Jump-sta
your
legal
research
on Westlaw.

PLI Treatises

PLI's treatises are authored by experts in their field and provide a wealth of information in every relevant legal area. PLI's treatises are updated annually (or as needed) to always reflect the latest developments in your field. Each book purchase includes Basic Upkeep Service. The PLI Library includes:

BANKING & COMMERCIAL LAW

635	Asset-Based Lending $225
626	Bankruptcy Deskbook $250
644	Documenting Secured Transactions $165
608	Equipment Leasing – Leveraged Leasing $350
625	Hillman on Commercial Loan Documentation $165
645	Revised Article 9 Opinion Manual $175
643	Structured Finance $185

BUSINESS, CORPORATE & SECURITIES

595	Accountants' Liability $160
661	Advising High Technology Companies $185
5047	Broker-Dealer Regulation $175
616	Corporate Law and Practice $140
601	Corporate Legal Departments $210
579	Directors' and Officers' Liability $160
585	Doing Business Under the Foreign Corrupt Practices Act $170
610	Financial Product Fundamentals $190
4376	GSI's Primer to SEC Research $35
627	How to Draft for Corporate Finance $190
596	Investment Adviser Regulation $150
648	Legal Opinions in Business Transactions $185
5519	Mutual Fund Regulation $185
4905	PLI's Guide to the Sarbanes- Oxley Act for Business Professionals $35
654	The Sarbanes-Oxley Deskbook $325
577	The Securities Law of Public Finance $195
641	Thinking Like a Writer $49
655	Understanding the Securities Laws $195
646	Working with Contracts: What Law School Doesn't Teach You $35

EMPLOYMENT

622	Disability Law Deskbook $170
4372	Employment Law Yearbook $190

ESTATE PLANNING AND ELDER LAW

628	Estate Planning & Chapter 14 $140
592	Income Taxation of Estates and Trusts $160
656	Manning on Estate Planning $225
587	New York Elder Law Handbook $160
617	Stocker and Rikoon on Drawing Wills and Trusts $180
636	Tax Planning with Real Estate $175

Continued on back...

CORPORATE LAW AND PRACTICE
Course Handbook Series
Number B-1505

Securities Litigation & Enforcement Institute 2005

Chairs

David Siegel
Colleen P. Mahoney

To order this book, call (800) 260-4PLI or fax us at (800) 321-0093.
Ask our Customer Service Department for PLI Order Number 6746,
Dept. BAV5.

Practising Law Institute
810 Seventh Avenue
New York, New York 10019

"This work is designed to provide practical and useful information on the subject matter covered. However, it is sold with the understanding that the publisher is not engaged in rendering legal, accounting or other professional services. If legal advice or other expert assistance is required, the services of a competent professional should be sought."

Foreword

This course handbook is one of about 200 published each year by the Practising Law Institute.

Its primary function is to serve as an educational supplement to each program. It may also be used as a reference manual by attorneys and related professionals unable to attend the sessions.

The method of reproduction utilized has been chosen to insure that registrants receive these materials as quickly as possible and in the most usable form practical.

The Practising Law Institute wishes to acknowledge its debt and extend its sincere appreciation to the authors who have rendered this valuable service. They exemplify the finest tradition of our profession by sharing their expertise with their colleagues.

Prepared for distribution at the
SECURITIES LITIGATION & ENFORCEMENT INSTITUTE 2005
Program
September 2005

<u>CONTENTS</u>:

PROSECUTING THE SECURITIES FRAUD ACTION

1

SECURITIES CLASS ACTIONS SINCE THE 1995 REFORM ACT: A PLAINTIFF'S PERSPECTIVE

Sherrie R. Savett

Berger & Montague, P.C.

Table of Contents

OVERVIEW

The Private Securities Litigation Reform Act of 1995 ("PSLRA") was enacted as part of Newt Gingrich's "Contract with America," over President Clinton's veto, in a Republican effort to protect the corporate elite from perceived abuses in class action litigation. The PSLRA placed a series of hurdles in place, over which a plaintiff must jump in order to pursue violations of the federal securities laws. The most noteworthy hurdle is the mandatory stay of discovery pending the resolution of a motion to dismiss. Similarly, the PSLRA's "heightened pleading requirements" and proportionate liability provisions were intended to thwart a plaintiff's ability to pursue and recover for securities fraud.

Unfortunately, the erection of litigation hurdles—combined with the unrealistic expectations associated with the Internet bubble—may have been a contributing factor in the massive proliferation of corporate fraud. With major financial scandals dominating the news over the last few years, it is clear that Congress should have been concerned with protecting public investors from corporate America's abuses—not protecting the corporate elite by fostering an atmosphere favorable to fraud.

This paper identifies and summarizes trends and developments in securities class action litigation following passage of the PSLRA, and examines the impact of corporate scandals and major reforms, including the Sarbanes-Oxley Act of 2002 ("SOA"). This article also explains what plaintiffs' counsel look for in deciding to sue, and suggests ways for defendants to avoid suit or minimize their liability exposure.

I. THE POST-PSLRA LANDSCAPE: TRENDS AND DEVELOPMENTS

A. Major Trends Causing the Litigation Pendulum to Swing Toward Plaintiffs

1. Enron and Other High-Profile Corporate Scandals Spur Class Action Filings; Accounting Allegations, Insider Trading Emphasized

The pro-corporate climate shifted dramatically with the collapse of Enron in December 2001, followed by the disclosure of the massive accounting fraud at WorldCom, and numerous other corporate scandals including Tyco, Adelphia Communications, and Global Crossing. In addition to these high-profile frauds, there have been allegations of widespread abuses in connection with initial public offerings ("IPOs"), analyst conflicts of interest, and mutual fund trading, fee structure, and distribution procedures. The most recent class actions include cases brought against insurance companies, alleging that their "bid-rigging" activities had artificially inflated the stock prices of these companies, and products liability securities class actions relating to the undisclosed health risks of COX-2 inhibitors. In addition, there has been an increase in ERISA filings accompanying securities class actions, which allege that the company's stock was not a prudent investment option for an ERISA plan, and that plan sponsors failed to perform their fiduciary duties under ERISA by including company stock as an investment option.

Most securities fraud complaints now allege either some form of accounting fraud, insider trading, or both. In 2004, 79% of securities cases contained allegations of misrepresentations in financial documents, and 48% of cases included GAAP violations.[1] Sixty percent of these complaints contained allegations of improper revenue recognition, while 17% of all cases with GAAP allegations included allegations of overstated accounts receivable, and 15% included allegations of overstatements of other assets or understatements of liabilities. Id. This is a significant increase from the 38% of cases alleging accounting fraud in the five years preceding the PSLRA. Id. In addition, 39% of cases filed in 2004 included allegations of insider trading. Id.

2. *Restatements Rise To Record Levels*

Restatements by public companies have increased dramatically in recent years, and a record number of companies revised their annual financial reports in 2004, according to a study by Huron Consulting Group.[2] There were 414 restatements of annual audited financial reports last year, up 28 % from the 323 restatements in 2003, and nearly double the number of restatements in 2000 (233). Id.

According to the Huron Report, the three most common reasons for corrections in 2004 included revenue recognition (16.4% of all restatements in 2004); equity (i.e. errors involving stock option accounting, EPS accounting, and accounting for warrants and other

---

1. See Cornerstone Research, Securities Class Action Case Filings 2004: A Year in Review, available at http://securities.stanford.edu ("Cornerstone Filings Report"), at 16.
2. See Huron Consulting Group, "Summary: 2004 Annual Review of Financial Reporting Matters," ("Huron Report"), at 1. Available at www.huronconsultinggroup.com.

equity instruments)(16%); and understated or overstated reserves, accruals, and contingencies (14.1%). Id. at 2. The large number of restatements involving reserves and contingent funds is particularly notable. Overstating reserves to reduce current profits and have money available later, or underestimating them in order to bolster revenue in the current period, is a common type of fraud.

Consistent with the recent upsurge in restatements, over half of all accounting cases filed in 2004 focus on restatements.[3] See Cornerstone Settlements Report at 17. Given the record number of restatements in 2004, this percentage will likely increase in the near future.

3. Dismissals Fall Sharply After Sarbanes-Oxley

In the wake of the unprecedented number and magnitude of corporate scandals revealed in 2002, the SOA was quickly enacted to restore investor confidence and prevent future Enrons. On July 30, 2002, Congress passed the SOA, a corporate-governance and accounting-oversight law. While the new law does not make it much easier for plaintiffs to plead a securities fraud case, the SOA does have several provisions favorable to shareholders, including:

- Lengthening the statute of limitations for private actions to 2 years after discovery of the violation or 5 years after the violation;
- Requiring preservation of key financial audit documents and e-mail for five years, and creating a 10-year felony for destroying such documents;
- Requiring CEOs and CFOs to certify financial reports;
- Requiring companies to immediately disclose "in plain English" material changes to their financial condition;
- Broadening the ability of whistleblowers to sue, and prohibiting retaliation against employees who provide or assist in an investigation relating to securities law violations; and
- Directing civil penalties from SEC enforcement actions to accounts that benefit investors victimized by securities fraud.

3. See Laura E. Simmons and Ellen M. Ryan, Post-Reform Act Securities Settlements: Updated Through December 2004, Cornerstone Research ("Cornerstone Settlements Report"), available at http://securities.stanford.edu/, at 17.

While the SOA did not remove the mandatory stay of discovery pending a decision on a motion to dismiss, or scale back the heightened pleading standards, its expansion of the statute of limitations is highly significant, and does, as a practical matter, increase the likelihood that those responsible for fraud may ultimately be held accountable. Furthermore, despite the absence of provisions directly relating to the pleading of a securities fraud complaint, dismissals have fallen sharply since the SOA, with one-third fewer dismissals since its July 2002 passage compared with the post-PSLRA, pre-SOA period.[4] As reported by NERA, 26 cases were dismissed in the first seventeen months since passage of the SOA, a substantial drop from the 39 dismissals that theoretically would have occurred if the number of dismissals kept pace with dismissals in the post-PSLRA, pre-SOA period. NERA Update at 4. The authors of the NERA study conclude that the lower rate of dismissal "suggests that either cases are proceeding more slowly or that judges are being more generous at the margin in evaluating the merits of cases on their desks, allowing a few more cases to proceed." Id.

According to a separate NERA study, considering the probability of a dismissal, the odds of a suit that continues beyond the motion to dismiss stage are up 41%.[5] The authors of the NERA 2003 Report conclude that the increase is likely the result of "a combination of more fraud during the late 1990s and more aggressive litigation of such fraud by the plaintiffs' bar, as well as more active enforcement by regulators." NERA 2003 Report, at 12.

4. *Widespread and Complex Frauds Lead to New Securities Cases*

The proliferation of financial fraud over the past four years has given rise to new types of securities cases alleging analyst conflicts of interest, fraud in connection with IPOs, and mutual fund trading, pricing, and sales practice abuses. The most recent non-traditional securities cases include suits alleging insurance "bid-rigging"; product liability securities class actions concerning the health risks of

---

4. See Elaine Buckberg, Todd Foster, and Stephanie Plancich, Recent Trends in Securities Class Action Litigation: 2003 Early Update, NERA Economic Consulting, Feb. 2004 ("NERA Update"), at 4.
5. See Elaine Buckberg, Todd S. Foster, Ronald I. Miller and Adam Werner, Recent Trends in Securities Class Action Litigation: Will Enron and Sarbanes-Oxley Change the Tides?, NERA Report, June 2003 ("NERA 2003 Report"), at 2.

COX-2 inhibitors; and ERISA cases alleging that the company stock was an imprudent investment option for the retirement plan.

IPO Cases

The first wave of new cases, filed in 2001, challenged improper IPO allocation practices, alleging that underwriters of certain "hot" IPOs during the high-tech boom of late 1999 and 2000:

- Engaged in illegal tactics by soliciting and receiving "kick-backs"—often in the form of excessive commissions—in exchange for allocations of portions of the Company's IPO;
- Required "tie-in" purchases creating an artificial demand for the stock; and
- Artificially inflated the price of the stock through "laddering"—requiring purchases of additional stock in the IPO after-market at escalating prices by customers who agreed to pay the underwriters "kickbacks," often in the form of excessive commissions.

See In re Initial Public Offering Securities Litigation, 241 F. Supp.2d 281, 293-94 (S.D.N.Y. 2003)("IPO Litigation"). In total, the plaintiffs in the consolidated IPO cases sued fifty-five underwriters, 309 issuers, and thousands of individual defendants. IPO Litigation, 241 F. Supp.2d at 294. In her 2003 opinion, Judge Shira A. Scheindlin upheld the vast majority of investors' claims against the underwriters and issuers and their officers. Id. at 295.

Analyst Cases

In 2002 and 2003, numerous cases against Wall Street analysts were filed, alleging that the analysts and their firms misled investors by issuing overly positive stock ratings of companies that also were investment banking clients. These cases were spurred by New York State Attorney General Eliot Spitzer's Wall Street analyst probe, which led to a host of reforms as well as a record $1.4 billion settlement with ten major brokerage firms over conflicts of interest. However, Judge Milton Pollack of the Southern District of New York dismissed suits against Merrill Lynch for failure to plead loss causation, holding that investors who gambled in the market and were exposed to ongoing press coverage of analysts' conflicts could not blame Merrill for the drop in their share prices. See In re Merrill

Lynch & Co. Research Reports Sec. Litig., 273 F. Supp.2d 351 (S.D.N.Y. 2003).

At least two other judges have allowed class actions against analysts to go forward. In DeMarco v. Robertson Stephens, Inc., 2004 U.S. Dist. LEXIS 265 (S.D.N.Y. Jan. 9, 2004), Judge Gerard E. Lynch upheld claims against former analysts at Robertson Stephens over their recommendations for the technology stock Corvis Corp. Similarly, in In re WorldCom, Inc. Secs. Litig., 2003 U.S. Dist. LEXIS 21161 (S.D.N.Y. Nov. 26, 2003), Judge Denise Cote held that press reports concerning widespread conflicts among analysts during market boom of the 1990s were not enough to put investors on notice about the allegedly "illicit relationship" between WorldCom and Salomon Smith Barney and its star telecommunications analyst, Jack Grubman.

Mutual Fund Cases

In 2003 and 2004, investigations of the mutual fund industry gathered steam, with far-ranging inquiries into late trading and market timing, a practice that involves the rapid trading in securities to take advantage of market-moving events. Also under investigation are marketing practices by mutual funds, including potential conflict and disclosure issues where broker-dealers push sales of particular funds in exchange for payments in the form of revenue sharing, soft dollars, or directed brokerage business from the fund company. In 2004, there were several new mutual fund cases filed with allegations relating to the mutual fund fee structure and distribution procedures.

Insurance "Bid-Rigging" Cases

On October 14, 2004, New York Attorney General Eliot Spitzer announced that he had charged several of the nation's largest insurance companies and largest broker with bid rigging and pay-offs that he said violated fraud and antitrust laws. Following this announcement, several securities class actions were filed, alleging that the insurance companies and an insurance broker's "bid-rigging" activities had artificially inflated the stock prices of these companies.

Product Liability Cases

In 2004, announcements relating to the health risks of COX-2 inhibitors led to the filing of several new product liability securities class actions.

ERISA Cases

An increasing number of ERISA cases are being filed by participants of company-sponsored retirement plans that included company stock as an investment option. The ERISA cases are often filed after the filing of a traditional securities class action. The plaintiffs in these cases allege that company stock was not an appropriate investment option for an ERISA plan, and that by including that investment option plan sponsors violated their fiduciary duties under ERISA.

5. Pension Funds And Other Institutions Are Increasingly Joining Cases As Lead Plaintiffs, Winning Bigger Settlements

Consistent with the intent of the PSLRA to encourage larger and more serious plaintiffs to serve as plaintiffs in securities cases, institutions are increasingly stepping forward as lead plaintiffs, which is in turn leading to bigger settlements. Institutions have served as lead plaintiffs in approximately 35% of all post-PSLRA cases.[6] While the general expectation was that the lead plaintiff provisions of the PSLRA would cause large institutional investors such as mutual funds to come forward, pension funds have been joining class actions at a far greater pace than other institutional investors. See Arden Dale, "Pensions Join Class-Action Suits At Faster Pace, Lending Clout," The Wall Street Journal, Jan. 14, 2004. The trend began soon after the California Public Employees Retirement System and the New York State Retirement Fund announced a record $2.8 billion settlement with Cendant in 1999. After the landmark Cendant settlement—which was more than 10 times larger than the previous record settlement—more and more funds were prompted to join suits as lead plaintiffs. The clout pension funds bring to cases is apparent in the huge settlements achieved in suits where pension funds served as lead plaintiffs.

B. Trends in Securities Class Action Filings

1. Filings in 2004 Increase Dramatically

Traditional securities fraud filings in 2004 totaled 212, significantly higher than the post-PSLRA average of 190 filings each year, and 17% higher than the 181 cases filed in 2003. See Cornerstone

6. See Cornerstone Settlements Report, at 9.

Filings Report at 2. As demonstrated in the chart below, the large number of "traditional" (i.e., not analyst, IPO, or mutual fund) securities class action filings in 2004 approached the highs seen in 2000 and 2002:

Federal Securities Class Action Filings: 1991- 2004
(Excluding "IPO Allocation," "Analyst," and "Mutual Fund" Filings)

Pre-PSLRA Year	Total "Traditional" Class Action Filings
1991	164
1992	202
1993	163
1994	233
1995	190

Post-PSLRA Year	Total "Traditional" Class Action Filings
1996	127
1997	193
1998	268
1999	241
2000	223
2001	195
2002	225
2003	175
2004	212

C. Settlement Amounts Reach Record Levels in 2004

While the PSLRA has resulted in more dismissals, the cases that survive motions to dismiss are generally strong, and institutional plaintiffs and lead plaintiffs with large losses are demanding larger settlements. As a result, the total value of cases settled has increased dramatically in recent years, with the number of exceptionally large settlements continuing to grow, raising overall average settlement amounts. See Cornerstone Settlements Report, at 1-2.

Total settlement values hit an all-time high in 2004, with a record $5.5 billion in total settlements, compared to $2.1 billion in 2003 and $4.5 billion in 2000 (the previous record-setting year). See Cornerstone Settlements Report, at 1-2. Even excluding the $2.6 billion WorldCom-

Citigroup settlement, reached in May 2004, settlements last year totaled $2.9 billion, the highest total value ever. This increase is due in part to an upsurge in exceptionally large settlements, as well as an increase in the total number of settlements in 2004. Id. In 2004, 118 cases settled, compared to 96 in 2003, a 23% increase. Id.

In addition, the average settlement amount in 2004 of $24.6 million represents a 25% increase over the $19.2 million average for all prior post-PSLRA years. Id. In 2004, there were seven settlements of $100 million or more, which represents an all-time high number of settlements that size. Id. at 3. Settlements in the $60 to $100 million range also increased substantially in 2004. Id.

Most recently, thirteen of WorldCom's investment banks settled for a total of more than $4 billion—the largest recovery ever achieved in a securities class action suit.

POST-PSLRA SETTLEMENTS OF CLASS ACTION SECURITIES FRAUD LAWSUITS IN EXCESS OF $50 MILLION AS OF MARCH 15, 2004

Rank	Issuer	Maximum Settlement Value
1.	WorldCom	$4 Billion[7]
2.	Cendant	$3.527 Billion[8]
3.	Lucent Technologies	$568 Million[9]
4.	Bank of America	$490 Million
5.	Waste Management II	$457 Million
6.	Raytheon	$410 Million[10]
7.	Rite Aid	$334 Million[11]

7. Partial settlement includes $2.65 billion from Citigroup defendants (2004); $428.4 million from ABN Amro, Mitsubishi Securities Internantional, BNP Paribas, and Mizuho International; $325 million from Deutsche Bank; $460.5 from Bank of America; and $112.5 million from West LB and Caboto Holdings.
8. Includes $3.185 billion in the common equity settlement and $340 million in the Prides derivative settlement.
9. Includes $148 million in cash, $315 million cash or stock (company's choice), $100 million in warrants (viable only if stock trades above $2.75 per share within 3 years of issue).
10. Includes cash payment of $210 million and warrants of Raytheon valued at $200 million.
11. Includes $193.5 million from the issuer, $125 million from the accounting firm, and $1.55 million from two individual defendants.

8.	Global Crossing	$325 Million[12]
9.	DaimlerChrysler	$300 Million
10.	Oxford Health Plans	$300 Million[13]
11.	3COM	$259 Million
12.	Waste Management I	$220 Million
13.	Dollar General	$162 Million
14.	Computer Associates	$152.6 Million
15.	Microstrategy	$150 Million
16.	Dayton Power & Light	$145.5 Million
17.	Charter Communications	$144 Million
18.	Informix	$142 Million
19.	Sunbeam	$125 Million
20.	Mattel	$122 Million
21.	Conseco	$120 Million
22.	Lernout & Hauspie	$115 Million[14]
23.	Interpublic	$115 Million
24.	GIO	$112 Million
25.	Ikon	$111 Million
26.	Prison Realty	$104 Million
27.	AT&T	$100 Million
28.	Honeywell	$100 Million
29.	Medaphis/Deloitte & Touche	$96 Million
30.	Real Estate Associates	$92.5 Million[15]
31.	Boeing	$92 Million
32.	Enron (ERISA claims)	$85 Million[16]
33.	Homestore Inc.	$85 Million
34.	I2 Technonlogies, Inc.	$84.5 Million
35.	Casden Properties, Inc.	$83 Million
36.	Aetna	$80 Million
37.	Hanover Compression	$80 Million

12. Includes $30 million from individual defendant Gary Winnick, and $19.5 million from the issuer's law firm.
13. Includes $225 million from the issuer, and $75 million from the accountant.
14. Partial settlement with KPMG.
15. Plus $25 million prejudgment interest.
16. Partial settlement.

38.	DuPont	$77 Million
39.	Alcatel	$75 Million
40.	Network Associates	$70 Million
41.	Sotheby's	$70 Million
42.	Providian	$65 Million
43.	Service Corporation Int'l	$65 Million
44.	Vesta	$61 Million
45.	Safeskin	$55 Million
46.	Enterasys	$50.4 Million (Cash and Stock)
47.	Sprint	$50 Million

1. Factors Increasing Settlement Amounts

The factors tending to increase settlement amounts include the following:

Institutional Investors as Lead Plaintiffs: As noted above, the increasing involvement of institutional investors—and particularly pension funds—in the post-PSLRA era is a significant factor boosting settlement amounts. According to the Cornerstone Settlements Report, approximately 35% of all post-PSLRA settlements to date have involved an institutional investor as lead plaintiff, and cases involving institutions as lead plaintiffs are associated with significantly higher settlement amounts. See Cornerstone Settlements Report at 9. The median settlements for cases with institutional investors as lead plaintiffs are about 20% higher than in cases not involving institutions. See NERA 2003 Report at 11.

Accounting Fraud Allegations: More than half of all post-PSLRA settlements have included accounting violations, and over half of those cases involve restatements. See Cornerstone Settlements Report at 7. In 2004, 60% of all cases settled during the year involved accounting allegations. See id. Settlements in cases involving GAAP allegations and restatements settle for approximately 46% more than non-accounting cases. Id. However, the lack of a restatement does not always get the issuer off the hook. Neither the Oxford Health Plans settlement nor the Bank of America settlement—each worth over $450 million—involved restatements.

Auditor Defendants: Approximately 14% of all post-PSLRA settlements have involved the issuer's accountant as a defendant.[17] These cases produced significantly higher settlements: In 2001, the median settlement value for a case where the accountant was named

($8.8 million) was 72% higher than the settlement value for cases where no accountant was named ($5.1 million). 2003 Cornerstone Settlements Report, at 9. In 2000, the disparity was even larger: the median values of settlements in which the accountant was a defendant ($14.8 million) were 195% higher than settlements with no auditor defendants ($5.0 million). Id.

Underwriter Defendants: Approximately 20% of cases settled through December 2004 involved Section 11 or 12(a)(2) claims. Cornerstone Settlements Report at 8. Post-PSLRA cases in which an underwriter was named as a defendant settled for approximately 64% more than cases with no underwriter defendants. See id.

Corresponding SEC Investigations: Over 20% of all post-PSLRA settlements involve a corresponding action by the SEC, which usually results in a higher settlement amount, probably because it demonstrates the case's merit. See id. at 10. Cases with corresponding SEC investigations also tend to involve accounting allegations as well as an accompanying derivative suit, both of which raise settlement values.

Corresponding Derivative Action: More than 15% of post-PSLRA class actions were accompanied by a derivative action. Id. at 12. Settlement amounts for class actions accompanied by derivative actions are significantly higher, probably because derivative cases tend to be associated with larger cases, accounting allegations, and an institutional lead plaintiff. Id.

Insider Trading: Slightly more than 25% of cases settled in 2004 involved insider trading allegations. Id. at 12. Cases including allegations of insider trading generally settle for higher amounts than cases with no insider trading. See id.

II. THE LEAD PLAINTIFF AND LEAD COUNSEL PROVISIONS OF THE PSLRA: RECENT DEVELOPMENTS

The PSLRA's detailed guidelines for selection of lead plaintiff begin with the requirement that a named plaintiff, within twenty days of filing a securities class action complaint, must publish a notice of the suit and advise class members of the opportunity to seek appointment as lead plaintiff. 15

17. See Laura E. Simmons and Ellen M. Ryan, Post-Reform Act Securities Lawsuits: Settlements Reported Through December 2003, Cornerstone Research ("2003 Cornerstone Settlements Report"), available at http://securities.stanford.edu/, at 9.

U.S.C. § 78u4(a)(3)(B)(vi). Within 90 days after publication of the notice, the court must appoint as lead plaintiff the "member or members of the purported plaintiff class that the court determines to be most capable of adequately representing the interests of class members." Id. 78u-4(a)(3)(B)(I).

The PSLRA establishes a rebuttable presumption that the person or persons with "the largest financial interest in the relief sought by the class" are the most capable of adequately representing the interests of class members. Id. § 78u-4(a)(3)(B)(iii). This presumption is rebuttable only upon a showing that the plaintiff will not fairly and adequately protect the interests of the class or is subject to unique defenses defeating adequate representation. Following appointment, the statute provides that "the most adequate plaintiff shall, subject to the approval of the court, select and retain counsel to represent the class." Id. § 78u-4(a)(3)(13)(v).

A. Lead Plaintiff Provisions Greatly Delay Cases

The lead plaintiff provisions of the PSLRA result in significant delay—there are often multiple notices of filings, and courts often take months to appoint a lead plaintiff. See, e.g., Raferty v. Mercury Fin. Co., No. 97 C 624, 1997 U.S. Dist. LEXIS 12439, at *2-3 (N.D. Ill. Aug. 7, 1997)(noting that statutory 90-day lead plaintiff appointment requirement had not been met). The subsequent stay of discovery pending resolution of a motion to dismiss, together with the lead plaintiff delays, often means that a case does not move forward to the merits for a year or more after filing. As reported by NERA, these delays have translated into slower settlements: Prior to the PSLRA, 61% of cases were disposed in three years and 77% in five years; post-PSLRA, only 44% have been disposed in three years and 62% in five years. NERA Report at 5.

B. Institutional Investors Are Seeking Appointment As Lead Plaintiff

As noted above, certain institutional investors—primarily large public pension funds—have taken a more active role in securities litigation, and frequently seek appointment as lead plaintiff. The increasing involvement of institutions is especially apparent in the more high-profile accounting fraud cases which involve large restatements. In most instances, the institutions are hiring traditional plaintiffs' class action lawyers.

C. Notice Requirements: Court Holds That The New York Times Is Not Adequate

Under the notice provisions of the PSLRA, the plaintiff or plaintiffs in a securities class action shall, within 20 days of filing their complaint, publish notice of the pendency of the suit "in a widely circulated national business-oriented publication or wire service." 15 U.S.C. § 78u-4(a)(3)(A)(i). The notice must inform the members of the purported class of the pendency of the action, the claims asserted, and the purported class period. Id. § 78u-4(a)(3)(A)(i)(I). Within 60 days of publication, any member of the class may move the court to serve as lead plaintiff. Id. § 78u-4(a)(3)(A)(i)(II).

In Haung v. Acterna Corp., 220 F.R.D. 255, 258 (D. Md. 2004), the court held that the PSLRA's publication requirement was not met where the plaintiffs' notice, though timely published, appeared in The New York Times. The court did not elaborate on its reasoning, but stated that it was "not satisfied" that publication in The Times met Congress' intent that the publication be "'reasonably calculated to reach, at the least, sophisticated and institutional investors.'" Id. (quoting Greebel v. FTP Software, Inc., 939 F. Supp. 57, 64 (D. Mass. 1996)). Thus, at least in the Haung court's view, The Times fails to meet the "widely-circulated national business-oriented publication" standard required by the PSLRA. Id.[18]

D. Lead Plaintiff Groups and Aggregation: Courts Approve Small Groups, Reject Large Groups of Unrelated Investors

1. *Most Courts Follow SEC's Position That Lead Plaintiff Groups Should Be Limited To 3 To 5 Investors*

The PSLRA provides that the most adequate plaintiff may be a "person or group of persons," or "member or members of the proposed plaintiff class." 15 U.S.C. § 78u-4(a)(3)(B)(iii)(I); § 78U-4(a)(3)(B)(i). The SEC, filing briefs as *amicus curiae* in several cases, has taken the position that courts should limit any proposed lead plaintiff group to a small number capable of managing the litigation, usually three to five investors. See, e.g., Memorandum of the

18. The Haung court also found that the content of the notice was inadequate since it did not "provide any information upon which a reader may rely to conduct an independent inquiry into the matter," and instead "reserves for the attorney the ability to screen lead plaintiffs and discourage greater participation by activist investors," a result "the PSLRA seeks to avoid." Id. at 257-58.

SEC, *Amicus Curiae*, Switzenbaum v. Orbital Sciences Corp., 187 F.R.D. 246 (E.D. Va. 1999); Memorandum of the SEC, *Amicus Curiae,* dated Sept. 24, 1998, in In re Vesta Insurance Group, Inc. Sec. Litig., Civil Action No. 98-AR-1407-S (N.D. Ala.); Memorandum of the SEC, *Amicus Curiae*, dated May 20, 1998, in In re Oxford Health Plans, Inc. Sec. Litig., No. MDL-1222 (S.D.N.Y.).

As the SEC argued in a brief *amicus curiae* filed in In re Baan Co. Sec. Litig., 186 F.R.D. 214, 217 (D.D.C. 1999):

> Construing the term 'group of persons' in light of the language and purposes of the Act, a court generally should only approve a group that is small enough to be capable of effectively managing the litigation and the lawyers. The commission believes that ordinarily this should not be more than three to five persons, a number that will facilitate joint decision making and also help to assure that each group member has a sufficiently large stake in the litigation.

In re Baan, 186 F.R.D. at 217 (quoting attached SEC brief *amicus curiae* at 16-17). Most courts, including the Third Circuit in In re Cendant Corp. Litig., 264 F.3d 201, 266 (3d Cir. 2001), have adopted this approach. In Cendant, 264 F.3d at 266, the court determined that although there is no "hard-and-fast-rule," courts should "generally presume that groups with more than five members are too large to work effectively," and therefore are not adequate lead plaintiffs. Id. (citing *amicus curie* brief submitted by the SEC).[19]

The Cendant court's analysis is consistent with the vast majority of decisions permitting appointment of a small group of unrelated investors. See, e.g., In re Cardinal Health, Inc. Sec. Litig., 2005 U.S. Dist. LEXIS 1431, *27 (S.D. Ohio Jan. 26, 2005); In re Gemstar-TV Guide Int'l, Inc. Sec. Litig., No. 02-02775 NM (C.D. Cal. Aug. 2, 2002) (appointing two public pension funds lead plaintiff over a group consisting of seven unrelated institutional and individual investors).[20]

---

19. The court in Cendant held that "[t]he PSLRA explicitly permits a 'group of persons' to serve as lead plaintiff." 264 F.3d at 266. The Cendant court in also rejected the position—advanced by several district courts—that a group of "unrelated individuals" is precluded from serving as lead plaintiff under the PSLRA: "The statute contains no requirement mandating that the members of a proper group be 'related' in some manner; it requires only that any such group 'fairly and adequately protect the interests of the class.'" Id.

2. *Other Approaches*

While most courts have been reluctant to appoint large lead plaintiff groups, others (primarily in the earlier cases) have found that the PSLRA does not limit group size. See, e.g., D'Hondt v. Digi Int'l, Inc., No. 97-5 (JRT/RLE), 1997 U.S. Dist. LEXIS 17700, at *13 (D. Minn. Apr. 3, 1997)(appointing 21-person group of lead plaintiffs and stating that "[a]n arbitrary limit on the number of proposed Lead Plaintiffs would be unrealistic if not wholly counterproductive"). In a variation on this approach, some courts have selected lead plaintiff and lead counsel based on the larger losses of the group, then appointed a smaller, subgroup of investors as lead plaintiff. E.g., Baan, 186 F.R.D. at 216 (appointing three members of 466-person group to serve as co-lead plaintiffs).

Courts have also appointed co-lead plaintiffs or a lead plaintiff group comprised of an individual and an institution in order to promote a diversity of class representation, reasoning that "the lead plaintiffs will represent a broader range of shareholder interests than if the Court appointed an individual or an institutional investor alone." Yousefi v. Lockheed Martin Corp., 70 F. Supp.2d 1061, 1070-71 (C.D. Cal. 1999). As the court explained in In re Oxford Health Plans, Inc., 182 F.R.D. 42, 49 (S.D.N.Y. 1998), naming an institution and individual lead plaintiffs "allows for broad representation and the sharing of resources and experience to ensure that litigation will proceed expeditiously...and will assure the court that any settlement when proposed will be provident." The court in Campbell Soup, 2000 U.S. Dist. LEXIS 5481, at *11, agreed with this approach, finding it "desirable to have both an institutional investor

20. See also, e.g., In re Orthodontic Centers of America, Inc. Sec. Litig., No. 01-949 Sec. "T", 2001 U.S. Dist. LEXIS 21816, at *15-16 (E.D. La. Dec. 17, 2001)(finding group of seven investors "is small enough to ensure manageability, yet diverse enough to prevent exposure of the class to disruption at a later point in the litigation"); In re Cell Pathways, Inc. Sec. Litig., 203 F.R.D. 189, 192 (E.D. Pa. 2001)(appointing group of four to serve as lead plaintiff); In re Ribozyme Pharmaceuticals, Inc., Sec. Litig., 192 F.R.D. 656, 662 (D. Colo. 2000)(appointing lead plaintiff group of four); In re Laborers Local 1298 Pension Fund v. Campbell Soup Co., 2000 U.S. Dist. LEXIS 5481, at *11 (D.N.J. 2000)(appointing institution and two individual investors as co-lead plaintiffs); In re Oxford Health Plans, Inc. Sec. Litig., 182 F.R.D. 42, 27 (S.D.N.Y. 1998)(using tri-partite lead plaintiff structure, with two institutions and one group of three individuals).

...and individual investors...included as lead plaintiffs since each may bring a unique perspective to the litigation."

A few courts have rejected aggregation altogether, based on the premise that a single investor—individual or institution—will better serve the class. See, e.g., In re Donkenny, Inc. Sec. Litig., 171 F.R.D. 156, 158 (S.D.N.Y. 1997)(single institution appointed lead plaintiff).

E. Courts Are Split On Whether Five-Case Limit on "Professional Plaintiffs" Applies to Institutions

The PSLRA prohibits a proposed lead plaintiff from serving in more than five securities class actions brought during any three-year period, 15 U.S.C. § 78u-4(a)(3)(B)(vi). Some courts, relying on the Conference Report for the PSLRA, have held that this limitation does not apply to institutional investors. See H. R. Conf. Rep. No. 104-396 of the 104th Congress at 35 (1999)("Institutional investors may need to exceed this limitation and do not represent the type of professional plaintiff this legislation seeks to restrict."). See also, e.g., In re Vicuron Pharms., Inc. Sec. Litig., 225 F.R.D. 508, 542 (E.D. Pa. 2004)("The [Conference] Report made it quite clear that the limitation against professional plaintiffs was not designed to be applied mechanically to institutional investors"); In re Gemstar-TV Guide, No.02–2775 NM, Order at 11-12 (concluding that "the PSLRA expressly authorizes courts to waive the restriction on professional plaintiffs to achieve the objectives of the statute," and appointing institution that had served in seven other cases in three years as lead plaintiff).[21]

---

21. See also, e.g., Smith v. Suprema Specialties, Inc., 206 F. Supp.2d 627 (D.N.J. 2002)(fact that institution had served as lead plaintiff five other times in the past three years did not automatically preclude it from serving as lead plaintiff); Naiditch v. Applied Micro Circuits Corp, No. 01-CV-0649-K-AJB, 2001 WL 1659115, at *6-9 (S.D. Cal. Nov. 5, 2001)(PSLRA's restrictions do not apply to institutional investors); In re Critical Path, Inc. Sec. Litig., 15 F. Supp.2d 1102 (N.D. Cal. 2001)(appointing institution, which was currently serving as lead plaintiff in six other securities class actions, to act as lead plaintiff); Piven v. Sykes Enters., Inc., 137 F. Supp.2d 1295, 1304 (M.D. Fla. 2000)(PSLRA "clearly grants the court the power to appoint a lead plaintiff despite its having served as lead plaintiff in five other suits in the past three years."); In re Network Assoc., Inc. Sec. Litig., 76 F. Supp.2d 1017, 1030 (N.D. Cal. 1999)(same); Blaich v. Employee Solutions, Inc., No. 97-545-PHX-RGS, 1997 WL 842417, at *2 (D. Ariz. Nov. 21, 1997)("the general restriction of serving in more than five cases as a lead plaintiff was not intended to apply to institutional investors....").

However, several courts have applied the 5-case restriction to institutions, particularly where more than one institutional investor seeks appointment as lead plaintiff. For example, in In re Enron Corp. Sec. Litig., 206 F.R.D. 427, 443-44 (S.D. Tex. 2002), the court, citing In re Telxon Corp. Sec. Litig., 67 F. Supp.2d 803, 821 (N.D. Ohio 1999), summarized the reasons why institutions should not automatically be excluded from the 5-case limit:

> [T]he statute itself contains no express blanket exception for institutional investors, the Conference Report is not the law, to create a blanket exception for institutional investors would turn the statute's grant of discretion into a requirement mandating that courts excuse institutional investors form the ["professional plaintiff"] bar and would 'transform the preference for institutional investors into a monopolization of the PSLRA actions by institutional investors.'

In re Enron, 206 F.R.D. at 444-43 (citing In re Telxon, 67 F. Supp.2d at 820-21). In Telxon, 67 F. Supp.2d 803, the court rejected the Florida State Board Administration's application for lead plaintiff because it was already lead plaintiff in more than five actions.[22]

F. Most Courts Hold That Defendants Do Not Have Standing to Challenge Lead Plaintiff Appointments

Most courts have held that defendants in securities class actions have no standing to object to the choice of lead plaintiff, and that the PSLRA vests that choice with the other plaintiffs and the court. See, e.g., Bell v. Ascendant Solutions, Inc., 2002 U.S. Dist. LEXIS 6850, *7 (N.D. Tex. Apr. 17, 2002); D'Hondt, 1997 U.S. Dist. LEXIS 17700, at *11 n.6 (stating that "it is doubtful" that defendants "have standing to object to the adequacy of the Lead Plaintiffs that have been proposed"); Baan, 186 F.R.D. at 215 n.1 ("Defendants generally have been held to

22. See also, e.g., Aronson v. McKesson HBOC, Inc., 70 F. Supp.2d 1146 (N.D. Cal. 1999)("this provision gives the court considerable discretion to bar repeat litigants, creating a rebuttable presumption that the same plaintiff should not direct more than five securities class actions in three years."); Ezra Charitable Trust v. Rent-Way, Inc., 136 F. Supp.2d 435, 441 and n.2 (W.D. Pa. 2001)(rejecting an institutional investor's bid for lead plaintiff, noting that the "FSBA was appointed lead plaintiff in seven separate securities class actions" and "is also a frequent non-lead plaintiff in securities actions"); In re Waste Management, Inc. Sec. Litig., 128 F. Supp.2d 401, 424 (S.D. Tex. 2000)("the PSLRA bars a person from serving as a lead plaintiff in more than five securities class actions during any three-year period").

lack standing to challenge appointment of lead plaintiffs."); Gluck v. Cellstar Corp., 976 F.Supp. 542 (N.D. Tex. 1997).

However, a few courts have held that the PSLRA does not prevent them from considering defendants' arguments on the presumption of adequacy, particularly where there are no other plaintiffs competing for lead plaintiff. In re Orthodontic Centers of America, No. 2001 U.S. Dist. LEXIS 21816, at *6-7. Accord, In re First Union Corp., Sec. Litig., 2000 U.S. Dist. LEXIS 2267 (W.D.N.C. Jan. 28, 2000). While the court in Orthodontic Centers heard defendants' objections, it ultimately rejected their arguments that the plaintiffs' notice to class members was defective, and that the proposed lead plaintiff group, consisting of four unrelated individuals and a church, was too large. Id. at *7-16.

Several courts have pointed out that while defendants lack standing to oppose a motion for appointment of lead plaintiff, they retain the right to challenge the Rule 23 requirements at the class certification stage. See, e.g., Netsky v. Capstead Mortgage Corp., 2000 U.S. Dist. LEXIS 9941, (N.D. Tex. 2000); Party City, 189 F.R.D. at 106 n.12.

G. Selection of Lead Counsel: Third Circuit Task Force, Most Courts Reject Auctions

The PSLRA entrusts the selection of lead counsel to the lead plaintiff. 15 U.S.C. § 78u-4(a)(3)(B)(v) ("The most adequate plaintiff shall, subject to approval of the court, select and retain counsel to represent the class."). Despite this clear language, a few courts sought to replace the lead plaintiff's choice of counsel through an auction process, requiring competitive bidding and appointing as counsel for the class the lowest bidder. See, e.g., In re Quintus Sec. Litig., 148 F. Supp.2d 967, 986-7 (N.D. Cal. 2001)(Walker, J.); In re Comdisco Sec. Litig., 141 F. Supp. 2d 951 (N.D. Ill. 2001)(Shadur, J.); In re Network Associates, Inc. Sec. Litig., 76 F. Supp.2d 1017 (N.D. Cal. 1999)(Alsup, J.).

However, the use of auctions to select class counsel and set attorneys' fees has been seriously criticized, including in the January 2002 report issued by the Third Circuit Task Force on the Selection of Class Counsel ("Task Force Report")[23] , and in Chief Judge Becker's recent opinion in Cendant, 182 F.R.D. at 271-280. In its Report, the Task Force concluded that "the risks and complications associated with a

23. See Proceedings of the 2001 Third Circuit Task Force on the Selection of Lead Counsel, available at www.ca3.uscourts.gov/classcounsel/.

judicially-controlled auction counsel against its use except under certain limited circumstances." Task Force Report at 18. The Task Force also determined that "[a]uctions are inconsistent with the goal of the PSLRA, which is to assure that the 'most adequate' plaintiff will choose counsel and negotiate a reasonable fee." Id. at 18-19. Therefore, "to the extent it is even permissible under the PSLRA," an auction

> should only be conducted if the lead plaintiff's choice of counsel, or process in choosing counsel, is so infirm as to rebut the presumption that the plaintiff is 'most adequate' under the statute, and then only if the alternative candidates for the 'most adequate plaintiff' do not appear willing or able to engage in a meaningful search for and negotiation with counsel.

Id. at 19.

The Cendant court came to the same conclusion, reasoning that the PSLRA

> evidences a strong presumption in favor of approving a properly-selected lead plaintiff's decisions as to counsel selection and counsel retention. When a properly-appointed lead plaintiff asks the court to approve its choice of lead counsel and of a retainer agreement, the question is not whether the court believes that the lead plaintiff could have made a better choice or gotten a better deal. Such a standard would eviscerate the Reform Act's underlying assumption that, at least in the typical case, a properly selected lead plaintiff is likely to do as good or better job than the court at these tasks.

Cendant, at 276. Accordingly, the Cendant court concluded that "the court's inquiry is appropriately limited to whether the lead plaintiff's selection and agreement with counsel are reasonable on their own terms." Id.[24]

Since the Third Circuit Task Force came out with its Report in January 2002, there has not been a single lead plaintiff/lead counsel determination based on bidding. The ever-increasing participation of institutional investors has in some cases led to lower fee percentages

---

24. See also, e.g., In re Razorfish, Inc. Sec. Litig., 143 F. Supp.2d 304, 311 (S.D.N.Y. 2001)(holding that auctioning class counsel was not "remotely consistent with the Reform Act," and stating that the court's authority under the PSLRA to reject the lead plaintiff's choice of counsel "cannot be transmogrified into a right to arrange a shotgun marriage between strangers"); In re Microstrategy, Inc. Sec. Litig., 110 F. Supp.2d 427, 437-8 (E.D. Va. 2000)(rejecting auction process and stating that "while plaintiff's selection of lead counsel is 'subject to the approval of the court,' approval should not be based on whether plaintiff's chosen counsel promises to charge a cheaper fee than anyone else.").

because those institutional investors negotiate lower fees with their chosen counsel than the court might otherwise award.

III. EXCEPTIONS TO THE PSLRA'S MANDATORY STAY OF DISCOVERY

Under the PSLRA, the filing of a motion to dismiss automatically stays "all discovery and other proceedings," unless a stay would create "undue prejudice," or "particularized discovery is necessary to preserve evidence." 15 U.S.C. § 78u-4(b)(3)(B). Attempts to limit the stay's effect have been largely unsuccessful, but courts are increasingly willing to lift the stay in particularly egregious cases, where the fraud is blatant and where defendants have already produced documents to governmental agencies conducting investigations or to plaintiffs in other actions, such as parallel ERISA or derivative suits.

Other exceptions to the automatic stay include: (1) informal interviews conducted by plaintiffs' counsel of former employees, which courts have concluded are not "discovery"; (2) where the mandatory disclosures of Rule 26(a) are treated separately from "discovery"; and (3) where a case includes state law claims over which the federal court has independent diversity jurisdiction.

A. Lifting the Stay to Avoid "Undue Prejudice" in Cases of Obvious Fraud and Where Documents have Already been Produced to Governmental Agencies

In the wake of Enron and other high-profile frauds, a number of courts have been willing to partially lift the PSLRA's discovery stay and have directed defendants to produce documents previously produced to government agencies or plaintiffs in ERISA or derivative actions. For example, in In re WorldCom, Inc. Sec. Master File Litig., 234 F. Supp.2d 301, 305 (S.D.N.Y. 2002), the court held that the intended purpose of the discovery stay—minimizing frivolous class action filings and preventing "fishing expeditions"—was not relevant to the circumstances of that case and should not prevent the securities plaintiff from having access to documents already made available to the U.S. Attorney, the SEC, and plaintiffs in a separate ERISA action. The court reasoned that production of the documents already produced to other parties was necessary to prevent "undue prejudice" to the interests of the putative investor class, which would otherwise "essentially be the only major interested party in the criminal and civil proceedings against WorldCom without access to documents that currently form the core of those proceedings." Id. Since settlement discussions were scheduled to begin in certain of the parallel cases, and since the company had already filed for bankruptcy protection, if the securities plaintiff was forced to "wait until the resolution of a motion to dismiss to obtain discovery and formulate its settlement or litigation strategy, it faces the very real risk that it will be left to pursue its action against defendants who no longer have anything or at least as much to offer." Id. at 306. Thus, the WorldCom court concluded that a stay of discovery is warranted "[w]here, as here, plaintiffs are not in any sense engaged in a fishing expedition or an abusive strike suit and do not thereby act in contravention of the fundamental rationales underlying the PSLRA discovery stay, and where plaintiffs would be substantially prejudiced by the maintenance of the stay[.]" Id.

More recently, the court in In re Royal Ahold N.V. Securities & ERISA Litig., No. 1:03-MD-01539, 2004 U.S. Dist. LEXIS 4048 (Mar. 12, 2004), lifted the discovery stay as to documents previously produced to regulatory agencies conducting investigations into irregularities at the company, including multibillion dollar accounting errors, restatements and admissions of "suspicious transactions." The court held that the "most compelling" reason for allowing the requested discovery was the risk of undue prejudice to the securities plaintiffs: "Without access to key documents that have already been produced to government investigators and that soon will be produced to the ERISA plaintiffs, the securities plaintiffs could suffer a severe disadvantage in formulating their litigation and settlement strategy—particularly if the parties proceed quickly to settlement negotiations, as the court has urged them to do." 2004 U.S. Dist. LEXIS 4048 at *23-24.

Noting that the plaintiffs' case was "far from frivolous," the court in Royal Ahold also found that the necessity to preserve evidence was "substantial," since the company was undertaking a wide-ranging reorganization which included the divestitures of key subsidiaries. Id. at *21-22. The court reasoned that "the divestitures add urgency to the discovery timetable, and discovery of the previously produced documents, which are likely to comprise the most critical evidence in the case, could help the plaintiffs identify other specific materials that [may] be at risk of loss." Id. at *21. The court also determined that the discovery request, which sought a potentially large volume of documents, was adequately particularized in light of the massive nature of the fraud. Id. at *18. However, the Royal Ahold court did not order production of investigative reports, which the government opposed, because it found that a "limited delay" in releasing the reports would not prejudice the parties or the court. In addition, because the plaintiffs' case against Royal Ahold's accountants was "not as apparent," the court declined to lift the stay as to the accountants. Id. at *27-28.

In a similar case, In re Tyco Int'l, Ltd. Multidistrict Litig., No. 02-1335-B (D.N.H. Jan. 29, 2003)(Practice and Procedure Order No. 5), at 9-11, the court refused to stay discovery in the ERISA and derivative actions merely because they had been consolidated with the securities actions for pretrial purposes, where the claims asserted in those actions "are not frivolous and defendants do not claim that plaintiffs' counsel are working together to thwart the stay provision." Id. at 9. The Tyco court concluded that lifting the stay was necessary to prevent "'undue prejudice' by placing all potential claimants on an equal footing with respect to discovery," an approach that "makes sense" in a case where:

> (1) the Securities Action plaintiffs would be at a serious disadvantage if they are denied access to documents that are produced to the other plaintiffs and government investigators; (2) the defendants will not incur any additional costs if the Securities Action plaintiffs are given access to the documents; (3) keeping all parties on an equal footing with respect to discovery serves important case management interests in this complex litigation; and (4) none of the claims at issue are frivolous."

Id. at 11. See also In re Enron Corp. Sec., Derivative & ERISA Litig., MDL-1446, 2002 WL 31845114, at *2 (S.D. Tex. Aug. 16, 2002)(ordering production of documents previously produced to numerous governmental entities).

Courts are also increasingly willing to lift the PSLRA stay with respect to documents already produced to the government even where the corporate defendant is not in bankruptcy and where there has been no restatement of financial results. See, e.g., In re AOL Time Warner, Inc. Securities & ERISA Litig., 2003 U.S. Dist. LEXIS 2731, at *3 (S.D.N.Y. Feb. 28, 2003) (ordering production of documents previously produced to government entities, where the plaintiff was not engaged in a fishing expedition or an abusive strike suit, and where providing a copy of discovery already produced to other parties would not burden the defendants); Singer v. Nicor Inc., No. 02 Civ. 5168 (N.D. Ill. Apr. 23, 2003)(ruling that the bankruptcy of the corporate defendant was not required for a partial lifting of the PSLRA stay).

B. Interviews of Former Employees and Validity of Confidentiality Agreements Between Former Employees and Companies

Several courts have concluded that informal, voluntary interviews with former employees of defendant companies conducted by plaintiffs' counsel do not constitute "discovery" under the PSLRA and are therefore not prohibited by the discovery stay. See In re JDS Uniphase Corp. Sec. Litig., No. C-02-1486 CW (EDL), slip. op. At 5-6 (N.D. Cal. Oct. 18, 2002). In JDS Uniphase, the court granted the plaintiffs' request for an order allowing former employees to speak voluntarily to plaintiffs' counsel about certain topics without fear of breaching the company's confidentiality agreements, reasoning that the plaintiffs were "not seeking discovery in the ordinary sense of the word...because plaintiffs are not using court process to require these third parties to provide information about the lawsuit." Slip Op. at 5. Instead, the court noted, "plaintiffs are merely seeking an order that would allow former employees to speak voluntarily if they wish to do so." Id. See also Tyco Int'l. Ltd. Sec. Litig., 2001 U.S. Dist. LEXIS 819 (D.N.H. 2001)("neither logic, tradition, the constitution nor the PSLRA prohibit interviewing prospective witnesses"); In re Flir Systems, Inc. Sec. Litig., 2000 WL 33201904 (D. Or. 2000).

In JDS Uniphase, the court explained that "the Reform Act was not intended to provide defendants with the means to bar all investigation into their conduct," or to provide defendants with "immunity from suit, but, rather, was intended to protect defendants from the burdens of defending against frivolous litigation." Slip. Op. at 7. The court pointed out that, "[i]n fact, the Reform Act's heightened pleading standard encourages plaintiffs to do more investigation before filing a complaint, not less." Id. at 6 (emphasis in original). Because the proposed interviews with former employees did not impose any burden or cost on the company, and did not fall within the definition of "discovery," the PSLRA's discovery stay had no bearing on the plaintiffs' request for an order permitting interviews with the former employees. Id. at 7. Accord, In re Flir Systems, 2000 WL 33201904, at *3 (stating that the PSLRA is "not to be a sword with which defendants can destroy the plaintiffs' ability to obtain information from third parties who are otherwise willing to disclose it.")

The court in JDS Uniphase also addressed the issue of whether a company's confidentiality agreements can lawfully be used to prohibit its former employees from providing whistleblower-type information about allegedly unlawful acts that occurred during their employment with the company. After concluding that disclosures of wrongdoing do not constitute revelations of trade secrets which can be prohibited by agreements binding on former employees, the court noted that Congress, in enacting the SOA, explicitly demonstrated a public policy in favor of whistleblowers in securities cases. Slip. Op. at 9. The recently-enacted SOA prohibits companies from discriminating against employees because of any lawful act by the employee to assist in the investigation of securities fraud. 18 U.S.C. § 1514A(a)(1). The court found that while this section applies only to investigations conducted by the company itself or the government, the public policy is clear, and the statute "certainly does not establish a public policy in favor of allowing employers to muzzle their employees with overbroad confidentiality agreements." Id.

Thus, under JDS Uniphase, companies cannot enforce typical confidentiality agreements against former employees to prevent them from providing non-trade secret, unprivileged information about the company's illegal activities. Since virtually every confidentiality agreement of this sort goes way beyond legitimate trade secrets, this ruling should be very helpful in thwarting defendants' efforts to assert confidentiality provisions as a bar to plaintiffs' counsel's right to speak with former employees.

C. Rule 26(a) Initial Disclosures

Application of the PSLRA's discovery stay to the initial disclosures required by Rule 26(a)(1) was addressed in the Ninth Circuit's mandamus decision in Medhekar v. United States Dist. Court, 99 F.3d 325 (9th Cir. 1996). In Medhekar, the court held in a per curiam opinion that "initial disclosures are a subset of discovery and, as such, they are included in the Act's stay provision." Id. at 328. Alternatively, the Medhekar court ruled that "such disclosures are at a minimum included in the ban on 'other proceedings' during the pendency of a motion to dismiss." Id. at 329.

Until recently, few challenges had been made to the 1996 Medhekar ruling. However, in In re Comdisco, 166 F. Supp.2d at 1262-3, Judge Shadur held that disclosure of insurance policies—one of the initial disclosures required by Rule 26(a)(1)—was not stayed by the PSLRA. Rejecting the Ninth Circuit's analysis in Medhekar, Judge Shadur determined that Rule 26(a)(1) disclosures do not qualify as "discovery" within the meaning of the PSLRA's stay provision simply because Rule

26 comes under the heading "Depositions and Discovery." Id. at 1262. In addition, Judge Shadur reasoned that production of the insurance policies was necessary to avoid "undue prejudice" to the plaintiffs, since "knowledge of the existence or nonexistence of insurance and the amount of any coverage are essential to the exercise of Class Counsel's ability to carry out that law firm's fiduciary obligations to its class member clients[.]" Id. at 1263.

D. State Law Claims

A court in the Southern District of New York has held that where jurisdiction is based on diversity, non-fraud common law claims are excepted from the PSLRA's stay of discovery. Tobias Holdings, Inc. v. Bank United Corp., 177 F. Supp.2d 162 (S.D.N.Y. 2001). However, in Angell Investments, L.L.C. v. Purizer Corp., 2001 U.S. Dist. LEXIS 17782, *4-7 (N.D. Ill. Oct. 2001), the court refused to permit discovery on the plaintiffs' negligent misrepresentation claim, reading Tobias Holdings narrowly as permitting an exception to the automatic stay only where discovery on the state law claims would not amount to "an improper end run around the PSLRA." The Angell Investments court reasoned that the negligent misrepresentation claim was related closely enough to the federal securities law claim that the discovery sought "would be precisely the same as what plaintiffs would seek on the securities violations claim absent the discovery stay." Id. at *7.

IV. PLEADING REQUIREMENTS UNDER THE PSLRA

A. Pleading Scienter: An Emerging "Middle Ground" Consensus

The PSLRA requires a plaintiff to "state with particularity facts giving rise to a strong inference" of scienter. 15 U.S.C. § 78u-4(b)(2). Since the passage of the PSLRA, every circuit court to consider the issue has agreed that some form of recklessness will suffice to establish scienter. Courts have differed, however, in their definitions of recklessness, and have split on the question of whether allegations of motive and opportunity can satisfy the PSLRA's pleading burden. Among circuit courts, three different standards have developed, with the "middle ground" standard—first outlined by the Sixth Circuit—emerging as the majority view.

1. The Second and Third Circuits: "Motive and Opportunity" Test Survives PSLRA

The Second Circuit has taken the position that the PSLRA did not alter its pleading standard for scienter, under which a plaintiff may **either** (a) allege facts to show that defendants had both motive and opportunity to commit fraud, **or** (b) allege facts that constitute strong circumstantial evidence of conscious behavior or recklessness. Press v. Chemical Investment Servs., 160 F.3d 529, 538 (2d Cir. 1999). In Novak v. Kasaks, 216 F.3d 300, 309-10 (2d Cir. 2000), the court clarified that the PSLRA did not change the pleading standard for scienter in the Second Circuit, except by the addition of the words "with particularity." Thus, in order to plead scienter, plaintiffs must "state with particularity facts giving rise to a strong inference that the defendant acted with the required state of mind." Id. at 311.

With respect to recklessness, the Second Circuit has held that to satisfy scienter pleading requirements, the conduct must have been "highly unreasonable" and "an extreme departure from the standards of ordinary care...to the extent that the danger was either known to the defendant or so obvious that the defendant must have been aware of it." In re Scholastic Corp. Sec. Litig., 252 F.3d 63, 76 (2d Cir. 2001)(citation omitted).

Like the Second Circuit, the Third Circuit, in In re Advanta Corp. Sec. Litig., 180 F.3d 525, 534 (3d Cir. 1999), held that scienter still may be established with allegations of motive and opportunity or circumstantial evidence of reckless or conscious behavior. The court in Advanta noted that the PSLRA "did not purport to alter the substantive contours of scienter," and found that stock sales "unusual in scope or timing may support an inference of scienter." Id.

2. The Ninth Circuit Minority View: "Deliberate Recklessness" is Required

The Ninth Circuit has adopted the most stringent standard for pleading scienter, holding that motive and opportunity pleadings alone can never satisfy the PSLRA's scienter pleading requirements, and requiring the pleading of "particular facts giving rise to a strong inference of deliberate recklessness." In re Silicon Graphics Sec. Litig., 183 F.3d 970, 979 (9th Cir. 1999). No other circuit court has followed the extreme position established in Silicon Graphics.

3. The "Middle Ground": Motive and Opportunity "Relevant" to Pleading Scienter in the First, Fifth, Sixth, Eighth, Tenth, and Eleventh Circuits

In what is emerging as the majority view, the First, Sixth, and Eleventh Circuits, joined recently by the Fifth, Tenth and Eighth Circuits, have taken a middle ground position regarding the pleading of scienter under the PSLRA. Under this view, first expressed by the Sixth Circuit, "plaintiffs may meet PSLRA pleading requirements by alleging facts that give rise to a strong inference of reckless behavior but not by alleging facts that illustrate nothing more than a defendant's motive and opportunity to commit fraud." In re Comshare, Inc. Sec. Litig., 183 F.3d 542, 551 (6th Cir. 1999). As the Sixth Circuit recently emphasized, even under this formulation, evidence of motive and opportunity may be "catalysts to fraud and so serve as external markers to the required state of mind." Helwig v. Vencor, 251 F.3d 540, (6th Cir. 2001). While "conclusory labels of motive and opportunity will not suffice," "facts presenting motive and opportunity may be of enough weight to state a claim under the PSLRA[.]" Id. Thus, the "middle ground position" espoused by the Sixth Circuit (and followed by an increasing number of other circuits) is actually quite close to the Second Circuit's standard.

The First Circuit followed the Sixth Circuit in Greebel v. FTP Software, Inc., 194 F.3d 185, 196-7 (1st Cir. 1999), holding that "merely pleading motive and opportunity, regardless of the strength of the inferences to be drawn of scienter, is not enough," and emphasizing that "whatever the characteristic patterns of the facts alleged, those facts must now present a strong inference of scienter." Significantly, however, the Greebel court held that "allegations of unusual insider trading by a defendant with access to material non-public information can support a strong inference of scienter." Id. at 198.

The Eleventh Circuit, in Bryant v. Avado Brands, Inc., 187 f.3d 1271, 1283, 1285 (11th Cir. 1999), stated that "we are in basic agreement with the Sixth Circuit," and held that allegations of motive and opportunity to commit fraud, standing alone, are not sufficient to establish scienter. The Eleventh Circuit also held that scienter can be shown with allegations of "severe" recklessness. Id. at 1284.

The Tenth Circuit has also taken a middle-ground position in holding that motive and opportunity allegations are "important," "but are typically not sufficient in themselves to establish a 'strong inference' of scienter." City of Philadelphia v. Fleming Cos., Inc.,

264 F.3d 1245, 1262 (10th Cir. 2001). Rather, evidence of motive and opportunity "may be considered as part of the mix of information that can come together to create the 'strong inference' of scienter required by the PSLRA." Id. at 1263. The key to reviewing a plaintiff's allegations of scienter is not "whether those allegations fall into defined, formalistic categories such as 'motive and opportunity,'" but "whether the plaintiff's allegations, taken as a whole, give rise to a strong inference of scienter." Id.

The Fifth Circuit has also concluded that allegations of motive and opportunity are "relevant" to pleading scienter and "may, on occasion, rise to the level of creating a strong inference of reckless or knowing conduct." Nathenson v. Zonagen, 267 F.3d 400, 407 (5th Cir. 2001). In addition, the Nathenson court held that the PSLRA did not change the substantive definition of scienter, which includes recklessness. Id.

The Eighth Circuit also appears to have taken a middle ground approach, stating that "motive and opportunity are generally relevant to a fraud case, and a showing of unusual or heightened motive will often form an important part of a complaint that meets the Reform Act standard." Florida State Board of Admin. V. Green Tree Financial Corp., 270 F.3d 645, 660 (8th Cir 2001). The court in Green Tree noted that in some cases—such as those alleging insider trading—"the same circumstantial allegations that establish motive and opportunity also give additional reason to believe the defendant's misrepresentation was knowing or reckless." Id. In such cases, the allegations of motive and opportunity "may meet the Reform Act standard, but if so it is because they give rise to a strong inference of scienter, not merely because they show establish motive and opportunity." Id.

Regardless of which pleading standard a court adopts, all circuits—including the Second Circuit—have been closely scrutinizing scienter allegations in Rule 10b-5 cases, looking for a "strong inference" of fraud. Cases that, prior to passage of the PSLRA, would have survived motions to dismiss, are now being dismissed as courts reject superficial allegations of scienter.

B. Lack of Restatement Does Not Negate Inference of Scienter

In Aldridge v. A.T. Cross Corp., 284 F.3d 72, 83 (1st Cir. 2002), the First Circuit—one of the more conservative on pleading standards—

reversed the dismissal of a securities fraud suit alleging accounting improprieties and improper sales practices, even where the company did not restate its earnings. The court in Aldridge emphasized that the lack of a restatement is not relevant to the inference of scienter:

> The company argues that because it has never restated any of its financials or otherwise indicated any error in the 1998 financial statements, and because its financial statements were audited by an independent accounting firm, no inference of accounting error, and so no inference of scienter, can be drawn. We disagree. Had the 1998 financials been restated, that might well have been useful to Aldridge. However, the fact that the financial statements for the year in question were not restated does not end Aldridge's case when he has otherwise met the pleading requirements of the PSLRA.

Id. To hold otherwise, the court reasoned, would "shift to accountants the responsibility that belongs to the court," and "would allow officers and directors of corporations to exercise an unwarranted degree of control over whether they are sued, because they must agree to a restatement of the financial statements." Id.

C. Knowledge May be Imputed to Defendants Where the Fraud Related to the Company's Core Business

Many courts have held that it is appropriate to impute to directors and officers knowledge about adverse developments affecting their company's core business. E.g., Cosmas v. Hassett, 886 F.2d 8, 12-13 (2d Cir. 1989) (directors rightfully imputed with knowledge of elimination of "potentially significant source of income for the company"); In Re World Access, Inc. Sec. Litig., 119 F. Supp.2d 1348, 1355-56 (N.D. Ga. 2000) (defendants' knowledge of severe problems with "flagship" product imputed); In re Aetna Inc., Sec. Litig., 34 F. Supp.2d 935, 953 (E.D. Pa. 1999) (knowledge imputed to key officials of problems with "core business" support strong inference of scienter); In re ValuJet, Inc., 984 F. Supp. 1472, 1479-80 (N.D. Ga. 1997) (allegations concerning executives who knew of safety problems while emphasizing ValuJet's safety record supportive of scienter).[25]

D. The PSLRA's "Basis" Requirement: Most Courts Hold That Disclosure of Confidential Sources is Not Required

The PSLRA requires that with respect to every allegation made on information and belief, a plaintiff must "state with particularity all facts on which that belief is formed." 15 U.S.C. § 78u-4(b)(2). Most courts have held that a plaintiff can comply with this requirement without naming confidential sources.

As the Second Circuit explained in Novak, 216 F.3d at 313:

> Our reading of the PSLRA rejects any notion that confidential sources must be named as a general matter. In our view, notwithstanding the use of the word 'all,' paragraph (b)(1) does not require that plaintiffs plead with particularity every single fact upon which their beliefs concerning false or misleading statements are based. Rather, plaintiffs need only plead with particularity sufficient facts to support those beliefs. Accordingly, where plaintiffs rely on confidential personal sources but also on other facts, they need not name their sources as long as the latter facts provide an adequate basis for believing that the defendants' statements were false.

Id. The Third, Fifth, and First Circuits have all explicitly adopted the reasoning and holding of Novak. See Cal. Pub. Employees' Retirement Sys. v. Chubb Corp., 394 F.3d 126, 146-47 (3d Cir. 2004); ABC Arbitrage Plaintiffs Group v. Tchuruk, 291 F.3d 336, 353 (5th Cir. 2002); In re Cabletron Systems, Inc., 311 F.3d 11, 29-31 (1st Cir. 2002). See also, Fla. State Bd. Of Admin. v. Green Tree Fin. Corp., 270 F.3d 645, 667-68 (8th Cir. 2001); Adams v. Kinder-Morgan, Inc., 340 F.3d 1083, 1103 (10th Cir. 2003)("plaintiffs are not required to disclose the documentary or personal sources from which they learned the facts alleged in an information and belief complaint").[26]

E. The Group-Published Information Doctrine: Majority Holds That It Survived The PSLRA

Under the group-published information or "group pleading" doctrine, a plaintiff may impute false or misleading statements conveyed in annual reports, quarterly and year-end financial statements and other

25. See also, e.g., In re Viropharma Sec. Litig., No. 02-1627, 2003 U.S. Dist. LEXIS 5623 at *31 (E.D. Pa. Apr. 3, 2003) (holding that knowledge can be imputed to defendants when the alleged fraud relates to a company's leading product); In re Cell Pathways, No. 99-752, 2000 U.S. Dist. LEXIS 8584 at *23 (E.D. Pa. June 20, 2000) ("where the alleged fraud relates to the core business of the company, knowledge of the fraud may be imputed to the individual defendants."); In re Tel-Save Sec. Litig., 1999 U.S. Dist. LEXIS 16800 at *14 (E.D. Pa. Oct. 19, 1999) ("Knowledge concerning a company's key businesses or transactions may be attributable to the company, its officers and directors"); Epstein v. Itron, Inc., 993 F. Supp. 1314, 1326 (E.D. Wash. 1998) (a company's top officers are presumed to know facts about the company's core products because those facts are so apparent); In re Campbell Soup Co. Sec. Litig., 145 F. Supp. 2d 574 (D.N.J. 2001).

group-published information to corporate officers. See, e.g., Wool v. Tandem Computers, Inc., 818 F.2d 1433, 1440 (9th Cir. 1987). Since the passage of the PSLRA, courts have debated whether the group-pleading doctrine survived that legislation. Recently, the Fifth Circuit rejected the group pleading doctrine, reasoning that "it cannot withstand the PSLRA's specific requirement that the untrue statements or omissions be set forth with particularity as to each defendant," and that the doctrine "conflicts with the scienter requirement of the PSLRA." Southland Secs. Corp. v. Inspire Ins. Solutions, Inc., 365 F.3d 353, 364-65 (5th Cir. 2004). Other circuit courts have largely avoided addressing the issue. See, e.g., In re Cabletron Sys., Inc., 311 F.3d 11, 40 (1st Cir. 2002)(noting that the First Circuit had previously recognized "a very limited version of the group pleading doctrine," but declining to decide whether group pleading survived the PSLRA).

The Tenth Circuit has recognized a group pleading exception to the particularity requirements of Rule 9(b). See Schwartz v. Celestial Seasonings, Inc., 124 F.3d 1246, 1254 (10th Cir. 1997). In addition, numerous district courts have determined that the group pleading doctrine is still viable after passage of the PSLRA. See, e.g., In re Rent-Way, 2002 U.S. Dist. LEXIS 12491, at *72 ("We see no reason to find that group pled allegations *per se* cannot meet the heightened pleading standards of Rule 9(b) or the PSLRA"); In re Raytheon Sec. Litig., 157 F. Supp.2d 131, 153 (D. Mass. 2001)("This Court agrees with the majority of courts that have held that the rationale behind the group pleading doctrine remains sound in the wake of the passage of the PSLRA."); In re SmarTalk Teleservices, Inc. Sec. Litig.,124 F. Supp.2d 527, 545 (S.D. Ohio 2000)(PSLRA did not abolish group-published rule); Baan,

---

26. Other courts agree that disclosure of confidential sources is not required. See, e.g., Johnson v. Tellabs, Inc., 262 F. Supp. 2d 937, 946 (N.D. Ill. 2003); In re Rent-Way Sec. Litig., 2002 U.S. Dist. LEXIS 12491, *46-47 (July 11, 2002)(following Novak); In re Campbell Soup Co. Sec. Litig., 145 F. Supp.2d 574, 599 (D.N.J. 2001)(adopting Second Circuit analysis); In re Theragenics Corp. Sec. Litig., 105 F. Supp. 1342, 1355 (N.D. Ga. 2000)("after extensively reviewing the Reform Act, its legislative history, and more than 50 cases, this Court agrees with the approach of the Second Circuit in its recent Novak decision"); In re Employee Solutions Sec. Litig., 1998 U.S. Dist. LEXIS 1644, at *13 (D. Ariz. 1998). But see, Party City, 147 F. Supp.2d 282, 304-5(PSLRA requires plaintiff to specifically name confidential sources); Blanca v. Paymentech, 2000 U.S. Dist. LEXIS 1704 (N.D. Tex. Feb. 8, 2000)(plaintiffs required to plead the "substance of the meetings with consultants" to support their allegations).

103 F. Supp.2d at 17; In re Sunbeam Sec. Litig., 89 F. Supp.2d 194, 219 (S.D.N.Y. 1999). However, a few courts have found that the PSLRA abolished the group published information doctrine. See, e.g., P. Schoenfeld Asset Mgmt. LLC v. Cendant Corp., 142 F. Supp.2d 589, 620-21 (D.N.J. 2001); Coates v. Heartland Wireless Communs., Inc., 26 F. Supp.2d 910, 916 (N.D. Tex. 1998).

F. "Controlling Person" Claims: Majority Holds That "Culpable Participation" Need Not Be Pled

Section 20(a) of the Exchange Act imposes secondary liability on "every person who, directly or indirectly, controls any person liable" under the provisions of the Exchange Act, and instructs that liability shall be imposed "unless the controlling person acted in good faith and did not directly or indirectly induce the act or acts constituting the violation or cause of action." 15 U.S.C. § 78t(a). While the statutory language is relatively clear, courts have disagreed about the appropriate pleading requirements for a Section 20(a) claim, and in particular, whether "culpable participation" must be alleged at the pleading stage.

The majority view holds that allegations of culpable participation are not required at the pleading stage. Under this view, in order to state a claim under Section 20(a), a plaintiff need only plead (1) the existence of a primary violation by a controlled person, and (2) the direct or indirect control of the primary violator by the defendant. See, e.g., Hollinger v. Titan Capital Corp., 914 F.2d 1564, 1574-75 (9th Cir. 1990)(culpable participation not required to establish controlling person liability under Section 20(a)); In re Worldcom, Inc. Sec. Litig., 294 F. Supp.2d 392, 415 (S.D.N.Y. 2003); In re Initial Public Offering Sec. Litig., 241 F. Supp.2d 281, 396 (S.D.N.Y. 2003); In re MicroStrategy, Inc. Sec. Litig., 115 F. Supp.2d 620, (E.D. Va. 2000).

Courts embracing the majority view reason that a plaintiff is not required to plead, or, in establishing liability, to prove, a defendant's culpable state of mind in connection with a Section 20(a) claim. See Worldcom, 294 F. Supp.2d at 415; IPO Litigation, 241 F. Supp.2d at 396. Instead, once a primary violation and control is shown, the burden shifts to the defendant to demonstrate good faith, or lack of involvement in the underlying securities violation. Worldcom, 294 F. Supp. at 414; Microstrategy, 115 F. Supp.2d at 660. In addition, since the plaintiff need not plead or prove a culpable state of mind, the PSLRA's heightened pleading standard does not apply to Section 20(a) claims. See id.; IPO Litigation at 396 (denying motion to dismiss on grounds that PSLRA does not apply to Section 20(a) claims and plaintiffs met pleading requirements).

A minority of courts—including the Third Circuit—require a plaintiff to establish not only primary liability and control, but also "that the defendant was a culpable participant in the fraud." Rochez Bros., Inc. v. Rhoades, 527 F.2d 880, 890 (3d. Cir. 1975). See also, Lanza v. Drexel & Co., 479 F.2d 1277, 1299 (2d Cir. 1973)("The intent of Congress...was obviously to impose liability only on those directors who fall within this definition of control and who are in some meaningful sense capable participants in the fraud perpetrated by controlled persons."); Carpenter v. Harris Upham & Co., 594 F.2d 388, 394 (4th Cir. 1979); In re Global Crossing, Ltd. Sec. Litig., 2004 U.S. Dist. LEXIS 5040, * (S.D.N.Y. Mar. 23, 2004)(stating that "[d]espite recent decisions within this Circuit arguing that no showing of culpable participation is necessary,...the Court here adheres to its prior position that the plaintiff must allege culpable participation."); In re Twinlab Corp. Sec. Litig., 103 F. Supp.2d 193 (S.D.N.Y. 2001). But see Marbury Mgmt. Inc. v. Kohn, 629 F.2d 705, 716 (2d Cir. 1980)(requiring only that the plaintiff plead an allegation of control and an underlying violation).[27]

Recently, courts within the Third Circuit have declined to apply the culpable participation test at the pleading stage, reasoning that "it is erroneous to conclude that culpable participation must be pled merely because it is an element of a prima facie case[.]" In re Rent-Way Secs. Litig., 209 F. Supp.3d 493, 523 (W.D. Pa. 2002). See also, In re Tel-Save Sec. Litig., 1999 U.S. Dist. LEXIS 16800 at *19-20 (E.D. Pa. Oct. 19, 1999); In re Campbell Soup Co. Sec. Litig., 145 F. Supp.2d 574, 600 (D.N.J. 1996); In re Mobile Media Sec. Litig., 28 F. Supp.2d 901, 940 (D.N.J. 1998).

V. PRIMARY LIABILITY OF "SECONDARY" ACTORS SUCH AS INVESTMENT BANKS, LAWYERS, JOINT VENTURERS, ACCOUNTANTS, AND SIMILAR ENTITIES

The unprecedented scope and scale of the Enron, WorldCom, and Global Crossing schemes, and the extensive reach of the IPO allocation, analyst,

27. The Second Circuit has not definitively determined whether a plaintiff must plead a culpable state of mind in connection with an alleged violation under Section 20(a), resulting in a split among district courts within the Second Circuit. See IPO Litigation, 241 F. Supp.2d at 394 (describing split and unsuccessful attempts to clarify the issue within the Second Circuit).

and mutual fund frauds, have made it unmistakably clear that third parties—including lawyers, bankers, underwriters, and accountants—are frequently active and essential participants in complex securities frauds. While third party defendants always argue that they are immune from liability under the prohibition of aiding and abetting liability established in Central Bank, N.A. v. First Interstate Bank, N.A., 511 U.S. 164 (1994), courts are beginning to read Central Bank more narrowly, and are finding that secondary actors can be primarily liable for their roles in a scheme to defraud as long as the requirements for liability under Rule 10b-5 have been satisfied and all pleading requirements are met.

A. Enron

In the Enron litigation, Judge Melinda Harmon held that primary securities fraud allegations were sufficiently stated against a number of third party actors, including the company's outside law firm, its auditor and commercial and investment banks. In re Enron Corp. Securities, Derivative & ERISA Litigation, 235 F. Supp.2d 549, 592 (S.D. Tex. 2002) ("Enron"). In so holding, the court adopted the SEC's "creation" test for primary liability of secondary actors, under which a person who creates a misrepresentation on which investors rely—whether or not they initiate the misrepresentation, and whether or not the identity of the author of the misrepresentation is disclosed—can be primarily liable if the person acts with scienter. Id. at 587-89. In addition, secondary actors who write misrepresentations for inclusion in a document to be given to investors can be primary violators even if the ideas for those misrepresentations came from someone else. Id. at 588.

The Enron court also upheld the plaintiffs' allegations of "scheme" liability, based on subsections (a) and (c) of Rule 10b-5, which prohibit the use of a manipulative or deceptive device or participation in a scheme to defraud. Id.; see 17 C. F. R. § 240.10b-5(a), (c). Thus, the court held that "[s]ecurities fraud actions under § 10(b) and Rule 10b-5 are not merely limited to the making of an untrue statement of material fact or omission to state a material fact," since "Section 10(b) prohibits 'any manipulative or deceptive contrivance,' which...includes 'a scheme to deceive' or 'scheme, plan or artifice." Id. at 577. The court concluded that "[m]arket manipulation, employment of a manipulative device, and engaging in manipulative schemes such as a scheme to artificially inflate or deflate stock prices, falsifying records to reflect nonexistent profits, and creating and distributing false research reports favorably reviewing a company are other types of conduct prohibited by § 10(b) and Rule 10b-5." Id. at 579.

Noting that "in recent months, this country has been overwhelmed with corporate scandals that place Congress' goal in enacting the PSLRA in a much wider perspective," the Enron court emphasized that "[t]he PSLRA's significance as a protective shield for business must be viewed within the context of the private right of action, granted decades before, to defrauded investors injured by corporate management, auditors, outside counsel, and investment bankers where their conduct allegedly violated the federal securities laws." Id. at 593.

The court also specifically rejected the "reputation" defense frequently raised by accountants and other third party defendants, who argue that it would be illogical and against defendants' own self-interest to risk their professional reputations to participate in or conceal the scheme merely for fees, payments and profits:

> This court notes that what may have been implausible two or three years ago is hardly so today, in light of the plethora of revelations, investigations, evidence, indictments, guilty pleas, and confessions of widespread corporate corruption and fraud by companies, auditors, brokerage houses, and banks. Lining one's pockets with gold, at the expense of investors, employees, and the public, appears too often to be a dominating ambition, and public skepticism about the market is very prevalent.

Id. at 356.

B. IPO Litigation

In another important decision, Judge Scheindlen found that the underwriters of more than 300 initial public offerings had acted to "line their pockets with gold" by creating an artificial demand for the stock of companies that conducted IPOs by requiring customers that received allocations of stock in the offerings to buy additional shares in the aftermarket. IPO Litigation, 241 F. Supp.2d at 293. The court also upheld allegations that the underwriters used the scheme to enrich themselves by requiring customers to pay them a portion of the profits they made by selling their IPO shares in the aftermarket. Id. at 295-96. Finding that the investors "successfully pled that all of the underwriters, both allocating and non-allocating, made material misstatements and omissions, which they had a duty to disclose, with the intent to defraud the public," the court emphasized that "the duty to disclose falls on all parties aware of the [market] manipulation, or who take advantage of it." Id. at 382. Thus, the court found it "unimportant that only Allocating Underwriters are directly liable for the market manipulation. It is enough that all Defendants—Underwriters, Issuers, and Individuals alike—are alleged to have known of or recklessly disregarded the manipulation, and to have used that knowledge to their advantage." Id. The Court concluded:

> Where insiders conspire to frustrate the efficient function of securities markets by exploiting their position of privilege, they have perpetrated a double fraud: they have manipulated the market, and they have covered up that manipulation with lies and omissions. When investors have been injured by these frauds, those insiders may be liable under the securities laws.

Id. at 295-96.

C. Lernout & Hauspie

Addressing the requirement of public attribution, the court in In re Lernout & Hauspie Sec. Litig., 230 F. Supp.2d 166-67 (D. Mass. 2002)("Lernout I"), refused to dismiss certain claims against Lernout & Hauspie's outside auditor, KPMG, where the auditor's role was widely disseminated to the public and it was "appropriate to infer that...investors reasonably attributed the statements" to the auditor. Although the statements at issue were not publicly attributed to KPMG, the involvement of KPMG"s United States affiliate had been widely disseminated to investors in annual reports. Id. Thus, the court determined that KPMG's participation in the fraudulent statements—including overseeing and preparing unaudited financial reports—was substantial enough that KPMG should be deemed to have "made" the statements. Id. The court noted that "absolving an auditor who prepares, edits, and drafts a fraudulent financial statement knowing it will be publicly disseminated simply because [it was signed by another, affiliated auditor] would stretch Central Bank's holding too far." Id. at 168.

In a later decision, In re Lernout & Hauspie Sec. Litig., 236 F. Supp.2d 161 (D. Mass. 2003)("Lernout II"), the court upheld fraudulent scheme allegations against a venture capital fund, an outside insurance company, and the insurance company's CEO, all of whom were alleged to have participated in a "strategic partner scheme" which included setting up sham entities and entering into bogus software licensing agreements with Lernout & Hauspie. Id. at 165. The plaintiffs argued that defendants could be liable under Section 10(b) even though they did not directly make misstatements, since they were integral participants in the fraud. Id. at 173. More specifically, "but for the formation and operation of the sham shell companies and the bogus licensing transactions," Lernout & Hauspie could not have created fictitious revenue and ultimately overstated profits in the company's financial reports. Id.

Accepting the plaintiffs' argument, the court concluded that the defendants could be primarily liable for their role in the fraudulent scheme or course of business:

> While both sides make strong arguments in an area of sparse law, the better reading of § 10(b) and Rule 10b-5 is that they impose primary liability on any person who substantially participates in a manipulative or deceptive scheme by directly or indirectly employing a manipulative or deceptive device (like the creation or financing of a sham entity) intended to mislead investors, even if a material misstatement by another person creates the nexus between the scheme and the securities market.

Id.

D. Global Crossing

The court in In re Global Crossing, Ltd. Sec. Litig., 2004 U.S. Dist. LEXIS 5040, *34-44 (S.D.N.Y. Mar. 23, 2004), upheld allegations of primary liability under Section 10(b) against Arthur Andersen LLP ("Andersen") for its role in reviewing, preparing, directing, and controlling certain press releases, unaudited quarterly statements, and "pro forma" financials issued by Global Crossing. Relying in part on the court's analysis in Lernout I, the Global Crossing court determined, first, that a "strict requirement of public attribution" was not necessary since Andersen's role as Global Crossing's auditor was "well known to investors, who could easily have relied on the accounting firm's involvement in making any public financial reports, even where a particular statement was not publicly attributed to it." 2004 U.S. Dist. LEXIS 5040, at *33. In addition, the court found that allegations that Andersen aggressively marketed its "novel" accounting strategies in a well-known document "raises an inference that sophisticated investors would have known of Andersen's role in creating the reporting practices behind [Global Crossing's] false statements." Id. at *33-34. Thus, plaintiffs' allegations were sufficient to raise an inference "not only that Andersen was one of the 'makers' of the statements, but also that investors viewed it as such." Id. at *34.

The Global Crossing court also upheld the plaintiffs' allegations of scheme liability, noting that "a cause of action exists under subsections (a) and (c) for behavior that constitutes participation in a fraudulent scheme, even absent a fraudulent statement by the defendant." Id. at *37-38. The plaintiffs alleged that Andersen "masterminded" the misleading accounting scheme at Global Crossing, "actively participated" in structuring the fraudulent transactions, "was intimately involved" in all of the company's accounting functions, and "directly participated" in the creation of misleading "pro forma" numbers that misled investors. Id. at *40. According to the court, "Andersen's allegedly central role in these schemes, as their chief architect and executor, leaves no doubt as to its potential liability as a primary violator under Section 10(b)." Id.

The court rejected Andersen's only argument against scheme liability—that claims under subsections (a) and (c) must involve "market manipulation" or illegal trading activity. Id. at *41-42. Manipulative conduct, the court pointed out, encompasses "[s]chemes used to artificially inflate the price of stocks by creating phantom revenue." As the court observed, "[i]f the behavior alleged does not make out a claim for engaging in 'any act, practice, or course of business which operates or would operate as a fraud or deceit upon any person,' then it is hard to imagine what would." Id. at *42 (quoting 17 C.F.R. § 240.10b-5(a), ©.

E. WorldCom

In re WorldCom Inc., Sec. Litig., 294 F. Supp.2d 392 (S.D.N.Y. 2003), involved claims against numerous defendants, including the company's officers, directors, auditors, underwriting syndicates, and its most influential outside analyst, Jack Grubman, and his firm, Salomon Smith Barney ("SSB"). The court refused to dismiss primary liability claims against SSB and Grubman based on misrepresentations they made in analyst reports and registration statements, stating that "[i]f the plaintiffs have succeeded in adequately pleading that the SSB Defendants acted with scienter in making material misrepresentations or omissions in documents that the SSB Defendants authored, then the plaintiffs have stated a violation of the federal securities laws." Id. at 426.

The claims against WorldCom's outside accountant, Andersen, were also upheld in In re WorldCom, Inc. Sec. Litig., 2003 U.S. Dist. LEXIS 10863 (S.D.N.Y. June 25, 2003). Judge Cote found that the plaintiffs adequately pleaded scienter, since "[t]he allegations identifying the steps Andersen should have taken and failed to take, and the fraud it would have discovered if it had taken those steps, create a strong inference that Andersen acted recklessly in conducting the

WorldCom audits." Id. at *22. However, the court rejected the plaintiffs' theory of fraudulent scheme liability against an Andersen partner, Andersen UK, and Andersen Worldwide SC, none of whom were alleged to have made a false statement. Id. at *33-34. The court stated that the complaint failed to allege "the existence of any scheme or artifice in which these defendants participated. It does not identify any false information that these defendants contributed to a scheme or actions they took to facilitate a scheme." Id. at *34.

VI. ACCOUNTANTS' LIABILITY UNDER THE PSLRA

A. Methods of Proving Scienter

The PSLRA's pleading requirements do not distinguish between corporate defendants and accountants. Therefore, a plaintiff must plead facts raising a "strong inference" that the accountant "acted with the required state of mind." 15 U.S.C. § 78u-4(b)(2).

1. Recklessness Standard

Some courts have set the bar for pleading accountants' recklessness particularly high, requiring that the plaintiff show that "the accounting practices were so deficient that the audit amounted to no audit at all or that no reasonable accountant would have made the same decisions if confronted with the same facts." In re MicroStrategy, Inc. Sec. Litig., 115 F. Supp.2d 620, 651 (E.D. Va. 2000). This standard has also been expressed as an "egregious refusal to see the obvious, or to investigate the doubtful." In re Oxford Health Plans, Inc. Sec. Litig., 51 F. Supp.2d 290, 295 (S.D.N.Y. 1999). The Second Circuit has described the recklessness standard for accountants as follows:

> For recklessness on the part of a non-fiduciary accountant to satisfy securities fraud scienter, such recklessness must be conduct that is highly unreasonable, representing an extreme departure from the standards of ordinary care. It must, in fact, approximate an actual intent to aid in the fraud being perpetrated by the audited company.

Rothman v. Gregor, 220 F.3d 81, 98 (2d Cir. 2000). Accord, e.g., In re Raytheon Sec. Litig., 157 F. Supp.2d 131, 154 (D. Mass. 2001)(dismissing case against auditor where allegations did not support "a **strong** inference of willful blindness" by accountant)(emphasis in original).

2. *"Red Flags"*

In order to satisfy this pleading burden, a plaintiff may allege that the auditor was aware of, but failed to investigate, certain "red flags" indicating fraud or suggesting the need to investigate further. See, e.g., In re Rent-Way, 2002 U.S. Dist. LEXIS 12491, at *43-45; In re Complete Mgmt., 153 F. Supp.2d 314 (S.D.N.Y. 2001); In re Health Management, Inc. Sec. Litig., 970 F. Supp. 192, 203 (E.D.N.Y. 1997). Examples of "red flags" sufficient to raise a strong inference of scienter include:

—facts indicating that the company's financial reporting systems were in disarray, and that its internal controls were severely deficient, together with the existence of an investigation into the company's internal controls and accounting practices by the New York Attorney General's office. In re Oxford Health Plans, 51 F. Supp.2d at 295;

—evidence that the company's employees had alerted the accountants to material misstatements in the company's financial statements, and facts demonstrating that the company's internal controls were virtually non-existent, together with a Barron's article accusing the company of manipulating its financial statements. In re Sunbeam Sec. Litig., 89 F. Supp.2d 1326, 1345 (S.D. Fla. 1999);

—the lack of complexity of the transactions at issue, and public statements of the CEO evidencing a "willingness to bend the truth," along with insider sales by several individual defendants. In re MicroStrategy, Inc. Secs. Litig., 115 F. Supp.2d 620 (E.D. Va. 2000) ;

—facts indicating the accountant's knowledge of a lack of internal controls. Great Neck Capital Apprec. Inv. P'ship, LP v. Pricewaterhouse Coopers, LLP, 137 F. Supp.2d 1114, 1124 (E.D. Wis. 2001);

—facts demonstrating the accountant's knowledge of a company's repeated failure to comply with auditor's requests for financial documents. In re Livent, Inc. Sec. Litig., 148 F. Supp.2d 331 (S.D.N.Y. 2001);

—receipt by accountant of a letter from an analyst specifically warning that the client had improperly inflated its accounts receivable. In re Health Mgmt., 970 F. Supp. at 203.

However, if a court finds that the auditor responded appropriately to red flags, or if the red flags became apparent only after the audit was performed, no inference of recklessness will be drawn. See In re Ikon Office Solutions, Inc. Sec. Litig., 277 F.3d 658 (3d Cir. 2002). In Ikon, the Third Circuit affirmed the district court's order granting the accounting firm's motion for summary judgment, holding that "the discovery of discrete errors after subjecting an audit to piercing scrutiny post-hoc does not, standing alone, support a finding of intentional deceit or of recklessness." Id. at 673.

Similarly, in Nappier v. PricewaterhouseCoopers LLP, 227 F. Supp.2d 263, 279-280 (D.N.J. 2002), the court, in dismissing the claims against the accountants, observed that in order to support an inference of scienter, "'red flags' must be closer to 'smoking guns' than mere warning signs." The Nappier court held that the plaintiffs failed to demonstrate the auditor's knowledge of improper accounting practices based on, among other things, documents suggesting improper practices prior to—but not during—the class period. Id.

3. Violations of GAAP or GAAS; Magnitude of Violation

Most courts have held that a violation of GAAP or GAAS, standing alone, is insufficient to support a strong inference of scienter, but scienter may be inferred when the GAAP or GASS violation is combined with other factors—such as "a drastic overstatement of financial results." Carley Capital Group v. Deloitte & Touche, LLP, 27 F. Supp.2d 1324, 1339 (N.D. Ga. 1998). Many courts have held that the sheer magnitude of the GAAP violations, overstatements, or write-offs are a sufficient "red flag" to support a strong inference of scienter. See, e.g., Global Crossing, 2004 U.S. Dist. LEXIS 5040, at *72 (concluding that conscious misbehavior or recklessness was pled where "plaintiffs have alleged a fraud of a magnitude only rarely seen—at least until recent years," and stating that "[i]n such cases, the scope of the fraud alleged may appropriately be considered in determining whether scienter has been adequately pled"); WorldCom, 2003 U.S. Dist. LEXIS 10863, at *7 ("although the size of the fraud alone does not create an inference of scienter, the enormous amounts at stake coupled with the detailed allegations regarding the nature and extent of [the client's] fraudulent accounting and Andersen's failure to conduct a thorough and objective audit create a strong inference that Andersen was reckless in not knowing that its audit opinions materially misrepresented [the company's] financial state."); Carley Capital, 27 F. Supp. at 1339 ("the totality and magnitude of the defendant's accounting violations constitute strong circumstantial evidence of reckless or conscious misbehavior"); Rehm v. Eagle Finance Corp., 954 F. Supp. 1246, 1256 (N.D. Ill. 1997)("[t]he magnitude of reporting errors may lend weight to allegations of recklessness where defendants were in a position to detect the errors.").

Other courts, however, disagree that the magnitude of the accounting violations can support a claim of fraudulent intent. See, e.g., Raytheon, 157 F. Supp.2d at 155 ("[t]he magnitude of the misstatement, combined with the internal documents...at most supports a garden-variety inference of recklessness or a strong inference of negligence—but that is not enough.")

4. Accountant's Motivation to Obtain Consulting Fees

While an accountant's desire for future auditing fees is insufficient to raise an inference of fraud, allegations that the accounting firm was also a consultant to the company may support the inference that the desire to obtain consulting fees "created incentives for the auditors to seek to please...management at the expense of accuracy and/or completeness." In re Complete Mgmt, 153 F. Supp.2d 314. See also, Global Crossing, 2004 U.S. Dist. LEXIS 5040, at *67-68 (finding motive was adequately pled where the complaint alleged that "the desire to increase its non-audit practice led Andersen to abandon its obligations as an independent auditor, and by pushing its auditing clients to adopt risky and misleading accounting practices, to participate actively in the Companies' schemes to defraud investors."); Enron, 235 F. Supp.2d at 679 (concluding that Andersen "turned a blind eye to the many red flags and continued to issue 'clean' audit opinions in order to generate big fees and increase the compensation of Arthur Andersen partners"); Carley Capital, 27 F. Supp.2d at 1339 (where defendant auditor was alleged to have performed extensive consulting services for company, court found that the "[d]efendant was not just an auditor. It was heavily involved in the management of Medaphis and had unrestricted access to its financial records and data," suggesting that "[d]efendant knew that its client was understating expenses and improperly recognizing revenue.").

B. Proportionate Liability

Under the PSLRA, traditional joint and several liability standards have been replaced with a system of proportionate liability for claims based on non-knowing conduct (i.e. claims based on recklessness, negligence or strict liability). 15 U.S.C. § 78u-4(g)(2)(B). Defendants who act knowingly remain jointly and severally liable for all damages. 15 U.S.C. § 78u4(g)(2)(A). Accountants fought hard for this change, since their culpability is almost always based on recklessness. To date, there have been no appellate court decisions on these provisions, and it is not clear how the change has affected post-PSLRA filings against accountants.

VII. THE PSLRA'S SAFE HARBOR FOR FORWARD-LOOKING STATEMENTS: RECENT DEVELOPMENTS

The PSLRA's "safe harbor" provision protects forward looking statements where the statement is "identified as forward-looking" and is "accompanied by meaningful, cautionary statements identifying important factors that could cause actual results to differ materially from those in the forward-looking statement." 15 U.S.C. § 78u-5(c)(1)(a). The safe harbor also protects forward-looking statements if defendants are not shown to have had actual knowledge of the falsity of the statements. 15 U.S.C. § 78u-5(c)(1)(b). Excluded from protection are forward-looking statements contained in registration statements, IPOs or tender offers, or financial statements. 15 U.S.C. § 78u-5 (b)(2).

Despite the increase in restatement and other accounting fraud cases, which generally do not involve forward-looking statements, defendants are increasingly invoking the protection of the safe harbor in motions to dismiss. As one defense counsel admits:

> It would appear that defendants are routinely invoking the safe harbor provision even in situations where the argument is very weak. There is an enormous incentive to move to dismiss every complaint because filing such a motion triggers the automatic stay of discovery. Defendants, it appears, thus continue to feel compelled to raise the issue at every turn."

Richard A. Rosen, "Safe Harbor for Forward-Looking Statements in the Courts: A Year 2001 Scorecard," 34 Sec. Reg. & Law Rep. (BNA) No. 3, at 94 (Jan. 21, 2002).The increase in safe-harbor-based motions to dismiss has not, however, translated into more dismissals: defendants lost all or part of their motion to dismiss in twenty-three of thirty-nine recently reported district court cases involving the safe harbor. See id.

A. Only Forward-Looking Statements are Protected

The safe harbor does not protect statements that misrepresent then-existing or historical facts. For example, in a recent case, In re Regeneron Pharmaceuticals, Inc. Sec. Litig., No. 03 Civ. 3111 (RWS), 2005 U.S. Dist. LEXIS 1350, at *39 (S.D.N.Y. Feb. 3, 2005), the court held that the defendants' statements regarding, among other things, the effectiveness, safety, and tolerability of a certain drug undergoing FDA testing involved representations of present or historical facts, and therefore the statements did not qualify for safe harbor protection. See also, e.g., In re Amylin Pharm., Inc. Sec. Litig., U.S. Dist. LEXIS 7667, No. 01cv1455 BTM(NLS), at *14, 16 (S.D. Cal. May 1, 2003) (defendants' statements were not forward-looking because the they involved "observed facts"about clinical trial results).[28] See also, Rosen, supra at 92 ("Fourteen of the cases decided in the last fifteen months reject application of the safe harbor provision on the ground that the challenged statement is not forward-looking at all, but rather a statement of present or historical fact.").

Courts have also held that a statement is not forward-looking if the truth or falsity of the statement is determinable when made. See Viropharma, 2003 U.S. Dist. LEXIS 5623, at *25; cf. Harris v. Ivax Corp., 182 F.3d 799, 805 (11th Cir. 1999)(a forward looking statement is one whose truth or falsity cannot be determined until after the statement has been made).[29]

---

28. Accord, In re Complete Mgmt. Inc. Sec. Litig., 153 F. Supp.2d 314 (S.D.N.Y. 2001); In re Premiere Technologies, Inc. Sec. Litig., 2000 U.S. Dist LEXIS 19207 (N.D. Ga. 2000); Sunbeam, 89 F. Supp.2d 1326; In re PSS World Med., Inc. Sec. Litig., 250 F. Supp. 2d 1335, 1351 (M.D. Fla. 2002) (challenged statements were not forward-looking because they concerned "primarily 'hard' financial reporting results for PSSI, as opposed to . . . projections or future financial analysis"); In re Physician Corp. of Am. Sec. Litig., 50 F. Supp. 2d 1304, 1318 (S.D. Fla. 1999) ("the statutory safe harbor, created to allow for projections, does not protect defendants from liability based on 'statements that misrepresent historical/hard or current facts'") (citation omitted). In re Valujet, Inc. Sec. Litig., 984 F. Supp. 1472 (N.D. Ga. 1997); Gross v. Medaphis Corp., 977 F. Supp. 1463 (N.D. Ga. 1997)

29. In Harris v. Ivax, 182 F.3d at 805, the safe harbor was successfully invoked by the defendants, as it was in Advanta, 180 F.3d at 525, where the Third Circuit concluded that the statement "as [Advanta] converts more than $5 billion in accounts that are now at teaser rates..." was forward-looking because it was a statement of plans and objectives for management for future operations. Id.

B. Cautionary Language Must Be "Meaningful" and Boilerplate Warnings will not Suffice

Courts are also scrutinizing the cautionary language used to see whether it was sufficiently "meaningful." For example, in Helwig v. Vencor, Inc., 251 F.3d 540, 559 (6th Cir. 2001), the Sixth Circuit refused to apply the safe harbor where the company offered only "blanket statements concerning pending legislation [that] offered investors no guidance about the consequences of health care reform upon the company's business." Similarly, In re Boeing Sec. Litig., 40 F. Supp.2d 1160, 1167-69 (W.D. Wash. 1998), the court found that the statement that Boeing "is experiencing a near-term decline in productivity" was not entitled to protection because the cautionary language was boilerplate and failed to warn investors "of factors that could cause a steeper decline in the Company's productivity or an extension of that period of inefficiency." Id.[30]

Boilerplate warnings that do not inform investors of specific, known risks are not meaningful and will not shield defendants from liability. For example, generic warnings about the risks of FDA approval in cases against pharmaceutical companies have been found insufficient to protect against liability for knowing or reckless false statements. See, e.g., Warshaw v. Xoma Corp., 74 F.3d 955, 959 (9th Cir. 1996) (the defendant's optimistic statements regarding FDA approval were actionable even though the defendant "did disclaim, in general terms, the risks of failure involved in the FDA process" because the defendant "knew, based on its clinical studies, that [its drug] might not work and would never be approved by the FDA."); Regeneron, 2005 U.S. Dist. LEXIS 1350, at *53-55 ("generic disclaimer concerning hypothetical future risks" associated with drug development was insufficiently precise where disclaimer did not refer to any of the specific, then-known problems with drug at issue); CV Therapeutics, 2004 U.S. Dist. LEXIS 17419, at *34 (warning that the "FDA **may** interpret...data differently, which could delay, limit or prevent regulatory approval of [company's drug]" did not shield defendants' statements from liability, since "they did not indicate the Company already knew that the FDA harbored serious doubts about [the drug]")(emphasis in original); In re Sepracor, Inc. Sec. Litig., 308 F. Supp.2d 20, 35 (D. Mass. 2004)("generic cau-

---

30. On the other hand, where risk factors are company-specific, detailed, and tailored to the particular risks, courts are finding that the safe harbor applies. E.g., Ehlert v. Singer, 245 F.3d 1313, 1319-20 (11th Cir. 2001).

tionary statements" about prospects for FDA approval were insufficient where defendants failed to disclose known facts about animal studies that undermined their predictions of drug's success); Amylin, 2003 U.S. Dist. LEXIS 7667 at *21 (warning investors that FDA may not approve the drug was not meaningful because it tells investors what they already know, and is boilerplate); Viropharma, 2003 U.S. Dist. LEXIS 5623, at *28-29 (purported cautionary language stating that clinical trials may fail insufficient because it did not advise investors of specific, known risks).[31]

C. Forward-Looking Statement Must be "Identified" as Such, and Cautionary Language Must "Accompany" Statement

Courts have denied safe harbor treatment where the forward-looking statement was not "identified" as such, or because the forward-looking statement was not "accompanied" by cautionary language, as required by the PSLRA. See, e.g., In re Campbell Soup Co. Sec. Litig., 145 F. Supp.2d at 574(no identification of forward-looking statement); Bryant v. Apple South, Inc., 25 F. Supp.2d 1372, 1382 (M.D. Ga. 1998)(cautionary language did not accompany statement).

D. Cautionary Statements Do Not Protect Against Liability for Knowingly False Statements

The safe harbor affords no protection to statements—forward-looking or not—when the speaker knows that such statements are contradicted by then-existing facts. 15 U.S.C. § 78u-5. The Conference Report for the PSLRA pointed out that "the applicability of the safe harbor provisions under subsection [15 U.S.C. § 78 u-5](c)(1)(B) shall be based on the 'actual knowledge' of the defendant and does not depend on the use of cautionary language.'" H.R. Conf. Rep. No. 104-369 at 47 (1995), U.S. Code Cong. & Admin. News at 746. Thus, "a plaintiff can defeat the safe harbor by demonstrating that the statement was made with actual knowledge...that the statement was false or misleading." Campbell Soup, 145 F. Supp.2d at 589. "In other words, the

31. See also, In re Ins. Mgmt. Solutions Group, Inc., Sec. Litig., 2001 U.S. Dist. LEXIS 9962, No. 8:00CV2013T26MAP, at *22-23, 33 (M.D. Fla. July 11, 2001) (detailed cautionary statements regarding risks of the company's flood-mapping services were deemed insufficient because the known undisclosed fact was that the company's flood-mapping services were declining due to problems with a merger); Rubinstein v. Collins, 20 F.3d 160, 171 (5th Cir. 1994) ("the inclusion of general cautionary language regarding a prediction would not excuse the alleged failure to reveal known material, adverse facts").

safe harbor provision does not afford corporations a free pass to lie to investors." In re AT&T, 2002 U.S. Dist. LEXIS 22219, at *41.

For example, in In re CV Therapeutics, Inc. Sec. Litig., No. C 03-03709 SI, 2004 U.S. Dist. LEXIS 17419, *33 (N.D. Cal. Aug. 5, 2004), the court found that statements concerning the possibility of FDA approval of the company's drug, Raxena, were not eligible for safe harbor protection since "defendants possessed and failed to disclose detailed information about the FDA's serious reservations concerning Raxena's safety and efficacy." The CV Therapeutics court noted, in addition, that "[t]he fact that defendants used those inadequately disclosed historical facts to support unsound projections does not shield their alleged misrepresentations as forward-looking statements." Id. (emphasis added). See also, Ruskin v. TGI Holdings, Inc., 2000 WL 1154278, at *7 (S.D.N.Y. Aug. 14, 2000)(declining to apply safe harbor and stating, "cautionary language does not protect material misrepresentations or omissions when defendants knew they were false when made"); Schaffer v. Evolving Sys., Inc., 29 F. Supp.2d 1213(D. Colo. 1998)(denying motion to dismiss based on safe harbor where plaintiffs adequately alleged that defendants issued quarterly earnings forecasts with actual knowledge that they would not be met).[32] However, where plaintiffs are unable to demonstrate actual knowledge of the falsity of defendants' forward-looking statements, courts are increasingly willing to grant motions to dismiss. See, e.g., In re Milestone Scientific Sec. Litig., 103 F. Supp.2d 425 (D.N.J. 2000); In re Ciena Corp. Sec. Litig., 99 F. Supp.2d 650 (D. Md. 2000).

E. Oral Statements Protected If Accompanied By Cautionary Warnings

Oral statements are protected under PSLRA where the statement is accompanied by a cautionary statement that (a) the particular oral statement is forward-looking, and (b) that actual results may differ materially from the results predicted. 15 U.S.C § 78u-5(c)(2)(A). The oral statement must also be accompanied by another oral statement indicating that additional meaningful cautionary language is contained in a readily identifiable written document and that the written document

---

32. See also, e.g., Employee-Teamster Joint Council Pension Trust Fund v. Am. West Holding Corp., 320 F. 3d 920, 937 n. 15 (9th Cir. 2003); In re PSS World Medical Inc. Sec. Litig., 2002 U.S. Dist. LEXIS 14887 at *43 (M.D. Fla. July 2, 2002); Milman v. Box Hill Sys. Corp., 72 F. Supp. 2d 220, 231 (S.D.N.Y. 1999) ("'[N]o degree of cautionary language will protect material misrepresentations or omissions where defendants knew their statements were false when made.'").

satisfies the standards for a written forward-looking statement. Id. The safe harbor for oral statements, which is often invoked by defendants in the context of analyst conference calls, has been applied in several cases. See, e.g., Queen Uno Ltd. Partnership v. Coeur D'Alene Mines Corp., 2 F. Supp.2d 1345 (D. Colo. 1998); Wenger v. Lumisys, 2 F. Supp.2d 1231 (N.D. Cal. 1998).

VIII. SUBJECT MATTER JURISDICTION UNDER THE FEDERAL SECURITIES LAWS IN TRANSNATIONAL FRAUD CASES

In today's economy, investors enjoy far broader access to markets, and in far greater numbers, than ever previously imagined. Over the last decade, the number of foreign securities and American Depository Receipts ("ADRs") traded in the United States on exchanges or in American over-the-counter-markets has skyrocketed. Not surprisingly, this rise has been accompanied by an increase in transnational fraud, leading to questions about the extent to which American securities laws may properly be applied to the claims of foreign plaintiffs.

Courts have responded to these changing circumstances by increasingly recognizing the breadth of American law to reach many transactions by foreigners on foreign securities markets. See, e.g., Itoba Ltd. v. LEP Group PLC, 54 F.3d 118, 124 (2d Cir. 1995); In re Laidlaw Stockholder Litig., No. 3:00-855-17, Order No. 65 on Class Certification, (D.S.C. Nov. 18, 2003)(certifying class including persons who purchased stock of Canadian company on Canadian stock exchanges, where "the heart of the fraud" was the issuer's U.S. subsidiaries); In re Gaming Lottery Sec. Litig., 58 F. Supp. 2d 62, 75 (S.D.N.Y. 1999) (certifying class of stock purchasers on both U.S. and foreign markets, finding subject matter jurisdiction "supported by substantial fraudulent activity in the United States directly causing harm abroad, the manner in which the same fraudulent scheme allegedly straddled both sides of the border, and the degree of economic activity connecting GLC [the issuer] to the United States.").

Numerous courts have exercised jurisdiction to protect innocent foreign investors where defendants committed some fraudulent conduct in the U.S. See, e.g., IIT v. Vencap, Ltd., 519 F.2d 1001 (2d Cir. 1975) (Although the shares were not offered or sold to U.S. citizens, subject matter jurisdiction was exercised because defendants drafted the investment agreement in the United States and used a New York office as a base for many transactions); Cont'l Grain (Austl.) Pty., Ltd. v. Pac. Oilseeds, Inc., 592 F.2d 409 (8th Cir. 1979) (Although the plaintiff was a foreign corporation, the foreign securities were neither registered nor traded on a national securities exchange, there was no impact or effect in the U.S. and the negotiations and conduct were largely outside of the U.S., the court exercised subject matter jurisdiction where defendants' conduct in the U.S. consisted of letters and telephone calls necessary to further the fraudulent scheme.); SEC v. Kasser, 548 F.2d 109 (3d Cir. 1977) (the investment contract was executed and records were kept in United States, conduct crucial to consummation of the fraud); Grunenthal GmbH v. Hotz, 712 F.2d 421 (9th Cir. 1983) (Subject matter jurisdiction was exercised over a transaction in foreign securities between foreign corporations and citizens of foreign states where the only connection with the U.S. was that the fraudulent securities contract was signed in the United States and instrumentalities of interstate commerce were used to effect the fraud.).

Courts have developed two basic tests for subject matter jurisdiction when foreign plaintiffs avail themselves of the United States securities laws—the "conduct" test and the "effects" test. Under the conduct test, the court examines whether "at least some activity designed to further a fraudulent scheme occurs within this country." Kasser, 548 F.2d at 113. Under the effects test, the court examines whether conduct outside the United States has had a substantial adverse effect on American investors or securities markets. Id. Satisfaction of either test will suffice to establish jurisdiction. See Starlight Int'l, Inc. v. Herlihy, 13 F. Supp. 2d 1178, 1182 (D. Kan. 1998); Alfadda v. Fenn, 935 F.2d 475, 478 (2d Cir. 1991); Cont'l Grain, 592 F.2d at 416-17.

Courts have grappled with what degree of domestic conduct will suffice to establish jurisdiction over foreign plaintiffs. For example, the applicable standard in the Third Circuit requires "at least some" domestic activity in furtherance of the fraud. Kasser, 548 F.2d at 114 (emphasis added). The stricter Second Circuit standard requires that the domestic conduct "directly" caused the losses abroad, and also requires that the defendant's conduct in the United States "was more than merely preparatory to the fraud[.]" Alfadda 935 F.2d at 478 (emphasis added); see Bersch v. Drexel Firestone, Inc. 519 F.2d 974, 993 (2d Cir. 1975).[33]

---

33. Other courts have acknowledged the Third Circuit's adoption of a more relaxed standard for exercising jurisdiction than the Second Circuit's strict formulation in Bersch. See, e.g., Kaufman v. Campeau Corp., 744 F. Supp. 808, 810 (S.D. Ohio 1990); Zoelsch v. Arthur Andersen & Co., 824 F.2d 27, 31 (D.C. Cir. 1987)("The Third, Eighth, and Ninth Circuits appear to have relaxed the Second Circuit's test.").

Recently, the Southern District of New York determined that the Second Circuit's standard was met where plaintiffs alleged that a French company's CEO and CFO were "principal actors" in the alleged scheme, having moved to the United States specifically "to better direct the corporate operations and more effectively promote misleading perceptions on Wall Street." In re Vivendi Universal, S.A. Sec. Litig., 2003 U.S. Dist. LEXIS 19431, *22 (S.D.N.Y. Nov. 3, 2003). The Vivendi court concluded that it was reasonable to infer that "the alleged fraud on the American exchange was a "'substantial' or 'significant contributing cause' of [foreign investors'] decisions to purchase" the company's stock abroad. Id. (quoting Itoba, 54 F.3d at 122).

Although the Third Circuit's standard is generally considered more relaxed, the court in Tri-Star Farms Ltd. v. Marconi, PLC, 225 F. Supp.2d 567, 576 (W.D. Pa. 2002), pointed out that while "the Third Circuit might be willing to accept some lesser quantum of conduct as sufficient to establish jurisdiction than that required to satisfy the 'direct causation' standard," this does not mean that "any conduct within the United States will suffice." Instead, "the level of domestic conduct, at the very least, must be significant and material to the fraud." Id. Thus, in Marconi, where "the alleged fraud was committed by foreign defendants on foreign individuals in a foreign country," and where the only fraudulent conduct alleged to have taken place in the U.S. was the inclusion of certain misrepresentations in SEC filings and the dissemination of statements published in the British press in the U.S., the claims of the foreign investors were "too tenuous" to support a finding of subject matter jurisdiction under the securities laws. Id. at 577-578.

By contrast, the court in Laidlaw, No. 3:00-855-17, Order No. 65, at 6, held that the conduct test was satisfied, and subject matter jurisdiction was properly exercised over Canadian investors who purchased Laidlaw stock on Canadian stock exchanges, where the Canadian company's operations within the U.S. were "at the heart of the fraud." The Laidlaw court noted that the individual defendants are were all alleged to have been involved in the fraud not just as officers and directors of Laidlaw, a foreign corporation, but also as officers and directors of the domestic subsidiaries, Safety-Kleen and AMR. Id. at 5.

The Laidlaw court relied, in part, on the decision in In re Gaming Lottery, 58 F. Supp. 2d at 74, where the court exercised subject matter jurisdiction over Canadian plaintiffs who purchased GLC stock on the Toronto Stock Exchange. In that case, plaintiffs alleged that Gaming Lottery ("GLC") made announcements of increases in earnings and stockholder equity incorporating the financials of an American company at a time when GLC had not completed the acquisition and was operating the American company without regulatory approval. Plaintiffs alleged that these activities were part of a single fraudulent scheme which included misstatements and omissions in the U.S. and Canada and impacted the price of GLC stock in Canadian as well as American securities markets. Id. at 74-75. The court found that this was sufficient conduct within the U.S. to support subject matter jurisdiction. Id.

IX. BUILDING A STRONG SUIT: WHAT PLAINTIFFS LOOK FOR IN DECIDING TO BRING A CASE

A. Indications of Fraud

What makes a strong case from the point of view of a plaintiff's counsel? The presence of some or all of the following factors will suggest a factually strong case:

1. **A large and sudden percentage drop in the price of the stock.** Generally, plaintiffs are looking for a drop of greater than 10-15% (depending on the company and the price), and a decline which is not consistent with the market or industry trend.

2. **A restatement of revenues or income, or a reclassification of assets.** By its very nature, a restatement is an admission that the financial statements were incorrect when issued. Therefore, restatement cases are among the highest quality cases from a plaintiff's point of view.

3. **An announcement of "financial irregularities" or a delay in the issuance of a company's Form 10-K or 10-Q in order to investigate irregularities.** Such a delay usually means the company is fighting with its auditors. If combined with a large stock drop, the company will probably be sued once the irregularities or delay is disclosed.

4. **Insider selling**, particularly when several senior executives sell in the period before the bad news. The selling must be "suspicious and unusual" to be considered an indicia of fraud.

5. **A change in management or accounting firms, or the firing or "resignation" of key officers**.

6. **Post-mortem admissions indicating fraud**. Plaintiffs are looking for explanations as to why the poor results that led to the stock drop occurred so they can plead with specificity. If the company says nothing or is vague or unclear, it will be more difficult for the plaintiff to plead a case. However, by issuing vague explanations, the company runs the risk that the market will not be satisfied with its explanation. In such a situation, analysts will likely uncover the reasons for the poor performance, the plaintiffs will be able to plead their case, and the stock will be hurt even more because of management's lack of credibility. If a company has a business-related, innocent, non-fraud explanation for the decline, it is best for the company to state it clearly. This "handcuffs" plaintiffs, but if the explanation is not true, the fraud is compounded and plaintiffs' case, if it survives motion practice, becomes even stronger. In some instances, plaintiffs will engage industry experts to get behind the official explanation.

7. **Evidence that the company was on an acquisition binge, using its stock as currency,** or other indications of motive, such as maintaining the illusion of success in order to attract new capital through public offerings or other means.

8. **Executive compensation packages tied to stock market performance or to the achievement of specific levels of revenues or earnings.**

B. Specific Types of Financial Fraud Plaintiffs Look For

1. **Phantom or Fictitious Revenue and/or Income.** Examples include shipping product to a warehouse instead of a customer, and booking the revenue on the warehoused goods ("shipping in place"), or booking revenue when a customer hasn't decided to buy the product (even if you shipped it).

2. **Income and Revenue Recognition Practices.** Suspect revenue and income recognition practices include:

   A. Booking revenue when the customer has the right to return the product;

   B. Providing oral agreements or side letters modifying an agreement with a customer;

   C. Contingent sales, or sales providing a right of return;

D. Highly liberal payment terms instituted at the end of a quarter in order to make the numbers (for example, an agreement that the distributor has nine months to pay for a product, and only if it is sold through to customers);

E. Offset transactions that amount to sham sales. For example, the company books the sale of a software license for $3 million, and simultaneously enters into an agreement with the customer that if a joint venture is not entered into, the customer will get $3 million from the company.

F. Swap transactions between two companies for equal or almost equal amounts of the same commodity that have no economic substance.

3. **Failure To Take Adequate Reserves**. The company may fail to take adequate reserves in the following situations:

a. For uncollectible accounts receivable;

b. For inventory obsolescence (for example, where a buyer has a right to return an old product and receive a newer one);

c. For price protection (the seller gives the buyer protection against the company lowering the price on a product by giving them a credit—the company must then create a reserve);

d. For loan losses. Cases based on inadequate loan loss reserves can be difficult for plaintiffs if the company sticks to established historical levels, but a known deviation from history or industry benchmarks can be a good case.

4. **Reserve Reversals.** This practice involves taking a pre-existing reserve and reversing it into income or reducing an expense reserve. Companies sometimes use this technique to mask declining operating earnings, setting up a "cookie jar" of reserves to reverse when the need arises. The timing of the reserve is critical. Plaintiffs must determine whether there was a legitimate reason to reserve at that time or whether it was done to artificially bolster income in order to make the numbers for the quarter. Thus, the two major questions are (1) was the reserve proper; and (2) even if it was proper, was it dis-

closed. Even if it was proper to take the reserve, there may be liability for non-disclosure since the quality of earnings presented by the company is misleading.

5. **Capitalization and Deferral of Expenses**. Companies sometimes capitalize and defer expenses in order to raise earnings. However, under GAAP, expenses may only be capitalized when there is a discernible future benefit. Examples of suspicious areas of capitalization include:

   a. Advertising expense;

   b. Start-up and pre-opening costs (restaurant chains, theater companies); and

   c. Executive compensation.

6. **Amortization and Depreciation of Assets.** By overstating the useful lives of assets, then amortizing or depreciating an asset over too long a period of time, a company may artificially raise current income. For example, in the waste management industry, if garbage trucks are generally amortized over 10 years, a company's practice of taking 15 years to amortize its trucks will be viewed suspiciously. Suspicions will also be raised if an accountant audits several companies in the same industry and treats useful lives differently. Therefore, if a company deviates from the industry standard, it should disclose that fact and explain the reason for the deviation in order to avoid a lawsuit.

7. **Failure to Write Down or Write Off An Impaired Asset.** This issue often arises with useless, outdated software that a company fails to write down. Recently, with the massive devaluation of assets related to the telecommunications and cable industries, this has become an important issue.

X. FACTORS DISCOURAGING SUIT

A company is less likely to be sued if some or all of these factors are present:

A. A gradual erosion in the company's stock price, rather than a sudden drop.

B. **Insider buying, a lack of insider selling, or a pattern of insider selling that occurs every year at the same time.** Courts will not consider insider selling an indicia of fraud if:

a. The selling is in the same pattern as prior years, and always in the same window;

b. A few top insiders sell, but most do not;

c. The stock sold represents a small percentage of the insider's total holdings;

d. There has been some simultaneous insider buying;

e. The company's policy on insider selling is adhered to; for example, the selling took place within appropriate window periods, was individually reported to General Counsel, etc.

C. Indications of **channel-stuffing and forward-looking statements**. These cases are much weaker and difficult to prove in light of the PSLRA's scienter requirements and safe-harbor protections.

D. **The company avoids speaking post-mortems**. With no explanation for the stock drop, it is very difficult to plead a defendant's scienter.

E. **No distinct speakers and/or few statements by top corporate officers**.

F. Indications of **industry-wide problems or a one-quarter problem** in an otherwise strong company.

G. **A quick rebound in the company's stock price**. When a company's stock recovers quickly, defendants can sometimes get plaintiffs to consider voluntary dismissal of the case.

XI. HOW TO AVOID A SUIT OR MINIMIZE EXPOSURE

A company and its executives can increase their chances of avoiding a securities fraud suit, or minimize their exposure, by doing the following:

A. **Implement an Internal Control System that is Clearly Documented, Articulated, and Monitored.** A company should have its auditors design good internal controls. Accounting policies and procedures should be set forth by management in clear, unambiguous terms. In a debatable area, if the accounting procedure is fully disclosed, the company may be able to discourage or avoid a lawsuit. An adequate internal control system should include:

1. Periodic exams by an internal audit staff, with written reports required, such as regular reports to the audit committee identifying any problems or red flags.

2. A regular internal reporting system.

3. Reporting of deviations from regular policies and procedures to the audit committee, as well as to outside auditors.By getting outside auditors involved in accounting decisions, management will be able to argue that their accountants' approval of the transactions or accounting treatment at issue negates defendants' scienter.

B. **Build a Strong Audit Committee.** A strong audit committee should have access to all financial information, should be able to interview anyone, and should be comprised of truly independent directors with experience in accounting issues. The company should make it widely known that the audit committee has access to all reports and will use its extensive powers. The audit committee members should conduct—and document—interviews of financial reporting personnel, sales people, and executives.

C. **Closely Monitor and Document Insider Sales.** As noted above, courts may draw an inference of fraud where a significant percentage of the insider's holdings are sold; where many executives sold at the same time; and where the pattern of selling differs from prior years or periods. Companies should monitor and document insiders' sales during "window" periods (sales are usually permitted beginning a few weeks after earnings are reported and ending at least a month before the end of a quarter). The reasons for the stock sales should be determined and documented before the sales take place—not in the context of litigation.

D. **Establish a Strong Board of Directors to Whom Management Must Seriously Report.** A strong Board will not be dominated by the company's CEO, and will promote a policy of disclosure and openness. It will be easier to put together a strong board if the company has adequate D & O coverage in place.

E. **Set Reasonable Corporate Goals.** In general, management must not create impossible goals which make executives feel inexorable pressure to lie or exaggerate. The roots of financial fraud usually come from a corporate culture—generated by top management—which demands quarter to quarter growth, whether or not such growth is realistic or possible.

F. **And When All Else Fails....** Have adequate D& O insurance; blame the accountants; and always hire great defense lawyers.

NOTES

NOTES

2

THE DEVIL IS IN THE DETAILS: APPLICATION OF THE PSLRA'S PROPORTIONATE LIABILITY PROVISIONS IS SO FRAUGHT WITH UNCERTAINTY THAT THEY MAY BE VOID FOR VAGUENESS

Stuart M. Grant

Megan D. McIntyre

Grant & Eisenhofer P.A.

Mr. Grant and Ms. McIntyre are directors of Grant & Eisenhofer P.A., a litigation boutique with offices in New York City and Wilmington, Delaware, representing institutional investors in securities litigation and corporate governance matters nationally. The views expressed in this article are those of the authors alone, and do not necessarily reflect the views of Grant & Eisenhofer P.A. or of the clients of the firm.

Until 1995, all defendants in private federal securities actions were subject to joint and several liability. That is, each defendant found to have violated the federal securities laws could be required to pay the full amount of any judgment to the plaintiff, regardless of whether that defendant was the primary violator or merely one of many violators. To the extent such a defendant believed that it had paid more than its fair share of the judgment, its recourse was to seek contribution from others.

In 1995, Congress enacted the Private Securities Litigation Reform Act (the "PSLRA"). During the Congressional hearings and debate surrounding that legislation, there was considerable discussion about the perceived unfairness of joint and several liability, including the perception that plaintiffs were taking advantage of the threat of joint and several liability to coerce settlements out of "deep pocket" defendants, who were willing to pay money to settle even very weak claims against them rather than risk a verdict in which they could be required to pay the judgment in its entirety.[1]

Through the PSLRA, Congress decided to eliminate joint and several liability in most federal securities actions, and to replace it with a proportionate liability regime. Thus, Congress included a provision in the PSLRA stating that, unless the trier of fact determines a "knowing" violation to have occurred,[2] a "covered person against whom a final judgment

---

1. See, e.g., Testimony of Richard C. Breeden, 1995 WL 57112 (Feb. 10, 1995) (under joint and several liability, "parties who are central to perpetuating a fraud often pay little, of anything," while "those whose involvement might be only peripheral and lacked any deliberate and knowing participation in the fraud often pay the most in damages"); 141 Cong. Rec. S9040 ("Joint and several is the engine that drives abusive securities lawsuits. Plaintiffs' class action lawyers know this and use it to extract settlements.") (statement by Senator Domenici) (June 26, 1995). See also S. Rep. No. 98, 104th Cong., 1st Sess., at 20-22 (June 19, 1995), reprinted in 1995 U.S.C.C.A.N. 679, at 699-701; H.R. Rep. No. 369, 104th Cong., 1st Sess. at 37-38 (Nov. 28, 1995), reprinted in 1995 U.S.C.C.A.N. 730, at 736-37.

2. The PSLRA retains joint and several liability for knowing violations of the federal securities laws. See 15 U.S.C. § 78u-4(f)(2)(A) ("Any covered person against whom a final judgment is entered in a private action shall be liable for damages jointly and severally only if the trier of fact specifically determines that such covered person knowingly committed a violation of the securities laws."). In addition, defendants can be held jointly and severally liable for a co-defendant's proportionate share of liability, if (i) the court finds that share to be uncollectible from the co-defendant, (ii) the plaintiff is an individual whose recoverable damages under the final judgment are equal to more than 10% of his/her net worth, and (iii) the plaintiff's net worth is $200,000 or less. Id. at § 78u-4(f)(4)(A)(i).

is entered in a private action shall be liable solely for the portion of the judgment that corresponds to the percentage of responsibility of that covered person ...."[3] The term "covered person" refers to each defendant in a private action under the Securities and Exchange Act of 1934, and each outside director who is a defendant in an action pursuant to Section 11 of the Securities Act of 1933.[4] Thus, after the PSLRA, joint and several liability will be imposed only on: (1) knowing violators of the Securities and Exchange Act of 1934, (2) outside directors who knowingly violate Section 11 of the Securities Act of 1933, (3) defendants other than outside directors who commit any violation of Section 11 of the Securities Act of 1933;[5] and (4) persons who are found liable as "controlling persons," where the controlled person is jointly and severally liable and the controlling person fails to establish that that he/she had no reason to know of the controlled person's violation.[6] All other defendants will be subject to proportionate liability.

In an apparent effort to assist the courts in determining each defendant's proportionate share of the liability, Congress included a provision in the PSLRA which requires the trier of fact to make specific findings "with respect to each covered person and each of the other persons claimed by any of the parties to have caused or contributed to the loss incurred by the plaintiff, including persons who have entered into settlements with the plaintiff or plaintiffs," concerning:

> (i) whether such person violated the securities laws;
>
> (ii) the percentage of responsibility of such person, measured as a percentage of the total fault of all persons who caused or contributed to the loss incurred by the plaintiff; and
>
> (iii) whether such person knowingly committed a violation of the securities laws.[7]

---

3. 15 U.S.C. § 78u-4(f)(2)(B)(i).
4. Id. at §78u-4(f)(10)(c).
5. Id.; 15 U.S.C. § 77k(f)(1).
6. See 15 U.S.C. § 77o (persons who control a violator of Section 11 or 12 of the Securities Act of 1933 are liable "jointly and severally with and to the same extent as such controlled person ... unless the controlling person had no knowledge of or reasonable ground to believe in the existence of the facts by reason of which the liability of the controlled person is alleged to exist"); 15 U.S.C. § 78t(a) (persons who control a violator of the Securities Exchange Act of 1934 are "liable jointly and severally with and to the same extent as such controlled person ... unless the controlling person acted in good faith and did not directly or indirectly induce the act or acts constituting the violation or cause of action").

In a case tried to a jury, the jury must answer special interrogatories which address these issues, and which "specify the total amount of damages that the plaintiff is entitled to recover and the percentage of responsibility of each covered person found to have caused or contributed to the loss incurred by the plaintiff or plaintiffs."[8] The statute goes on to prescribe the factors which the jury "shall consider" when evaluating a person's percentage of responsibility:

> (i) the nature of the conduct of <u>each covered person</u> found to have caused or contributed to the loss incurred by the plaintiff or plaintiffs; and
>
> (ii) the nature and extent of the causal relationship between the conduct of <u>each such person</u> and the damages incurred by the plaintiff or plaintiffs.[9]

The foregoing provisions—which this article will refer to as the "Fault Allocation Provisions" of the PSLRA—are hopelessly vague and inherently contradictory. The flaws in the statute, while perhaps not readily apparent when reading the statutory language in a vacuum, become quite clear when one tries to apply the Fault Allocation Provisions in a real-world trial setting. While one provision requires the trier of fact to determine the percentage of responsibility of covered persons <u>and</u> "each of the other persons claimed by any of the parties to have caused or contributed to the loss incurred by the plaintiff,"[10] the provision that tells the trier of fact how to make that determination only makes reference to the nature of the conduct of <u>covered</u> persons and the causal relationship between <u>covered</u> persons' conduct and the plaintiffs' loss. Moreover, neither the PSLRA nor its legislative history provide any guidance as to the meaning or intended breadth of the term "each of the other persons claimed by any of the parties to have caused or contributed to the loss," and it is susceptible to widely varying interpretations.

Defendants read this language broadly, and seek to require juries to allocate responsibility for the plaintiffs' losses among as many persons as possible, in the hopes that this will minimize the defendants' own liability.[11] Defendants thus argue that, according to the plain language of the statute, they need do no more than "claim" that another person "caused or contributed to" the plaintiff's loss in order to ask the jury to allocate

---

7. 15 U.S.C. § 78u-4(f)(3)(A) (emphasis added).
8. <u>Id.</u> at § 78u-4(f)(3)(B).
9. 15 U.S.C. § 78u-4(f)(3)(C) (emphasis added).
10. <u>Id.</u> at § 78u-4(f)(3)(A).

responsibility to that person. Defendants also advocate the inclusion of both individuals and the entities that employ them in the allocation formula, even when the liability of the entity is alleged to be derivative of the individual's liability.

Plaintiffs, on the other hand, want as few persons as possible to be included in the allocation, since even a large verdict will be a pyrrhic victory if a substantial amount of the fault is allocated to non-defendants from whom the plaintiffs cannot collect. Accordingly, plaintiffs argue that there must be some sort of meaningful threshold for a defendant to meet in order to succeed in submitting a non-defendant's name to the jury for purposes of apportioning fault. For example, plaintiffs contend that fault should not be apportioned to non-defendants unless there is a sufficient factual and legal basis for a finding that those persons actually could have been held liable to the plaintiff, had they been named as defendants. Additionally, plaintiffs point out that when the liability of an entity is derivative of the liability of one of its directors, officers, or employees, it may be inappropriate to allocate separate shares of liability to both the individual and the entity, since to do so can result in double-counting.

The Fault Allocation Provisions give rise to other practical concerns as well. No matter how they are interpreted, they will lengthen and complicate securities trials which are, invariably, already long and complex. Instead of focusing on the liability or non-liability of the defendants, the parties and the court now must also address questions of whether non-parties contributed to the loss. Questions abound as to when and how the allegedly responsible non-parties must be identified, and who bears the burden of proof as to whether they violated the securities laws and/or contributed to the plaintiff's loss. At trial, the issue of non-parties' responsibility can easily give rise to a trial within a trial—one in which the non-parties are not there to defend themselves, leaving the plaintiffs in the awkward position of having to step into the non-parties' shoes and argue to the jury that those non-parties are <u>not</u> responsible.

From the non-party's perspective, the Fault Allocation Provisions raise interesting questions of fairness, since they may result in a jury finding that a non-party violated the federal securities laws and caused or contrib-

---

11. Some defendants have taken this so far as to seek to include plaintiffs as well as the Securities & Exchange Commission in the list of those who have "contributed to the loss incurred by the plaintiff." While absurd on its face, this effort conceivably conforms to the statutory language because the statute does not seem to require illegal conduct, only conduct that caused or contributed to the loss.

uted to the plaintiff's losses, and yet that result can be reached in a proceeding from which the non-party is completely absent, and of which they may have no notice. Even if they are aware of the proceeding, they have no right or ability to defend themselves or clear their names. Although the verdict would not be legally binding on an absent party, it may well cause significant reputational damage. No prominent businessperson would want a jury verdict holding him or her responsible for a percentage of a plaintiff's loss in a securities fraud trial, without the ability to offer a defense, yet the PSLRA's Fault Allocation Provisions seem to permit precisely that result.

Because only a small number of private federal securities cases have gone to trial since the PSLRA was enacted,[12] few courts have been called upon to interpret the Fault Allocation Provisions and there are no published opinions addressing these issue. As the authors discovered during a recent securities class action trial, however[13]—and as any court trying to navigate these uncharted waters in the future will find—these provisions can be interpreted in any number of ways, each with a different yet significant impact upon the rights and interests of the parties. The Fault Allocation Provisions are so vague that they are likely to be unconstitutional, because they provide neither plaintiffs nor defendants with ample notice of how liability will be allocated at the end of a case, or what they must do in order to protect their rights during earlier stages of the proceedings.

To illustrate the unconstitutionality of the Fault Allocation Provisions, this article will first examine the language of the PSLRA, and the competing interpretations of these provisions by plaintiffs and defendants, including some of the arguments for and against those interpretations and

---

12. The authors are aware of only nine federal securities class actions which have gone to trial based on post-PSLRA conduct during the ten years since the PSLRA was enacted. Of those, five settled during the course of trial or resulted in judgments as a matter of law, before the case was submitted to the jury. See Bruce Carton, "Counting Up the Securities Class Action Trials, Part III," Securities Litigation Watch (June 24, 2005), available at http://slw.issproxy.com.

13. The authors were sole lead counsel for the plaintiff class in In re Safety-Kleen Corp. Bondholders Litigation, No. 3:00-1145 17 in the United States District Court for the District of South Carolina, which went to trial in March 2005. There was considerable debate among the parties regarding the appropriate interpretation of the Fault Allocation Provisions, and the extent to which non-defendants should be included in the special interrogatories to be submitted to the jury regarding the allocation of fault. In the end, the dispute was not resolved, because the trial judge found two defendants to have committed knowing violations of the federal securities laws (thus subjecting them to joint and several liability) and the plaintiffs settled their claims against the remaining defendants before the case was submitted to the jury.

the consequences that will befall each group of litigants if their interpretation is ultimately not accepted by the trial judge. We will then examine the legislative history behind the PSLRA for clues as to how Congress intended the Fault Allocation Provisions to be applied. Finally, the article will explain why the Fault Allocation Provisions are susceptible to a constitutional challenge based on vagueness.

The Language of the PSLRA's Fault Allocation Provisions

The Fault Allocation Provisions of the PSLRA provide, in pertinent part, as follows:

> (2) Liability for damages
>
> (A) Joint and several liability
>
> Any covered person[14] against whom a final judgment is entered in a private action shall be liable for damages jointly and severally only if the trier of fact specifically determines that such covered person knowingly committed a violation of the securities laws.
>
> (B) Proportionate liability
>
> (i) In general
>
> Except as provided in subparagraph (A), a covered person against whom a final judgment is entered in a private action shall be liable solely for the portion of the judgment that corresponds to the percentage of responsibility of that covered person, as determined under paragraph (3).
>
> * * *
>
> (3) Determination of responsibility
>
> (A) In general
>
> In any private action, the court shall instruct the jury to answer special interrogatories, or if there is no jury, shall make findings, with respect to each covered person and each of the other

---

14. The term "covered person" is defined in the PSLRA to mean "(i) a defendant in any private action arising under [the Securities Exchange Act of 1934]; or (ii) a defendant in any private action arising under section [11] of [the Securities Act of 1933], who is an outside director of the issuer of the securities that are the subject of the action." 15 U.S.C. § 78u-4(f)(10)(C).

persons claimed by any of the parties to have caused or contributed to the loss incurred by the plaintiff, including persons who have entered into settlements with the plaintiff or plaintiffs, concerning—

(i) whether such person violated the securities laws;

(ii) the percentage of responsibility of such person, measured as a percentage of the total fault of all persons who caused or contributed to the loss incurred by the plaintiff; and

(iii) whether such person knowingly committed a violation of the securities laws.

(B) Contents of special interrogatories or findings

The responses to interrogatories, or findings, as appropriate, under subparagraph (A) shall specify the total amount of damages that the plaintiff is entitled to recover and the percentage of responsibility of each covered person found to have caused or contributed to the loss incurred by the plaintiff or plaintiffs.

(C) Factors for consideration

In determining the percentage of responsibility under this paragraph, the trier of fact shall consider-

(i) the nature of the conduct of each covered person found to have caused or contributed to the loss incurred by the plaintiff or plaintiffs; and

(ii) the nature and extent of the causal relationship between the conduct of each such person and the damages incurred by the plaintiff or plaintiffs.[15]

The "percentage of responsibility" as determined pursuant to the Fault Allocation Provisions also comes into play in other aspects of the PSLRA. For example, the PSLRA's provisions regarding contribution in favor of persons found to be jointly and severally liable state:

> A covered person who becomes jointly and severally liable for damages in any private action may recover contribution from any other person who, if joined in the original action, would have been liable for the same damages. A claim for contri-

---

15. 15 U.S.C. § 78u-4(f)(2)-(3).

bution shall be determined based on the percentage of responsibility of the claimant and of each person against whom a claim for contribution is made.[16]

In other words, non-defendants may be held liable for contribution, but only if they could have been held liable if they had been joined in the action as defendants. Additionally, if a covered person agrees to a settlement prior to final judgment, the PSLRA requires the subsequent final judgment to be reduced by the greater of (i) the amount that corresponds to the settling person's percentage of responsibility, or (ii) the amount paid by the settling person to the plaintiff.[17] These provisions illustrate why it was necessary for Congress to provide for the allocation of percentages of responsibility to certain persons who do not qualify as "covered persons"—namely, non-defendants who could have been held legally responsible for the plaintiff's loss, and former defendants who have settled with the plaintiff. They do not, however, reveal any justification for the allocation of responsibility to persons who could not have been held legally responsible if sued by the plaintiff.

Competing Views As To How The Fault Allocation Provisions Should Be Applied

The scope of the phrase "other persons claimed by any of the parties to have caused or contributed to the loss incurred by the plaintiff" is susceptible to numerous different interpretations. Among other things, there is substantial room for disagreement as to the meaning of the terms "claimed," "caused," "contributed to," and "loss." Is it enough to make a bare claim that a non-party caused a loss, or must there be an evidentiary showing to support that claim? When must the "claim" be made—at the pleadings stage, at the time the case is submitted to the jury, or somewhere in between? What is the "loss" for purposes of allocation of fault—is it the plaintiff's entire economic loss, or only the portion which is recoverable as legal damages? And can a person be claimed to have "caused" or "contributed to" a "loss" if that person could not be held liable for any damages to the plaintiff, even if they had been named as a defendant? These are merely some of the questions—predictably answered in diametrically different ways by plaintiffs and defendants—with which the courts and the parties must struggle when trying to apply the Fault Allocation Provisions.

16. Id. at § 78u-4(f)(8).
17. Id. at § 78u-4(f)(7)(B).

1. The Defense Perspective

The primary interest of defendants in securities fraud cases is, of course, in avoiding liability altogether. As a fallback position, however, in the post-PSLRA environment defendants will invariably argue that their conduct was not "knowing" (thereby making joint and several liability unavailable), and that to the extent they have any liability, it is small in comparison to that of others. Under the proportionate liability regime of the PSLRA, such an argument, when successful, will minimize the ultimate amount of that defendant's liability to the plaintiff.

The PSLRA's Fault Allocation Provisions provide defendants with a golden opportunity to try to shift blame for the plaintiff's loss away from themselves and onto others. The statute says that the jury must affix each defendant's percentage of responsibility by comparing their individual responsibility with "the total fault of all persons who caused or contributed to the loss incurred by the plaintiff."[18] As a further invitation for juries to consider the fault of non-defendants, the PSLRA says that the jury must make findings regarding the percentage of responsibility of each defendant "and each of the other persons claimed by any of the parties to have caused or contributed to the loss incurred by the plaintiff."[19] Thus, defendants typically argue that they need do no more than "claim" that a non-defendant "caused or contributed to the loss" in order to have that person's name sent to the jury as a potentially responsible party.

From a policy standpoint, defendants argue that their interpretation of the Fault Allocation Provisions is consistent with Congressional intent, because its effect is to limit each defendant's ultimate liability to that portion of the loss for which the defendant is actually found to be responsible. Using an overly simplified example, if one assumes that there are ten persons who are equally responsible for a plaintiff's loss, yet the plaintiff elects to sue only four of them, why should those defendants be required to pay 25% of the plaintiff's loss, when they are only responsible for 10%? This is an appealing argument on its face, but, as discussed below, it begs the question of what it means to be responsible for a plaintiff's loss. Or, in the words of the statute, how does one determine whether a particular person "caused or contributed to" the plaintiff's loss?

Defendants' interests are best served by arguing in favor of a broad interpretation of the phrase "caused or contributed" to the plaintiff's loss. After all, the more persons who can be deemed to have caused or contrib-

---

18. 15 U.S.C. § 78u-4(f)(3)(A).
19. Id.

uted to loss, the better the chances that liability will be spread across a larger group of persons, and that each defendant's individual liability will decrease. Thus, many defendants will argue that a person can cause or contribute to a loss, even if that person did not actually violate the federal securities laws. These defendants interpret the Fault Allocation Provisions to mean that, even if the jury answers "no" to the first question they are required to answer—i.e., whether a person violated the securities laws—they must nonetheless proceed to the second question—i.e., that person's percentage of responsibility. This interpretation clearly serves the defendants' self-interests, but it can leave the plaintiffs without a remedy for substantial amounts of their losses.

Assume, for example, that a plaintiff brings a Rule 10b-5 case against a company's directors and outside auditor, alleging that they caused the company to issue financial statements which were materially false as the result of fraudulent accounting. Often, there will have been numerous lower and mid-level employees in the company's accounting and finance departments who participated, perhaps unwittingly, in making the accounting entries by which the fraud was committed. When it comes time for allocation of liability at trial, the director and auditor defendants might claim that those lower and mid-level employees "caused or contributed to" the loss by making those entries. Defendants might further contend that the jury should be asked to allocate fault to those employees regardless of whether they could be held liable on the federal securities claim in question (e.g., in a Rule 10b-5 case, regardless of whether they acted with scienter or engaged in the type of conduct that is necessary to give rise to primary Rule 10b-5 liability). The result of the defendants' approach could well be the allocation of large percentages of fault to persons against whom the plaintiffs could not possibly state a claim.

The defense position on this issue has been credited by at least one commentator, who wrote that the Fault Allocation Provisions "invite[] the fact-finder to place blame on a variety of persons who bear no legal responsibility (and perhaps including the plaintiffs themselves) and so further dilute the liability of the reckless violators."[20] As he explained:

> Importantly, this allocation is not limited to defendants to the action. All responsible parties, named as defendants or not, are included; it is the plaintiffs' problem if a party allocated some of the blame is not named as a defendant. As will be dis-

20. Donald C. Langevoort, The Reform of Joint and Several Liability Under the Private Securities Litigation Reform Act of 1995: Proportionate Liability, Contribution Rights and Settlement Effects, 51 Bus. Law. 1157, 1162 (Aug. 1996) (emphasis added).

> cussed, it is quite possible to read the statute as including within the allocation persons (perhaps even the plaintiff himself) who are not liable for any damages at all....
>
> The key issue here has to do with the meaning of the phrase "persons claimed by any of the parties to have caused or contributed to the loss incurred by the plaintiff." [footnote omitted.] Reading the legislative history, one finds no evidence that Congress intended to do anything except have the fact-finder allocate responsibility among all the violators, whether named as defendants in the lawsuit or not. But this provision says plainly that the jury is to allocate responsibility among all those who caused or contributed to the loss; the aggregate of all such responsibility becomes the denominator in the allocation of damages to each defendant. That, presumably, could include the plaintiff, as well as other persons who contributed to the fraud even if they are not legally responsible. Read this way, there could be a substantial reduction in expected recoveries in those cases where there was no solvent defendant with joint and several liability.
>
> * * *
>
> One obvious strategy for the defendants is to maximize the number of persons, especially unnamed ones, to whom the jury should assign at least some percentage points of responsibility, because each percentage point put somewhere else is not other defendants' problem unless joint and several liability is triggered. Collectively, the defendants' best story is one of mass diffusion of responsibility, suggesting to the jury that they are just innocent scapegoats and hinting of conspiracies and involvements by phantom defendants well beyond the case that the plaintiff is presenting. And, of course, much attention will presumably be given to the plaintiffs' own responsibility in cases where the investors seemed a bit careless themselves.[21]

Another defense strategy is to seek an allocation of fault among individuals as well as the entities which employ them. For example, assume that a plaintiff alleges that a company and its Chief Executive Officer and Chief Financial Officer violated the federal securities laws by issuing false press releases, and that the conduct giving rise to the company's liability is the very same conduct giving rise to the two individual defendants' liability. In other words, the plaintiff alleges that the company is subject to liability because the actions and state of mind of the officers are imputed to the company.[22] Assuming that the jury finds all three defendants to be liable, how should the fault be allocated under the PSLRA? The officer defendants would argue that it should be apportioned at least three ways—i.e., among the two of them and the company. Arguably, however, the allocation should only be between the two officers, since the company's liability is derivative of the officers' liability. This can be a sig-

21. Id. at 1166-68 (emphasis added).

nificant issue, particularly in cases where the company itself is in bankruptcy and unable to pay a judgment.[23] Additionally, including all three defendants in the allocation can result in verdicts that are susceptible to challenge. For instance, a jury which is asked to allocate fault among all three defendants could conceivably allocate 40% to the Chief Executive Officer, 40% to the Chief Financial Officer, and 20% to the company. Given the vicarious nature of the company's liability, however, one could argue that its share of the fault should be equal to that of its officers. The PSLRA does not address this issue at all, thus creating an inherent ambiguity which is likely to lead to post-trial challenges to jury verdicts.

Finally, to the extent the Fault Allocation Provisions permit a party to make a "claim" that a non-defendant is responsible for the plaintiff's loss, thereby justifying allocation of fault to that non-defendant, the statute does not specify when that "claim" must be made. Defendants may argue that, in the absence of any statutory time limit, they can make that claim at any time prior to the submission of the case to the jury.

2. Plaintiffs' Perspective

Plaintiffs' interests are in achieving full recovery for their losses. However, the Fault Allocation Provisions of the PSLRA, if construed as defendants do, threaten to prevent plaintiffs from achieving that goal in a large number of cases. In deciding whom to name as defendants in a private securities action, plaintiffs are limited by a number of factors, not the least of which are the provisions of the PSLRA which heightened the pleading standards for certain elements of such cases. Thus, in the accounting fraud example discussed above, many plaintiffs would elect not to sue the com-

---

22. Because a company can only act through its agents, the actions and states of mind of its agents can be imputed to it for purposes of the federal securities laws. See Piper Jaffray Cos., Inc. v. National Union Fire Ins. Co. of Pittsburgh, 38 F. Supp. 2d 771, 779 (D. Minn. 1999) ("any liability faced by ... a corporate entity under rule 10b-5 requires a demonstration that at least one agent of the corporation ... possessed the requisite scienter"). See also In re Sunbeam Sec. Litig., 89 F. Supp. 2d 1326 (S.D. Fla. 1999); Rowe v. Marietta Corp., 955 F. Supp. 829, 833 (W.D. Tenn. 1996); American Gen. Ins. Co. v. Equitable Gen. Corp., 493 F. Supp. 721, 747 (E.D. Va. 1980).
23. The PSLRA does provide some protection for investors against judgment-proof defendants, insofar as it allows a plaintiff to recover a portion of the liability attributed to an insolvent defendant from the other defendants. 15 U.S.C. § 78u-4(f)(4). However, except in rare circumstances, the solvent defendants cannot be required to pay more than an additional 50% of their own liability toward the share of the insolvent defendant, and the plaintiff will be unable to collect the full judgment. See id. at § 78u-4(f)(4)(A)(i)-(ii).

pany's lower or mid-level accounting staff even though those persons may have contributed to the plaintiff's loss in some fashion, because claims against those persons would be doomed for dismissal due to the absence of any evidence of scienter, and/or because those persons' roles did not rise above the level of aiding and abetting.[24] These staff members will typically not have signed any of the Company's public filings or had any direct communications with investors, and thus would be deemed by many courts not to have "made" any statements in connection with the purchase or sale of securities for purposes of a Rule 10b-5 claim. Likewise, they probably would not be among the persons potentially subject to liability under Section 18 of the Securities & Exchange Act of 1934[25] or Section 11 of the Securities Act of 1933.[26] Moreover, lower level employees typically assert that they were merely following orders, did not know there was anything wrong with what they were doing, and therefore acted in good faith and without scienter. Under these circumstances, when there is no evidence to support a legally viable claim against a person, the law should discourage the filing of suit against such person. Yet, if the defendants' broad interpretation of the Fault Allocation Provisions is correct, those persons can still be allocated responsibility for a portion of the plaintiff's loss, and the plaintiff will have no ability to recover that portion.

Most plaintiffs would agree that, if they fail to sue defendants against whom they know they have legitimate claims, then it is fair to include those persons in the allocation of fault. For example, if there are viable securities fraud claims against a company's Chief Financial Officer, investment banks, and outside auditing firm, and yet the plaintiff sues only the "deep pocket" investment banks and auditing firm, those entities could persuasively argue that the jury should apportion fault not only to themselves, but also to the Chief Financial Officer. In those circum-

---

24. The Supreme Court has ruled that there is no private cause of action for aiding and abetting a securities law violation. Central Bank of Denver, N.A. v. First Interstate Bank of Denver, N.A., 511 U.S. 164, 191, 114 S. Ct. 1439, 1455 (1994).

25. Liability under Section 18 is limited to persons who make or cause to be made false statements in certain documents filed with the Securities and Exchange Commission pursuant to the Securities Exchange Act of 1934. See 15 U.S.C. § 78r.

26. Section 11 liability is limited to underwriters of securities, persons who sign a false registration statement, directors of the issuer, and other professionals (such as accountants) who give authority to statements made in the registration statement. 15 U.S.C. § 77k(a).

stances, any other result would frustrate the intent behind the PSLRA's shift to a proportionate liability scheme, as it would enable plaintiffs to force "deep pocket" defendants to pay more than their fair share of plaintiffs' losses.

By the same token, however, plaintiffs argue that defendants' interpretation of the Fault Allocation Provisions swings the pendulum too far in the other direction, since it would prevent the plaintiffs in many cases from recovering the full amount of their losses from those who were proven to have committed fraud. Thus, plaintiffs argue that the Fault Allocation Provisions require something more than a bare "claim" by a defendant that a non-defendant contributed to a loss, before the jury can be required to allocate fault to that non-defendant. The question is: What is that "something more," and how can the plaintiffs' position be squared with the language of the PSLRA?

The answer may lie in the interplay between the various provisions of the PSLRA relating to the percentage of responsibility. There is only one reference in the statute to "other persons claimed by any of the parties to have caused or contributed to the plaintiff's loss." That reference occurs in the section of the statute requiring the trier of fact to make findings regarding three distinct issues as to those persons: whether or not they violated the securities laws; their percentage of responsibility; and whether they committed a knowing violation. One could argue that, if the answer to the first question is "no"—i.e., if the jury finds that the "other person" did not violate the securities laws—then the jury should be instructed to stop there, as the second and third questions (regarding the percentage of responsibility and whether the violation was "knowing") are moot.[27] This would prevent the allocation of fault to non-defendants who did not violate the federal securities laws, while preserving Congress's intent to protect "deep pocket" defendants by requiring the allocation of fault to persons who violated the securities laws but are not named as defendants in the complaint. Under this approach, a jury would not be asked to allocate fault to a non-defendant on the basis of a bare "claim" that the non-defendant contributed to the loss, but only upon a showing

---

27. Accord John C. Coffee, Jr., Developments Under the Private Securities Litigation Reform Act of 1995: The Impact After Two Years, ALI-ABA Course of Study, Corporate Governance: Current and Emerging Issues, at 420-421 (Dec. 11, 1997) ("the better argument is that [the Fault Allocation Provisions] contemplate[] allocation of the loss only among the tortfeasors because it expressly requires the factfinder to determine first 'whether such person violated the securities laws.'").

sufficient to establish that the non-defendant is legally responsible for the loss.

The plaintiffs' interpretation is consistent with the approach taken by several courts in other circumstances requiring apportionment of fault. As one court has stated, "in the absence of substantial evidence, an attorney cannot make an 'empty chair' argument and blame an absent tortfeasor for a plaintiff's injury."[28] Similarly, in Hardin v. Manitowoc-Forsythe Corporation,[29] the Tenth Circuit Court of Appeals held that, in order to present the name of a non-defendant to the jury for purposes of allocation of fault, the defendants had to present sufficient evidence of that non-party's liability that the court would deny a motion for a directed verdict by that non-party. Professor John Coffee has also expressed the view that "the better argument is that [the Fault Allocation Provisions] contemplate[] allocation of the loss only among the tortfeasors because it expressly requires the factfinder to determine first 'whether such person violated the securities laws.'"[30]

Another argument made by plaintiffs is that a "claim" by the defendants that a non-party is partially responsible for the plaintiff's loss must be made well before the time the special interrogatories to the jury are drafted. Otherwise, plaintiffs will have no notice that a defendant intends to blame an absent party, and will have no opportunity to join that party as a defendant, or otherwise present evidence regarding the non-party's alleged fault. The Tenth Circuit has held, in the comparative negligence context, that "[t]he defense that a phantom party contributed to the plaintiff's injuries is in the nature of an avoidance and normally would be required to be pleaded affirmatively in the answer" in accordance with Rule 8(c) of the Federal Rules of Civil Procedure.[31] The Court also recognized that this requirement could be overridden if the plaintiff consented to treat the non-party's fault as an issue for trial, but that "courts must be particularly careful to scrutinize the record to ensure that plaintiff had adequate notice and opportunity to rebut the tardily-raised Rule 8(c) defense before finding that it was tried by consent."[32] Similarly, plaintiffs may argue that the Fault Allocation Provisions of the PSLRA do not give

---

28. Rowe v. Sisters of the Pallottine Missionary Society, 560 S.E.2d 491 (W. Va. 2001).
29. 691 F.2d 449 (10th Cir. 1982).
30. John C. Coffee, Jr., Developments Under the Private Securities Litigation Reform Act of 1995: The Impact After Two Years, ALI-ABA Course of Study, Corporate Governance: Current and Emerging Issues, at 420-421 (Dec. 11, 1997).
31. Hardin v. Manitowoc-Forsythe Corp., 691 F.2d 449, 458 (10th Cir. 1982).

defendants license to disregard the requirement of Rule 8(c) that defenses be presented in their answers, and that the reference in the PSLRA to a "claim" of fault by another party must be construed to mean a claim or defense which is appropriately raised in that party's pleadings.

On the question of whether the plaintiffs themselves can be allocated a portion of the fault under the Fault Allocation Provisions of the PSLRA, the plaintiffs will answer that such a result should not be permitted. Defendants will undoubtedly try to identify the plaintiffs as "other persons claimed by any of the parties to have caused or contributed to the loss ..." in at least some cases, particularly those where the plaintiffs were aware of risks associated with the securities at the time they purchased them. However, to the extent that a jury finds the plaintiffs themselves to have been responsible for a portion of their losses, that finding will likely result in a reduction in the total damages awarded to the plaintiff. In fact, defense experts will often present damage figures which purport to exclude from damages any losses caused by the plaintiff's own conduct. Allocating a portion of the liability for the final damage figure to the plaintiff would result in a "double-counting" of the plaintiff's responsibility, penalizing the plaintiff twice for the same conduct.

The Legislative History

Unfortunately, the legislative history of the PSLRA provides no answers to the questions raised above. It sheds no light on whether, or to what extent, Congress actually intended to have juries allocate fault in securities cases to persons who could not be found to have violated the federal securities laws, and provides no guidance as to the nature or timing of the "claim" that must be made by a party in order to justify including a non-party in the apportionment of fault. Although changes in the language of the Fault Allocation Provisions can be traced through the various iterations of the House and Senate bills that ultimately became the PSRLA, as discussed below, the Congressional debates and reports do not reveal the reasons for those changes.

For example, the proportionate liability provisions in the House versions of the bill, H.R. 1058, expressly permitted a jury to take into account a plaintiff's responsibility when allocating fault, stating:

> The trier of fact shall determine the percentage of responsibility of the plaintiff, of each of the defendants, and of each of the other persons or entities alleged by the

---

32. Id. See also O'Gilvie v. International Playtex, Inc., 821 F.2d 1438, 1445 (10th Cir. 1987).

parties to have caused or contributed to the harm alleged by the plaintiff. In determining the percentages of responsibility, the trier of fact shall consider both the nature of the conduct of each person and the nature and extent of the causal relationship between that conduct and the damage claimed by the plaintiff.[33]

The initial version of the Senate bill, on the other hand, did not provide for allocation of responsibility to plaintiffs, and instead stated:

> In an implied private action in which more than 1 person contributed to a violation of this title, the court shall instruct the jury to answer special interrogatories, or if there is no jury, shall make findings, concerning the degree of responsibility of each person alleged to have caused or contributed to the violation of this title, including persons who have entered into settlements with the plaintiff....[34]

Unlike the House bill, which contemplated apportionment among persons alleged to have caused or contributed to the "harm," the early Senate bill contemplated apportionment only among persons alleged to have caused or contributed to a violation of the securities laws.

A later version of the Senate bill, adopted on June 20, 1995, contained language similar to that in the initial Senate bill, but added a requirement that the jury make findings as to whether the defendants knowingly violated the securities laws:

> In any private action arising under this title in which more than 1 person is alleged to have violated a provision of this title, the court shall instruct the jury to answer special interrogatories, or if there is no jury, shall making findings, concerning-
>
> (A)the percentage of responsibility of each of the defendants and each of the other persons alleged by any of the parties to have caused or contributed to the violation, including persons who have entered into settlements with the plaintiff or plaintiffs, measured as a percentage of the total fault of all persons who caused or contributed to the violation; and
>
> (B)whether such defendant committed knowing securities fraud.[35]

In the Senate Report accompanying S. 240, the section-by-section analysis of the proposed bill explained the mechanics of the Fault Allocation Provisions as follows:

> In cases involving multiple defendants, the court shall instruct the jury to determine (i) each defendant's percentage of responsibility, including any settling defendants, and (ii) whether each defendant committed knowing securities fraud.

33. H.R. 1058, Sec. 4, § 10A(e)(3)(a) (March 1, 1995, March 10, 1995 and March 12, 1995 versions) (emphasis added).
34. S. 240, Sec. 203(a), § 41(C) (Jan. 22, 1995 version) (emphasis added).
35. S. 240, Sec. 202, § 38(c) (June 20, 1995 version); H.R. 1058, Sec. 202, § 38(c) (June 29, 1995 version).

The defendants who did not commit knowing securities fraud will only be liable for the portion of the damages attributable to their percentage of responsibility.[36]

No reference was made to any requirement that the jury make findings regarding the percentages of responsibility of non-defendants other than defendants who have already settled.

On June 29, 1995, the Senate passed H.R. 1058, after striking all but the enacting clause and replacing the text with the June 20, 1995 version of S. 240. The House, however, would not approve the Senate's amendments to the bill (albeit for reasons unrelated to the proportionate liability provisions). Accordingly, members of the House and Senate subcommittees met in November 1995 in an effort to reconcile their differences, and they ultimately agreed upon the final language of the PSLRA, which modified the proportionate liability provisions in several respects. First, whereas the June 29, 1995 version of the bill spoke in terms of allocating responsibility among persons who are alleged to have caused or contributed to a "violation" of the federal securities laws, the final language contemplates allocation among those who are claimed by any party to have caused or contributed to the plaintiff's "loss." The final language of the PSLRA also adds a requirement that the factfinder make a finding which would not have been expressly required under the prior versions of the bill: i.e., whether the various persons who are claimed to have caused or contributed to the loss actually violated the federal securities laws. This provision was inserted as the first of three questions to be addressed by the factfinder, preceding the requirements of findings regarding percentage of responsibility and whether the person committed a "knowing" violation. Plaintiffs may argue that this supports their interpretation of the PSLRA, because it demonstrates that Congress sought to require a finding that a person actually violated the federal securities laws before the jury would be required to assign that person a percentage of responsibility. Defendants will counter that the language of the PSLRA does not clearly make the assignment of responsibility contingent upon a finding of a violation. The final bill also did not contain the language from the House bill which would have expressly required the trier of fact to consider the plaintiff's percentage of fault, which one can argue demonstrates an intent by Congress to exclude plaintiffs from the apportionment equation.

---

36. S. Rep. No. 98, 104th Cong., 1st Sess. at 29 (June 19, 1995), reprinted in 1995 U.S.C.C.A.N. 679, at 708.

The final bill was accompanied by a Statement of Managers which explained the rationale behind the proportionate liability provisions as follows:

> One of the most manifestly unfair aspects of the current system of securities litigation is its imposition of liability on one party for injury actually caused by another. Under current law, a single defendant who has been found to be 1% liable may be forced to pay 100% of the damages in the case. The [final bill] remedies this injustice by providing a "fair share" system of proportionate liability....[37]

No explanation is provided, however, for the variations in the language between the final language of the Fault Allocation Provisions and the prior versions of the bill. No real attention was given (or at least none is reflected in the legislative record) as to the mechanics of how the Fault Allocation Provisions would operate in a trial setting, or whether the requirement that the jury make certain findings regarding covered persons and "other persons claimed by any of the parties to have caused or contributed to the loss" actually was intended to require the apportionment of fault to persons who would not have been subject to legal liability had they been sued by the plaintiff. In sum, the legislative history leaves unanswered the numerous questions that arise when trying to determine how to apply the Fault Allocation Provisions in practice.

The Fault Allocation Provisions Are Susceptible to a Facial Constitutional Challenge for Vagueness

The federal courts are required "to interpret the language of the statute enacted by Congress."[38] That interpretation begins with the plain language of the statute, and "where the statutory language provides a clear answer, it ends there as well."[39] Whether the language of a statute is plain or ambiguous "is determined by reference to the language itself, the specific context in which that language is used, and the broader context of the statute as a whole."[40] As discussed above, the language of the PSLRA's Fault Allocation Provisions is ambiguous on a number of issues, including in particular the meaning and scope of the phrase "other persons claimed by any of the parties to have caused or contributed to the loss

---

37. H.R. Rep. No. 369, 104th Cong., 1st Sess. at 37 (Nov. 28, 1995), reprinted in 1995 U.S.C.C.A.N. 730, at 736.
38. Barnhart v. Sigmon Coal Co., 534 U.S. 438, 461 (2002).
39. Hughes Aircraft Co. v. Jacobson, 525 U.S. 432, 438 (1999); Raila v. United States, 355 F.3d 118, 120 (2d Cir. 2004).
40. Robinson v. Shell Oil Co., 519 U.S. 337, 341 (1997) (cited in In re Worldcom, Inc. Sec. Litig., 2005 WL 335201, at *10 (S.D.N.Y. Feb. 14, 2005)).

incurred by the plaintiff." This ambiguity arises from the uncertain meanings of words such as "claimed," "caused," "contributed to," and "loss," all of which are subject to multiple competing interpretations. The ambiguity is further compounded by the fact that the PSLRA, when prescribing the factors to be considered when assessing percentages of responsibility, tells the jury to consider the conduct of the covered persons (defined to excluded non-defendants), and omits any reference to non-covered persons. The legislative history of the PSLRA, meanwhile, is silent as to how Congress intended these provisions to be interpreted.

Given the ambiguous nature of the PSLRA's Fault Allocation Provisions, the courts and the parties are left guessing about how to apply them in a real-world setting. Ultimately, it is up to the courts to decide what form of special interrogatories to submit to the jury regarding the allocation of responsibility, and to determine what non-defendants, if any, the jury will be asked to consider when performing the allocation. That determination—which will not come until the end of what is likely to have been a lengthy litigation process—can have far-reaching effects on the parties. If the court decides to include only defendants and settling defendants in the allocation, the potential liability of each defendant will be increased. If the court includes non-defendants, particularly ones against whom the plaintiffs cannot assert a viable claim, then the plaintiff may find itself unable to recover its full damages. If the court decides at the time the case is submitted to the jury that the special interrogatories will only inquire into the responsibility of those non-defendants for whom the defendants have presented evidence to support a finding of liability, the defendants will claim prejudice if they did not know at an earlier stage of the proceedings that they would be required to satisfy such a burden. Conversely, if the court allows the jury to allocate responsibility to non-defendants who were not identified as potentially responsible parties in the defendants' pleadings, the plaintiffs may claim prejudice because they were not put on notice of the need to either join that non-defendant as a defendant, or demonstrate at trial why the non-defendant is not culpable. And, of course, there are questions about who bears the burden of proof as to the non-party's responsibility: Is it up to the plaintiffs to disprove the non-parties' responsibility as part of their case-in-chief, or is it the defendants' burden to prove the non-parties' responsibility in the nature of an affirmative defense? While a "trial within a trial" on these issues seems inevitable, the scope of that trial can be significantly affected by the trial court's interpretation of the ambiguous Fault Allocation Provisions.

A civil statute like the PSLRA—which does not reach constitutionally protected conduct—is subject to challenge as unduly vague, in violation of due process, when it is "impermissibly vague in all of its applications."[41] Stated differently, it has been said that such a statute is void for vagueness if it is "substantially incomprehensible."[42] Thus, while the courts recognize that "we can never expect mathematical certainty from our [statutory] language,"[43] a law will be deemed unconstitutionally vague when it involves an "unascertainable standard," or no standard at all, such that "men of common intelligence must necessarily guess at its meaning."[44] As the Supreme Court has explained:

> Vague laws offend several important values. First, because we assume that man is free to steer between lawful and unlawful conduct, we insist that laws give the person of ordinary intelligence a reasonable opportunity to know what is prohibited, so that he may act accordingly. Vague laws may trap the innocent by not providing fair warning. Second, if arbitrary and discriminatory enforcement is to be prevented, laws must provide explicit standards for those who apply them. A vague law impermissibly delegates basic policy matters to policemen, judges, and juries for resolution on an *ad hoc* and subjective basis, with the attendant dangers of arbitrary and discriminatory applications.[45]

As discussed above, the Fault Allocation Provisions of the PSLRA fail to provide explicit standards for the courts who must apply them, and do not provide litigants with a clear picture of what they must do during the early stages of a case to ensure that the Fault Allocation Provisions are not interpreted in a way that will cause them prejudice at the end of the case. As the Tenth Circuit stated in Hardin, a non-PSLRA case involving the apportionment of fault to non-defendants where the non-defendants were not identified in the pleadings and the court gave mixed signals about what the jury would be told about those non-defendants:

---

41. Village of Hoffman Estates v. Flipside, Hoffman Estates, Inc., 455 U.S. 489, 497, 102 S. Ct. 1186, 1193 (1982).

42. Exxon Corp. v. Busbee, 644 F.2d 1030, 1033 (5th Cir. 1981), cert. denied, 454 U.S. 932, 102 S. Ct. 430 (1981).

43. Grayned v. City of Rockford, 408 U.S. 104, 110, 92 S. Ct. 2294, 2300 (1972).

44. Coates v. City of Cincinnati, 402 U.S. 611, 91 S.Ct. 1686 (1971) (citation omitted). See also Smith v. Goguen, 415 U.S. 566, 572, 94 S. Ct. 1242, 1246 (1974); Hotel and Restaurant Employees and Bartenders Int'l Union Local 54 v. Read, 832 F.2d 263, 268 (3d Cir. 1987) ("A statute can ... be held unconstitutionally vague if the discretion of those who enforce it is not limited by explicit legislative standards.").

45. Grayned, 408 U.S. at 108-109, 92 S. Ct. at 2298-99 (footnotes omitted).

> The court's apparent confusion about the standards governing consideration, as opposed to actual submission, of phantom party fault, together with the lack of pleading notice before trial, enhanced the possibility of a slippery, undisciplined trial in which the parties had no notice of the governing standards and were likely to be prejudiced in the presentation of their cases.[46]

While the Hardin case did not involve a constitutional challenge, it demonstrates the potential prejudice which can result when courts are left to divine the meaning of the PSLRA's ambiguous provisions regarding the attribution of responsibility to non-defendants, with no meaningful standards or guidance. Although Congress's intent to protect "deep pocket" defendants by eliminating joint and several liability is clear, neither the language of the PSLRA nor its legislative history provide any guidance as to whether Congress meant to go so far as to allow the apportionment of responsibility to persons who did not even violate the federal securities laws, thereby creating a situation in which plaintiffs cannot be made whole. Absent such guidance, there is a colorable argument that the Fault Allocation Provisions "impermissibly delegate[] basic policy matters"— such as whether and to what extent defendants in securities cases can reduce their own liability and the plaintiff's overall recovery by pointing their fingers at non-defendants who did not violate the securities laws— for resolution by the courts "on an *ad hoc* and subjective basis, with the attendant dangers of arbitrary and discriminatory applications."[47] As such, there is a strong possibility that the Fault Allocation Provisions will—if the issue is ever addressed by a court—be declared unconstitutionally vague. Until then, litigants in the federal securities arena must proceed at their own peril, not fully knowing the consequences of their decisions regarding who to join (or not join) as parties in the case, and not knowing the extent to which a verdict in favor of the plaintiff may actually become a hollow victory by virtue of apportionment to persons without legal liability.

---

46. Hardin, 691 F.2d at 459 n.7.
47. Grayned, 408 U.S. at 109, 92 S. Ct. at 2299.

NOTES

NOTES

DEFENDING THE SECURITIES CLASS ACTION

3

RECENT DEVELOPMENTS IN SHAREHOLDER DERIVATIVE ACTIONS

Seth Aronson

Sharon L. Tomkins

Tristan Sorah-Reyes

O'Melveny & Myers, LLP

Table of Contents

I. DERIVATIVE ACTIONS BROUGHT IN STATE AND FEDERAL COURT

A. Defining Derivative Claims

1. What Is A Derivative Action?

a. A derivative action is actually two causes of action: it is an action to compel the corporation to sue and it is an action brought by a shareholder on behalf of the corporation to redress harm to the corporation. *Aronson v. Lewis*, 473 A.2d 805, 811 (Del. 1984) ("The nature of the action is two-fold. First, it is the equivalent of a suit by the shareholders to compel the corporation to sue. Second, it is a suit by the corporation, asserted by the shareholders on its behalf, against those liable to it."); *Brown v. Tenney*, 532 N.E.2d 230, 232 (Ill. 1988) (a derivative action is in effect two actions: "one against the directors for failing to sue; the second based upon the right belonging to the corporation.").

b. A derivative action allows shareholders to monitor and redress harm to the corporation caused by management where it is unlikely that management will redress the harm itself. *Meyer v. Fleming*, 327 U.S. 161, 167 (1946) ("the purpose of the derivative action [is] to place in the hands of the individual shareholder a means to protect the interest of the corporation from the misfeasance and malfeasance of 'faithless directors and mangers'"); *Kamen v. Kemper Financial Services, Inc.*, 500 U.S. 90, 95 (1991) (same) (quoting *Cohen v. Beneficial Indus. Loan Corp.*, 337 U.S. 541, 548 (1949); *Jones v. H. F. Ahmanson & Co.*, 1 Cal. 3d 93 (1969) ("A shareholder's derivative suit seeks to recover for the benefit of the corporation and its whole body of shareholders when injury is caused to the corporation that may not otherwise be redressed because of failure of the corporation to act. Thus, 'the action is derivative, i.e., in the corporate right, if the gravamen of the complaint is injury to the corporation, or to the whole body of its stock or property without any severance or distribution among individual holders, or if it seeks to recover assets for the corporation or to prevent the dissipation of its assets.").

c. An action is derivative when brought by a shareholder on behalf of the corporation for harm suffered by all shareholders in common. *See Levine v. Smith*, 591 A.2d 194, 200 (Del. 1991) ("A shareholder derivative suit is a uniquely equitable remedy in which a shareholder asserts on behalf of a corporation a claim belonging not to the shareholder, but to the corporation."); *Lewis v. Knutson*, 699 F.2d 230, 237-38 (5th Cir. 1983) ("When an officer, director, or controlling shareholder breaches [a] fiduciary duty to the corporation, the shareholder has no 'standing to bring [a] civil action at law against faithless directors and managers,' because the corporation and not the shareholder suffers the injury[; e]quity, however, allow[s] him to step into the corporation's shoes and to seek in its right the restitution he could not demand on his own."); *Avacus Partners, L.P. v. Brian*, CCH Fed. Sec. L. Rep. ¶ 96,232 (Del. Ch. 1990) (action is derivative because it is brought by one or more shareholders on behalf of the corporation rather than by the corporation itself); *see also*, *Katz v. Halperin,* 1996 WL 66006, at *4 (Del. Ch. Feb. 5, 1996) ("A proven claim of mismanagement resulting in corporate waste is a direct wrong to the corporation, and all stockholders experience an indirect wrong. Corporate waste claims are derivative, not individual.").

(1) "Although most derivative suits involve claims by a shareholder on behalf of a corporation, derivative suits also may be filed by members of an unincorporated association, such as a limited partnership." *Draper Fisher Jurvetson Mgmt. Co. V, LLC v. I-Enterprise Co. LLC*, 2004 WL 2944055, at *2 (N.D. Cal. Dec. 15, 2004) (plaintiff invested in venture capital funds, then alleged damages in the millions as a result of the defendants' fraudulent and negligent misrepresentation, breach of contract, breach of fiduciary duty, etc.; court held that most of the plaintiff's claims were derivative and had to be brought on behalf of the funds, of which plaintiff was a limited partner).

d. In contrast, an action brought by a shareholder for harm done to an individual shareholder or a group of shareholders is a direct action. *See Kahn v. Kaskel*, 367 F. Supp. 784

(S.D.N.Y. 1973) (a class action by shareholders is based upon individual rights belonging to each member of the class); *Von Brimer v. Whirlpool Corp.*, 367 F. Supp. 740 (N.D. Cal. 1973), *aff'd in part, rev'd on other grounds*, 536 F.2d 838 (9th Cir. 1976) (if the injury is to one of the shareholders and not the corporation, it is direct); *Behrens v. Aerial Comm., Inc.* Del . Ch., No. 17436 (May 18, 2001) ("The distinction between a direct and derivative claim... turns on the existence of direct or 'special' injury to the plaintiff stockholder.").

(1) A direct action can take many forms. *See, e.g., In re Worldcom, Inc.*, 323 B.R. 844, 850 (Bankr. S.D.N.Y. 2005) ("Common examples of direct actions include suits to compel the payment of a dividend, to protest the issuance of shares impermissibly diluting a shareholder's interest, to protect voting rights or to obtain inspection of corporate books and records."); *The Winer Family Trust v. Queen*, 2004 WL 2203709, at *25 (E.D. Pa. Sept. 27, 2004) ("If the injury is one to the plaintiff as an individual shareholder, as where the action is based on a contract to which the shareholder is a party, or on a right belonging severally to the shareholder, or on a fraud affecting the shareholder directly, or if there is a duty owed to the individual independent of the person's status as a shareholder, the shareholder may assert a direct action on his own behalf.")

2. How to Distinguish Between Direct and Derivative Actions?

a. It is not always easy to tell whether an action is derivative or direct. *Abelow v. Symonds*, 156 A.2d 416, 420 (Del. Ch. 1959) ("the line of distinction between derivative suits and those brought for the enforcement of personal rights asserted on behalf of a class of stockholders is often a narrow one, the latter type of actions being designed to enforce common rights running against plaintiffs' own corporation or those dominating it, while the former are clearly for the purpose of remedying wrongs to the corporation itself"). Often, the same set of facts gives rise to both direct and derivative claims. *Grimes v. Donald*, 673 A.2d 1207, 1212 (Del. 1996); *see e.g., H. F. Ahmanson & Co.*, 1 Cal. 3d at

107 ("The individual wrong necessary to support a suit by a shareholder need not be unique to that plaintiff. The same injury may affect a substantial number of shareholders. If the injury is not incidental to an injury to the corporation, an individual cause of action exists."); *Behrens*, Del. Ch., No. 17436 ("The distinction between a direct and derivative claim, which is difficult to apply in specific circumstances, turns on the existence of direct or 'special' injury to the plaintiff stockholder.").

b. Courts "have wide discretion" to determine whether an action is derivative or direct. *See e.g., Hanson v. Kake Tribal Corp.*, 939 P.2d 1320 (Alaska 1997) (looking to the adequacy of the remedies under derivative and direct actions).

c. Deciding whether an action is direct or derivative has been greatly complicated by courts that use a "special injury" test to determine whether a claim is direct or derivative. These courts require shareholders to show that they have suffered a special or distinct injury from other shareholders in order to bring a direct claim. *See, e.g., Geer v. Cox*, 242 F. Supp. 2d 1009, 1018 (D. Kan. 2003) ("Because plaintiff has failed to show that there was any duty owed to him that was not owed to all shareholders . .. or that he suffered any harm individually, his direct claim must be dismissed . . .") (interpreting Delaware law); *Pate v. Elloway*, 2003 WL 22682422 (Tex.App.Hous. (1 Dist.) Nov. 13, 2003) ("To have standing to assert a direct or individual claim, a stockholder must allege an injury that is separate and distinct from other stockholders . . .") (applying Delaware law). Other cases, however, have rejected this line of reasoning. *See, e.g., Strougo v. Bassini*, 282 F.3d 162, 172 (2nd Cir. 2002) ("where shareholders suffer a distinct injury, i.e., an injury that does not derive from corporate injury, they may bring direct suit, even if their injury is undifferentiated among them.") (interpreting Maryland law and rejecting "undifferentiated effect on shareholders" standard followed in other jurisdictions); *Kennedy v. Venrock Associates*, 348 F.3d 584, 591-592 (7th Cir. 2003) ("The charge that [the corporation's] directors issued a misleading proxy statement in violation of their fiduciary obligation is a legitimate direct claim . . . since the effect of the reincorporation was to reduce the shareholders' power over the corporation's affairs rather than to reduce the value of the corporation. It shows by the way that a direct suit is not necessarily precluded by the common shareholders' having suffered an 'undifferentiated harm.' They can suffer such a harm without the corporation's being injured.").

d. The Delaware Supreme Court, acknowledging the prior "confusing jurisprudence on the direct/derivative dichotomy," recently "disapprove[d] [of] the use of the concept of 'special injury' as a tool" in analyzing whether a claim is direct or derivative. *Tooley v. Donaldson, Lufkin & Jenrette, Inc.*, 845 A.2d 1031, 1035 (2004). The Court held: "We set forth in this Opinion the law to be applied henceforth in determining whether a stockholder's claim is derivative or direct. That issue must turn *solely* on the following questions: (1) who suffered the alleged harm (the corporation or the suing stockholders, individually); and (2) who would receive the benefit of any recovery or other remedy (the corporation or the stockholders, individually)?" *Id.* at 1033. The Court disapproved the concept that a claim is necessarily derivative if it affects all stockholders equally. *Id.* Rather, the focus, under the new test, is whether the stockholder has shown that he or she has suffered an injury that is not dependent on injury to the corporation. *Id.* at 1036.

(1) In *Tooley*, plaintiff stockholders brought a purported class action alleging that the members of the board of directors breached their fiduciary duties by agreeing to a 22-day delay in closing a proposed merger. Plaintiffs alleged that the delay cost them the lost time-value of the cash paid for their shares. *Id.* at 1033. The Court held that plaintiffs failed to state a derivative claim because they did not show an "injury to the corporate entity" or seek relief that "would go the corporation. Accordingly, there is no basis to hold that the complaint states a derivative claim." *Id.* at 1039.

(2) *See also, Agostino v. Hicks,* 845 A.2d 1110, 1121 (Del. Ch. 2004) ("what must be discarded is the notion of using special injury, *i.e.*, 'injury which is separate and distinct from that suffered by other shareholders' as a talismanic

entreaty to the assertion of an individual claim. . . [T]he more grounded approach [is to ask] whether the plaintiff has suffered injury 'independent of any injury to the corporation.'").

(3) Many courts have subsequently applied the principles set forth in *Tooley. See, e.g., Marcoux v. Prim*, 2004 WL 830393, at *12 (N.C. Super. April 16, 2004) (relying on *Tooley*, held that plaintiffs stated a direct breach of fiduciary duty claim that directors failed to get a fair price for the corporation's stock in a merger because the injury was to the shareholders, not the corporation); *In re Syncor Int'l Corp. S'holders Litig.*, 857 A.2d 994, 996-97 (Del. Ch. 2004) (applying *Tooley*, the court found that shareholders did not have a direct claim against the company for the reduced price they received for their shares in a merger due to the misconduct of the company's founder and former chairman; rather, the claim was derivative because "the alleged misconduct was in connection with Syncor's core business activities and, if proven, would involve a breach of the duty of loyalty owed to Syncor. Moreover, although the immediate effect of the misconduct might have been to benefit Syncor through increased sales and profits, there is no mistaking that the alleged misconduct caused substantial injury to Syncor, which became the focus of multiple criminal and civil proceedings."); *Dieterich v. Harrer*, 857 A.2d 1017 (Del. Ch. 2004) (mismanagement that precluded company from entering more lucrative merger transaction deemed derivative under *Tooley*); *Smith v. Waste Mgmt, Inc.*, 407 F.3d 381, 385 (5th Cir. 2005) (using the test articulated in *Tooley*, the court held that "when a corporation, through its officers, misstates its financial condition, thereby causing a decline in the company's share price when the truth is revealed, the corporation itself has been injured," and not just the shareholder); *Schuster v. Gardner*, 127 Cal. App. 4th 305, 313, 315-316 (2005) (action arising from alleged mismanagement improprieties of officers and directors of corporation and the attendant decline in company's stock value deemed derivative

under either California or Delaware (applying *Tooley*) law).

e. An increasing number of courts have also abandoned the distinction between direct and derivative actions in the context of closely held corporations. *See Marcuccilli v. Ken Corporation*, 766 N.E. 2d 444, 450 (Ind. Ct. App. 2002) (quoting *Barth v. Barth*, 659 N.E. 2d 559 (Ind. 1995)) (quoting A.L.I., *Principles of Corporate Governance* § 7.01(d)) ("[i]n the case of a closely held corporation, the court in its discretion may treat an action raising derivative claims as a direct action, exempt it from those restrictions and defenses applicable only to derivative actions, and order an individual recovery, if it finds that to do so will not (i) unfairly expose the corporation or the defendants to a multiplicity of actions, (ii) materially prejudice the interests of creditors of the corporation, or (iii) interfere with a fair distribution of the recovery among all interested persons."); *see also Sharkey v. Emery,* 272 B.R. 574, 582-583 (Bankr. D.N.J. Nov. 2001) (relying on *Brown v. Brown*, 323 N.J. Super. 30, 36 (App. Div. 1999) (the distinction between derivative and direct actions in a closely held corporation is immaterial where defendants will not be exposed to a multiplicity of actions, creditors interests could be protected, and proceeds could be distributed fairly among interested persons); *Hubbard v. Tomlinson*, 747 N.E. 2d 69, 71-72 (Ind. Ct. App. 2001) (quoting the Indiana Supreme Court in *G & N Aircraft, Inc. v. Boehm*, 743 N.E. 2d 227, 236 (2001)) ("a shareholder in a close corporation need not always bring claims of corporate harm as derivative actions[;] rather, in such an arrangement, the shareholders are more realistically viewed as partners, and the formalities of corporate litigation may be bypassed."); *DeHoff v. Veterinary Hospital Operations Of Central Ohio, Inc.,* 2003 WL 21470388, at *14 (Ohio App. 10 Dist. June 26, 2003) (allowing minority shareholder of closely held corporation to bring a direct action for breach of fiduciary duty against controlling shareholder because a derivative remedy would primarily benefit the alleged wrongdoers); *Fritzmeier v. Krause Gentle Corporation*, 669 N.W. 2d 699, 707-708 (2003) (allowing shareholders of wholly-owned corporations to pursue a direct action because there is no distinction between the shareholder and the corporation, and thus, no danger of duplicative recovery); *but see Mynatt v. Collis*, 57 P.3d 513, 529-30 (Kan. 2002) (although it recognized the "close corporation exception," the Court emphasized that "the decision whether to allow a party to proceed with a direct suit in lieu of a derivative action is entrusted to the court's discretion"; even if all three prongs are met (as discussed in *Marcuccilli* above) a court, "in its equitable power and discretion," can deny a shareholder from bringing a direct action); *Redeker v. Litt*, 2005 WL 1224697, at *5 (Iowa Ct. App. May 25, 2005) ("If a closely held corporation operates more like a partnership, some jurisdictions allow the shareholders to bring an individual action, even though the cause of action may technically be that of the corporation."); *Woolard v. Davenport*, 601 S.E.2d 319, 324-25 (N.C. Ct. App. 2004) (quoting *Norman v. Nash Johnson & Sons' Farms, Inc.*, 537 S.E.2d 248, 258 (N.C. Ct. App. 2000)) ("[I]t seems particularly appropriate to allow minority shareholders to file individual actions when a dispute arises within the context of a family owned corporation, or other corporation in which all shares of stock are held by a relatively small number of shareholders . . . . When the close relationships between the shareholders in a 'family' or closely held corporation tragically break down, the majority of shareholders are obviously in a position to exclude the minority shareholders from management decisions, leaving the minority shareholders with few remedies."); *Durham v. Durham*, 871 A.2d 41, 46 (N.H. 2005) ("A direct action may be appropriate in this case because all of the corporation's shareholders are before the court as either the plaintiff or defendants; thus, there is no risk that a direct suit would expose the corporation to a multiplicity of actions.").

f. Most states, including Delaware, however, have yet to adopt this so-called "closely held corporation exception." *See* Ferrara, Abikoff, Gansler, *Shareholder Derivative Litigation: Besieging the Board* §1.02[2] (hereinafter "Ferrara, et al."); *see also Glod v. Baker*, 851 So.2d 1255, 1264-1267, 1276 (La.App.3rd Cir. Aug. 6, 2003) (shareholders in closely held corporations, partnerships and limited liability companies could not pursue individual claims on their own behalf even though they were "severely personally damaged as a result of the wrongs done to their entities" because the right of action belonged solely to the entities).

3. State Law Applies

a. State law controls the determination of whether an action is derivative or direct in diversity actions brought in federal court. *Sax v. World Wide Press, Inc.*, 809 F.2d 610, 613 (9th Cir. 1987) (characterization of an action as derivative or direct question of state law); *Seidel v. Allegis Corp.*, 702 F. Supp. 1409 (N.D. Ill. 1989) (same); *Gadd v. Pearson*, 351 F. Supp. 895 (M.D. Fla. 1972) (same).

B. Standing Requirements

1. Plaintiffs Must Be A Shareholder At Time Of Suit

a. Most states and Federal Rule of Civil Procedure 23.1 require a plaintiff to be a shareholder of the corporation at the time a derivative action is filed and at the time of the challenged transaction. *See* Ferrara, et al. §4.02[1] and [2] and cases and statutes cited therein; *see also* Wright, Miller & Kane, *Federal Practice and Procedure: Civil 2d* § 1826 and § 1828 and cases cited therein. The second requirement is often known as the "contemporaneous ownership" requirement. This requirement is designed to curtail strike suits by prohibiting potential plaintiffs from buying into a lawsuit or commencing a derivative action by simply purchasing shares after the alleged wrong has occurred. *See, e.g., Brambles USA, Inc. v. Blocker*, 731 F. Supp. 643 (D. Del. 1990); *In re Penn Cent. Transp. Co.*, 341 F. Supp. 845 (E.D. Pa. 1972).

b. In diversity actions brought under Federal Rule 23.1, a threshold question is whether the court looks to state or federal law to determine a plaintiff's standing. The first requirement (i.e., that the plaintiff be a shareholder of the corporation at the time the action was filed) is governed by state law. *See* Wright & Miller § 1826 and cases cited therein. Courts have also generally held that the contemporaneous ownership requirement is procedural and have applied the contemporaneous ownership requirement found in Federal Rule 23.1 in the face of inconsistent state law. *See, e.g., Kona Enterprises, Inc. v. Estate of Bishop*, 179 F.3d 767, 769 (9th Cir. 1999); *Perrott v. U.S. Banking Corp.*, 53 F. Supp. 953 (D. Del. 1944); *Piccard v. Sperry Corp.*, 36 F. Supp. 1006 (S.D.N.Y.), *aff'd without opinion*, 120 F.2d 328 (2nd Cir. 1941).

c. The size of plaintiff's financial stake in the corporation is immaterial. *Koster v. (American) Lumbermens Mut. Cas. Co.*, 330 U.S. 518 (1947); *Subin v. Goldsmith*, 224 F.2d 753, 761 (2nd Cir. 1955). The only time a plaintiff's financial stake may be of consequence is where state law provides security-for-expenses. States that have adopted security-for-expenses statutes include Arizona, California, Colorado, Florida, Nebraska, New Jersey, New York, Pennsylvania, and Wisconsin. For a general discussion on securities-for-expenses statutes *see* Wright & Miller § 1835 and cases cited therein.

2. The Requirement That A Shareholder Own Stock When A Derivative Action Is Started

a. Maryland and New York have statutes that expressly require stock ownership at the time an action is commenced. *See* Md. Code Ann. § 4A-802 and N.Y. Bus. Corp. L. § 626. Other jurisdictions have judicially imposed this requirement. *See, e.g., Weffel v. Kramarsky*, 61 F.R.D. 674, 679 (S.D.N.Y 1974).

b. In some jurisdictions, beneficial owners are not permitted to bring derivative actions. *See* Ferrara, et al. § 4.02[1]. Other states expressly allow beneficial owners to bring such suits. *See id.* and statutes cited therein.

The Court of Appeals of Kansas, in a case that involved record, butnot beneficial owners of stock, held that a shareholder need not bea beneficial owner of stock in the corporation to have standing,finding that a "mere nominal owner of stock" has standing to bringa derivative suit because the nominal owner has an ongoingproprietary interest in the corporation. *Quality Developers, Inc. v.Thorman*, 31 P.3d 296, 301-302 (Kan. Ct. App. 2001).

c. In some community property states, a spouse has a beneficial interest arising from the other spouse's ownership of stock. *See, e.g.*, *American Guarantee & Liability Insurance Company v. Keiter*, 360 F.3d 13, 18 (1st Cir. 2004) ("In Washington, a community property state, one spouse is deemed to have a beneficial interest in stock owned by the other spouse by virtue of the one-half community property interest" and is not contingent upon the other spouse's death because the non-ownership spouse is not merely a legatee, but rather, is an owner of the one-half community interest).

d. Those jurisdiction that do not have statutes addressing the issue, such as Delaware, look to see if the plaintiff has an equitable interest in the stock. *Quality Developers*, 31 P.3d at 301-302. (citing *Anadarko Petroleum Corp. v. Panhandle Eastern Corp.*, 545 A.2d 1171, 1176 (Del. 1988); *Harrf v. Kerkorian*, 324 A.2d 215, 218 (Del. Ch. 1974), *aff'd in part, rev'd in part* 347 A.2d 133 (Del. 1975); *Rosenthall v. Burry Biscuit Corp.*, 60 A.2d 106, 113 (Del. Ch. 1948)).

3. The Contemporaneous Ownership Requirement

a. In most jurisdictions, a derivative plaintiff must have been a shareholder at the time of the challenged transaction and must remain a shareholder pending the outcome of the litigation. *See, e.g., Lewis v. Anderson*, 477 A.2d 1040, 1049 (Del. 1984) ("a plaintiff who ceases to be a shareholder, whether by reason of a merger or for any other reason, loses standing" to sue derivatively); *see also Brambles USA, Inc.*, 731 F. Supp. at 648 ("a derivative plaintiff [must] be a shareholder of the corporation at the time of the transaction of which he complains . . . [and] must also maintain that status throughout the lawsuit"); *Schilling v. Belcher*, 582 F.2d 995, 996 (5th Cir. 1978) ("a shareholder who sells his stock pending appeal of a favorable judgment in a stockholder's derivative suit . . . loses standing to further prosecute or defend the case"); *Strategic Asset Mgmt., Inc. v. Nicholson*, 2004 WL 2847875, at *3 (Del Ch. Nov. 30, 2004) (rejecting the argument that a shareholder need not maintain his or her status as a shareholder in situations where a settlement agreement has been reached; holding, instead, that a settlement agreement "without a final judgment by the Court" does not terminate the litigation). The purpose of this rule is "to prevent what has been considered an evil, namely, the purchasing of shares in order to maintain a derivative action designed to attack a transaction which occurred prior to the purchase of stock." *Burry Biscuit Corp.*, 60 A.2d at 111.

b. Exceptions To The Contemporaneous Ownership Rule

(1) Statutory Exceptions

(a) Several state statutes provide exceptions to the contemporaneous ownership rule. *See, e.g.,* Alaska Stat. § 10.06.435; Cal. Corp. Code § 800; Ill. Ann. Stat., Ch. 32, § 7.80; 15 Pa. Stat. § 1782; Va. Code Ann. § 13.1-672.1.

(b) Factors used to determine whether the exception should apply include: (1) whether there is a strong *prima facie* case in favor of the claim; (2) whether a similar action has or is likely to be commenced; (3) whether the shareholder acquired shares in the corporation before public disclosure of the alleged misconduct; (4) whether the defendant(s) will be permitted to retain ill-gotten gains if the suit does not go forward; and (5) whether the suit, if successful, will result in unjust enrichment to the shareholder. Ferrara, et al. § 4.02[3] collecting factors from Alaska's and California's statutes.

(2) The Continuing Wrong Doctrine

(a) Under the continuing wrong doctrine, the contemporaneous ownership requirement will not apply where the alleged wrong is occurring at the time the shareholder bought stock even if it began before the shareholder purchased the stock. *See, e.g., Brambles USA, Inc.*, 731 F. Supp. at 643; *Noland v. Barton*, 741 F.2d 315 (10th Cir. 1984); *see also* cases cited in Wright & Miller § 1828.

(b) Recently, the Second Circuit, declining to adopt an expansive interpretation of the continuing wrong doctrine, held that plaintiff "must have acquired his or her stock in the corporation before the core of the allegedly wrongful conduct transpired." *In re Bank of New York Derivative Litigation*, 320 F.3d 291, 298 (S.D.N.Y. 2003). *See also Lerner v. Allaire*, 2003 WL 22326504, at *3 (D. Conn. Sept. 30, 2003) ("a proper plaintiff must have acquired his or her stock in the corporation before the core of the allegedly wrongful conduct transpired").

(c) The cost of defending against related class action lawsuits and the negative impact of a company's standing in the financial markets does not constitute continuing harm. *In re Omnivision Technologies, Inc.*, 2005 WL 2397586, at *3 (N.D. Cal. Oct. 26, 2004) (concluding that "such open-ended injuries" as a company's "legal woes" and "reduced standing" in the capital markets "are well outside the bounds of the continuing wrong doctrine" because they could "continue for years").

(d) Not all courts allow a plaintiff to allege a continuing wrong to overcome the contemporaneous ownership rule. *See, e.g., Pullman-Peabody Co. v. Joy Mfg.*, 662 F. Supp. 32 (D.N.J. 1986) (rejecting continuing wrong exception to the contemporaneous ownership rule); *Herald Co. v. Seawell*, 472 F.2d 1081 (10th Cir. 1972) (same); *Lowell Wiper Supply Co. v. Helen Shop, Inc.*, 235 F. Supp. 640, 647 (S.D.N.Y. 1964) (shareholder could not maintain action on the theory that payment of dividends subsequent to plaintiff's ownership constituted continuing wrong).

(3) The Contemporaneous Ownership Rule And Mergers

(a) Normally, a merger destroys a derivative claim. Thus, under the general rule, a plaintiff loses standing to maintain a derivative action where a merger has occurred. *See, e.g., Schreiber v. Carney*, 447 A.2d 17, 21 (Del. Ch. 1982) ("upon the merger the derivative rights pass to the surviving corporation which then has the sole right or standing to prosecute the action"); *Lewis v. Anderson*, 477 A.2d 1040, 1047 (Del. 1982) ("[a] merger which eliminates ownership of stock eliminates standing to pursue a derivative claim."); *see also, Lewis v. Ward*, 852 A.2d 896, 904 (Del. 2004) (affirming *Lewis v. Anderson*) (court concluded that "the established principle of Delaware corporate law recogniz[es] the separate corporate existence and identity of corporate entities, as well as the statutory mandate that the management of every corporation is vested in its board of directors, not its stockholders.")

(b) There, however, are exceptions to this rule. For example, Delaware allows a shareholder to maintain a derivative action if the merger is the subject of a fraud claim and was perpetrated merely to deprive shareholders of standing. *See Kramer v. Western Pac. Indus.*, 546 A.2d 348, 354 (Del. 1988); *see also Arnett v. Gerber Scientific, Inc.*, 566 F. Supp. 1270, 1273 (S.D.N.Y. 1983) (shareholders had standing to sue after merger because "(1) plaintiffs' disposition of the stock was involuntary; (2) the disposition was related to the allegedly illegal acts of defendants; and (3) the remedy sought [rescission of the merger] would result in plaintiffs regaining shareholder status"). This exception is difficult to plead. *See,e.g., Lewis v. Ward*, 2003 WL 22461894, at *5 (Del. Ch. Oct. 29, 2003) (the exception to the contemporaneous ownership rule in the merger context "requires a showing that the sole basis for [the corporation's] decision to enter the merger was to divest the plaintiff of derivative standing"; the absence of well-pled facts suggesting that defendants' derivative liability was so substantial as to have been the motivating factor for a pre-textual merger with another company is fatal). Shareholders relying on this exception must plead with particularity facts showing the fraud. *Id.* at *4-5.

(c) A shareholder also has standing to bring a derivative suit if the merger is simply a reorganization that does not affect plaintiff's ownership in the business enterprise. *See Kramer*, 546 A.2d at 354; *see also Schreiber*, 447 A.2d at 17 (because the "structure of the old and new companies [was] virtually identical" and thus "had no meaningful effect on the plaintiff's ownership of the business enterprise," the plaintiff did not lose standing to maintain derivative action).

(d) Recently, the American Law Institute has proposed a rule that would allow a derivative plaintiff to maintain suit following the loss of stockholder status if that loss is the result of corporate action in which the holder did not acquiesce, and either: (1) the derivative action was commenced prior to the corporate action terminating the holder's status, or (2) the court finds that the holder is better able to represent the interests of the shareholders than any other holder who has brought suit. Principles of Corp. Governance § 7.02(a)(2) (2003).

(e) *Compare FirstCom, Inc. v. Qwest Corp.*, 2004 WL 2315289, at *2-3 (D. Minn. Oct. 13, 2004) (underMinnesota's Business Corporations Act,shareholders of defunct company still had standingto bring derivative suit).

C. The Demand Requirement

1. As discussed above, a derivative action redresses harm to the corporation. *See, e.g.*, H. F. Ahmanson & Co., 1 Cal. 3d at 93("'A stockholder's derivative suit is brought to enforce a cause of action which the corporation itself possesses against some third party, a suit to recompense the corporation for injuries which it has suffered as a result of the acts of third parties.'"). Thus, there is a presumption that the corporation, through its directors and officers, controls the decision to pursue a claim on behalf of the company. Accordingly, a shareholder that wishes to maintain a derivative action must attempt to secure corporate action through a demand to the board that it initiate the litigation. *See Grimes*, 673 A.2d at 1207 (citing *Kamen*, 500 U.S. at 90); see also *Delaware & Hudson Co. v. Albany & Susquehanna R.R. Co.*, 213 U.S. 435, 447 (1909) (the demand requirement "recognizes the right of the corporate directory to corporate control; in other words, to make the corporation paramount, even when its rights are to be protected or sought through litigation"). The demand requirement is not limited to corporations, but also applies to business trusts and investment funds. See *ING Principal Protection Funds Derivative Litigation*, 2005 WL 1107072, at *4 (D. Mass. May 9, 2005) (universal demand requirement applies to derivative actions brought on behalf of business trusts). One way around

this requirement, as discussed below, is to allege demand futility.

2. To satisfy the demand requirement, a complaint must "allege with particularity the efforts, if any, made by the plaintiff to obtain the action the plaintiff desires . . and the reasons for the plaintiff's failure to obtain the action or for not making the effort." Del. Ch. Ct. R. 23.1; *see also* Cal. Corp. Code § 800(b)(2) ("plaintiff [must] allege in the complaint with particularity plaintiff's efforts to secure from the board such action as plaintiff desires, or the reasons for not making such effort"); N.Y. Bus. Corp. Law § 626(c) ("complaint shall set forth with particularity the efforts of the plaintiff to secure the initiation of such action by the board or the reasons for not making such effort"). Because of the particularity requirement, notice pleading is insufficient. *Grobow v. Perot*, 539 A.2d 180, 187 (Del. 1989) ("conclusionary allegations of fact or law not supported by allegations of specific fact [are] not [to] be taken as true"); *Allison ex rel. General Motors Corp. v. General Motors Corp.*, 604 F. Supp. 1106, 1112 (D. Del. 1985) (Rule 23.1 "is a marked departure from the 'notice' pleading philosophy of the Federal Rules of Civil Procedure").

3. To make a demand a shareholder generally must send a letter or draft complaint or other comparable communication to the board of directors although some state statutes and Federal Rule 23.1 do allow a demand to be made on someone other than the board if that party is of "comparable authority." For a list of state statutes allowing demand on "comparable authority" *see* Ferrara, et al. § 3.03[1] n.11.

   a. The following cases have looked at the issue of who besides the board of directors may be served with a demand: *Kaster v Modification Systems, Inc.*, 731 F.2d 1014, 1017-19 (2nd Cir. 1984) (demand on individual who was president and chairman of the board and who owned 71% of voting stock was not sufficient); *Greenspun v. Deb E. Webb Corp.*, 634 F.2d 1204, 1209 (9th Cir. 1980) (demand to individual who was president, director, and general counsel of company insufficient); *In re Penn Cent. Sec. Litig.*, 335 F. Supp. at 1026 (demand on receiver or trustee for a bankrupt company sufficient); *Kemper v. American Broadcasting Cos.*, 365 F.

Supp. 1272, 1274 (S.D. Ohio 1973) (same); *Womble v. Dixon*, 585 F. Supp. 728, 731 (E.D. Va. 1983), *aff'd in part, vacated in part* 752 F.2d 80 (4th Cir. 1984) ("demand to bring suit on the savings and loan association's behalf must be made on the receiver or agency possessing the right to assert the associations claim").

b. The demand does not need to "assume a particular form . . . [or] be made in any special language." *Stoner v. Walsh*, 772 F. Supp. 790, 796 (S.D.N.Y. 1991). It must simply "fairly and adequately apprise the directors of the potential cause of action so that they, in the first instance, can discharge their duty of authorizing actions that 'in their considered opinion . . .[are] in the best interest of the corporation.'" *Id.* Accordingly, the demand typically must (1) identify the alleged wrongdoers; (2) describe the factual basis for the allegations; (3) describe the harm caused to the corporation; and (4) describe the request for relief. *See, e.g., Levner v. Saud*, 903 F. Supp. 452, 456 (S.D. N.Y. 1994), *aff'd* 61 F.3d 8 (2nd Cir. 1995); *Seidel v. Allegis Corp.*, 702 F. Supp. 1409, 1412 (N.D. Ill. 1989); *Lewis On Behalf of National Semiconductor Corp. v. Sporck*, 646 F. Supp. 574, 578 (N.D. Cal. 1986).

4. A new demand is not typically required where there has been a change in the board's make up. *See Nelson v. Pacific Southwest Airlines Industries, Inc., Shareholder Litig.*, 399 F. Supp. 1025 (S.D. Cal. 1975); *In re Fuqua Indus.*, 1997 WL 257460 (Del. Ch. May 13, 1997) (new demand not required even where the entire membership of the board has changed). But where an amended complaint raises issues not previously included in the earlier demand, these issues need to be presented to the board, absent futility, before they can be litigated. *In re Fuqua Indus.*, 1997 WL at 257460.

5. In assessing the reasonableness of the time between a demand and the filing of a derivative action, courts balance the needs of a corporation to make a conscientious decision against the potential desire of the corporation to delay the suit by engaging in "idle ceremony." See *Mills v. Esmark, Inc.*, 91 F.R.D. 70, 73 (N.D. Ill. 1981) (failure to respond to demand within three months tantamount to admitting demand futility); *but compare Recchion on Behalf of Westinghouse Electric Corp. v. Kirby*,

637 F. Supp. 1309, 1319 (W.D. Pa. 1986) (two months deemed insufficient to complete adequate investigation); *see also, Mozes on Behalf of General Electric Co. v. Welch*, 638 F. Supp. 215, 221 (D. Conn. 1986) (eight months deemed insufficient where investigation impeded by parallel criminal proceedings); *General Motors Corp.*, 604 F. Supp. at 1117-18 ("amount of time needed for a response will vary in direct proportion to the complexity of the technological, quantitative, and legal issues raised by the demand"); *MacCoumber v. Austin*, 2004 WL 1745751, at *4 (N.D. Ill. Aug. 2, 2004) ("courts have not formulated a specific rule as to what constitutes a reasonable response time," instead, they "determine reasonable response time by examining the complexity of the issues presented by the demand and the surrounding circumstances").

6. Choice of Law Considerations

   a. The U.S. Supreme Court in *Kamen v. Kemper Financial Services* settled the issue of what law governs the determination of whether a plaintiff has made an adequate demand or has been excused from making such a demand. 500 U.S. 90 (1991). In *Kamen* the Supreme Court held that the demand requirement of Federal Rule 23.1 "speaks only to the adequacy of the shareholder representative's pleadings," and does not itself create a demand requirement. *Id.* at 97 ("the function of the demand doctrine in delimiting the respective powers of the individual shareholder and of the directors to control corporate litigation clearly is a matter of 'substance,' not 'procedure.'") Accordingly, state law (i.e., the law of the state of incorporation), rather than federal law determines whether a demand is required and if so whether the demand was adequate. *Id.; see also, Hicks v. Lewis,* 2003 WL 22309482 (Tenn.Ct.App. Oct. 7, 2003) ("After a thorough review of the applicable case law, this Court has found no case decided after *Kamen* applying the substantive law of any state other than the state of incorporation to issues relating to the demand requirement").

D. Demand Futility

1. There are certain circumstances where a demand will be excused and a majority of courts still recognize a futility

exception to the demand requirement. *See, e.g., Aronson*, 473 A.2d at 814; *In re Abbott Labs. Derivative S'holder Litig.*, 325 F.3d 795, 803 (7th Cir. 2003); I*n re Prudential Ins. Co. Derivative Litig.*, 659 A.2d 961, 970 (N.J. Super. Ct. Ch. Div. 1995). The growing trend, however, has been for states to adopt a rule of universal demand. *See Ritter v. Dollens*, 2004 WL 1771597, at *1 (S.D. Ind. July 13, 2004) (noting that "nineteen states, including eight since 1997, have adopted the universal demand standard," this includes, Arizona, Connecticut, Florida, Georgia, Hawaii, Michigan, North Carolina, Texas and Virginia). *See also, Warden v. McLelland*, 288 F.3d 105, 111 (3rd Cir. 2002) ("Pennsylvania law no longer recognizes a futility exception"); *McCann v. McCann*, 61 P.3d 585, 593 (Idaho 2002) ("There is no futility exception in Idaho's Business Corporations Act"); *Equitec-Cole Roesler LLC v. McClanahan*, 2003 U.S. Dist. LEXIS 4340, at *11 (S.D. Tex. 2003) ("Under Texas law plaintiff must make a demand regardless of whether such a demand would be futile"); *ING Principal Protection Funds Derivative Litigation*, 2005 WL 1107072 (D. Mass. May 9, 2005) (Under Massachusetts' new "universal demand" statute, "demand must be made prior to the commencement of every derivative case, whether or not the directors are independent with respect to the matter subject to the demand.").

2. Acknowledging the growing trend toward universal demand, some courts that still recognize the demand futility analysis have nonetheless come to apply it quite narrowly. *See, e.g., Scalisi v. Fund Asset Management, L.P.*, 380 F.3d 133, 140-141 (2nd Cir. 2004) (applying Maryland law as stated in *Werbowsky v. Collomb,* 766 A.2d 123 (2001)) (allegations made by shareholders of mutual fund that directors of the fund's investment adviser would not authorize a suit against the fund for fear they would lose their highly paid positions were inadequate to excuse the demand requirement under Maryland law, citing *Werbowsky*'s firm adherence to the importance of the demand requirement even when a director "would be hostile to the action;" the court further noted the value of allowing "directors — even interested, non-independent directors—an opportunity to consider, or reconsider, the issue in dispute" (quoting *Werbowsky*)).

3. Rule 23.1 of the Delaware Chancery Court, as well as most of its counterparts, and Federal Rule 23.1 require a shareholder who fails to make a pre-suit demand to plead with particularity reasons why a demand was not made. *See e.g.*, Delaware Court of Chancery Rule 23.1, Fed. R. Civ. P. 23.1, N.Y. Bus. Corp. L. § 626, Cal. Corp. Code § 800(b)(2).

4. The plaintiff bears the burden of showing that a demand would be futile. *See, e.g., In re Oxford Health Plans, Inc. Sec. Litig.*, 192 F.R.D. 111 (S.D.N.Y. 2000); *Siegman v. Tri-star Pictures, Inc.*, 1989 WL 48746 (Del. Ch. May 5, 1989). Conclusory allegations that a demand would be futile are insufficient. As the California Court of Appeal held in *Shields v. Singleton*: "[B]road, conclusory allegations against all directors of a corporation are insufficient to establish demand futility." 15 Cal.App.4th 1611, 1621 (1993) (citing *Findley v. Garrett*, 109 Cal. App.2d 166, 174 (1952)); see also *Simon v. Becherer*, 775 N.Y.S.2d 313, 318 (N.Y. App. Div., 1st Dept. 2004) (plaintiffs failed to meet Delaware's pleading requirement that demand futility be supported by particularized facts where allegations failed to specify board members who allegedly participated in fraudulent transactions and lacked specific facts regarding the nature of the purported "systematic failure" to provide appropriate oversight and the "myriad" of "red flags" that were allegedly ignored; without such facts, plaintiffs failed to show that directors faced substantial likelihood of liability, and therefore, lacked disinterest); *In re SONUS Networks, Inc. Derivative Litigation*, 2004 WL 2341395, at *2 ("If a plaintiff does not actually make demand prior to filing suit, he or she 'must set forth . . . particularized factual statements that are essential to the claim.' The pleading requirements of Rule 23.1 are 'an exception to the general notice pleading standard' and 'more onerous than that required to withstand a Rule 12(b)(6) motion to dismiss.'" (citations omitted); *see additionally, Brehm v. Eisner*, 746 A.2d 244 (Del. 2000); *Scattered Corp. v. Chicago Stock Exchange Inc.*, 701 A.2d 70 (Del. 1997); *Grimes*, 673 A.2d at 1207; *Lewis v. Graves*, 701 F.2d 245 (2nd Cir. 1983); *In re E.F. Hutton Banking Practices Litig*, 634 F. Supp. 265 (S.D.N.Y 1986).

5. Determining whether a shareholder has met the burden is "predominately a factual issue." *Kaster*, 731 F.2d at 1014.

6. While most jurisdictions recognize this exception, the contours of the exception vary. The following are the demand futility tests for Delaware, New York, and California:

a. The Delaware Test

(1) A court's decision on whether a demand is futile is reviewed *de novo*. *Brehm*, 746 A.2d at 244 ("review of decisions of the Court of Chancery applying Rule 23.1 is *de novo* and plenary").[1] Demand futility is to be determined solely from the well-pled allegations of the Complaint. *Aronson, 473 A.2d at 814-17.*

(2) Delaware, which has the most developed body of law concerning demand futility, applies a two-prong test to determine whether demand futility has been adequately pled. For demand to be excused, a shareholder must allege facts that if taken as true raise a reasonable doubt that (1) a majority of the directors are disinterested and independent or (2) the challenged transaction was otherwise "the product of a valid business judgment." *Aronson*, 473 A.2d at 805. If either prong is met, demand is excused. *Id.* at 814.

(a) This test was first articulated in *Aronson v. Lewis* and, as discussed below, has been refined in later cases. In *Aronson*, a shareholder brought a derivative action against Meyers Corporation and its directors to challenge the compensation package of, and certain loans to a director who owned 47% of the stock. The shareholder alleged that a demand would be futile because (1) all of the current directors were named as defendants; (2) they all approved or acquiesced to the challenged transaction; and (3) the other board members and officers were "controlled" and "dominated" by the

---

1. Until the decision in *Brehm*, the Delaware courts had operated, based on dicta beginning in *Aronson*, 473 A.2d at 805, that a court's decision would be reviewed for an abuse of discretion, the standard used by the federal court's. *See, e.g.*, *Kaster*, 731 F.2d at 1020 (the determination of "whether the complaint pleads sufficient facts to establish that . . . a demand on the directors would be futile is within the sound discretion of the district court"). To the extent that *Aronson* and its progeny imply otherwise, those decisions have been overruled on that basis but otherwise remain good law.

director owning 47% of the shares. The court rejected these arguments, holding that the shareholder had failed to meet the two-prong test articulated by the court. 473 A.2d at 814 ("even proof of majority ownership of the company does not strip the directors" of the protection of the business judgment rule, nor do allegations that a majority of the members of the board approved of or acquiesced to the challenged transaction).

(3) *Pogostin v. Rice* amplified the *Aronson* test. 480 A.2d 619 (Del. 1984). The court stated: "As to the first *Aronson* inquiry, the court reviews the factual allegations to determine whether they create a reasonable doubt as to the disinterestedness and independence of the directors . . . Directorial interest exists wherever divided loyalties are present, or a director either has received, or is entitled to receive, a personal financial benefit from the challenged transaction which is not equally shared by the stockholders. The question of independence flows from an analysis of the factual allegations pertaining to the influences upon the directors' performance of their duties generally, and more specifically in request to the challenged transaction. . . .Thus, the *Aronson* test examines the alleged wrong to the corporation in relation to issues of independence, interest, and the exercise of business judgment by the directors." *Id.* at 624-25.

(a) *Pogostin v. Rice* arose as a result of a tender offer for shares of City Investing Company by Tamco Enterprises, Inc. The plaintiff shareholders claimed that the board rejected Tamco's tender offer in an effort to retain control of the company. The shareholders did not make a pre-suit demand, alleging that such a demand would have been futile because "each of the directors participated in the wrongs alleged" and because "the directors could not and would not sue themselves." *Pogostin*, 480 A.2d at 623. The court rejected the shareholders' claim that a pre-suit demand was excused. *Id.* at 626-27 ("An informed decision to reject a takeover proposal, hostile or friendly, will not excuse demand absent particularized allegations of a breach of fiduciary duty, such as self-dealing, fraud, overreaching, or lack of good faith.").

(4) The *Aronson* test was further amplified in *Grobow v. Perot.* 539 A.2d at 180. Rejecting the trial court's reading of *Aronson*, the *Grobow* court stated: "The test for demand futility should be whether the well-pleaded facts of the particular complaint support a reasonable doubt of business judgment protection, not whether the facts support a judicial finding that the directors' actions are not protected by the business judgment rule." *Grobow*, 539 A.2d at 186. The court declined to create a hard rule for determining when a plaintiff has established reasonable doubt under *Aronson*: "It would be neither practicable nor wise to attempt to formulate a criterion of general application for determining reasonable doubt. The facts necessary to support a finding of reasonable doubt either of director disinterest or independence, or whether proper business judgment was exercised in the transaction will vary with each case. Reasonable doubt must be decided by the trial court on a case-by-case basis employing an objective analysis." *Id.*

(a) In *Grobow*, General Motors' decision to repurchase shares of its own stock from Ross Perot was challenged. Plaintiffs alleged that the repurchase agreement was motivated by the board's desire to maintain control of GM and that a demand to the board would have been futile. The court disagreed, finding that the plaintiffs failed to raise a reasonable doubt that the directors were not disinterested in the transaction or that the directors were not independent. *Id.* at 189.

(b) The *Grobow* plaintiffs filed a second-amended complaint several months later based on newly acquired evidence. The case was consolidated with another derivative action. *See Levine*, 591 A.2d at 194. After dismissal based on Rule 23.1 of the consolidated action, plaintiffs' appealed. On appeal, the Supreme Court further clarified the *Aronson* test: "[A] plaintiff in a demand futility case must plead particularized facts creating a reasonable doubt as to the 'soundness' of the challenged business transaction sufficient to rebut the presumption that the business judgment rule attaches to the transaction. The point is that in a claim of demand futility, there are two alternative hurdles, either of which a derivative shareholder complaint must overcome to successfully withstand a Rule 23.1 motion." *Id.* at 205-06.

(5) The Court in *In re The Walt Disney Company Derivative Litigation*, 825 A.2d 275 (Del. Ch. 2003), further refined the business judgment hurdle imposed under *Aronson.* The Court stated that for demand to be excused under the second prong of *Aronson*, "plaintiffs must allege particularized facts sufficient to raise (1) a reason to doubt that the action was taken honestly and in good faith or (2) a reason to doubt that the board was adequately informed in making the decision." *Id.* at 286. Although it stated that "[i]t is rare when a court imposes liability on directors of a corporation for breach of the duty of care, and this Court is hesitant to second-guess the business judgment of a disinterested and independent board of directors"[,] the Court, nevertheless, did just that, stating that the *Disney* directors "failed to exercise *any* business judgment and failed to make *any* good faith attempt to fulfill their fiduciary duties" in approving an executive compensation contract for then president, Michael Ovitz, as well as implicitly approving a non-fault termination provision that resulted in a substantial monetary award to Ovitz after barely one year of employment. *Id.* at 278. The Court found that "all of the alleged facts, if true, imply that the defendant directors *knew* that they were making material decisions without adequate information and without adequate deliberation, and that they simply did not care if the decisions caused the corporation and its stockholders to suffer injury or loss. Viewed in this light, plaintiffs' new complaint sufficiently alleges a breach of the directors' obligation to act honestly and in good faith in the corporation's best interests for a Court to conclude, . . . , that the defendant directors' conduct fell outside the protection of the business judgment rule." *Id.* at 289.

(6) The Court also held that "[w]here a director consciously ignores his or her duties to the corporation, thereby causing economic injury to its stockholders, the director's actions are either 'not in good faith' or 'involve intentional misconduct'[,] [and] . . . fall *outside* the liability waiver provided under Disney's certificate of incorporation[,] [which is based on 8 *Del. C.* § 102(b)(7)]." *Id.* at 290. The Court additionally found that Ovitz had also breached his fiduciary duties to the company. The Court explained that because Ovitz was a "fiduciary during both the negotiation of his employment contract and the non-fault termination, he had an obligation to ensure the process of his contract negotiation and termination was both impartial and fair [to the corporation]." *Id.* at 290-291. Citing *Telxon Corp. v. Meyerson*, 802 A.2d 257, 265 (Del. 2002), the *Disney* Court noted that "directoral self-compensation decisions lie outside the business judgment rule's presumptive protection, so that, where properly challenged, the receipt of self-determined benefits is subject to an affirmative showing that the compensation arrangements are fair to the corporation." *Id.* The Court held that Ovitz had breached this duty to negotiate honestly and in good faith by working together with his close friend, Michael Eisner, to develop a "secret strategy" to attain the maximum benefit from his contract, all without board approval. *Id.* at 291.

(a) In *Disney*, plaintiffs brought a derivative action alleging that defendant directors breached their fiduciary duties when they blindly approved an employment contract with defendant Michael Ovitz and then, again without adequate deliberation or information, ignored defendant Michael Eisner's negotiations with Ovitz regarding his non-fault termination deal. The Court found that the board had breached its fiduciary duty of care because: (1) the board failed to review the actual draft employment agreement, including details of Ovitz's salary and severance provisions, basing its decision instead, on a summary of an incomplete agreement with no additional information or investigation; (2) no expert was available to advise the board as to the details of the agreement, outlining the pros and cons of either the salary or non-fault termination provisions or analyzing comparable industry standards for such agreements; and (3) the board, after approving Ovitz's hire under these circumstances, appointed CEO, Michael Eisner, a close friend of Ovitz for over 25 years, to negotiate the unresolved terms of the employment contract, never reviewing the final terms, which varied significantly from the draft agreement presented to the board in that the terms for the stock options and the non-fault termination were much more favorable to Ovitz. *Disney*, 825 A.2d at 287-289.

(b) The *Disney* Court noted similar failings regarding Ovitz's subsequent termination deal, again negotiated by his close friend Eisner. The deal included a payout of more that $38 million in cash and three million in "A" stock options, "all for leaving a job that Ovitz had allegedly proven incapable of performing." *Disney*, 825 A.2d 290-291. The Court noted that the board was neither informed of nor consulted on this deal, even though a formal board approval appeared necessary for such an action. Moreover, when the board learned of the agreement, it failed to ask any questions, did not seek to negotiate with Ovitz regarding his departure, and did not consider whether to seek a termination based on fault. *Id.* The Court indicated that if the "board had taken the time or effort to review these or other options, perhaps with the assistance of expert legal advisors, the business judgment rule might well protect its decision." *Id.* Having failed to pursue any of these options, the Court held that the board's conduct fell outside the protection of the business judgment rule. *Id.*

(7) Delaware courts apply a slightly different test where the board takes no action. In such cases, "no business judgment has been made and thus the second prong of the *Aronson* test . . . is inapplicable." *Rales v. Blasband*, 634 A.2d 927, 933-34 (Del. 1993). "Where there is no conscious decision by directors to act or refrain from acting, the business judgment rule has no application." *Id.* The

second prong of the *Aronson* test is also inapplicable where a majority of the board that undertook the challenged transaction has been replaced or where the challenged transaction was made by a board of a different corporation, such as might occur where there has been merger or sale. *Id.* at 933-34. In these circumstances, the court must determine whether the allegations in the complaint "create a reasonable doubt that, as of the time the complaint is filed, the board of directors could have properly exercised its independent and disinterested business judgment in responding to a demand." *Zimmerman v. Braddock*, 2002 WL 31926608, at *6 (Del. Ch. Dec. 20, 2002) (citing *Rales*, 634 A.2d at 934); *see also*, *Guttman v. Huang*, 823 A.2d 492, 503 (Del. Ch. 2003) (director's impartiality compromised when facing a substantial likelihood of personal liability for actions not covered under company's exculpatory charter provisions); *Rattner v. Bidzos*, 2003 WL 22284323 (Del. Ch. Oct. 7, 2003) ("Directors are considered disinterested . . . when they 'appear on both sides of a transaction [or] expect to derive any personal financial benefit from it in the sense of self-dealing, as opposed to a benefit which devolves upon the corporation or all stockholders generally.' Directorial interest may also be said to exist when 'a corporate decision will have a materially detrimental impact on a director, but not on the corporation and the stockholders.") (citations omitted). When director liability is predicated upon a failure to properly monitor or oversee the management of the corporation or other liability-creating activities, "only a sustained or systematic failure of the board to exercise oversight—such as an utter failure to attempt to assure a reasonable information reporting system exists—will establish the lack of good faith that is a necessary condition to liability." *Salsitz v. Nasser*, 208 F.R.D. 589, 592 (E.D. Mich. 2002) (quoting *McCall v. Scott*, 239 F.3d 808, *amended in part by* 250 F.3d 997, 999 (6th Cir. 2001) (quoting *In re Caremark International Inc. Derivative Litigation*, 698 A.2d 959, 971 (Del. Ch. 1996); *see also, Simon v. Becherer*, 775 N.Y.S. 2d 313, 318 (2004) (directors who are sued for failure to oversee subordinates have a disabling interest when the potential for liability is not a "mere threat" but instead a "substantial likelihood"). The Delaware Chancery Court recently dismissed the novel argument that this duty includes the duty to monitor the personal and financial affairs of the corporation's directors, or at least those directors who are "closely identified" with the success and welfare of the corporation. *See, e.g., Beam v. Stewart*, 833 A.2d 961, 971 (Del. Ch. 2003) ("it is unreasonable to impose a duty upon the Board to monitor [a director's] personal affairs because such a requirement is neither legitimate nor feasible.").

b. The New York Test

(1) The standard for demand futility under New York law is set forth in *Marx*, 666 N.E.2d at 1034, and is similar to the *Aronson* test. To establish demand futility under *Marx*, a plaintiff must allege with particularity that (1) a majority of the directors is interested in the challenged transaction; (2) the board of directors did not fully inform themselves to the extent reasonably appropriate under the circumstances; or (3) the challenged transaction was so egregious on its face that it could not have been the product of a sound business judgment. *Id.* at 1039; *see also, Bansbach v. Zinn*, 769 N.Y.S. 2d 175, 183 (2003) (demand excused and directors held to be dominated and controlled by the corporation's president where directors voted to indemnify all legal costs and expenses incurred by the president even after the president admitted in open court, under penalty of perjury, that he misused corporate funds to violate federal campaign finance laws).

(2) The principal difference between the New York and Delaware tests are the degree of certainty with which a plaintiff must allege demand futility. New York has expressly rejected a "reasonable doubt" standard. *Id.* at 1039. Instead, a plaintiff must show a greater degree of certainty that the board lacked independence or care or failed to exercise sound business judgment.

c. The California Test

(1) Under California law, demand futility is established when "the court [is] apprised of facts specific to each director from which it can conclude that the particular director could or could not be expected to fairly evaluate the claims of the shareholder plaintiff." *Shields*, 15 Cal. App. 4th at 1622 (1993).

(a) Plaintiff in *Shields* brought a derivative action against the directors and officers of Teledyne, Inc. and a number of employees and consultants of one of its subsidiaries to recover damages that the company allegedly suffered as a result of defendants intentional and negligent breach of their fiduciary duties by failing to prevent criminal acts of the subsidiary's employees. The court of appeals, rejecting plaintiff's claim that a demand was futile, stated, "[T]he general allegations which plaintiff here indiscriminately level against all the directors of the Company are insufficient to establish that demand on the board would have been futile." 15 Cal. App. 4th at 1622.

(2) Although there is relatively little case law discussing demand futility under California law, a litigant should be able to use Delaware law as persuasive authority. "There is obviously no problem where the laws of the two states [Delaware and California] are identical . . . Defendants do not argue that a different result would obtain if Delaware, rather than California, law is applied, or even that the laws of the two jurisdictions are in conflict." *Shields*, 15 Cal. App. 4th at 1621.

7. Many demand futility cases rely on acts of entrenchment by the board, allegations of domination and control by a majority shareholder, and director compensation levels to prove the requisite director interest or lack of independence. *See California Pub. Employees' Ret. Sys. v. Coulter*, 2002 WL 31888343, at *8 (Del. Ch. Dec. 18, 2002) ("Directors are presumptively 'interested' in . . . actions taken for entrenchment purposes" and "golden parachute" agreements for incumbent directors, especially after receiving serious complaints from shareholders, raised a reasonable doubt as to directors' disinterest);

Orman v. Cullman, 794 A.2d 5, 25 (Del. Ch. 2002) (where court defined "controlled" director as one who is dominated by another, whether through close personal or familial relationship or through force of will; director may also be "controlled" by another if he or she is beholden to the allegedly controlling entity, such as when the entity has the unilateral power to decide whether the director continues to receive a benefit upon which the director is so dependent or of such subjective importance that the threatened loss of the benefit might create a reason to question whether the director can objectively consider the corporate merits of the challenged transaction); *see also In re The Limited, Inc. Shareholders Litig.*, 2002 WL 537692, at *5-6 (Del. Ch. March 27, 2002) ("as a general matter, compensation from one's principal employment is 'typically of great consequence' to the employee" and it was reasonable to infer that director lacked independence from majority shareholder of corporation where position in corporation provided director his principal employment and an average salary of $1.8 million); *In re The Student Loan Corp. Derivative Litig.*, 2002 WL 75479, at *3 (Del. Ch. Jan. 8, 2002) (where a majority of the directors owe their livelihood to the corporation, it is "difficult to conceive . . . how any of them could impartially consider a demand in this case."); *In re National Auto Credit, Inc. Shareholders Litig.*, 2003 WL 139768, at *10 (Del. Ch. Jan. 10, 2003) (although directors' fees usually do not suggest a conflict of interest, fees that constitute a "massive increase" over existing fees, such as $1000 per meeting increased to $55,000 annually, could reasonably be inferred to compromise a director's ability to properly consider a demand); *In re Ebay, Inc. Shareholders Litig.* 2004 WL 253521, at *3 (Del. Ch. Feb. 11, 2004) (outside, non-managing director deemed to lack independence because value of his stock options "potentially run into the millions of dollars" and "one cannot conclude realistically that [the director] would be able to objectively and impartially consider a demand to bring litigation against those to whom he is beholden for his current position and future position on [the corporation's] board"); *but compare In re Merrill Lynch Focus Twenty Fund Investment Company Act Litig.*, 218 F.R.D. 377, 380-381 (E.D. N.Y. 2003) (directors' service on multiple boards associated with the corporation, with significant remuneration ($160-260,000), was not enough to demonstrate demand futility) (applying Maryland law) aff'd *by Scalisi*, 380 F.3d 133 (2nd Cir. 2004); *In re Sagent Technology, Inc., Derivative Litig.*, 278 F. Supp. 2d 1079, 1089 (N.D. Cal. 2003) ("demand futility cannot be pled merely on the basis of allegations that directors acted or would act to preserve their position" in the Company, even in situations concerning the directors' principal occupation); *Jacobs v. Yang*, 2004 WL 1728521, at *4 (Del. Ch. Aug. 2, 2004) (receipt of director's fees or remuneration not enough for purposes of pleading demand futility where director defendants do not control the nomination, election and continued tenure of directors on the company's board).

8. Plaintiffs in a number of recent cases have relied on allegations of insider stock sales to prove that directors lack disinterest. Recently, the Delaware Chancery Court noted the differences between archetypical claims of self-dealing and insider trading claims, concluding that "it is unwise to formulate a common law rule that makes a director 'interested' whenever a derivative plaintiff cursorily alleges that he made sales of company stock in the market at a time when he possessed material, non-public information." *Rattner*, 2003 WL 22284343, at *11. The Court held that a more balanced approach is to focus the impartiality analysis on whether the plaintiffs "have plead particularized facts regarding the directors that create a sufficient likelihood of personal liability because they have engaged in material trading activity at a time when . . . they knew material, non-public information about the company's financial condition." *Id.* (citing *Guttman*, 823 A.2d at 502). *See also, Sagent*, 278 F. Supp. 2d at 1089 (held director not disinterested because plaintiffs "fail[ed] to plead particularized facts raising a reasonable doubt that [the director] face[d] a substantial likelihood of liability for the alleged insider trading."); *Mitzner v. Hastings*, 2005 WL 88966, at *5 (N.D. Cal. Jan. 14, 2005) (plaintiff failed to plead particularized facts that directors lacked disinterest because of alleged insider stock sales where the "complaint does not contain particular facts showing that the outside directors knew about the alleged inside information or connecting particular trades to information acquired at particular times . . . Nor does the plaintiff place the allegedly

insider trades in the context of the defendant's trading histories.").

9. The futility analysis has also focused on the extent to which personal or business relationships affect a director's independence. For example, the Delaware Supreme Court held that "[a]llegations of a mere personal friendship or a mere outside business relationship, standing alone, are insufficient to raise a reasonable doubt about the director's independence"; such allegations "largely boil down to a 'structural bias' argument, which presupposes that the professional and social relationships that naturally develop among members of a board impede independent decision making." *Beam*, 845 A.2d at 1050-1051. *See also, Yang*, 2004 WL 1728521, at *6 (directors with outside business ties to Yahoo! were not prevented from considering a demand independently and free from "extraneous influences" where the complaint failed to allege "sufficient facts to support the inference that the [Insider Directors] had the authority or ability to cause Yahoo! to terminate its relationships" with these outside companies; complaint also failed to show that the outside business relationships were "material").

   a. In *Beam,* a shareholder of Martha Stewart Living Omnimedia, Inc. ("MSO") brought a derivative action against Martha Stewart for allegedly breaching her fiduciary duties of loyalty and care by illegally engaging in insider trading and mishandling the media attention that followed, thereby jeopardizing the financial future of MSO. *Id.* at 1044. Defendants moved to dismiss, citing plaintiff's failure to make a demand. The Court granted defendants' motion and held that demand was not futile because the majority of the board, consisting of three outside, non-managing directors, were deemed to be independent, even though the outside directors were "longstanding personal friends" of Martha Stewart. *Id.*

   b. The Court held that "[a]llegations that Stewart and the other directors moved in the same social circles, attended the same weddings, developed business relationships before joining the board, and described each other as 'friends,' even when coupled with Stewart's 94% voting power, are insufficient, without more, to rebut the presumption of independence. . . Whether they arise before board membership or later as a result of collegial relationships among the board of directors, such affinities—standing alone—will not render presuit demand futile." *Id.* at 1051. The Court went on to note that the outside directors all held significant positions in other businesses and companies so that a "reputation for acting as a careful fiduciary" was essential to their careers and was an issue in which they would have a material interest. *Id.* at 1047.

10. The presumption of independence and/or disinterest is particularly strong for outside, non-managing directors. To "create a reasonable doubt about an outside director's independence, a plaintiff must plead facts that would support the inference that because of the nature of a relationship or additional circumstances other than the interested director's stock ownership or voting power, the non-interested director would be more willing to risk his or her reputation than risk the relationship with the interested director." *Beam*, 845 A.2d at 1052; *see also, Marcoux v. Prim*, 2004 WL 830393, at *16-17 (N.C. Super. April 16, 2004) (allegations that outside directors served on the same boards, belonged to the same social clubs, vacationed together, and had prior business relationships with interested directors not sufficient to show that outside directors were beholden and lacked independence); *see also, Mitzner,* 2005 WL 88966, at *6 (outside directors found not interested because they were unlikely to face substantial likelihood of liability for false and misleading statements in prospectuses, registration statements, annual reports, press releases, or other "group-published information" since the complaint failed to se forth particularized facts to show that the outside directors either participated in day-to-day corporate activities or had a special relationship with the corporation).

11. Recent cases that have focused on the business judgment prong in determining demand futility have found that plaintiffs were successful in raising a reasonable doubt that the board's decision was a valid exercise of business judgment. *See e.g., Geer v. Cox*, 292 F.Supp.2d 1282, 1294, (D. Kan. 2003) (reasonable doubt sufficiently alleged where directors accepted a liquidation for 50 per cent of market value and failed to seek required

shareholder approval for the action or have any valid business reason to choose such a transaction, particularly when an alternative transaction (sale of the assets by consignment) would have yielded 90 per cent of fair market value); *California Pub. Employees' Ret. Sys.*, 2002 WL 31888343, at *12 (demand excused where directors relied on investment bank valuation report alleged to have contained some opinions that were fabricated and unfounded; moreover, special litigation committee designated to approve the challenged transaction was found to have abdicated its role to CEO and other directors); *In re Abbott Labs.*, 325 F.3d at 808-09 (directors' failure to respond to repeated warnings for six years about quality control abuses, which resulted in $100 million fine by FDA, was sufficient to overcome presumption of business judgment rule) (decided under Illinois law, which follows Delaware); *compare White v. Panic*, 783 A.2d 543, 552-555 (2001) (plaintiff failed to overcome the presumption that the board's decisions were a valid exercise of business judgment even though board settled several sexual harassment lawsuits because of CEO's alleged behavior for $3.5 million, failed to take any action against the CEO for this behavior, and made a loan to the CEO to settle a paternity suit brought against him); *cf. In re SONUS Networks, Inc. Derivative Litigation*, 2004 WL 2341395, at *4 (generalized complaints alleging poor supervision over financial statements, particularly as to controls over how the statements were prepared, and a lack of particularized allegations as to any specific act by any particular board member individually or by the board as a whole, cannot overcome the presumption of a valid business judgment).

12. Certain actions, such as self-compensation decisions and knowing violations of the law, have been held to be outside the protections of the business judgment rule. *See, e.g., Telxon Corp. v. Meyerson*, 802 A.2d 257, 265 (Del. 2002) ("Like any other interested transaction, directoral self-compensation decisions lie outside the business judgment rule's presumptive protection."); *Padgett v. McGee*, 2004 WL 1098986, at *7 (Cal. Ct. App. May 18, 2004) ("good faith reliance on the advice of counsel, without any further inquiry, is ordinarily presumed to be an appropriate and protected exercise of business judgment"; if, however, "directors have knowledge that would

make them suspect [that this] reliance is unwarranted, then the failure to conduct further inquiry is . . . unprotected by the business judgment rule"); *Landy v. D'Alessandro*, 2004 WL 1045783, at *17 (D. Mass. March 30, 2004) (a "knowing violation of the law renders a decision outside the business judgment rule . . .").

E. Board Response

1. The effect of making a demand "is to place control of the derivative litigation in the hands of the board of directors." *Spiegel v. Buntrock*, 571 A.2d 767, 773 (Del. 1990) ("The purpose of the pre-suit demand is to assure that the stockholder affords the corporation the opportunity to address the alleged wrong without litigation, to decide whether to invest the resources of the corporation in litigation and to control any litigation which does occur."); *Stotland v. GAF Corp.*, 469 A.2d 421, 422 (Del. 1983) ("once a demand has been made, absent a wrongful refusal, the stockholders' ability to initiate a derivative suit is terminated") .

2. After a demand has been made, the board can decide whether to pursue the litigation, resolve the grievance short of litigation, or reject the demand. *Weiss v. Temporary Inv. Fund, Inc.*, 692 F.2d 928, 941 (3d Cir. 1982) (in response to a demand the board "can exercise their discretion to accept the demand and prosecute the action, to resolve the grievance internally without resort to litigation, or to refuse the demand"), *vacated and remanded on other grounds*, 465 U.S. 1001 (1984); *see also, Zapata Corp. v. Maldonado*, 430 A.2d 779, 783 (Del. 1981).

3. Directors served with a demand cannot stand neutral. *Spiegel*, 571 A.2d at 767 (board of directors confronted with a derivative action cannot stand neutral); *Grimes*, 673 A.2d at 1207 (board may not assume position of neutrality with respect to demand). Some courts have viewed neutrality as tacit approval for the continuation of the derivative litigation. *See Kaplan v. Peat, Marwick, Mitchell & Co.*, 540 A.2d 726, 729 (Del. 1988) (neutral position by the board will "be viewed as tacit approval for the continuation of the litigation[,]" thus excusing demand); *Halprin v. Babbitt*, 303 F.2d 138 (1st Cir. 1962). *But see, Benak v. Alliance Capital Management L.P.*, 2005 WL

1285652, at *2-3 (D.N.J. May 23, 2005) (applying Maryland law) (court rejected holding by Delaware Supreme Court that a corporate board's position of neutrality excuses demand).

4. The board assumes control of the litigation if it accepts the demand. *See Daily Income Fund, Inc v. Fox*, 464 U.S. 523, 533 (1984) ("If, in the view of the directors, litigation is appropriate, acceptance of the demand places the resources of the corporation, including its information, personnel, funds and counsel behind the suit.").

5. Frequently, the board of directors will reject a shareholders demand as not being in the best interest of the corporation. This is the most likely scenario. *See* Ferrara, et al. § 7.02, citing *A.L.I., Principles of Corporate Governance: Analysis and Recommendations* § 7.08, Reporter's Note 9 (Proposed Final Draft, March 31, 1992). If after board rejection of a demand, a shareholder decides to move forward with the suit, the shareholder must prove that the board's decision to reject the demand was wrongful. *See Levine v. Smith*, 1989 WL 150784, at *4 (Del. Ch. Nov. 27, 1989) (a shareholder "will be permitted to proceed with his derivative suit if the Court is satisfied that the board's rejection of the demand was wrongful."), aff'd, 591 A.2d 194 (Del. 1991); see also *Grimes*, 763 A.2d at 1207; *Stepak v. Addison*, 20 F.3d 398 (11th Cir. 1994); *Miller v. Thomas*, 656 N.E.2d 89 (Ill. App. 1995).

6. To show that a board's decision to reject the demand was wrongful, a shareholder must overcome the presumption that the board acted in good faith, with due care and in the honest belief that the action taken was in the best interest of the corporation. Citron v. Fairchild Camera & Instrument Corp., 569 A.2d 53, 64 (Del. 1989); Aronson, 473 A.2d at 812. This calls into play the business judgment rule.

7. Demand Rejected and Business Judgment Rule

   a. The business judgment rule determines when a shareholder may bring a derivative action after a demand has been rejected. *Mt. Moriah Cemetery v. Moritz*, CCH Fed. Sec. L. Rep. ¶ 95,900 (Del. Ch. April 4, 1991) ("Where demand is made and refused by a board, a plaintiff may proceed with a derivative action only if the Court is satisfied that the board's rejection of the demand was wrongful. The business judgment rule is used in reviewing a board's refusal to act pursuant to a stockholder demand"); *Zapata Corp.*, 430 A.2d at 784 n.10 ("when stockholders, after making demand and having their suit rejected, attack the board's decision as improper, the board's decision falls under the 'business judgment' rule and will be respected if the requirements of the rule are met"); *Stoner*, 772 F. Supp. at 800-01 ("business judgment inquiry is proper whenever a board or a committee of the board is charged with wrongfully preventing shareholder litigation of a corporate cause of action"); *United Copper Sec. Co. v. Amalgamated Copper Co.*, 244 U.S. 261 (1917) (Whether or not a corporation shall seek "to enforce in the courts a cause of action for damages is, like other business questions, ordinarily a matter of internal management and is left to the discretion of the directors").

(1) Absent such a showing, a shareholder lacks standing to maintain a suit on behalf of the corporation. Z*apata Corp.*, 430 A.2d at 784 ("Absent wrongful refusal, the stockholder [where a demand has been made and refused] lacks managerial power.").

b. The business judgment rule provides that absent evidence of bad faith, fraud or lack of due care, courts will defer to the business judgment of corporate directors. *Zapata Corp.*, 430 A.2d at 782 ("The 'business judgment' rule is a judicial creation that presumes propriety, under certain circumstances, in a board's decision").

(1) In some jurisdiction, such as California, the business judgment rule is codified. *See* Cal. Corp. Code § 309. In other jurisdictions, such as Delaware the rule is judicially imposed. *See,* e.g., *Brehm v. Eisner*, 746 A.2d 244 (Del. 2000).

c. The business judgment rule "creates 'a presumption that in making a business decision, the directors of a corporation'" met their fiduciary duties to the corporation, that is that that they "acted on an informed basis (i.e., with due care), in good faith, and in the honest belief that the action taken was in the best interest of the company." *Citron*, 569 A.2d at 64 (quoting *Aronson*, 473 A.2d at 812); *see also Schreiber v.*

Pennzoil Co., 419 A.2d 952, 956 (Del. Ch. 1980) ("The business judgment rule is a presumption that a rational business decision of the officers or directors of a corporation is proper unless there exists facts which remove the decision from the protection of the rule.").

(1) In most circumstances, the business judgment rule places the burden on the party challenging the board decision to introduce evidence that the board either lacked good faith, acted in self-interest, or acted without due care. *Citron*, 569 A.2d at 64. *But see, e.g., Sadler v. Jorad, Inc.*, 2004 WL 1175773, at *5-6 (Neb. May 28, 2004) (burden is shifted in close corporation where defendants control the books and the business).

(2) A 2002 case from the New Jersey Supreme Court, however, explicitly holds otherwise. In *In re PSE & G Shareholder Litig.*, 173 N.J. 258, 286 (N.J. 2002), the Court stated that a "modified" version of the business judgment rule is the proper standard of review to apply when evaluating whether a corporation's board of directors has responded properly in rejecting a shareholder's demand or terminating existing litigation in a demand-excused context. In this "modified" version, the initial burden is actually on the directors to demonstrate that they "(1) were independent and disinterested, (2) acted in good faith and with due care in their investigation of the shareholder's allegations, and that (3) the board's decision was reasonable." *Id.* Moreover, "shareholders in these circumstances must be permitted access to corporate documents and other discovery 'limited to the narrow issue of what steps the directors took to inform themselves of the shareholder demand and the reasonableness of its decision.'" *Id.* The court also noted that an appellate court's review of a trial court's decision in this context is *de novo* on the record. *Id.* at 287. The court pointed to renewed questions about the objectivity and responsibility of corporate directors in the marketplace as a basis for their decision in this matter. *Id.* at 297.

8. Absent a showing that the directors failed to meet their fiduciary obligations, the business judgment rule shields directors

from personal liability. *Citron*, 569 A.2d at 64 (If the party challenging a board decision "fails to meet [the] burden of establishing facts rebutting the presumption, the business judgment rule, as a substantive rule of law, will attach to protect the directors and the decisions they make.").

9. As with other business decisions a board's decision "not to pursue legal recourse pursuant to a shareholder's complaint" is given "great deference under the business judgment rule." *Lewis v. Hilton*, 648 F. Supp. 725, 727 (N.D. Ill. 1986). Accordingly, courts seldom interfere with a board decision not to pursue litigation unless "the directors are guilty of misconduct equivalent to a breach of trust, or where they stand in a dual relation which prevents an unprejudiced exercise of judgment." *United Copper Securities Co.*, 244 U.S. at 261; *see also Aronson*, 473 A.2d at 812.

   a. To demonstrate that the decision of the board in rejecting a demand violated the business judgment rule, a shareholder must allege particular facts that "create a reasonable doubt that the directors' action was entitled to the protections of the business judgment rule." *Aronson*, 473 A.2d at 808.

      (1) Delaware courts held that shareholders concede the disinterestedness and independence of a board as to the underlying claims by making a pre-suit demand. *See, e.g., Spiegel*, 571 A.2d at 773-77 (act of making a demand on a board of directors is a concession that demand is not futile); *Levine*, 591 A.2d at 212 (plaintiff's "complaint based on wrongful refusal of demand not only tacitly concedes lack of self-interest and independence of a majority of the Board, but expressly concedes both issues"); *see also Thorpe v. CERBCO, Inc.*, 611 A.2d 5, 10 (Del. Ch. 1991); *Abbey v. Computer & Comm. Tech. Corp.*, 457 A.2d 368 (Del. Ch. 1983).

      (2) But in other jurisdictions a plaintiff can, even after a demand has been made, show that the board improperly rejected the demand because the board lacked independence and was under the influence of an improper party. *See Findley v. Garrett*, 109 Cal. App. 2d 166, 174 (1952).

10. Successful wrongful refusal claims tend to involve allegations that the business judgment rule does not apply to a board's decision to reject a demand because either the board lacked due care or did not demonstrate good faith in reviewing and responding to a derivative demand. *See, e.g., Stepak*, 20 F.3d at 398 (finding that the board lacked due care in rejecting a demand because of the board's reliance on counsel who had previously represented the company's officers and directors in criminal investigations relating to the subject matter of the demand; "[b]oard members were merely passive recipients of the product of an 'investigation' orchestrated by counsel"); *Syracuse Television, Inc. v. Channel 9, Syracuse, Inc.*, 273 N.Y.S.2d 16 (N.Y. Sup. 1966) ("[B]oard took none of the many actions which might be anticipated in view of the gravity of the charges. It did not direct an investigation, it did not direct an audit, it did not refer the matter to committee, it did not amend the motion, the motion was tabled."); *see also Mt. Moriah Cemetery*, CCH Fed. Sec. L. Rep. at ¶95,900 ("In responding to plaintiff's demand letter, as in every other business decision, the directors of D&B had a duty to inform themselves of 'all material information reasonably available to them. In deciding whether directors have made an informed decision, the standard is gross negligence. Thus, the alleged deficiencies in the Special Committee's investigation must rise to the level of gross negligence if the directors' decision is to be condemned as uninformed.").

11. Even if the derivative action proceeds, the business judgment rule can come into play to determine whether liability exists for the underlying transaction if it involved a decision by the board. *Aronson*, 473 A.2d at 812 ("The function of the business judgment rule is of paramount significance in the context of a derivative action. It comes into play in several ways—in addressing a demand, in the determination of demand futility, in efforts by independent disinterested directors to dismiss the action as inimical to the corporation's best interests, and generally, as a defense to the merits of the [underlying] suit.").

12. Special Litigation Committees

    a. Use of a Litigation Committee to Review a Demand

(1) A board may act as a whole in reviewing a shareholder's demand or it may choose to appoint a committee to investigate the facts underlying a demand and make a report and recommendation regarding the suit. *See, e.g., Spiegel,* 571 A.2d at 767; *Seminaris v. Landa*, 662 A.2d 1350 (Del. Ch. 1995); *Abbey,* 457 A.2d at 368.

(a) The Chancery Court in *Abbey* called into question whether the appointment of a committee to review a shareholder's demand concedes the board's lack of independence to the demand. 457 A.2d at 368 ("[B]y divesting itself of any power to make a decision on the pending suit, and by adding a new and independent director and by designating him as a Special Litigation Committee of one with the final and absolute authority to make the decision on behalf of the corporation, the incumbent board of directors, in effect, conceded the circumstances alleged in the complaint justified the initiation of the suit by the plaintiff. This is so because the incumbent board opted for the possible use of the new *Zapata* procedure and, as I read *Zapata*, that procedure necessarily presumes a suit properly initiated by a shareholder.").

(b) Later cases, however, have clarified that the statement in *Abbey*, conceding the board's lack of independence is not a per se rule. *See Spiegel v. Buntrock*, 571 A.2d 767 (Del. 1990) ("[W]e find that the Court of Chancery properly rejected Spiegel's argument that *Abbey* stands for the proposition that a board of directors, *ipso facto*, waives its right to challenge a shareholder plaintiff's allegation that demand is excused by the act of appointing a special litigation committee and delegating to that committee the authority to act on the demand."); *Peller v. Southern Co.*, 911 F.2d 1532 (11th Cir. 1990) (applying Delaware law) ("In determining whether a shareholder is excused from making a demand, Delaware courts examine the response of a challenged board when first confronted with a derivative suit. If a board responds to a derivative suit by appointing a special litigation committee with the sole authority to evaluate whether to pursue the litigation before making a motion to dismiss for failure to make a demand, then a court may conclude that the board has conceded its disqualification and therefore demand may be excused. By contrast, if a board responds before appointing a special litigation committee to evaluate the suit, a court may not find that such a board has conceded that demand is excused.").

(c) A more recent Delaware decision on the issue rejected the view that *Abbey* or *Spiegel* establish a bright-line rule about when a board concedes independence by forming a committee to review a shareholder complaint. *See Seminaris*, 662 A.2d at 1350. The court in *Landa* held that where a plaintiff claims that the formation of a committee before a motion to dismiss constitutes concession of the independence issue, "a derivative plaintiff must allege particularized facts that support a factual finding that the board made the concession." *Id.* at 1353. This decision strongly undercuts the view that the formation of the committee constitutes a per se concession of lack of independence. That said, a board confronted with a demand should take care not to be perceived as having conceded its lack of independence.

(2) Cases that have rejected the decisions of special litigation committees have largely focused on the independence or good faith of the committee members and the reasonableness of the investigations. *See e.g., Janssen v. Best & Flanagan*, 662 N.W. 2d 876, 888-889 (2003) (committee's decision rejected because committee "acted more like a legal advisor than a neutral decision maker" and conducted inadequate factual investigation, especially given that plaintiff and plaintiff's attorneys were not interviewed; board of directors have only "one opportunity to exercise its business judgment" before plaintiff is allowed to proceed with the action); *Kloha v. Duda*, 226 F. Supp. 2d 1342, 1344 (M.D. Fla. 2002) (it was "impossible" for committee members to maintain their independence given that members received salary and retirement benefits from corporation and faced potential "crippling" personal liability from derivative suit that was not cov-

ered by corporation's indemnification policy.); *Klein v. FPL Group, Inc.*, 2003 WL 22768424, at *20-24 (S.D. Fla. Sept. 26, 2003) (Florida court, seeking guidance from Delaware law, rejected the decision of the special litigation committee and held that its members were not independent given that they were involved and/or approved the challenged transactions, faced substantial financial liabilities because of these transactions, were hand-selected by the defendant CEO and approved by the board without any inquiry into their independence or objectivity, did not have the authority to make a final determination on the issue, and were assisted by outside counsel that had a past and ongoing relationship with the corporation and its senior officers; the court also found it "troublesome" that the company's management had issued public statements "opining on the legality of the issue in question prior to a final decision from the committee"); *cf. Powell v. First Republic Bank*, 274 F. Supp. 2d 660, 669-671 (E.D. Penn. 2003) (directors justified in not pursuing derivative action based on recommendation of one independent investigator, even though directors hired the investigator and the investigator failed to interview all interested parties, where the court otherwise found the investigation to be thorough and complete); *Brady v. Calcote*, 2005 WL 65535, at *4-6 (Tenn. Ct. App. Jan. 11, 2005) (trial court's decision to uphold conclusion of special litigation committee affirmed where committee members, a lawyer and certified public accountant, were (1) deemed to be independent as they were neither shareholders, directors or officers of the company and had many years experience investigating/auditing unsound banking practices (the issue at hand) and (2) found to have made a good faith effort to investigate the alleged misconduct as they spent "several months" conducting interviews of involved parties, "reviewed various documents including FDIC reports and financial statements of the Bank for the period at issue" and interviewed independent experts by questioning directors for other local banking corporations; the court also found that the committee's conclusion was sound because (1) it was supported by the fact that there was little likelihood that plaintiff would succeed on the merits, (2) there was no evidence of damages suffered by the shareholders or the company, and (3) the benefit of pursuing the claim against the directors would likely outweigh the costs of bringing the derivative action).

(3) Some courts permit limited discovery to assess the independence and good faith of the special litigation committee members and the reasonableness of the investigation that was undertaken. *See, e.g., Klein*, 2003 WL 22768424, at *8-9.

b. Formation Of A Special Litigation Committee In The Demand-Excused Context

(1) A special litigation committee may also be appointed to review and make a binding determination with respect to a pending derivative action where a demand has been excused.

(a) Most courts and legislatures that have considered the use of special litigation committees in the demand excused context have concluded that such a committee may, under certain circumstances, terminate the pending derivative suits. *See e.g., Auerbach v. Bennett*, 393 N.E.2d 994 (N.Y. 1979); *Zapata Corp.*, 430 A.2d at 779; *see also* Ferrara, et al. § 8.01 n.10.

(b) *See* Ferrara, et al. § 8.01 n.10 for cases and statutes approving the appointment of such committees; *but see Miller v. Register & Tribune Syndicate, Inc.* 336 N.W.2d 709 (Iowa 1983) (holding that a tainted board lacks the authority to pass on a shareholder's demand).

(2) Unlike a committee formed in response to a demand, which makes a recommendation to the full board, a special litigation committee in the demand-excused context must be given the authority to make a binding determination as to the derivative suit without seeking approval from the full board. Absent such delegation, the special litigation committee is an ineffective means of insulating the corporation's response to the derivative suit from the taint of interested directors. *See e.g., In re Par Pharmaceutical Inc.*, 750 F. Supp. 641, 646 (S.D.N.Y. 1990).

(3) Courts that allow a special litigation committee in the demand excused context have adopted a number of approaches. The following are the New York and Delaware approaches. For other approaches *see* Ferrara, et al. §§ 8.04, et seq.

(a) The New York Approach

(i) Under New York law, a court may review the procedures used by the special litigation committee, but the conclusions reached by the committee are "outside the scope" of the court's review. To that decision, the business judgment rule attaches. *Auerbach*, 393 N.E.2d at 994 (Review of the merits of the special litigation committee's decision "would go to the very core of the business judgment made by the committee. To permit judicial probing of such issues would be to emasculate the business judgment doctrine as applied to the actions and determinations of the special litigation committee.").

(ii) This approach has been adopted by a number of courts. *See Atkins v. Hibernia Corp.*, 182 F.3d 320 (5th Cir. 1999) (predicting Louisiana law); *Genzer v. Cunningham*, 498 F. Supp. 682 (E.D. Mich. 1980) (predicting Michigan law); *Lewis v. Anderson*, 615 F.2d 778 (9th Cir. 1979) (predicting California law); *Desaigoudar v. Meryercord*, Fed. Sec. L. Rep. P91,204 (Cal. Ct. App. 2003); *Roberts v. Alabama Power Co.*, 404 So.2d 629 (Ala. 1981); *Hirsch v. Jones Intercable, Inc.*, 984 P.2d 629 (Colo. 1999); *Curtis v. Nevens*, 31 P.3d 146, 153 (Colo. 2001) (Supreme Court of Colorado affirmed the New York approach and added that in a pre-investigation context, the trial court "may determine the independence of the SLC but may not, absent extraordinary circumstances . . . review the reasonableness of the SLC's proposed procedures"); *Drilling v. Berman*, 589 N.W.2d 503 (Minn. Ct. App.), *rev. denied* (Minn. 1999); *Miller v. Bargaheiser*, 591 N.E.2d 1339 (Ct. App. Ohio 1990).

(b) The Delaware Approach

(i) Under Delaware law, a court retains the ability to review the substantive merits of a decision by a special litigation committee to dismiss an action. *Zapata Corp.*, 430 A.2d at 779.

(ii) The court first looks at the good faith and independence of the committee in its investigation as well as the reasonableness of the information on which it relied.

(iii) If this has been met, the court either grants the committee's motion to dismiss or may, at its discretion, apply its own independent business judgment to determine whether the committee's decision is valid. *Id.* at 789. "[T]he discretionary second-step analysis . . . contemplates the balancing of two potentially off-setting premises, namely, the good faith and reasonably supported view of an independent Committee that it would be in the best interests of the corporation and its shareholders to dismiss the derivative action versus a theoretical valid cause of action." *Kaplan v. Wyatt*, 484 A.2d 501, 509 (Del. Ch. 1984), *aff'd* 499 A.2d 1184 (Del. 1985).

(iv) A recent Delaware decision has held that shareholders could not voluntarily dismiss a derivative action once the corporation's special litigation committee was involved and opposed the dismissal. *In re Oracle Corp. Derivative Litig.*, 808 A.2d 1206, 1213 (Del. Ch. 2002).

(v) The Delaware approach has been followed by other states. *Strougo v. Padegs*, 27 F. Supp. 2d 442, 447 (S.D.N.Y. 1998) (applying Maryland law); *Rosengarten v. Buckley*, 613 F. Supp. 1493 (D. Md. 1985) (applying Maryland law); *Abella v. Universal Leaf Tobacco Co.*, 546 F. Supp. 795 (E.D. Va. 1982) (applying Virginia law); *Peller v. Southern Co.*, 707 F. Supp. 525 (N.D. Ga. 1988), *aff'd* 911 F.2d 1532 (11th Cir. 1990) (applying Georgia law); *Allied Ready Mix Co. ex rel Gobel Mattingly v. Allen*, 994

S.W.2d 4 (Ky. Ct. App. 1998), rev. denied (Ky. 1999); *Alford v. Shaw*, 358 S.E.2d 323 (N.C. 1987), *withdrawing* 349 S.E.2d 41 (N.C. 1986), *aff'g and modifying* 324 S.E.2d 878 (N.C. App. 1985); *but compare Atkins v. Topp Comm, Inc.*, 874 So. 2d 626, 627-28 (Fla. Dist. Ct. App. 2004) ("trial courts in [Florida] are not required to evaluate the reasonableness of an independent investigator's final recommendation, pursuant to the second-step analysis in Zapata").

c. Characteristics of a Special Litigation Committee

(1) The following guidelines should be followed in setting up a special litigation committee:

(a) The committee should be vested with full and unconditional authority to act on behalf of the board to investigate the allegations and to determine if litigation is in the company's best interest. *See Abbey*, 457 A.2d at 368.

(b) The board needs to appoint truly independent and disinterested directors. *See, e.g., Melton v. Blau*, 2004 WL 2095317, at *6 (Conn. Super. Ct. Aug. 26, 2004) ("Without a statutory definition, the court looks to the common and ordinary meaning of 'independent.' Basically, to be 'independent' means that one is free from the influence, control or determination of someone or something. . . . [T]o be 'independent,' a director should be 'disinterested.'") Courts are reluctant to accept a special litigation committee's recommendation when it suspects that personal interests motivated the committee's determination. *See, e.g., , Lewis v. Fuqua*, 502 A.2d 962, 966 (Del. Ch. 1985); *Biondi v. Scrushy*, 820 A.2d 1148, 1156-1157 (Del. Ch. 2003) (court held that committee was "fatally compromised" because of members' strong friendship with key defendant, inadequate delegation of authority to the committee, and fact that chairman of the committee publicly and prematurely issued statements exculpating one of the key defendants before the committee finished its investigation).

(c) In *In re Oracle Corp. Derivative Litig.*, 824 A.2d 917 (Del. Ch. 2003), the Court broadened the basis for questioning a special litigation committee's independence. In *Oracle*, shareholders brought a derivative action alleging insider trading by certain of the company's officers and directors. The special litigation committee appointed to investigate the matter subsequently moved for dismissal after conducting an investigation which the Court acknowledged was, "by any objective measure, extensive." *Id.* at 925. The Court stated that in order for the committee to prevail in its motion to dismiss, it must show that: "(1) its members were independent; (2) that they acted in good faith; and (3) that they had reasonable bases for their recommendations" (citations omitted). *Id.* at 928. Basing its decision solely on the independence factor, the Court held that the two-member committee had failed to demonstrate its independence. *Id.* at 942-945. This decision was based on the fact that both members were professors at Stanford University, and all of the defendant directors and officers accused of wrong doing in the derivative action had important ties to the University. *Id.* The Court arrived at this conclusion despite acknowledging that the committee members were not in key fundraising positions that would call into question their impartiality, and were both tenured professors whose current jobs would not be threatened by whatever good faith decision they made as committee members. The Court, instead, emphasized the following relationships between the committee members and defendants: (1) one of the defendants, also a Stanford professor, taught one of the committee members when the committee member was a Ph.D. candidate and both individuals currently serve on the same economic research committee at Stanford; (2) another defendant, a Stanford alumnus, is chair of the advisory board of the same economic research committee mentioned above and has made substantial monetary donations to departments and committees at Stanford that are closely affiliated to one of the committee members and from which the member has directly benefited; and (3) another defendant, Oracle's CEO, has made millions of dollars in donations to Stanford, and was considering donating his $100 million house and a $170 million scholarship program to Stanford at around the time that the committee members were added to Oracle's board. *Id.*

(d) The Court, broadening the independence analysis by using a "contextual approach," which takes into account all relevant facts and circumstances that may affect a committee member's impartiality, focused on "bias-creating" factors beyond the usual economic factors in coming to its decision. *Id.* The Court ultimately found that even though the committee members were not "dominated" or "controlled" by any of the defendants in the traditional economic sense, the members were not independent due to other social and collegial factors, such as the difficulty of accusing a fellow professor, whom one might see at the faculty club or at academic conferences, of insider trading. *Id.* The Court also suggested that these types of relationships might be of particular concern when committee members are called upon to make subjective determinations about defendants' state of mind or when the committee's decision can result in potentially severe consequences. *Id.*

(e) A special litigation committee should also consist of two or more members. In a jurisdiction where a one-member special litigation committees is permitted, that member must, "like Caesar's wife, be above reproach." *Houle v. Low*, 556 N.E.2d 51 (1990). Committee members should be qualified. Qualifications depend on (1) the nature of the issues involved; (2) the complexity of the information obtained during the course of the investigation; and (3) the extent that the committee obtained expert advice. *See Lewis*, 502 A.2d at 966.

(f) The committee should retain independent counsel to assist it in its investigation. *See In re Par Pharmaceutical Inc.*, 750 F. Supp. 641, 647 (S.D.N.Y. 1990) ("Both

New York and Delaware law contemplate that a special litigation committee be represented by independent counsel."). To avoid the appearance of a conflict of interest, outside counsel is preferable to in-house counsel. Counsel should be free of any conflicts that might interfere with its ability to render unbiased legal advice to the committee. *See, e.g., General Electric Co. v. Rowe*, 1992 WL 277997 (E.D. Pa. Sept. 30, 1992); *In re Par Pharmaceutical Inc.*, 750 F. Supp. 641, 647 (S.D.N.Y. 1990).

(g) The committee must fully and thoroughly investigate the allegations underlying the derivative suit and draft a report of its findings of fact and conclusion of law, which should address the merits of the plaintiff's claims and provide sufficient information to demonstrate that the investigation was reasonable and thorough. *See, e.g., Electra Inv. Trust PLC v. Crews*, 1999 WL 135239 (Del. Ch. Feb. 24, 1999).

II. THE ABILITY TO REMOVE DERIVATIVE ACTIONS TO FEDERAL COURT UNDER THE SECURITIES LITIGATION UNIFORM STANDARDS ACT OF 1998

A. SLUSA Background

1. In 1998, Congress enacted the Securities Litigation Uniform Standards Act ("SLUSA") in an effort to prevent litigants from strategically pursuing frivolous class action suits in state court under state law in order to evade the heightened pleading requirements and restrictions established under federal law. SLUSA attempts to curtail these abuses by preempting and requiring that any "covered class action" based on state law that alleges a misrepresentation or omission of a material fact or act of deception in connection with the purchase or sale of a covered security be removed to federal court. *See* 15 U.S.C. § 77p; 15 U.S.C. § 78bb. SLUSA's removal provision, however, do not appear to extend to shareholder claims based on holders, as opposed to purchasers and sellers, of a covered security. *See, e.g., Meyer v. Putnam International Voyager Fund*, 220 F.R.D. 127, 129 (D. Mass. 2004). There also seems to be a split in authority on whether the provision extends to claims based

exclusively on the Securities Act of 1933. *See, e.g., In re Tyco International, LTD. Multidistrict Litigation*, 2004 WL 1403009, at *4 n.1 (D.N.H. June 21, 2004).

2. SLUSA explicitly states that actions that are "exclusively derivative" in nature are excluded from the definition of "covered class actions." 15 U.S.C. § 77p(f)(2)(B); 15 U.S.C. § 78bb(f)(5)(c). Recently, several federal courts have interpreted the application of SLUSA in the context of shareholder derivative suits and have decided to remand these suits back to state court.

3. In *Coykendall v. Kaplan*, 2002 U.S. Dist. LEXIS 22483, at *9-11 (N.D. Cal. 2002), defendants argued that the "exclusively derivative" exemption under SLUSA should be given a broad functional construction and that if a complaint could have alleged claims that would be subject to SLUSA, SLUSA should apply. The court rejected this argument and held that even though plaintiffs' complaints could have been actionable as securities fraud, the fact that plaintiffs sought relief on behalf of the corporation rather than for a class of injured investors was determinative and remanded the case back to state court. *See also Arlia v. Blankenship*, 234 F. Supp. 2d 606, 612-613 (S.D. W. Va. 2002) (case remanded back to state court because "statute itself makes clear that the shareholder derivative action was not one of the mass actions that Congress intended to cover" under SLUSA).

4. In *Shen v. Bohan*, 2002 U.S.Dist. LEXIS 22485, at *6-7 (C.D. Cal. 2002), the court rejected the defendants' argument that plaintiffs' request for damages made the action a "covered class action" within the purview of SLUSA. The court held that since plaintiffs' requests for damages clearly related to their shareholder derivative actions, the request for damages did not render the action removable under SLUSA. The court also found that removal to federal court was improper because plaintiffs' allegations regarding improper dilution of shareholder interests were not misrepresentations "in connection with" the purchase or sale of a security and there was no indication that plaintiffs were "fraudulently pleading to circumvent SLUSA." *Id.* at 11.

5. In *Greaves v. McAuley*, 264 F. Supp. 2d 1078 (N.D. Ga. 2003), the court found that some of plaintiffs' claims were specifically preempted by SLUSA because they were a "covered class action" and the alleged misrepresentations were "in connection with" the purchase or sale of a covered security. *Id.* at 1082-1083. The court, however, also found that plaintiffs' claims, which alleged that a proxy statement provided by defendant directors contained material misstatements and omissions concerning a proposed merger, were expressly preserved by the Delaware carve-out exception under SLUSA.[2] In resolving this conflict, the court held that according to the "plain language of the statute, the court is to consider the propriety of remand after determining the propriety of removal . . . If remand is appropriate, the entire lawsuit must be returned to state court, irrespective of the court's decision regarding removal . . . the remand provision trumps the removal provision, and the entire lawsuit must be remanded." *Id.* at 1085-1086. Moreover, the court supported its decision by stating that "[b]ecause removal jurisdiction raises significant federalism concerns, federal courts are directed to construe removal statutes strictly . . . [and] all doubts about jurisdiction should be resolve in favor of remand to state court." (citations omitted). *Id.* at 1086. Thus, the entire cause of action was remanded to state court.

6. In *Young v. Antioco*, 2003 WL 23201342, at *2-3 (N.D. Tex. Aug. 6, 2003), the court—in addressing whether plaintiff's references to the federal securities laws and claim for damages due in part to the pendency of the federal class action suits implicates those federal statutes to such a degree as to federalize the derivative suit such that the SLUSA removal provision attach—held that removal was improper because the alleged federal securities laws violations served solely to illuminate the alleged state law derivative claims. *See also, Fathergill v. Rouleau*, 2003 WL 21467570 (N.D. Tex. June 23, 2003) ("fact

---

2. The Delaware carve-out exception preserves actions that involve "(1) any recommendation, position, or other communication with respect to the sale [of securities of] any issuer; (2) that is made by or on behalf of the issuer or an affiliate of the issuer to holders of equity securities of the issuer; and (3) concerns decisions of such equity holders with respect to voting their securities, acting in response to a tender or exchange offer, or exercising dissenters' or appraisal rights." (citations omitted). *Id.* at 1083.

that conduct that violates federal law serves as a basis for a state-law claim does not make a federal right an essential element of that claim[,]" necessitating removal under SLUSA).

B. Exercising SLUSA Power to Stay Discovery

1. Under SLUSA, "a court may stay discovery proceedings in any private action in a State court, as necessary in aid of its jurisdiction, or to protect or effectuate its judgments, in an action subject to a stay of discovery pursuant to this paragraph." 15 U.S.C. § 78u-4(b)(3)(D). Courts have applied this provision with mixed results.

2. *In re DPL Inc., Sec. Litig.*, 285 F. Supp. 2d 1053, 1062 (S.D. Ohio 2003), the court refused to vacate its prior stay of discovery because the purpose of the stay had not yet been realized. The purpose of the stay in the state court proceeding was to "ensure that a motion to dismiss the federal securities claims could be filed, heard and decided before discovery had commenced." *Id.* In addition, the court initially issued the stay so that the plaintiffs would "not use discovery in the state court litigation to acquire information in order to 'resuscitate a complaint that [would] otherwise [be] subject to dismissal'" under the PSLRA. *In re DPL Inc., Sec. Litig.*, 247 F. Supp. 2d 946, 951 (S.D. Ohio 2003).

3. In *City of Austin Police Ret. Sys. v. ITT Educ. Servs., Inc.*, 2005 WL 280345, at *1 (S.D. Ind. Feb. 2, 2005), the court held that SLUSA does not warrant a stay in a shareholder action to inspect defendants' records pursuant to Section 220 of the Delaware Corporation Code even with a parallel federal securities fraud action. *Id.* Although the court had the authority under SLUSA to stay the state inspection suit, as a type of "discovery proceeding," the defendants failed to make a "proper showing" that the state action would interfere with the federal action. *Id.* The defendants argued "that a federal court should stay discovery in a state case when a defendant shows that discovery is being conducted or attempted in a state court proceeding any time the facts at issue and the discovery are related to and overlap with the federal securities fraud case." *Id.* at 9. The court rejected this argument, finding that the "defendants' proposed standard would apply far too broadly, reaching state court

cases in which the claims would be entirely different, and in which the federal defendants would not even need to be parties." *Id.*

4. In *Cardinal Health, Inc. Sec. Litig.*, 365 F.Supp.2d 866 (S.D. Ohio 2005), the court came to a different conclusion, exercising its power under SLUSA to allow a stay of discovery in the state derivative action. *Id.* at 867. In deciding to stay discovery, the court relied on the fact that the state derivative claim was "predicated almost entirely on the gravaman of the complaints pending [before the] Court: securities fraud." *Id.* at 875. "Thus, were discovery to reach accidentally the federal Plaintiffs, the information would likely be applicable to the federal case because both involve the same substantive arguments." *Id.*

III. IMPACT OF THE SARBANES-OXLEY ACT OF 2002 ON DERIVATIVE ACTIONS

Congress enacted the Sarbanes-Oxley Act ("SOX") on July 30, 2002, in an effort to restore public confidence in the securities market after a series of high-profile corporate accounting scandals and to protect investors from improper business conduct. *In Re Enron Corporation Securities, Derivative & Erisa Litigation*, 258 F. Supp. 2d 576, 588 (S.D. Texas 2003). SOX seeks to accomplish this task by enacting procedural and structural reforms in corporate governance, auditor independence, and auditor oversight and greatly increasing the responsibilities and obligations of officers and directors of public companies. *See, e.g.,* 15 U.S.C. §§ 7211-7219; §§ 7231-7234 and §§ 7241-7246. These new rules and regulations consists of some of the most intense corporate governance reforms since the post-Depression activities that led to the Securities Act of 1933 and the Securities Exchange Act of 1934, and will consequently have an impact on the litigation of future derivative actions.

There are several provisions in the Act that may have an impact on shareholder derivative actions. The most substantial provision requires lawyers who are practicing or appearing before the SEC to report evidence of a material violation of the securities laws or breach of fiduciary duty to the corporation's chief legal counsel or chief executive officer. 15 U.S.C. § 7245(1). Moreover, if the lawyer finds that appropriate remedial measures or sanctions have not been taken, the lawyer must report the evidence to the corporation's audit committee or another comparable committee composed of independent directors or board members. 15 U.S.C. §

7245(2). The Act also requires corporations to have audit committees composed only of independent directors with at least one member who is financially sophisticated. 15 U.S.C. § 78j-1; *see also* SEC Release No. 33-8177. These new provisions will likely increase the number of civil actions, including derivative actions, that are filed against public companies, directors and officers, and may provide derivative plaintiffs with added incentive and opportunity to engage in discovery.

For example, a shareholder derivative action was brought, in part, on the claim that company directors failed to address the impropriety of the company's payment of split-dollar insurance policy premiums to the company's Chairman and CEO, Martha Stewart. *Beam*, 833 A.2d at 975. Because the premiums for these policies are paid entirely or in large part by the employer, some have suggested that this type of insurance policy constitutes an interest-free loan to the employee on whose behalf the policy is purchased. *Id.* at 970. As such, these policies *may* run afoul of the SOX provisions that ban loans to corporate executives and directors. *See* Sarbanes-Oxley Act of 2002, Pub.L. No. 107-204 §402(a), 15 U.S.C. § 78m(k). The Court, however, dismissed the claim because plaintiff failed to plead facts to show that the payment of these premiums were in fact unlawful. Moreover, the company had disclosed the existence of the policy, and the company's lawyers and accountants were looking into whether the policy should be discontinued in light of the new SOX provisions. *Beam*, 833 A.2d at 975.

NOTES

4

CURRENT ISSUES UNDER THE SECURITIES LITIGATION UNIFORM STANDARDS ACT

Seth Aronson

Amy J. Longo

Kristina Hersey

O'Melveny & Myers LLP

Table of Contents

I. OVERVIEW OF SLUSA

A. Enacted in 1998, SLUSA extremely limits most securities fraud class actions based on state law, whether pursued in state or federal court. The Act amends Section 16 of the Securities Act of 1933 (the "1933 Act") (15 U.S.C. § 77p) and Section 28 of the Securities Exchange Act of 1934 (the "1934 Act") (15 U.S.C. § 78bb), to provide that any "covered class action" involving a "covered security" that is filed in state court is preempted, and "shall be removed" to the federal court for the district in which the action is pending. SLUSA was expressly enacted to curtail the plaintiffs' practice of filing securities cases in state courts to avoid the proscriptions of the Private Securities Litigation Reform Act of 1995, 15 U.S.C. §§ 78u-4, 78u-5 *et seq.* ("PSLRA"). *See* Conference Report of the Committee of Conference, H.R. 105-803 (October 9, 1998) (SLUSA's dual purposes are "prevent[ing] plaintiffs from seeking to evade the protections that Federal law provides against abusive litigation by filing suit in State, rather than in Federal, court" and "implement[ing] a uniform law of securities fraud").

B. SLUSA provides that:

No covered class action based upon the statutory or common law of any State or subdivision thereof may be maintained in any State or Federal court by any private party alleging—

1. an untrue statement or omission of a material fact in connection with the purchase or sale of a covered security; or
2. that the defendant used or employed any manipulative or deceptive device or contrivance in connection with the purchase or sale of a covered security. 15 U.S.C. § 77p(b); 15 U.S.C. § 78bb(f)(1).

C. Thus, SLUSA has four elements: (1) a covered class action; (2) that is based on state law; (3) alleging a misrepresentation or omission of material fact or the use of any manipulative or deceptive device or contrivance; (4) "in connection with" the purchase or sale of a covered security.

D. **Retroactivity Analysis.**

1. SLUSA applies to all lawsuits filed after its enactment, regardless of when the underlying events occurred. *See Blaz v. Belfer*,

368 F.3d 501 (5th Cir. 2004) (Plaintiff filed suit more than three years after SLUSA's enactment, with a proposed class period ending shortly before SLUSA's enactment; plaintiff claimed that retroactive application of SLUSA to preenactment conduct denied meaningful relief to the proposed class. Affirmed district court's application of SLUSA to pre-enactment conduct because SLUSA's provisions are procedural and do not impair any substantive rights. *Accord Professional Mgmt. Assocs., Inc. Employees' Profit Sharing Plan v. KPMG LLP*, 335 F.3d 800, 803-04 (8th Cir. 2003), *cert. denied*, 124 S. Ct. 1176 (2004); *Gray v. Seaboard Secs., Inc.*, 241 F. Supp. 2d 213, 218 (N.D.N.Y. 2003); *W.R. Huff Asset Mgmt. Co., LLC v. Kohlberg Kraus Roberts & Co., L.P.*, 234 F. Supp. 2d 1218, 1226-27 (N.D. Ala. 2002).

E. **Timing of Removability Determination.**

1. Under 28 U.S.C. § 1446, defendants have 30 days from receipt of notice of the filing of the complaint or of an "amended pleading, motion, order or other paper" giving rise to removal jurisdiction.

2. The four corners of the complaint, motion, order or other document must indicate that grounds exist for removal for the thirty-day clock to begin running. Until the service of a pleading or other document giving rise to a basis for removal, therefore, SLUSA does not come into play. *See Desmond v. BankAmerica Corp.*, 120 F. Supp. 2d 1201, 1203-04 (N.D. Cal. 2000) (Actions alleging violations of the California securities fraud laws were filed prior to the effective date of SLUSA. After the first motion for class certification was denied, plaintiffs proposed to amend the complaint to add plaintiffs who were proposed as class representatives and defendants removed. Held: Even if the amended complaint would make the case removable under SLUSA, removal was premature because plaintiffs had not yet filed a pleading on which basis the action was removable).

3. Because jurisdiction is determined at the time of removal, subsequent pleading amendments do not eliminate jurisdiction. *See Behlen v. Merrill Lynch*, 311 F.3d 1087 (11th Cir. 2002), *cert. denied*, 123 S. Ct. 2583 (2003) (Plaintiff argued that once he amended his complaint to attempt to eliminate any allega-

tions giving rise to SLUSA preemption, the district court lost subject matter jurisdiction to decide the motion to remand. Held: the district court had the discretion to retain jurisdiction over the amended complaint. Provided that the allegations gave rise to subject matter jurisdiction at the time of removal, subsequent actions did not divest the court of jurisdiction).

4. ***Removability Based on Proposed Jury Instruction.*** In *Burns v. Prudential Secs., Inc.*, 218 F. Supp. 2d 911, 914-15 (N.D. Ohio 2002), defendants removed the action two years after it was filed, on the morning trial was to commence. The plaintiff-investors asserted claims for breach of fiduciary duty and misrepresentation against the brokerage firm and broker who managed their accounts, for improperly liquidating their accounts without authorization. *Id.* at 913. Plaintiffs initially indicated an intent to rely on evidence of fraud, but only to rebut defendants' ratification defense, and not as an affirmative claim. When plaintiffs proposed a jury instruction on fraud, however, defendants requested that plaintiffs amend the complaint to assert a fraud claim. Plaintiffs instead withdrew the instruction, and defendants filed a motion in limine to bar evidence of fraud. Denying the motion, the court ruled that fraud was part of the pleading. Defendants then removed. The court found the removal timely under 28 U.S.C. § 1446(b), holding that defendants did not have a basis for removal until receipt of plaintiffs' proposed jury instruction. However, the case was remanded because the claims did not arise in connection with the sale of securities.

F. Reviewability of Remand Order.

1. There is currently a circuit court split as to whether SLUSA remand orders are reviewable on appeal. The Second, Ninth and Eleventh Circuits have held that remand orders under SLUSA are not subject to appellate review, while the Seventh Circuit has ruled that such orders are reviewable.

2. **Not Reviewable: Second, Ninth and Eleventh Circuits.**

   a) In *Spielman v. Merrill Lynch, Pierce, Fenner & Smith, Inc.*, 332 F.3d 116 (2d Cir. 2003), the customer alleged that the defendant brokerage company misrepresented the nature and amount of transaction fees associated with the type of deposit account, constituting breach of contract, breach of implied covenant of good faith and fair dealing, fraud, negligent misrepresentation, breach of fiduciary duty, and violation of New York's consumer protection statute. The district court remanded on the basis that the allegations were not sufficiently connected to the value of or consideration for covered securities to be in connection with purchase or sale. *Spielman v. Merrill Lynch, Pierce, Fenner & Smith, Inc.*, Fed. Sec. L. Rep. (CCH) ¶ 91,619, at 97,645 (S.D.N.Y. Oct. 9, 2001). On appeal, the Second Circuit held that because the remand was based on lack of subject matter jurisdiction, it was not a reviewable order. 332 F.3d at 122, 127.

b) In *Abada v. Charles Schwab & Co., Inc.*, 300 F.3d 1112 (9th Cir. 2002), the plaintiff-investor asserted exclusively state law claims for unfair business practices and negligent and intentional misrepresentation against the defendant-brokerage company, based on allegedly misleading statements about its capacity to conduct internet trading transactions. After the district court denied a motion to remand under SLUSA, plaintiffs added a claim under § 10(b). The case was then transferred to a different judge. In opposing defendants' motion to dismiss, plaintiffs asked the court to reconsider the denial of the motion to remand. The district court then remanded on the basis that federal question jurisdiction was lacking because only some of the state law claims in the complaint were preempted by SLUSA. *Abada v. Charles Schwab & Co., Inc.*, 127 F. Supp. 2d 1101 (S.D. Cal. 2000). The Ninth Circuit held that because the remand was nondiscretionary and was based on lack of subject matter jurisdiction, there was no basis for appellate review under 28 U.S.C. § 1447(d). Since federal question jurisdiction must exist at the time of removal, the amendment to add a claim under Section 10(b) did not give rise to federal question jurisdiction. 300 F.3d at 1117-18.

(a) Following the denial in *Shaw*, the California trial court ruled that because the federal court's determination of whether or not SLUSA applied was jurisdictional, it was not *res judicata*. The court then found that the claims were preempted, and dismissed the action under SLUSA. *Shaw v. Charles Schwab & Co., Inc.*, Fed. Sec. L. Rep. (CCH) ¶ 92,413, at 92,090 (Cal. Super. Ct. Mar. 7, 2003).

c) In *Williams v. AFC Enterprises, Inc.,* 389 F.3d 1185 (11th Cir. 2004), the plaintiff alleged that the defendants violated the 1933 Act. The defendants removed, and the plaintiffs filed a timely motion to remand, arguing that SLUSA precludes the removal of a securities action asserting only federal claims. The district court concluded that the defendants' right of removal was unclear and remanded the case, then certified its remand order for an interlocutory appeal. The Eleventh Circuit found that the district court granted the motion to remand because it determined that it was without removal jurisdiction to hear the case. The Eleventh Circuit held that it lacked jurisdiction to review the district court's remand order because the remand was based on either lack of subject matter jurisdiction or a defect other than lack of subject matter jurisdiction entered in response to a timely motion to remand. *Cf. Cogdell v. Wyeth,* 366 F.3d 1245 (11th Cir. 2004) (District court remanded, concluding that by filing a motion to dismiss the case in state court, the defendant waived his right to remove it to federal court. Remand order that was based on waiver of the right to remove was not a remand order contemplated by 28 U.S.C. § 1447(c)).

3. ***Reviewable: Seventh Circuit.*** In *Kircher v. Putnam Funds Trust*, 373 F.3d 847 (7th Cir. 2004), the Seventh Circuit, in an opinion by Judge Easterbrook, diverged from the Second, Ninth and Eleventh Circuit's view. In a proposed class action based on state law alleging that a mutual fund and its investment adviser engaged in misconduct, which allegedly caused a decline in the fund's shares, the district court granted remand on the ground that the claims were not asserted in connection with the purchase or sale of securities. The Seventh Circuit concluded that the remand order was reviewable on appeal. The court reasoned that while a remand based on lack of subject matter jurisdiction under Section 1447(c) is barred from review by Section 1447(d), the finding that the action was preempted by SLUSA is not a finding of the federal courts' "lack [of] adjudicatory competence" but a substantive decision under

authority of federal statute; therefore, remand orders are appealable in federal court. The court found this outcome consistent with SLUSA's goal to promote uniform application of the federal securities laws.

II. DEFINITION OF "COVERED CLASS ACTIONS"

A. SLUSA defines "covered class actions" to include:

1. any single lawsuit in which—

a) damages are sought on behalf of more than 50 persons or prospective class members, and questions of law or fact common to those persons or members of the prospective class, without reference to issues of individualized reliance on an alleged misstatement or omission, predominate over any questions affecting only individual persons or members; or

b) one or more named parties seek to recover damages on a representative basis on behalf of themselves and other unnamed parties similarly situated, and questions of law or fact common to those persons or members of the prospective class predominate over any questions affecting only individual persons or members; or

2. any group of lawsuits filed in or pending in the same court and involving common questions of law or fact, in which—

a) damages are sought on behalf of more than 50 persons; and

b) the lawsuits are joined, consolidated, or otherwise proceed as a single action for any purpose. 15 U.S.C. § 77p(f)(2)(A); 15 U.S.C. § 78bb(f)(5)(B).

B. For purposes of calculating the number of persons involved in a class action, corporations, investment companies, pension plans, partnerships and other entities, provided they have not been established for the purpose of the action, are treated as a single person under SLUSA. 15 U.S.C. § 77p(f)(2)(C); 15 U.S.C. § 78bb(f)(5)(D).

1. Thus, a bankruptcy litigation trust may be deemed more than one person under SLUSA. *See, e.g., Cape Ann Investors LLC v. Lepone*, 296 F. Supp. 2d 4, 10 (D. Mass. 2003) (trustee in

bankruptcy trust created to pursue litigation was not "one person" under SLUSA).

C. **No Need for Class Determination.** In *Behlen*, 311 F.3d at 1092, the plaintiff argued that until the state court had determined whether or not class certification would be granted, the action was not removable as a covered class action. Held: determination of removability does not require a ruling on class certification, but only the assertion of class claims. *Id.* To hold otherwise would lead to lengthy state court motion practice that would undermine the purpose of SLUSA, namely, to shift covered class actions to federal court. *Id.* at 1093.

1. Moreover, SLUSA not only provides for removal of class actions, but also for removal of non-class actions asserted on behalf of 50 more plaintiffs, including actions that are consolidated (for discovery or otherwise) on behalf of groups of plaintiffs. 15 U.S.C. § 77p(f)(2); 15 U.S.C. § 78bb(f)(5).

D. **Effect on 1933 Act Claims in State Court.**

1. The first reported decision to consider whether SLUSA allows the removal of 1933 Act claims filed in state court was *In re Waste Mgmt., Inc. Sec. Litig.*, 194 F. Supp. 2d 590, 596 (S.D. Tex. 2002), which held that such claims were not removable.

2. Several other district courts have followed *Waste Management* in holding that 1933 Act claims are not removable under SLUSA.

a) *See Zia v. Medical Staffing Network, Inc.*, 336 F. Supp. 2d 1306 (S.D. Fla. 2004) (concluding that the plain language of SLUSA bars preemption where the claims are based on a federal statute);

b) *In re Tyco-Int'l Ltd.*, 322 F. Supp. 2d 116 (D.N.H. 2004) (concluding that 1933 Act claims originally filed in state court should be remanded; reasoning that statutory language compelled this result, and statutory history did not indicate otherwise);

c) *Hawaii Structural Ironworkers Pension Trust Fund v. Calpine Corp.*, No. 03CV0714BTM(JFS), 2003 WL 23509312 (S.D. Cal. Aug. 27, 2003) (following *Waste Management*; remand granted); *Nauheim v. Interpublic Group of*

Cos., Inc., No. 02-C-9211, 2003 WL 1888843 (N.D. Ill. Apr. 16, 2003).

3. Other courts have disagreed with *Waste Management.*

   a) In *Brody v. Homestore, Inc.*, 240 F. Supp. 2d 1122 (C.D. Cal. 2003), the court denied a motion to remand 1933 Act claims filed in California state court based on alleged accounting violations. The court concluded that Congress intended to authorize broad removal of securities actions filed in state court, including 1933 Act claims. The court also found that the amendment to § 77v(a) to provide that 1933 Act claims are not removable "except as set forth" in § 77p(c) would be meaningless under any other analysis. *Id.* at 1124.

   b) *Accord Alkow v. TXU Corp.*, Fed. Sec. L. Rep. ¶ 92,495 (N.D. Tex. May 8, 2003).

E. **Actions Seeking Damages.**

1. In general, actions that seek relief other than monetary damages are not within the purview of SLUSA. *See, e.g. Wald v. C.M. Life Insur. Co.*, No. CIV 3:00-CV-2520-H, 2001 WL 256179 (N.D.Tex. Mar. 8, 2001) (granting motion to remand; action alleged only declaratory and injunctive relief against issuer of variable annuities; Held: action was not a "covered class action" because no damages were or could be sought).

2. ***Meaning of Damages***. In *Feitelberg v. Merrill Lynch & Co., Inc.*, 234 F. Supp. 2d 1043, 1046-1048 (N.D. Cal. 2002), *aff'd*, 353 F.3d 765 (9th Cir. 2003), plaintiffs sought restitution and disgorgement under California's unfair business practices statute, Cal. Bus. & Prof. Code § 17200, based on the defendant's settlement of an investigation by the New York State Attorney General into alleged analyst misconduct. Plaintiff sought remand on the basis that disgorgement and restitution are not "damages" under 15 U.S.C. § 78bb(f)(5). The court found that under federal law, these monetary remedies fall within the type of actions preempted by SLUSA.

3. ***Damages in Primarily Derivative Action***. In *Shen v. Bohan*, Fed. Sec. L. Rep. (CCH) ¶ 92,223 (C.D. Cal. Oct. 17, 2002), two derivative actions for breach of fiduciary duty arising out

of a merger transaction were consolidated. An amended complaint added a class action claim for breach of fiduciary duty arising from the failure to conduct a shareholders' meeting. Following the amendment, defendants removed. Granting plaintiffs' motion to remand, the court held that the damages prayer related to the derivative, rather than the class claim, and that the claims therefore did not constitute a covered class action.

F. **Presence of Uncovered Claims.** Courts are divided over SLUSA's effect on complaints that include a mixture of preempted and non-preempted claims.

1. *Compare Rowinski v. Salomon Smith Barney Inc.,* 398 F.3d 294 (3d Cir. 2005) (Plaintiff argued that the Court should separately determine whether each claim is preempted. The court "question[ed] whether preemption of certain counts and remand of others [was] consistent with the plain meaning of SLUSA," but held that because plaintiff had incorporated every allegation into every count of his complaint, the court need not decide the issue); *Greaves v. McAuley,* 264 F. Supp. 2d 1078 (N.D. 2003) (Plaintiff argued based on § 77p(d)(4) that the presence of one unremovable claim required remand of the entire action. Defendants argued based on 15 U.S.C. § 77p(c) that because the action was a "covered class action," all claims were preempted. Held: because the court lacked jurisdiction over the claims affected by the Delaware carve-out, the entire action was remanded); *with*

2. *Falkowski v. Imation Corp.*, 309 F.3d 1123 (9th Cir. 2002), *as amended by* 320 F.3d 905 (9th Cir. 2003) (fraud claim preempted; breach of contract claim permitted to proceed); *Gray v. Seaboard Secs., Inc.*, 241 F. Supp. 2d 213, 219-20 (N.D.N.Y. 2003) (court determined SLUSA preemption as to each claim); *Premium Plus Partners, L.P. v. Davis,* No. 04 C 1851, 2005 WL 711591 (N.D. Ill. Mar. 28, 2005) (plaintiff's complaint alleged both state and federal law claims, the court determined SLUSA preemption separately as to plaintiff's state law claims); *Vohs v. Miller,* 323 F. Supp. 2d 965 (D. Minn. 2004) (plaintiff's complaint alleged both federal claims and state law claims for fraudulent misrepresentation and civil conspiracy,

the court determined SLUSA preemption separately as to plaintiff's state law claims).

III. SCIENTER

A. To be removable under SLUSA, a claim must involve some level of scienter, though courts have reached different conclusions about the requirement of an element of deceptive misstatement.

1. Element of deception required; action preempted.

a) *See Feitelberg*, 234 F. Supp. 2d at 1049-1051 (although complaint did not directly allege "scienter" and state unfair competition statute did not require it, allegations that brokerage firm issued favorable research reports in order to increase investment banking revenues sufficiently alleged deceptive conduct such that claim fell within SLUSA) ("In other words, if it looks like a securities fraud claim, sounds like a securities fraud claim and acts like a securities fraud claim, it is a securities fraud claim, no matter how you dress it up.");

b) *Denton v. H&R Block Fin. Advisors, Inc.*, Fed. Sec. L. Rep. (CCH) ¶ 91,618 (N.D. Ill. Oct. 4, 2001) (fiduciary duty claim sufficiently alleged deception to be preempted);

c) *Burekovitch v. Hertz,* No. 01-CV-1277 (ILG), 2001 WL 984942 (E.D.N.Y. Jul. 24, 2001) (where shareholder alleged that the controlling shareholder/CEO breached his fiduciary duty by failing to disclose that a large percentage of his holdings were pledged for trading in a personal margin account, claim was barred by SLUSA).

2. Element of deception required; action remanded.

a) *See Magyery v. Transamerica Financial Advisors, Inc.*, 315 F. Supp. 2d 954 (N.D. Ind. 2004) (investor's proposed class claim against broker and brokerage firm alleging unauthorized trading, based on state law breach of contract, conversion, breach of fiduciary duty and negligent supervision, was not subject to SLUSA preemption because the complaint did not allege any fraudulent misstatements);

b) *MDCM Holdings Inc. v. Credit Suisse First Boston Corp.*, 216 F. Supp. 2d 251 (S.D.N.Y. 2002) (fiduciary duty and breach of implied covenant claims did not sufficiently allege deception to be preempted);

c) *Simon v. Internet Wire, Inc.*, Fed. Sec. L. Rep. (CCH) ¶ 91,408 (C.D.Cal. Apr. 3, 2001) (motion to remand granted; action alleged negligence and negligent misrepresentation arising from company's publication of counterfeit press release; Held: because action alleged merely negligence, rather than securities fraud, it was not meant to be preempted by SLUSA).

B. Negligence.

1. One court has held that even common law negligence claims can be preempted by SLUSA. *See In re WorldCom, Inc.*, 263 F. Supp. 2d 745 (S.D.N.Y. 2003) (claim for common law negligence against an audit firm was preempted; although negligence is not actionable under Section 10(b), SLUSA bars more than simply state law claims requiring scienter).

IV. THE "IN CONNECTION WITH" REQUIREMENT

A. Most of the caselaw under SLUSA has developed around the issue of whether alleged misrepresentations or omissions occur "in connection with" the purchase or sale of a covered security.

B. Though decided under Rule 10b-5 and not involving SLUSA, the Supreme Court's decision in *SEC v. Zandford*, 535 U.S. 813 (2002), is the current touchstone for the "in connection with" requirement. In *Zandford*, an investor alleged that his broker converted customer funds for personal use. Giving a broad construction to the phrase "in connection with" under Section 10(b), the Court held that it requires only that the "scheme to defraud and the sale of securities coincide," for the conduct to be actionable under Rule 10b-5. *Id.* at 821-22.

C. All of the circuit courts that have issued opinions interpreting the "in connection with" requirement have held that phrase to have the same meaning in SLUSA as it has under Section 10(b) and Rule 10b-5 case law. *See Dabit v. Merrill Lynch, Pierce, Fenner & Smith, Inc.*, 395 F.3d 25 (2d Cir. 2005), *petition for cert. filed,*

73 U.S.L.W. 3632 (U.S. April 11, 2005) (No. 04-1271); *Rowinski v. Salomon Smith Barney Inc.*, 398 F.3d 294 (3d Cir. 2005); *Kircher v. Putnam Funds Trust*, 403 F.3d 478 (7th Cir. 2005); *Green v. Ameritrade,* 279 F.3d 590 (8th Cir. 2002); *Falkowski v. Imation Corp.*, 309 F.3d 1123 (9th Cir. 2002); *Riley v. Merrill Lynch, Pierce, Fenner & Smith, Inc.*, 292 F.3d 1334 (11th Cir. 2002).

D. **Holder Actions:** There is a split in the circuits on the issue of whether SLUSA preempts claims that do not allege that class members purchased or sold securities in reliance upon the defendant's alleged misconduct. All of the circuits that have ruled on this issue agree that the meaning of the "in connection with" language in SLUSA is coterminous with the meaning of that phrase in Section 10(b) of the 1934 Act. The courts diverge when analyzing whether the rule outlined in *Blue Chip Stamps v. Manor Drug Stores,* 421 U.S. 723 (1975), which limits private rights of action under Section 10(b) to individuals who either purchased or sold securities, preempts state cases where there is no allegation that the class members purchased or sold securities.

a) The lone circuit that has found that holder actions can be preempted by SLUSA is the Seventh Circuit. In an opinion by Judge Easterbrook, the court extended SLUSA's preemptive effect to litigants who neither purchased nor sold shares during the class period. In *Kircher v. Putnam Funds Trust*, 403 F.3d 478 (7th Cir. 2005), the plaintiff defined all but one of the classes as "investors who held shares of a given mutual fund between two specified dates." *Id.* at 482. The court held that SLUSA's preemption applies to Rule 10b-5 actions where the plaintiffs are neither purchasers nor sellers of securities. The court reasoned that "[i]nvocation of [the Rule 10b-5] anti-fraud rule does not depend on proof that the agency…purchased or sold securities; instead the 'in connection with' language ensures that the fraud occurs in securities transactions rather than some other activity." *Id.* at 483.

b) Every other court to consider this issue has ruled that holder actions are not preempted by SLUSA. In *Dabit v. Merrill Lynch, Pierce, Fenner & Smith, Inc.*, 395 F.3d 25 (2005), the court held that "in enacting SLUSA Congress sought only to ensure that class actions brought by plaintiffs who satisfy the *Blue Chip* purchaser-seller rule are subject to the federal securities laws." *Id.* at 43. To be preempted, an action must allege a purchase or sale of a covered security made by the plaintiff or class member. *Id.* at 43-44. The court held that when the defined class included both persons who purchased or sold securities and those that merely held securities, and the complaint provides no meaningful way to distinguish between the two, SLUSA requires the claim be dismissed. *Id.* at 47. *See also Green,* 279 F.3d at 598; *Falkowski,* 309 F.3d at 1130-31, *Riley,* 292 F.3d at 1343-45; *Davis v. Kozlowski,* No. MDL 02-1335-PB, Civ. 04-1338-PB, 2005 WL 662694 at *2 (D.N.H. March 17, 2005); *Atencio v. Smith Barney, Citigroup, Inc.,* No. 04 Civ. 5653 (MBM), 2005 WL 267556 at *4 (S.D.N.Y. Feb. 2, 2005); *Grabow v. PriceWaterhouseCoopers LLP,* 313 F. Supp. 2d 1152 (N.D. Okla. 2004).

E. Treatment of the "in connection with" requirement

1. In *Rowinski,* 398 F.3d 294, customers sued a brokerage firm for breach of contract, unjust enrichment, and unfair business practices, alleging that the company failed to ensure that its research reports were not improperly influenced by investment banking relationships with issuers, leading brokerage customers to overpay for research reports. The court stated that there were several factors relevant in distinguishing between preempted claims and state law claims: (a) whether the covered class action alleges a 'fraudulent scheme' that 'coincides' with the purchase or sale of securities; (b) whether the complaint alleges a material misrepresentation or omission 'disseminated to the public in a medium upon which a reasonable investor would rely; (c) whether the nature of the parties' relationship is such that it necessarily involves the purchase or sale of securities; and (d) whether the prayer for relief 'connects' the state law claims, to the purchase or sale of securities. The court held that the customers allegations of material misrepresentations were in connection with the purchase or sale of securities.

2. In *Falkowski,* 309 F.3d at 1130-32, the complaint, filed on behalf of former employees, alleged breach of contract and fraud in connection with certain stock options granted as part

of a merger. Looking to the 1933 and 1934 Acts' definitions of "security," which include unconsummated contracts to buy or sell securities, the court held that the complaint sufficiently alleged a more-than-tangential nexus between the alleged fraud and the purchase or sale of securities, and was preempted by SLUSA. *Id.*

3. In *Behlen*, 311 F.3d at 1094, the plaintiff, an investor in mutual funds, asserted claims for breach of contract, breach of implied covenants, breach of fiduciary duty, unjust enrichment, negligence and money had and received, based on allegedly improper commissions. Plaintiff alleged that he was mistakenly sold a class of funds with a higher commission than those he had agreed to purchase, arguing that the alleged failure to disclose the nature of the commissions was incidental to, rather than in connection with, his purchase of securities. Held: the commissions were an integral part of the transaction and the claim was barred. *Id.*

4. In *Herndon v. Equitable Life Assurance Soc'y*, 253 F. Supp. 2d 1364, 1369 (S.D. Ga. 2002), *aff'd*, 325 F.3d 1252 (11th Cir. 2003), the complaint alleged that the insured under a variable life insurance policy was mis-designated as higher risk in order to charge higher premiums. Held: claims were in connection with a covered security and action was removable).

5. Similarly, in *Dudek v. Prudential Secs., Inc.*, 295 F.3d 875 (8th Cir. 2002), the plaintiff alleged that the defendant investment firm improperly sold tax-deferred annuities with increased fees to accounts that were already tax-deferred. Held: the asserted misrepresentations were in connection with the purchase of the securities; the claims were barred. *Id.* at 879.

6. Under varying fact patterns, district courts have reached different conclusions about what allegations satisfy SLUSA's "in connection with" requirement.

   a) Decisions finding claims to be asserted in connection with the purchase or sale of securities and therefore preempted by SLUSA:

      (1) *Cinicolo v. Morgan Stanley Dean Witter & Co.*, No. 01 Civ. 6940 (GBD), 2004 U.S. Dist. LEXIS 24896 (S.D.N.Y. Dec. 9, 2004) (Customers sued brokerage

firm for breach of fiduciary duty, Section 349 of New York State General Business Law, and unjust enrichment, alleging that company compromised the integrity and value to retail customers of its equity research in order to obtain investment banking business from public companies. Held: the alleged misrepresentations were in connection with the purchase or sale of a security because the plaintiffs were seeking the disgorgement of commissions paid to the company and because the recommendations made by the company affected the public's interest in a particular corporation's stock;

(2) *Premium Plus Partners,* 2005 WL 711591 at *19 (Plaintiff claimed losses from alleged insider trading of treasury bonds. Plaintiff alleged that preemption did not apply because its alleged losses occurred when it bought Treasury Options as opposed to Treasury Bonds. Held: There is no requirement that plaintiff itself trade in securities. Plaintiff alleged more than misconduct coinciding with a securities transaction, instead plaintiff focused on trading of government securities on the basis of material non-public information. This cause of action is specifically what was intended to be preempted by SLUSA.

(3) *Ray v. Citigroup Global Markets, Inc.*, No. 03C3157, Fed. Sec. L. Rep. (CCH) ¶ 92,625 (N.D. Ill. Nov. 20, 2003) (Investors sued a brokerage firm and broker, asserting claims for violations of Rule 10b-5 as well as state law claims for conspiracy, negligent misrepresentation and negligent supervision, claiming that they were fraudulently induced to purchase and hold shares of an issuer based on misrepresentations about the issuer's prospects. Defendants moved to dismiss the state law claims under SLUSA. Plaintiffs argued that the claims were not preempted because they were directed at plaintiffs' purchase and hold of the issuer's stock. The district court disagreed with plaintiffs, finding that the complaint alleged a "uni-

tary scheme of fraud" both before and after the purchases);

(4) *Feitelberg*, 234 F. Supp. 2d at 1052 (allegations that misleading analysts' research reports affected the prices of securities asserted claims in connection with the sale of securities);

(5) *In re Merrill Lynch & Co., Inc. Research Reports Sec. Litig.*, Nos. 02 MDL 1484 (MP), 03 CV 1428 (MP), 03 CV 1429 (MP), 03 CV 1430 (MP), 2003 WL 21036085 (S.D.N.Y. May 6, 2003) (motion to remand claims under New York statutory and common law for misrepresentations and omissions relating to investment firms' research reports denied; leave to amend denied); *see also In re Merrill Lynch & Co., Inc. Research Reports Sec. Litig.*, Nos. 02 MDL1484 (MP), 02 CV4051 (MP), 02 CV8472 (MP), 02 CV4205 (MP), 02 CV9487 (MP), 2003 WL 1872820 (S.D.N.Y. Apr. 10, 2003) (same);

(6) *Shaw*, Fed. Sec. L. Rep. (CCH) ¶ 92,413, at 92,090-92,091 (Brokerage customer's claim that defendant misrepresented the commissions on its brokerage accounts was preempted. Citing *Zandford*, the court held that "in connection with" under SLUSA should have the same meaning as under Section 10(b), *i.e.*, that it should be interpreted flexibly, and should reach even transactions that merely coincide with alleged misconduct).

b) Decisions holding that claims were not asserted in connection with the purchase or sale of securities and therefore SLUSA did not apply:

(1) *Norman v. Salomon Smith Barney Inc.*, 350 F. Supp. 2d 382 (S.D.N.Y. 2004) (brokerage customers with discretionary accounts sued brokerage firm alleging breach of fiduciary duty and breach of contract on the basis that investment recommendations were based on analysts' research that was tainted by conflicts of interest; court found that allegations were

not made in connection with any purchases or sales of securities and no fraud or misrepresentation was alleged);

(2) *Grabow v. PricewaterhouseCoopers LLP*, 313 F. Supp. 2d 1152 (N.D. Okla. 2004) (shareholders sued corporation's auditor, claiming that alleged misrepresentations in financial statements caused them to retain shares; court found that because claims dealt with retention of shares, they did not arise in connection with the purchase or sale of securities);

(3) *Bradfisch v. Templeton Funds, Inc.*, 319 F. Supp. 2d 897 (S.D. Ill. 2004) (holders of open-ended mutual fund sued fund manager alleging breach of duties of care and loyalty based on asserted stale pricing; court found that claims were not asserted in connection with purchase or sale because claims were asserted on behalf of holders and alleged only dilution in value);

(4) *Meyer v. Putnam International Voyager Fund*, 220 F.R.D. 27 (D. Mass. Jan. 27, 2004) (Court found that claims by a mutual fund investor alleging breach of fiduciary duty because of market timing were not preempted by SLUSA. Because the complaint asserted claims on behalf of "holders" of the mutual funds, rather than purchasers or sellers, the court ruled that the asserted claims did not arise in connection with purchase or sale of the mutual fund shares);

(5) *Seaboard Secs.*, 241 F. Supp. 2d at 220-23 (Claims for fraud in the inducement under New York General Business Law Section 349 and breach of contract were not preempted, because they asserted that plaintiffs contracted for services based on misrepresentations, rather than traded securities based on misrepresentations. Claims for fraud and misrepresentation were preempted, but claims for negligence and negligent supervision were not);

(6) *Burns*, 218 F. Supp. 2d at 915-16 (granting motion to remand complaint that asserted breach of fiduciary duty and misrepresentation based on broker's unauthorized liquidation of plaintiff's accounts and the brokerage firm's failure to disclose the liquidation. Held: any alleged misrepresentations occurred after the purchases or sales of securities and were therefore not in connection with them, *Zandford* distinguished on the basis that the sales and the representations did not coincide);

(7) *Dacey v. Morgan Stanley Dean Witter & Co.*,, 263 F. Supp. 2d 706, 711-12 (S.D.N.Y. 2003) (Motion to remand granted in part and denied in part. The plaintiff sued his investment advisor for failing to meet NASD standards, on the basis that the advisor's research reports were improperly influenced by investment banking relationships. The complaint asserted claims for breach of contract on behalf of both investors who purchased securities on the basis of the alleged reports and investors who were holding securities at the time the reports were issued. Held: the claims of the latter group did not arise in connection with the purchase or sale of securities and were not preempted);

(8) *Shen*, Fed. Sec. L. Rep. (CCH) ¶ 92,223, at 91,262-91,263 (claim for breach of fiduciary duty through dilution of voting rights arising out of merger did not state claim in connection with sale of securities).

V. "COVERED SECURITIES" DEFINED

A. SLUSA defines "covered securities" as including securities that meet the standards of Section 18(b)(1) or 18(b)(2) of the 1933 Act at the time of the alleged misrepresentation or omission, except debt securities that are exempt under Section 4(2) of the 1933 Act.

1. Section 18(b)(1) applies to nationally traded securities, including those traded on any of the national exchanges as well as

securities of these same issuers that are equal or senior to their listed securities.

2. Section 18(b)(2) applies to the securities of registered investment companies, whether open or closed-end funds.

3. Only those actions pertaining to the purchase or sale of the securities defined as "covered securities" by SLUSA are preempted.

4. **Variable Annuities**. It is now widely recognized that variable annuities are covered securities under SLUSA. *See Herndon*, 253 F. Supp. 2d at 1369 (fact that after complaint was filed, plaintiff reallocated premiums to a money market account did not change holding); *accord Dudek*, 295 F.3d at 878; *Patenaude v. Equitable Life Assurance Soc'y*, 290 F.3d 1020, 1025-26 (9th Cir. 2002); *Lander v. Hartford Life & Annuity Insur. Co.*, 251 F. 3d 101, 109-15 (2d Cir. 2001) (affirming denial of motion to remand; Held: variable annuity policies were "covered securities" under SLUSA; McCarran-Ferguson Act, which has a provision barring federal preemption of insurance regulation, does not preclude application of SLUSA to variable annuities); *Lasley v. New England Variable Life Ins. Co.*, 126 F. Supp. 2d 1236, 1238-39 (N.D. Cal. 1999) (denying motion to remand granting motion to dismiss complaint alleging fraud, negligent misrepresentation, negligence, breach of contract and interference with economic advantage in connection with marketing of life insurance products; Held: because complaint involved allegations relating to variable life insurance policies, which are covered securities under SLUSA, entire complaint was removable); *In re Lutheran Bros. Variable Ins. Prods. Co. Sales Practices Litig.*, 105 F. Supp. 2d 1037, 1039-40 (D.Minn. 2000) (denying motion to remand; Held: variable life insurance policies were covered securities under SLUSA).

5. **Stock Options**. In *Falkowski*, 309 F.3d at 1129, the court held that alleged misrepresentations in connection with options to purchase stock that met the definition of a covered security fell within SLUSA.

6. **Certificates of Deposit**. In *Kenneth Rothschild Trust v. Morgan Stanley Dean Witter*, 199 F. Supp. 2d 993 (C.D. Cal.

2002), the plaintiffs purchased CDs, and claimed that the bank misrepresented the interest payable between the deposit of funds and the actual purchase of the CD, constituting a violation of California's consumer protection statute, consumer law fraud, negligent misrepresentation and breach of contract. In the interim period, the deposited funds were invested in a money market mutual fund that was a covered security. The court held that although the CDs themselves were not "covered securities," the alleged misrepresentations pertained to the interest payable while the funds were invested in the money market shares, which were covered securities and therefore the claims were subject to SLUSA.

7. **Specific Securities**. In *Seaboard Secs.*, 241 F. Supp. 2d at 219, the plaintiffs, holders of accounts with a brokerage firm, asserted claims for breach of contract, fraud and negligence against the firm, based on its alleged representations about the extent to which its services were based on, and its commissions priced to include, proprietary research from another, larger firm, also named as a defendant. Plaintiffs asserted that because the complaint did not reference particular securities, the action did not involve covered securities. Held: because all of the securities at issue were listed on national exchanges, the action pertained to covered securities and was barred.

8. **Stock Issued Pursuant to a Merger Agreement.** In *Madden v. Deloitte & Touche, LLP,* Nos. 02-56976, 02-56982, 03-55408, 03-56891. D.C. Nos. CV-99-01516-TJW, CV-99-01516-TJW, CV-99-01516-TJW, D.C. No. CV-99-01516-LAB, 118 Fed. Appx. 150 (9th Cir. Nov. 23, 2004) (unpublished) *petition for cert. filed,* 73 U.S.L.W. 3720 (U.S. June 2, 2005) (No. 04-1636) plaintiffs argued that common stock issued pursuant to a merger agreement was not a 'covered security' because the actual shares of stock were not listed on Nasdaq until after the alleged misrepresentations occurred. Held: because plaintiffs alleged that the common stock of the company was traded on Nasdaq, the plaintiffs received some of that stock, the SEC had approved registration of the plaintiffs' stock and the alleged fraud induced plaintiffs to acquire the common stock, the complaint sufficiently alleged that the stock was a 'covered security.'

VI. PRESERVED ACTIONS AND THE DELAWARE CARVE-OUT

A. Four general categories of actions are preserved by SLUSA, including exclusively derivative actions, actions under contractual agreements between issuers and indenture trustees, actions by states or their subdivisions, and certain actions under the state law of an issuer's state of incorporation.

B. **Derivative Actions Excluded**. Actions that are exclusively derivative in nature are excluded from the definition of "covered class actions", whereas three other categories of actions are explicitly "preserved" by SLUSA. 15 U.S.C. § 77p(f)(2)(B); 15 U.S.C. § 78bb(f)(5)(c).

1. ***Deference to Characterization of Derivative Action.*** Under the plain meaning of the statute, if plaintiff labels the claim derivative, the court will consider it not preempted. In *Arlia x rel. Massey Energy Co. v. Blankenship*, 234 F. Supp. 2d 606, 612-13 (S.D. W.Va. 2002), the complaint asserted a derivative claim for breach of fiduciary duty, including a misappropriation theory of insider trading. Defendants argued that the complaint essentially asserted a class action claim for insider trading, which could not recover for harm to the corporation, but only to shareholders. Held: the plain meaning of the statute exempted the claim under the Delaware carve out, despite the fact that West Virginia law may not recognize a derivative cause of action for insider trading.

C. **State Actions**. "State actions" are one category of preserved actions. SLUSA provides that "Notwithstanding any other provision of this section, nothing in this section may be construed to preclude a State or political subdivision thereof or a State pension plan from bringing an action involving a covered security on its own behalf, or as a member of a class comprised solely of other States, political subdivisions, or State pension plans that are named plaintiffs, and that have authorized participation, in such action." 15 U.S.C. § 77p(d)(2)(A); 15 U.S.C. § 78bb(f)(3)(B).

D. **Trustee Actions**. Also preserved are actions under contractual agreements between issuers and indenture trustees. Specifically, SLUSA provides that covered class actions that "seek to enforce a contractual agreement between an issuer and an indenture trustee" can be brought in federal or state court "by a party to the agreement or a successor to such party." 15 U.S.C. § 77p(f)(d)(3); 15 U.S.C. § 78bb(f)(3)(B)(i).

E. **Delaware Carve-Out**. Actions based on the law of the state of incorporation, along with the exception for derivative actions, are known as "the "Delaware carve-outs."

1. For a non-derivative action based on the law of the state of incorporation to fall within the Delaware carve-out, it must involve either: (1) the purchase or sale of securities by the issuer or an affiliate of the issuer exclusively from or to holders of equity securities of the issuer; or (2) a recommendation, position, or other communication with respect to the sale of the issuer's securities that is made by or on behalf of the issuer or its affiliate to equity holders, and concerns the equity holders' decisions with respect to voting their securities, responding to a tender or exchange offer, or exercising dissenters' or appraisal rights.

2. Several cases have now interpreted the scope of the Delaware carve-out.

   a) *See G.F. Thomas Investments, L.P. v. Cleco Corp.*, 317 F. Supp. 2d 673 (W.D.La. 2004) (Plaintiffs filed proposed class action under state law on behalf of shareholders of energy company; plaintiffs argued that action fell within exception for actions involving purchase or sale of securities by the issuer exclusively from or to holders of the issuer's securities; defendants argued that because shares were offered on open market, they were not offered exclusively from or to holders of the issuer's securities; action dismissed), *aff'd,* 123 Fed. Appx. 155 (5th Cir. 2005) (unpublished);

   b) *Alessi v. Beracha*, 244 F. Supp. 2d 354 (D. Del. 2003) (Plaintiff alleged that company failed to disclose ongoing merger discussions during a stockholder buyback, thereby purchasing shares for less than their value. Held: action was subject to Delaware carve out and SLUSA did not apply. Court rejected a narrow reading of "tender or exchange offer," finding that where gravamen of claim was breach of duty of disclosure, matters were intended to be entrusted to Delaware state court);

c) *Greaves v. McAuley*, No. CIV A 1:03-CV-0207-B, 264 F. Supp. 2d 1078 (N.D. Ga. 2003) (Plaintiff, a shareholder of the defendant company, challenged the company's announced plan to merge, asserting breach of fiduciary duty based on inadequate consideration to the public shareholders. The amended complaint included class and derivative claims, among them a claim for misrepresentations in the proxy statement regarding the consideration and the process of considering the merger. On receipt of the amended complaint, defendants removed under SLUSA. Held: the majority of the claims were excluded from SLUSA under the Delaware carve-out because they involved communications to shareholders under the law of the state of incorporation concerning decisions whether or not to vote for the merger).

VII. THE SLUSA DISCOVERY STAY

A. One of the key elements of the PSLRA is the stay of discovery pending a court's determination on a motion to dismiss the complaint. After the PSLRA's enactment, plaintiffs would frequently file parallel federal and state proceedings in order to circumvent the discovery stay by obtaining discovery in the state court actions. By restricting plaintiffs' ability to file in state court, SLUSA was intended to close this loophole. *See* Report of the House Committee on Commerce, H.R. 105-640, July 21, 1998, at 9.

B. In addition to generally augmenting the reach of the PSLRA's federal discovery stay through its preemptive effect, SLUSA also expressly provides that "upon a proper showing, a court may stay" discovery in a state action, "as necessary in aid of its jurisdiction, or to protect or effectuate judgments … ." 15 U.S.C. § 77z-1(b)(4); 15 U.S.C. § 78u-4(b)(3)(D).

C. In the first appellate court decision to address the discovery stay, the Fifth Circuit in *Newby v. Enron Corp.*, 338 F.3d 467 (5th Cir. 2003), affirmed its applicability to an individual action filed in state court. The Fifth Circuit refused to read into the plain language of SLUSA a requirement that the state court action be a class action, finding this contrary to the meaning and purpose of the discovery stay.

D. **Overlapping State and Federal Claims.**

1. In *Schwartz v. TXU Corp.,* No. Civ.A.3:02-CV-2243-K, 2004 WL 1732477 (N.D. Tex. July 30, 2004), the plaintiffs argued that the scope of the state court suit was much narrower than the federal action, and discovery should therefore not be stayed. The court held that even though the claims in the state court action were narrower, they still overlapped with the federal claims. The court issued the stay on discovery in the state court action.

2. *Compare In re Gilead Sciences Sec. Litig.,* No. C 03-4999 MJJ, 2004 U.S. Dist. LEXIS 27309 (N.D. Cal. Nov. 22, 2004). The court relied on the following factors to determine whether to grant a stay of discovery: (1) whether there is a risk of the federal plaintiffs obtaining the state plaintiffs' discovery and to what extent a confidentiality agreement and/or protective order with defendants would minimize that risk; (2) whether the state and federal actions contain overlapping legal claims and underlying facts; and (3) the scope of the discovery needed to amend the state complaint, and the corresponding burden on defendants. The court held that even though both the state and federal causes of action were based on the same operative facts and the defendants would be forced to respond to duplicative discovery if the stay was not granted, a protective order would be effective to protect the defendants and the duplicative discovery was not overly burdensome, therefore the stay was not issued.

E. **Derivative Actions**. The SLUSA discovery stay may be invoked to stay discovery in a state court derivative action. *See In re Cardinal Health, Inc. Securities Litigation,* 365 F. Supp. 2d 866 (S.D. Ohio 2005); *In re DPL Inc., Sec. Litig.*, 247 F. Supp. 2d 946, 949 (S.D. Ohio 2003).

1. In *In re Cardinal Health,* 365 F. Supp. 2d 866, plaintiff argued that SLUSA did not broadly apply to derivative actions, but instead only applied where the defendant could demonstrate the plaintiff's intent to circumvent the PSLRA's stay provision. The court rejected plaintiff's argument, stating that Congress did not intend to limit the provision to state private securities class action lawsuits and that the defendant need not prove that the state action was intended to circumvent the PSLRA.

2. In *In re DPL,* 247 F. Supp. 2d 946, defendants in a federal securities action moved to invoke the SLUSA discovery stay as to four state court derivative actions based on similar allegations. The court rejected the argument that because derivative actions are themselves exempt from SLUSA, discovery may not be stayed, noting that the stay may extend to "'any private action' pending in a state court," not only to "covered class actions." *Id.* at 948-49. In granting the stay, the court applied the two-part test previously set forth in *Lapicola v. Alternative Dual Fuels, Inc.*, Fed. Sec. L. Rep. (CCH) ¶ 91,765, at 98,653 (N.D. Tex. Apr. 5, 2002), which requires that the stay be necessary both to: (1) prevent an unreasonable burden on defendants before the disposition of a motion to dismiss; and (2) avoid allowing plaintiffs to use discovery to support claims that do not meet the PSLRA pleading requirements. *DPL*, 247 F. Supp. 2d at 950. The *DPL* court disagreed with *In re Transcrypt Int'l Sec. Litig.*, 57 F. Supp. 2d 836 (D. Neb. 1999), which had held that only discovery in state class actions could be stayed. *Id.* at 948 n.6.

3. *Compare City of Austin Police Ret. Sys. v. Itt Educ. Serv., Inc.*, No. 1:04-CV-0380 DFH-TAB, 2005 WL 280345 (S.D. Ind. Feb. 2, 2005) (Held: Congress did not intend for SLUSA to allow federal courts to halt any state actions' discovery. Congress intended the provision to apply to almost exclusively to state securities fraud actions, unless defendants could show that plaintiffs intended to circumvent the PSLRA's stay provision.

F. **Bankruptcy Actions**. In *In re Recoton Corp.*, 307 B.R. 751 (S.D.N.Y. 2004), the unsecured creditors' committee sought to obtain documents and testimony from directors and officers of the bankrupt entity who were simultaneously defending a series of securities class actions. The directors and officers argued that discovery in the bankruptcy action would circumvent the purpose of the stay. The court found that since the bankruptcy claims were pending in federal rather than state court, the discovery stay did not apply.

G. **Third Party Standing to Invoke Stay**. In addition to litigants, third parties also have standing to invoke the discovery stay. *See In re Adelphia Communications Corp.*, 294 B.R. 39, 42-45

(S.D.N.Y. June 12, 2003) (Third party accounting firm objected to the form of proposed order on a motion staying discovery, to the extent that it permitted discovery in a related state court action. Held: while the auditor had standing to object, the court declined to exercise its discretion to stay document discovery; no discovery against the third party was presently sought, hence the issue could be decided by the state or federal trial courts).

H. **Staying Actions to Inspect Books and Records pursuant to Section 220 of the Delaware Corporation Code.** The Delaware Corporations Code provides shareholders a right to inspect the books and records of a corporation before bringing a shareholder derivative suit. A few cases have addressed the issue of whether SLUSA's discovery stay operates to stay Section 220 actions.

1. *City of Austin Police Retirement System,* 2005 WL 280345 (held that a Section 220 action is a discovery proceeding within the meaning of SLUSA, but that pursuit of the Section 220 action will not interfere with the court's consideration or disposition of the federal securities fraud case. The court held that because there was no indication that the plaintiff was going to share the information with the plaintiffs in the federal action, thus circumventing the requirements of the PSLRA, the Section 220 action would not be stayed. *See also Cohen v. El Paso Corporation,* No. Civ.A. 551-N, 2004 WL 2340046 (Del. Ch. Oct. 18, 2004) (held that the text and legislative history of both the PSLRA and SLUSA reveal that the automatic stay of discovery rules were meant to deal exclusively with discovery in federal securities class actions, and do not prevent a state court from considering a books and records demand or similar state law claims).

NOTES

NOTES

5

ISSUER CLASS ACTIONS: NOTEWORTHY DECISIONS AND TRENDS OF 2004/2005

Laurie Smilan

Latham & Watkins LLP

This article is submitted by Laurie B. Smilan, a partner and Co-Chair of the Securities Litigation and Professional Liability Practice Group at Latham & Watkins LLP. Ms. Smilan, her partners Pamela S. Palmer and Jeff G. Hammel, and associates David A. Becker, J. Christian Word, Gregory A. Harris, and Heather M. McPhee contributed to this article.

Table of Contents

Introduction

Although the Private Securities Litigation Reform Act was enacted nearly a decade ago, its key provisions continue to be litigated and their contours determined—and not always uniformly—by the federal courts. These reforms were put in place at a time when the conventional wisdom was that securities suits were, more often than not, "abusive" and "meritless" and a constraint on the efficient operation of the capital markets. Held to the stringent pleading standards the Act imposed and unaided by discovery, due to the statute's mandatory stay provisions, plaintiffs had an increasingly difficult time maintaining a claim. While there has been no sustained reduction in the number of cases filed, the number of fraud-by-hindsight strike suits based on failed financial forecasts and garden variety business reversals has significantly declined and dismissals have become more common—reported as reaching 39% of cases filed in 2004.[1]

The corporate scandals that rang in the new millennium, however, resulted in decisions that took back some of the ground that was gained. The protections of the Reform Act are at risk of significant erosion due to seeming back-tracking by the courts and examples of outright disregard for the express language, as well as the legislative intent, behind the Reform Act's reforms.

There were bright spots on the loss causation front. The Supreme Court's decision in *Dura Pharmaceuticals* has captured our attention. In *Dura Pharmaceuticals*, the Supreme Court firmly established that the efficient market theory, which permits class actions by means of the presumption of reliance on the market price is a two-way street.

In addition to *Dura* however, other important developments merit close examination. First, it appears that there are troubled waters ahead for the Reform Act's safe harbor, as witnessed by the Seventh Circuit's recent decision in *Asher v. Baxter*, the evisceration of the "actual knowledge" standard for forward-looking statements on remand and the Ninth Circuit's total failure to apply the safe harbor at all in Oracle. Second, a series of decisions in the Ninth Circuit reversed a stunning string of decisions affirming dismissal, representing a retreat from *Silicon Graphics* and its progeny, which established the strictest scienter pleading requirements in the nation. In another retreat from *Silicon Graphics*, the Ninth Circuit in I*n re Daou Systems, Inc. Securities Litigation*, 2005 WL 1431833 (9th Cir. 2005), articulated relatively lenient standards for

1. National Economic Research Associates, Inc.

assessing the credibility of confidential witnesses, at least when compared to the more stringent application of those same standards, derived from the Second Circuit's decision in *Novak v. Kasaks*, 216 F.3d 300, 310 (2d Cir. 2000), or by the Third Circuit in *California Public Employees' Retirement System v. The Chubb Corporation*, 394 F.3d 126 (3d Cir. 2004). Finally, the Reform Act's discovery stay provision is no longer sacrosanct, as recent cases reveal.

All in all, in the last two years we have seen a number of decisions that reflect that the skepticism towards securities class action lawsuits that led to the Reform Act is now being balanced by skepticism about corporate America. As the Ninth Circuit said in signaling its retreat from *Silicon Graphics:* "in this era of corporate scandal, when insiders manipulate the market with the complicity of lawyers and accountants, we are cautious to raise the bar of the PSLRA any higher than that which is required under its mandates."[2] Indeed, the bar is being lowered, for better or for worse.

I. LOSS CAUSATION: *DURA PHARMACEUTICALS* AND THE SUPREME COURT'S CHOICE

In *Dura Pharmaceuticals, Inc. v. Broudo*, --- US ---, 2005 WL 885109 (Apr. 19, 2005), the United States Supreme Court reversed the Ninth Circuit's "price inflation" theory of loss causation. This theory, at odds with the standards applied by almost all other federal courts, would have allowed investors to sue a company merely by claiming that they paid too much for the company's stock because of a defendant's alleged misrepresentations. The Supreme Court unanimously rejected the theory with eight words: "In our view, the Ninth Circuit is wrong." Lower courts have already begun to apply *Dura* in dismissing pending cases and, there is no doubt about the significance of this opinion in securities litigation for years to come.

A. What Is "Loss Causation" and Does it Matter?

The Private Securities Litigation Reform Act of 1995 (the "PSLRA") codified the many judicial decisions holding that Rule 10b-5 required plaintiffs to prove that their investment losses were caused by the defendant's misrepresentations. This causation requirement has two components: (i) transaction causation (that the plaintiff relied on the defendant's alleged misrepresentations in making the investment

2. *No. 84 Employer-Teamster Joint Council Pension Trust Fund v. America West Holding Corp.,* 320 F.3d 920, 946 (9th Cir. 2003).

decision), and (ii) loss causation (that the alleged misrepresentation caused the plaintiff's investment loss). These requirements are designed to insure that defendants are only held liable for investment losses actually resulting from their misrepresentations - and not for stock price declines attributable to other factors, such as adverse changes in market conditions or other negative business developments.

In 1988, the United States Supreme Court enabled so-called "stock drop" class actions by allowing plaintiffs to plead the first component of causation—transaction causation or reliance—based on a "fraud-on-the-market" theory. In *Basic v. Levinson*, 485 US 224 (1988), the Court held that all investors who trade stock in an "efficient market"—such as the New York Stock Exchange or the NASDAQ—inherently rely on the integrity of the market price because that price should rapidly reflect all available material information. Accordingly, class action plaintiffs may plead transaction causation by alleging that a defendant's material misrepresentation was a fraud-on-the-market that artificially inflated the stock price on which investors relied.

The efficient market theory also comes into play in the second component of causation - loss causation. The so-called "truth-on-the-market" theory is that, in an efficient market, an artificially inflated stock price remains inflated until the "truth" comes out. As the Supreme Court in *Dura* explained, this means that investors do not suffer an economic loss "caused" by the alleged misrepresentations until their falsity is disclosed and absorbed by the efficient market causing the stock price to drop (deflate). It logically follows that any adverse price movement prior to a corrective disclosure is caused by events other than the alleged misrepresentation because the negative truth is not yet known and, therefore, not reflected in the stock price. Thus, investors who buy after the misrepresentation but sell before the truth comes out have not been injured.

Herein lay the problem with the Ninth Circuit's *Dura* decision: it permitted plaintiffs to maintain a securities fraud suit even though they plead only that the stock price was inflated due to the defendant's alleged fraud, but not that the price fell following a corrective disclosure.

B. The Ninth Circuit's Decision In Dura

The plaintiffs alleged that defendant Dura Pharmaceuticals artificially boosted the price of its stock at the beginning of the alleged class period by misrepresenting the prospects for FDA approval of its asthma-spray device. The plaintiffs sued when the stock price dropped after Dura announced lower than expected earnings due to slow drug sales, even though the "truth" about FDA approval was not disclosed. It was not until eight months later, after the close of the class period, that Dura disclosed that the FDA failed to approve the asthma-spray device. Plaintiffs' sole allegation regarding their economic loss was that they had "paid artificially inflated prices for Dura securities." The Ninth Circuit reversed the trial court, holding that this allegation was sufficient to plead loss causation.

C. The Supreme Court's Decision In Dura

The Supreme Court, in a short and unanimous opinion authored by Justice Breyer, held that in fraud-on-the-market cases such as *Dura*, "an inflated purchase price will not itself constitute or proximately cause the relevant economic loss." The decision rests on three points.

First, the Court rejected the notion that mere price inflation means that the investor has suffered an economic loss. "For one thing," the Court observed, "as a matter of pure logic, at the moment the [stock purchase] takes place, the plaintiff has suffered no loss; the inflated purchase payment is offset by ownership of a share that at that instant possesses equivalent value." An investor who sells the stock before the truth is disclosed may suffer a loss if the price decline, but that loss is not attributable to the misstatements because the decline is unrelated to the inflation. Moreover, even after the "relevant truth" is learned by the market, a "lower price may reflect, not the earlier misrepresentation, but changed economic circumstances, changed investor expectations, new industry-specific or firm-specific facts, conditions or other events." Thus, at most, "an initially inflated purchase price might mean a later loss." (emphasis added.)

Second, the Court concluded that the price inflation theory of loss causation has no historical support in the common law of fraud and deceit on which the federal anti-fraud securities statutes are based. The judicial consensus, as reflected in the Restatement of Torts, is that a person who "misrepresents the financial condition of a corporation in order to sell its stock" is liable "for the loss" sustained by the purchaser "when the facts … become generally known" and, as a result, share value depreciates. "Given the common-law roots of the securities fraud class action," the Court observed that "it is not surprising that the other courts of appeals have rejected the Ninth Circuit's 'inflated purchase price' approach to proving causation and loss."

Third, the Court found that the price inflation theory was inconsistent with the purpose of the federal securities statutes. These statutes "seek to maintain public confidence in the marketplace" they are "not to provide investors with broad insurance against market losses" that are not caused by defendant's misrepresentations. The Ninth Circuit's approach "would allow recoveries where a misrepresentation leads to an inflated purchase price but nonetheless does not proximately cause" an investor's economic loss - as, for instance, when a drop in stock price is caused by factors other than disclosure of "the truth."

In *Dura*, the truth about FDA approval was not known at the close of the alleged class period. Rather, the drop in stock price that the plaintiffs sought to recover followed an announcement of other unrelated negative developments about Dura's business. Thus, the plaintiffs could not demonstrate loss causation.

One may wonder why the plaintiffs simply did not extend the class period until the disclosure of the news about FDA approval. The answer appears to be that they would not have been able to demonstrate damages under the PSLRA. When the alleged "truth" was revealed, Dura's stock price momentarily dipped but then quickly recovered. Under the PSLRA's so-called "90-day bounce-back" provision, this meant that the plaintiffs likely did not suffer any recoverable damages.

D. What Is The Effect Of The Dura Decision?

The Supreme Court's rejection of the price inflation theory of loss causation may have the most effect in the Ninth and Eighth Circuits where the *Dura* decision closes the door to a speculative genre of stock drop class actions in which plaintiffs need not plead any loss in stock value due to a defendant's alleged fraud. In all jurisdictions, however, the lasting impact of the Dura decision will depend on how parties use and courts interpret the Supreme Court's reasoning.

The Supreme Court's embrace of the logical consequences of the efficient market theory strongly supports certain defense arguments in fraud-on-the-market cases. The Court perceptively noted that even a decline in stock price after the "truth" is revealed may not necessarily be attributable to the alleged misrepresentation where other factors are operating on the market price. This supports the long-standing argument that defendants are not liable for the portion of a drop in stock price attributable to factors unrelated to an alleged corrective disclosure, the conclusion reached by the Second Circuit in *Dabit v. Merrill Lynch* and the Northern District of California in *McKesson*. The

Court's reasoning also seems to support the defense argument that the absence of any negative market reaction to disclosure of "the truth" establishes that the alleged misrepresentation was not material and, therefore, not actionable, as the Third Circuit held in *Oran v. Stafford.*

One aspect of the Court's decision, however, may be welcomed by plaintiffs. Because *Dura* was dismissed at the pleading stage, the Court considered the level of detail at which plaintiffs must plead loss causation. The Court "assume[d]," rather than held, "that neither the [Federal] Rules nor the securities statutes impose any special further requirement" for pleading loss causation. As a result, the Court evaluated the complaint pursuant to the "short and plain statement" pleading standard of Rule 8 of the Federal Rules of Civil Procedure. The Court observed that, measured only by the requirements of Rule 8, "it should not prove burdensome for a plaintiff who has suffered an economic loss to provide a defendant with some indication of the loss and the causal connection that the plaintiff has in mind." Because most securities fraud class actions are decided at the pleading stage, the manner in which the lower courts for loss causation will affect whether at least some securities fraud class actions survive the pleading phase. Presumably, even under Rule 8, the lower courts will reject purely conclusory allegations absent some logical stock price reaction reasonably related to the disclosure of the facts alleged to have previously been misrepresented or concealed.

In the end, while courts and commentators still have plenty of issues to wrestle with in the wake of *Dura*, the decision is a significant victory for public companies and others named as defendants in securities fraud cases.

II. TROUBLED WATERS IN THE SAFE HARBOR

The Reform Act's safe harbor protecting forward-looking information is one of its most important provisions. In adopting the Reform Act, Congress concluded that "understanding a company's own assessment of its future potential [is] among the most valuable information shareholders and potential investors could have about a firm."[3] Congress also determined, however, that fear of strike suits second-guessing projections of future performance was having a "chilling effect . . . on the robustness and candor of disclosure," and on "the willingness of corporate managers to

---

3. H.R. Conf. Rep. No. 104-369 (1995), reprinted in 1995 U.S.C.C.A.N. 730 (the "Conference Report"), at 43 (citation omitted).

disclose information to the marketplace," because "companies and their officers [were] subjected to potentially limitless liability if they disclosed projections that later turn out to be inaccurate."[4] Accordingly, the "safe harbor" was enacted in order "to . . . encourag[e] companies to disclose forward-looking information" without fear of liability.[5] The goal of the safe harbor is "to provide certainty that forward-looking statements will not be actionable by private parties . . . if they are accompanied by a meaningful" risk disclosure.[6] Thus, the safe harbor immunizes a forward-looking statement so long as it is "accompanied by meaningful cautionary statements identifying important factors that could cause actual results to differ materially from those in the forward-looking statement."[7]

Consistent with its goal of encouraging forward-looking disclosure, Congress did not intend to make it overly burdensome for a company to comply with the safe harbor. Thus, as the legislative history makes clear, a company is not required to identify or caution against every conceivable factor that may cause results to differ from its projections.[8] A company is not even required to identify the actual risks that ultimately caused the forward-looking statement not to come true.[9] The idea is not that the cautionary disclosure turn out to be right, but that investors are warned that the projections are not guarantees. Thus, a risk factor is deemed "important" and "meaningful" if it "could actually affect whether the forward-looking statement is realized."[10]

The safe harbor has a second "prong," which serves as an "alternative inlet[]" to the "meaningful cautionary statements" prong. This second prong immunizes forward-looking statements from liability even if not accompanied by meaningful cautionary language unless the plaintiffs plead particularized facts sufficient to satisfy their burden of showing that

---

4. *Id.* at 42-43.
5. A "forward-looking" statement is defined as a projection of financial items, a description of management's plans for future operations or economic performance, or the stated assumptions underlying these projections. 15 U.S. C. § 78u-5(i)(1).
6. Conference Report at 43-44 (emphasis added).
7. 15 U.S.C. § 78u-5(c)(1)(A); *Harris v. Ivax Corp*, 182 F.3d 799, 803 (11th Cir. 1999).
8. *See Ivax*, 182 F.3d at 807.
9. *Id.* Further, the Reform Acts directs courts to determine at the pleading stage whether forward-looking statements are protected by the safe harbor. 15 U.S.C. 78u-5(e). Corporations who comply with the safe harbor by properly warning investors of meaningful risks, can therefore expect to be protected without first facing the crushing costs of litigation.
10. Conference Report at 43-44.

the defendants made the statements with actual knowledge that they could not be achieved.[11]

Numerous courts throughout the country have dismissed cases on a motion to dismiss because the challenged statements are inactionable forward-looking statements protected by the safe harbor.[12] Two recent appellate court decisions—the Seventh Circuit's *Asher v. Baxter*[13] (together with the District Court's decision on remand in *Baxter*[14]), and the Ninth Circuit's *Nursing Home Pension Fund, Local 144 v. Oracle Corp*[15]—call into question the extent to which the Reform Act's "safe harbor" can be relied upon to protect forward-looking statements, and discuss whether these decisions represent a trend.

A. A Brewing Storm—Asher v. Baxter International, Inc.

1. Required Risk Disclosures under the Safe Harbor

One of the fundamental precepts of the immunity provided by the safe harbor is that a company's risk disclosures need not, in hindsight, have necessarily disclosed the "right" risks facing the company (*i.e.,* those that ultimately cause the predictions not to come to pass).[16] The Conference Committee explained that "[f]ailure to include the particular factor that ultimately causes the forward-looking statement not to come true will not mean that the statement is not protected by the safe harbor."[17] Forward-looking statements are, after all, simply a company's estimation about its future performance; Congress recognized that just as a Company ought not to be subject to liability for incorrectly predicting future results, it also ought not to be held liable for failing to predict what risks may, in the future, come to pass and cause a projection not to be achieved.

---

11. 15 U.S.C. § 78u-5(c)(1); Conference Report at 44.
12. *See, e.g., Rombach v. Chang*, 355 F.3d 164, 173 (2d Cir. 2004); *Miller v. Champion Enterprises,* 346 F.3d 660 (6th Cir. 2003); *Harris v. Ivax Corp.*, 182 F.3d 799 (11th Cir. 1999); *Ehlert v. Singer*, 245 F.3d 1313 (11th Cir. 2001).
13. *Asher v. Baxter International Inc.,* 377 F.3d 727 (7th Cir. 2004).
14. *Asher v. Baxter International Inc.,* 2005 WL 331572 (N.D. Ill. Feb. 3, 2005).
15. 380 F.3d 1226 (9th Cir. 2004).
16. *See, e.g., Ivax,* 182 F.3d at 807; *Halperin v. eBanker USA.COM, Inc.,* 295 F.3d 352, 359 (2d Cir. 2002); *Helwig v. Vencor, Inc.*, 251 F.3d 540, 558-59 (6th Cir. 2001) (en banc); *Ehlert v. Singer*, 245 F.3d 1313, 1320 (11th Cir. 2001); *Semerenko v. Cendant Corp.*, 223 F.3d 165, 182-83 (3d Cir. 2000) (same).
17. Conference Report at 44.

Any other result would eviscerate the safe harbor and be antithetical to the important policy interest of encouraging the disclosure of forward-looking information. Accordingly, Congress required only that the risk factors be meaningful, *i.e.*, sufficient to alert investors that a projection is not a guarantee. Thus, as one court aptly put it: "[M]ust the cautionary language explicitly mention the factor that ultimately belies a forward-looking statement? We think not....When an investor has been warned of risks of a significance similar to that actually realized, she is sufficiently on notice of the danger of the investment to make an intelligent decision about it according to her own preferences for risk and reward."[18]

Congress also intended that where the requisite "meaningful" and "important" risk factors are disclosed, "a court may...decide a motion to dismiss, without examining the state of mind of the defendant."[19] Accordingly, courts have recognized that where such risk factors are disclosed, "the defendants' state of mind is irrelevant."[20] Indeed, courts and commentators have recognized that the safe harbor thus protects forward-looking statements accompanied by sufficient cautionary statements even where the defendant decided not to disclose a risk that might undermine its projections because, inter alia, the risk was deemed too remote or too competitively sensitive to publicly disclose.[21]

2. The Baxter Decision and its Implications

Judge Easterbrook's recent decision in *Asher v. Baxter,* if left to stand and followed, casts grave doubt on whether companies, at least in the Seventh Circuit, can confidently continue to rely on the safe harbor when making financial projections and predictions of future performance. *Baxter* purports to weigh the adequacy of a company's risk disclosures in hindsight, in order to assess, *prima facie,* if it is apparent that an issuer disclosed the "principal risks" that existed at the time of the projection. Where a company is prescient enough to identify the risk that ultimately comes to fruition, this approach will

18. *See Ivax,* 182 F.3d at 807.
19. Conference Report at 44.
20. *Ivax,* 182 F.3d at 803 ("If a statement is accompanied by 'meaningful cautionary language,' the defendants' state of mind is irrelevant.")
21. *See Miller v. Champion Enterprises,* 346 F.3d 660 at 672; Richard A. Rosen, "The Statutory safe harbor for Forward-Looking Statements: A Scorecard in the Courts from January 2002 through April 2003," 35 SEC. REG. & L. REP. (BNA) ANALYSIS & PERSPECTIVE at 5 (June 16, 2003)

still, presumably, protect the forward-looking statement from challenge. However, where the risk that comes to pass is not among those identified, *Baxter* predicts that it will be difficult, if not impossible, to determine whether the "principal risks" existing at the time the forward-looking statement was made were identified without permitting plaintiffs to conduct costly discovery with respect to that issue. This result not only is contrary to the legislative intent that the "meaningfulness" of risk factors, like the accuracy of predictions, not be litigated in hindsight, but is also inconsistent with the intent that courts resolve the merits of suits challenging forward-looking statements at the pleading stage <u>without</u> discovery.

In *Baxter,* shareholders of Baxter International, a manufacturer of medical products, brought suit against the company after its stock dropped on the announcement of disappointing financial results.[22] The plaintiffs, in classic fraud-by-hindsight fashion, alleged that Baxter's forecasts of revenue growth and significant "operational cash flow," repeated throughout the nine-month class period, were misleading because, at the time these projections were made, Baxter allegedly already knew of the problems which ultimately caused it not to achieve its forecasts. Judge Easterbrook acknowledged that Baxter accompanied its forward-looking statements with numerous risk disclosures, many of which were not mere boilerplate, but were "specific to the company and the health care arenas in which it operates."[23] These included statements that the following factors could cause the company's result to differ materially from its projections:

- Regulatory, legal or other developments relating to three specific series of the company's dialyzers;
- Demand and market acceptance risks for new and existing products, technologies and health care services;
- Manufacturing capacity and new plant start-ups;
- Commercialization factors; product development risks, including technological difficulties; and results of product testing;
- Impacts of competitive products and pricing;
- Continued price competition;

---

22. 377 F.3d at 728.
23. *Id.* at 730.

- Ability to enforce patents;
- Technological advances in the medical field;
- Reimbursement policies of government agencies.[24]

On the basis of these risk factors, the District Court for the Northern District of Illinois dismissed the case on the grounds that the challenged forward-looking statements were protected from liability by the safe harbor.[25]

On appeal, Judge Easterbrook rejected the plaintiffs' proffered per se rule that companies be required to disclose the risks that ultimately came to pass, finding that non-disclosure of the "right" risk "can't be dispositive; otherwise the statute would demand prescience."[26] Instead, Judge Easterbrook held that, "[t]he PSLRA does not require the most helpful caution; it is enough to "identify[] important factors that could cause actual results to differ materially from those in the forward-looking statement."[27] To this point, the decision is consistent with the spirit of the safe harbor and with the interpretation of its "meaningful cautionary language" prong by the majority of courts (*see, e.g.,* the Eleventh Circuit's seminal decision in *Harris v. Ivax.)*[28]

However, *Baxter* then parted company from prior case law and the clear intent of the statute in holding that the cautionary language must "point to the <u>principal contingencies</u> that could cause actual results to depart from the projection."[29] The *Baxter* court expressed skepticism about whether the "principal contingencies" had been identified by Baxter, because, during the nine-month class period, "the cautionary language remained fixed even as the risks changed," *i.e.*, as various adverse events (such as manufacturing problems and plant closures) occurred[30] Because it could not be established on the pleadings whether it was in fact these undisclosed adverse events that had caused Baxter to miss its projections (not the test envi-

---

24. Id.
25. *Asher v. Baxter International, Inc.,* 2003 WL 21825498 (N.D. Ill. July 17, 2003).
26. 377 F.3d at 730; *see also* 377 F.3d at 733 (noting that Baxter's disclosures included company-specific information and "highlighted some parts of the business that might cause problems.").
27. *Id.* at 734.
28. 182 F.3d 799 (11th Cir. 1999).
29. 377 F.3d at 734 (emphasis added).
30. *Id.* at 734.

sioned by the statute), and thus, whether the "principal" risks had been disclosed (also not the proper test), Judge Easterbrook opined that discovery was necessary and dismissal had been improper. The court observed:

> There is no reason to think—at least, no reason that a court can accept at the pleading stage, before plaintiffs have access to discovery—that the items mentioned in Baxter's cautionary language were those that at the time were the (or any of the) "important" sources of variance. The problem is not that what actually happened went unmentioned; issuers need not anticipate all sources of deviations from expectations. Rather, the problem is that there is no reason (on this record) to conclude that Baxter mentioned those sources of variance that (at the time of the projection) were the principal or important risks.[31]

The Baxter court's requirement that issuers disclose "principal risks" cannot be squared with the clear legislative intent that companies only need disclose "meaningful" and "important" risks to avail themselves of safe harbor protection. Perhaps even more troubling, Judge Easterbrook's reasoning imports an element of hindsight back into the safe harbor inquiry, seeking to divine whether a company had correctly identified the "principal risks" it faced, <u>after</u> the company reveals that its performance has suffered. Further, because such an inquiry implicates the question of exactly what a company knew at the time it made specific risk disclosures, it becomes extraordinarily difficult if not impossible at the pleading stage to determine whether the company's forward-looking statements qualify for safe harbor protection—thus necessitating discovery to reach a determination. *Baxter*'s implication, therefore, is that unless the ultimately dispositive risk is identified when a forward-looking statement is made, it will be necessary to proceed to discovery to determine what the "principal risks" were when the projection was made before the applicability of the safe harbor can be evaluated. Again, this problematic result runs directly to counter to all of the animating principles behind the Reform Act: (1) to preclude meritless cases at the pleading stage, (2) to avoid costly discovery, and (3) to encourage forward-looking statements by providing <u>certainty</u> that they will not be subject to hindsight second guessing by plaintiffs or the courts.

Judge Easterbrook's *Baxter* decision can be understood, in large part, as stuck in time and rooted in the pre-Reform Act "bespeaks caution" doctrine, or the more limited safe harbor applied in the Sev-

---

31. *Id.*

enth Circuit's (*i.e.*, Judge Easterbrook's) old *Wielgos* decision.[32] Under the bespeaks caution doctrine and the old safe harbor, courts routinely examined how "meaningful" the risk factors were in light of subsequent developments. *Baxter* also echoes decisions applying the bespeaks caution doctrine which held that warnings of a potential risks a company *might* face cannot shield the company from liability when the risks have *already* occurred.[33] Indeed, it was precisely because courts were continuing to assess the "meaningfulness" of risk factors under the old bespeaks caution doctrine and the prior safe harbor, that Congress adopted a more automatic, less discretionary, safe harbor which was meant, after all, to provide certainty that projections would not be second-guessed in hindsight.[34]

3. Fallout from Baxter

On March 22, 2005, the U.S. Supreme Court denied Baxter's petition for *certiorari*, which had been supported by *amicus curiae* briefs from the American Society of Corporate Secretaries, the National Investor Relations Institute, the New England Legal Foundation, the Washington Legal Foundation, and the Business Roundtable. Although *Baxter* will thus remain the controlling decision in the Seventh Circuit on these issues for the foreseeable future, other courts outside of the Seventh Circuit seem unlikely to adopt *Baxter's* approach. Indeed, in the First Circuit's even more recent decision in *Baron v. Smith*[35], the Court accepted relatively superficial risk disclosures as sufficient to immunize the defendant's projections under the safe harbor, a result seen previously in the decisions of many courts.[36] At least two courts have followed *Baxter* in refusing to dis-

32. *Wielgos v. Commonwealth Edison Co.,* 892 F.2d 509 (7th Cir. 1989).

33. A number of courts, using oft-quoted language from such a case, *In re Prudential Securities Inc. Limited Partnerships Litigation,* 930 F. Supp. 68, 72 (S.D.N.Y. 1996), improperly grafted this concept onto the Reform Act's safe harbor holding that "the safe harbor provision 'provides no protection to someone who warns his hiking companion to walk slowly because there might be a ditch ahead when he knows with near certainty that the Grand Canyon lies one foot away.'" *See, e.g., In re Compuware Sec. Litig.*, 301 F. Supp. 2d 672, 685-86 (E.D. Mich. 2004), *quoting Prudential,* 930 F. Supp. at 72; *see also In re FirstEnergy Corp. Sec. Litig.*, 316 F. Supp. 2d 581, 596 (N.D. Ohio 2004) (same).

34. Conference Report at 44 ("The safe harbor seeks to provide certainty that forward-looking statements will not be actionable by private parties under certain circumstances. Forward-looking statements will have safe harbor protection if they are accompanied by a meaningful cautionary statement.")

35. 380 F.3d 49 (1st Cir. 2004).

36. 380 F.3d 49, 53-54 (1st Cir. 2004).

miss claims based on forward-looking statements—as did the district court in Baxter on remand. In *Ong v. Sears, Roebuck & Co.*[37], the District Court for the Northern District of Illinois addressed the defendants' forward-looking statements regarding the outlook for Sears' credit card receivables portfolio, which had deteriorated significantly during the alleged class period. The court found that Sears had made projections, and disclosed that the projections were subject to changes in delinquency rates and charge-off trends in the company's credit card portfolio. The court held that these risk factors were insufficient to provide safe harbor immunity, because plaintiffs alleged that the defendants knew (but omitted) that the credit portfolio was already deteriorating.[38] Though it acknowledged that "the disclaimers did include some Sears-specific information, the court held that it could not determine without discovery whether the disclosed risks that accompanied Sears' projections were "those thought at the time to be the (or any of the) 'important' sources of variance."[39] The court also rejected the defendants' argument that its risk disclosures "were not only realistic; they actually came true," finding that "[i]t is inappropriate to entertain such an argument at the pleading stage."[40]

In State of New Jersey v. Sprint Corp.,[41] the defendants projected that Sprint's two top executives—the company's chairman and CEO, and its president and COO—would remain with the company for the "long-term."[42] Sprint's forward-looking statements in this regard were unaccompanied by any cautionary language; therefore, the question was whether the plaintiffs adequately alleged that the defendants actually "knew" the two executives would soon be leaving the company.[43] Although, as discussed *infra, Baxter* wholly ignored the second "actual knowledge" prong of the safe harbor, the *Sprint* court—perhaps presaging the District Court's holding after Baxter was remanded purported to follow the Seventh Circuit's deci-

37. 2004 WL 2534615 (N.D.Ill. September 27, 2004).
38. *Id.* at *31-32.
39. *Id.*
40. Id. at *32. One court in the Northern District of Illinois, in a decision published after Baxter, dismissed challenges to the defendants' forward-looking statements because they were protected under the safe harbor. *In re Midway Games, Inc. Sec. Litig.*, 332 F. Supp. 2d 1152, 1163-68 (N.D. Ill. 2004).
41. 2004 WL 1960130, *10 (D. Kan. Sept. 3, 2004).
42. *Id.* at *3.
43. *Id.* at *9-10.

sion in Baxter holding that it could not determine such a question without discovery.[44]

B. *Rough Sailing—The Courts of Appeal in Baxter and Oracle Ignore the Second, "Actual Knowledge" Inlet Of The Safe Harbor While the Baxter District Court Renders the Requirement a Nullity*

The Seventh Circuit's decision in *Baxter* is troubling not only for what it says about the first prong of the safe harbor but also because it says nothing about the second, "alternative inlet." As noted above, even where a company's forward-looking statements are not accompanied by sufficiently meaningful cautionary language, the safe harbor still immunizes forward-looking statements unless plaintiffs show (it is their burden) that defendants had "actual knowledge" their projections could not come true.[45] As one court aptly articulated the standard, "[t]o demonstrate actual knowledge for...statements about future economic performance, plaintiffs would have to demonstrate that [the defendant] knew the growth he was predicting was not possible."[46]6

The Seventh Circuit ought not to have reversed and remanded *Baxter* without addressing this requirement. Indeed, since the express language of the safe harbor makes clear that plaintiffs have the pleading burden ("forward-looking statements are protected unless plaintiffs show . . . actual knowledge"), the fact that the court could not determine on the basis of the pleadings what was known or knowable when the projections were made was plaintiffs' problem and should have resulted in dismissal.

Because the Seventh Circuit did not address the second-prong "actual knowledge" defense, *Baxter* raised this defense on its renewed motion to dismiss. This resulted in more bad law. The District Court denied the motion—despite the lack of any direct evidence that demonstrated actual knowledge.[47] Instead, the court rested its decision on the

44. *Id.* at *10.
45. 15 U.S.C. § 78u-5(c)(1); Conference Report at 44.
46. *In re Ascend Communications Sec. Litig.*, Case No. CV 97-8861 NW (C.D. Cal. February 2, 1999) *reprinted at* http://securities.stanford.edu/1011/ASND97/110.html, at 13 (emphasis added). Judge Pfaelzer observed in *Ascend* that under the safe harbor, "for each forward-looking statement, a complaint must now allege facts suggesting materiality, lack of meaningful cautionary language, and the actual knowledge of the speaker that the statement was false or misleading."
47. *Asher v. Baxter International Inc.*, 2005 WL 331572, *4-*9 (N.D. Ill. Feb. 3, 2005).

plaintiffs' allegations that the defendants, as "hands-on," "high-level managers," routinely accessed Baxter's revenue reports on the company's computer system, and that this information "would have shown them that the predictions...were unrealistic."[48] The district court also relied on significant stock sales by the eleven defendants, and Baxter's alleged use of its "inflated" stock price to consummate a merger more cheaply, as additional evidence that the defendants "actually knew" their projections were unachievable.[49] The holding that allegations of "motive and opportunity" are sufficient to demonstrate "actual knowledge" has little logical or precedential support. But it is the court's conclusion that senior management's "actual knowledge" that their predictions were unachievable can be inferred from the mere presence of adverse sales reports in the company's computer system that is the most alarming aspect of the decision.

The Ninth Circuit's recent decision in *Nursing Home Pension Fund, Local 144 v. Oracle Corp.*[50] is similarly troubling. In *Oracle*, although virtually all of the challenged statements were forward-looking, and the defendants' briefs specifically raised the safe harbor as a defense, the Ninth Circuit did not mention the safe harbor at all in reaching its decision. In *Oracle*, the defendant software company's second quarter 2000 report projected robust third quarter earnings, revenues, and sales growth.[51] Subsequently, Oracle reiterated these expectations.[52] Ultimately, when Oracle realized that it would not meet its earnings and revenue projections, it promptly announced the shortfall.[53] The next day, Oracle stock prices fell from $19.50 to $16.88. Plaintiffs, Oracle's shareholders, filed suit alleging that the company's financial projections were fraudulent.

Despite the forward-looking nature of the statements at issue—Oracle's predictions of its third quarter 2000 performance—the court did not reference either the safe harbor or the pre-Reform Act "bespeaks caution" doctrine (which may apply even when the safe harbor's requirements are not met).[54] Moreover, the Oracle court stated that "the required state of mind is one of 'deliberate recklessness,'"[55] and con-

48. *Id.* at *8-*9.
49. *Id.* at *9.
50. 380 F.3d 1226 (9th Cir. 2004).
51. *Id.* at 1228.
52. *Id.*
53. *Id.* at 1229.

cluded that the allegations were "sufficient to create a strong inference that defendants acted with deliberate or conscious recklessness."[56]

While the *Oracle* court did not address the issue under the safe harbor, it appears that the *Oracle* court, like *Baxter*, was concerned that the problems that ultimately caused Oracle's projections not to come to pass might have existed at some point before Oracle announced its earnings miss. In *Oracle,* the court concluded that, because sales figures were recorded in Oracle's computer system and Oracle's senior management said they monitored those figures, it could be inferred that senior management "must have known"—classic fraud-by-hindsight language—that the forecasts could not be met. The court accepted plaintiffs' allegations that

> since all sales information was in this database, and since the top executives admit to having monitored the database, Oracle must have been aware that it was not going to meet its sales projections earlier in the third quarter, and that its statements to the contrary were therefore made with scienter.[57]

C. Conclusion—Charting the Shoals of the Safe Harbor

Baxter and *Oracle* are dangerous because it is almost always possible, with the benefit of hindsight, to identify information that could

---

54. The Conference Report made clear that the safe harbor was not intended to limit the bespeaks caution doctrine: "The Conference Committee does not intend for the safe harbor provisions to replace the judicial 'bespeaks caution' doctrine or to foreclose further development of that doctrine by the courts." Conference Report at 46.

55. 380 F.3d at 1230 (emphasis added), *citing Silicon Graphics*, 183 F.3d at 973.

56. *Id.* at 1234. Although the court found the complaint raised a strong inference that the statements "were known to be false when made," and discussed the means by which a plaintiff can plead that "the party making the statement knew that it was false," the court made no mention of "actual knowledge" as the applicable standard. *Id.* Other courts—including other Courts of Appeals—have not ignored, but instead have misapplied, the applicable standard when examining allegations that forward-looking statements were fraudulent. For example, in *Rombach v. Chang*, 355 F.3d 164 (2d Cir. 2004), the Second Circuit dismissed plaintiffs' challenges to the defendant's forward-looking statements, but did so under the lesser standard of "conscious misbehavior or recklessness" applicable to false statements of present fact. *Id.* at 176-77, *citing Rothman v. Gregor,* 220 F.3d 81, 90 (2d Cir. 2000) (applying "conscious misbehavior or recklessness" standard). Similarly, in *GSC Partners CDO Fund v. Washington,* 368 F.3d 228 (3d Cir. 2004), although the Third Circuit found the challenged statements protected by the safe harbor, the court ignored the existence of the "actual knowledge" inlet to the safe harbor, in much the same way as the *Baxter* court, and purported to apply a "recklessness" standard to the claims at issue. *Id.* at 237-39.

57. *Id.* at 1231 (emphasis added).

have led management to determine, at an earlier point in time, that its forecasts would not be achieved. It was just that sort of second-guessing that the safe harbor was meant to prevent, by rendering both the projection and the accompanying risk factors immune from attack simply because things turn out differently than anticipated when the projection was made. It is to prevent such second-guessing that Congress required a showing of "actual knowledge" that a projection could not possibly come true, not merely that the data available in the complex MIS systems of a mega-corporation, interpreted correctly, could—or even should—lead to that conclusion. In short, these cases have it all wrong.

Not surprisingly, the *Baxter* decision has met with a negative reaction in the corporate world. The National Investor Relations Institute (NIRI) filed an *amicus* brief in support of Baxter's petition for certiorari.[58] NIRI predicts, or rather cautions, that if *Baxter* is left to stand, "[c]ompanies that have provided vital forward-looking information for investors... may well revert to less disclosure—in effect going back to square one. More importantly... plaintiffs' lawyers across the country will press for discovery to cause companies to settle these cases"exactly the sort of abuses the Reform Act was meant to remedy. As the U.S. Supreme Court recognized nearly 30 years ago in *Blue Chip Stamps v. Manor Drug Stores*,[59] securities lawsuits are particularly susceptible to abuse, because of their "*in terrorem*" threat to a Company can be used to drive up settlement value even in cases without merit. Although the Reform Act blunted this threat, *Baxter* potentially provides it with renewed vigor.

Baxter raises the question of what measures a company can take to protect itself if it desires to continue to provide financial projections to investors. Plainly, thorough and carefully-considered non-boilerplate risk disclosures are required. Moreover, it may be advisable specifically to identify the risks disclosed as themselves being predictions, adding language that risks are "among the primary risks we foresee at the present time."

Most importantly, *Baxter* counsels that companies must evaluate their risk disclosures over time within the company and counsels in favor of updates to risk disclosures, even as any duty to update is disclaimed as conditions change. Although this task is daunting and

---

58. Louis M. Thompson, Jr., "President's Note—November 2004," available at www.niri.org/news_media_center/irupdate/200411PresNote.cfm.

59. 421 U.S. 723, 741 (1975).

clearly not required by statute, it is nonetheless good practice to continually evaluate and update the company's risk warnings every time a press release or public filing is issued. Hopefully, *Baxter* will be reversed or limited. Hopefully, too, it will serve as a cautionary tale for companies and their counsel, resulting in better and frequently-updated risk disclosures not because they are required, but because they are the best practice.

III. SCIENTER: MOVEMENT IN THE CIRCUITS?

Another major reform adopted by the Reform Act was the heightening of the pleading standards with respect to scienter. Rule 9(b) was found to be insufficient to stem abusive securities litigation because, while it requires that the details of an alleged fraud be plead with particularity, it permits scienter to averred generally. Before the Reform Act, many courts had begun to impose more stringent pleading requirements for scienter in the context of securities class actions. The Second Circuit led the way in this regard, requiring that plaintiffs in a securities fraud class action plead facts with sufficient particularity that give rise to a "strong inference" of fraud. The Third Circuit followed suit. Other courts, however—most notably in the Ninth Circuit—continued to permit generalized pleading of scienter, resulting in vastly different standards in the disposition of securities actions among Circuits.

In adopting the Reform Act, Congress looked to the Second Circuit's then-existing standard as a starting point, adopting its requirement that securities fraud plaintiffs plead facts giving rise to a "strong inference" of scienter. However, in the Conference Report, Congress indicated that it meant to strengthen existing standards and, thus, did not intend to codify Second Circuit decisional law.[60]

In the decade since the Reform Act passed, the courts of appeal have continued to debate the proper method for pleading facts giving rise to the requisite "strong inference" of scienter, as well as the manner in which such facts should be assessed at the pleading stage. In this section, we discuss the middle-of-the-road approach adopted by most circuits, the departures therefrom on either side of the spectrum (and on opposite sides of the country), and the fact that, in practice, the different formulations have either moderated and/or been applied such that differing results reached in

60. It was this decision that led to President Clinton's veto of the Reform Act—a veto that was subsequently overridden by a 2/3 vote in each chamber of Congress.

the cases are explained less by differing formulations of a standard than by differences in the facts (and the finders of fact).

A. The "Same Old, Same Old" Approach

Shortly after the Reform Act was adopted, the Second and then the Third Circuits held that the Reform Act merely codified the Second Circuit's pre-existing standard for pleading scienter. Under that standard, a plaintiff can satisfy the "strong inference" requirement for scienter by alleging either (a) facts showing that the defendants had motive and opportunity to commit fraud, *or* (b) facts constituting strong circumstantial evidence of conscious misbehavior or recklessness.[61] Before and after the Reform Act, the Second Circuit has repeatedly held that motive requires a showing that defendants actually obtain concrete, personal benefits—not merely generic, generalized, hypothetical or inchoate ones—and that stock sales, the *sine qua non* for pleading scienter in most cases, are alone insufficient to give rise to any inference of scienter unless made in suspicious amounts and at suspicious times. The Second Circuit also repeatedly held, both before the PSLRA and after, that, while lack of motive does not necessarily defeat a showing of scienter, it necessarily undermines any such inference, requiring that plaintiff come forward with even stronger circumstantial evidence of conscious misbehavior.[62]

B. The Ninth Circuit

After the Reform Act, the circuits that had not previously adopted the Second Circuit's "strong inference" standard, again used the old Second Circuit cases applying that standard as a starting point. In assessing what kinds of facts might suffice to give rise to a strong infer-

---

61. *See Novak v. Kasaks*, 216 F.3d 300, 310 (2d Cir. 2000) (stating that Reform Act "did not change the basic pleading standard for scienter in this Circuit"); *In re Advanta Corp. Sec. Litig.*, 180 F.3d 525, 534 (3d Cir. 1999) ("We believe Congress's use of the Second Circuit's language compels the conclusion that the Reform Act establishes a pleading standard approximately equal in stringency to that of the Second Circuit.").

62. "Where motive is not apparent, it is still possible to plead scienter by identifying circumstances indicating conscious behavior by the defendant . . . though the strength of the circumstantial allegations must be correspondingly greater." *Beck v. Manufacturers Hanover Trust Co.*, 820 F.2d 46, 50 (2d Cir. 1987), *cert. denied,* 484 U.S. 1005, 108 S. Ct. 698, 98 L. Ed. 2d 650 (1988), *overruled on other grounds by United States v. Indelicato,* 865 F.2d 1370 (2d Cir. 1989) (en banc) (internal citations omitted). *See also Kalnit v. Eichler,* 264 F.3d 131, 142 (2d Cir. 2001); *Powers v. British Vita, P.L.C.*, 57 F.3d 176, 184 (2d Cir. 1995).

ence of scienter, the Ninth Circuit, which had the most lenient standard prior to the Reform Act, reversed course and adopted the most stringent standard. Beginning with *Silicon Graphics*, the Ninth Circuit issued a series of more than 20 opinions, all affirming motions to dismiss, which: uniformly held that motive alone was never enough; that stock sales below a significant percentage (*e.g.,* 43.6% in *Silicon Graphics*) were not probative of scienter; never found that a strong inference of scienter had been established where there were no stock sales; steadfastly refused to credit merely plausible or even reasonable inferences where alternative inferences were possible;[63] and determined that circumstantial facts had to be plead in almost evidentiary detail (names of witnesses, contents of documents, etc.) in order to be deemed credible enough even to merit analysis as to whether they were probative of scienter.[64]

C. The Middle of the Road Approach

The First, Fourth, Fifth, Sixth, Eighth, Tenth, and Eleventh Circuits[65] have taken a middle position. These courts agree that the Reform Act was intended to strengthen existing pleading standards beyond the Second Circuit standard and, as a result, hold that allegations of motive and opportunity—while highly relevant to an overall analysis of scienter—are not alone sufficient to give rise to the required "strong inference" of scienter.[66] However, rather than posit "bright line" or *"per se"* rules or presumptions, such as those described by the Ninth Circuit decisions, the cases in these middle-ground circuits reflect a more fact-intensive, "totality of the circumstances" analysis.

---

63. In *Gompper v. VISX, Inc.*, the Ninth Circuit stated that "when determining whether plaintiffs have shown a strong inference of scienter, the court must consider all reasonable inferences to be drawn from the allegations, including inferences unfavorable to the plaintiffs." 298 F.3d 893, 897 (9th Cir. 2002) (emphasis added). The *VISX* court felt that doing otherwise—such as applying the traditional motion to dismiss standard set forth in *Silicon Graphics*, according to which all reasonable inferences are drawn *in favor* of the non-moving party—"would thwart Congress' basic purpose in raising the bar in the first place; namely, to eliminate abusive and opportunistic securities litigation and to put an end to the practice of pleading fraud by hindsight." *Id.* at 897.
64. *In re Vantive Corp. Securities Litigation,* 283 F.3d 1079, 1093 (9th Cir. 2002) (74%); *In re Silicon Graphics Inc. Sec. Litig.,* 183 F.3d 970, 1001 (9th Cir. 1999) (43.6%).

D. A Movement Towards The Middle?

As discussed below, a trilogy of recent decisions from the Ninth Circuit, including *Oracle*, seem to be tending towards this middle ground. Thus, for example, while acknowledging that the Ninth Circuit's interpretation of the PSLRA's pleading requirement is "more stringent than that of our sister circuits," and never purporting to overrule it, the Ninth Circuit in *America West, Dura Pharmaceuticals,* and *Oracle* has adopted a more flexible approach, considering in each case "whether the total of plaintiffs' allegations, even though individually lacking, are sufficient to create a strong inference that defendants acted with deliberate or conscious recklessness."[67] In each of these cases, the Ninth Circuit reversed the district courts' decisions to dismiss the claims, which had been based on the Court of Appeals' earlier precedents. Moreover, while the Second and Third Circuit have articulated a

---

65. *See Rombach v. Chang,* 355 F.3d 164, 176 (2d Cir. 2004); *GSC Partners CDO Fund v. Washington*, 368 F.3d 228, 238 (3d Cir. 2004); *In re Alpharma Inc. Sec. Litig,* 372 F.3d 137, 152 (3d Cir. 2004). *Ottoman v. Hanger Orthopedic*, 353 F.3d 338 (4th Cir. 2003). In *Ottoman*, the Fourth Circuit stated that "courts should not restrict their scienter inquiry by focusing on specific categories of facts, such as those relating to motive and opportunity, but instead should examine all of the allegations in each case to determine whether they collectively establish a strong inference of scienter." *Id.* at 345. Adopting such a "flexible, case-specific" approach was reasonable, the *Ottoman* court argued, especially in light of the absence of any statutory language addressing particular methods of pleading and PSLRA's inconclusive and conflicting legislative history. *Id.* In *Southland Sec. Corp. v. Inspire Ins. Solutions Inc.,* the Fifth Circuit reiterated its stance that "our court requires more than allegations of motive and opportunity to withstand dismissal." 365 F.3d 353, 368 (5th Cir. 2004). Although it acknowledged that "appropriate allegations of motive and opportunity may meaningfully enhance the strength of the inference of scienter," the court held that the stock transactions at issue were not probative of scienter because they were neither "in suspicious amounts" nor "at suspicious times." *Id* at 368. In *In re Ford Motor Co. Sec. Litig.*, the Sixth Circuit affirmed the district court's dismissal reaffirming that "the bare pleading of motive and opportunity does not, standing alone, constitute the pleading of a strong inference of scienter," although "facts concerning motive and opportunity," nonetheless, may be relevant to "pleading circumstances from which one could infer a strong inference of fraudulent scienter." 381 F.3d 563, 568 (6th Cir., 2004). In *PR Diamonds v. Chandler,* the Sixth Circuit enumerated the various factors that are probative, although not determinative, of scienter, including: "insider trading at a suspicious time or in an unusual amount" and the "divergence between internal reports and external statements on the same subject." 364 F.3d 671, 682-691 (6th Cir. 2004). Remarkably, the Seventh Circuit has not yet opined on the issue; indeed, *Baxter*, discussed, *supra*, is the first PSLRA decision to come out of that court of appeals. The DC Circuit also has yet to opine as to the applicable standard.

rule that posits the possibility that motive alone might be sufficient to give rise to a strong inference, and have eschewed an absolute requirement that evidentiary details (names, dates, etc.) be plead, in most, if not all, of the cases in which a strong inference of scienter has been found, evidence of motive is, not surprisingly, supplemented by other well-detailed circumstantial evidence of scienter.[68]

The single most common characteristic in the cases finding that a strong inference of scienter has been plead is a fact pattern that ought not to be surprising: the existence of internal information inconsistent with the defendants' public statements. The conclusion as to whether the internal information alleged suffices to give rise to a strong inference of scienter, then, depends on: (1) whether there are other indicia of fraud (most typically the existence or absence of trading at times and in amounts that appear to have been calculated to maximize profits and/or inconsistent with past patterns or practices); (2) whether the information existed contemporaneously, or whether it reflects subsequent developments, including improved information or understanding; (3) the strength of the inferences to be drawn from the evidence (*e.g.*, whether it is equally subject to innocuous or benign inferences); and (4) the specificity of the allegations (generic reports or information systems with generally described content, versus specific reports with specific authors, recipients and content).[69]

---

66. *See, e.g., Aldridge v. A.T. Cross Corp.*, 284 F.3d 72, 82 (1st Cir. 2002) ("[W]hile mere allegations of motive and opportunity alone may be insufficient, together with additional factual support, evidence of motive and opportunity may establish a strong inference of scienter."); *Abrams v. Baker Hughes Inc.,* 292 F.3d 424, 430 (5th Cir. 2002) ("Allegations of motive and opportunity, standing alone, are no longer sufficient to plead a strong inference of scienter, although appropriate allegations of motive and opportunity may enhance other allegations of scienter"); *In re Comshare Inc. Sec. Litig.*, 183 F.3d 542, 551 (6th Cir. 1999) (holding that scienter may not be pled by "alleging facts that illustrate nothing more than a defendant's motive and opportunity to commit fraud"); *In re Navarre Corp. Sec. Litig.*, 299 F.3d 735, 747 (8th Cir. 2002) ("[A]n allegation that defendants had the motive and opportunity to make false or misleading statements is insufficient to support the strong inference of scienter required after the PSLRA."); *City of Philadelphia v. Fleming Cos.*, 264 F.3d 1245, 1263 (10th Cir. 2001) ("[A]llegations of motive and opportunity, with nothing more, could allow potentially frivolous lawsuits to go forward with only minimal allegations of scienter."); *Bryant v. Avado Brands, Inc.*, 187 F.3d 1271, 1283 (11th Cir. 1999) ("[W]e hold that [the Reform Act] does not codify the 'motive and opportunity' test formulated by the Second Circuit.").

67. *Nursing Home Pension Fund, Local 144 v. Oracle Corp.,* 380 F.3d 1226, 1230 (9th Cir. 2004). *See also No. 84 Employer-Teamster Joint Council Pension Trust Fund v. America West Holding Corp.,* 320 F.3d 920, 938 (9th Cir. 2003); *Broudo v. Dura Pharmaceuticals, Inc.,* 339 F.3d 933, 940 (9th Cir. 2003).

E. The Ninth Circuit Shift

In addition, the Fifth and Sixth Circuit issued apparently conflicting decisions on "collective" or "corporate" scienter, (*i.e.,* the concept of corporate scienter was rejected by the Fifth Circuit and permitted by the Sixth Circuit in cases where no individual defendant was found to have acted with scienter).[70]

The Ninth Circuit's uninterrupted string of more than 20 decisions affirming dismissals on scienter grounds was abruptly interrupted two years ago in *No. 84 Employer-Teamster Joint Council Pension Trust Fund v. America West Holding Corp.*[71] Certainly, the facts alleged in America West were problematic: "[m]ost of the individuals sold 100% of their shares, with the lowest percentage being 88%," "all nine of the individuals' sales occurred in succession over a three month period when *America West* officials were making optimistic statements regarding the company's financial outlook and reassuring analysts that [a controversial] settlement agreement would have no economic effect," and "[n]one of the individual defendants sold stocks during the twenty months preceding the ten month class period."[72] Against this backdrop, the Ninth Circuit's conclusion that "the sudden flurry of massive insider trading over this three month period of time, after an extended period of inactivity" in amounts "dramatically out of line with their prior trading practices at times calculated to maximize the

---

68. Hence, in *Rombach v. Chang*, 355 F.3d 164, 176 (2d Cir. 2004) for instance, the Second Circuit reiterated that one way for a plaintiff to plead scienter is by alleging facts showing that a defendant had both the motive and opportunity to commit fraud. While the Third Circuit also continues to hold that scienter can be plead on the basis of motive and opportunity, its decision in *GSC Partners CDO Fund v. Washington* and *In re Alpharma Inc. Sec. Litig.*, affirmed dismissals holding, respectively, that "motives that are generally possessed by most corporate directors and officers," 368 F.3d 228, 237 (3d Cir. 2004) and stock transactions that were not "unusual in scope," fail to give rise to a strong inference of scienter, 372 F.3d 137, 152 (3d Cir. 2004).
69. Of course, some decisions can only be explained as wrongly decided.
70. Compare In *Southland Sec. Corp. v. Inspire Ins. Solutions Inc.*, 365 F.3d 353, 366 (5th Cir. 2004) (courts look to "the state of mind of the individual corporate official or officials who make or issue [an allegedly misleading] statement . . . rather than generally to the collective knowledge of all the corporation's officers and employees acquired in the course of their employment.") with *City of Monroe Employees Retirement System v. Bridgestone Corp.*, 387 F.3d 468, 502 (6th Cir. 2004) (finding scienter with respect to Firestone and Bridgestone without finding knowledge or action by any particular corporate officer or director).
71. 320 F.3d 920 (9th Cir. 2003).
72. *Id.* at 939.

personal benefit from undisclosed inside information"—"appears unusual," seems, if anything, understated.[73]

The Ninth Circuit's most recent decision finding a "strong inference" of scienter, *Oracle,* also involves "unusual," indeed "novel" stock sales by a individual defendants.[74] However, while the stock sales in question in *America West* constituted between 88% and 100% of the individuals' shares, in Oracle, Larry Ellison, the CEO, sold only 2% of his holdings. However, Mr. Ellison's 2% stake equated to almost $1 billion in proceeds—enough, in the Court's view, to provide a "motive" supportive of, albeit not alone sufficient to, give rise to a strong inference of scienter. As the Ninth Circuit put it, although "[i]n the past, we have given great weight to the percentage of stock sold, . . . where, as here, stock sales result in a truly astronomical figure, less weight should be given to the fact that they may represent a small portion of the defendant's holdings."[75]

On the theory that bad facts, or big stock sales—either in percentages or amounts—make bad law, one could disregard and/or distinguish *America West* and *Oracle.* However, because the Ninth Circuit continues to hold that motive and opportunity alone are insufficient and that other indicia of fraud must be taken into account,[76] the analyses in these two cases did not end with the finding that the defendants sold and/or profited in large amounts. Instead, the Ninth Circuit in each of these cases looked at plaintiffs' other allegations to determine if they, too, supported a finding of scienter. It is the evaluation of these other factors in these decisions that is troubling.

In both *America West* and *Oracle*, the Ninth Circuit reasoned backward from the fact that the company subsequently missed its projections in finding support for an inference of scienter. In *America West*, the company had announced that it did not expect that a settlement with the FAA (the terms of which were well publicized) would have a mate-

---

73. *Id.* at 939-940 (Note that the plaintiffs provided a chart showing, "[f]or each defendant, . . . the individual's holdings, his class period sales, when the sales occurred, the percentage of owned shares that were sold, and the total proceeds that were generated from the sale," as well as a summary of their trading history prior to the class period).

74. 380 F.3d 1226, 1232 (9th Cir. 2004).

75. *Id.*

76. While the decision actually says that the timing and amount of sales supports a "strong inference" of scienter, the court elsewhere emphasizes the need to view all of the alleged indicia of scienter together and does not base its ruling solely on the ground that the sales alone were sufficient.

rial adverse effect on the Company's operations—a forward-looking statement. Plaintiffs claimed that this statement was later shown to be false and known to be false because America West subsequently missed its earnings forecast due, in part, to operational disruptions. Significantly, however, there were no facts alleged, but merely plaintiffs' bald assertions, that linked the operational disruptions that led to the miss with any issues addressed in the settlement. Still, the Ninth Circuit accepted plaintiffs' allegations in this regard.

Similarly, in *Oracle*, plaintiffs claimed that because Oracle kept track of all of its sales data in sophisticated MIS systems which Mr. Ellison claimed regularly to monitor, and because Mr. Ellison was personally involved in deals that did not close, he "must have been aware,"[77] at some unspecified time before the earnings miss was disclosed, that the Company's projections would not be achieved. Again, the Ninth Circuit credited the suggested "must have known" inference, stating that "[i]t is reasonable to believe that Oracle had known, prior to its [announcement] that it would not reach its projected earnings."[78] As noted, the district court in *Baxter,* on remand from the Seventh Circuit, reached a similar conclusion. Again, neither court explains how mere access to information can give rise to the requested "strong inference" of actual knowledge that forward-looking projections will not be met.

These holdings are troubling for a number of reasons. First, as just suggested they are inconsistent with prior precedent holding that the Reform Act's "strong inference" requirement trumps the general rule granting plaintiffs the benefit of inferences that are merely "reasonable," as is the case in a typical 12(b)(6) motion. Two years before, *in Gompper v. VISX, Inc.,* the Ninth Circuit held that, under the Reform Act, a plaintiff, seeking to establish scienter, is not entitled to an inference merely because it is reasonable; instead, in order to support the requisite *strong* inference, the inference plaintiffs seek to draw must be the most plausible of competing inferences.[79] Thus, in *VISX,* the Ninth Circuit held that "[W]hen determining whether plaintiffs have shown a strong inference of scienter, the court "must consider all reasonable

---

77. In *Daou,* 2005 WL 1431833 (9th Cir. 2005), the Ninth Circuit recently held, although not in the context of forward-looking statements, that conclusory allegations that executives ran their namesake company from "top to bottom" and that their alleged accounting manipulations were "known throughout the Company" were sufficient, together with their more specific averments to give rise to a strong inference of scienter.
78. 380 F.3d at 1232.
79. 298 F.3d 893 (9th Cir. 2002).

inferences to be drawn from the allegations, including inferences unfavorable to the plaintiffs."[80] The America West decision, while purporting to acknowledge this rule in VISX, criticized the district court for not crediting plaintiffs' allegations, chiding that "in this era of corporate scandal, when insiders manipulate the market with the complicity of lawyers and accountants, we are cautious not to raise the bar of the PSLRA any higher than that which is required under its mandates" and opining that "the District Court's failure to accept Plaintiffs' allegations as true and construe them in the light most <u>favorable</u> to Plaintiffs does just that."[81]

Second, in crediting plaintiffs' hindsight allegations based on failed projections, the Ninth Circuit flaunts many of the underlying purposes behind the Reform Act: Preventing fraud by hindsight lawsuits based on failed forecasts; encouraging forward-looking statements, such as the financial projections in *Oracle* and the projection in *America West* that the settlement would have no material effect; and requiring a strong inference, not just a plausible inference, of scienter on the basis of particularized facts.

There are, however, recent Ninth Circuit cases that appear to downplay the significance of *America West* and *Oracle*. For instance, in *In re Read-Rite Corp. Sec. Litig.*, the Ninth Circuit affirmed a dismissal of securities fraud claims because the allegations did not satisfy the "express heightened pleading standards set forth in *Silicon Graphics*, a standard to which [the Ninth Circuit] continue[s] to adhere."[82] The court also made clear that its decision in *America West* had no bearing on *Read-Rite* because "[t]he facts asserted by the *America West* plaintiffs were far more compelling than those alleged here."[83]

Moreover, in *Employers Teamsters Local Nos. 175 & 505 Pension Trust Fund v. Clorox Co.*, the Ninth Circuit explicitly relied on *VISX* in

---

80. *Id.* at 897. The First, Sixth, and Eighth Circuits had previously recognized that the heightened pleading standards for scienter meant that plaintiffs were entitled only to the most plausible of competing inferences, or, at least, that plaintiffs were not automatically entitled to the most reasonable inference. *See, e.g., In re K-Tel Int'l Sec. Litig.*, 300 F.3d 881 (8th Cir. 2002); *Aldridge v. A.T. Cross Corp.*, 284 F.3d 72 (1st Cir. 2002); *Helwig v. Vencor, Inc.*, 251 F.3d 540 (6th Cir. 2001). The Sixth Circuit recently reaffirmed this standard in *Fidel v. Maiden,* which holds that the "strong inference requirement creates a situation in which plaintiffs are entitled only to the most plausible of competing inferences . . ." 2004 WL 2901274, at *5 (6th Cir. Dec. 16, 2004) (internal citation omitted).

81. 320 F.3d 920, 946 (9th Cir. 2003) (emphasis added).

82. 335 F.3d 843, 848 n. 1 (9th Cir. 2003)

83. *Id.*

rejecting appellant's contention that the district court abused discretion in refusing to permit certain claims to proceed based on certain declarations attached to the complaint.[84] In holding that the declarations should not be accorded great weight, the court reaffirmed the rule set forth in *VISX* that "the court must consider all reasonable inferences to be drawn from the allegations, including inferences unfavorable to the plaintiffs."[85] Significantly, there are no references or citations to *America West* in the *Clorox* opinion.

IV. STAY OF DISCOVERY: TWO TICKETS TO LIMITED DISCOVERY

Another mechanism designed to protect securities defendants from unnecessary burden and expense in defending meritless claims is the Reform Act's discovery stay.[86] The stay, which remains in place until a court sustains the sufficiency of a complaint, has two purposes: 1) to prevent plaintiffs from filing securities fraud lawsuits as a vehicle for conducting fishing expedition discovery "in the hope of finding a sustainable claim not alleged in the complaint;"[87] and 2) to minimize incentives for plaintiffs to file frivolous securities class actions in the hope that corporate defendants will settle, rather than bear the high cost of discovery.[88]

The PLSRA's discovery stay provision is not absolute. However, in order to obtain relief from the stay, the plaintiff must show that at least one of two exceptional circumstances exist: 1) a need to preserve evidence; or 2) the likelihood of undue prejudice if the stay remains in place.[89] A party asserting that discovery is necessary to preserve evidence must make a specific showing that "the loss of evidence is imminent as

---

84. 353 F.3d 1125 (9th Cir. 2004).
85. *Id.* at 1134 (quoting *VISX*, 298 F.3d at 897).
86. The Reform Act provides: "in any private action arising under this chapter, all discovery and other proceedings shall be stayed during the pendency of any motion to dismiss, unless the court finds upon the motion of any party that particularized discovery is necessary to preserve evidence or to prevent undue prejudice to that party." *15 U.S.C. § 78u-4(b)(3)(B).*
87. *See* S. Rep. No. 104-98 at 14, *reprinted in* 1995 U.S.C.C.A.N. 679, 693. "Manifest in the Reform Act is the mandate that courts assess the legal sufficiency of plaintiffs' securities fraud allegations according to what plaintiffs know at the time the complaint is filed, rather than what they wish to learn through discovery and recover from defendants merely by reason of commencing an action charging fraud." *In re Livent, Inc. Noteholders Sec. Litig.*, 151 F. Supp. 2d 371,423 (S.D.N.Y. 2001)(emphasis added).
88. *See* H.R. Conf. Rep. No. 104-369 at 37 (1995), *reprinted in* 1995 U.S.C.C.A.N. 730, 736.
89. 15 U.S.C. § 78u-4(b)(3)(B). 15 U.S.C. § 78u-4(b)(3)(B).

opposed to merely speculative,"[90] or must specifically identify some "improper or unfair treatment amounting to something less than irreparable harm."[91] The exceptions contemplate limited aided targeted discovery which must be particularized and shown to be "necessary to remedy" the extraordinary circumstances.[92]

From the start, Plaintiffs sought to circumvent the PLSRA's discovery stay using varied methods, including the assertion of a right to conduct discovery in related state court actions and the issuance of discovery requests in unrelated cases. This practice became so prevalent that Congress acted to close the loophole by enacting the Securities Litigation Uniform Standards Act ("SLUSA").[93] Other, sometimes creative, attempts at an end-run around the stay have met with limited success.[94]

Recently, however, plaintiffs have successfully overcome the Reform Act's discovery stay by claiming that civil plaintiffs ought to have the right to obtain access to discovery provided by defendants in the course of government actions and investigations. In some high-profile cases, plaintiffs' counsel have effectively (albeit incorrectly) argued that the concerns animating the discovery stay provisions are not implicated and the burden on defendants is minimal since the production has already been made to the government. Although, increasingly, companies who are subjects of government investigations have little choice but to provide cooperative discovery, including privileged materials to the government, these cases portend that such production threatens to weaken the protections of the discovery stay in civil litigation.

In the past two years, highly publicized cases involving alleged financial fraud at *Enron* and *WorldCom*, as well as Royal Ahold NV, have generated decisions granting relief from the Reform Act's stay. Follow-

---

90. *In re CFS-Related Secs. Fraud Litig. AUSA,* 179 F. Supp. 2d 1260, 1265 (N.D. Okla. 2001).

91. *Sarantakis v. Gruttadauria,* Civ. A. No. 02-1609, 2002 WL 1803750, at *2 (N.D. Ill. Aug. 5, 2002) (citations omitted); *see also, In re CFS-Related Secs. Fraud Litig.,* 179 F. Supp. 2d at 1265 ("Undue prejudice is prejudice that is improper or unfair under the circumstances").

92. *Sarantakis,* 2002 WL 1803750 at *2.

93. Moreover, a few courts, sitting in diversity jurisdiction, have permitted discovery regarding the state law claims. *See, e.g., Tobias Holdings, Inc. v. Bank United Corp.,* 177 F. Supp. 2d 162 (S.D.N.Y. 2001). Most courts, however, have rejected this approach. Thus, for example, in *Winer Family Trust v. Michael Queen* the court held that ". . . Congress' attempt to address concerns of discovery abuse would also be rendered meaningless if securities plaintiffs could circumvent the PSLRA stay (and relevant case law) by simply asserting pendant state law claims in conjunction with defendant's cross-claim." 2004 U.S. Dist. LEXIS 1825 at *9 (E.D. Pa., Feb. 6, 2004).

ing the *Enron* and *Worldcom* decisions, however, several courts have acknowledged that the circumstances of those cases were, in fact, extraordinary, and have concluded that the mere fact that defendants were compelled (even if acting "voluntarily") to provide documents in connection with government investigations is an insufficient basis to exclude such information from the protections of the Reform Act's stay.

A. Absence of Frivolity and "Slight" Burdens

1. Enron

In *Newby v. Enron Corp.,* securities plaintiffs sought relief from the Reform Act's discovery stay for materials the company had previously produced in the course of a federal government investigation.[95] The court first ordered Enron to produce all documents and materials provided to the government and later ordered Enron to produce transcripts of witness interviews and depositions as well.[96] Explaining its reasoning for lifting the stay with regard to the ERISA-related materials, the Court noted that a central concern motivating the Reform Act's discovery stay—the prevention of expensive and burdensome "fishing expeditions in frivolous securities lawsuits"—was not implicated.[97] Noting that in the Enron case, there was significant evidence of fraud and wrong-doing the Court concluded that "[The stay] was not designed to keep secret from counsel in securities cases documents that have become available for review by means other than discovery in the securities case."[98]

---

94. For example, in *ATSI Communications, Inc. v. The Shaar Fund, Ltd.,* 2003 WL 1877227 (S.D.N.Y. April 9, 2003), the court interceded when plaintiffs in a securities class action issued subpoenas and discovery requests to the NASD and National Securities Clearinghouse Corporation ("NSCC"), in an entirely separate case but sought information only about transactions relating to the defendants in the Shaar Fund case. *Id* at *3. The court worried that plaintiffs' counsel actions might "have been intended to facilitate an end-run around the PSLRA and Rule 45(b)(1) . . . and may have been motivated . . .by a desire to seek discovery for the purpose of attempting to file an amended complaint." *Id.* at *4. Plaintiffs were ordered to provide copies of the subpoenas, discovery requests, and related correspondence, and to make complete disclosure of all materials obtained in response and prohibited plaintiffs from conducting *any* discovery in any action relating to the securities of plaintiff ATSI Communications, Inc. or the Shaar Fund defendants, without prior notice to defendants.
95. No. H-01-3624 (S.D. Tex. Feb. 27, 2002) (Scheduling Order).
96. *Id.*
97. *Id.* at 3-4.
98. *Id.*

The court also agreed with the plaintiff's assertion that "the burden would be slight because Enron has already found, reviewed and organized the documents."[99]

2. *Worldcom*

A similar decision was reached in another highly publicized case, *In re Worldcom, Inc. Sec. Litig.*,[100] Worldcom was ordered to produce documents and other materials which had been previously produced in connection with various government investigations, as well as documents and materials previously produced to the Special Investigative Committee of the Board of Directors, after its counsel produced its final report. However, unlike *Enron,* the corporation was not ordered to produce witness interview notes. Notably, both the SEC and the U.S. Attorney had submitted requests to the court that the corporation not be ordered to produce those witness interview notes.[101]

The *Worldcom* court explained its decision to lift the discovery stay by pointing to the simultaneous existence of three key circumstances: 1) the absence of the primary concerns animating Congress's enactment of the Reform Act's stay—the prevention of "fishing expedition" discovery and forced settlement of frivolous actions; 2) the relatively small burden imposed on the corporation, since the requested documents had already been gathered and previously produced; and 3) the concern that proceedings were "moving apace," and lead plaintiff could be prejudiced by an "inability to make informed decisions . . . in a rapidly shifting landscape," including impending court-ordered settlement negotiations.[102] The court specifically noted that none of the circumstances alone would have warranted a lift in the stay.

Discussing the threat of prejudice faced by plaintiffs (which warrants relief from the stay pursuant to the prevention of "undue prejudice" prong of 15 U.S.C. § 78u-4(b)(3)(B)), the court expressed concern that the plaintiffs would not only be at a disadvantage in crafting their strategy, but also that their lack of information would severely disadvantage their chance of obtaining any recovery: "If [lead plaintiff] must wait until the resolution of a

---

99. *Id.*
100. 234 F. Supp. 2d 301 (S.D.N.Y. 2002).
101. *Id.* at 305.
102. *See Id.* at 305.

motion to dismiss to obtain discovery and formulate its settlement or litigation strategy, it faces the very real risk that it will be left to pursue its action against defendants who no longer have anything or at least as much to offer."[103]

3. Royal Ahold

In re Royal Ahold N. V. Sec. & ERISA Litig. plaintiffs sought relief from the Reform Act's discovery stay for production of documents (excluding witness statements and interview notes) that had been produced to government agencies, including the SEC, US Attorney's Office, the NYSE, and the NASD.[104] The *Royal Ahold* plaintiffs also sought the company's internal investigation documents, which had not been produced to government agencies. The government agencies intervened arguing against production to the private plaintiffs on the theory that the provision of such information might interfere with their ongoing investigations. Although the volume of requested documents consisted of over one million pages, the court determined that the request met the PSLRA' s requirement of "particularity." Citing *Worldcom*, the court concluded that the burden on defendant would be "slight," since they had already produced the requested documents.[105]

Like the Enron and *Worldcom* actions, the court held that the key concern motivating the stay provision—deterrence of frivolous cases—was not implicated, as the claims were based upon a 400-plus page Consolidated Amended Complaint containing "detailed allegations"[106] and *Ahold* had admitted culpability. The court explicitly acknowledged that the apparent strength of plaintiffs' case "may factor into [its] determination as to the necessity of allowing discovery under the PLSRA."[107]

The Ahold court also noted that the facts of defendant's "wide-ranging corporate reorganization," which included substantial divestitures of key subsidiaries, showed that plaintiffs' concerns about potential evidentiary loss was not "not wholly speculative." [108] The court refused to credit defendant's assertion that evidence would be preserved.[109] Finally, citing *Worldcom*,

---

103. *Id.* at 306.
104. 220 F.R.D. 246; 2004 U.S. Dist. LEXIS 4048 (D. Md. Apr. 12, 2004).
105. *Id.* at 253.
106. *Id.* at 251.
107. *Id.*
108. *Id.*

the *Ahold* court noted that relief from the stay was also warranted because plaintiffs would be unduly prejudiced compared to other post-bankruptcy claimants by the non-securities plaintiffs' ability to gain discovery and proceed with their claims.[110]

4. *LaBranche*

In *LaBranche* the court granted relief from the discovery stay after determining that, in light of the status of the case, doing so would not frustrate Congress' purpose in enacting the PLSRA.[111] Like *Enron, Worldcom* and *Ahold, LaBranche* had been the subject of SEC (and NYSE) investigations resulting in a settlement pursuant to which defendant agreed to pay over $63 million in penalties and disgorgement.[112]

In these circumstances, the Court found that:

> If the stay remains in place, Lead Plaintiffs will be the only interested party without access to those documents and will be prejudiced by their inability to make informed decisions about their litigation [or settlement] strategy in this rapidly shifting landscape.[113]

Additionally, citing *Worldcom* and *Enron*, the court noted that—since the documents had previously been compiled, reviewed and produced to regulators, the burden on defendants would be slight (noting, too, that lead plaintiffs agreed to bear the costs of production).[114]

B. Nothing Special Here: Maintaining the Stay, Regardless of Government Investigation Discovery

1. *AOL Time Warner*

In *In re AOL Time Warner, Inc. Sec. & ERISA Lit.* matter, the court initially granted a lift in the stay, citing *Enron* and *Worldcom.*[115] However, several weeks later, the court vacated that order and after subsequent briefing, the court refused to order production of documents that had been previously produced to various governmental entities, determining that the key concerns moti-

109. *Id.*
110. *Id.* at 252.
111. *In re: LaBranche Sec. Litig.*, 333 F. Supp. 2d 178, 181 (S.D.N.Y. 2004).
112. *Id.* at 181.
113. *Id.* at 183.
114. *Id.*
115. 2003 U.S. Dist. LEXIS 9979, at *1 (S.D.N.Y. April 2, 2003).

vating the stay remained operative: "Defendants in this action have only recently filed their motion to dismiss the amended complaint. It cannot be concluded that 'evidence from discovery might not be the subject of controversy as to a claim in the complaint if leave to replead to were granted."[116] The court also noted its concern with that the plaintiffs would use information contained in the materials documents in their opposition to a motion to dismiss. The court ultimately determined that the mere fact that documents had been produced to the government was not sufficient to warrant lifting the stay, and that in this case, unlike *Worldcom* plaintiffs, there was no "impending settlement that could prejudice plaintiffs' possible recovery. [117]

2. Vivendi, Rampersad, Merrill Lynch, and Lantronix

Decisions issued by several courts subsequent to *Enron* and *Worldcom* establish, consistent with *AOL*, that the mere fact of prior production to a government agency does not alone necessarily warrant a lift in the discovery stay.

Thus, in *In re Vivendi Universal, S.A., Sec. Litig.,* the court refused plaintiffs' request to lift the stay as to "documents already produced by defendants to the United States Department of Justice, Securities and Exchange Commission, [and various French agencies]...produced in connection with civil and criminal investigations...."[118] The *Vivendi* court determined that plaintiff failed to demonstrate "exceptional circumstances," that would result in "undue prejudice"; accepting defendants "represent[ation] in open court" that documents produced to government agencies had been and would continue to be preserved.[119] Similarly, in *In re Merrill Lynch & Co., Inc. Research Reports Sec. Litig.*, the court held that plaintiff failed to show extraordinary circumstances warranting a lifting of the stay; there was no "imminent risk" that evidence would be lost,[120] and that defendant's representations to the court that it will preserve the evidence were satisfactory.

116. *In re AOL Time Warner, Inc. Sec. & ERISA Lit.,* 2003 U.S. Dist. LEXIS 12846, at *5 (July 25, 2003).
117. *Id.* at *5-6.
118. 2003 WL 21035383, at *1 (S.D.N.Y. May 6, 2003).
119. *Id.*
120. 2004 WL 305601, at *1. (S.D.N.Y. Feb. 18, 2004).

In re Lantronix, Inc. Sec. Lit., is to the same effect rejecting a request the discovery stay be lifted for documents already produced to regulators and government agencies.[121] Indeed, the court found that the risk that the evidence would be lost was negligible given the fact that the documents had already been produced and so were in the custody of third parties—a twist on the finding of the WorldCom and other courts that prior production worked against defendants' claim of burden.[122] The court determined that one of the main concerns animating the stay provision was implicated in that case, because: "[i]t cannot be concluded that evidence from discovery might not be the subject of controversy as to a claim in the complaint if leave to replead were granted. Nor can it be assured that plaintiffs will not attempt to use the discovery materials in opposition to the recently filed motion."[123] Moreover, despite the court did not find the fact that the defendant had recently settled with a different group of plaintiffs in another action compelling: "Plaintiff here makes no showing of how the discovery materials sought are necessary at this moment to effectuate a settlement in this case or how one settlement in another case creates anything more than the routine delay contemplated by the PSLRA."[124]

In sum, it appears for now that the discovery stay will continue to be enforced in all but the most egregious of cases. Nonetheless, the determination by the courts that have permitted relief from the stay that the cases were not "not frivolous" is a concerning development, particularly if the holdings of these cases are applied in circumstances less notorious than *WorldCom* and *Ahold*.

V. SHOWDOWN OVER SLUSA

Recently, the Seventh Circuit Court of Appeals issued its second decision in the *Putnam Funds* securities litigation, holding that the Securities Litigation Uniform Standards Act's ("SLUSA") preemption of state law claims in certain cases is not limited to actions in which the plaintiffs purchased or sold covered securities. This decision opens a clear rift with the Second Circuit, which, while broadly interpreting the scope of SLUSA's preemption held that SLUSA did not preempt so-called "holder" cases, in

121. 2003 U.S. Dist. LEXIS 19593 at *4-*6 (C.D. Cal. Sept. 26, 2003).
122. *Id.* at 7.
123. *Id.* at 6 (internal quotations omitted).
124. *Id.* at 6-7.

which the plaintiff class consists entirely of investors who neither bought nor sold securities during the purported class period. Interestingly, this is the *second* SLUSA-related split to arise between the Second and Seventh circuits as the result of the *Putnam Funds* litigation: in 2004, the Seventh Circuit held—in contrast to recent Second Circuit case law—that a district court's decision to remand an action removed to federal court under the auspices of SLUSA was appealable.[125] The ultimate resolution of these two issues will affect the ability of securities class action plaintiffs to circumvent the strict pleading requirements and other restrictions imposed by the Private Securities Litigation Reform Act of 1995 (the "Reform Act")[126] by filing suit in state court.

A. Background

In the wake of the Reform Act's passage, the securities plaintiffs' bar made increasing use of parallel state court claims to circumvent the discovery stay and strict pleading standards to which private actions in federal court now were subject.[127] The temporary decline in federal securities class action cases that occurred after the Reform Act became effective was accompanied by a corresponding increase in state court filings.[128] In California, for example, the number of state court securities claims quintupled from 1995 to 1997.[129] Moreover, the vast majority of these new cases were filed in conjunction with a nearly-identical federal court action—often by the same plaintiffs' firms. By this transparent "end-run" around the Reform Act, plaintiffs were able to propound discovery in state courts in aid of their pleading efforts in federal court. This tactic obviously "prevented [the Reform Act] from fully achieving its objectives."[130]

In 1998, Congress, having determined that securities plaintiffs often sought "to evade the protections that Federal law provides against abusive litigation by filing suit in State, rather than Federal, court,"[131]

---

125. *Kircher v. Putnam Funds Trust,* 373 F.3d 847 (7th Cir. 2004) ("*Putnam Funds I*").
126. Pub. L. No. 104-67, 109 Stat. 737 (1995) (codified as amended throughout 15 U.S.C. §78u-4, *et seq.*).
127. H.R. Conf. Rep. No. 105-803, at 14-15 (1998).
128. H.R. Conf. Rep. No. 105-803, at 14 (1998), citing Joseph A. Grundfest & Michael A. Perino, *Securities Litigation Reform: The* First *Year's Experience: A Statistical and Legal Analysis of Class Action Securities Fraud Litigation under the Private Securities Litigation Reform Act of 1995*, Stanford Law School, PLI Order No. B4-7199 (February 27, 1997).
129. H.R. Conf. Rep. No. 105-803, at 15 (1998).
130. H.R. Conf. Rep. No. 105-803, at 15 (1998).

adopted SLUSA[132] to establish exclusive venue in federal court for most securities class action litigation. Specifically, the statute states that:

> No covered class action based upon the statutory or common law of any State or subdivision thereof may be maintained in any State or Federal Court by any private party alleging—
>
> (1) an untrue statement or omission of a material fact in connection with the purchase or sale of a covered security; or
>
> (2) that the defendant used or employed any manipulative or deceptive devise or contrivance in connection with the purchase or sale of a covered security.[133]

The language in subsections (1) and (2) should be familiar, as it hews closely to § 10(b) of the 1934 Act[134] and Rule 10b-5.[135] As a result, most courts examining the ambit of SLUSA have drawn from earlier case law discussing the reach of §10(b) and Rule 10b-5. They have, however, reached starkly different conclusions regarding the extent to which the "purchase or sale" requirement limits the scope of SLUSA preemption.

B. Court-Imposed Limitations on SLUSA's Reach

Prior to the Seventh Circuit's recent *Putnam Funds* decisions, the circuit courts had imposed two major limitations on the ability of securities fraud defendants to utilize SLUSA to preempt the filing of state law claims designed to circumvent the Reform Act's protections.

1. A Procedural Limitation

The first limitation on SLUSA's preemptive effect was strictly procedural—the Second and Ninth Circuits held that a district court's decision to remand an action that had been removed to federal court under SLUSA was *not* appealable. In so holding, these courts relied on 28 U.S.C. § 1447(d), which states that "[a]n order remanding a case to the State court from which it was removed is not reviewable on appeal."

131. H.R. Conf. Rep. No. 105-803, at 13 (1998)

132. Pub. L. No. 105-353, 112 Stat. 3227 (1998) (codified in part as 15 U.S.C. § 77p and 15 U.S.C. § 78bb).

133. *See* 15 U.S.C § 77p(b) (1933 Act, as amended by SLUSA) and 15 U.S.C. § 78bb(f)(1) (1934 Act, as amended by SLUSA).

134. 15 U.S.C. § 78j(b).

135. 17 C.F.R. § 240.10b-5.

While §1447(d)'s language is sweeping, its ambit has been limited by a series of United States Supreme Court decisions to include only those cases remanded due to either (1) lack of subject-matter jurisdiction, or (2) irregularities with the procedure of removal.[136] Drawing on these decisions, the First, Second and Ninth Circuits issued a string of opinions holding that a district court's determination that a case removed under SLUSA should be remanded due to lack of subject-matter jurisdiction fell squarely within the (Supreme Court-circumscribed) limits of §1447(d) and its prohibition of appellate review.[137] These decisions, therefore, limited the ability of securities defendants to seek redress for even a clearly-erroneous district court decision to remand a SLUSA-preempted action.

2. A Substantive Limitation

The second limitation on SLUSA's preemptive effect was substantive in nature. In January, the Second Circuit issued its decision in *Dabit v. Merrill Lynch, Pierce, Fenner & Smith, Inc.* ("*Dabit*"), holding that SLUSA does not preempt state law actions brought by, or on behalf of, "holders," defined as investors who neither purchased nor sold, but rather "held" shares in reliance on alleged corporate misrepresentations.[138] In so holding, the Second Circuit joined the Eighth, Ninth, and Eleventh Circuits in finding that SLUSA's "in connection with the purchase or sale of covered securities" requirement was modeled on—and has the same scope as—its antecedent in §10(b) and Rule 10b-5.[139] The *Dabit* court reasoned that the purchaser-seller rule of *Blue Chip Stamps v. Manor Drug Stores*,[140] in which the United States Supreme Court analyzed the

136. *See, e.g., Thermtron Products, Inc. v. Hermansdorfer*, 423 U.S. 336 (1976); *Things Remembered, Inc. v. Petrarca*, 516 U.S. 124 (1995); *Quackenbush v. Allstate Insurance Co.*, 517 U.S. 706 (1996).

137. *Abada v. Charles Schwab & Co.*, 300 F.3d 1112 (9th Cir. 2002); *United Investors Life Insurance Co. v. Waddell & Reed, Inc.*, 360 F.3d 960 (9th Cir. 2004); and *Spielman v. Merrill Lynch, Pierce, Fenner & Smith, Inc.*, 332 F.3d 116 (2d Cir. 2003).

138. 395 F.3d 25 (2d Cir. 2005).

139. *Dabit*, 395 F.3d at 34-36. *See also Green v. Ameritrade, Inc.*, 279 F.3d 590, 596-97 (8th Cir. 2002); *Falkowski v. Imation Corp.*, 309 F.3d 1123, 1131 (9th Cir. 2002), amended, 320 F.3d 905 (2003); *Riley v. Merrill Lynch,* Pierce, *Fenner & Smith, Inc.*, 292 F.3d 1334, 1342-43 (11th Cir. 2002). Subsequent to the *Dabit* decision, both the Third and Seventh Circuits concurred. *Rowinski v. Salomon Smith Barney Inc.*, 398 F.3d 294, 299 (3d Cir. 2005); *Kircher v. Putnam Funds Trust,* 403 F.3d 478, 482 (7th Cir. 2005) ("*Putnam Funds II*").

140. 421 U.S. 723 (1975).

scope of private actions under Rule 10b-5, "applies as a limit on SLUSA's 'in connection with' requirement such that SLUSA does not preempt claims that do not allege purchases or sales made by the plaintiff or the alleged class members."[141] Thus, "holder" claims could not be subject to SLUSA preemption.

In reaching this decision, the Second Circuit considered, but ultimately rejected, the SEC's *amicus* argument warning that the policy issues underlying SLUSA militated strongly against applying *Blue Chip Stamps'* purchaser-seller rule. The SEC argued that the effect of applying this rule to limit SLUSA's preemptive powers would, perversely, be to exempt from the Reform Act the very sort of claims identified by the Supreme Court in *Blue Chip Stamps* as posing a particularly high risk of vexatious litigation. While agreeing with the SEC that Congress likely did not intend to limit the scope of SLUSA preemption by imposing a purchaser-seller requirement, the *Dabit* court held that Congress nonetheless did so "by borrowing language with a settled judicial interpretation in the context of private damages actions, and such borrowing implicates the strong presumption that Congress is aware of and approves that construction."[142] Thus, because *Blue Chip Stamps* interpreted the language of Rule 10b-5 as allowing private litigants to bring an action only when they themselves purchased or sold securities during the period of allegedly fraudulent conduct, the *Dabit* court held that SLUSA's preemptive powers—couched in language taken directly from §10(b)—must similarly be limited to cases in which the private litigants purchased or sold securities.[143]

The Second Circuit's *Dabit* decision thus re-opened, in a more limited fashion, the state court loophole securities class action plaintiffs can use to avoid the strictures of the Reform Act—so long as such claims are asserted only on behalf of "holders" who neither purchased nor sold in the relevant period. Moreover, this limited loophole appears wide enough to allow the sort of expensive, time-consuming discovery that led to the settlement of meritless strike suits prior to the enactment of the Reform Act.

141. *Dabit,* 395 F.3d at 28.
142. *Dabit,* 395 F.3d at 40.
143. *Blue Chip,* 421 U.S. at 754-55.

C. The Seventh Circuit Creates a Split: Appealability of SLUSA Remands

Enter the Seventh Circuit. In June 2004, Judge Easterbrook authored an opinion in *Kircher v. Putnam Funds Trust ("Putnam Funds I")*[144] that directly challenged the trio of Second and Ninth Circuit opinions holding that §1407(d) precluded federal appellate review of a district court's decision to remand a SLUSA-removed action for lack of subject-matter jurisdiction. More precisely, the *Putnam Funds I* court found that, when a district court reviews and then remands a case removed to federal court under the auspices of SLUSA, the remand is *not*—despite the language used by the district court—based on a lack of subject-matter jurisdiction. To support this somewhat startling proposition, Judge Easterbrook drew on two recent United States Supreme Court decisions, *Kontrick v. Ryan*[145] and *Scarborough v. Principi*,[146] which held that a court lacks subject-matter jurisdiction *only when* (1) the Constitution forbids adjudication; or (2) Congress has not authorized the federal judiciary to resolve the sort of issue presented by the case. "There may be many other reasons why a court should not resolve a dispute," Judge Easterbrook concludes, "but these differ from the lack of subject-matter jurisdiction."[147]

According to the Seventh Circuit, then:

> We must distinguish between a decision that 'this court lacks adjudicatory competence' and a decision that 'the court has been authorized to do X and having done so should bow out.' The former implies lack of subject-matter jurisdiction, as *Kontrick* and *Scarborough* explain; the latter implies the presence of jurisdiction.[148]

In the context of claims removed to federal court under SLUSA, then, the district court "ma[kes] a substantive decision under authority granted by federal statute" (*i.e.,* SLUSA) and then, having done so, should bow out.[149] Because, under *Kontrick* and *Scarborough*, this does not constitute a finding that the district court lacked adjudicatory competence, it does not imply—regardless of the terminology used by the district court—an actual lack of subject-matter jurisdiction.

144. *Kircher v. Putnam Funds Trust,* 373 F.3d 847 (7th Cir. 2004).
145. 124 S. Ct. 906, 914-16 (2004).
146. 124 S. Ct. 1856, 1864-65 (2004).
147. *Putnam Funds I,* 373 F.3d at 849.
148. *Putnam Funds I,* 373 F.3d at 850.
149. *Id.*

Moreover, the Seventh Circuit found that "[n]ormal remands, for which §1447(d) is designed, leave all substantive issues open to plenary resolution in the state court."[150] A district court remand under SLUSA, by contrast, represents the end product of the "one specific substantive decision in securities litigation [that] must be made by the federal rather than the state judiciary."[151]

In penning the *Putnam Funds I* opinion, Judge Easterbrook was aware of other circuits' decisions—including those of the Second Circuit—which drew on earlier Supreme Court precedent to hold that SLUSA remands were not appealable. He therefore advanced two lines of argument to undercut the courts' reasoning in those cases. First, he noted that the majority of these opinions were authored prior to the Supreme Court's *Kontrick* and *Scarborough* decisions, and therefore could not apply the high court's new guidance regarding when, precisely, a district court lacks subject-matter jurisdiction. Second, he asserted that "[b]oth the Second and Ninth Circuits were mesmerized by the [district courts' use of the] word 'jurisdiction' and did not see the difference between a case that never should have been removed and a case properly removed and remanded only when the federal job is done."[152]

With these two arguments, Judge Easterbrook left open the possibility that the Second and Ninth Circuits, when presented with the opportunity to revisit their prior decisions in light of the Supreme Court's guidance in *Kontrick* and *Scarborough,* might choose to follow the Seventh Circuit's lead and, in this way, repair the split between the circuits. Judge Easterbrook's next SLUSA-related opinion, however, would widen the rift between the circuits, leaving far less hope for a meeting of the minds to bridge the gap.

D. The Seventh Circuit Creates a Second Split: Preemption of "Holder" Claims

In May, Judge Easterbrook authored the Seventh Circuit's second opinion in *Kircher v. Putnam Funds Trust* ("*Putnam Funds II*"),[153] holding that SLUSA preemption applied even to "holder" claims that do not directly involve the purchase or sale of securities in reliance on

---

150. *Id.*
151. *Id.*
152. *Putnam Funds I,* at 851.
153. *Kircher v. Putnam Funds Trust,* 403 F.3d 478 (7th Cir. 2005).

alleged corporate misrepresentations. This holding, directly contradicts the Second Circuit's decision in *Dabit, issued just months earlier.*

Whereas in Putnam Funds I, the Seventh Circuit determined that the Northern District of Illinois' decision to remand several Illinois state-law claims was, in fact, appealable, in *Putnam Funds II,* the circuit court took up the merits of the appeal, examining the district courts' determination that SLUSA preemption does not apply to "holders" claims. The district courts, applying the same logic as the Second Circuit's *Dabit* decision, held that because "holders" claims do not directly implicate "the purchase or sale of covered securities," they fall outside the boundaries of SLUSA's preemptive language.[154]

The Seventh Circuit disagreed, finding that SLUSA preemption is *not* limited to actions where the plaintiffs are purchasers or sellers of securities, but also includes "holder" classes, such as those at issue in the Putnam Fund litigation. For example, one of the Putnam Fund complaints carefully defined its class to include "all investors who *held* the fund's securities during a defined period *and neither purchased or sold shares* during that period."[155] As seen above, such artful pleading would be enough to avoid SLUSA's grasp under the Second Circuit's decision in *Dabit.*

The Putnam Funds II decision, however, reexamined the underlying premise behind the *Dabit* ruling—the United States Supreme Court's interpretation, in *Blue Chip Stamps,* of §10(b)'s "in connection with a purchase or sale" language. In analyzing *Blue Chip Stamps,* the *Dabit* court—and others—found that the Supreme Court read the "in connection with" language to limit the scope of §10(b) and Rule 10b-5 to include only those plaintiffs who purchased or sold stock in reliance on the alleged misrepresentation. To Judge Easterbrook, however, this reading of *Blue Chip Stamps* and §10(b) is erroneous:

> Section 10(b) defines a federal crime, and it also permits the SEC to enforce the prohibition through administrative proceedings. Invocation of this anti-fraud rule does not depend on proof that the agency or United States purchased or sold securities; instead the "in connection with" language ensures that the fraud occurs in securities transactions rather than some other activity.
>
> . . .

---

154. *See, e.g., Kircher v. Putnam Funds Trust*, 2004 U.S. Dist. LEXIS 10327 (S.D. Ill. 2004).

155. *Putnam Funds II,* 403 F.3d at 483 (emphasis added).

> *Blue Chip Stamps* came out as it did not because §10(b) and Rule 10b-5 are limited to situations in which the plaintiff itself traded securities, but because a private right of action to enforce these provisions is a judicial creation and the Court wanted to confine these actions to situations where litigation is apt to do more good than harm. The Justices observed that anyone can *say* that a failure to trade bore some relation to what the issuer did (or didn't) disclose, but that judges and juries would have an exceedingly hard time knowing whether a given counterfactual claim ("I *would have* traded, if only . . .") was honest. The Court thought it best to limit private actions to harms arising out of actual trading, which narrows the affected class and simplifies proof, while leaving other securities offenses to public prosecutors.[156]

Judge Easterbrook's novel reading of *Blue Chip Stamps* challenges the premise upon which the *Dabit* court held that SLUSA did not apply to "holders" claims. If the Supreme Court's decision deals only with which plaintiffs may assert a private action, and does not restrict coverage of §10(b) and Rule 10b-5, then the *Dabit* decision's foundations are considerably weakened.

There is some reason to believe that Judge Easterbrook's interpretation of *Blue Chip Stamps* may accurately reflect the Supreme Court's reasoning. Several Supreme Court decisions issued subsequent to *Blue Chip Stamps* appear to indicate that the decision does not truncate the overall scope of §10(b) and Rule 10b-5.[157] Moreover, Judge Easterbrook advances a compelling public policy argument that echoes the SEC's *amicus* concerns in *Dabit.* The *Putnam Funds* plaintiffs' careful construction of "non-purchaser-non-seller" classes represent a transparent attempt to avoid the reach of the Reform Act "in the hope that a local judge or jury may produce an idiosyncratic award . . . the very sort of maneuver that SLUSA is designed to prevent."[158] Returning to the subject of *Blue Chip Stamps*, Judge Easterbrook finds that "[i]t would be more than a little strange if the Supreme Court's decision to block private litigation by non-traders became the opening by which that very litigation could be pursued under state law, despite the judgment of Congress (reflected in SLUSA) that securities class actions must proceed under federal securities law or not at all."[159]

---

156. *Id.*
157. *See United States v. O'Hagan*, 521 U.S. 642, 664 (1997); *Holmes v. SIPC*, 503 U.S. 258, 284 (1992); *United States v. Naftalin*, 441 U.S. 768, 774 n.6 (1979)
158. *Putnam Funds II,* 403 F.3d at 484.
159. *Id.*

E. What is at Stake?

With the publication of *Putnam Funds II*, the initial split between the Second and Seventh Circuits has widened considerably. Judge Easterbrook's opinion challenges nearly every aspect of the *Dabit* decision, leaving the Second Circuit either to fundamentally reverse itself and admit an erroneous interpretation of *Blue Chip Stamps* or to allow the *Putnam Funds* challenge to go unanswered. In either event, the prospects for "bridging" this gap without outside intervention—through Congressional action or a petition to the Supreme Court—appear dim.

For issuers and securities fraud defendants, the resolution of this matter will have significant consequences. As an initial matter, SLUSA's promise of national uniformity in securities class actions is at stake, as "holder" claims are recognized by some states, but not by others. Moreover, because state court claims are not subject to the Reform Act's discovery stay, they may be used in conjunction with federal securities actions to increase the costs of defense and force settlement of even meritless suits. In addition to using state-law "holder" suits to circumvent the strict Reform Act-imposed standards of federal securities litigation, plaintiffs may find in them a convenient means of avoiding the much-despised board demand requirements of shareholder derivative suits. The ultimate risk, however, is that of having to defend two (or more) actions arising from the same set of facts, but subject to radically different substantive and procedural requirements, which may produce inconsistent substantive rulings.

Absent further Congressional action to tighten SLUSA's grasp, the best hope for issuers and securities litigation defendants lies in Merrill Lynch's recent filing of a petition for a writ of certiorari to the United States Supreme Court, seeking review of the Second Circuit's *Dabit* opinion.[160] This petition—and the amicus brief jointly filed by the Securities Industry Association and the Bond Market Association[161]—urges the Court to resolve the split between the Second and Seventh Circuits. Ultimately, the Supreme Court itself may decide whose reading of its *Blue Chip Stamps* decision is correct. At stake is the realization of Congress's intent to protect issuers (and their officers and directors) with a uniform, national standard for securities class actions.

---

160. *See* No. 04-1371, 73 USLW 3632 (Apr. 11, 2005).
161. Available at http://www.bondmarkets.com/assets/files/DabitAmicusBrief.pdf.

NOTES

NOTES

LOSS CAUSATION AND DAMAGES

6

A REVIEW OF THE SUPREME COURT'S *DURA V. BROUDO* OPINION, AND WHAT IT PORTENDS FOR INVESTORS SEEKING TO PLEAD AND PROVE "LOSS CAUSATION" IN OPEN-MARKET FRAUDS

Patrick J. Coughlin

Eric Alan Isaacson

Joseph D. Daley

Lerach Coughlin Stoia Geller Rudman & Robbins LLP

The authors are partners in the law firm of Lerach Coughlin Stoia Geller Rudman & Robbins LLP who represented the plaintiffs before the Supreme Court in *Dura Pharmaceuticals, Inc. v. Broudo*, No. 03-932. Mr. Coughlin argued the case on January 12, 2005.

Table of Contents

I. INTRODUCTION

On April 19, 2005, the United States Supreme Court in *Dura Pharmaceuticals, Inc. v. Broudo* ruled on the issue of loss causation in private securities open market-fraud actions.[1] The issue as framed in *Dura* was a narrow one—whether an allegation of price inflation alone due to a material misrepresentation or omission was sufficient to establish loss causation. Reversing a Ninth Circuit panel that had held that an inflated purchase price itself sufficiently "establishes" loss causation,[2] the Supreme Court determined that defrauded investors need to prove that defendants' misrepresentation proximately caused an economic loss.[3] Having determined plaintiffs need to prove causation leading to economic loss, the Court unremarkably held that plaintiffs' pleadings must provide defendants with fair notice of plaintiffs' claim.

The Court declined to adopt the argument that Fed. R. Civ. P. 9(b) particularity applied to the elements of causation and economic loss, or that the Private Securities Litigation Reform Act of 1995 ("PSLRA") had raised the pleading standards as to these elements,[4] but rather "conced[ed] that the Federal Rules of Civil Procedure require only 'a short and plain statement of the claim showing that the pleader is entitled to relief,'" providing the defendant with "'fair notice of what the plaintiff's claim is and the grounds upon which it rests.'"[5] As a result, the Court found "it should not prove burdensome for a plaintiff who has suffered an economic loss to provide a defendant with some indication of the loss and the causal connection that the plaintiff has in mind."[6]

---

1. *Dura Pharmaceuticals, Inc. v. Broudo*, S. Ct. No. 03-932 (Apr. 19, 2005) (hereafter "Slip op.").
2. *Broudo v. Dura Pharmaceuticals, Inc.*, 339 F.3d 933, 938 (9th Cir. 2003), *cert. granted*, ___ U.S. ___, 124 S. Ct. 2904 (2004).
3. Slip op. at 5-6, 9.
4. Both the Solicitor General and Dura had argued that loss-causation allegations must be stated with particularity under Fed. R. Civ. P. 9(b). Brief for the United States as Amicus Curiae Supporting Petitioners ("U.S. Br.") at 15; Dura Reply Br. at 10-11. The Solicitor General also argued that loss-causation allegations must satisfy the heightened pleading requirements of the PSLRA. At argument the Supreme Court Justices expressed their skepticism of these arguments (*e.g.*, Justice Ginsburg, Transcript of January 12, 2005, Oral Argument ("Tr.") at 20) and did not impose the heightened pleading requirements requested as to the elements of causation and economic loss. Slip op. at 9-10.
5. *Id.* at 9 (quoting Fed. R. Civ. P. 8(a)(2) and *Conley v. Gibson*, 355 U.S. 41, 47 (1957)).
6. *Id.* at 10.

The Supreme Court also declined Dura's request for a rule that required a stock drop directly tied to a corrective disclosure. Instead, the Court seemed to recognize that inflation could be removed any number of ways.[7] Even the Solicitor General recognized "fraud can be revealed by means other than a corrective disclosure and a drop in the stock price may not be a necessary condition for establishing loss causation in every fraud-on-the-market case."[8] According to the Solicitor General, inflation attributable to a misrepresentation might be reduced or eliminated even if there were a net increase in price"[9]—a concept the Supreme Court specifically acknowledged but declined to address.[10]

This review examines what *Dura* does—and does not—hold, examining in particular certain positions taken by Dura and its *amici* that the Court declined to adopt.

II. THE SUPREME COURT'S *DURA* DECISION: WHAT IT DOES —AND DOES NOT—HOLD

A careful reading of the *Dura* decision reveals that the opinion consists of two sections—(A) and (B)—dealing with matters of "proof" and "pleading" respectively.

Section A of the opinion deals only with what securities-fraud plaintiffs must *prove* to establish loss causation and concludes "that a plaintiff must prove that the defendant's misrepresentation (or other fraudulent conduct) proximately caused the plaintiff's economic loss."[11] While this proof may take a variety of forms, the Supreme Court declined to define

7. Justice Breyer, at oral argument, noted that inflation might come out in many different ways, not simply an announcement "I'm a liar." According to Justice Breyer, inflation could "ooze[] out as earning reports come in, but it has to come out." Tr. at 38-39.
8. U.S. Br. at 19. The Supreme Court nowhere requires there be a corrective disclosure tied to a stock drop. The Court speaks in terms of the truth leaking out or making it to the market, thereby eliminating inflation. Slip op. at 5.
9. U.S. Br. at 19-20.
10. Slip op. at 5-6. Prior to the Supreme Court's ruling, Professor John C. Coffee, Jr., wrote a draft article deriding the Ninth Circuit's "loss causation" decision that the Supreme Court was to address in *Dura*. In *Causation By Presumption? Why the Supreme Court Should Reject Phantom Losses and Reverse Broudo*, Professor Coffee joined defendants and their *amici* in urging the Supreme Court not only to reverse the Ninth Circuit, but to adopt the stock drop rule urged by Dura and its *amici*. 60 Bus. Law. 533 (2005). The paper was cited by Dura in a supplemental pleading accepted by the Supreme Court just weeks before the Court's decision. Thus, all of Professor Coffee's views were before the Court.
11. Slip op. at 9.

its parameters, whether substantive or temporal. It holds only that plaintiffs must ultimately prove the economic loss they suffered as the "relevant truth begins to leak out," or as "the truth makes its way into the market place."[12] Importantly, although the Dura defendants (and Dura's numerous *amici* in the securities and business arenas) had urged stringent loss causation/proximate cause rules that would have required proof of a *direct* tie between any subsequent stock decline and a previous misrepresentation, the Supreme Court expressly declined to go that far: "We need not, and do not, consider other proximate cause or loss-related questions."[13]

The "pleading" section of the *Dura* opinion contains the core of the Court's guidance, for the underlying case is currently at the motion-to-dismiss stage and the Court knew that the Ninth Circuit had already granted plaintiffs leave to amend their complaint.[14] *Dura* confirms that securities-fraud plaintiffs face no enhanced burdens in satisfactorily alleging loss causation. Rather, to successfully plead loss causation in a securities-fraud action, plaintiffs simply need to allege a "'short and plain statement'" of the loss and how defendants caused it, sufficient to provide defendants with "'fair notice.'"[15] This should not be difficult, the Court explains: satisfactory loss-causation allegations need only "provide a defendant with some indication of the loss and the causal connection that the plaintiff has in mind."[16]

Clearly, the Court means for this pleading exercise to be a fairly simple one, focusing on the *plaintiff's* subjective belief of how defendant caused her loss. Twice, in fact, the Supreme Court explains that the plaintiff needs only to allege an "indication" of the economic loss and proximate cause that "*the plaintiff has in mind.*"[17] This language, considered in conjunction with the Court's earlier acknowledgment that a "tangle of factors" related to price will have to be sorted out at the proof stage,[18] makes

12. *Id.* at 5.
13. *Id.* at 9.
14. At oral argument, plaintiffs' counsel Patrick Coughlin reminded the Supreme Court that the Ninth Circuit had already granted leave to amend, and explained that plaintiffs could add more facts explaining their losses caused by defendants' AlSpiros misstatements. In its opinion, the Supreme Court remands the case to the Ninth Circuit "for further proceedings consistent with this opinion." *Id.* at 11.
15. *Id.* at 9 (citing *Conley*, 355 U.S. at 47).
16. *Id.* at 10.
17. *Id.* (emphasis added).
18. *Id.* at 6.

clear that the Court does not intend for the motion-to-dismiss stage to become a mini-trial on loss-causation scenarios.

While the foregoing explains what the Supreme Court's *Dura* opinion holds, the opinion is also notable for what it does *not* hold. Defendants and their *amici* had tried mightily to convince the Supreme Court to raise both the proof, and pleading bars, of securities-fraud actions well out of reach of many defrauded investors. By any reasoned analysis of the *Dura* opinion, their efforts failed.

Specifically, Dura (and commentators like Columbia Law Professor John Coffee, Jr.) hoped the Court might reconsider *Basic Inc. v. Levinson.*[19] *Basic*'s rebuttable presumption of plaintiffs' reliance on the integrity of a security's market price, according to Professor Coffee, could have been significantly curtailed.[20] The Court instead repeatedly cites *Basic* with approval, using *Basic* to lay out a securities-fraud action's basic elements, and reaffirming a rebuttable presumption of investors' reliance on a stock's public market price.[21]

Nor does the Court adopt the argument, urged by Dura and its *amici*, that loss causation requires that there always exist a corrective disclosure—really, an admission by defendants—specifically linked to a final stock drop.[22] (A more pernicious extension of that argument further urged the Court to hold that the final drop in response to such a disclosure is in every case the *total* measure of plaintiffs' damages.)[23] Instead, the Supreme Court explains in *Dura's* "proof" discussion that plaintiffs' economic loss may occur as the "relevant truth begins to leak out," or as *"the*

19. 485 U.S. 224 (1988).
20. Coffee, *supra*, 60 Bus. Law. at 544, 547.
21. Slip op. at 4, 8.
22. Several commentators have specifically noted the absence of any requirement that there be a corrective disclosure linked to a final stock drop. "'That did not happen,' said Donald Langevoort, a Georgetown University Law Center professor. 'The Court deals with this on the narrowest of possible grounds.'" Dana Wilkie, *Drugmaker wins in stock fraud lawsuit: Supreme Court declines to ease standard on claims*, Copley News Service, Apr. 20, 2005, at http://www.signonsandiego.com/news/business/20050420-9999-1b20dura.html. Professor John Coffee from Columbia recently conceded that, while he had argued that courts should interpret loss causation to require a net stock-market decline in the security's price in order to preclude what he had termed "phantom losses," the Supreme Court did not adopt his position—or Dura's for that matter. *See* John C. Coffee, Jr., *Loss Causation After 'Dura': Something for Everyone*, N.Y.L.J., May 19, 2005, at 5 ("But the Court has not done that.").
23. Then, using the PSLRA's 90-day look-back provision (15 U.S.C. §78u-4(e)(1)), defendants would be able to argue that because the stock eventually bounced back above its post-disclosure final drop, there was *no loss at all* in the case.

truth makes its way into the market place."[24] Importantly, the Court does not require that an explicit corrective *disclosure*—whether by defendants themselves, or sleuthing outsiders—be the mechanism by which the truth "leak[ed]" out.[25] As plaintiffs' counsel Patrick Coughlin explained at oral argument, there are myriad ways in which the truth involving defendants' fraud can be communicated to the market, thereby removing inflation from the stock price and harming investors. The Supreme Court has now confirmed that plaintiffs need only provide defendants with "some indication" of the connection between that leakage and plaintiffs' claimed economic loss.[26]

Finally, Dura and the Solicitor General had urged the Supreme Court to hold that loss causation needed to be pleaded, like falsity and scienter, with Rule 9(b) particularity.[27] The Justices reacted to that argument with skepticism at the oral argument, and their opinion does not adopt the Solicitor General or Dura's position that Rule 9(b) applies in this context.[28] In fact, *Dura* reaffirms the vitality of *Conley v. Gibson* and the requirement that, absent special pleading rules, a complaint need only provide a "'short and plain statement'" of loss causation.[29] "[I]t should not prove burdensome," explained the Court, "for a plaintiff who has suffered an economic loss to provide a defendant with some indication of the loss and the causal connection that the plaintiff has in mind."[30] That explanation is consistent with the Court's earlier observation that the "tangle of factors affecting price" will be part of the *proof* of loss causation[31]—a fact-intensive inquiry clearly reserved for trial.

---

24. Slip op. at 5. At oral argument Justice Breyer recognized the truth might come out in "subtle ways as well as direct ways." Tr. at 55.
25. Slip op. at 5.
26. Slip op. at 10.
27. U.S. Br. at 15; Dura Reply Br. at 11.
28. Justice Ginsburg, for example, specifically stated to the government during oral argument: "I thought you pointed to the 9(b) rule because fraud must be pleaded with particularity, but causation does not, not under the rules and not under the statute." Tr. at 20.
29. Slip op. at 9 (citation omitted). The Solicitor General had also argued that allegations dealing with the element of loss causation "must satisfy the pleading requirements added to the 1934 Act by the PSLRA, see 15 U.S.C. 78u-4(b)(1) and (2)." U.S. Br. at 15. This argument, as replied to at oral argument by Justice Ginsburg (*see* above footnote) faired little better than the Solicitor General's Rule 9(b) contention.
30. Slip op. at 10.
31. *Id.* at 6.

III. REAL-WORLD EXPERIENCE BELIES THE NOTION THAT A DROP ON DISCLOSURE OF FRAUD IS THE ONLY SENSIBLE WAY TO DETERMINE LOSS

Dura, its *amici*, and several commentators had insisted on significant market reactions to corrective disclosures as the only accurate, reliable determinants of loss. For example, absent a dramatic reaction to a disclosure contradicting defendants' earlier representations, Professor Coffee had asserted that loss determinations are necessarily speculative or hypothetical.[32] Economists surely disagree—and Professor Coffee conceded as much, writing that "[f]rom an economic perspective, [the] theory is coherent: if you make a material misstatement, it must inflate the market price and so the shareholders purchasing at that inflated price are injured."[33] Despite that economic truism, the Supreme Court now holds that plaintiffs cannot rely upon that initial inflation alone to prove their economic loss, requiring them to show how the security's value subsequently declined for reasons related to the fraud—such as a subsequent leakage of the "truth" into the marketplace.[34] The Supreme Court, however, did not adopt the corrective-disclosure stock-drop rule urged by Dura and its *amici*.

The Justices at oral argument recognized that inflation can be removed in a number of ways—not just with corrective disclosures. For example, Justice Breyer recognized that fraud-based inflation "might come out in many different ways," not just an admission or corrective disclosure from a corporate executive that "I'm a liar."[35] It could come out because that corporate executive "doesn't say anything but it sort of oozes out as earning reports come in, but it has to come out."[36] Even the Solicitor General did not require a corrective disclosure, simply that "the truth was revealed (at least in part) and the inflation in the price of the security attributable to

---

32. Coffee, *supra*, 60 Bus. Law. at 533, 538.

33. *Id.* at 536-37. Professor Coffee was speaking to the "theory" advanced in a companion article by his Columbia Law School colleague Merritt Fox, that the *Dura* plaintiffs satisfactorily pleaded causation without having to allege a subsequent stock drop. *Id.* (citing Merritt B. Fox, *Demystifying Causation in Fraud-on-the-Market Actions*, 60 Bus. Law. 507 (2005)). To the extent that they both agree a stock drop following disclosure is unnecessary to show loss causation, the *Dura* plaintiffs' and Professor Fox's "theor[ies]" are equivalent. That said, however, counsel has never agreed *completely* with Professor Fox's overall loss-causation analysis—disagreeing with Fox's suggestion that the transaction/loss dichotomy be abandoned.

34. Slip op. at 5-6.

35. Tr. at 38.

36. *Id.* at 39.

the misrepresentation was thereby eliminated (or reduced) to the plaintiff's detriment."[37] The Solicitor General specifically noted that "fraud can be revealed by means other than a corrective disclosure, and a drop in the stock price may not be a necessary condition for establishing loss causation in every fraud-on-the-market case. To the extent that courts or litigants have suggested otherwise, they are mistaken."[38] In addition, the Solicitor General asserted that "inflation attributable to a misrepresentation might be reduced or eliminated even if there were a net *increase* in price"[39]—a scenario the Supreme Court acknowledged, but declined to address.[40] As an example, the Solicitor General found that inflation could be eliminated without a drop in the price—but perhaps even a rise—if a company were to "correct[] the false information and at the same time issue[] unrelated positive information."[41] The reasons for this are not complex.

Market valuations are based upon expected future cash flows discounted by the cost of capital—commonly referred to as discounted cash flows.[42] Open-market frauds commonly manipulate stock-market prices, then, by artificially raising cash-flow *expectations*. Conversely, cash-flow expectations just as easily can be lowered, thereby reducing fraud-induced inflation *without* an overt disclosure of the fraud, by further statements—true or false—that *on their face* may or may not appear to be directly related to the original fraud. So long as they provide some indication of the true state of defendants' operations, however, the statements may be regarded as having caused plaintiffs' economic loss.[43]

---

37. U.S. Br. at 16. The Supreme Court's opinion speaks in terms of the "relevant truth" reaching the market—not of corrective disclosures tied to stock drops. Slip op. at 5. That the inflation only need be "reduced," according to Professor Coffee, requires very little. Coffee, *supra*, 60 Bus. Law. at 547.
38. U.S. Br. at 19.
39. *Id.* (emphasis in original).
40. Slip op. at 5-6.
41. U.S. Br. at 19-20.
42. *See* Burton G. Malkiel, *Is the Stock Market Efficient?*, 243 Sci. 1313, 1316 (1989); Merton H. Miller & Franco Modigliani, *Dividend Policy, Growth, and the Valuation of Shares*, 34 J. Bus. 411, 415-16 (1961); Richard A. Brealey & Stewart C. Myers, *Capital Investment and Valuation* 77 (2003); Richard A. Brealey, *An Introduction to Risk and Return From Common Stocks* 67-72, 78 n.1 (1983); Eugene F. Fama & Merton H. Miller, *The Theory of Finance* 87-89 (1972); *see also* Jay W. Eisenhofer, Geoffrey C. Jarvis & James R. Banko, *Securities Fraud, Stock Price Valuation, and Loss Causation: Toward a Corporate Finance-Based Theory of Loss Causation*, 59 Bus. Law. 1419, 1421-24 (2004).
43. Slip op. at 5-6.

Even the passage of time itself will dissipate a major fraud's impact on a stock's price. Inflation from sales or asset overstatements ages with time, for instance, as does inflation due to earnings misstatements.[44] This occurs again as a new picture of the company's operations hits the market over time. Because investors rely on recent earnings to project future cash flows, the effect of an overstatement fades with the passage of each subsequent quarter. Section 10(b) claims must be filed within five years of the violation,[45] but five years is eons in the stock market. Justice Breyer suggests that time can make the connection between fraud and loss more attenuated.[46] While time may certainly make it tougher to disentangle other market forces, etc., this is for the proof stage of the litigation—not the pleading stage—and the subject of expert analysis.

Thus, truthful disclosure of falsified quarterly earnings that would have been quite material to the market at the time of the earnings announcement may be rendered far less important years later, when more-recent quarterly-performance information is available, *i.e.*, a truer picture of the company's operations. But the lack of a visceral, dramatic stock decline accompanying that final disclosure does not mean that the "truth" has not leaked into the market during the ensuing years, and if plaintiffs can plead and prove that the leakage caused them economic loss, the loss-causation element has been satisfied.[47] Indeed, if a stock has become worthless because the company has failed, a disclosure that its former strong financial results and ostensibly bright prospects were all the product of fraud can have no market impact. Yet recovery should not be denied merely because the defendants manage to conceal their fraud until after the company failed and its stock was worthless.[48]

Because stock drops are not the exclusive barometers of investors' "loss," reliance on such market drops on disclosures is simply mis-

---

44. *See* Marcia Kramer Mayer, Ph.D., *Loss Causation and Damages: Dura and Beyond* (NERA Economic Consulting, Sept. 30, 2004); *see also In re Initial Pub. Offering Sec. Litig.*, 297 F. Supp. 2d 668, 673 (S.D.N.Y. 2003) ("ordinary market forces affect the rate of artificial inflation" because in some circumstances "the normal functioning of the securities market causes the inflationary effect to dissipate over time"); A. A. Berle, Jr., *Liability for Stock Market Manipulation*, 31 Colum. L. Rev. 264, 269 (1931) ("a false statement . . . some years ago would have little appreciable effect on the price of the stock today").

45. *See* Pub. L. 107-204 §804, 116 Stat. 745, 801 (2002), *codified at* 28 U.S.C. §1658(b).

46. "Other things being equal, the longer the time between purchase and sale, the more likely that this is so, *i.e.*, the more likely that other factors caused the loss." Slip op. at 6.

47. *Id.* at 5-6, 9-10.

placed.[49] The reason: "Executives can be marvelously creative when they have to disclose disappointing results to investors."[50] A disclosure's negative effect may be obscured by defendants who downplay its significance, who pair the bad news with good, *or who lie again.*[51] Dura's November 3, 1998, press release, for example, downplayed the product's failure so blatantly that the U.S. Food and Drug Administration ("FDA") cited the company.[52]

The Dura defendants' proposed rule would have given those who choose to commit fraud many opportunities to game the system, and to avoid liability with manipulative disclosures.[53] The loss-causation issue is in play only if a defendant has already told one lie, *i.e.*, a lie that inflated the price of the stock for some period of time while investors were purchasing it. Telling two lies would, under the bright-line causation rule that had been sought by Dura and their *amici*, allow lying insiders to avoid liability. There is no room under our securities laws for a rule that encourages corporate insiders to tell a second lie to avoid liability for their first lie. Dura's proposed rules would have made it hardest for victims of the most egregious frauds to plead a claim. It is important that the Supreme Court rejected these draconian proposals.[54]

In sum, *Dura* is not the resounding victory defense counsel hoped for. The decision confirms the basic notice pleading standard as to causation and economic loss, acknowledges that in the real world the truth can reach

---

48. Commentary to §548A of the Restatement (Second) of Torts specifies that far from barring damages, the company's insolvency may in appropriate cases provide the basis for *additional* recovery. Comment b explains that "when the financial condition of a corporation is misrepresented and it is subsequently driven into insolvency by reason of the depressed condition of an entire industry, which has no connection with the facts misrepresented, it may still be found that the misrepresentation was a legal cause of the . . . loss, since it may appear that if the company had been in sound condition it would have survived the depression, and hence that a loss of this kind might reasonably have been expected to follow."

49. As noted above, SEC/United States' *amicus* brief in *Dura* admits that "fraud can be revealed by means other than a corrective disclosure, and a drop in the stock price may not be a necessary condition for establishing loss causation in every fraud on-the-market case." U.S. Br. at 19. "To the extent that courts or litigants have suggested otherwise, they are mistaken." *Id.* Indeed, inflation "might be reduced or eliminated even if there were a net *increase* in price." *Id.* (emphasis in original). The Supreme Court acknowledges as much when it alludes to a plaintiff's "claim that a share's higher price is lower than it would otherwise have been," but notes that that is "a claim we do not consider here." Slip op. at 5-6.

50. Gretchen Morgenson, *Finding Holes in Corporate Excuses*, N.Y. Times, Aug. 1, 2004.

the market in many ways—not just through admissions—and does not require a stock drop to maintain an action. While defense counsel may tout the count a 9-0 victory, plaintiffs' counsel feel the *Dura* opinion is really a diamond in the rough—validating the oft-repeated phrase that "beauty is in the eye of the beholder."[55]

IV. EPILOGUE

As of late June 2005, when these materials were finalized, the *Dura* decision had already begun to percolate in the lower courts. In *In re Daou Sys., Inc., Sec. Litig.*, No. 02-56989 (9th Cir. June 21, 2005), for example, after receiving full briefing from the parties on *Dura*'s significance, the Ninth Circuit became the first circuit-level court to issue a for-publication ruling applying *Dura*'s loss-causation holding. The *Daou* panel held that plaintiffs satisfied *Dura* by providing defendants with "some indication that the drop in Daou's stock price was causally related to Daou's financial misstatements."[56] Importantly, the *Daou* panel rejected the district court's insistence upon express "'negative public statements, announcements or disclosures . . . that Defendants were engaged in improper

---

51. *See, e.g., No. 84 Employer-Teamster Joint Council Pension Trust Fund v. Am. West Holding Corp.*, 320 F.3d 920, 934-35 (9th Cir. 2003); *Gray v. First Winthrop Corp.*, 82 F.3d 877, 882-83, 886 (9th Cir. 1996); *Goldberg v. Household Bank, F.S.B.*, 890 F.2d 965, 966 (7th Cir. 1989) ("a firm that lies about some assets cannot defeat liability by showing that other parts of its business did better than expected, counterbalancing the loss") (Easterbrook, J.).
52. JA110a-111a (¶136); *see* Nov. 6, 1998, FDA letter, *available at* http://www.fda.gov/cder/warn/nov98/7258.pdf.
53. *See* Eisenhofer, *supra*, 59 Bus. Law. at 1443.
54. For example, a stock may decline, before any disclosure, as insiders bail out. In *Dirks v. SEC*, 463 U.S. 646 (1983), the Supreme Court noted that surreptitious stock sales by investors with access to adverse inside information regarding a company's accounting improprieties drove its stock from $26 per share to less than $15 per share in two weeks—causing the New York Stock Exchange to halt trading—before any public disclosure of the accounting fraud. *Id.* at 649-50; *see also Dirks v. SEC*, 681 F.2d 824, 831-32 (D.C. Cir. 1982), *rev'd*, 463 U.S. 646 (1983). In *SEC v. Shapiro*, 494 F.2d 1301, 1307 n.3 (2d. Cir. 1974), trading by insiders who knew of undisclosed favorable information "pushed the price of [the] stock by February 18 to nearly three-and-one-half times what it had been at the beginning of the year." These insider sales led to a "truer" picture of the company's operations well before any corrective disclosure. As Justice Breyer recognized, the truth can reach the market in many subtle and indirect ways. Tr. at 5.
55. Proverb credited to Margaret Wolfe Hungerford, *Molly Bawn* (1878).
56. *Daou*, slip op. at 7357.

accounting practices.'"[57] Instead, under *Dura* loss causation was adequately pleaded by alleging the disclosure of the defendant company's "true financial health" in an earnings-shortfall release, and that the company's "stock [price] fell precipitously after defendants began to reveal figures showing the company's true financial condition."[58]

A district court within the Ninth Circuit has similarly held that loss causation is satisfied by allegations that defendants' misrepresentations caused the company's stock price to rise to inflated levels, and that the stock price "'collapse[d] as the truth regarding [a company product] emerged.'"[59] "In the present matter, Plaintiff's Complaint contains the very allegations regarding share price decrease and public exposure to the truth" that the Supreme Court found lacking in the *Dura* complaint.[60]

---

57. *Id.* at 7356 (citation omitted).
58. *Id.* at 7356-58.
59. *In re Immune Response Sec. Litig.*, No. 01CV1237 J (WMc) 2005 U.S. Dist. LEXIS 12602, at *94 (S.D. Cal. June 7, 2005) (citation to complaint omitted).
60. *Id.* at *95-*96. *But see D.E. & J. P'ship v. Conaway,* Nos. 03-2334, 03-2417, 2005 U.S. App. LEXIS 11267 (6th Cir. June 10, 2005) (unpublished disposition holding that complaint failed to provide defendants notice of relevant economic loss or causal connection between loss and defendants' misrepresentations); *In re Initial Pub. Offering Sec. Litig.*, No. MDL 1554 (SAS), 2005 U.S. Dist. LEXIS 9318, at *17 (S.D.N.Y. May 16, 2005) (plaintiffs failed to allege disclosure that would "correct" defendants' omissions or misrepresentations).

NOTES

7

DURA PHARM., INC. V. BROUDO —*THE LEAST OF ALL EVILS*

Alan Schulman

Niki Mendoza

Bernstein Litowitz Berger & Grossmann LLP

Alan Schulman is the Partner in Charge of the San Diego office of Bernstein Litowitz Berger & Grossmann LLP. Niki Mendoza is an associate in the same office. Priscilla Vargas, an associate, also in the San Diego office, assisted in the preparation of this article.

When the Supreme Court granted the petition for writ of certiorari to the Ninth Circuit in *Dura Pharmaceuticals, Inc. v. Broudo* in June 2004, the defense bar expected a lot, and plaintiffs' bar feared the worst. Most expected that the Supreme Court would reject the "price inflation" theory of loss causation, but worried how far the Court would go in granting defendants' and industry amici's "wish list" including requiring a specific corrective disclosure followed by a stock price drop, eliminating the presumption of reliance, and imposing a heightened standard for pleading loss causation. But in the end, the unanimous Supreme Court opinion in *Dura* was not a bad decision for plaintiffs—defendants got the price inflation theory win, and nothing else, and the plaintiffs' bar ended up with the best of all possible non-prevailing scenarios.

A little background is necessary. Courts have long implied a private right of action for damages under § 10(b) of the Securities Exchange Act of 1934 and SEC Rule 10b-5. To sufficiently plead such a claim, a private plaintiff must allege (1) a material misrepresentation or omission or fraudulent scheme; (2) in connection with the purchase or sale of a security; (3) scienter; (4) reliance; (5) an economic loss; and (6) "loss causation." *See Dura Pharms, Inc. v. Broudo,* 125 S. Ct. 1627, 1631 (April 19, 2005); *see also* 15 U.S.C. § 78u-4; 17 C.F.R. § 240.10b-5(a)-(c). The last two elements were at issue in *Dura.* The controversy arose from the Ninth Circuit's acceptance of pleading artificial price inflation on the date of purchase, as sufficient to allege loss causation. *See, e.g., Dura,* 339 F.3d 933, 938 (9th Cir. 2003). "Because the Ninth Circuit's views about loss causation differ from those of other Circuits that have considered this issue," the Supreme Court granted Dura's petition for certiorari. 125 S. Ct. at 1630. In a concise five-page opinion, Justice Breyer rejected the price inflation theory, finding it "inconsistent with the law's requirement that a plaintiff prove that the defendant's misrepresentation (or other fraudulent conduct) proximately caused the plaintiff's economic loss." *Id.* at 1633. Explaining that "[w]e need not, and do not, consider other proximate cause or loss-related questions," however, the Court gave little guidance on what allegations would satisfy the Court's loss causation requirement.

What is notable to securities plaintiffs (and a disappointment to the defense bar) is what the *Dura* decision does **not** say.

No Specific Corrective Disclosure Requirement

Dura does not, for example, adopt the position urged by defendants and their amici, that plaintiff must allege "a corrective disclosure followed by a stock price drop." Pet. Br. at *10. Despite substantial briefing and colloquy about this issue at argument, the Court endorsed neither petitioner's "corrective disclosure" nor its "stock price drop" arguments. Instead, the Court's narrow ruling said only that the Ninth Circuit's price-inflation-at-purchase theory was "inconsistent with the law's requirement that a plaintiff prove that the defendant's misrepresentation (or other fraudulent conduct) proximately caused the plaintiff economic loss, and that an "'artificially inflated purchase price' is not itself a relevant economic loss" in a § 10(b) action. 125 S. Ct. at 1634. *Dura* does not foreclose establishing loss causation by means other than a specific corrective disclosure of the truth linked to a stock price drop.

Had the Court adopted defendants' proposed requirement of a specific corrective disclosure of the truth—by confession or otherwise—linked to a drop in stock price, the pleading hurdle could have been "insurmountable." [Resp. Br. at *9.] Plaintiffs argued that "[s]ophisticated individuals who would commit market manipulation and fraud are likely to be adept at concealing it. Expectations can be lowered, thereby reducing fraud-induced inflation without disclosure of the fraud, by further false statements. Even the passage of time itself will dissipate a fraud's impact on a stock's price."[1] Indeed, it is not unusual for a company with a problem to strategically leak multiple negative information at different times, or to combine negative events and disclose them at once to confound plaintiffs' ability to isolate the cause of their losses. In many complex cases, the full extent of the fraud is not revealed until long after the stock price collapses.

There are myriad ways in which the truth may be revealed, for example: 1) whistleblower claims; 2) analysts question financial results or other company "explanations"; 3) CFOs or auditors resign; 4) the company lowers earning expectations; and/or 5) the company announces changes in accounting treatment going forward. *See* John C. Coffee, *Loss Causation After 'Dura': Something for Everyone*, N.J. L.J., May 19, 2005 (explaining that requiring a "disclosure of corrective information" "ignores that the market can learn of fraud or suspected fraud well before a formal corrective disclosure").

---

1. Resp. Br. at *10 (citing, *inter alia*, Jay W. Eisenhofer, Geoffrey C. Jarvis & James R. Banko, *Securities Fraud, Stock Price Valuation, and Loss Causation: Toward a Corporate Finance-Based Theory of Loss Causation*, 59 Bus. Law. 1419, 1443 (2004) and *In re Initial Pub. Offering Sec. Litig.*, 297 F. Supp. 2d 668, 673 (S.D.N.Y. 2003) ("ordinary market forces affect the rate of artificial inflation" because in some circumstances "the normal functioning of the securities market causes the inflationary effect to dissipate over time")).

Nothing in *Dura* precludes plaintiffs from pleading loss causation through a ***partial*** disclosure. Indeed, as a recent decision interpreted *Dura*: "plaintiffs need only allege 'that the misstatement or omission concealed something from the market that, when disclosed, negatively affected the value of the security,' and loss causation does not require *full* disclosure and can be established by *partial* disclosure during the class period which causes the price of shares to decline." *Montoya v. Mamma.com Inc.*, 2005 WL 1278097, at *2 (S.D.N.Y. May 31, 2005) (citing *Dura* and *Lentell v. Merrill Lynch & Co.*, 396 F.3d 161, 174 (2d Cir. 2005)) (emphasis in original).[2]

In its first post—*Dura* decision, the Ninth Circuit implicitly rejected defendants' position that *Dura* requires that the revealed "truth" must precisely mirror the specific allegations in the complaint. In *Daou Systems*, defendants argued that the complaint did not allege that the truth "about the Company's alleged violation of the [percentage-of-completion] method" became known when the stock price fell, but the Ninth Circuit held the complaint sufficiently alleged loss causation because it alleged the company's stock fell precipitously "*after defendants began to reveal figures showing the company's true financial condition*." *In re Daou Systems, Inc.*, 2005 WL 1431833, at *15-*16 (9th Cir. June 21, 2005).

---

2. *Montoya* addressed *Dura* in the context of competing motions for lead plaintiff. There, certain competing plaintiffs argued that the purported damages of "in and out purchasers" should not be included in computing which movant has the largest financial interest (and is, therefore, presumptively the most adequate lead plaintiff under the PSLRA), because, under *Dura,* none of these losses could be attributable to the fraud. The court noted that "in and out purchasers" "obfuscate loss calculations" but that because under *Dura* only a partial disclosure need affect the value of the security, the court appointed the movants with the largest purported loss, including "in and out purchasers," which, the court noted, were not "unique." 2005 WL 1278097, at *2.
Dictum in the Ninth Circuit's Amended Opinion in *Daou*, discussed *infra*, likewise arguably interprets *Dura* as potentially affecting damage calculations: "We note that, as the TAC currently reads, at the time when Daou began to reveal its true financial health in August 1998, its stock was trading at $18.50 per share and not at the class high of $34.375. The TAC does not allege any revelation of Daou's true financial health prior to August 1998. Thus, as the TAC reads now, any loss suffered between $34.375 and $18.50 cannot be considered causally related to Daou's allegedly fraudulent accounting methods because before the revelations began in August 1998, the true nature of Daou's financial condition had not yet been disclosed." 2005 WL 1431833, at *16. *Dauo,* however, discussed the issue in the context of a motion to dismiss, not in the context of evidence of damages presented at trial.

No Price Decline Requirement

The Supreme Court also did not adopt defendants' argument that a "loss" can only occur when the stock price ***declines,*** and not when the stock price experiences an overall net increase due to, for example, the mixed disclosure of both negative and positive information. Pet. Br. at *13, *36. The untruth will ***generally*** be removed through an absolute decline in the price of the security, ***but could also be removed through an increase in the price that is smaller than it otherwise would have been.*** The *Dura* court acknowledged that when "a share's higher price is lower than it would otherwise have been," the same reasoning applies as does when a purchaser subsequently resells shares at a lower price.[3]

Likewise, *Dura* does not require plaintiff to demonstrate that the entirety of their economic loss was caused ***exclusively*** by defendants' fraud. Indeed, *Dura* emphasizes that loss causation deals with the concept of proximate cause, drawn from common law principles. *See Dura,* 125 S. Ct. at 1631-32. Those principles require only that fraud be a substantial cause of loss—not that it be the exclusive cause. *See Sosa v. Alvarez-Machain,* 124 S. Ct. 2739, 2750 (2004) ("Proximate cause is causation substantial enough and close enough to the harm to be recognized by law, but a given proximate cause need not be, and frequently is not, the exclusive proximate cause of harm."). Thus, the Court also left open the door on ways to allege, and prove, loss.

The Presumption of Reliance Remains

The *Dura* Court also did not accept defendants' invitation to re-evaluate the rebuttable fraud-on-the-market presumption it accepted in *Basic Inc. v. Levinson,* 485 U.S. 224 (1988), by arguing the plaintiffs must also plead *separate* transaction causation. Instead, the Court reiterated that transaction causation and reliance are synonymous in most securities class actions and can be established through the fraud-on-the-market presumption. 125 S. Ct. at 1631; *see also id.* at 1633, 1634.[4]

---

3. 125 S. Ct. at 1632. Specifically the Court explained: "If the purchaser sells later after the truth makes its way into the market place, an initially inflated purchase price *might* mean a later loss. But that is far from inevitably so. When the purchaser subsequently resells such shares, even at a lower price, that lower price may reflect, not the earlier misrepresentations, but changed economic circumstances, changed investor expectations, new industry-specific or firm-specific facts, conditions, or other events, which taken separately or together account for some or all of that lower price. (***The same is true in respect to a claim that a share's higher price is lower than it would otherwise have been—a claim we do not consider here***.)." 125 S. Ct. at 1631-32 (emphasis added).

No Heightened Pleading Standard

Justice Breyer's discussion of the applicable pleading standard is particularly noteworthy.[5] Defendants and their amici argued that loss causation allegations must satisfy the heightened pleading standards of Federal Rule of Civil Procedure 9(b) and the PSLRA. The Securities Industry Association even argued that the PSLRA requires the complaint to include expert testimony supported by "[a]n event study . . . a statistical regression analysis that examines the effect of an event, such as an allegedly fraudulent statement or omission, on a dependent variable, such as a company's stock price." Sec. Ind. Ass'n Br. at 9-10, n.6.

The Court did not adopt these positions, but instead "assume[d], at least for argument's sake, that neither the Rules nor the securities statutes impose any special further requirement in respect to the pleading of proximate causation or economic loss." *Dura,* 125 S. Ct. at 1634. The Court analyzed the loss causation allegations under Federal Rule of Civil Procedure 8(a), requiring "a short and plain statement of the claim showing that the pleader is entitled to relief," which provides a defendant with "fair notice of what the plaintiff's claim is and the grounds upon which it rests."[6]

Applying "ordinary pleading rules" to the complaint before it, the Court, found that "the complaint nowhere else provides the defendants with notice of what the relevant economic loss might be or of what the causal connection might be between that loss and the misrepresentation . . . ." 125 S. Ct. at 1634. In apparent guidance going forward, the Court commented, "We concede that ordinary pleading rules are not meant to impose a great burden upon a plaintiff. [citation omit-

---

4. Indeed, the district court in the District of New Jersey has since relied on the Supreme Court's Opinion in *Dura* in denying defendants' motion to dismiss, stating:

> ***The Court is satisfied that the allegations relating to transaction causation in this short-selling context are sufficient to withstand a motion to dismiss based on loss causation. . . .*** Read in the light most favorable to short-selling Plaintiffs, the inference to be drawn from the allegations of the Amended Complaint is that the false financial statements artificially inflated [Lernout & Hauspie] stock, which, in turn, forced Plaintiffs to make cover transactions and incur significant losses. ***Fact-intensive issues related to causation and whether a given misstatement 'substantially contributed' to Plaintiffs' losses . . . are not properly resolved at this juncture.***

Rocker Management, L.L.C. v. Lernout & Hauspie Speech Products N.V., 2005 WL 1366025, at *7 (D. N.J. June 8, 2005) (emphasis added).

ted]. But it should not prove burdensome for a plaintiff who has suffered an economic loss to provide a defendant with some indication of the loss and the causal connection that the plaintiff has in mind." *Id.* at 1634.

***Case Outcomes Remain Unchanged After* Dura**

In the first published circuit court decision to apply *Dura*, the Ninth Circuit in *Daou Systems,* 2005 WL 1431833 (9th Cir. June 21, 2005), reached the same result as it had prior to *Dura.* In its *original* opinion (issued a month after the argument in *Dura*) the Ninth Circuit held that the district court erred in dismissing the complaint for failure to sufficiently allege loss causation. The district court had concluded that Daou's improper use of the percentage-of-completion accounting method was not linked to the decline in Daou's share price and that analysts' suspicions were "merely speculation." *Daou,* 397 F.3d 704, 722 (9th Cir. Feb. 2, 2005). On appeal, the Ninth Circuit found significant that "the price of the stock fell precipitously after defendants revealed figures vastly different than those reported in a press conference two weeks prior. The complaint also anonymously quotes an analyst who allegedly stated, '[w]hen you say one thing on the conference call and report something different on the 10-Q, that raises concern. . . . *You have got to question whether they are manufacturing earnings.*" *Id.* at 722. The Ninth Circuit in its original opinion concluded: "Although some of the allegations do call for speculation, the foregoing, if assumed true, is sufficient to show that the drop in Daou's stock price was the direct result of their financial misstatements and, in turn, caused plaintiffs' damages." *Ibid.*

After the Supreme Court issued its decision in *Dura,* the Ninth Circuit ordered the parties to submit supplemental briefs "addressing the impact of the Supreme Court's decision in [*Dura*] on the opinion in this case."

---

5. Several securities and non-securities cases have since cited *Dura*'s explanation of the appropriate pleading standard. *See, e.g., Rocker Management, L.L.C. v. Lernout & Hauspie Speech Products N.V.*, 2005 WL 1366025, at *7 (D. N.J. June 8, 2005) (citing *Dura*'s standard that the complaint need only "provide a defendant with some indication of the loss and the causal connection that the plaintiff has in mind"); *Pfeiffer v. Integrated Fund Servs, Inc.*, 2005 WL 1163998, at *3 (S.D.N.Y. May 18, 2005) ("[t]he federal rules allow simple pleadings and rely on liberal discovery rules and summary judgment motions to define disputed facts and issues and to dispose of unmeritorious claims," citing *Dura*); *Edelberg v. Roberts*, 2005 WL 1006000, at *2 (D.D.C. Apr. 29, 2005) (legal malpractice case citing *Dura* regarding general federal pleading standard); *Allied Van Lines, Inc. v. Gulf Shores Moving & Storage, Inc.*, 2005 WL 1027463, at *1 (M.D. Fla. May 2, 2005) (conversion claim citing *Dura* regarding general federal pleading standard). Several other cases merely cite *Dura* for its recitation of the elements of a § 10(b) claim.

Defendants' argued that the *Daou Systems* complaint "never meets the threshold *Dura* requirement of a moment when the truth became known," because (1) the complaint does not allege a specific date on which the relevant truth became known; and (2) the "truth" that became known must specifically mirror the complaint's allegations that the company violated GAAP through the misuse of the percentage-of-completion method.[7]

On June 21, 2005, the Ninth Circuit issued an Amended Opinion repeating the loss causation paragraphs contained in its original Opinion, and in implicitly rejecting defendants' supplemental arguments. The Ninth Circuit concluded that the alleged facts were "sufficient to provide Daou with ***some indication that the drop in Daou's stock price was causally related to Daou's financial misstatements reflecting its practice of prematurely recognizing revenue before it was earned.*** 2005 WL 1431833, at *16 (citing "*Dura Pharms.,* 125 S. Ct. at 1634 (requiring 'a plaintiff who has suffered an economic loss to provide a defendant with some indication of the loss and the causal connection that the plaintiff has in mind')") (emphasis added). The Ninth Circuit also added a new section entitled "Economic Loss":

> ***Plaintiffs' economic loss was not that they purchased stock at inflated prices; rather, their economic loss was the decline in their stock value that was the direct result of Daou's misrepresentations.*** *See Dura Pharms.,* 125 S. Ct. at 1631-32. Here, the TAC's assertions of a steep drop in Daou's stock price follow-

---

6. 125 S. Ct. at 1634. Although the Court did not expressly decide the issue, by their terms neither Rule 9(b) nor the PSLRA apply to the loss causation element of a Rule 10b-5 action. Rule 9(b) imposes a particularity requirement in only two specific instances. It states in full: "In all averments of fraud or mistake, the circumstances constituting fraud or mistake shall be stated with particularity. Malice, intent, knowledge, and other condition of mind of a person may be averred generally." The PSLRA similarly imposes particularized pleading requirements for only falsity (when false statements or omission, as opposed to fraudulent scheme, are alleged) and scienter allegations, not loss causation. *See* 15 U.S.C. § 78u-4(b)(1), (2); *see also Gebhardt v. ConAgra Foods, Inc.,* 335 F.3d 824, 830 n.3 (8th Cir. 2003) ("The new statute does not change traditional pleading rules with respect to" loss causation). The PSLRA expressly addresses loss causation only in the trial stage: "the plaintiff shall have the burden of proving that the act or omission of the defendant alleged to violate this title caused the loss for which the plaintiff seeks to recover damages." 15 U.S.C. § 78j-4(b)(4). For a scholarly analysis of the interplay between Rule 9(b) and the PSLRA, see Judge Scheindlin's opinion in *In re Initial Pub. Offering Sec. Litig.,* 241 F. Supp. 2d 281 (S.D.N.Y. 2003).
7. Defendants/Appellees/Cross-Appellant's Post-Appellate Brief Addressing The Impact On This Appeal Of The Supreme Court Decision In *Dura Pharmaceuticals, [sic] Inc. v. Broudo,* at 3, 8, *In re Daou Systems, Inc. Sec. Litig.* (9th Cir.) (Nos. 02-56989 and 02-57018).

> ing the revelation of Daou's true financial situation are sufficient to enable the complaint to survive a motion to dismiss under Federal Rule of Civil Procedure 12(b)(6).

2005 WL 1431833, at *16 (emphasis added).[8]

Judge Scheindlin also re-examined a prior opinion in *In re IPO* in light of *Dura.* In the court's initial opinion issued April 1, 2005 (just 18 days before the Supreme Court's *Dura* decision), the court predicted that "any ruling by the Supreme Court in *Dura Pharms.* will certainly affect the pleading standard for misrepresentation cases like this one." *In re Initial Pub. Offering Sec. Litig.,* 2005 WL 743550, at *6 n.68 (S.D.N.Y. Apr. 1, 2005). But, upon reconsideration after the *Dura* decision was published, Judge Scheindlin noted that "*Dura* itself does not define a pleading standard for loss causation; rather, it simply rejects the Ninth Circuit's standard as overly permissive," and concluded that the Second Circuit's loss causation standard "is undisturbed by *Dura.*" 2005 WL 1162445, at *3 n.23 (S.D.N.Y. May 6, 2005). As in *Daou Systems,* the outcome did not change after *Dura*, but the court "supplement[ed]" its loss causation analysis. *Id.* at *4. Using the Second Circuit analysis, in her supplemental opinion Judge Scheindlin found that the complaint's allegations were insufficient because they did not allege that, "at some point, the concealed scheme was disclosed to the market." *Id.* at *3.[90] She continued: "It is illustrative to consider what kind of event could have disclosed the actual fraud alleged, thereby permitting a determination of whether the alleged fraud actually caused any losses," and surmised that a single news article

---

8. A district court within the Ninth Circuit after *Dura* likewise found the complaint sufficiently alleged loss causation. In *In re Immune Response Sec. Litig.,* Case No. 01-1237 J (S.D. Cal. June 7, 2005), Judge Napoleon Jones denied defendants' motion to dismiss because, although *Dura* "reversed well-established Ninth Circuit case law regarding what is required to withstand a motion to dismiss on this issue," reviewed under Rule 8(a)(2)'s pleading standard, the complaint contained "the very allegations regarding share price decrease and public exposure to the truth the Supreme Court found lacking in the *Dura* complaint." *Id.* at 44-45. The court continued: "Moreover, the Complaint adequately notifies Defendants of the losses claimed and the causal connection between the losses and Defendants' allegedly fraudulent conduct. Whether the alleged omissions and misstatements actually were the cause-in-fact of the price of IRC stock raises an issue of fact and, as such, is a question properly reserved for a motion for summary judgment or for the trier of fact." *Id.* at 45.

9. Judges Stein and Kaplan, also sitting in the Southern District of New York, similarly cited *Dura* but then performed the loss causation analysis pursuant to the Second Circuit's prior decisions. *See Louros v. Kreicas,* 367 F. Supp. 2d 572, 592 (S.D.N.Y. Apr. 25, 2005) (denying summary judgment as to loss causation); *Dresner v. Utility.com., Inc.,* 2005 WL 1185636, at *19 (S.D.N.Y. May 18, 2005) (granting motion to dismiss).

stating, for example, that one of the defendants had engaged in the "common and deceptive practice of deliberately understating a company's expected earnings" in an effort to avoid missing estimates, "could have constituted a disclosing event." *Id.* at *4. But because the complaint alleged no such disclosures, Judge Scheindlin dismissed the complaint. *Ibid.*

The Sixth Circuit reached the same result in an unpublished decision after *Dura, D.E. & J. Ltd. P'ship v. Conaway,* 2005 WL 1386448 (6th Cir. June 10, 2005), a case brought against several former Kmart executives and PricewaterhouseCoopers. In affirming dismissal of the complaint, the Sixth Circuit reasoned that the complaint did "not differ in any material respect from Broudo's [in *Dura*]. Like Broudo, [plaintiff] did not plead that the alleged fraud became known to the market on any particular day, did not estimate the damages that the alleged fraud caused, and did not connect the alleged fraud with the ultimate disclosure or loss. Rather, the heart of [plaintiff's] causation theory looks remarkably like Broudo's allegations in his complaint." 2005 WL 1386448, at *5.[10]

The Sixth Circuit rejected plaintiffs' arguments that: (1) their complaint was materially different from the *Dura* complaint because the *Conaway* complaint alleged a stock drop following the company's disclosure that it had filed for reorganization under Chapter 11; and (2) the stock drop following the restatement announcement was sufficient, albeit not alleged in the complaint. The Sixth Circuit rejected both arguments because "[n]either of these observations (one in the complaint, the other on appeal) 'provide[d] the defendants with notice of what the relevant economic loss might be or of what the causal connection might be between the loss and the misrepresentation.'" *Id.* at *6 (quoting *Dura,* 125 S. Ct. at 1634). The court explained: "As to the bankruptcy filing, [plaintiff] never alleged that Kmart's bankruptcy announcement disclosed

---

10. Specifically, the *Conaway* complaint, echoing that in *Dura,* alleged only the following with respect to loss causation:

> Plaintiffs and the Class have suffered damages in that, in reliance on the integrity of the market, they paid artificially inflated prices for Kmart publicly traded securities. Plaintiffs and the Class would not have purchased Kmart publicly traded securities at the prices they paid, or at all, if they had been aware that the market prices had been artificially and falsely inflated by defendants' misleading statements. As a direct and proximate result of defendants' wrongful conduct, plaintiffs and the other members of the Class suffered damages in connection with their purchases of Kmart publicly traded securities during the class period.

Conaway, 2005 WL 1386448, at *5 (quoting complaint).

any prior misrepresentations to the market. . . . And, of course, the filing of a bankruptcy petition by itself does not a security fraud allegation make." *Id.* The court further explained, "[h]ere, [plaintiff] has done nothing more than note that a stock price dropped after a bankruptcy announcement, never alleging that the market's acknowledgment of prior misrepresentations caused that drop." *Id.* at *6.

The court further noted the complaint's failure to allege the five cent drop in Kmart's stock price the day Kmart announced its restatements on May 15, 2002. Implying that such allegations, if actually alleged in the complaint (rather than merely argued on appeal), would satisfy the pleading requirements, the court commented: "By failing even to note that Kmart's stock dropped in price after the company restated its financial records and by failing to present this argument to the district court, [plaintiff] simply never pleaded that the defendants' alleged misrepresentations caused economic losses on May 15, 2002." *Id.*

NOTES

NOTES

8

JUST HOW MUCH DAMAGE DID THOSE MISREPRESENTATIONS ACTUALLY CAUSE AND TO WHOM?: DAMAGES MEASUREMENT IN "FRAUD ON THE MARKET" SECURITIES CLASS ACTIONS

Daniel P. Lefler

Irell & Manella LLP

Allan W. Kleidon

Cornerstone Research

Mr. Lefler is Director of Irell & Manella's Securities Litigation Workgroup. Dr. Kleidon is Senior Vice President, Cornerstone Research and Lecturer in Finance, Graduate School of Business, Stanford University.

The views expressed herein are solely those of the authors and do not necessarily reflect the views of Irell & Manella LLP, Cornerstone Research or their clients.

Table of Contents

I. INTRODUCTION

The field of securities litigation has generated a well-developed jurisprudence in many areas (*e.g.*, pleading standards, class certification, scope of discovery). There are, however, relatively few judicial opinions addressing damages issues, specifically, how damages are to be calculated at trial. Given that most securities cases settle—and they used to settle well before trial—this relative paucity of case law is not surprising since there historically have been few pre-trial opportunities for parties to litigate the details of damages measurement.

This trend appears to be changing. Last term the United States Supreme Court articulated the standards for pleading and proving "loss causation" in its decision in *Dura Pharmaceuticals, Inc. v. Broudo*, 544 U.S. ___, 125 S. Ct. 1627 (2005). Additionally, a number of recent securities cases have proceeded to the brink of trial—or even into trial—before settling, and have produced a set of opinions that will shape the damages debate in future cases.

These new opinions touch on each of the three key issues in damages measurement: the measurement of per share damages, the proper method for calculating damages at the investor level, and the validity of using estimates of aggregate (or class-wide) damages at trial. This article will look at each of these issues in turn.

II. PER SHARE DAMAGES: HOW MUCH DAMAGE DID THE MISREPRESENTATIONS ACTUALLY CAUSE?

A. The Out-of-Pocket Measure

Until recently, most of the limited case law that does exist regarding damages measurement in open market securities fraud cases was focused on the out-of-pocket rule. The out-of-pocket rule, which is the traditional measure of damage in a common law fraud case, provides that the plaintiff may recover the difference between the price she paid for a security and the price she would have paid "but for" the fraud. *See, e.g.*, Restatement (Second) of Torts § 549; Cal. Civ. Code § 3343. In *Affiliated Ute Citizens of Utah v. United States*, 406 U.S. 128, 155 (1972), the Supreme Court adopted this measure of damages as appropriate for cases brought under Section 10(b) of the Securities Exchange Act of 1934 (the "1934 Act"). *Affiliated Ute,* however, was not a "fraud on the market" case, and it did not therefore address how the out-of-pocket rule should be or could be applied in open market fraud cases.[1] This question was thus left to the lower courts.

In what proved to be an influential concurring opinion in *Green v. Occidental Petroleum*, 541 F.2d 1335, 1344 (9th Cir. 1976), Judge Sneed argued that the out-of-pocket rule could be implemented in a "fraud on the market" case by creating a "value line." The "value line" would represent an expert's opinion regarding the fair price of the stock on each day of the class period "but for" the alleged fraud. Per share damages could then be computed by simply subtracting the actual stock price during the period of artificial inflation from the estimate of fair value.

Damages experts adopted this approach. Initially, plaintiffs' experts used the price at the end of the class period as the measurement of assumed fair value throughout the class period, and created a "value line" by simply "backcasting" the end price over the class period. A refinement to this simple "backcasting" approach adjusted the "value line" through time for movements in a broad index such as the NYSE or NASDAQ.

A more recent "backcasting" approach uses some elements of finance theory. Typically, the first step in this estimation process is to use a standard statistical tool known as regression analysis to isolate the portion of a firm's stock price movements that are attributable to company-specific information, as opposed to market-wide or industry information. The expert then uses the company-specific price decline on the day (or days) when information correcting the fraud entered the market as the basis for estimating the "value line." Say, for example, the firm-specific price decline was 10% on the day the truth entered the market. A typical "backcasting" approach used by plaintiffs' damages experts would estimate fair value at approximately 90% of the company's actual stock price throughout the period of the fraud. *See, generally,* Bradford Cornell and R. Gregory Morgan, "Using Finance Theory to Measure Damages in Fraud on the Market Cases," 37 U.C.L.A. Law Review 883 (1990). Damages ("inflation") would be estimated for each day during the class period by subtracting the estimated fair value from

1. In fact, the damages issue addressed in *Affiliated Ute* was whether the plaintiffs could recover more than the out-of-pocket measure. In *Affiliated Ute*, unlike the typical case, the plaintiffs sold securities at prices they claimed were artificially depressed by the defendants' omissions. The issue in *Affiliated Ute* was whether the plaintiffs could recover the amount of the defendants' benefit from the fraud if that amount exceeded the plaintiffs' out-of-pocket loss. The Court held that they could. *Affiliated Ute*, 406 U.S. at 155.

the actual price (less an adjustment if the shares were resold during the class period when the price was still inflated, as discussed below). In cases with multiple corrective disclosures a similar procedure would be adopted taking into account the firm-specific price reaction on the date of each disclosure.

B. But What About Loss Causation?

While the use of a "value line" approach to measure out-of-pocket loss (often based on "backcasting") was widespread, the case law also acknowledged that there are two elements of legal causation, "transaction causation" and "loss causation." *See, e.g.*, *Binder v. Gillespie*, 184 F.3d 1059 (9th Cir. 1999). "Transaction causation" was typically analogized to the tort law concept of "but for" causation, and "loss causation" was typically analogized to the concept of proximate causation. *Binder*, 184 F.3d at 1065-66.

The "value line" approach to damages measurement suggested by Judge Sneed in *Green* was centered around the concept of "but for" damages—that is, the goal of the "value line" approach was to measure damages based on what the company's stock price would have been without the fraud. Given that "but for" causation was typically equated with transaction causation, it was unclear what role loss causation played in the estimation of damages. This question gained in importance when Congress enacted the Private Securities Litigation Reform Act of 1995 ("PSLRA") explicitly establishing loss causation as a statutorily required element of a claim under Section 10 of the 1934 Act.[2]

Thereafter, several Courts of Appeals issued decisions holding that proof that a stock price was inflated at the time of purchase is not sufficient to satisfy the loss causation requirement. *See, e.g.*, *Emergent Capital Investment Management, LLC v. Stonepath Group, Inc.*, 343 F.3d 189 (2d Cir. 2003); *Semerenko v. Cendant Corp*, 223 F.3d 165 (3d Cir. 2000); *Robbins v. Koger Properties, Inc.*, 116 F.3d 1441 (11th Cir. 1997). The Ninth Circuit, however, reached the opposite conclusion in its opinion in *Broudo v. Dura Pharmaceuticals*, 339 F.3d 993 (9th Cir. 2003). This circuit split set the stage for the Supreme Court's decision in *Dura*.

---

2. *See* 15 U.S.C. § 78u-4(b)(4) ("[i]n any private action arising under this title, the plaintiff shall have the burden of proving that the act or omission of the defendant alleged to violate this title caused the loss for which the plaintiff seeks to recover damages").

C. The Supreme Court's Decision In *Dura Pharmaceuticals*

Dura was a private securities class action arising under Rule 10b-5, in which the plaintiffs claimed that a company's stock price had been artificially inflated pursuant to a "fraud on the market." *Dura Pharmaceuticals, Inc. v. Broudo*, 544 U.S. ___, 125 S. Ct. 1627, 1631 (2005). (A copy of the *Dura* opinion is reproduced as Exhibit 1). The plaintiffs in *Dura* alleged, among other things, that a drug company made misstatements about a new drug application with the FDA. *Id.* at 1630. The district court dismissed these allegations on loss causation grounds. The class period ended in February 1998, but the FDA's rejection of the new drug was not known or disclosed to the market until about eight months later in November 1998. The district court therefore concluded that the complaint failed to allege a causal connection between the claimed fraud and the plaintiffs' loss. *Id.* The plaintiffs argued that loss causation existed because the complaint alleged that at the time of purchase the stock price was artificially inflated by the statements about the FDA application. *Id.* The district court held that this allegation was insufficient to satisfy the loss causation requirement and dismissed the complaint.

The Ninth Circuit reversed. The Court of Appeals held that "plaintiffs establish loss causation if they have shown that the price *on the date of purchase* was inflated because of the misrepresentation." *Broudo v. Dura Pharmaceuticals, Inc.*, 339 F.3d 933, 938 (9th Cir. 2003) (emphasis added). The Court of Appeals therefore concluded that a plaintiff need not prove that the revelation of the fraud caused the company's stock price to decline in order to establish a causal link between the fraud and the damages.

The Supreme Court reversed the Ninth Circuit in a unanimous opinion. The Court held that a plaintiff *cannot* satisfy the requirement of "loss causation" "simply by . . . establishing that the price of the security *on the date of purchase* was inflated because of the misrepresentation." *Dura*, 125 S. Ct. at 1629 (emphasis in original; internal quotations omitted).

The Court began its analysis by pointing out that an investor who purchases stock at an inflated price does not have any damages at the time of purchase. The Court explained that "as a matter of pure logic, at the moment the transaction takes place, the plaintiff has suffered no loss; the inflated purchase payment is offset by ownership of a share that *at that instant* possesses equivalent value." *Id.* at 1631 (emphasis in original). The Court pointed out that if "the purchaser sells the shares quickly before the relevant truth begins to leak out, the misrepresentation will not have led to any loss." *Id.*

Moreover, the Court noted, even if the price of the stock were to decline after some disclosure correcting the fraud, it does not necessarily follow that the plaintiff has suffered a loss that was caused by the claimed fraud. The Court explained that:

> If the purchaser sells later after the truth makes its way into the market place, an initially inflated purchase price *might* mean a later loss. But that is far from inevitably so. When the purchaser subsequently resells such shares, even at a lower price, that lower price may reflect, not the earlier misrepresentation, but changed economic circumstances, changed investor expectations, new industry-specific or firm-specific facts, conditions, or other events, which taken separately or together account for some or all of that lower price.

Id. at 1632 (emphasis in original).

Given that stock prices can decline for a multitude of reasons, and given that the 1934 Act "expressly imposes on plaintiffs 'the burden of proving' that the defendant's misrepresentations 'caused the loss for which the plaintiff seeks to recover,'" *id.* at 1633, the Court held that a plaintiff can satisfy the loss causation requirement *only* by proving that the claimed misrepresentations were the "proximate cause" of an "economic loss." *Id.* The Court pointed out that the "judicial consensus" for establishing proximate cause "says that a person who misrepresents the financial condition of a corporation in order to sell its stock becomes liable to a relying purchaser for the loss the purchaser sustains *when the facts become generally known and as a result share value depreciates.*" *Id.* at 1633 (internal quotes, ellipsis and citation omitted; emphasis added).[3]

The Court explained that this standard is important in light of the policy objectives of the securities laws. The Court pointed out that pri-

---

3. The Court left open the possibility that proximate cause might be shown in some cases through other types of proof. This makes sense given that Section 10(b) and Rule 10b-5 prohibit a wide range of manipulative and deceptive practices, and give rise to various types of criminal, regulatory and civil proceedings. Nevertheless, in a private class action that is based on the "fraud on the market" theory, it is difficult to see how the proximate cause standard could be met by any proof other than that described by the Supreme Court—*i.e.*, disclosure of corrective information accompanied by a price decline. Injury in a "fraud on the market" case is established by showing that the stock's price deviated from its fair value due to misinformation in the marketplace. Therefore, a causal connection between misrepresentation (or omission) and loss in such a case would appear to require a corrective disclosure accompanied by a price change.

vate lawsuits are "available, not to provide investors with broad insurance against market losses, but to protect them against those economic losses that misrepresentations *actually cause*." *Id.* (emphasis added). Because recoverable damages are limited to losses that were *actually caused* in the real world by the claimed misrepresentations, the question of what the stock price *would have been* on the date of purchase "but for" the claimed fraud is not by itself the proper measure of recovery. As the Supreme Court expressly held, "an inflated purchase price will not itself constitute or proximately cause the relevant economic loss." *Id.* at 1631. In short, the key consideration for loss causation purposes is what losses were actually sustained in the real world based on the facts that actually occurred, not what the company's stock price would have been had the facts been different.

D. *Dura's* Implications

1. In-And-Out Trades Before The First Corrective Disclosures Do Not Result In Any Loss Caused By The Fraud

Dura expressly precludes any recovery based on stock price declines that occur before the market learned about the fraud. 125 S. Ct. at 1632. This is a sensible holding since any such price decline necessarily resulted from non-fraud-related factors. Investors are supposed to bear non-fraud-related investment risks and therefore recovery for such declines should be precluded. *Id.* at 1633 (private lawsuits are "available, not to provide investors with broad insurance against market losses, but to protect them against those economic losses that misrepresentations actually cause").

Dura, therefore, leaves little room for debate that an in-and-out investor—*i.e.*, an investor who purchased and then resold securities during the class period—will have no recoverable damages if his sales occurred before the first corrective disclosure.[4] This rule can have a significant impact on damages calculations. Indeed, in cases where there is only one corrective disclosure at the end of the class period, this rule effectively means that there are no recoverable in-and-out damages.

---

4. Thus, the statement of the court in *Wool v. Tandem Computers,* 818 F.2d 1433, 1437 (9th Cir. 1987), that "an in-and-out trader . . . may suffer recoverable damages under the out-of-pocket rule even in the absence of corrective disclosures" is no longer good law.

2. *Damages Must Be Measured In Dollar Terms, Not Percentage Terms*

There has been an ongoing debate between plaintiffs' experts and defendants' experts about whether damages should be measured in percentage terms or in dollar terms. In cases where stock prices are declining over the class period—the pattern in virtually all of the cases contemporaneous with the bursting of the Internet "bubble"—use of a percentage method typically will result in much larger damages estimates.

An example is useful to illustrate the point. Assume that a company's stock is trading at $50, and that the residual price drop (that is, the price drop controlling for market and industry forces) is $5 when the "truth" about a fraud is revealed. Investors who bought while the stock was inflated suffered a $5 loss that was actually caused by the fraud.

Converting that $5 loss into percentage terms and using the percentage to measure purchase price inflation will result in a windfall if the company's stock price was declining through the class period. In percentage terms, the $5 price drop is 10%. Assume that thirty days earlier during the class period and before any corrective disclosure, the company's stock price was $100. Measuring purchase price inflation in percentage terms will result in $10 of inflation per share, not $5.

Recovery of $10 in this example is flatly inconsistent with the Supreme Court's ruling in *Dura* because the additional five dollars in inflation that results from using a percentage approach was not "actually caused" by the fraud. That additional inflation results solely from the drop in price from $100 to $50—a price decline that, by definition, was based on factors other than the claimed fraud since it occurred before any alleged corrective disclosure. As the Supreme Court noted, lower stock prices can result from "changed economic circumstances, changed investor expectations, new industry-specific or firm-specific facts, conditions, or other events." *Dura*, 125 S. Ct. at 1632. Because it awards recoveries based on price declines that are unrelated to the fraud, the percentage approach introduces through the back door price declines that the Supreme Court expressly held in *Dura* do not meet the test for "loss causation."

Plaintiffs' experts typically argue that a percentage approach is correct because as a matter of economics, stock prices react to new information in percentage terms. To refer back to our hypothetical example, plaintiffs would argue that if the revelation of the "truth" caused a 10% residual decline when the stock price was $50 (a $5 drop), that same information would have caused a 10% residual decline thirty days earlier when the stock price was $100 (a $10 drop), had it been disclosed earlier. Whether or not this argument is correct as a matter of economics (and this is often a matter of dispute between experts), after *Dura* it should be legally irrelevant to the question of what loss was caused by a claimed fraud. Even if the price reaction in dollar terms would have been larger had the facts been different on the date of purchase, under *Dura*, the principle of loss causation limits recovery to the price reaction that *actually occurred* at the time of the disclosure (or disclosures) that actually occurred. The "but for" argument from economics is simply not the legal measure of recovery.

In short, a percentage methodology that increases recovery based on stock price declines that are not fraud-related is inconsistent with *Dura*. This is an enormously important issue to any company facing a lawsuit during a period when its stock price was generally declining—the pattern observed in most cases with class periods that include the severe market declines of 2000 and 2001.

3. Any Observed Price Decline Must Be Allocated Across Inflating Events

Another implication of the *Dura* decision is the need to allocate any loss resulting from corrective disclosures across the inflationary events.

Consider the following example. XYZ Corp. issues first quarter financial statements that overstate earnings by $10 million. The second quarter financial statements overstate earnings by $40 million, and the third quarter financial statements overstate earnings by $20 million. In the fourth quarter, the fraud is discovered and the entire $70 million in earnings overstatement from the previous three quarters is revealed on one day. The residual stock price drop—after controlling for market and industry factors—is $10 per share.

The $10 stock price drop is not the appropriate damages award for all investors in this case. Logic dictates that an investor who purchased after the first quarter earnings announcement (when the total misstatement was $10 million), but before the second quarter earnings announcement suffered a smaller loss than an investor who purchased after the third quarter financial statements (when the total earnings misstatement had grown to $70 million), but before XYZ Corp. disclosed the fraud. Since *Dura* limits recovery to losses "actually cause[d]" by the fraud, 125 S. Ct. at 1633, the losses recoverable by the first investor should be less than the losses recoverable by the second.

This notion is supported by case law over the fairness of plans of allocation. For example, the court in *In re California Micro Devices Sec. Litig.*, 965 F. Supp. 1327 (N.D. Cal. 1997), explained that the damages expert:

> used the actual amount of the price declines [that occurred on corrective disclosure dates] as his measure of total inflation.
>
> Because a number of misstatements were made over a period of months, [the expert] needed to apportion the total inflation among the various alleged misstatements. Each misstatement involved an overstatement of earnings. [The expert's] method assumed that the percentage of the total inflation attributable to a given misstatement was the same as that statement's share of the total overstatement of earnings. Thus, if earnings were overstated by ten dollars per share over the class period and a single quarterly announcement overstated earnings by one dollar, ten percent of the total inflation was attributed to that announcement.

965 F. Supp. at 1333 (emphasis added); *see also In re Cendant Corp. Sec. Litig.*, 109 F. Supp. 2d 235, 256 (D.N.J. 2000) (approving settlement plan of allocation where total estimated inflation was allocated over time based on "the actual amount by which each earnings release was overstated over the three year [class] period.") In both *California Micro Devices* and *Cendant* that fact that the plan of allocation took into account the different quantum of loss suffered by purchasers at different times in the class period was an element of the plan's overall fairness.

Dura's requirement that recoverable losses be limited to loss actually caused by the fraud, provides additional support for the argument that experts must allocate the claimed dollar loss resulting from corrective disclosures over the claimed inflationary events. This would require a higher degree of specificity in damages opinions than has generally been provided in the past.

4. Are Plaintiffs' Counsel Required To Prepare An Event Study Prior to Filing A Securities Fraud Complaint?

Dura's explicit recognition that stock prices fluctuate based on many non-fraud-related factors raises potential hazards for plaintiffs' counsel. The mere fact that a company's stock price declined on a day when information correcting earlier disclosures is disseminated is arguably not a sufficient basis for the filing of a complaint.

Say, for example, a complaint were filed in a case alleging a single corrective disclosure. Assume further that the corrective disclosure did not result in a statistically significant change in the company's stock price—that is, the price reaction was within a normal range when controlling for market and industry factors. In such a case, a defendant could argue that plaintiffs' counsel failed to conduct a pre-suit investigation sufficient to comply with Rule 11 of the Federal Rules of Civil Procedure.

This possibility, when coupled with the PSLRA's requirement that the district court issue findings regarding Rule 11 compliance "upon the final adjudication" of a private securities case, 15 U.S.C. § 78u-4(c), suggests that plaintiffs' counsel would be well-advised in many cases to prepare an event study even before the filing of a complaint. In some cases the causal relationship between corrective disclosures and price declines will be obvious, but that is not always so.

5. Does Dura Effectively Overrule The Out-Of-Pocket Measure Of Damages?

Dura does not abolish the out-of-pocket measure of damages. Instead, *Dura* simply establishes that the principle of loss causation limits recovery in cases where the loss that actually results from a fraud is less than the out-of-pocket measure. That is why the Supreme Court said in *Dura* that "an inflated purchase price will not *itself* constitute or proximately cause the relevant economic loss." 125 S. Ct. at 1631 (emphasis added). The out-of-pocket measurement determines the amount of inflation on the date of purchase. That is not *itself* the relevant economic loss because the principle of loss causation requires proof of a causal connection between the claimed fraud and the actual economic loss.

The relationship between the out-of-pocket measure and the principle of loss causations was explained by the Eleventh Circuit in *Robbins*—a case that the Supreme Court cited in *Dura*. *See* 125 S. Ct. at 1630, 1633. Echoing the distinction between "damages" and "recovery" that is found in Section 11 of the Securities Act of 1933, the court in *Robbins* noted that "[t]he proper measure of damages utilizes the out-of-pocket rule." 116 F.3d at 1447 n.5. Nevertheless, "in determining recoverable damages," the court explained, "contributing forces" to an "investment's decline in value" that are not related to the fraud, "must be isolated and removed." *Id.* As the court pointed out, "[p]roof of damages under the out-of-pocket rule is not proof of loss causation." *Id.*

The fact that loss causation limits recoveries in cases where the out-of-pocket measure is greater than the loss actually caused does not mean that the out-of-pocket measure has been abolished. A simple hypothetical illustrates the point. Assume that a company intentionally misstated its earnings and the result was $5 in purchase price inflation. Assume that Investor 1 purchased when inflation was $5. Assume that a quarter later, the company intentionally misstated earnings again, causing inflation to rise to $10. Investor 2 purchased when inflation was $10. When the fraud was revealed, the price dropped by $10. Investor 1 has an out-of-pocket (or "but for") loss of $5. He is not entitled to recover $10, even though that is the amount of the price drop on the date of the corrective disclosure. His recovery is limited to his out-of-pocket loss, or $5. Investor 2 recovers $10. His out-of-pocket loss was $10, and he actually suffered that loss when the truth about the fraud was revealed and the stock price declined by $10.

In sum, *Dura* has important implications in measuring per share damages. Limiting recoveries based on *Dura*'s loss causation principles can have a significant impact, particularly in cases involving significant non-fraud-related market declines.

III. COMPUTING LOSS AT THE INVESTOR LEVEL: WHO ACTUALLY LOST MONEY DUE TO THE FRAUD, AND HOW IS THAT LOSS MEASURED?

The methodologies and procedures required for establishing per share damages do not by themselves determine the recovery of any particular investor, let alone the total recovery of all investors in the aggregate. Proceeding from per share damages estimates to the actual recoveries due to actual investors, if any, requires consideration of other damages-related legal rules. This is a subject that, again, has received little attention in the case law.

Specifically, it is a fundamental tenet of tort law that a plaintiff can recover only if he was harmed by the defendant's wrongdoing. In the securities litigation context, therefore, the first step in evaluating the recovery of any particular investor (assuming liability and a determination of per share damages) should be to determine whether that investor was a net winner or a net loser from the fraud. In simple terms, purchases at inflated prices generate inflation losses, while sales from inflated prices generate inflation gains. Any investor whose inflation gains exceed inflation losses, has no damages. As the court explained in *Arenson v. Broadcom Corporation*, No. SA CV 02-301 GLT, 2004 WL 2353646 (C.D. Cal. Dec. 6, 2004) (a copy of the *Arenson* opinion is reproduced as Exhibit 2):

> The authority is clear: where a plaintiff engages in multiple purchases and sales during the period in which the stock is inflated, the proper damages methodology is to take all the inflation losses resulting from all purchases at the inflated price and reduce this amount by all the inflation gain resulting from all sales at the inflated price.

Id. at *2.[5] As basic as the proposition is, it has often been overlooked in the class action securities litigation context, probably due to the widespread use of trading models which do not account for inflationary gains to estimate aggregate damages.

The calculation described in the *Arenson* case is only the first step in determining recoverable damages. The difference between total inflationary loss and total inflationary gain ("net inflationary loss") represents an investor's maximum possible recovery. Obviously, any investor with a negative net inflationary loss (*i.e.*, a net inflationary gain) benefited from the fraud and is entitled to no recovery whatsoever (as was the case for many of the plaintiffs in *Arenson*).

To determine the proper amount of recovery, if any, a separate analysis should be conducted applying *Dura*'s loss causation rules. This requires exclusion of any in-and-out trades prior to the first corrective disclosure.[6] Once these in-and-out trades have been excluded, recoverable loss must be measured using the lower of (i) purchase price inflation (*i.e.*, the out-of-pocket measure); or (ii) the amount of the price decline occurring on the date of the pertinent corrective disclosure or disclosures as allocated across purchase dates.

---

5. A team of lawyers at Irell & Manella LLP, including Mr. Lefler, represented Broadcom in the *Arenson* matter, as well as in the *In Re Broadcom* lawsuit referred to below. A team of professionals at Cornerstone Research, including Dr. Kleidon, provided consulting support in both cases.
6. This process requires a matching assumption to determine which sales are attributable to which purchases. The most logical matching assumption is the last-in-first-out assumption ("LIFO"), in which each share sold is matched up to the last share purchased. Another possible matching assumption would be first-in-first-out ("FIFO"), considering only transactions that occurred after the beginning of the class period.

The final step should be to compare the results of the prior two analyses. The investor recovers the lesser of his net inflationary loss or his loss applying *Dura*'s loss causation standards (subject, of course, to the PSLRA bounceback rule).

IV. ARE AGGREGATE DAMAGES MODELS ADMISSIBLE AT TRIAL?

Determining the amount of damages caused by a fraud on a per share basis does not, by itself, reveal the total amount of damages suffered by a class of purchasers. Making that determination with precision would require access to the actual trading records of the class members so that the type of analysis described in Section III could be performed on an investor-by-investor basis and then totaled.

Typically, however, plaintiffs are eager to present the jury with expert testimony concerning the total amount of damages suffered by the class.[7] In order to arrive at an estimate of aggregate damages, plaintiffs' experts use stock trading models that purport to estimate trading activity for the class as a whole at the aggregate level.

While trading models have their uses (particularly in the context of valuing a case for settlement purposes), whether they are sufficiently reliable to be introduced into evidence before a jury has long been a hard-fought issue. In particular, defendants have argued that stock trading models lack sufficient indicia of reliability to pass muster under the Supreme Court's decisions in *Daubert v. Merrell Dow Pharms., Inc.*, 509 U.S. 579 (1993) and *Kumho Tire Co. Ltd. v. Carmichael*, 526 U.S. 137 (1999).

In *Kaufman v. Motorola, Inc.*, No. 95 C 1069, 2000 WL 1506892 (N.D. Ill. Sept. 21, 2000), the court granted a *Daubert* motion precluding the plaintiffs' expert from offering testimony on class-wide damages based on an early trading model known as the proportional trading model. The court cited *Daubert*'s four factors—(1) whether the theory or technique can be and has been tested; (2) whether the technique or theory has

7. Plaintiffs' counsel might argue from the "common fund" cases that their fee award can be based on the jury's aggregate damages award. *See The Boeing Co. v. Van Gemert*, 444 U.S. 472 (1980). This argument is probably incorrect in securities cases. Pursuant to 15 U.S.C. § 78u-4(a)(6), attorney fee awards in 1934 Act class action cases are restricted to "a reasonable percentage of the amount of any damages and prejudgment interest actually paid to the class." Therefore, fee awards should be calculated based on the amounts actually paid to class members, not based on estimated aggregate damages awarded by juries.

been subject to peer review and publication; (3) the known or potential rate of error, and (4) the 'general acceptance' of the theory.

The court concluded that "[t]he proportional trading model does not meet *any* of the *Daubert* standards." *Id.* at *2 (emphasis added). To the contrary, the court noted that "the proportional trading model has never been tested against reality" and that the plaintiffs' expert in that case candidly admitted that "there was no way to actually test the reliability of the proportional trading model." *Id.* Deciding to exclude the model from the trial, the court explained that "the proportional trading model has never been accepted by professional economists. It seems to be a theory developed more for securities litigation than anything else." *Id.*

Since the *Kaufman* decision, common stock trading models have been excluded from trials in a number of cases including:

- *In re Clarent Corporation Sec. Litig.*, C-01-3361 CRB (N.D. Cal.);
- *Employer-Teamsters Joint Council No. 84 Pension Trust Fund v. America West Holdings Corp.*, CV-99-399-PHX-EHC(OMP), (D. Ariz.); and
- *In re Raytheon Company Sec. Litig.*, C.A. No. 99-12142 PBS (D. Mass.).[8]

The *Clarent*, *America West* and *Raytheon*, decisions did not result in formal written opinions, but reliability concerns were expressly mentioned at *Daubert* hearings in both the *Clarent* and *Raytheon* cases.[9]

There are, however, cases that have ruled admissible aggregate damages testimony premised on the output from a trading model, including:

- *In re Oxford Health Plans, Inc. Sec. Litig.*, 244 F. Supp. 2d 247, 252 (S.D.N.Y. 2003); and

---

8. In *Raytheon,* the court ruled on a motion by the company that the plaintiffs' expert would not be permitted to offer aggregate damages testimony at trial based on a trading model that used a statistical model known as the Weibull curve. Thereafter, the company settled and the auditors argued that the PSLRA's joint and several liability rules require aggregate damages testimony (a highly debatable proposition which, to our knowledge, has not been adopted by any court). Based on the position taken by the auditor the court suggested that it might admit aggregate testimony based on a different trading model. The auditor settled shortly thereafter and before the issue was definitively resolved.
9. A trading model was also excluded in *Bell v. Fore Systems, Inc.*, No. Civ. 97-1265, 2002 WL 32097540 at * 5 (W.D. Pa. Aug. 2, 2002). The court in *Bell*, however, did not reach *Daubert* issues. Instead, the court concluded that the trading model was inconsistent with the 90-day bounceback calculation required by the PSLRA, and therefore excluded the model on legal grounds.

- *In re Worldcom Inc., Sec. Litig.*, No. 02 Civ. 3288 DLC, 2005 WL 375313 (S.D.N.Y. Feb. 17. 2005).

The courts in *Oxford* and *Worldcom*, however, both concluded that if the judgment based on the aggregate damages estimate exceeded the amount ultimately claimed by class members, the defendants would be entitled to a refund of the excess. *Oxford*, 244 F. Supp. at 252; *In re Worldcom Inc., Sec. Litig.*, No. 02 Civ. 3288 DLC, 2005 WL 491397, *3 (S.D.N.Y. Feb. 17. 2005). Therefore, even in the cases where aggregate damages testimony has been ruled admissible, the trading model would not necessarily establish the total amount of the defendants' liability. As a practical matter the aggregate award would function as a cap.

As of this writing, the most recent case considering the admissibility of a common stock trading model is *In re Broadcom Corporation Sec. Litig.*, No. SA CV 01-275 GLT, 2005 WL 1403756 (C.D. Cal. June 3, 2005) (a copy of the *In re Broadcom* opinion is reproduced as Exhibit 3). The model at issue in *Broadcom* was a multi-trader model, not the earlier proportional trader model that was excluded in *Kaufman*. Following a two-day evidentiary hearing concerning the reliability of the multi-trader model, the court in *Broadcom* concluded that:

> the proposed trading model probably does not satisfy the *Daubert* test for submission to the jury. The technique has not been tested against "real world" conditions, and probably cannot be so tested unless a different set of test protocols is established. It has not been subjected to the sort of critical peer review and publication that one would expect as a prerequisite for jury acceptance. The potential error rate is highly questionable, and is based on a set of criteria that undermines the claimed error rate as being truly representative of the facts sought to be proved. Although held out by litigation professionals as useful in securities litigation, most notably as a settlement aid, the technique is not generally accepted in what is the relevant scientific community—professional economists.

2005 WL 1403756, at *2.

In addition to these reliability concerns, the court in *Broadcom* noted that an aggregate damages award based on estimates derived from a trading model is of limited utility given that the precise amount of damages to be paid to the class can be determined through the claims process—a process that is required in all circumstances to distribute any recovery. The court explained that "[t]he Court need not use a proof method of questionable reliability when an alternative, completely reliable method is available through the claims administration process." *Id.* at *3.

In sum, while there are cases going both ways, courts appear to be increasingly willing to exclude aggregate damages testimony that is premised on common stock trading models. For the reasons explained in the recent *Broadcom* opinion, this trend to exclude aggregate damages estimates is, in the authors' opinion, the better reasoned view.

V. CONCLUSION

While the jurisprudence concerning damages measurement in open-market class action securities cases is not well-developed, recent cases have touched on key issues that will shape the debate into the future.

In particular, the Supreme Court's articulation of loss causation standards in *Dura* should have a significant impact on the estimation of per share damages in many cases. In addition, recent case law concerning the calculation of damages at the investor level and the admissibility of aggregate damages testimony suggests that determining a total amount of damages for a class in the aggregate in a trial setting may be more difficult than has been assumed in the past.

H

Briefs and Other Related Documents

Supreme Court of the United States
DURA PHARMACEUTICALS, INC., et al.,
Petitioners,
v.
Michael BROUDO et al.
No. 03-932.

Argued Jan. 12, 2005.
Decided April 19, 2005.

Background: Purchasers of stock in pharmaceutical company brought securities fraud action against company and certain managers and directors, alleging that defendants' false statements regarding expected future Food and Drug Administration (FDA) approval of a new asthmatic spray device artificially inflated price of stock. The United States District Court for the Southern District of California, 2000 WL 33176043, M. James Lorenz, J., dismissed without prejudice, and following filing of amended complaint dismissed with prejudice. Purchaser appealed. The Court of Appeals, 339 F.3d 933, reversed and remanded. Certiorari was granted.

Holdings: The Supreme Court, Justice Breyer, held that:
(1) an investor may not establish loss causation by alleging that security price was inflated because of misrepresentation, and
(2) investors' allegations were insufficient to state fraud claim.
Reversed and remanded.

West Headnotes

[1] Securities Regulation 🔑60.47
349Bk60.47
An investor claiming securities fraud under the Securities Exchange Act cannot satisfy the requirement of proving that the fraud caused an economic loss simply by alleging in the complaint, and subsequently establishing, that the price of the security on the date of purchase was inflated because of the misrepresentation. Securities Exchange Act of 1934, § 21D(b)(4), as amended, 15 U.S.C.A. § 78u-4(b)(4).

[2] Securities Regulation 🔑60.53
349Bk60.53
Investors' allegations that they paid artificially inflated prices for securities of pharmaceutical company, due to false statements regarding expected future Food and Drug Administration (FDA) approval of a new asthmatic spray device, and suffered damages, implying that the investors' loss consisted of the artificially inflated purchase price, were insufficient to state securities fraud claim under Securities Exchange Act; investors failed to claim that share price fell significantly after truth became known. Securities Exchange Act of 1934, § 21D(b)(4), as amended, 15 U.S.C.A. § 78u-4(b)(4).

***1628** Syllabus [FN*]

FN* The syllabus constitutes no part of the opinion of the Court but has been prepared by the Reporter of Decisions for the convenience of the reader. See *United States v. Detroit Timber & Lumber Co.,* 200 U.S. 321, 337, 26 S.Ct. 282, 50 L.Ed. 499.

Respondents filed a securities fraud class action, alleging that petitioners, Dura Pharmaceuticals, Inc., and some of its managers and directors (hereinafter Dura), made, *inter alia,* misrepresentations about future Food and Drug Administration approval of a new asthmatic spray device, leading respondents to purchase Dura securities at an artificially inflated price. In dismissing, the District Court found that the complaint failed adequately to allege "loss causation"--*i.e.,* a causal connection between the spray device misrepresentation and the economic loss, 15 U.S.C. § 78u-4(b)(4). The Ninth Circuit reversed, finding that a plaintiff can satisfy the loss causation requirement simply by alleging that a security's price at the time of purchase was inflated because of the misrepresentation.

Held:

1. An inflated purchase price will not by itself constitute or proximately cause the relevant economic loss needed to allege and prove "loss causation." The basic elements of a private securities fraud action--which resembles a common-law tort action for deceit and misrepresentation--include, as relevant here, economic loss and "loss causation." The Ninth Circuit erred in following an inflated purchase price approach to showing causation and loss. First, as a matter of pure logic, the moment the transaction takes place, the plaintiff has suffered no loss because the inflated purchase price is offset by ownership of a share that possesses equivalent value at that instant.

And the logical link between the inflated purchase price and any later economic loss is not invariably strong, since other factors may affect the price. Thus, the most logic alone permits this Court to say is that the inflated purchase price suggests that misrepresentation "touches upon" a later economic loss, as the Ninth Circuit found. However, to touch upon a loss is not to *cause* a loss, as 15 U.S.C. § 78u-4(b)(4) requires. The Ninth Circuit's holding also is not supported by precedent. The common-law deceit and misrepresentation actions that private securities fraud actions resemble require a plaintiff to show not only that had he known the truth he would not have acted, but also that he suffered actual economic loss. Nor can the holding below be reconciled with the views of other Courts of Appeals, which have rejected the inflated purchase price approach to showing loss causation. Finally, the Ninth Circuit's approach is inconsistent with an important securities law objective. The securities laws make clear Congress' intent to permit private securities fraud actions only where plaintiffs adequately allege and prove the ***1629** traditional elements of cause and loss, but the Ninth Circuit's approach would allow recovery where a misrepresentation leads to an inflated purchase price, but does not proximately cause any economic loss. Pp. 1630- 1634.

2. Respondents' complaint was legally insufficient in respect to its allegation of "loss causation." While Federal Rule of Civil Procedure Rule 8(a)(2) requires only a "short and plain statement of the claim showing that the pleader is entitled to relief," and while the Court assumes that neither the Rules nor the securities statutes place any further requirement in respect to the pleading, the "short and plain statement" must give the defendant "fair notice of what the plaintiff's claim is and the grounds upon which it rests," *Conley v. Gibson,* 355 U.S. 41, 47, 78 S.Ct. 99, 2 L.Ed.2d 80. The complaint here contains only respondents' allegation that their loss consisted of artificially inflated purchase prices. However, as this Court has concluded here, such a price is not itself a relevant economic loss. And the complaint nowhere else provides Dura with notice of what the relevant loss might be or of what the causal connection might be between that loss and the misrepresentation. Ordinary pleading rules are not meant to impose a great burden on a plaintiff, but it should not prove burdensome for a plaintiff suffering economic loss to provide a defendant with some indication of the loss and the causal connection that the plaintiff has in mind. Allowing a plaintiff to forgo giving any indication of the economic loss and proximate cause would bring about the very sort of harm the securities statutes seek to avoid, namely the abusive practice of filing lawsuits with only a faint hope that discovery might lead to some plausible cause of action. Pp. 1634-1635.

339 F.3d 933, reversed and remanded.

BREYER, J., delivered the opinion for a unanimous Court.

Thomas G. Hungar, for United States as amicus curiae, by special leave of the Court, supporting the petitioners.

Patrick J. Coughlin, for respondents.

William F. Sullivan, Counsel of Record, Christopher H. McGrath, Tracey L. DeLange, Paul, Hastings, Janofsky & Walker, LLP, San Diego, CA, Attorneys for Petitioners.

Justice BREYER delivered the opinion of the Court.

A private plaintiff who claims securities fraud must prove that the defendant's fraud caused an economic loss. 109 Stat. 747, 15 U.S.C. § 78u-4(b)(4). We consider a Ninth Circuit holding that a plaintiff can satisfy this requirement--a requirement that courts call "loss causation"--simply by alleging in the complaint and subsequently establishing that "the price" of the security "*on the date of purchase* was inflated because of the misrepresentation." 339 F.3d 933, 938 (9th Cir.2003) (internal quotation marks omitted). In our view, the Ninth Circuit is wrong, both in respect to what a plaintiff must prove and in respect to what the plaintiffs' complaint here must allege.

I

Respondents are individuals who bought stock in Dura Pharmaceuticals, Inc., on the public securities market between April 15, 1997, and February 24, 1998. They have brought this securities fraud class action against Dura and some of its managers ***1630** and directors (hereinafter Dura) in federal court. In respect to the question before us, their detailed amended (181 paragraph) complaint makes substantially the following allegations:

(1) Before and during the purchase period, Dura (or its officials) made false statements concerning both Dura's drug profits and future Food and Drug Administration (FDA) approval of a new asthmatic spray device. See, *e.g.,* App. 45a, 55a,

89a.

(2) In respect to drug profits, Dura falsely claimed that it expected that its drug sales would prove profitable. See, *e.g., id.,* at 66a-69a.

(3) In respect to the asthmatic spray device, Dura falsely claimed that it expected the FDA would soon grant its approval. See, *e.g., id.,* at 89a-90a, 103a-104a.

(4) On the last day of the purchase period, February 24, 1998, Dura announced that its earnings would be lower than expected, principally due to slow drug sales. *Id.,* at 51a.

(5) The next day Dura's shares lost almost half their value (falling from about $39 per share to about $21). *Ibid.*

(6) About eight months later (in November 1998), Dura announced that the FDA would not approve Dura's new asthmatic spray device. *Id.,* at 110a.

(7) The next day Dura's share price temporarily fell but almost fully recovered within one week. *Id.,* at 156a.

Most importantly, the complaint says the following (and nothing significantly more than the following) about economic losses attributable to the spray device misstatement: *"In reliance on the integrity of the market, [the plaintiffs] ... paid artificially inflated prices for Dura securities" and the plaintiffs suffered "damage[s]" thereby. Id.,* at 139a (emphasis added).

The District Court dismissed the complaint. In respect to the plaintiffs' drug-profitability claim, it held that the complaint failed adequately to allege an appropriate state of mind, *i.e.,* that defendants had acted knowingly, or the like. In respect to the plaintiffs' spray device claim, it held that the complaint failed adequately to allege "loss causation."

The Court of Appeals for the Ninth Circuit reversed. In the portion of the court's decision now before us--the portion that concerns the spray device claim--the Circuit held that the complaint adequately alleged "loss causation." The Circuit wrote that "plaintiffs establish loss causation if they have shown that the price *on the date of purchase* was inflated because of the misrepresentation." 339 F.3d, at 938 (emphasis in original; internal quotation marks omitted). It added that "the injury occurs at the time of the transaction." *Ibid.* Since the complaint pleaded "that the price at the time of purchase was overstated," and it sufficiently identified the cause, its allegations were legally sufficient. *Ibid.*

Because the Ninth Circuit's views about loss causation differ from those of other Circuits that have considered this issue, we granted Dura's petition for certiorari. Compare *ibid.* with, *e.g., Emergent Capital Investment Management, LLC v. Stonepath Group, Inc.,* 343 F.3d 189, 198 (C.A.2 2003); *Semerenko v. Cendant Corp.,* 223 F.3d 165, 185 (C.A.3 2000); *Robbins v. Koger Properties, Inc.,* 116 F.3d 1441, 1447-1448 (C.A.11 1997); cf. *Bastian v. Petren Resources Corp.,* 892 F.2d 680, 685 (C.A.7 1990). We now reverse.

II

Private federal securities fraud actions are based upon federal securities statutes and their implementing regulations. Section 10(b) of the Securities Exchange Act ***1631** of 1934 forbids (1) the "use or employ[ment] ... of any ... deceptive device," (2) "in connection with the purchase or sale of any security," and (3) "in contravention of" Securities and Exchange Commission "rules and regulations." 15 U.S.C. § 78j(b). Commission Rule 10b-5 forbids, among other things, the making of any "untrue statement of material fact" or the omission of any material fact "necessary in order to make the statements made ... not misleading." 17 CFR § 240.10b-5 (2004).

The courts have implied from these statutes and Rule a private damages action, which resembles, but is not identical to, common-law tort actions for deceit and misrepresentation. See, *e.g., Blue Chip Stamps v. Manor Drug Stores,* 421 U.S. 723, 730, 744, 95 S.Ct. 1917, 44 L.Ed.2d 539 (1975); *Ernst & Ernst v. Hochfelder,* 425 U.S. 185, 196, 96 S.Ct. 1375, 47 L.Ed.2d 668 (1976). And Congress has imposed statutory requirements on that private action. *E.g.,* 15 U.S.C. § 78u-4(b)(4).

In cases involving publicly traded securities and purchases or sales in public securities markets, the action's basic elements include:

(1) *a material misrepresentation (or omission),* see *Basic Inc. v. Levinson,* 485 U.S. 224, 231-232, 108 S.Ct. 978, 99 L.Ed.2d 194 (1988);

(2) *scienter, i.e.,* a wrongful state of mind, see *Ernst & Ernst, supra,* at 197, 199, 96 S.Ct. 1375;

(3) *a connection with the purchase or sale of a security,* see *Blue Chip Stamps, supra,* at 730-731, 95 S.Ct. 1917;

(4) *reliance,* often referred to in cases involving public securities markets (fraud-on-the-market cases) as "transaction causation," see *Basic, supra,* at 248-249, 108 S.Ct. 978

(nonconclusively presuming that the price of a publicly traded share reflects a material misrepresentation and that plaintiffs have relied upon that misrepresentation as long as they would not have bought the share in its absence);
(5) *economic loss,* 15 U.S.C. § 78u-4(b)(4); and
(6) *"loss causation,"* *i.e.,* a causal connection between the material misrepresentation and the loss, *ibid.;* cf. T. Hazen, Law of Securities Regulation, §§ 12.11[1], [3] (5th ed.2002).

Dura argues that the complaint's allegations are inadequate in respect to these last two elements.

A

[1] We begin with the Ninth Circuit's basic reason for finding the complaint adequate, namely, that at the end of the day plaintiffs need only "establish," *i.e.,* prove, that "the price *on the date of purchase* was inflated because of the misrepresentation." 339 F.3d, at 938 (internal quotation marks omitted). In our view, this statement of the law is wrong. Normally, in cases such as this one (*i.e.,* fraud-on-the-market cases), an inflated purchase price will not itself constitute or proximately cause the relevant economic loss.

For one thing, as a matter of pure logic, at the moment the transaction takes place, the plaintiff has suffered no loss; the inflated purchase payment is offset by ownership of a share that *at that instant* possesses equivalent value. Moreover, the logical link between the inflated share purchase price and any later economic loss is not invariably strong. Shares are normally purchased with an eye toward a later sale. But if, say, the purchaser sells the shares quickly before the relevant truth begins to leak out, the misrepresentation will not have led to any loss. If the purchaser***1632** sells later after the truth makes its way into the market place, an initially inflated purchase price *might* mean a later loss. But that is far from inevitably so. When the purchaser subsequently resells such shares, even at a lower price, that lower price may reflect, not the earlier misrepresentation, but changed economic circumstances, changed investor expectations, new industry-specific or firm-specific facts, conditions, or other events, which taken separately or together account for some or all of that lower price. (The same is true in respect to a claim that a share's higher price is lower than it would otherwise have been--a claim we do not consider here.) Other things being equal, the longer the time between purchase and sale, the more likely that this is so, *i.e.,* the more likely that other factors caused the loss.

Given the tangle of factors affecting price, the most logic alone permits us to say is that the higher purchase price will *sometimes* play a role in bringing about a future loss. It may prove to be a necessary condition of any such loss, and in that sense one might say that the inflated purchase price suggests that the misrepresentation (using language the Ninth Circuit used) "touches upon" a later economic loss. *Ibid.* But, even if that is so, it is insufficient. To "touch upon" a loss is not to *cause* a loss, and it is the latter that the law requires. 15 U.S.C. § 78u-4(b)(4).

For another thing, the Ninth Circuit's holding lacks support in precedent. Judicially implied private securities-fraud actions resemble in many (but not all) respects common-law deceit and misrepresentation actions. See *Blue Chip Stamps, supra,* at 744, 95 S.Ct. 1917; see also L. Loss & J. Seligman, Fundamentals of Securities Regulation, 910-918 (5th ed.2004) (describing relationship to common-law deceit). The common law of deceit subjects a person who "fraudulently" makes a "misrepresentation" to liability "for pecuniary loss caused" to one who justifiably relies upon that misrepresentation. Restatement (Second) of Torts § 525, p. 55 (1977) (hereinafter Restatement of Torts); see also *Southern Development Co. v. Silva,* 125 U.S. 247, 250, 8 S.Ct. 881, 31 L.Ed. 678 (1888) (setting forth elements of fraudulent misrepresentation). And the common law has long insisted that a plaintiff in such a case show not only that had he known the truth he would not have acted but also that he suffered actual economic loss. See, *e.g., Pasley v. Freeman,* 3 T.R. 5:1, 100 Eng. Rep. 450, 457 (1789) (if "no injury is occasioned by the lie, it is not actionable: but if it be attended with a damage, it then becomes the subject of an action"); *Freeman v. Venner,* 120 Mass. 424, 426 (1876) (a mortgagee cannot bring a tort action for damages stemming from a fraudulent note that a misrepresentation led him to execute unless and until the note has to be paid); see also M. Bigelow, Law of Torts 101 (8th ed.1907) (damage "must already have been suffered before the bringing of the suit"); 2 T. Cooley, Law of Torts § 348, p. 551 (4th ed.1932) (plaintiff must show that he "suffered damage" and that the "damage followed proximately the deception"); W. Keeton, D. Dobbs, R. Keeton, & D. Owen, Prosser and Keeton on Law of Torts § 110, p. 765 (5th ed.1984) (hereinafter Prosser and Keeton) (plaintiff "must have suffered substantial damage," not simply nominal damages, before "the cause of action can arise").

Given the common-law roots of the securities fraud action (and the common-law requirement that a plaintiff show actual damages), it is not surprising that other courts of appeals have rejected the Ninth Circuit's "inflated purchase price" approach to proving causation and loss. See, ***1633** *e.g., Emergent Capital,* 343 F.3d, at 198 (inflation of purchase price alone cannot satisfy loss causation); *Semerenko,* 223 F.3d, at 185 (same); *Robbins,* 116 F.3d, at 1448 (same); cf. *Bastian,* 892 F.2d, at 685. Indeed, the Restatement of Torts, in setting forth the judicial consensus, says that a person who "misrepresents the financial condition of a corporation in order to sell its stock" becomes liable to a relying purchaser "for the loss" the purchaser sustains "when the facts ... become generally known" and "as a result" share value "depreciate[s]." § 548A, Comment *b,* at 107. Treatise writers, too, have emphasized the need to prove proximate causation. Prosser and Keeton § 110, at 767 (losses do "not afford any basis for recovery" if "brought about by business conditions or other factors").

We cannot reconcile the Ninth Circuit's "inflated purchase price" approach with these views of other courts. And the uniqueness of its perspective argues against the validity of its approach in a case like this one where we consider the contours of a judicially implied cause of action with roots in the common law.

Finally, the Ninth Circuit's approach overlooks an important securities law objective. The securities statutes seek to maintain public confidence in the marketplace. See *United States v. O'Hagan,* 521 U.S. 642, 658, 117 S.Ct. 2199, 138 L.Ed.2d 724 (1997). They do so by deterring fraud, in part, through the availability of private securities fraud actions. *Randall v. Loftsgaarden,* 478 U.S. 647, 664, 106 S.Ct. 3143, 92 L.Ed.2d 525 (1986). But the statutes make these latter actions available, not to provide investors with broad insurance against market losses, but to protect them against those economic losses that misrepresentations actually cause. Cf. *Basic,* 485 U.S., at 252, 108 S.Ct. 978 (White, J., joined by O'CONNOR, J., concurring in part and dissenting in part) ("[A]llowing recovery in the face of affirmative evidence of nonreliance--would effectively convert Rule 10b-5 into a scheme of investor's insurance. There is no support in the Securities Exchange Act, the Rule, or our cases for such a result" (internal quotation marks and citations omitted)).

The statutory provision at issue here and the paragraphs that precede it emphasize this last mentioned objective. Private Securities Litigation Reform Act of 1995, 109 Stat. 737. The statute insists that securities fraud complaints "specify" each misleading statement; that they set forth the facts "on which [a] belief" that a statement is misleading was "formed"; and that they "state with particularity facts giving rise to a strong inference that the defendant acted with the required state of mind." 15 U.S.C. §§ 78u-4(b)(1), (2). And the statute expressly imposes on plaintiffs "the burden of proving" that the defendant's misrepresentations "caused the loss for which the plaintiff seeks to recover." § 78u-4(b)(4).

The statute thereby makes clear Congress' intent to permit private securities fraud actions for recovery where, but only where, plaintiffs adequately allege and prove the traditional elements of causation and loss. By way of contrast, the Ninth Circuit's approach would allow recovery where a misrepresentation leads to an inflated purchase price but nonetheless does not proximately cause any economic loss. That is to say, it would permit recovery where these two traditional elements in fact are missing.

In sum, we find the Ninth Circuit's approach inconsistent with the law's requirement that a plaintiff prove that the defendant's misrepresentation (or other fraudulent conduct) proximately caused the plaintiff's economic loss. We need ***1634** not, and do not, consider other proximate cause or loss-related questions.

B

[2] Our holding about plaintiffs' need to *prove* proximate causation and economic loss leads us also to conclude that the plaintiffs' complaint here failed adequately to *allege* these requirements. We concede that the Federal Rules of Civil Procedure require only "a short and plain statement of the claim showing that the pleader is entitled to relief." Fed. Rule Civ. Proc. 8(a)(2). And we assume, at least for argument's sake, that neither the Rules nor the securities statutes impose any special further requirement in respect to the pleading of proximate causation or economic loss. But, even so, the "short and plain statement" must provide the defendant with "fair notice of what the plaintiff's claim is and the grounds upon which it rests." *Conley v. Gibson,* 355 U.S. 41, 47, 78 S.Ct. 99, 2 L.Ed.2d 80 (1957). The complaint before us fails this simple test.

As we have pointed out, the plaintiffs' lengthy complaint contains only one statement that we can fairly read as describing the loss caused by the defendants' "spray device" misrepresentations. That statement says that the plaintiffs "paid artificially inflated prices for Dura's securities" and suffered "damage[s]." App. 139a. The statement implies that the plaintiffs' loss consisted of the "artificially inflated" purchase "prices." The complaint's failure to claim that Dura's share price fell significantly after the truth became known suggests that the plaintiffs considered the allegation of purchase price inflation alone sufficient. The complaint contains nothing that suggests otherwise.

For reasons set forth in Part II-A, *supra,* however, the "artificially inflated purchase price" is not itself a relevant economic loss. And the complaint nowhere else provides the defendants with notice of what the relevant economic loss might be or of what the causal connection might be between that loss and the misrepresentation concerning Dura's "spray device."

We concede that ordinary pleading rules are not meant to impose a great burden upon a plaintiff. *Swierkiewicz v. Sorema N. A.,* 534 U.S. 506, 513-515, 122 S.Ct. 992, 152 L.Ed.2d 1 (2002). But it should not prove burdensome for a plaintiff who has suffered an economic loss to provide a defendant with some indication of the loss and the causal connection that the plaintiff has in mind. At the same time, allowing a plaintiff to forgo giving any indication of the economic loss and proximate cause that the plaintiff has in mind would bring about harm of the very sort the statutes seek to avoid. Cf. H.R. Conf. Rep. No. 104-369, p. 31 (1995), U.S.Code Cong. & Admin.News 1995, pp. 679, 730 (criticizing "abusive" practices including "the routine filing of lawsuits ... with only a faint hope that the discovery process might lead eventually to some plausible cause of action"). It would permit a plaintiff "with a largely groundless claim to simply take up the time of a number of other people, with the right to do so representing an *in terrorem* increment of the settlement value, rather than a reasonably founded hope that the [discovery] process will reveal relevant evidence." *Blue Chip Stamps*, 421 U.S., at 741, 95 S.Ct. 1917. Such a rule would tend to transform a private securities action into a partial downside insurance policy. See H.R. Conf. Rep. No. 104-369, at 31, U.S.Code Cong. & Admin.News 1995, pp. 679, 730; see also *Basic,* 485 U.S., at 252, 108 S.Ct. 978 (White, J., joined by O'CONNOR, J., concurring in part and dissenting in part).

For these reasons, we find the plaintiffs' complaint legally insufficient. We reverse the judgment of the Ninth Circuit, and we ***1635** remand the case for further proceedings consistent with this opinion.

It is so ordered.

125 S.Ct. 1627, 161 L.Ed.2d 577, 73 USLW 4283, Blue Sky L. Rep. P 74,529, Fed. Sec. L. Rep. P 93,218, 05 Cal. Daily Op. Serv. 3273, 2005 Daily Journal D.A.R. 4419, 18 Fla. L. Weekly Fed. S 233

Briefs and Other Related Documents (Back to top)

. 2005 WL 1333264T2 (Appellate Brief) Motion of Respondents for Leave to File Supplemental Brief After Argument; Supplemental Brief%tc (Apr. 14, 2005)Original Image of this Document (PDF)

. 2005 WL 1397051T2 (Appellate Brief) Motion of Petitioners for Leave to File Supplemental Brief after Argument and Supplemental Brief%tc (Feb. 07, 2005)Original Image of this Document (PDF)

. 2004 WL 2988614T2 (Appellate Brief) Reply Brief%tc (Dec. 22, 2004)Original Image of this Document (PDF)

. 2004 WL 2652613T2 (Appellate Brief) Brief of City of New York Pension Funds, the California Public Employees' Retirement System, the California State Teachers' Retirement System, Los Angeles County Employees Retirement Association and Alan G. Hevesi, Comptroller of the State of New Yor k, as Trustee of the New York State Common Retirement Fund and as Administrative Head of this New York State and Local Retirement Systems as Amici Curiae in Support of Respondents%tc (Nov. 17, 2004)Original Image of this Document (PDF)

. 2004 WL 2652616T2 (Appellate Brief) Brief of Amicus Curiae the Regents of the University of California in Support of Respondents%tc (Nov. 17, 2004)Original Image of this Document (PDF)

. 2004 WL 2671450T1 (Appellate Petition, Motion and Filing) Respondents' Brief (Nov. 17, 2004)

. 2004 WL 2678597T2 (Appellate Brief) Brief for James J. Hayes as Amicus Curiae Supporting Respondents%tc (Nov. 17, 2004)Original Image of this Document (PDF)

. 2004 WL 2898976T2 (Appellate Brief) Brief of the North American Securities Administrators

Association, Inc., as Amicus Curiae in Support of Respondents Broudo et al.%tc (Nov. 17, 2004)Original Image of this Document (PDF)

. 2004 WL 2652617T2 (Appellate Brief) Brief of State of New Jersey Department of the Treasury and its Division of Investment as Amicus Curiae in Support of Respondents%tc (Nov. 15, 2004)Original Image of this Document (PDF)

. 2004 WL 2597149T2 (Appellate Brief) Brief for Amici Curiae National Association of Shareholder and Consumer Attorneys, AARP, and the Consumer Federation of America in Support of Respondents (Nov. 12, 2004)Original Image of this Document (PDF)

. 2004 WL 2045248T2 (Appellate Brief) Brief for the American Institute of Certified Public Accountants as Amicus Curiae in Support of Petitioners (Sep. 13, 2004)Original Image of this Document (PDF)

. 2004 WL 2069560T2 (Appellate Brief) Brief of the Chamber of Commerce of the United States As Amicus Curiae in Support of Petitioners (Sep. 13, 2004)Original Image of this Document (PDF)

. 2004 WL 2069561T2 (Appellate Brief) Brief for Technology Network as Amicus Curiae in Support of Petitioners (Sep. 13, 2004)Original Image of this Document (PDF)

. 2004 WL 2069562T2 (Appellate Brief) Brief of Amici Curiae the Securities Industry Association and the Bond Market Association in Support of Petitioners (Sep. 13, 2004)Original Image of this Document (PDF)

. 2004 WL 2069563T2 (Appellate Brief) Brief of Washington Legal Foundation as Amicus Curiae in Support of Petitioners (Sep. 13, 2004)Original Image of this Document (PDF)

. 2004 WL 2069564T2 (Appellate Brief) Brief for the United States as Amicus Curiae Supporting Petitioners (Sep. 13, 2004)Original Image of this Document (PDF)

. 2004 WL 2075751T2 (Appellate Brief) Brief of Broadcom Corporation as Amicus Curiae in Support of Petitioners (Sep. 13, 2004)Original Image of this Document (PDF)

. 2004 WL 2075752T2 (Appellate Brief) Brief for Petitioners (Sep. 13, 2004)Original Image of this Document (PDF)

. 2004 WL 2092648T2 (Appellate Brief) Brief for Merrill Lynch & Co., Inc. as Amicus Curiae in Support of Petitioners (Sep. 13, 2004)Original Image of this Document (PDF)

. 2004 WL 2307122T1 (Joint Appendix) (Sep. 13, 2004)

. 2004 WL 1400170T1 (Appellate Petition, Motion and Filing) Supplemental Brief for Petitioners (Jun. 18, 2004)

. 2004 WL 1205204T1 (Appellate Petition, Motion and Filing) Brief for the United States as Amicus Curiae (May. 28, 2004)

. 2004 WL 329364T1 (Appellate Petition, Motion and Filing) Reply Brief (Feb. 17, 2004)

. 2004 WL 239396T1 (Appellate Petition, Motion and Filing) Motion for Leave to File a Brief as Amicus Curiae and Brief for the Securities Industry Association as Amicus Curiae in Support of Petitioners (Feb. 04, 2004)

. 2004 WL 239397T1 (Appellate Petition, Motion and Filing) Response in Opposition to Petition for a Writ of Certiorari (Feb. 04, 2004)

. 03-932 (Docket) (Jan. 05, 2004)

. 2003 WL 23146437T2 (Appellate Petition, Motion and Filing) Petition for a Writ of Certiorari (Dec. 24, 2003)Original Image of this Document with Appendix (PDF)

END OF DOCUMENT

ENTERED

DEC - 7 2004

CLERK, U S DISTRICT COURT
CENTRAL DISTRICT OF CALIFORNIA
SANTA ANA OFFICE
BY DEPUTY

Priority
Send
Clsd
Enter
JS-5/JS-6
JS-2/JS-3

FILED

DEC 06 2004

CLERK, U S DISTRICT COURT
CENTRAL DISTRICT OF CALIFORNIA
SOUTHERN DIVISION AT SANTA ANA
BY DEPUTY

THIS CONSTITUTES NOTICE OF ENTRY
AS REQUIRED BY FRCP, RULE 77(d).

UNITED STATES DISTRICT COURT

CENTRAL DISTRICT OF CALIFORNIA

SOUTHERN DIVISION

JOSEPHINE TUCKER ARENSON et al., Plaintiffs, vs. BROADCOM CORPORATION et al., Defendants.

Case No. SA CV 02-301-GLT (MLGx)

ORDER GRANTING DEFENDANTS' MOTION FOR SUMMARY JUDGMENT AS TO PLAINTIFFS WHO BENEFITTED FROM ALLEGED INFLATION

Defendants' motion for summary judgment as to Plaintiffs who benefitted from alleged inflation is GRANTED.

I. BACKGROUND

Plaintiffs, stockholders of Defendant Broadcom, allege Defendants inflated the company's reported earnings and misled investors through a series of misrepresentations and fraudulent accounting methods between July 31, 2000 and February 26, 2001. Plaintiffs allege causes of action under section 10(b) of the Securities Exchange Act and Rule 10b-5. Plaintiffs opted not to join a consolidated class action against the Defendants; instead, they sue as individuals.

Defendants move for summary judgment on damages. Defendants argue twenty-six of the forty-seven Plaintiffs cannot establish damages because they profited from the alleged fraud by selling their shares of stock at an artificially inflated price. Because damages is an element of Plaintiffs' prima-facie case, and because Plaintiffs cannot establish it, Defendants ask the Court to grant their motion for summary judgment.

Following oral argument on October 4, 2004, the Court took under submission Defendants' motion and Plaintiffs' request for additional briefing. On October 6, 2004, the Court ordered additional briefing. The briefing is now in, and the Court rules as follows.

II. DISCUSSION

Summary judgment is proper if "there is no genuine issue as to any material fact and . . . the moving party is entitled to a judgment as a matter of law." Fed. R. Civ. P. 56(c).

Defendants contend twenty-six Plaintiffs actually profited from selling Broadcom stock at an artificially inflated price. (Defs.' Supplemental Mem. Supp. Summ. J. at 2.) Defendants conclude Plaintiffs cannot establish damages, which is a required element under their prima-facie case.

Plaintiffs argue Defendants' contention is based on applying the "last in, first out" ("LIFO") accounting methodology, which is not supported by the case law. The case law, according to Plaintiffs, supports application of the "first in, first out" ("FIFO") methodology. Moreover, Plaintiffs' expert claims the FIFO methodology is customarily required in calculating damages in this type of case, not the LIFO methodology (Hakala Decl. ¶¶ 6-7), and applying the FIFO methodology demonstrates the presence of damages.

A number of courts have spoken clearly on this issue, treating it as a pure question of law and finding the FIFO methodology improper.

See, e.g., In re Cable & Wireless, PLC, Sec. Litig., 217 F.R.D. 372, 378-79 (E.D. Va. 2003) ("[C]ourts have generally rejected FIFO as an appropriate means of calculating losses in securities fraud cases.") (internal quotation marks omitted); In re Clearly Canadian Sec. Litig., Nos. C-93-1037-VRW, C-93-1278-VRW, C-93-4313-VRW, C-95-0699-VRW, C-95-2295-VRW, 1999 WL 707737, at *4 (N.D. Cal. Sept. 3, 1999) ("[U]se of the 'first in, first out' method . . . will identify damages where in reality there may be none; the 'FIFO' assumption is in no way based on actual trading practices in general, let alone the trades of actual claimants.").

In re Comdisco Securities Litigation, 150 F. Supp. 2d 943, 945-46 (N.D. Ill. 2001) also rejected the FIFO methodology, stating:

> when the Class Period . . . is focused upon, PASERS' claim that it suffered some $2.4 million in losses in connection with its investment in Comdisco common stock is only a mirage created by PASERS' adoption of a FIFO (first-in-first-out) approach to its dealings in the stock. . . . And when those transactions are properly matched, rather than by the impermissible application of a FIFO methodology . . . PASERS' Class Period sales at inflated prices caused it to derive unwitting benefits rather than true losses from the alleged securities fraud . . . . There are a host of cases . . . that reject the kind of artificial "loss" that is manufactured by PASERS' attempted FIFO construct in favor of a calculation that properly nets out purchases and sales during the class period and determines gains or losses in those terms.

Id.

Plaintiffs' expert claims FIFO is "customarily required" in

calculating damages. (Hakala Decl. ¶ 6.) As the cases demonstrate, however, the issue of which accounting methodology applies is a question of law, not fact, for the Court to decide. Crow Tribe v. Racicot, 87 F.3d 1039, 1045 (9th Cir. 1996).

Plaintiffs cite In re Chipcom Corp. Securities Litigation, No. CIV. A. 95-11114-DPW, 1997 WL 1102329, at *24 (D. Mass. June 26, 1997), in support of their position. This case is inapposite. While it does include seemingly on-point language -- "the FIFO (first-in-first-out) matching basis will be applied" -- the language is recited in the court's summary of the parties' settlement agreement; the decision itself does not address the issue.

Applying a LIFO methodology is supported by adequate authority, especially in light of the body of case law rejecting FIFO.

The authority is clear: where a plaintiff engages in multiple purchases and sales during the period in which the stock is inflated, the proper damages methodology is to take all the inflation losses resulting from all purchases at the inflated price and reduce this amount by all the inflation gain resulting from all sales at the inflated price. See Wool v. Tandem Computers Inc., 818 F.2d 1433, 1437 & n.4 (9th Cir. 1987); In re Seagate Tech. II Sec. Litig., 843 F. Supp. 1341, 1349 n.7 (N.D. Cal. 1994).

Plaintiffs attempt to distinguish Wool, arguing the Wool plaintiffs bought and sold stock during the period of inflation and, therefore, the Ninth Circuit did not need to decide what sales and purchases to match (i.e., what accounting methodology to apply). Here, Plaintiffs argue stock was held before the period of inflation, thereby raising the issue of methodology.

This factual distinction does not overcome the language in Wool, which establishes a general principle applicable here. In re Seagate makes the point even clearer.

III. DISPOSITION

Defendants' motion for summary judgment as to Plaintiffs who benefitted from alleged inflation is GRANTED. The following Plaintiffs cannot show they were damaged as a result of the conduct alleged in the First Amended Complaint:

1. Alexander R. Brishka, as an individual
2. Ilma Brishka, as an individual
3. Alexander R. Brishka and Ilma Brishka, as trustees of the Brishka Trust
4. Timothy J. Buckley, as an individual
5. Compass Communications, a Grand Cayman Islands Company
6. Robert J. Follman, as an individual
7. Carole A. Follman, as an individual
8. Robert J. Follman and Carole A. Follman, as trustees of the Robert J. and Carole A. Follman Living Trust
9. Robert J. Follman and Carole A. Follman, as administrators of the Robert J. Follman IRA Rollover
10. Robert J. Follman and Carole A. Follman, as administrators of the Carole A. Follman IRA
11. Jeff D. Martin, as an individual
12. Jill D. Martin, as an individual
13. Jeff D. Martin and Jill D. Martin, as trustees of the J. & J. Martin Trust
14. Jeff D. Martin and Jill D. Martin, as administrators of the Jeff Martin IRA
15. Jeff D. Martin and Jill D. Martin, as administrators of the

Jill Martin IRA

16. Scott McCarter, as an individual

17. Scott McCarter, as an administrator of the Scott McCarter SEP-IRA

18. Sarajen Capital, LLC, a California limited liability company

19. Ronald E. Tendler, as an individual

20. Ronald E. Tendler, as trustee of the Tendler Family Trust

21. Ronald E. Tendler, as administrator of the J. Edward Company Money Purchase Pension Plan

22. Thomas T. Tierney, as an individual

23. Elizabeth C. Tierney, as an individual

24. Thomas T. Tierney and Elizabeth C. Tierney, as trustees of the Thomas T. and Elizabeth C. Tierney Trust

25. Thomas E. Tucker, as an individual

26. Thomas E. Tucker, as trustee for the Tucker Family Trust

DATED: December 6, 2004

GARY L. TAYLOR
UNITED STATES DISTRICT JUDGE

Priority X
Send X
Enter
Closed
JS-5/JS-6
JS-2/JS-3
Scan Only

FILED
JUN - 3 2005
CLERK, U.S. DISTRICT COURT
CENTRAL DISTRICT OF CALIFORNIA
SOUTHERN DIVISION AT SANTA ANA
BY DEPUTY

UNITED STATES DISTRICT COURT

CENTRAL DISTRICT OF CALIFORNIA

SOUTHERN DIVISION

IN RE BROADCOM CORPORATION SECURITIES LITIGATION	Master File No. SA CV 01-275-GLT (MLGx)
JOSEPHINE TUCKER ARENSON, v. BROADCOM CORPORATION et al.,	Consolidated for Trial with Case No. SA CV 02-301-GLT (ANx)
	CLASS ACTION
	RULING ON MOTIONS RE PROOF OF AGGREGATE DAMAGES

The Court finds that, under the unique circumstances of this particular case, the aggregate damages prove-up, employing a trading model, will not be used. Instead, a per share damage per day determination, aided by the claims administration process, will be used.

I. DISCUSSION

This is a case under the Private Securities Litigation Reform Act of 1995 ("PSLRA"), 15 U.S.C. § 78u-4 (1997). Before the Court is Defendants' motion to exclude aggregate damages testimony of Scott D. Hakala and Plaintiffs' cross-motion to permit aggregate damages evidence. The Court held a two-day evidentiary hearing on the Daubert issue concerning the trading model. After reviewing all of the parties' evidentiary showing and extensive briefing, the Court now makes its ruling.

The issue presented on these motions is whether, under the particular circumstances of this case, a prove-up of aggregate damages is appropriate, or an alternative method is better. Plaintiffs suggest use of a trading model to prove aggregate damages, while Defendants suggest final prove-up through the claims administration process is more appropriate.

The small body of case law the parties cite as dealing with this issue is far from dispositive.[1]

On the side supporting aggregate damages or a trading model, In re Oxford Health Plans, Inc. Securities Litigation, 244 F. Supp. 2d 247, 249-52 (S.D.N.Y. 2003), held aggregate damages testimony was admissible, but stated it expressed no opinion on the validity or admissibility of plaintiffs' proposed damages calculation. Robbins v. Deloitte & Touche, LLP, 1995 WL 17205104, at *1 (M.D. Fla. 1995), rev'd on other grounds by 116 F.3d 1441 (11th Cir. 1997), permitted a jury to render an aggregate damages verdict. In re Worldcom, Inc. Securities Litigation, 2005 WL 491397, at *2-4 (S.D.N.Y. 2005), held evidence of an aggregate damages figure was appropriate where there was actual trading data available for over fifty percent of the trades at issue and the permissibility or reliability of a stock trading model was not at issue. In re Raytheon Co. Securities Litigation, (D. Mass. 2004), first excluded a "Weibull trading model" (which Dr. Hakala described in this

---

[1] Of the following cases, there is no case citation for Lazar, Employer-Teamsters Joint Counsel, Raytheon, Clarent Corp., or Helionetics, so the reference is based on trial court transcripts or minute orders.

case as merely a different mathematical formulation for reaching the same result as his two-trader model), but, after uncontested argument that the PSLRA requires aggregate damages, evidence of aggregate damages was accepted without objection. In re Helionetics, Inc. Securities Litigation, SA CV 94-1069 (C.D. Cal. 1998), used a trading model at trial to estimate damages, where use of the model was apparently not challenged.

Of the cases rejecting proof of aggregate damages or a trading model under the facts of those particular cases, Kaufman v. Motorola, Inc., 2000 WL 1506892, at *2 (N.D. Ill. 2000), rejected an older proportional trading model on Daubert grounds, held proof of aggregate damages is unnecessary, and found an adequate remedy would be for the jury to determine per share damages, followed by the filing of claims by each damaged shareholder. Bell v. Fore Systems, Inc., 2002 WL 32097540, at *1, 5-6 (W.D. Pa. 2002), noting its decision was "at odds with current litigation practices" and "based on practicalities rather than precedent," held the PSLRA requires "an individualized damages limitation for each plaintiff" and excluded Dr. Hakala's aggregate damages testimony. Lazar v. Biogen, Inc., (D. Mass. 1998), ruled only actual damages are recoverable, and the jury would be asked to calculate the damage amount per share, rather than in the aggregate. Employer-Teamsters Joint Counsel No. 84 Pension Trust Fund v. America West Holdings Corp., (D. Ariz. 2004), without describing the expert testimony offered or explaining the court's reasoning, held the jury would not be permitted to estimate and award aggregate damages using a trading model. In re Clarent Corp. Securities Litigation, (N.D. Cal. 2005), commented early in the hearing that there was "plenty of science" in Dr. Hakala's work, and it thought the model would survive a Daubert challenge, but it was inclined to exclude the model as not helpful to the jury; but, Dr. Hakala's aggregate damages testimony was eventually excluded apparently (on review of the transcript) on Daubert grounds.

This Court concludes that, although each of these cases provides persuasion and guidance on this subject, none of them is controlling or dispositive under the unique facts of this particular case.

After review of the PSLRA, the Court concludes the statute neither requires nor prohibits proof of aggregate damages. The statute leaves it open for a court to select the most reliable method of damages proof that is available in that particular case.

This conclusion is consistent with the history of class action precedent. Rule 23 allows district courts to devise imaginative solutions to problems created by the presence of individual damages issues in a class action litigation. Carnegie v. Household Int'l, Inc., 376 F.3d 656, 661 (7th Cir. 2004) (Posner, J.). Proof by the aggregate approach is the traditional method, see 3 Alba Conte & Herbert B. Newberg, Newberg on Class Actions § 10:2, at 477-79 (4th ed. 2002), and so it is usable in a PSLRA case, unless it is shown to be unreliable and a more accurate method is available. There is no hard-and-fast rule on the use of aggregate damages, and the determination whether that method is appropriate is governed by considerations of economy, fairness, and other equitable considerations. In re Worldcom, Inc. Sec. Litig., 2005 WL 491397, at *5 (quoting Jaroslawicz v. Engelhard Corp., 724 F. Supp. 294, 299 (D.N.J. 1989)).

The question is whether, under the unique facts of this particular case, proof of aggregate damages will be sufficiently reliable to justify its use when weighed against other available alternatives.

The evidentiary hearing showed that the proposed trading model probably does not satisfy the Daubert test for submission to the jury. The technique has not been tested against "real world" conditions, and probably cannot be so tested unless a different set of test protocols is established. It has not been subjected to the sort of critical peer review and publication that one would expect as a prerequisite for jury acceptance. The potential error rate is highly questionable, and is based on a set of criteria that undermines the claimed error rate as being truly representative of the facts sought to be proved. Although held out by litigation professionals as useful in securities litigation, most notably as a settlement aid, the technique is not generally accepted in what is the relevant scientific community -- professional economists. The Daubert criteria are not exclusive, and the Court has considered others suggested by Plaintiffs, but the Court is unable to find other indicators of reliability or acceptability that would satisfy Daubert's requirement.

In addition to probably failing the Daubert test, the trading model has been shown to be of highly questionable reliability and accuracy under the unique facts of this particular case. The model does not account for the entire class. It is based on broad estimates and assumptions that may not apply to this class. The model's adjustments are of uncertain application here. Defendants' evidence shows the error rate is based on questionable criteria, and may be much larger than Plaintiffs acknowledge. In short, the trading model provides a "rough and ready" calculation that is undoubtedly useful for trial preparation, settlement, and mediation, and may be helpful at trial if the needs of a particular case fit its capabilities. However, that has not been shown to be the situation in this unique case.

Other than the trading model technique, no other method of

aggregate damages proof has been proposed.

The Court does not need to finally decide whether the trading model technique passes the Daubert test. All that need be decided is that, because of its Daubert shortcomings, and because it is of questionable accuracy, the trading model technique is of significantly questionable reliability. The Court need not use a proof method of questionable reliability when an alternative, completely reliable method is available through the claims administration process.

Under the PSLRA, the law requires a claims administration process. The Court finds the jury can determine per share damage per day, and the Court can easily use the claims administration process to supply the remaining information to calculate an accurate, reliable total damage figure and payout.

The Court has considered the suggested disadvantages of using the claims administration technique. Plaintiffs argue the public is entitled to know the full amount of the harm; but, the lawsuit's purpose is to compensate claims lawfully made, not to declare a degree of harm. Plaintiffs argue they have a possessory right in a common fund; but, this would only apply to the amount for which Defendants are lawfully liable after receipt of claims. Plaintiffs argue that, without an adjudged aggregate amount, there is nothing for the class "to look to or hang onto," and fewer claims will be submitted; however, it is not the function of the lawsuit to provide that comfort to the class, and the "ballpark" of total recovery will probably be known. Plaintiffs argue an aggregate award would provide a source for fees and expenses during the claims process; but, the Court can order an unsuccessful defendant to deposit a reasonable sum for fees and expenses pending that process. The Worldcom case suggests it is best for the jury to make all the determinations it can; the reply, however, is that an unreliable determination by the jury is not helpful. Worldcom also points out an aggregate award might permit earlier appellate review; however, appellate review of an unreliable determination is not productive and, in any event, an interlocutory appeal can be sought under 28 U.S.C. § 1292(b).

At the evidentiary hearing, Defendants disclaimed any broader right to advisory participation in the claims administration process if the claims process is used to complete the damages calculation, than they would have if there were an aggregate damages prove-up.

The Court finds that, under the unique facts of this particular case, the advantage of certainty in the claims process damages calculation outweighs the disadvantages. The aggregate damages prove-up employing a trading model, suggested by Plaintiffs, will not be used. A per share damage per day determination aided by the claims administration process, suggested by Defendants, will be used.

II. DISPOSITION

Defendants' motion to exclude aggregate damages testimony of Dr. Hakala is GRANTED. Plaintiffs' cross-motion to permit evidence of aggregate damages at trial is DENIED. Defendants' ex parte application to strike has previously been denied. The Court makes no ruling at this time on Plaintiffs' motion to qualify expert witnesses, pending a future motion on whether the witnesses can testify on other topics.

DATED: June 3, 2005

GARY L. TAYLOR
UNITED STATES DISTRICT JUDGE

S:\GLTLC1\Civil\2001\01-275\01-0275-ord.aggregate motion

NOTES

9

LOSS CAUSATION AND THE CRIMINAL PROSECUTION OF SECURITIES LAW VIOLATIONS

Lawrence J. Zweifach
Marny Zimmer
Heller Ehrman LLP

Table of Contents

I. INTRODUCTION

The federal securities laws provide that individuals, corporations and other business entities can be subject to criminal prosecution for "wilfull" violations of most of the substantive provisions of those laws and the regulations thereunder. Consequently, judicial interpretations of the securities laws in civil cases, including SEC enforcement proceedings and private actions, are an important part of the jurisprudence that courts consider when interpreting the securities laws in the context of criminal prosecutions. While courts often look to civil case law for purposes of determining the essential elements of a criminal securities law violation, they infrequently have looked to the civil law of damages for guidance at sentencing.

This article discusses a case in which the sentencing court was recently called upon to rely on the civil law of damages for guidance. In *United States v. Daniel Bayly, et al.* (CR. No. H-03-363, S.D. Texas)(the "Nigerian Barge case"), a criminal prosecution brought by the Enron Task Force, the defendants and the United States Chamber of Commerce as *amicus curiae* requested that the United States District Court for the Southern District of Texas consider and apply "loss causation," a principle rooted in the civil law of damages, for purposes of determining appropriate sentences for the defendants who were convicted after trial.[1] In its memorandum, the Chamber of Commerce discussed the importance of the sentencing proceeding in Nigerian Barge case as follows:

> The legal rules crafted in high profile cases such as this one have economic effects across the board. The Chamber submits that it is vital that the rule of law that emerges from this case fit logically within the structure of securities law and reflect the focused purpose of the "loss" requirement under securities law and the Sentencing Guidelines. It is important that hard cases not make bad law, even when the hard cases involves Enron. Rather, the governing rule of law used by this Court should maintain the balance between the appropriate punishment of criminal wrongdoing and the reasonable limits on liability reflected in corporate law generally and securities law specifically.

Memorandum of *Amicus Curiae* United States Chamber of Commerce Concerning Interpretation of "Loss" ("Chamber Mem.") at 3-4.

As explained by the Chamber of Commerce, one of the principal issues at the sentencing proceeding in the Nigerian Barge case, the proper

1. The authors of this article represented one of the defendants in the Nigerian Barge case, James A. Brown, at the trial of the case and at sentencing. The appeal of the case is currently pending before the United States Court of Appeals for the Fifth Circuit.

definition of "loss" in cases arising out of allegations of securities fraud, "is a recurring question of great importance to the business community." Chamber Mem. at 1-2. After having considered extensive briefing on the issue of loss causation, the sentencing court in the Nigerian Barge case declined to apply the government's "stock inflation" theory in determining the amount of "loss" under the Sentencing Guidelines. Given the spate of criminal prosecutions in recent years arising out of numerous, alleged accounting fraud scandals, it is likely that courts will continue to be called upon in the near future to consider the application of loss causation at sentencing proceedings.

II. LOSS CAUSATION: STATUTORY AND COMMON LAW BACKGROUND

The principle of law causation is well-established in both civil case law and statute. In 1995, the Private Securities Litigation Reform Act ("PSLRA") codified the loss causation requirement in civil securities actions. S. Rep. No. 104-98 at 15 (1995). Section 21D(b)(4) provides that "[i]n any private action arising under this chapter, the plaintiff shall have the burden of proving that the act or omission of the defendant alleged to violate this chapter caused the loss for which the plaintiff seeks to recover damages." 15 U.S.C. § 78u-4(b)(4).

Prior to the enactment of the PSLRA, loss causation existed in case law as a judicial creation. It was originally articulated as an independent requirement in securities actions in *Schlick v. Penn-Dixie Cement Corp.* 507 F.2d 374 (2d Cir. 1974). The *Schlick* court defined loss causation as "the misrepresentations or omissions [that] caused the economic harm." *Id.* at 380. The court differentiated between loss causation and "transaction causation," which the court defined as a showing that "the violations in question caused the [plaintiff] to engage in the transaction in question." *Id.* The court's articulation of transaction causation, similar to reliance and the tort concept of "but for causation," focused on the relationship between defendant's misrepresentation and plaintiff's investment decision. Loss causation, on the other hand, "requires one further step in the analysis: even if the investor would not otherwise have acted, was the misrepresented fact a proximate cause of the loss? The plaintiff must prove not only that had he known the truth, he would not have acted, but in addition that the untruth was in some reasonably direct, or proximate, way responsible for his loss." *Huddleston v. Herman & MacLean*, 640 F.2d 534, 549 (5th Cir. 1981).

Loss causation requires that plaintiffs prove that the loss was linked, in a direct and foreseeable way, to the defendant's fraud. *See Rousseff v. E.F. Hutton Co.*, 843 F.2d 1326, 1329 n.2 (11th Cir. 1988). It is similar to the common law principle of proximate cause. *Citibank, N.A. v. K-H Corp.*, 968 F.2d 1489 (2d Cir. 1992). The Restatement of Torts explains proximate causation as follows:

> [O]ne who misrepresents the financial condition of a corporation in order to sell its stock will become liable to a purchaser who relies upon the misinformation for the loss that he sustains when the facts as to the finances of the corporation become generally known and as a result the value of the shares is depreciated on the market, because that is the obviously foreseeable result of the facts misrepresented. On the other hand, there is no liability when the value of the stock goes down after the sale, not in any way because of the misrepresented financial condition, but as a result of some subsequent event that has no connection with or relation to its financial condition. There is, for example, no liability when the shares go down because of the sudden death of the corporation's leading officers. Although the misrepresentation has in fact caused the loss, since it has induced the purchase without which the loss would have occurred, it is not a legal cause of the loss for which the maker is responsible.

RESTATEMENT (SECOND) OF TORTS § 548A (1977).

Thus, loss causation is required to prevent plaintiffs from recovering for investment losses that stem from causes unrelated to a defendant's fraud. Instead, the loss must be linked, directly, to defendant's fraud.

III. THE *DURA PHARMACEUTICALS* CASE

Prior to the Supreme Court's recent decision in *Dura Pharmaceuticals, Inc. et al. v. Broudo*, 125 S. Ct. 1627 (2005), the circuits were split with respect to the requirements for pleading and proving loss causation in securities cases. The Eighth and Ninth Circuits held that a showing of artificial price inflation satisfied the requirement of loss causation. *See, e.g., Gebhardt v. ConAgra Foods, Inc.*, 335 F.3d 824, 831 (8th Cir. 2003); *Broudo v. Dura Pharmaceuticals, Inc. et al.*, 339 F.3d 933, 937-38 (9th Cir. 2003). The Second, Third and Eleventh Circuits held that plaintiffs had to show that they bought at an inflated price *and* suffered an injury due to defendant's misrepresentation. *See Emergent Capital Inv. Mgmt., LLC v. Stonepath Group, Inc.*, 343 F.3d 189, 198 (2d Cir. 2003); *Semerenko v. Cendant Corp.*, 223 F.3d 165, 185 (3d Cir. 2000); *Robbins v. Koger Props., Inc.*, 116 F.3d 1441, 1448-49 (11th Cir. 1997). "To plead loss causation, therefore, a plaintiff must allege something more than mere price inflation—something that explains the plaintiff's loss." *In re*

Initial Pub. Offering Sec. Litig., 297 F. Supp. 2d 668, 671 (S.D. N.Y. 2003).

The Supreme Court addressed the Circuits' differing views on loss causation in the *Dura Pharmaceuticals* case. In *Dura*, the Supreme Court considered a Ninth Circuit holding that a plaintiff can satisfy the loss causation requirement in a securities fraud case by alleging in the complaint and subsequently establishing that the defendant's fraud inflated the purchase price of the security. *Id.* at 1629. Plaintiffs were individuals who bought stock in Dura Pharmaceuticals, Inc. ("Dura"). *Id.* at 1629-1630. They alleged that before and during the purchase period, Dura made false statements that caused its stock price to be inflated. In their complaint, plaintiffs stated: "[i]n reliance on the integrity of the market, [plaintiffs] paid artificially inflated prices for Dura securities... and suffered damages" as a result. *Id.* at 1630.

The Ninth Circuit reversed the district's court dismissal of the complaint for failing to allege loss causation. 339 F.3d 933 at 938. The Ninth Circuit held that the complaint met the pleading requirements for loss causation because respondents alleged "that the price on the date of purchase was inflated because of the [defendant's] misrepresentation." *Id.* at 938. The court added that "the injury occurs at the time of the transaction." *Id.*

The Supreme Court reversed, stating that the Ninth Circuit was wrong in holding that plaintiffs need only establish the purchase price was artificially inflated in order to prove loss causation. 125 S. Ct. at 1631. The Court noted that at the time a plaintiff purchases a stock, he has not suffered a loss. *Id.* Rather, at the time of purchase, the plaintiff owns a security that possesses the equivalent value that he paid for it. If the purchaser sells the share before the relevant misrepresentation is revealed, the misrepresentation will not have led to any loss. *Id.* at 1631-32. Further, if the plaintiff sells the security for a loss, the loss may be due to various factors including changed economic conditions, changed investor expectations or changed industry factors. *Id.* at 1632. Therefore, the Court stated:

> [the inflated purchase price] may prove to be a necessary condition of any such loss, and in that sense one might say that the inflated purchase price suggests the misrepresentation [] "touches upon" a later economic loss. But, even if that is so, it is insufficient. To "touch upon" a loss is not to *cause* a loss, and it is the latter that the law requires.

Id. at 1632 (citations omitted).

The Court also noted that the Ninth Circuit's holding lacked support in precedent. *Id.* Securities fraud actions resemble common-law deceit and misrepresentation actions in many respects. *Id.* at 1632-33. Common law actions require a plaintiff to show not only that had he known the truth he would not have acted but also that he suffered an actual economic loss. *Id.* at 1632. "Given the common-law roots of the securities fraud action (and the common-law requirement that a plaintiff show actual damages), it is not surprising that other courts of appeals have rejected the Ninth Circuit's 'inflated purchase price' approach to proving causation and loss." *Id.* at 1632-33 (citations omitted).

Lastly, explained the Supreme Court, the Ninth Circuit's approach overlooked an important securities law objective. *Id.* at 1633. The securities statutes seek to deter fraud through private actions, not to provide investors with insurance against market losses. *Id.* The statutes are designed to protect investors against those economic losses that misrepresentations actually cause. Therefore, the statutes impose on "plaintiffs 'the burden of proving' that the defendant's misrepresentations 'caused the loss for which the plaintiff seeks to recover.'" *Id.* (citing 15 U.S.C. § 78u-4(b)(4)).

IV. LOSS UNDER THE FEDERAL SENTENCING GUIDELINES

Section 2B1.1 of the Federal Sentencing Guidelines addresses the sentencing calculation for fraud-based crimes, including those involving securities fraud. United States Sentencing Guidelines § 2B1.1, "Theft, Embezzlement, Receipt of Stolen Property, Property Destruction and Offense Involving Fraud or Deceit."[2] Section 2B1.1 provides a base offense level for fraud-based crimes that may be increased due to various factors, including the amount of loss attributed to the offense. Other factors increasing the base offense level include the number of victims affected (§ 2B1.1(b)(2)) and the violation of a securities law (§ 2B1.1(b)(15)(A)).

The Guidelines explain that "loss serves as a measure of the seriousness of the offense and the defendant's relative culpability and is a principal factor in determining the offense level under this guideline." USSG § 2B1.1, Background. The Guidelines treat the amount of loss as a "specific

2. The Sentencing Commission adopted an amendment that impacted sentences after November 1, 2001. The amendment consolidated the fraud and theft guidelines, adjusted the loss table, and provided the definition of loss discussed below.

offense characteristic." Therefore, as the amount of loss increases, the offense level calculation increases, and thus the sentence increases. USSG § 2B1.1(b)(1). There are sixteen steps of two-level increases, from 0 for losses of $5000 or less, up to 30 for losses exceeding $400 million. *Id.* If the loss exceeds $400,000,000, a base offense of 7 can be increased to 37. As result, a defendant's sentence in a securities case, where losses can be high, depends heavily upon the calculation of loss under the Guidelines. Guidance for determining the meaning of "loss" within the Guidelines is found in Application Note 2 to the theft/fraud guideline. USSG § 2B1.1, cmt. (n.2). Application Note 2 defines actual loss as "the reasonably foreseeable pecuniary harm that resulted from the offense." *Id.* Pecuniary harm means the harm that is monetary or that otherwise is readily measurable in money. *Id.* The court shall use the gain that resulted from the offense as an alternative measure of loss only if there is a loss but it reasonably cannot be determined. *Id.*

When considering the amount of loss attributable to a defendant's conduct, the Guidelines require only that courts make a reasonable estimate of the loss, given the available information. USSG § 2B1.1, Application Note 3(C). The sentencing judge should consider the "reduction that resulted from the offense in the value of equity securities or other corporate assets," as well as the "approximate number of victims multiplied by the average loss to each victim." USSG § 2B1.1, Application Note 3(c)(iii)-(iv).[3] In calculating losses under the Guidelines, courts have used various methods including the out-of-pocket method and rescission. *See, e.g., United States v. Grabske,* 260 F. Supp. 2d 866 (N.D. Cal. 2002) ("While 'out-of-pocket' damages are the traditional measure of loss in securities fraud cases, another method is rescissory damages.").

V. THE NIGERIAN BARGE CASE

The Nigerian Barge case involved a commercial transaction between Merrill Lynch and Enron in which Merrill Lynch agreed to invest $7 million in three energy producing barges located off the coast of Nigeria. The theory of the prosecution was that the $7 million equity investment by Merrill Lynch was actually a secret loan to Enron for purposes of improperly inflating Enron's earnings. According to the government, as a result of

3. The number of victims is important in its own right, not just for its effect on the loss calculation. The Guidelines provide 2 step increases for different ranges of victims. If the fraud involves more than 250 victims, the base offense level is increased by 6 levels. USSG § 2B1.1(b)(2).

this $7 million "loan," Enron was able to record improperly approximately $12 million in earnings. Prior to the time that Enron commenced bankruptcy proceedings, there was never any public disclosure that the Nigerian Barge transaction was fraudulent or otherwise resulted in Enron recording earnings improperly. However, the government presented expert testimony to the effect that, as a result of the Nigerian Barge deal, Enron's stock was artificially inflated by approximately $43.8 million. The government's position at sentencing was that the amount by which Enron's stock was inflated should be deemed the "loss" under the Sentencing Guidelines.

VI. ARGUMENTS PRESENTED AT THE SENTENCING OF THE NIGERIAN BARGE CASE DEFENDANTS

A. The Government's Position: Artificial Inflation Is a Valid Measure of Loss

The government argued that measuring the loss by the artificial inflation in the stock price was reasonable under the Guidelines provision stating that the amount of actual loss "is the amount by which the stock was overvalued."[4] Govt Br. at p. 7 (citing USSG § 2F1.1, comment (n. 8(a)). Further, artificial inflation was the proper method because the inflation harmed investors by causing them to overpay for the stock. Id. at p. 8. If one investor sells the stock at the artificially inflated price to another "unsuspecting victim," there is no change in the harm; "some investor has still paid too much for the stock. Through the overpayment, investors have lost something valuable. The intrinsic value of what they hold, the stock, is worth less than the price they paid for it." Id. at p. 8. The investors were subject to the risk that the artificial inflation could disappear from the stock, "rendering them unable to recoup their purchase price." Id. at p. 9.

In arguing for the enhancement under the Guidelines, the government noted that offense levels for fraud crimes are largely governed by

---

4. The government argued in the alternative that even if the Court accepted defendants' argument that there was no actual loss for Guidelines purposes until the artificial inflation in the stock price was removed, it could still prove an intended loss of $43 million. According to this argument, the defendants intended to artificially inflate Enron's stock by engaging in the barge transaction. As a result, their sentences could be enhanced by the amount of the inflation.

the amount of loss involved in the offense and "reflect the Sentencing Commission's considered judgment that the greater of the actual or intended loss attributable to the offense reasonably reflects the magnitude of the offense." Govt. Br. at p. 6. Because the barge transaction allowed Enron to book inflated earnings and hide its true financial condition, the government argued that the artificial inflation in Enron's stock was a reasonable, and "even minimal," measure of the actual losses caused by the fraud. Citing to *United States v. Devours,* the government stated, "[t]he Fifth Circuit has clearly adopted this position, which is of course consonant with and called for by the Sentencing Guidelines." Govt. Br. at p. 9. (citing 219 F.3d 400, 402-04 (5th Cir. 2000). In *Devours,* the Court refused to reduce the defendants' liability in a Ponzi scheme by the amount of money the defendants returned to the victims, "since those profits simply came from other investor victims." *Id.* at 402; *see also United States v. Lane*, 323 F.3d 568, 587-88 (7th Cir. 2003) (loss should not be reduced by amount victim is able to recover from third-party guarantor, as such recoupment by victim "does not decrease the magnitude of [defendant's crime]."

With regard to the issue of loss causation, the government argued that civil loss causation principles, requiring that the artificial inflation be removed from the stock in order to prove loss, do not apply to sentencing in criminal cases. Differentiating civil securities fraud cases from criminal, the government pointed out that the purpose of a private civil suit primarily is to redress harm suffered by particular individuals. Govt. Br. at p. 13. The concern that loss causation addresses in the civil context, that an individual plaintiff can always sell the stock until the artificial inflation is removed, at the artificially inflated price, "is [] inapposite in the criminal context, where the passing of the loss from one investor to the other does not mitigate defendant's culpability one iota." *Id.* "The purpose of determining loss in a criminal sentencing proceeding is to assess the magnitude of the harm to society and the culpability of the defendant, not to recompense a particular individual in a civil suit." *Id.* at p. 15 (citation omitted). Therefore, the "harm to society is reasonably measured by the overpayment and the resulting deprivation to the investor caused by the artificial inflation." *Id.*

Alternatively, the government argued that the barge transaction was disclosed to the market, and Enron's stock fell as a result; accordingly the civil loss causation standard was met. Govt. Br. at 24. The disclosures in the Fall of 2001 that Enron had been engaged in earnings manipulation resulted in a massive stock price decline. The barge transaction was a piece of the earnings manipulation that was disclosed at that time. *Id.* Under *Huddleston v. Herman & MacLean*, the loss causation requirement is satisfied where "the misrepresentation touches upon the reasons for the investment's decline in value." *Id.* at 25; 640 F.2d 534, 549 (5th Cir. 1981) (internal citation omitted), *aff'd in part and rev'd in part*, 459 U.S. 375 (1983). The Nigerian barge fraud "touch[ed] upon" the overall earnings manipulation at Enron, therefore, the government satisfied the civil loss causation requirement. Govt. Br. at 25.

B. The Defendants' Position: Mere Inflation of Stock Price Does Not Prove Loss

The defendants who were former Merrill Lynch employees (the "Merrill Defendants") argued that the artificial inflation theory of loss was flawed because, although the government contended that the barge transaction inflated the stock, the government did not contend that investors lost the inflation in the value of their stock as a result of the fraud. Merrill Br. at p. 8. Mere artificial inflation in the stock price, the defendants contended, does not prove a loss. *Id.* at p. 10. In order to prove the loss, the government had to prove that the artificial inflation was removed from the stock price because of a public disclosure of the alleged fraud. The government could not make such an argument because the Enron investors lost the value of their stock for reasons unrelated to the barge transaction—the massive fraud that sent Enron into bankruptcy. *Id.*

The Merrill Defendants relied on both civil and criminal cases which held that artificial inflation in stock price is insufficient to prove loss, without further proof that the fraud caused the stock price to decline. *See, e.g., Robbins v. Koger Prop. Inc.* 116 F.3d 1141 ("[The] showing of price inflation, however, does not satisfy the loss causation requirement."); *Grabske*, 160 F. Supp. 2d at 869 ("[T]he government has not adequately explained how the defendant's fraud *caused* [] investors to lose $1.9 million."). The Merrill defendants noted that the federal courts of appeals consistently held that "mere artificial inflation is simply not enough to prove loss in a securities fraud case. *Id.* at 14 (citations omitted). The Merrill Defendants also pointed to a number of criminal cases measuring loss by subtracting the stock price "following announcement of the fraud" from the average stock price for a period of time before the announcement. *See, e.g., United Stated v. Snyder*, 291 F.3d 1291, 1296 (11th Cir. 2002).

The Merrill Defendants emphasized that six months after Merrill Lynch's purchase of the three barges from Enron, Merrill Lynch sold the barges to another entity, LJM2. In the later part of 2000, Enron arranged for the sale of nine barges, including the three Merrill Lynch previously owned, to a third party. As a result of this sale, Enron profited $53 million. Merrill Br. at p. 33. Even if the sale to Merrill Lynch allowed Enron to book a gain too early for the sale of the barges, the gain was not fictitious, and Enron shareholders ultimately profited. *Id.* As a result, the barge transaction could not have caused Enron's stock price to fall.

Finally, the Merrill Defendants argued that there was no evidence that the barge transaction was ever disclosed to the public. *Id.* at 30-32. To assert that the barge transaction had at least some "connection with or relation to" the earnings manipulation engaged in by Enron in order to meet the loss causation requirement, would be "causation run riot." Merrill Br. at p. 31 (citing *Miller v. Schweickart*, 413 F. Supp. 1062 (S.D. N.Y. 1976)). According to the defendants, the government did not put forth any facts to meet its burden of proof that the barge transaction was disclosed as part of Enron's widespread earnings manipulation. Merrill Br. at 32.

C. The Chamber of Commerce: The Word "Loss" in Guideline § 2F1.1 Should Be Given Its Established Meaning Under Securities Law and The Common Law—The Decline In Price Attributable To A Defendant's Misrepresentation

The Chamber of Commerce argued in its *amicus* brief that: i) in order to increase the defendants' sentences for "actual loss," the government must prove that the defendants' misrepresentations caused an actual decline in the price of Enron's stock; ii) the government cannot use the decline in Enron's stock—a decline that preceded disclosure of the misrepresentation at issue in the Nigerian Barge case—as proof that the stock declined as a result of the defendants' misrepresentations; and iii) the word "loss" has the same definition in Guideline § 2F1.1's phrases "actual loss" and "intended loss." Chamber Mem. at 4. According to the Chamber of Commerce, the term "loss" in § 2F1.1 should be defined as it has been defined under securities law and in the common law of fraud. Chamber Mem. at 9-10. In the Barge case, explained the Chamber of Commerce, there was no market-based decline to measure loss; instead, there was only an "expert's speculation" about what would have happened if the misrepresentation had been disclosed before the stock price went down. Chamber Mem. at 2. "Under civil law, such speculation is legally inadequate to demonstrate 'loss'; the Chamber submits that it is even more problematic to use that speculation to increase exponentially criminal punishment." *Id.*

VII. CONCLUSION

At sentencing in the Barge case, the Court declined to apply the government's stock inflation theory for purposes of measuring "loss" under Section 2F1.1. The Court reasoned that it could not do so without engaging in "pure conjecture and speculation." Transcript of Sentencing in *United States v. Bayly, et al.*, at 20.

As argued by the Chamber of Commerce, the stock inflation theory "is particularly troubling in the Guideline setting where substantially increased criminal sanctions will occur arbitrarily in some cases but not others, based on subjective and unpredictable opinion testimony." Chamber Mem. at 17. Given the potentially draconian sentences that can be meted out in securities fraud prosecutions, it can be expected that the role of loss causation in criminal sentencing proceedings will continue to be vigorously contested by the government and the criminal defense bar.

NOTES

10

SHINING A LIGHT OR CURSING THE DARKNESS?—THE IMPACT OF *DURA PHARMS., INC. V. BROUDO*

Lyle Roberts

Paul Chalmers

Wilson Sonsini Goodrich & Rosati

Lyle Roberts is a partner and Paul Chalmers a special counsel in the Reston, Virginia office of Wilson Sonsini Goodrich & Rosati. The views expressed in this article are those of the authors, and do not necessarily represent the views of Wilson Sonsini Goodrich & Rosati or its clients.

This article is current as of July 2005.

Biographical Information

LYLE ROBERTS is a partner with Wilson Sonsini Goodrich & Rosati's Securities Litigation Group in the firm's Reston, Va. office. Mr. Roberts defends public corporations in class actions, derivative actions, mergers and acquisitions litigations, and SEC enforcement actions. Representative clients include Cree, Inspire Pharmaceuticals, and Krispy Kreme. Mr. Roberts recently argued before the U.S. Court of Appeals for the Fourth Circuit and won an affirmance of the lower court's dismissal in the PEC Solutions securities class action. He also counsels clients with respect to securities regulatory issues, including listing and delisting on the Nasdaq Stock Market.

Mr. Roberts is a frequent writer and lecturer on securities litigation topics. He is the author of The 10b-5 Daily (www.the10b-5daily.com), a weblog devoted to news and analysis related to securities class actions, and serves as an Adjunct Professor at the George Mason University School of Law.

Mr. Roberts received his undergraduate and masters degrees in international relations from The Johns Hopkins University. He received his J.D. from the University of Chicago, where he was a member of the Law Review. After law school, Mr. Roberts clerked for Judge Donald S. Russell on the United States Court of Appeals for the Fourth Circuit. Mr. Roberts is admitted to practice in Maryland, Virginia, the District of Columbia, and numerous federal courts.

He can be reached by phone at (703) 734-3174, by fax at (703) 734-3199 and by e-mail at lroberts@wsgr.com.

Table of Contents

In a highly-publicized decision earlier this year, *Dura Pharms., Inc. v. Broudo*, __ U.S. __, 125 S. Ct. 1627 (2005), the Supreme Court addressed what a plaintiff must show to demonstrate that an alleged securities fraud caused his loss (*i.e.,* loss causation), an issue that had sharply divided the lower courts. The main question was whether plaintiffs needed to demonstrate a decline in the value of their securities after revelation of the fraud, or whether it was enough for plaintiffs to demonstrate that the alleged fraud had inflated the price of the securities when they were purchased. In *Dura*, the Supreme Court sided with those courts that require a causal connection between the alleged misrepresentations and a subsequent decline in the stock price.

The narrowly-tailored decision, however, raised as many questions as it answered. While the Court categorically rejected the price-inflation approach to loss causation, it failed to provide lower courts with any real guidance on how to assess whether a plaintiff has adequately plead or proven loss causation—an omission that is already leading to extensive litigation (and contradictory decisions) in the lower courts.

Background

Loss causation is the requirement that a plaintiff plead and prove that the alleged fraud caused him to suffer an economic loss. *See* 15 U.S.C. § 78u-4(b)(4). Prior to *Dura*, courts disagreed as to how a plaintiff could satisfy this requirement, and developed two conflicting approaches.

The first approach, followed by the Eight and Ninth Circuits, was the price inflation approach.[1] Under this approach, the court focused on the moment the plaintiff purchased his security. If the plaintiff could show that his purchase price was inflated due to the defendants' misconduct, he had established loss causation. The plaintiff did not need to allege a subsequent price decline.

The second approach, followed by the Second, Third, Seventh, and Eleventh Circuits, was the price decline approach.[2] Under this approach,

1. *See Broudo v. Dura Pharms., Inc.*, 339 F.3d 933 (9th Cir. 2003); *Gebhardt v. ConAgra Foods, Inc.*, 335 F.3d 824 (8th Cir. 2003).

2. *See, e.g., Lentell v. Merrill Lynch & Co.,* 396 F.3d 161 (2d Cir. 2005); *Semerenko v. Cendant Corp.*, 223 F.3d 165 (3d Cir. 2000); *Robbins v. Koger Props., Inc.*, 116 F.3d 1441 (11th Cir. 1997); *Bastian v. Petren Res. Corp.*, 892 F.2d 680 (7th Cir. 1990).

not only must the plaintiff show that the defendants fraudulently inflated the stock price at the time of his purchase, he must also show that he lost some or all of his overpayment, usually by alleging a corrective price decline after revelation of the fraud.

Dura—The Lower Courts' Rulings

In *Broudo*, the plaintiff alleged that the defendants made misleading statements about clinical trials needed for FDA approval of Dura's Albuterol Spiros asthma medication delivery device. On February 24, 1998, Dura revealed that it expected lower than forecast 1998 revenues and 1998 earnings per share, causing Dura's stock price to decline by 47%. The announcement did not mention the Albuterol Spiros delivery system, and it was not until November 1998, nearly nine months after the end of the class period, that Dura announced the FDA had "found the Albuterol Spiros device not approvable. . . ." *Broudo v. Dura Pharms., Inc.,* 339 F.3d 933, 936 (9th Cir. 2003). The district court found that the plaintiffs had failed to properly plead loss causation because the complaint did "not contain any allegations that the FDA's non-approval [of the Albuterol Spiros device] had any relationship to the February price drop." *Id.* at 937.

The Ninth Circuit reversed. It held that the plaintiffs did not need to allege "that a disclosure and subsequent drop in the market price of the stock have actually occurred, because the injury occurs at the time of the transaction." *Id.* at 938 (citation omitted). In a "fraud on the market case," loss causation "merely requires pleading that the price at the time of purchase was overstated and sufficient identification of the cause." *Id.*

Dura—The Supreme Court's Decision

The Supreme Court, in turn, reversed the Ninth Circuit, rejecting that court's price inflation theory. Instead, the Supreme Court held that a plaintiff must plead and prove that there was a causal connection between the alleged misrepresentations and a subsequent decline in the stock price. *Dura*, 125 S. Ct. at 1631. In explaining its decision, the Court dismissed the idea that price inflation is the equivalent of an economic loss. The Court noted that "as a matter of pure logic, at the moment the transaction takes place, the plaintiff has suffered no loss; the inflated purchase payment is offset by ownership of a share that *at that instant* possesses equivalent value." *Id.* (emphasis in original) Moreover, it is not inevitable that an initially inflated purchase price will lead to a later loss. A subsequent resale of the stock at a lower price may result from "changed economic circumstances, changed investor expectations, new industry-specific or firm-specific facts, conditions, or other events, which taken separately or together account for some or all of that lower price." *Id.* at 1632.

The Court also found that the price inflation theory has no support in the common law. The common law has "long insisted" that a plaintiff in a deceit or misrepresentation action "show not only that had he known the truth he would not have acted but also that he suffered actual economic loss." *Id.* Accordingly, it was "not surprising that other courts of appeals have rejected the Ninth Circuit's 'inflated purchase price' approach." *Id.* (citations omitted)

Finally, the Court noted that the price inflation theory of loss causation was arguably at odds with the objectives of the securities statutes, including the Private Securities Litigation Reform Act of 1995 ("PSLRA"). *Id.* at 1633. These statutes make private securities fraud actions available "not to provide investors with broad insurance against market losses, but to protect them against those economic losses that misrepresentations actually cause." *Id.* In particular, the PSLRA "makes clear Congress' intent to permit private securities fraud actions for recovery where, but only where, plaintiffs adequately allege and prove the traditional elements of causation and loss." *Id.*

Revealing The Fraud

While the *Dura* decision resolved the substantive standard for establishing loss causation, it provided virtually no guidance on how courts should apply that standard. Most significantly, the Supreme Court declined to address what constitutes a revelation of the fraud beyond making some opaque references to when "the relevant truth begins to leak out" and "after the truth makes its way into the market place." 125 S. Ct. at 1631-32. The open question is whether the revelation of the fraud must take the form of a corrective disclosure leading to a stock price drop, or whether the plaintiff can allege that the truth reached investors in some other, less direct fashion.

The importance of this issue—and the room left for judicial disagreement—can be seen in a pair of divergent post-*Dura* appellate decisions. In the first circuit court decision to apply the Supreme Court's holding, the Sixth Circuit affirmed the dismissal of a securities class action based on the plaintiffs' failure to adequately plead loss causation. *D.E.&J. L.P. v. Conaway,* No. 03-2334, 2005 WL 1386448 (6th Cir. June 10, 2005) (unpublished). The case was brought against several former Kmart executives and PricewaterhouseCoopers. The plaintiffs alleged that the defendants misled Kmart's investors in 2000 and 2001 prior to the company's bankruptcy. The court found that the plaintiffs "did not plead that the alleged fraud became known to the market on any particular day, did not estimate the damages that the alleged fraud caused, and did not connect the alleged fraud with the ultimate disclosure or loss." *Id.* at *5. In the end, the plaintiffs relied entirely on allegations that they had paid artificially inflated prices for their Kmart stock and that Kmart's stock price declined after the company announced its bankruptcy. The court held: (a) the Supreme Court had expressly rejected price inflation as an adequate basis for pleading loss causation; and (b) the plaintiffs "never alleged that Kmart's bankruptcy announcement disclosed any prior misrepresentations to the market." *Id.* at *6.

By contrast, the Ninth Circuit has taken a much less stringent approach. *In re Daou Sys., Inc.*, __F.3d__, No. 02-56989, 2005 WL 1431833 (9th Cir. June 21, 2005). In *Daou*, the plaintiffs alleged that the company prematurely recognized revenue. The lower court found that loss causation had not been adequately plead, however, because the complaint did not "allege that there were any negative public statements, announcements or disclosures at the time the stock price dropped that Defendants were engaged in improper accounting practices." *Id.* at *15. The Ninth Circuit reversed, noting that the complaint alleged that the "price of Daou's stock fell precipitously after defendants began to reveal figures showing the company's true financial condition." *Id.* In particular, the court pointed to a series of warnings by the company during the third quarter of 1998 that its "operating expenses and margins were deteriorating"; the company's announcement several months later that third quarter revenues had missed expectations; and a statement by an unnamed securities analyst that, given this course of events, "you have got to question whether they are manufacturing earnings." *Id.* The court held that the plaintiffs' allegations "if assumed true, are sufficient to provide Daou with some indication that the drop in Daou's stock price was causally related to Daou's financial misstatements reflecting its practice of prematurely recognizing revenue before it was earned." *Id.* at *16

It is difficult to reconcile the holdings of the two appellate courts, which appear to have different concepts of what constitutes a disclosure of the "relevant truth."[3] Does a plaintiff have to point to a disclosure revealing that the alleged misrepresentations were false when made (6th Circuit) or is it sufficient to point to a disclosure that deflates the market's expectations about the company (9th Circuit)? To put it another way, a bankruptcy filing is certainly a revelation of a company's "true financial condition," but the Sixth Circuit does not appear to agree with the Ninth Circuit that financial revelations (unless the revelations also disclose the existence of misrepresentations) are sufficient to connect a stock price drop to an alleged fraud. If these early decisions are any indication, the Supreme Court may have simply reframed the circuit split over loss causation rather than resolved it.

Other Issues

Dura raises some additional concerns for the securities litigation bar:

Pleading With Particularity—The Supreme Court also left another contentious issue unresolved: whether loss causation must be plead with particularity. Because the plaintiffs' allegations were deemed to be insufficient even under Fed. R. Civ. P. 8's "short and plain statement" requirement, the Court "assume[d], at least for arguments sake," that neither the PSLRA nor Fed. R. Civ. P. 9(b) impose "any special further [pleading] requirement" as to loss causation. *Dura*, 125 S. Ct. at 1634. The Court concluded that even under a notice pleading standard "it should not prove burdensome for a plaintiff who has suffered an economic loss to provide a defendant with some indication of the loss and the causal connection that the plaintiff has in mind." *Id.*

At least one lower court has seized on this language and concluded that there is no heightened pleading standard for loss causation allegations. *See Rocker Management, L.L.C. v. Lernout & Hauspie Speech Prods. N.V.*, No. Civ. A. 00-5965(JCL), 2005 WL 1366025, at *7 (D.N.J. June 8, 2005). Other courts (*e.g.,* the Ninth Circuit in *Daou*) appear to

3. Another interesting post-*Dura* decision on this question is *In re Initial Public Offering Sec. Litig.*, No. MDL 1554(SAS), 2005 WL 1162445 (S.D.N.Y. May 6, 2005). The plaintiffs alleged a scheme by an investment bank and several issuers to systematically set the issuers' announced earnings forecasts below internal forecasts. When earnings consistently beat the announced forecasts, plaintiffs alleged, the resulting excitement in the market drove the issuers' stock prices up. The plaintiffs alleged that this scheme was ultimately revealed to the market through a series of pronouncements disclosing that earnings were below expectations or warning that future earnings would not meet expectations. The plaintiffs alleged that these announcements ended "the fraudulently induced expectation of continuing upside surprises. . . ." *Id.* at *3. The court rejected the plaintiffs' reliance on these disclosures because they were not "corrective disclosures." The court explained that "[t]o allege loss causation, plaintiffs must allege that, at some point, the concealed scheme was disclosed to the market." *Id.* None of the disclosures relied on by the plaintiffs, however, implied that there had been a fraudulent scheme. *Id.*

have simply assumed that "some indication" is all that is required. Although no court appears to have engaged in a direct examination of whether, for example, loss causation is a "circumstance" of the alleged securities fraud and therefore must be plead with particularity pursuant to Fed. R. Civ. P. 9(b), a decision on this issue seems inevitable.

Appointment of Lead Plaintiff or Class Representative—There is an active district court split over whether in-and-out traders (*i.e.,* investors who both bought and sold their shares during the class period) are subject to a unique loss causation defense and therefore should not be named as the lead plaintiff or class representative in a securities class action. *Compare In re Bally Total Fitness Sec. Litig.*, No. 04C5350, 2005 WL 627960 (N.D. Ill. Mar. 15, 2005) *with Montoya v. Mama.com, Inc.*, No. 05 Civ. 2313(HB), 2005 WL 1278097 (S.D.N.Y. May 31, 2005). The Supreme Court's finding that if a "purchaser sells the shares quickly before the relevant truth begins to leak out, the misrepresentation will not have led to any loss," would appear to bolster the position that in-and-out traders should not be appointed to these positions.

Class Certification—For class certification to be proper, the plaintiff must show, *inter alia*, that common issues predominate over individual ones. Fed. R. Civ. P. 23(b). Thus, the plaintiff "must present a methodology for determining loss causation that may be commonly applied to all members of the class." *In re Initial Public Offering Sec. Litig.*, 227 F.R.D. 65, 111 (S.D.N.Y. 2004). Under *Dura*, this means that the plaintiff needs to provide a mechanism for showing that the alleged misrepresentation caused a price decline that affected all class members. *Id.* at 111-12. Class members whose shares were not so affected (*e.g.*, they sold before the decline, bought afterwards, or a netting of all of their relevant stock trades reveals no real loss) would be differently situated, meaning loss causation would not be a common issue. *Id.* This suggests that a plaintiff will have to carefully define and limit his proposed class to take account of these factors. It also raises the possibility of intra-class conflicts that may require the establishment of sub-classes and whether a class action, in some cases, will be superior to other available methods of adjudication.

Damages Analysis—Although the Court noted that a variety of factors, besides an alleged fraud, could cause a stock price decline (125 S. Ct. at 1632), it did not provide guidance as to how plaintiffs can meet their burden of proof for loss causation in cases where some or all of these other factors are present. To put it another way, the Court called for a "battle of the experts" without establishing any rules of engagement. Given *Dura*'s mandate that plaintiffs link their losses to the alleged misrepresentations, damages models that do not exclude stock price fluctuations attributable to factors other than the alleged misrepresentations are of dubious validity. A number of popular plaintiff-friendly damages models, including the constant true value, constant percent ribbon method, and index method models, will be subject to challenge.[4]

Conclusion

The relevance of *Dura*—and the questions it presents—will depend on the facts before the court. Many securities fraud claims provide a direct link between the alleged fraud and a stock price decline. If a company, for example, announces a financial restatement and the announcement leads to a stock price decline, plaintiffs will have little difficulty establishing that the stock price decline was related to the earlier financial misstatements. As the link becomes more tenuous, however, loss causation becomes an increasingly viable defense. With a divide already opening on the key question of what constitutes a disclosure of the "relevant truth," it is almost certain that the judicial debate on loss causation will continue, and possibly with the same mixed results that led the Supreme Court to intervene in the first place.

4. It is already the case that some courts have rejected the use of aggregate trading models to establish damages as insufficiently reliable. *See, e.g., In re Broadcom Corp. Sec. Litig.*, No. SA CV 01275GLTMLGX, 2005 WL 1403756 (C.D. Cal. June 3, 2005); *Kaufman v. Motorola, Inc.*, No. 95 C 1069, 2000 WL 1506892 (N.D. Ill. Sept. 21, 2000). The *Dura* decision is likely to add further fuel to that fire.

NOTES

11

LOSS CAUSATION

Scott D. Musoff

Joanne Gaboriault

Skadden, Arps, Slate, Meagher & Flom LLP

Scott D. Musoff is a partner and Joanne Gaboriault is an associate at Skadden, Arps, Slate, Meagher & Flom LLP.

Table of Contents

I. INTRODUCTION

In cases involving publicly traded securities and purchases or sales in public securities markets, the basic elements for a claim under Section 10(b) of the Securities Exchange Act of 1934 (the "Exchange Act"), 15 U.S.C. 78j(b) and Rule 10b-5 promulgated thereunder, 17 C.F.R. § 240.10b-5 (2005) include:

(1) a material misrepresentation (or omission), see Basic Inc. v. Levinson, 485 U.S. 224, 231-32 (1988);

(2) scienter, i.e., a wrongful state of mind, see Ernst & Ernst v. Hochfelder, 425 U.S. 185, 197, 199 (1976);

(3) a connection with the purchase or sale of a security, see Blue Chip Stamps v. Manor Drug Stores, 421 U.S. 723, 730-31 (1975);

(4) reliance, often referred to in cases involving public securities markets (fraud-on-the-market cases) as "transaction causation," see Basic Inc., 485 U.S. at 248-49 (nonconclusively presuming that the price of a publicly traded share reflects a material misrepresentation and that plaintiffs have relied upon that misrepresentation as long as they would not have bought the share in its absence);

(5) economic loss, 15 U.S.C. § 78u-4(b)(4); and

(6) "loss causation," i.e., a causal connection between the material misrepresentation and the loss, id.; cf. 3 Thomas Lee Hazen, The Law of Securities Regulation § 12.11[1], [3] (5th ed. 2005).

Dura Pharms. Inc. v. Broudo, 125 S. Ct. 1627, 1631 (2005) (listing elements and authorities).

Even though the Private Securities Litigation Reform Act of 1995, Pub. L. No. 104-67, 109 Stat. 737 (the "PSLRA"), codified certain pleading requirements, including that plaintiff must plead and prove that the act or omission complained of caused the loss for which plaintiff seeks damages, see 15 U.S.C. § 78u-4(b)(4) (enacted by the PSLRA) until recently, the element of loss causation had not been a heavily litigated issue at the pleading stage. However, the combination of the bursting of the technology bubble in 2000-2001—which led to large declines in market capitalization—and the proliferation of novel claims brought against non-issuers (e.g., research claims brought against financial institutions), has propelled the defense of failure to plead loss causation into an increasingly important and highly litigated subject.

Indeed, the issue of what is necessary to plead loss causation in a "fraud on the market" case has percolated to the United States Supreme Court, resulting in the decision in Dura Pharmaceuticals, Inc. v. Broudo, 125 S. Ct. 1627 (2005) on April 19, 2005, which resolved a split in the circuits. Prior to the Dura Pharmaceuticals decision, the majority view (Second, Third, Seventh and Eleventh Circuits) was that, to sufficiently plead loss causation, a plaintiff must adequately allege a causal connection between the loss and the alleged misstatement upon which plaintiff relied. Thus, in a "fraud on the market" case, plaintiff must allege both that the price of the security was "artificially inflated" at the time of purchase by the alleged misstatements (reliance or "transaction causation") and that the circumstance concealed by the alleged misstatement was the actual cause of the asserted loss. Loss causation is (typically) pleaded by alleging a decline in the price of the security when the subject matter of the alleged fraud is revealed.

The minority view (Eighth and Ninth Circuits) held that loss causation is sufficiently pled where plaintiff has pled that plaintiff purchased securities at a price "artificially inflated" by the alleged fraud. These circuits reasoned that plaintiff's "loss" occurs at the time of purchase—when he or she overpays for the security.

II. BASICS OF LOSS CAUSATION

A. **Transaction causation or reliance as distinguished from loss causation**: To plead a claim under Section10(b) of the Exchange Act 15 U.S.C. § 78j(b), a plaintiff must allege that his or her injuries were caused by the defendant's conduct. There are two different types of causation.

1. **Transaction causation**: This is generally thought of as the "reliance" or "but for" prong of causation, i.e., "that but for the fraudulent statement or omission, plaintiff would not have entered into the transaction." Suez Equity Investors, L.P. v. Toronto-Dominion Bank, 250 F.3d 87, 95 (2d Cir. 2001).

a. **"Fraud on the Market" Theory**: The securities fraud plaintiff need not plead actual reliance or "transaction causation." Instead, in well-developed, so-called "efficient markets" plaintiffs may, at the pleading stage, invoke a "rebuttable presumption" of transaction causation as a surrogate for actual reliance. See Basic Inc. v. Levinson, 485 U.S. 224, 241-50 (1988).

b. This efficient market hypothesis posits that the market price of a security reflects all material information disclosed to the market and that investors may be presumed to rely on the integrity of the price of a security when deciding to purchase or sell.

2. **Loss causation**: This is more akin to the tort concept of "proximate causation" or "legal causation." This is the connection between the defendant's alleged misconduct and the economic harm suffered by the plaintiff.

3. **Summary**: Thus, while transaction causation concerns plaintiff's decision to enter into the securities transaction, loss causation addresses the requirement that the alleged misrepresentation be the actual cause of plaintiff's alleged economic loss, i.e., the reason the transaction turned out to be a losing one.

B. **History of loss causation**

1. **Common law**: Initially, loss causation was a judicially inferred element of a Section 10(b) cause of action.

a. Cases decided before the enactment of the PSLRA in 1995 held that the plaintiff had to prove "that the untruth was in some reasonably direct, or proximate, way responsible for his loss." Huddleston v. Herman & MacLean, 640 F.2d 534, 549 (5th Cir. Unit A Mar. 1981), aff'd in part, rev'd in part on other grounds, 459 U.S. 375 (1983); see also Schlick v. Penn-Dixie Cement Corp., 507 F.2d 374, 380-81 (2d Cir. 1974), overruled on other grounds by Virginia Bankshares v. Sandberg, 501 U.S. 1083 (1991).

b. One rationale for this requirement is that an investor should not recover for a decline in value that is unrelated to the alleged misrepresentation. See Huddleston, 640 F.2d at 549.

c. "If the plaintiffs would have lost their investment regardless of the fraud, any award of damages to them would be a windfall." Bastian v. Petren Res. Corp., 892 F.2d 680, 684-85 (7th Cir. 1990); see also id. at 685 ("No social purpose would be served by encouraging everyone who suffers an investment loss because of an unanticipated change in market conditions to pick through offering memoranda with a fine-tooth comb in the hope of uncovering a misrepresentation.").

2. **PSLRA codification**: In Section 21D(b)(4) of the Exchange Act, 15 U.S.C. 78u-4(b)(4) (enacted by the PSLRA), Congress codified loss causation as an element of a Section 10(b) claim. See 15 U.S.C. § 78u-4(b)(4).

a. "[T]he plaintiff shall have the burden of proving that the act or omission of the defendant alleged to [have] violate[d] [the Exchange Act] caused the loss for which the plaintiff seeks to recover damages." Id.

b. Congress thus established that a misrepresentation and a loss are not sufficient: plaintiff must plead and prove that the alleged misrepresentation caused the alleged loss. See id.

c. The legislative history indicates that the PSLRA's intent was "to reduce the cost of raising capital" by, inter alia, "codifying the requirement under current law that plaintiffs prove that the loss in the value of their stock was caused by the Section 10(b) violation and not by other factors." S. Rep. No. 104-98, at 7 (1995), reprinted in 1995 U.S.C.C.A.N. 679, 686.

d. The PSLRA also enacted a 90-day "look back" period which limits plaintiff's recovery to "the difference between the purchase or sale price paid or received, as appropriate, by the plaintiff for the subject security and the mean trading price of that security during the 90-day period beginning on the date on which the information correcting the misstatement or omission that is the basis for the action is disseminated to the market." 15 U.S.C. § 78u-4(e)(1) (emphasis added).

(1) This provision assumes a connection between that plaintiff's asserted loss and a disclosure revealing the alleged misstatement.

(2) The legislative history reveals that the 90-day average was intended to reduce the level of uncertainty in calculating damages, "thereby limiting damages to those losses caused by the fraud and not by other market conditions." S. Rep.

No. 104-98 at 20 (1995), reprinted in 1995 U.S.C.C.A.N. 679, 699.

III. CIRCUITS THAT HELD THAT PLEADING PRICE INFLATION IS SUFFICIENT TO PLEAD LOSS CAUSATION

A. **Introduction**: Two circuits have held that to plead loss causation adequately in a fraud-on-the market case, plaintiffs do not have to allege that information revealing the alleged misstatements was disclosed to the market, causing a decline in the price of the security. These courts hold that loss causation is sufficiently pled if plaintiff alleges that the misrepresentation created a disparity between the market price and the stock's "true" value at the time of the purchase ("purchase-time disparity").

1. **Eighth Circuit**: Gebhardt v. ConAgra Foods, Inc., 335 F.3d 824 (8th Cir. 2003). In this case, plaintiffs alleged defendants fraudulently overstated revenues which ultimately led to an earnings restatement. However, when the disclosure regarding the restatement was made, the stock price dropped about two percent, but quickly recovered and ninety days later, was trading higher than before the disclosure. See id. at 827-28.

   a. The court rejected defendants' argument that because the stock's trading price increased soon after the announcement, there could be no connection between the misrepresentation and any loss. See id. at 831-32.

   b. The court held that stockholders could "be damaged in other ways" than a price depreciation, such as less of an appreciation had there been no fraud. Id.

   c. The court held that the absence of a stock price decline upon disclosure of the facts allegedly concealed by the fraud was not dispositive of the issue of whether the alleged fraud caused a loss; the court would first have to consider "expert testimony, which cannot be considered" on a motion to dismiss. Id. at 832.

   d. The court reasoned that plaintiffs adequately pleaded loss causation because they could invoke the fraud-on-the market theory and assume that the misrepresentations inflated the stock's price: "Our finding of materiality allows the plaintiffs to invoke the fraud-on-the market theory and assume that the misrepresentations inflated the stock's price. Paying more for something than it is worth is damaging. " Id. at 831.

2. **Ninth Circuit**: Broudo v. Dura Pharmaceuticals, Inc., 339 F.3d 933 (9th Cir. 2003), rev'd, 125 S. Ct. 1627 (2005). In Broudo, the Ninth Circuit held that plaintiff had adequately pled loss causation as to the company's alleged misstatements concerning the "efficaciousness" of a medical device it was testing and developing in coordination with the FDA. On the last day of the putative class period, the company had announced that it expected a revenue short-fall but did not mention anything about the medical device, which, as it later turned out, was not approved by the FDA. See Broudo, 339 F.3d at 936-37, 941.

   a. The Ninth Circuit held that loss causation was sufficiently pled as to the medical device misstatement because plaintiff alleged that the stock price on the date of purchase was inflated because of the misrepresentation. See id. at 938-39. "[I]njury occurs at the time of the transaction," and therefore it is unnecessary to plead a corrective disclosure and stock price decline. Id. at 938.

   b. The Ninth Circuit rejected the lower court's holding that because there were no corrective disclosures during the class period regarding the medical device, the complaint could not allege a causal relationship between plaintiffs' loss and the alleged misstatements. See id. at 938-39. Under the Ninth Circuit's precedents, plaintiff need only allege that the stock price was overstated at the time of the purchase and "sufficient[ly] identif[y] . . . the cause for this overvaluation." Id. at 939.

IV. CIRCUITS THAT REQUIRED PLAINTIFFS TO ALLEGE THAT THE FRAUD IS THE REASON FOR THE DECLINE IN THE INVESTMENT

A. **Eleventh Circuit**: Robbins v. Koger Properties, Inc., 116 F.3d 1441 (11th Cir. 1997). In Robbins, plaintiffs alleged that the issuer's accountant fraudulently overstated the issuer's cash flows. Following the issuer's announcement that it was cutting its dividend, stock prices declined by more than fifty percent. The alleged fraud by the accountant was not revealed until long after the end of the class period. See id. at 1443-45.

1. The court expressly rejected the Eighth and Ninth Circuit standards: "Our cases do not hold that proof that a plaintiff purchased securities at an artificially inflated price, without more, satisfies the loss causation requirement." Id. at 1448.

2. Loss causation was not adequately pled where there was no evidence that the price inflation due to the accounting fraud was removed from the stock price at the end of the class period. See id. at 1448-49. There must be "proof of a causal connection between the misrepresentation and the investment's subsequent decline in value." Id. at 1448.

B. **Third Circuit**: Semerenko v. Cendant Corp., 223 F.3d 165 (3d Cir. 2000). In Semerenko, plaintiffs alleged the defendant made false statements regarding its financial condition in connection with a planned tender offer, which, in turn, increased the price of the target's stock. The court found that loss causation had been pled because when the misrepresentations were disclosed, the price of the target's stock fell. See id. at 169-71, 185-86.

1. Citing Robbins v. Koger Properties, Inc., 166 F.3d 1441 (11th Cir. 1997) with approval, the Third Circuit held that unless plaintiff alleges that the "artificial inflation" allegedly created by the misrepresentation was removed from the stock price when the "truth" was made known, "it cannot be said that there is in fact an economic loss attributable to that misrepresentation." Semerenko, 223 F.3d at 185.

C. **Seventh Circuit**: Bastian v. Petren Resources Corp., 892 F.2d 680 (7th Cir. 1990) (Posner, J.). The court affirmed dismissal of a securities fraud complaint relating to the purchase of oil and gas limited partnerships where defendants had allegedly misrepresented in the offering memorandum facts relating to their "competence and integrity." Plaintiff's purchases took place amid a peak in the price of oil that declined steadily thereafter. Id. at 682-84.

1. The court rejected plaintiffs' contention that the fraud was the cause of their loss because "they would not have invested but

for the fraud; [and] if they had not invested, they would not have lost their money." Id. at 683.

2. The Seventh Circuit explained that "[i]f the defendants' oil and gas ventures failed not because of the personal shortcomings that the defendants concealed but because of industry-wide phenomena that destroyed all or most such ventures, then the plaintiffs, given their demonstrated desire to invest in such ventures, lost nothing by reason of the defendants' fraud and have no claim to damages." Id. at 685.

D. **Second Circuit**: Emergent Capital Investment Management. LLC v. Stonepath Group, Inc., 343 F.3d 189 (2d Cir. 2003). The Second Circuit held that an allegation of a purchase-time value disparity, standing alone, cannot satisfy the loss causation pleading requirement.

> By claiming that it incorrectly appraised the value of [the] securities and purchased them at an inflated price, [plaintiff] simply asserts that, had it known about [the allegedly omitted information], it would not have agreed to buy [the] stock at the offering price. Hence, its "investment quality" allegation amounts to nothing more than a paraphrased allegation of transaction causation. While it may explain why plaintiff purchased the . . . stock, it does not explain why it lost money on the purchase, the very question that the loss causation allegation must answer.

Id. at 198.

V. SECOND CIRCUIT'S RECENT PRONOUNCEMENT: LENTELL V. MERRILL LYNCH & CO.

A. **Introduction**: Recently, the Court of Appeals for the Second Circuit affirmed dismissal of two of several class actions brought against Merrill Lynch and one of its research analysts seeking damages for alleged losses plaintiffs incurred investing in internet stocks. The complaints—brought by persons who were not even customers of Merrill Lynch and had not read or relied upon the allegedly false "Buy" and "Accumulate" ratings in Merrill Lynch's research reports—alleged that their losses stemmed from their having purchased the subject stocks at prices allegedly inflated by the ratings. See Lentell v. Merrill Lynch & Co., 396 F.3d 161, 164-67, 172, 175 (2d Cir. 2005).

1. Affirming the district court's dismissal for failure to plead loss causation, the court unequivocally held that to plead loss causation, a plaintiff must allege "that the misstatement or omission concealed something from the market that, when disclosed, negatively affected the value of the security. Otherwise the loss in question was not foreseeable." Id. at 173.

2. Thus,

   a. the decline in value of the securities must be directly related to subject matter of the alleged misrepresentations or omissions; and

   b. the loss complained of must be a foreseeable result of the challenged conduct. See id. at 173-74.

3. Judge Dennis Jacobs, writing for the court, emphasized that although a 2001 case, Suez Equity Investors, L.P. v. Toronto Dominion Bank, 250 F.3d 87 (2d Cir. 2001), "can be (mis-) read to say that this Circuit has rejected the 'materialization of risk' approach," the Second Circuit's precedents both before and after Suez Equity, require "that the loss be caused by the materialization of the concealed risk." Lentell, 396 F.3d at 173.

B. **Analysis**: The court began by reiterating the court's long established requirement "that a securities-fraud plaintiff 'must prove both transaction [causation] and loss causation.'" Id. at 172 (citation omitted).

1. Transaction causation was not at issue in this appeal and historically has not often been challenged at the pleading stage. See, e.g., Hevesi v. Citigroup Inc., 366 F.3d 70, 78-79 n.6 (2d Cir. 2004) ("On motions to dismiss . . . courts are required to assume the truth of well-pleaded allegations, including allegations that an analyst's misrepresentations affected the market price of securities.").

2. The court reiterated its holding in the 2003 case, Emergent Capital Investment Management, LLC v. Stonepath Group, Inc., 343 F.3d 189 (2d Cir. 2003), that an allegation "that a defendant's misrepresentations and omissions induced a 'purchase-time value disparity' between the price paid for a security and its 'true "investment quality"' . . . is 'nothing more than a paraphrased allegation of transaction causation'—[it]

explains why a particular investment was made, but does not speak to the relationship between the fraud and the loss of the investment." Lentell, 396 F.3d at 174 (quoting Emergent Capital, 343 F.3d at 198).

a. Note that such "purchase time disparity" allegations are precisely what have been held sufficient to plead loss causation by the Eighth and Ninth Circuits.

3. The court explained that the although the loss causation pleading requirement is analogous to the common law element of proximate cause, the analogy is imperfect:

a. "A foreseeable injury at common law is one proximately caused by the defendant's fault, but it cannot ordinarily be said that a drop in the value of a security is 'caused' by the misstatements or omissions made about it, as opposed to the underlying circumstance that is concealed or misstated." Lentell, 396 F.3d at 173.

b. Thus, plaintiff must plead "'that the subject of the fraudulent statement or omission was the cause of the actual loss suffered.'" Id. (quoting Suez Equity, 250 F.3d at 95); see also Emergent Capital, 343 F.3d at 199.

4. The court also emphasized that "'when the plaintiff's loss coincides with a marketwide phenomenon causing comparable losses to other investors, the prospect that the plaintiff's loss was caused by the fraud decreases, 'and a plaintiff's claim fails when 'it has not adequately ple[]d facts which, if proven, would show that its loss was caused by the alleged misstatements as opposed to intervening events.'" Lentell, 396 F.3d at 174 (alteration in original) (quoting First Nationwide Bank v. Gelt Funding Corp., 27 F.3d 763, 772 (2d Cir. 1994)). "Though all reasonable inferences are drawn in the plaintiff's favor on a motion to dismiss on the pleadings, 'conclusions of law or unwarranted deductions of fact are not admitted.'" Lentell, 396 F.3d at 174-75 (quoting First Nationwide Bank, 27 F.3d at 771).

C. **Application to the allegations in Lentell**: The Second Circuit held that plaintiffs' loss causation allegations were fatally flawed because there was (i) "no allegation that the market reacted negatively to a corrective disclosure regarding the falsity of Merrill's 'buy' and 'accumulate' recommendations" and (ii) "no allegation that Merrill misstated or omitted risks that did lead to the loss." Lentell, 396 F.3d at 175.

1. Plaintiffs pled no causal relationship between the research reports containing the allegedly fraudulent "Buy" and "Accumulate" ratings and the declines in plaintiffs' investments in internet securities. See id.

   a. There was "no allegation that the market reacted negatively to a corrective disclosure regarding the falsity of Merrill's 'buy' and 'accumulate' recommendations." Id.

   b. The court rejected plaintiffs' contention that they adequately pled loss causation by alleging that the trading prices declined when the stocks were downgraded (e.g., from "Buy" to "Accumulate"), holding that downgrades are not corrective disclosures "because they do not reveal to the market the falsity of the prior recommendations." Id. at 175 n.4.

   c. Indeed, the court noted that plaintiffs had affirmatively argued (and the complaints withstood a statute of limitations reversal on the strength of that argument) that they did not know of the falsity until well after the close of their putative class periods. See id.

2. Plaintiffs failed "to allege facts to establish that the [defendant]'s misstatements and omissions concealed the price-volatility risk (or some other risk) that materialized and played some part in diminishing the market value of [their internet securities]." Id. at 176-77.

   a. The court found it "incontestible that the risk price volatility—and hence, the risk of implosion—is apparent on the face of every report challenged." Id. at 176.

   b. The court held that "where, (as here) substantial indicia of the risk that materialized are unambiguously apparent on the face of the disclosures alleged to conceal the very same risk, a plaintiff must allege (i) facts sufficient to support an inference it was defendant's fraud—rather than other salient factors—that proximately caused plaintiff's loss; or (ii) facts sufficient to apportion the losses between the disclosed and concealed portions of the risk that ultimately destroyed an investment. Plaintiffs have done neither . . . ." Id. at 177 (emphasis added).

3. With respect to plaintiffs' allegations concerning allegedly undisclosed conflicts of interest, the court noted that such alleged conflicts "do not, standing alone, evidence fraud," id. at 170, and found that plaintiffs had simply made no attempt to connect these alleged omissions with any "concealed . . . risk of a significant devaluation of [the internet securities]." Id. at 177.

VI. THE SUPREME COURT'S DECISION IN DURA PHARMACEUTICALS, INC. V. BROUDO

A. The Supreme Court's decision in Dura Pharmaceuticals, Inc. v. Broudo, 125 S. Ct. 1627 (2005), addressed the question of whether it is sufficient for purposes of pleading loss causation to allege "'that the price *on the date of purchase* was inflated because of the misrepresentation.'" Id. at 1630 (citation omitted).

B. Concluding that it was not, the Court held that, "as a matter of pure logic," there cannot be a loss at the time of purchase because the artificial inflation created by the alleged misrepresentation "is offset by ownership of a share that *at that instant* possesses equivalent value." Id. at 1631. The Court explained that in a "fraud on the market" case, it is *necessary* that the misrepresentation be revealed to the market before there can be any economic loss attributable to it. See id. at 1631-32.

C. However, revelation of the misrepresentation may not be *sufficient* to show a loss attributable to it:

> [The] lower price may reflect, not the earlier misrepresentation, but changed economic circumstances, changed investor expectations, new industry-specific or firm-specific facts, conditions, or other events, which taken separately or together account for some or all of that lower price. . . . Other things being equal, the longer the time between purchase and sale, . . . the more likely that other factors caused the loss.

Id. at 1632.

D. Rejecting the Ninth Circuit's approach that it is sufficient to allege that the price of a security was inflated by an alleged misrepresentation at the time of purchase, the Supreme Court explained that private rights of action under the anti-fraud provisions of the securities laws are "available, not to provide investors with broad insurance against market losses, but to protect them against those economic losses that misrepresentations actually cause." Id. at 1633.

E. "Given the common-law roots of the securities fraud action (and the common-law requirement that a plaintiff show actual damages), it is not surprising that other courts of appeals have rejected the Ninth Circuit's 'inflated purchase price' approach to proving causation and loss."Id. at 1632-33 (citing Emergent Capital Inv. Mgmt., LLC v. Stonepath Group, Inc., 343 F.3d 189, 198 (2d Cir. 2003); Semerenko v. Cendant Corp., 223 F.3d 165, 185 (3d Cir. 2000); Robbins v. Koger Props., Inc., 116 F.3d 1441, 1448 (11th Cir. 1997); Bastian v. Petren Res. Corp., 892 F.2d 680, 685 (7th Cir. 1990)). Moreover, "[t]he [PSLRA] makes clear Congress' intent to permit private securities fraud actions for recovery where, but only where, plaintiffs adequately allege and prove the traditional elements of causation and loss." Dura Pharms., 125 S. Ct. at 1633.

F. The Supreme Court concluded:

> In sum, we find the Ninth Circuit's approach inconsistent with the law's requirement that a plaintiff prove that the defendant's misrepresentation (or other fraudulent conduct) proximately caused the plaintiff's economic loss. We need not, and do not, consider other proximate cause or loss-related questions.

Id. at 1633-34 (emphasis added).

VII. CERTAIN POST-DURA PHARMACEUTICALS CASES

A. D.E. & J. Limited Partnership v. Conaway, No. 03-2334, 2005 WL 1386448 (6th Cir. June 10, 2005) (not for publication): The Sixth Circuit found that the complaint did "not differ in any material respect from Broudo's. Like Broudo, D.E. & J. did not plead that the alleged fraud became known to the market on any particular day, did not estimate the damages that the alleged fraud caused, and did not connect the alleged fraud with the ultimate disclosure and loss." Id. at *5.

B. In re Immune Response Securities Litigation, No. 01CV1237JWMC, 2005 WL 1579484 (S.D. Cal. June 7, 2005):

Court held that loss causa tion allegations satisfied Dura Pharmaceuticals because "[p]laintiffs allege that the price of the stock 'collapse[d] as the truth regarding REMUNE emerged.' . . . The Complaint specifically pleads that when the disappointing study results and Agouron's decision to terminate funding were finally revealed, the price of IRC's stock went from $18.31 to $2.00 per share." Immune Response, 2005 WL 1579484, at *32 (second alteration in original).

C. Joffe v. Lehman Brothers, Inc., No. 04 Civ.3507 RWS, 2005 WL 1492101 (S.D.N.Y. June 23, 2005): Court held that loss causation allegations did not satisfy Dura Pharmaceuticals because the complaint "contained no allegations of a causal connection between the alleged misrepresentations and a subsequent economic loss suffered by the [p]laintiffs." Joffe, 2005 WL 1492101, at *9.

D. In re Daou Systems, Inc. Securities Litigation, No. 02-56989, 2005 WL 1431833 (9th Cir. June, 21, 2005) (to be published in F.3d): Ninth Circuit held that "assertions of a steep drop in Daou's stock price following the revelation of Daou's true financial situation are sufficient to enable the complaint to survive a motion to dismiss." Id. at *16.

E. In re Initial Public Offering Securities Litigation, No. MDL 1554 (SAS), 2005 WL 1529659 (S.D.N.Y. June 28, 2005): Court dismissed complaint for failing to plead loss causation, holding that "Dura did not disturb Second Circuit precedent regarding loss causation." Initial Pub. Offering, 2005 WL 1529659, at *1. The court held in connection with a research opinion, relying on Lentell, that "where the alleged misstatement is an intentionally false opinion, the market will not respond to the truth until the falsity is revealed—i.e. a corrective disclosure." Initial Pub. Offering, 2005 WL 1529659, at *6 & n.56.

VIII. CONCLUSION

A. Loss causation will surely continue be a highly litigated topic.

B. The Supreme Court's decision in Dura Pharmaceuticals should add to the arsenal available to litigants defending federal securities actions. However, as it was narrowly decided, its impact on motions to dismiss, class certification, summary judgment and damages remains to be seen.

C. A central issue going forward will be how courts define a "corrective disclosure," including how a "correction" might occur over time and what is required plead it.

D. The Second Circuit's decision in Lentell should dispose of many analyst and other cases currently in the courts and will deter the filing of speculative claims.

NOTES

SETTLEMENT PROCEDURES AND TRENDS IN SECURITIES ACTIONS

12

SETTLEMENT ISSUES IN SECURITIES CLASS ACTIONS: THE DEFENSE PERSPECTIVE IN 2005

Bruce D. Angiolillo

Simpson Thacher & Bartlett LLP

Mr. Angiolillo is a senior litigation partner at Simpson Thacher & Bartlett LLP (www.simpsonthacher.com).

Table of Contents

INTRODUCTION

Defendants do not want securities class actions settled—they want them dismissed. As Justice Rehnquist recognized, writing for the Supreme Court more than twenty-five years ago, a complaint that survives a motion to dismiss "has a settlement value to the plaintiff out of any proportion to its prospect of success at trial."[1] Congress enacted the Private Securities Litigation Reform Act ("Reform Act"), in large part to hinder the filing of frivolous securities actions for this very reason. One of the primary vehicles to achieve this goal was making it more difficult for these cases to get to trial.[2] As a consequence, a plaintiff's expectations about a case's settlement value may well be influenced by surviving a post-Reform Act motion to dismiss. In light of these dynamics, this paper will consider securities class action settlements from the defense perspective in two parts: the first will provide an overview of the technical requirements of structuring a settlement in a securities class action and the second will discuss six practical issues and challenges confronting modern settlements: (i) jurisdiction; (ii) funding the settlement; (iii) settlement implications of the Reform Act; (iv) corporate governance; (v) directors' and officers' insurance; and (vi) partial settlements.

I. SETTLING SECURITIES CLASS ACTIONS UNDER THE REFORM ACT

Although an independently negotiated contract between the parties, a settlement must satisfy the technical requirements presented by the Federal Rules of Civil Procedure and the law that has grown up around the process of settlement. This section provides a general overview of these technical requirements that provide the background to negotiations between the parties over the content of their settlement.

In recognition of the competing interests of those negotiating the settlement and the wide array of interests of the class members, Rule 23(e) of the Federal Rules of Civil Procedure provides that a "class action shall not be dismissed or compromised without the approval of the court and notice of the proposed dismissal or compromise shall be given to all members of the class in such manner as the court directs."[3] This rule addresses the fact that when settling class actions, the interests of the lead plaintiffs

1. *Blue Chip Stamps v. Manor Drug Stores*, 421 U.S. 723, 740 (1975).
2. Tamara Loomis, *Securities Reform—What Went Wrong?*, New York L.J. (Oct. 27, 2000).
3. Fed. R. Civ. P. 23(e).

may diverge from those of the class as a whole at the expense of the rest of the class. As the Second Circuit recognized, it "is no secret that in 'seeking court approval of their settlement proposal, plaintiffs', attorneys', and defendants' interests coalesce and mutual interest may result in mutual indulgence.'"[4] While the statute recognizes this risk, it also prevents courts from fashioning settlements themselves. The Supreme Court has described this balance wherein Rule 23(e) "wisely requires court approval of the terms of any settlement of a class action, but . . . does not authorize the court to require the parties to accept a settlement to which they have not agreed."[5] After negotiation has yielded an agreement, parties submit to the court a joint statement of settlement that sets forth the terms of the agreement along with briefs and affidavits establishing the fairness and adequacy of the settlement.[6] In this way, the court provides a check on parties' settlements but does not impose its own terms. Parties submit their settlement to the court for its approval pursuant to this Rule in two stages: (i) a preliminary court review and then, after notice is provided to the class, (ii) the final fairness hearing.

The court's preliminary consideration of the settlement establishes a presumption of fairness if the court finds that: (1) the negotiations

---

4. *Kaplan v. Rand*, 192 F.3d 60, 67 (2d Cir. 1999) (citations omitted); *see also In re Warner Communications Sec. Litig.*, 798 F.2d 35, 37 (2d Cir. 1986) (stating that it is not the function of the court to modify the terms of the settlement for the parties).
5. *Evans v. Jeff D.*, 475 U.S. 717, 726 (1986).
6. John C. Coffee, Jr. & Joel Seligman, Securities Regulation: Cases and Materials 1218 (9th ed. 2003); William S. Lerach, *"The Private Securities Litigation Reform Act of 1995—27 Months Later": Securities Class Action Litigation Under the Private Securities Litigation Reform Act's Brave New World*, 76 Wash. U. L.Q. 597 (1998); Tower C. Snow, Jr. et al., *The Settlement of Class and Derivative Claims, in Securities Litigation* 1996, at 1105, 1111 (PLI Corporate Law Practice Course, Handbook Series No. 958, Sept.-Oct. 1996). While settlements may be submitted to the court for approval before the class is certified, the class negotiated for and described in the settlement must still meet the prerequisites for class certification outlined in Fed. R. Civ. P. 23(a) and 23(b). *See also Amchem Prods., Inc. v. Windsor*, 521 U.S. 591, 621 (1997) (Rule 23's "[s]ubdivisions (a) and (b) focus court attention on whether a proposed class has sufficient unity so that absent members can fairly be bound by decisions of class representatives. That dominant concern persists when settlement, rather than trial, is proposed."). Class certification can also take place as part of the approval of the settlement. In order to ensure fairness, settlements with uncertified classes will also be subject to a higher standard of review. *Id.* at 620 ("specifications of the rule—those designed to protect absentees by blocking unwarranted or overbroad class definitions—demand undiluted, even heightened, attention in the settlement context"). *See also* 5 *Moore's Federal Practice*, §23.82[2], at 23-336.2 (Matthew Bender 3d ed.).

occurred at arm's length; (2) there was sufficient discovery; (3) the proponents of the settlement are experienced in similar litigation; and (4) the number of actual or anticipated objectors is small relative to the size of the class.[7] If the settlement survives this first review, the court schedules the formal fairness hearing. The Reform Act provides standards for notice that ensure class members receive adequate information about the settlement after the preliminary review.[8] Once notice has been provided to the class, the parties proceed with the fairness hearing where they defend the terms of their agreement as measured against the factors and criteria listed above. Class members who oppose the settlement also have the opportunity to present their views at this hearing. If no one comes forward and the court is satisfied with the settlement, the court may expedite the hearing to approve the settlement and bar further claims against the settling defendants. While Rule 23(e) provides no specific guidance for the court's approval of class action settlements, courts universally focus on whether the settlement is fair, reasonable, and adequate to the plaintiff class.[9]

When applying these three criteria to a settlement, courts in different Circuits apply a wide array of factors.[10] The complexity of settlements defies blanket balancing tests and courts have used any number of the fol-

---

7. *In re General Motors Corp. Pick-Up Truck Fuel Tank Prods. Liab. Litig.*, 55 F.3d 768, 785 (3d Cir. 1995) (hereinafter *GM Pick-Up*) (*citing* 2 Herbert B. Newberg & Alba Conte, *Newberg on Class Actions* § 11.41, at 11-9 (3d ed. 1992)); *see also Moore's Federal Practice*, *supra* note 6, § 23.85[3].

8. After the fairness hearing is scheduled, the parties must give notice of the settlement to the class. The Reform Act lays out six specific elements for this notice including such "other information as may be required by the court." The Reform Act requires parties' notice of settlement to include: (i) the amount of the settlement in the aggregate and on an average per share basis; (ii) the average amount of damages per share that would be recoverable if the plaintiff had prevailed, if the settling parties can agree on that amount; or if the settling parties cannot agree on such amount, a statement from each settling party concerning the issue(s) on which the parties disagree; (iii) a statement indicating which parties or counsel intend to make an application for attorneys' fees, the amount of fees and costs that will be sought (including the amount of such fees and costs determined on an average per share basis) and a brief explanation supporting the fees and costs sought; (iv) the name, telephone number, and address of one or more representatives of counsel for the plaintiff class who will be reasonably available to answer questions from class members; and (v) a brief statement explaining the reasons why the parties are proposing the settlement. *See* 15 U.S.C. §§ 77z-1(a)(7), 78u-4(a)(7). The Federal Rules do not provide rigid requirements for individual notice, and most parties elect to effect service through mail. Often in the interests of economy, courts will allow notice under Rule 23(e) to be combined with Rule 23(c) notice. *See* David F. Herr, *Annotated Manual for Complex Litigation*, § 30.41, at 282 (3d ed. 2001).

9. *See generally Moore's Federal Practice*, *supra* note 6, § 23.85.

lowing considerations when evaluating a given settlement: the plaintiff's potential recovery at trial; the complexity, expense, and likely duration of the litigation; the interests and views of the creditors; the stage of the proceedings; the experience and expertise of class counsel; the arrival at settlement through arm's length bargaining; the risks of establishing liability, proving damages and maintaining the class action through trial; and the defendant's ability to withstand a greater judgment.[11]

Courts have also considered the fairness of the settlement and whether it was the product of collusion or fraud.[12] Practical considerations like the plaintiff's need for immediate relief,[13] and the potential difficulties confronting distribution of the settlement to the class also may play a role.[14] Courts will also look to the potential outcomes of the trial, the likelihood the insurer will disclaim liability under the policy if the case is tried, the size of the settlement fund compared to the best possible recovery, the scope of the settlement fund compared to a possible recovery in light of the risks of pursuing litigation, and the reaction of class members to the settlement, including the number of objectors and the sizes of their holdings.[15]

Using a combination of these factors the court determines whether the settlement is fair, reasonable, and adequate and will either approve or disapprove the entire settlement. As noted above, the court has no power under Rule 23(e) to modify the terms of the settlement, however, if the court disapproves the proposed settlement, it may indicate in an opinion what changes need to be made in order for the court to approve the next settlement.[16] While not generally the rule, several courts have stated that a

10. *See* 2 Herbert Newberg & Alba Conte, *Newberg On Class Actions*, § 22.85 (3d ed. 1992), for consideration of various Circuits' approaches to the "fair, reasonable and adequate" standard.
11. Arnold S. Jacobs, *Litigation & Practice Under Rule 10b-5*, Part 12 § 301.6 (1997-2000); *Varljen v. H.J. Meyers & Co.,* No. 97 CIV. 6742 (DLC), 2000 U.S. Dist. LEXIS 16205, at *9 (S.D.N.Y. Nov. 6, 2000) (*citing In re Drexel Burnham Lambert Group, Inc.*, 960 F.2d 285, 292 (2d Cir. 1992)); *Hawkins v. Comm'r of the N.H. Dep't of Health and Human Servs.*, No. 99-143-JD, 2004 U.S. Dist. LEXIS 807, at *15 (D.N.H. Jan. 3, 2004).
12. *GM Pick-Up*, 55 F.3d at 805; *In re Cylink Sec. Litig.*, 274 F. Supp. 2d 1109, 1112 (N.D. Cal. 2003).
13. *Kirkorian v. Borelli*, 695 F. Supp. 446, 450 (N.D. Cal. 1988); *Vigil v. Finesod*, 779 F. Supp. 522, 525, 527 (D.N.M. 1990).
14. *In re Flight Transp. Corp. Sec. Litig.*, 730 F.2d 1128, 1135 (8th Cir. 1984); *Yates v. Forker* (*In re Patriot Co.*), 303 B.R. 811, 815 (B.A.P. 8th Cir. 2004).
15. Jacobs, *supra* note 11, Part 12 § 301.6.
16. *See In re California Micro Devices Sec. Litig.*, No. C-94-2817-VRW, 1995 WL 476625, at *6 (N.D. Cal. Aug. 4, 1995).

"district court is required to address the issues of attorneys' fees before approving a class action settlement."[17] The Reform Act also provides that apart from reasonable costs and expenses directly related to representing the class, named plaintiffs shall not receive special compensation from the settlement.[18]

Once a court makes its determination that the settlement is fair, reasonable, and adequate, objectors may appeal. Courts of appeals grant district courts' decisions great deference because of their unique understanding of the facts, the dynamics of the case and the potential risks of future litigation. A district court's decision will be overturned, however, where there has been an abuse of discretion.[19] Abuses of discretion include decisions that rest on clearly erroneous findings of fact, erroneous applications of law or improper applications of law to fact.

II. PRACTICAL CONSIDERATIONS FOR NEGOTIATING MODERN SETTLEMENTS

While defendants navigate the technical requirements of settling their action, they must also consider the strategic issues that impact their ability to negotiate their settlement with plaintiffs. The following section focuses on six issues that may factor in this bargaining process: jurisdiction, funding the settlement, Reform Act implications, corporate governance, directors' and officers' insurance and partial settlements. Each of these factors affects defendants' positions in negotiations and affects their ability to shape robust, advantageous settlements. Faced with increasing demands for higher cash settlements and emerging demands for corporate gover-

---

17. *Moore's Federal Practice*, *supra* note 6, § 23.85[7]. The Reform Act states that the total attorneys' fees and expenses should not exceed a reasonable percentage of the amount of any damages and interest paid to the class. *See* 15 U.S.C. §§ 77z-1(6)(4), 78u-4(a)(6). Specific preference for either the "lodestar" or "percentage" methods is not explicit in the statute and courts have found up to 20-30% of the damages award an acceptable range for attorneys' fees. *In re Aetna Inc.*, No. Civ. A. MDL 1219, 2001 WL 20928, at *13-15 (E.D. Pa. Jan. 4, 2001) (approving attorneys' fees of 30% of net settlement where support by the class inferred from lack of objections); *cf. In re: Dreyfus Aggressive Growth Mutual Fund Litig.*, No. 98 Civ. 4318, 2001 WL 709262 (S.D.N.Y. June 22, 2001) ("The determination that 15% is a reasonable fee tracks the emerging trend within the [Second] Circuit of awarding attorneys considerably less than 30% of the common funds in securities class actions, even where there is a considerable contingency risk.").
18. *See* 15 U.S.C. §§ 77z-1(a)(4), 78u-4(a)(4); *see also Moore's Federal Practice*, *supra* note 6, § 23.101[4].
19. *See generally Moore's Federal Practice*, *supra* note 6, § 23.86.

nance changes, defendants who are aware of the relationship between these various issues will be in a better position to take advantage of their strengths in negotiations and shape agreements that meet their strategic interests.

A. Jurisdiction

The question of jurisdiction arises in two important contexts in the course of negotiating settlements: first, in the determination of whether the same court that approved the settlement may adjudicate subsequent claims regarding that settlement and second, as the site of potential conflict between state and federal actions. As defendants negotiate settlements they should consider whether it is advantageous to retain the court's jurisdiction over their settlement and how their settlement will be treated by other jurisdictions.

For the court to retain jurisdiction over the enforcement of a settlement, it must either explicitly reserve jurisdiction or incorporate the terms of the settlement in its dismissal order.[20] Even though their approval is required, district courts do not have an inherent power to enforce a settlement in the event of a breach.[21] Merely requesting or agreeing to the court's continuing jurisdiction is insufficient; parties must prevail on the court to exercise its discretion to incorporate the terms of their agreement in its dismissal order. If the settlement agreement is incorporated into the dismissal order, a breach of the agreement then violates the court order and grounds the court's jurisdiction.[22] Parties who seek to adjust the deadlines of an approved settlement, however, may be able to rely on the court's equitable jurisdiction to modify the settlement. The Second Circuit has upheld a district court's power to modify the deadlines of a settlement on the grounds that in "a class action settlement, a court retains special responsibility to see to the administration of justice . . . [as] the District Court retains the 'ultimate responsibility' for the protection of class members."[23] Notwithstanding this exception, parties who seek to have the original court retain juris-

---

20. *Arata v. Nu Skin Int'l, Inc.*, 96 F.3d 1265, 1268-69 (9th Cir. 1996) (*citing Kokkonen v. Guardian Life Ins. Co. of Am.*, 511 U.S. 375 (1994)); *see also Stewart v. O'Neill*, 225 F. Supp. 2d 6, 8 (D.D.C. 2002).
21. *Arata*, 96 F.3d at 1268-69.
22. *See Moore's Federal Practice*, *supra* note 6, § 23.87.
23. *In re Cendant Corp. Prides Litig.*, 233 F.3d 188, 194 (3d Cir. 2000) (*citing Maywalt v. Parker & Parsley Petroleum*, 67 F.3d 1072, 1078 (2d Cir. 1995)). The court also pointed to Fed. R. Civ. P. 6(b)(2) as the source for the power to modify the deadlines of the settlement. *Id.* at 195.

diction should request that the court incorporate their agreement into its dismissal order.

Defendants who negotiate settlements for class actions must also consider the potential for multiple actions in state and federal courts. The Securities Litigation Uniform Standards Act of 1998 ("SLUSA") was enacted to preempt 'covered class actions' relating to 'covered securities' brought in state courts and authorizes federal courts to stay discovery in state court actions.[24] The Supreme Court's decision in *Matsushita Electrical Industrial Co., Ltd. v. Epstein,* 516 U.S. 367 (1996), further provides that settlements in state court class actions may contain provisions that release exclusive federal claims.[25] In *Matsushita,* state and federal claims were being litigated simultaneously, when the state claim was settled with a provision barring all federal claims. The Supreme Court upheld this provision under the Full Faith and Credit clause. While SLUSA limits the impact of the *Matsushita* decision, one of the exceptions to SLUSA allows state pension funds to bring state claims and avoid preemption leaving the possibility of multiple state and federal claims.[26]

Other state claims that may escape SLUSA preemption include "holder claims," i.e., claims related to the holding of securities as opposed to their purchase or sale. For SLUSA to apply, a claim must fulfill the following requirements: (1) it must be a covered class action, (2) the action must be based on state law, and (3) it must allege a misrepresentation or omission of material fact "in connection with" the purchase or sale of (4) a covered security.[27] There are differing views among the Circuits as to whether SLUSA preempts state law actions that are based on the holding of securities.[28]

---

24. SLUSA defines a "covered class action" as an action in which there are more than 50 people filing claims with similar issues of law and fact. *See* 15 U.S.C. § 78bb (f)(1). It defines a "covered security" as any security listed or authorized for listing on the NYSE, ASE, NASDAQ, or NMS or systems with similar standards. *See* 15 U.S.C. § 78bb (f)(5)(B). The statute provides four exceptions to the preemption rule: (1) actions under state laws of state of incorporation such as breach of fiduciary duty; (2) state pension funds; (3) actions based on indenture trustee agreements; and (4) shareholder derivative actions. *See* 15 U.S.C. § 78bb (f)(3).
25. *See* generally Bruce D. Angiolillo, Managing Multiple Federal State Securities Actions: The Defense Perspective, in Securities Litigation 2000, at 425, 450 (PLI Corporate Law Practice Course, Handbook Series No. 1199, Sept.-Oct. 2000).
26. *See* 15 U.S.C. § 78bb (f)(3).
27. Id. § 78bb(f)(1-2); *Green v. Ameritrade*, 279 F.3d 590, 598-599 (8th Cir. 2002).

B. Settlement Implications of the Reform Act

In addition to heightened pleading standards and restrictions on discovery by plaintiffs, the Reform Act replaced the common law regime of joint and several liability and contribution rights with proportionate share liability for all defendants in cases brought under the Securities Exchange Act of 1934 who lack "actual knowledge" of fraud. This change also applies to non-"knowing" outside director defendants in suits brought under Section 11 of the Securities Act of 1933.[29] Under the Reform Act, there is no joint and several liability unless the defendant has "knowingly committed a violation of the securities laws."[30] "Knowing" must reach beyond recklessness to actual knowledge that a misrepresentation or omission was false and that persons were likely to rely upon that misrepresentation or omission.[31] If the defendant was non-"knowing," the Reform Act imposes proportionate share liability, meaning the defendant is liable only for the amount of damages consistent with his "percentage of responsibility," or share of the total fault.[32] Thus, absent a "knowing" violation, a defendant's trial exposure will not exceed his proportionate share.[33]

There are two situations where a non-"knowing" defendant may be required to pay more than his proportionate share. First, if the plaintiff is unable to collect from an insolvent defendant, any solvent co-defendant will be required to increase his share of the payment by up to an additional 50% of his proportionate share. Second, if a plaintiff has a

---

28. *See Kircher v. Putnam Funds Trust and Putnam Inv. Mgmt., LLC, et al.*, 403 F.3d 478 (7th Cir. 2005) (holding SLUSA preempts state action that defined its class as investors who held shares between two specified dates but did not purchase or sell shares during that period and state actions that define their classes according to holding of shares between specified dates); *Dabit v. Merrill Lynch, Pierce, Fenner & Smith, Inc.*, 395 F.3d 25 (2d Cir. 2005) (finding SLUSA's preemption provision does not apply to non-purchaser/non-seller claim); *Falkowski v. Imation Corp.*, 309 F.3d 1123 (9th Cir. 2002) (determining state claim preempted because alleged fraud took place in connection with the purchase or sale of a covered security under SLUSA); *Riley v. Merrill Lynch, Pierce, Fenner & Smith, Inc.* 292 F.3d 1334 (11th Cir. 2002) (holding suit alleging that defendant made material misrepresentations and omissions that induced shareholders to purchase and retain shares of business trust covered by SLUSA and not properly brought in state court); *Green*, 279 F.3d at 598 (stating "nonsellers and nonpurchasers of securities are not covered by SLUSA's preemption provision").

29. *See* Denis T. Rice, *A Practitioner's View of the Private Securities Litigation Reform Act of 1995*, 31 U.S.F.L. Rev. 283, 283-85 (1997).

30. 15 U.S.C. § 78u-4(f)(2)(A).

31. *Id.* § 78u-4(f)(10)(A-B); Rice, *supra* note 29, at 287.

32. *Id.* § 78u-4(f)(2)(B).

33. Rice, *supra* note 29, at 299-300.

net worth of under $200,000 and has suffered damages exceeding 10% of his net worth, the defendant will be jointly and severally liable for supplemental payments to satisfy any uncollectible portion.[34]

C. Funding the Settlement

Obviously, a defendant's ability to pay for a settlement is an important criteria for courts when determining if a given settlement structure is reasonable. The district court when evaluating the settlement in *In re American Bank Note Holographics, Inc. Securities Litigation,* 127 F. Supp. 2d 418 (S.D.N.Y. 2001), found that the defendant's precarious financial situation militated in favor of settlement. Among the obstacles to the plaintiffs' recovery after a trial, the court recognized that while there appeared to be some culpability on the part of some of the defendants, "their lack of assets rendered them substantially judgment proof absent sufficient insurance coverage."[35] Approving the settlement, the court also recognized that potential criminal liability could trigger policy exclusions that would further thwart plaintiffs' attempts to fund their settlement.

Out of economic necessity, securities class action settlements often contain a mixture of cash and non-cash consideration. The mixture of both cash and non-cash elements, however, presents a challenge when attempting to evaluate the settlement. Given the fluctuating nature of stocks, options, warrants and other "paper" elements of the settlement, the valuation date of the securities becomes one of the most crucial points of negotiation. [36] A valuation or calculation date before the announcement of the proposed settlement may be an advantage for plaintiffs in the event that a positive market response to the announcement results in a higher yield in stock for distribution to the class. Collar provisions provide one solution to the problems presented by market fluctuations in settlements. Written into the settlement, a collar provision creates both a ceiling and a floor for the price of the paper element of the settlement consideration, and provides a means of rescinding the settlement if these limits are exceeded. This arrangement is designed to address plaintiffs' and defendants' concerns

34. *Id.* § 78u-4(f)(4)(A)(i-ii); John L. Latham and Jenna L. Freuchtenicht, *Securities Regulation*, 48 Mercer L. Rev. 1677, 1692-93 (1997).
35. *In re American Bank Note Holographics, Inc.*, 127 F. Supp. 2d 418, 425 (S.D.N.Y. 2001).
36. *See* Joseph P. Monteleone and James M. McCarrick, *Settlement Issues in Securities Litigation Involving Directors and Officers*, Insights, Sept. 1996, at 9-10.

regarding adverse changes in the stock price after the settlement is negotiated.

In addition to fluctuations in the value of the settlement consideration, there are also fluctuations in the numbers of class members to whom the settlement is distributed. Inevitably, some plaintiffs choose to opt out of the settlement, changing the structure of the distribution or resulting in unclaimed funds. To control the impact of excessive opt-outs, defendants and their insurers generally prefer a settlement on the basis of claims made as well as an aggregate amount.[37] This method determines a per-share amount for each class member and leaves open the possibility of reverter of funds to the defendants or the insurance company. A settlement agreement may also incorporate a "blow provision," which sets a ceiling on the percentage of class members who can opt out before the defendants may rescind the settlement agreement, or a "claw back provision," which reduces the total settlement amount based on the percentage of opt outs.[38]

In some circumstances, residual funds remain unclaimed after distribution to the class. Courts that have retained jurisdiction over the settlement may use the doctrine of cy pres, sometimes described in the class action context as "fluid class recovery," as a means of allocating these funds to the next best use that would provide indirect benefit to the class. In the class action context, the doctrine of cy pres has been used to provide payment for scholarship funds at universities and fund research institutions.[39] Cy pres may be attractive to defendants who have suffered negative publicity as a result of damaging revelations in discovery and are working to repair their public image. Attempting to capitalize on this opportunity, charities like the Federal Judicial Center Foundation have begun to suggest language to class action attorneys that can be incorporated into settlements that would require counsel to give special consideration to particular causes agreed to by the parties when distributing remaining funds.[40]

---

37. *Id.* at 8. If insurers are expected to pay a large part of the settlement, they may prefer distribution on a claims-made basis rather than lump sum. In a claims-made settlement, the parties agree to set aside an aggregate settlement fund and a per-share settlement amount. If the anticipated class members do not all come forward, left over funds are then returned to the contributing defendants in a manner proportional to their initial contributions.
38. *See generally* Snow, *supra* note 6, at 1133.
39. *In re Three Mile Island Litig.*, 557 F. Supp. 96, 97 (D.C. Pa. 1982); *Powell v. Georgia-Pacific Corp.*, 119 F.3d 703, 706-07 (8th Cir. 1997); *see generally* Newberg, *supra* note 7, § 11.20.

D. Corporate Governance

While relatively new to class action settlements, changes to corporate governance are a familiar aspect of the settlement landscape in derivative actions.[41] These changes provide companies further nonmonetary concessions to offer as part of their settlements and typically involve adjustments to the numbers of independent directors on various corporate boards or the creation of committees to oversee the kind of conduct that has given rise to the litigation. Changes in corporate governance are justified as a benefit to the corporation and its current shareholders pursuant to the theory that they act as deterrents to future conduct of the kind alleged in the underlying litigation.[42]

While courts recognize that "nonpecuniary benefits to the corporation may support a settlement,"[43] corporate governance changes still present difficulties when courts attempt to evaluate their benefit to the shareholder class, many of whom are no longer shareholders. Courts recognize that this "difficulty in valuing therapeutic relief poses significant risks [as] Parties may capitalize on the valuation problem and exchange cosmetic 'reforms' for plaintiffs' fees, concealing a collusive settlement."[44] Accordingly, courts will refuse to approve settlements where corporate governance changes are included that are practically ineffective, fail to address the underlying claims of the litigation, or are not in the best interests of the corporation.[45]

---

40. Contact: Dianne M. Nast, Chair, Federal Judicial Center Foundation, One Columbus Circle N.E., Washington, DC 20002-8003.

41. *See generally* Mark J. Loewenstein, *Shareholder Derivative Litigation and Corporate Governance*, 24 Del. J. Corp. L. 1 (1999).

42. Keith L. Johnson, *Deterrence of Corporate Fraud Through Securities Litigation: The Role of Institutional Investors*, 60 AUT Law & Contemp. Probs. 155, 164 (1997) ("Management changes and imposition of good corporate governance practices can be effective tools to protect shareholders from corporate wrongdoers."); *see also* Keith Johnson, *Deployment of Institutions on the Securities Class Action Wars*, 38 Ariz. L. Rev. 627, 635 (1996).

43. *Bell Atlantic Corp. v. Bolger*, 2 F.3d 1304, 1311 (3d Cir. 1993) (*citing Granada Invs., Inc. v. DWG Corp.*, 962 F.2d 1203, 1207 (6th Cir. 1992) (corporation received release from potential liability to settling plaintiff shareholder and settlement called for changes in corporate governance aimed at limiting corporation's disbursements to settling defendant director and controlling shareholder); *Zimmerman v. Bell*, 800 F.2d 386, 391 (4th Cir. 1986) (nonmonetary derivative settlement relief adequate when it provided guidelines for "future management responses to tender offers and takeover bids"); *Maher v. Zapata Corp.*, 714 F.2d 436, 466 (5th Cir. 1983) (nonmonetary relief adequate settlement relief); *cf. Mills v. Electric Auto-Lite Co.*, 396 U.S. 375, 391-92 (1970)).

44. *Id.* at 1311-1312.

In the settlement of *In re Cendant Corp.*, 109 F.Supp.2d 235, 240 (D.N.J. 2000), *aff'd*, 264 F.3d 201 (3d Cir. 2001), these kinds of remedies were incorporated in a securities class action settlement. The high profile of this case raises the question of what the long-term impact such concessions may have on settlement negotiations. The *Cendant* settlement was at the time the largest securities class action settlement in history and was primarily comprised of a $2.8 billion cash payment from Cendant, a $335 million payment from Ernst & Young, LLP ("E&Y") and a potential class recovery of 50% of the net recovery from subsequent litigation against E&Y.[46] In addition to the cash portion of the settlement, Cendant agreed to the following changes to its corporate structure:

> (i) the Board's Audit Committee, Nominating Committee, and Compensation Committee will each be comprised entirely of independent directors; (ii) the majority of the Board will be independent within two years following final approval of the settlement in this action; (iii) Cendant will take the steps necessary to provide that all directors shall be elected annually; and (iv) no employee stock option shall be "re-priced" following its grant without an approving vote of shareholders.[47]

In submissions made to the court regarding the approval of the settlement, two parties objected to the imposition of corporate governance changes. One argued that these concessions were obtained in lieu of additional cash recovery for the class[48] and the other asserted that the corporate governance concessions should be "entitled to no weight in [the] Court's consideration of the settlement because they provide only illusory benefit to the class members."[49] Over these objections, the court approved the settlement and found that there had not been "the slightest indication that the cash portion of the settlement was related

---

45. *See, e.g.*, *Fischer & Porter Co. by Lepow Equities Corp. v. Tolson*, No. CIV. A. 91-7822, 1993 WL 319622, at *4 (E.D. Pa. Aug 18, 1993), *amended by* No. CIV. A. 91-7822, 1993 WL 427351 (E.D. Pa. Oct. 19, 1993) (finding settlement that included therapeutic relief that only lasted three years and did not affect defendant's control was only "marginally valuable to the company" and thus unreasonable to the class).
46. *Cendant*, 109 F. Supp. 2d at 240.
47. Bernstein Litowitz Berger & Grossmann LLP, *In re Cendant Corporation Litigation, Master File No. 98-1664(WHW)(D.N.J), FACT SHEET*, *at* http://www.blbglaw.com/cases/home.html; *see also* William S. Lerach, *Achieving Corporate Governance Enhancements Through Litigation*, Keynote Address at the Council of Institutional Investors Spring Meeting, Washington, DC, March 27, 2001, *at* http://www.milberg.com/misc/corp_gov.html.
48. *Cendant*, 109 F. Supp. 2d at 251-252.
49. *Id.* at 247.

to, dependent upon, or intertwined with the governance proposals."[50] Standing in stark contrast to these criticisms, the institutional plaintiffs were very vocal about the importance of the corporate governance changes that were instituted as part of the settlement.

Immediately after the settlement was announced, representatives of the institutional investor plaintiffs commented on its corporate governance aspects. New York City Comptroller Alan Hevesi stated that "[n]ot only did we win the largest recovery ever, but we also forced the company to institute governance reforms that will help prevent this kind of behavior from recurring."[51] Charles P. Valdes, Chairman of CalPERS Investment Committee also emphasized the impact of corporate governance changes on the future of the company, arguing that "[n]ot only have we recovered the losses incurred by all class members, but the company is emerging from the lawsuit stronger and worthy of greater confidence by the financial markets."[52] Despite these institutional shareholders' enthusiasm and claims to increased influence over the corporate governance of the company, defense counsel should consider whether such concessions pose a potential threat to the proper autonomy of corporate governance and management.

Other settlements show that the trend towards including corporate governance reforms in settlement agreements may be lasting. In May 2003, Hanover Compressor Co. settled a securities class action for $80 million and "sweeping corporate governance reforms that went far beyond the mandates outlined in Sarbanes-Oxley."[53] Significant provisions focusing on board independence included a requirement that 2/3 of the members, as well as all members of the Compensation, Audit, and Nomination Committees, be "independent," institution of a lead independent director for the purpose of coordinating all other directors, shareholder nomination of one or two directors, insider trading controls, and shareholder approval of changes in executive option plans.[54]

---

50. *Id.* at 252.
51. *Press Release*, "News From the Office of the New York State Comptroller," H. Carl McCall, Dec. 7, 1999, *at* http://www.osc.state.ny.us/press/releases/dec99/12799.htm.
52. *Id.*
53. Amalia Deligiannis, *SEC Plan Fuels Heated Debate Over Shareholder Access*, Corporate Legal Times, Jan. 2004, at 20.
54. *Settlement of Hanover Shareholder Litigation Produces Unprecedented Corporate Governance Reforms & Recovery of More Than $80 Million for Investors*, Lerach, Coughlin, Stoia & Robbins, LLP, *available at* http://www.lcsr.com/lcsr-cgi-bin/mil?templ=hanover_settle.html.

In December 2003, a $50 million settlement resolving shareholder claims in two lawsuits stemming from Sprint Corporation's failed merger with WorldCom, Inc. included significant non-monetary relief.[55] Sprint agreed to a number of corporate governance changes, including the requirement that two thirds of the board be composed of "independent" directors, the appointment of a lead independent director, and the evaluation of all shareholder proposals by an independent committee of the board.[56]

The increased role of institutional investors as lead plaintiffs, coupled with the developments in settlement structures, suggests that defense counsel will be confronted with increasingly frequent demands for changes to corporate governance in settlement negotiations.[57] There is the danger in these settlement provisions, however, of tying the hands of the corporation's board and management to the ultimate disadvantage of investors.

One important check on this dynamic is the requirement for court approval. Proposals for corporate governance changes should be tested by whether they address the issues that have given rise to the underlying litigation and in light of what value they provide to the corporation.[58] Given the potentially long-term impact of changing the structure of corporate governance, these ramifications should be carefully considered. Needless to say, such corporate governance changes do not remedy any past injury to shareholders and provide no benefit to those class members who have sold their stock.[59]

---

55. Christopher Brown, *Settlements: $50M Settlement Approved in Suits Over Failed Sprint-WorldCom Merger*, Corporate Accountability and Fraud Daily, Jan. 15, 2004 (citing *In re Sprint Corp. Securities Litigation* (D. Kan., No. 01-4080-CM, Dec. 16, 2003) and *Amalgamated Bank v. Lemay* (Mo. Cir. Ct., No. 00-CV-230077, Dec. 16, 2003)).

56. *Sprint Corporate Governance Enhancements*, Lerach, Coughlin, Stoia & Robbins, LLP, *available at* http://www.lcsr.com/lcsr-cgi-bin/mil?templ=featured/sprint_enhance.html.

57. *See* Lerach, *supra* note 47.

58. Notably, plaintiffs' attorneys in the *Cendant* settlement did not ascribe any value to corporate governance changes when determining the value of the settlement on which to base their fees. *In re Cendant*, 109 F. Supp. at 299 n.8.

59. The Third Circuit has noted the potential for intra-class conflict between plaintiffs who have sold their shares and those who continue to hold the defendant's stock. "Sell Plaintiffs" will seek the largest possible recovery, while "Hold Plaintiffs" will favor a settlement maximizing total settlement *plus* the value of the stock the plaintiff continues to hold. *In re Cendant Corp. Litig.*, 264 F.3d at 244 n.25 (3d Cir. 2001). These diverging interests may require courts to consider certifying separate classes or sub-classes to ensure satisfaction of Rule 23(e).

E. Directors' and Officers' Insurance

Settlement negotiations are significantly influenced by the presence and extent of Directors' and Officers' ("D&O") insurance coverage.[60] In fact, some commentators have argued that given the extent to which modern settlements rely on insurance to provide the cash portion of the settlement, insurance can sometimes have a more significant role in shaping the settlement than the merits of the case itself.[61] Given the importance of insurance and the fact that most policies require the insurer's consent for settlement, the insurance company is an important party in settlement negotiations. Insurers will frequently play a consultative role in the assessment of the case, the cash component of the settlement, the form of disbursement, the form of payment and any releases contained in the settlement.

Insurers generally work with their insured to assess the insured's exposure in the underlying lawsuit. This involves an evaluation of the plaintiffs' claims against the insured and the insured's defenses to those claims. Through such an evaluation, the insurer and insured attempt to arrive at a shared assessment of the settlement value of the case. In exchange for the insurer's participation in the settlement of the underlying litigation, the insured provides a release from subsequent claims.[62] If an insurer declines coverage either because it believes the suit is baseless or falls outside the parameters of the policy, the settlement may proceed and then be followed by subsequent litigation against the insurer for contribution.[63]

Plaintiffs recognize that the presence of the insurer is often a prerequisite for meaningful settlement negotiations as insurance policies are frequently a primary source of cash in securities class action settle-

---

60. *See* Monteleone & McCarrick, *supra* note 36, at 7 (discussing the importance of the insurance companies' financial commitments and consequent control over a class action litigation and settlement).

61. James M. McCarrick & Karen A. Reardon, *When the Merits Don't Matter: The Influence of Insurance on Settlements in Securities Class Actions*, 4 No. 8 Andrews Sec. Litig. & Reg. Rep. 1 (1998).

62. While there are three types of insurance releases (litigation, claim, and policy), most settlements include either claims or policy releases. One part of the negotiations between the insurer and insured focuses on the scope of the release with respect to claims associated with and arising out of the settled litigation. Parties are less likely to offer a policy release as it offers protection from all matters pertaining to the insurance coverage. *See* McCarrick & Reardon, *supra* note 61.

63. This litigation may include claims from either the insured in a coverage dispute or in the event of a settlement between plaintiffs and the insured, from the plaintiffs for a cash recovery of the settlement fund.

ments. Accordingly, plaintiffs will want the insurer at the bargaining table. In the absence of explicit language in the policy, negotiations may also take place over the allocation of contributions between insured and uninsured defendants.[64] Ultimately, defendants must first establish that they are covered by the insurance policy and then cooperate with the insurance company to ensure that both defendants' and their insurers' interests are served by the dynamics of settlement negotiations with plaintiffs.[65]

Certain developments in shareholder derivative litigation may negatively impact the corporate indemnification rights of officers and directors and their access to insurance coverage. First, in *In re The Walt Disney Company Derivative Litigation*, 825 A.2d 275, 289 (Del. Ch. 2003), the Delaware Chancery Court held that the Disney board's alleged failure to review an executive compensation agreement, which resulted in an award of over $140 million to Michael Ovitz upon his termination as Disney's president, could potentially constitute a breach of the directors' duty of good faith to the corporation.[66] Describing the board's conduct as a "'we don't care about the risks' attitude," the Court found that such a lack of involvement would go beyond just a violation of the duty of due care.[67] This difference would negatively impact a director's indemnification rights. Under Section 102(b)(7) of the Delaware corporations code, actions not taken in good faith are non-indemnifiable by the corporation and would leave the director exposed to personal liability.[68]

Second, in *Tafeen v. Homestore, Inc.*, No. 023-N, 2004 Del. Ch. LEXIS 38, at *36 (Del Ch. Mar. 22, 2004), the court noted in dicta that the Sarbanes-Oxley Act has created potential uncertainty about the continuing viability of the advancement of defense costs to officers and directors. Although the court found in favor of the officer's claim for

---

64. Snow, *supra* note 6, at 1127-1128 (allocation between defendants and insurers can become problematic if the insurer tries to distinguish between the corporation's liability and that of the directors and officers, *see Nordstrom, Inc. v. Chubb & Son, Inc.*, 54 F.3d 1424 (9th Cir. 1995), and as a consequence should be negotiated beforehand).
65. When assessing the value of a settlement offer compared to the merits of the plaintiffs' claim, insurers are constrained by the law of bad faith wherein failure to settle the underlying claims within the policy's limits leaves the insurer potentially liable for any verdict in excess of policy limits as well as additional attorneys' fees and punitive damages.
66. *In re The Walt Disney Co. Derivative Litig.*, 825 A.2d 275, 289 (Del. Ch. 2003).
67. *Id.* at 286, 289.
68. *Id.* at 286.

advancement of defense costs, it raised the issue of the possible preemption of Section 145(e) of the Delaware corporations code, which permits corporations to advance money to directors and officers for their attorneys' fees and other expenses incurred in defending litigation claims, by Section 402 of the Sarbanes-Oxley Act, which bars corporations from making personal loans to officers and directors.[69] The court did not directly rule on the federal-state law question, instead holding that Section 402's use of the phrase "current directors and officers" made it inapplicable to the "former" officer involved.[70]

Should Section 402 of the Sarbanes-Oxley Act be deemed to preempt Delaware and other states' laws regarding the advancement of defense costs as constituting non-allowable personal loans, this could have dramatic and negative implications for directors and officers accused of wrongdoing. Many D&O insurance policies are drafted with this state law indemnification framework in mind. Conflicts may therefore arise amongst D&O insurers, corporations, and directors and officers regarding the extent to which directors and officers would be covered in the event that corporate indemnification was not available. This air of uncertainty, combined with rising premiums and the greater use of policy exclusions, may make it increasingly advisable for directors and officers to obtain individual director liability insurance policies or to ensure that any applicable D&O policy will provide for the advancement of defense costs in the event that Section 402 precludes a corporation from doing so.[71]

The most recent development in this area—and the one many directors and officers may find most unsettling—are the agreements of certain directors of Enron Corp. and WorldCom, Inc.[72] to personally pay millions of dollars to settle shareholder suits. In the *WorldCom* settlement, the former chairman agreed to pay a total of $4.5 million and 11 other former directors agreed to pay a total of $20.25 million—more than 20% of the aggregate net worth of these individuals—from their

69. *Tafeen v. Homestore, Inc.*, No. 023-N, 2004 Del. Ch. LEXIS 38, at *36 (Del. Ch. Mar. 22, 2004), *aff'd, Homestore, Inc. v. Tafeen,* No. 223-N, 2005 Del. Ch. LEXIS 217 (Del. Sup. Ct. Jun 8, 2005) .

70. *Id.* at *37-41.

71. *See* Carl Kaplan and Manny Rivera, *Board Protection: Individual Liability Insurance for Independent Directors*, Startup & Emerging Companies Strategist, Dec. 22, 2003, at 1.

72. Initially, Judge Denise Cote of the Southern District of New York rejected the proposed settlement for limiting the financial capability of the settling director defendants. *In re WorldCom, Inc. Sec. Litig.*, No. 02 Civ. 3288, 2005 WL 335201, *15 (S.D.N.Y. Feb. 14, 2005).

own pockets to settle the claims asserted against them.[73] Likewise, in *Enron*, 10 former outside directors agreed to contribute personally $13 million towards their $168 million settlement.[74] Historically, individual directors have not paid out of their own pockets sums such as these and have relied nearly exclusively on funding from D&O insurance coverage or the companies. Some commentators have suggested that the scope of the alleged corporate frauds at issue in the *Enron* and *WorldCom* litigations, including huge accounting restatements and bankruptcy, posed unique risks for the individual director defendants.[75] In their view, it was these risks which resulted in the directors' willingness to make their personal contributions to the settlements. This development raises questions about the scope of personal liability for corporate directors under the securities laws.[76] These agreements may increase the likelihood of similar concessions by settling directors in the future and may make the recruitment of directors for the boards of public companies more difficult.[77]

F. Partial Settlements

The possibility of future litigation by non-settling parties historically threatened the integrity of partial settlements.[78] In an attempt to provide more stability in this area, the Reform Act now provides that a defendant "who settles any private action at any time before final ver-

73. *In re WorldCom, Inc. Sec. Litig.*, No. 02 Civ. 3288, Preliminary Approval Order Regarding Settlement with James C. Allen, et al. (S.D.N.Y. March 21, 2005).
74. *In re Enron Corp. Sec. Litig.*, No. H-01-3624, Order Preliminarily Approving Settlement (S.D. Tex. Feb. 4, 2005).
75. *See* David J. Berger, *Stormy Weather; The Enron and WorldCom Settlements Make Waves*, D and O Advisor (April 1, 2005).
76. *See* Peter Wallison, *The WorldCom and Enron Settlements: Politics Rears Its Ugly Head*, 1486 PLI/Corp 955 (May 2005). Such settlements antagonize a primary objective of the Sarbanes-Oxley Act, which to place matters of financial disclosure by public companies under the control of independent directors. *Id.*
77. Partial settlements involving insurance proceeds may partially or fully exhaust policy limits yet release less than all of the insureds, leaving some nonsettling officer or director defendants without sufficient insurance coverage. *See Rite Aid,* 146 F. Supp. 2d at 718. The proper resolution of such competing claims to insurance proceeds — and whether insurers must set aside funds for the nonsettling insured — remains a live issue.
78. *See generally,* Dianne M. Hansen, *The Effect of Partial Settlements on the Rights of Non-settling Defendants in Federal Securities Class Actions: In Search of a Standardized Uniform Contribution Bar Rule*, 60 UMKC L. Rev. 91 (1991) (identifying three conflicting interests with regard to partial settlements: (1) the federal judicial policy that encourages settlement; (2) the duty to see that the deterrent effect of securities law is not comprised and (3) the need to protect the equitable interest of non-settling defendants).

dict or judgment shall be discharged from all claims for contribution brought by other persons."[79] This provision requires courts to enter a "bar order," both protecting defendants from contribution claims and preventing them from seeking contribution claims from third parties.[80]

While the language of the statute requires courts to include a bar order preventing contribution claims both by and against settling defendants, it leaves open the question of whether defendants can incorporate other broadly constructed bar orders in their settlements.[81] Addressing this issue, a district court has recently held that in light of the fact that the Reform Act "contains no provision that explicitly limits [a court's] ability to enter a bar order that precludes indemnification claims," courts are free to consider the reasonableness of bar orders that deal with indemnification and other claims.[82] While the court denied the bar order in question, it rejected plaintiffs' argument that "the text of the Reform Act prevents the entry of a bar order that precludes indemnification claims."[83] This decision suggests that defendants can use broad language in their settlements to bar further indemnification claims and encourage more parties to join their settlements.[84]

In addition to protecting settling defendants through the use of bar orders, the Reform Act also protects non-settling defendants by requiring the reduction of subsequent verdicts or judgments "by the greater of (i) an amount that corresponds to the percentage of responsibility of that covered person; or (ii) the amount paid to the plaintiff by that covered person."[85] This provision effectively shifts from defendants to plaintiffs the risk of settling for less than the other defendants' propor-

---

79. 15 U.S.C. § 78u-4(f)(7)(A).
80. This bar order may not preclude, however, independently grounded state actions. *See In re Cendant Corporation Sec. Litig.*, 139 F. Supp. 2d 585, 596 (D.N.J. 2001), *aff'd in part, rev'd in part*, 147 F.3d 132 (3d Cir. N.J. 2001) (holding that independent "state law cross claims for negligence, fraud, breach of contract and breach of fiduciary duty are not barred [by the Reform Act] as de facto securities claims").
81. 15 U.S.C. § 78u-4(f)(7)(A).
82. *In re Rite Aid Corp. Sec. Litig.*, Nos. MDL 1360, 99-CV-1349, Civ.A. 99-2493, 2001 WL 632941, at *14 (E.D. Pa. June 8, 2001).
83. *Id.*
84. Indeed, the broad bar order in *Rite Aid* included non-party insurers that were "critical participant[s] and contributor[s] to the overall settlement," and, therefore, properly included in the bar order despite their non-party status. *Id.* at 732 & n.37 (disallowing bar order on other grounds).
85. 15 U.S.C. § 78u-4(f)(7)(B).

tionate fault and spreads the benefits of large settlements to all defendants without disproportionately benefiting plaintiffs.[86]

In an effort to shift the risk of low or disproportionate settlements back to defendants, plaintiffs may attempt to condition a partial settlement on getting non-settling defendants to waive rights under the judgment reduction provision. In the civil securities fraud litigation stemming from Enron's collapse, for example, the press reported that plaintiffs' counsel were prepared to settle on an ability-to-pay basis with Arthur Andersen for approximately $300 million, a figure allegedly representing nearly all of Andersen's remaining, but dwindling assets. Plaintiffs' counsel conditioned this proposed partial settlement on the non-settling defendants, including the financial institution defendants, waiving their rights to reduce any subsequent verdict or judgment by Andersen's proportional responsibility for the shareholder losses. As such a waiver would lead to almost limitless potential liability if a large civil judgment were to be rendered against the non-settling defendants, plaintiffs' waiver proposal was apparently rejected.[87]

The WorldCom court recently rejected a similar effort to reallocate the risk of disproportionate settlements. In January 2005, the *WorldCom* plaintiffs and certain outside director defendants proposed a settlement with a judgment reduction provision that deviated from the statutory framework. Their proposed "contribution credit" provided for a settlement discharge based on the settling directors' assessed proportion of the judgment, but reduced to the amount the individuals would have been able to pay.[88] Thus, rather than reduce a judgment by the greater of the settlement amount or the directors' proportionate fault, as set forth in Section 21D(7) of the Reform Act, the proposed reduction formula would have reduced a judgment against nonsettling defendants by the greater of the "contribution credit," the actual settlement amount, or the amount of insurance coverage available. Given the billions of dollars at issue in the litigation, the proposed contribution credit could have resulted in a multi-billion dollar increase in the damages exposure of the nonsettling defendants.

---

86. Donald C. Langevoort, *The Reform of Joint and Several Liability Under the Private Securities Litigation Reform Act of 1995: Proportionate Liability, Contribution Rights and Settlement Effects, in Symposium on the Private Securities Litigation Reform Act of 1995*, 51 Business Lawyer 1157, 1173 (1996).

87. Jonathan Weil, Devon Spurgeon & Cassell Bryan-Low, *Arthur Andersen Breaks Off Talks to Settle Criminal Case*, Wall St. J., Apr. 19, 2002, at A1.

88. *In re WorldCom, Inc. Sec. Litig.*, No. 02 Civ. 3288, 2005 WL 335201, *8 (S.D.N.Y. Feb. 14, 2005).

The district court rejected the settlement's "contribution credit" as inconsistent with the unambiguous reduction formula set forth in the statute.[89] But the court also recognized the practical consequence of enforcing the statute as written, noting it would be "extraordinarily difficult for outside directors to settle Section 11 claims before all deep-pocket defendants facing joint and several liability have done so."[90] Thus, the proportionate liability system of the Reform Act—designed in part to protect outside directors—in fact may inhibit these same directors from settling early.

Whether there are circumstances where a non-settling defendant should consider surrendering any of the protection afforded by the judgment reduction provision is a very difficult question and depends on many factors, including the size of the partial settlement as compared with the magnitude of shareholder losses, and the respective potential culpability of the settling and non-settling defendants.

CONCLUSION

To achieve settlements that best meet the needs of corporate defendants and their shareholders, defense counsel must consider a wide range of factors that may influence the settlement of complex securities class actions. As the costs of settlement continue to increase, defendants are being subjected to increasing pressure for larger cash awards and more creative non-monetary settlement structures. The continuing challenge for defense counsel will be to fashion comprehensive settlements that provide plaintiffs sufficient value without hamstringing corporate governance and management over the long term.

89. *In re WorldCom*, 2005 WL 335201, at *15.
90. *Id.* at *10.

NOTES

13

RECENT TRENDS IN SHAREHOLDER CLASS ACTION LITIGATION: ARE WORLDCOM AND ENRON THE NEW STANDARD?

Elaine Buckberg, Ph.D.

Todd Foster

Ronald Miller, Ph.D.

NERA Economic Consulting

This edition of NERA's research on recent trends in securities class action litigation expands on previous work by our colleagues Lucy Allen, Frederick C. Dunbar, Vinita M. Juneja, Denise Neumann Martin, Stephanie Plancich and David I. Tabak. We gratefully acknowledge their contribution to previous editions as well as this current version. In addition, the authors thank Christopher Enright and D.J. Percella for supervising the research effort. These individuals receive credit only for improving this paper; all errors and omissions are ours.

Table of Contents

A. WORLDCOM: A NEW RECORD SETTLEMENT

The WorldCom shareholder class action settlement has now topped $6.1 billion, reflecting the contributions of eight investment banks, Arthur Andersen, and personal contributions by its directors.[1] The WorldCom settlement is nearly 75% larger than the prior record settlement in Cendant, which reached $3.5 billion including the Cendant PRIDES settlement. The WorldCom settlement is striking not only in its size, but also in its composition. Outside co-defendants have financed nearly the entire settlement, with the exception of the directors' contributions. Whereas settlements on behalf of directors are typically wholly paid by D&O insurance, several insurers rescinded their coverage on grounds that their policies do not apply in the event of a finding of fraud. Plaintiffs succeeded in compelling ten WorldCom directors to make settlement payments of $18 million, negotiated as 20% of their personal assets, toward a settlement of $54 million on their behalf.[2]

The Enron shareholder class action may be on track for a yet-larger settlement, following preliminary settlement agreements by JPMorgan Chase for $2.2 billion, Citigroup for $2.0 billion, and over $500 million from members of the board of directors, Arthur Andersen, and two other investment banks.[3] Former directors will contribute $13 million in personal assets toward a settlement of $168 million on their behalf.[4] Another five investment banks which have not yet settled are named as underwriter defendants.

The record breaking WorldCom settlement compensates record breaking investor losses, larger by a substantial multiple than in any other settled case filed since 1991, even if common stock alone is considered, although the WorldCom class also included a substantial amount of debt. Investor losses, a simplified plaintiffs' style measure of damages, is the single most powerful predictor of settlement size.[5] In the Enron case,

---

1. With the exception of Citigroup's $2.575 billion contribution, the components of the settlement remain tentative, pending court approval. WorldCom, which emerged from bankruptcy as MCI in April 2004, made no contribution.
2. "Ex-directors of WorldCom in $54 mln settlement," Reuters, January 7, 2005, 1:10 p.m. and Stipulation of Settlement, *In Re* WorldCom, Inc. Securities Litigation, Master File No. 02 Civ. 3288, January 7, 2005.
3. Citigroup and JPMorgan Chase's settlements have not yet received court approval.
4. "Enron directors agree to $168 mln settlement," Reuters, January 7, 2005, 6:39 p.m.
5. We use investor losses as a proxy for the damages estimates presented by plaintiffs' side prior to settlement because we generally do not have access to plaintiffs' figures.

investor losses on common stock would rank fourth if compared to other settled cases; the Enron class action also includes debt and other securities, where each additional security type included in the class can dramatically increase settlement size.

Top Ten

Securities Class Action Settlements

Ranking (1)	Company (2)	Year (3)	Settlement Value ($MM) (4)
1	WorldCom, Inc. *	2005	$6,127
2	Enron Corp. **	2005	4,747
3	Cendant Corp. ***	2000	3,528
4	Lucent Technologies, Inc.	2003	517
5	BankAmerica Corp. and NationsBank Corp.	2002	490
6	Raytheon Company	2004	460
7	Waste Management Inc.	2002	457
8	Rite Aid Corporation	2003	320
9	DaimlerChrysler AG	2003	300
10	Oxford Health Plans, Inc.	2003	300

* Includes settled and pending settlements from the following parties: ABN Amro, Arthur Andersen LLP, Bank of America, Citigroup, Deutsche Bank, JP Morgan Chase, Lehman Brothers, Credit Suisse First Boston Corp., UBS Warburg, Goldman Sachs, WestLB AG, and various directors.

** This is a partial settlement involving Bank of America, Andersen Worldwide Societe Cooperative, Enron's Board of Directors, and Lehman Brothers. It also includes tentative settlements with Citigroup and JP Morgan Chase for a total of $4.2 billion (as of June 20, 2005).

*** The settlement value incorporates a $341 million settlement in the Cendant Prides case.

B. FILINGS DIP IN EARLY 2005

Based on the 109 filings through June 15, 2005, courts will receive fewer filings this year. If filings continue at the same pace for the remainder of the year, plaintiffs will file 201 cases in 2005, compared to 241 in 2004 and a post-PSLRA average of 211 filings each year, excluding the laddering, analyst, and mutual fund cases.[6] However, the slowing in early 2005 may be reversed by a faster than normal pace of filings in the remaining months of the year.

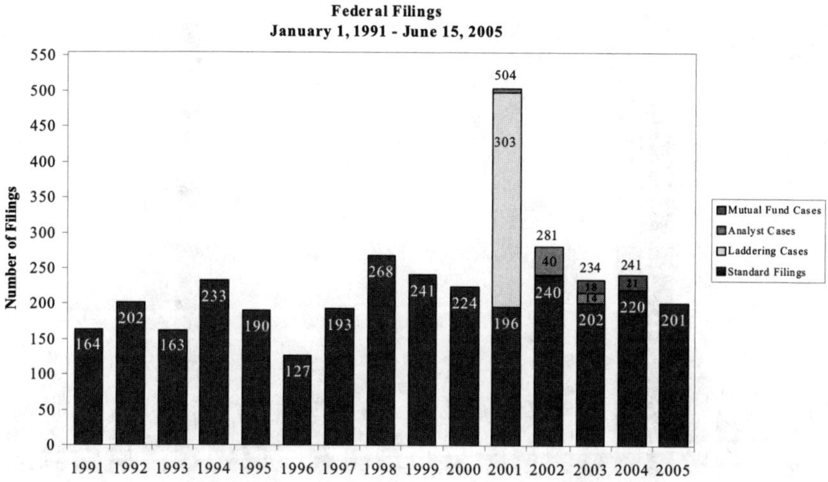

The drop in federal filings in the first six months of the year can be attributed to a sharp drop in Ninth Circuit filings. It may be that plaintiffs' firms in the Ninth Circuit chose to delay certain filings until after the *Dura* decision[7] by the Supreme Court in order to determine what they would need to do to plead loss causation. The Supreme Court's April 19, 2005 decision reversed the Ninth Circuit's decision in *Dura* and rejected the Ninth Circuit's view that a demonstration of inflation on date of purchase was sufficient to satisfy the loss causation requirement. Instead, plaintiffs' counsel must ultimately prove that a misrepresentation proximately caused plaintiffs' economic loss. Ninth Circuit plaintiffs' firms may file an unusually high number of cases in the remaining months of 2005, including cases that they would otherwise have filed earlier in the year.

---

6. The post-PSLRA average is calculated for 1996-2004, excluding all laddering, analyst, or mutual fund cases. Excluding 1996, the 1997-2004 average is 223 standard filings per year.
7. Broudo, et al. v. Dura Pharmaceutical, et al., 339 F.3d 933 (9th Cir. 2003).

2004 versus Projected 2005 Federal Filings by Circuit

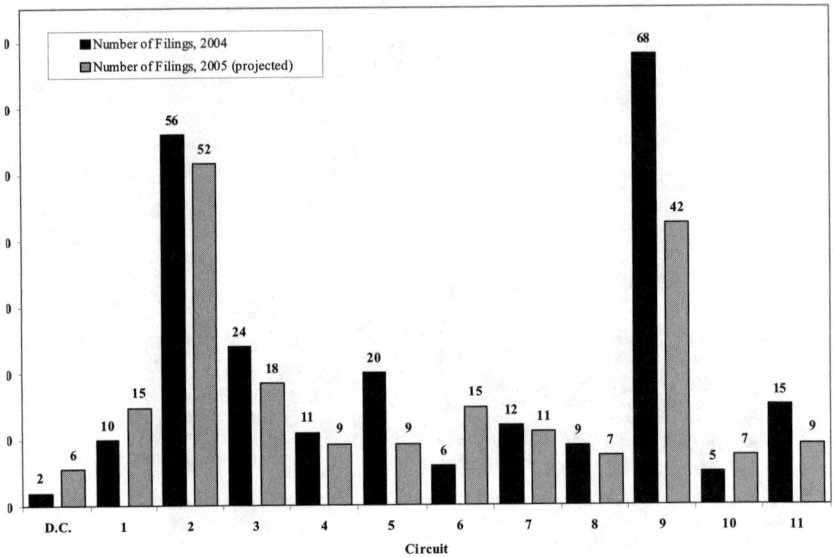

Based on the 2004 filing rate, over a five-year period, the average public corporation faces a 10% probability that it will face at least one shareholder class action lawsuit.[8] The annual likelihood of a suit has risen 25% since 1995, from 1.6% to 2.0%. However, the increased likelihood of a suit is offset by the increased dismissal rate such that the probability of a company facing a suit that survives a motion to dismiss is nearly constant, at 1.2% in 2004 versus 1.3% in 1995.

8. The probability of not facing a suit is 98.0% per year. Assuming that the probability of facing a suit in each year is independent and compounding over five years yields a 90.4% chance of no suit, or a 9.6% chance of at least one suit, in five years.

Companies Face a 2% Chance of a Suit Each Year

	1995	2004	% Change
No. of Publicly Traded Companies	11,688	11,875	1.6 %
Annual Filings	190	241	26.8
Probability of Securities Class Action (SCA)	1.6%	2.0%	24.8
Less: Probability of Dismissal	20.3%	39.3%	93.6
Probability of SCA that Survives Motion to Dismiss	1.3%	1.2%	-4.9

C. DISMISSALS

Dismissal rates nearly doubled after PSLRA.[9] Of cases filed between 1995 and 1999, dismissals accounted for 20.3% of dispositions. Of cases filed between 1996 and 2002, dismissals account for 39.3% of dispositions, a statistically significant increase of over 90%.[10] Our post-PSLRA dismissal rate may be slightly overstated, as it may include some dismissals without prejudice that will be reversed by amended and better-pled complaints or dismissals with prejudice that will be successfully appealed.

Dismissal rates vary by circuit. Both the Second and Ninth Circuits, which together receive the preponderance of cases, dismiss approximately 25% of cases within two years of the filing date. The Fourth Circuit has the highest rate, dismissing nearly 45% of filings within two years.

9. Our dismissal statistics include summary judgments but exclude partial dismissals.

10. Because it is not uncommon for judges to take up to two years from the filing date to rule on motions to dismiss, it would be premature to evaluate dismissal rates of cases filed in 2003-2005.

Dismissal Rates by Circuit
Within Two Years of Filing

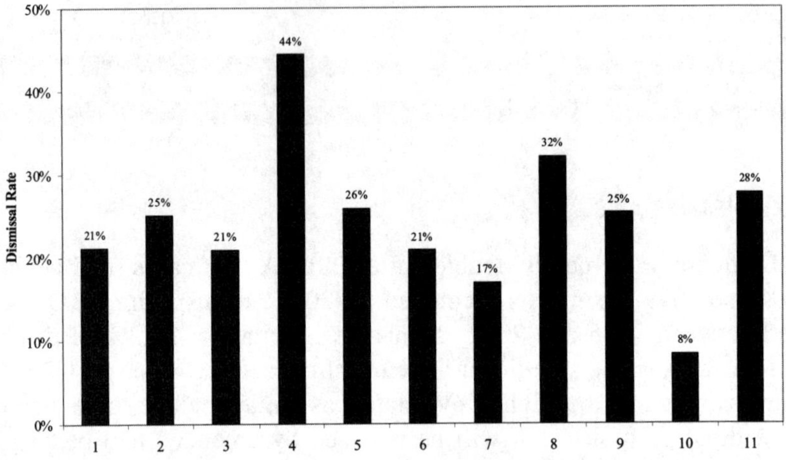

D. SETTLEMENTS HEAD FOR NEW HIGHS IN 2005

Even if we exclude the WorldCom and Enron settlements, 2005 is likely to bring new highs in both mean and median settlements. In the first six months of 2005, the mean settlement value reached $25.8 million, exceeding the prior high of $23.5 million in 2002.[11]

11. Excluding Cendant from the 2000 average.

Average Settlements Have Been Rising

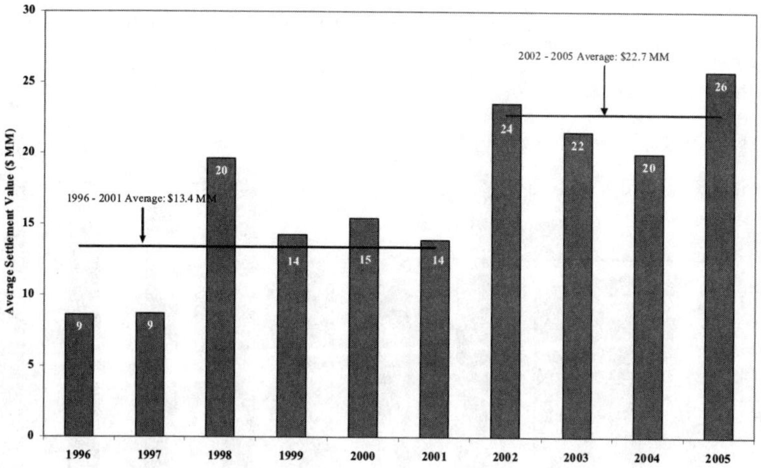

E. GOODBYE TO NUISANCE SUITS

If we look at median settlement values, 2005 will set another record. In the first six months of the year, the median settlement value rose to $6.8 million from $5.3 million in 2004, a 28% increase. The driving factor behind this increase is the sharp reduction in settlements under $3 million, which accounted for nearly 45% of settlements in 1996 but account for less than 26% of settlements thus far in 2005. Taken with the substantial increase in dismissal rates since PSLRA, this suggests that cases that formerly settled for small sums are instead being dismissed.

With Fewer Nuisance Settlements, Median Settlements Will Hit a New High in 2005

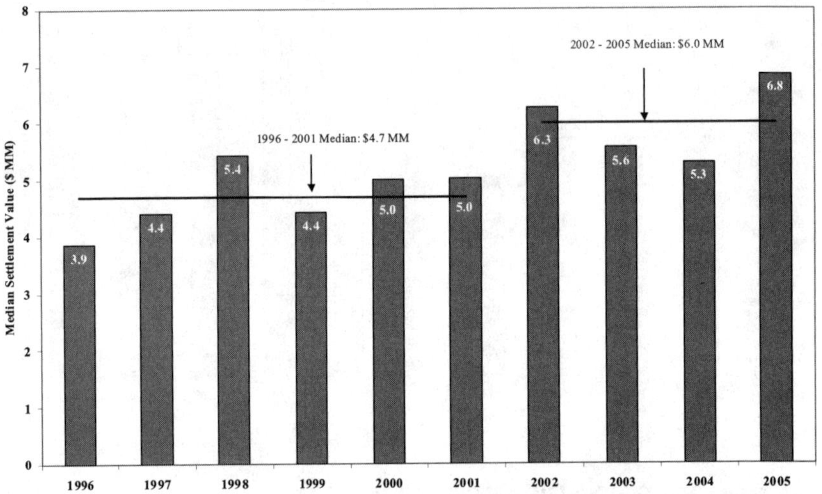

F. SETTLEMENTS MAY HAVE FURTHER TO FALL, BUT IT MAY TAKE A FEW YEARS

Settlements in 2002-2005 have been substantially higher than in the prior post-PSLRA years of 1996-2001, averaging $22.7 million versus $13.4 million for the earlier years.[12] Our analysis indicates that this is due to higher investor losses in suits settled in 2002-2005, including a number of lawsuits with class periods ending during the collapse of the stock market bubble in 2000-2002.

We expect this trend of high settlements to continue for several more years as other cases with class periods ending during the 2000-2002 bubble deflation period reach settlement. Our projection rests on our analysis of median investor losses by end-of-class-period year for settled cases. For settled cases, median investor losses for cases with class periods in 2000-2002 are $397 million—more than 80% higher than the maximum for any prior end-of-class-period year. If the size of investor losses does

12. These statistics exclude the Cendant, Enron, and WorldCom settlements; if we include them, the jump is from an average of $17.1 million to $57.4 million.

not affect the speed of settlement, then we can expect that unsettled cases with class periods ending in 2000-2002 will settle for amounts similar to the already settled cases from the same period.

Because just under 50% of cases that settle do so within five years of the filing date, it will be several more years before most of these cases with class periods ending in 2000-2002 are settled. If cases continue to progress at their historical rates, approximately half of cases with class periods ending in 2000 will have settled by the end of 2005. Approximately half of those cases with class periods ending in 2001 will have settled by the end of 2006, and half of those with class periods ending in 2002 will have settled by the end of 2007.[13]

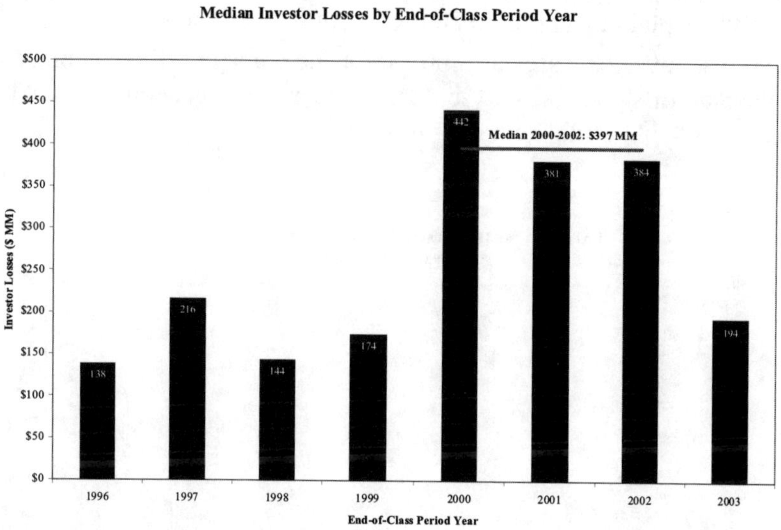

We find no statistically significant change in settlement values since the passage of Sarbanes-Oxley, once we control for other factors including investor losses. Higher investor losses explain the rise in settlements, as we will discuss further below.

13. This approximation assumes that most suits are filed in the same year as the class period ends, although the statute of limitations allowed one year from disclosure to filing prior to the passage of Sarbanes-Oxley on July 25, 2002 and two years since the passage of Sarbanes-Oxley.

G. EXPLAINING SETTLEMENTS

NERA has estimated a settlement prediction model that explains over 60% of the variation in settlements, using data on settled cases filed after January 1, 1996. This section discusses the sensitivity of settlement values to various lawsuit characteristics, based on that model; all the sensitivity measures described are calculated controlling for other characteristics of the suit and changes in the consumer price index.

Trends in investor losses explain both the headline settlements of recent years and trends in median settlements. On average, a 1.0% increase in investor losses results in a 0.4% increase in the size of the expected settlement, meaning that settlements tend to increase far less than one-for-one with investor losses. Investor losses—an estimate of what investors lost over a class period relative to an investment in the S&P—are the single most powerful, publicly available determinant of settlements, explaining approximately 50% of the variation.

We use investor losses as a proxy for the damage estimates presented by the plaintiffs' side prior to settlement because we generally do not have access to the plaintiffs' actual figures.

Investor Losses Have Risen More Rapidly than Settlements...
1991 - June 15, 2005

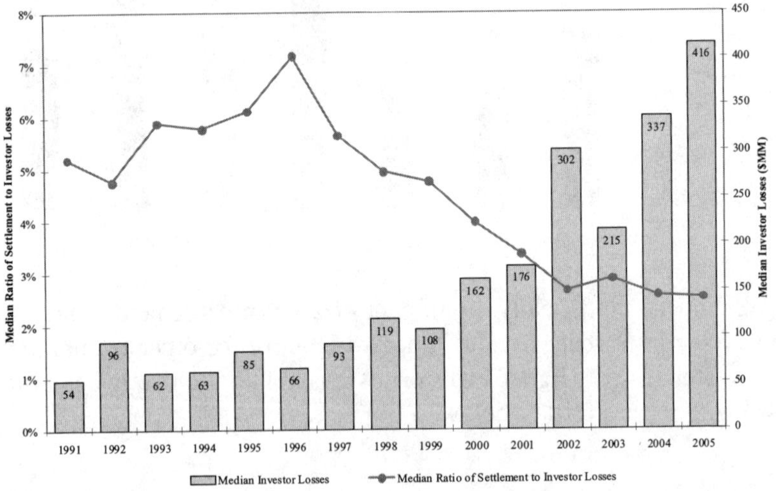

Following the bursting of the 1990s stock market bubble, average investor losses ballooned from $140 million in the average suit settling in 1996 to $1.0 billion in 2002 and $2.5 billion in 2003. After dipping to

$1.7 billion in 2004, average investor losses in cases settling in the first six months of 2005 have set a new high of $3.5 billion (excluding WorldCom and Enron). Median investor losses have risen steadily in the last two years to $416 million for cases settling in early 2005 from $337 million in 2004 and $215 million in 2003. Taking a longer-term perspective, 2005 median investor losses were more than five times the 1996 median of $66 million.

Settlement values rise dramatically with the inclusion of each class of securities other than common stock in a class action suit. Effectively, the claims of the holders of these other securities represent losses above and beyond—and not captured by our measure of—investor losses on common stock.

Settlements increase with the depth of the defendants' pockets. For each 1.0% increase in the company's market capitalization on the day after the end of the class period, the typical settlement will increase 0.1%. But this effect may be offset if the company's fortunes change on the way to settlement. If the defendant firm is in bankruptcy or has a stock price of less than $1.00 per share on the settlement date, the settlement will typically be approximately one-third lower. The involvement of company co-defendants can lead to larger settlements. In cases with an accounting firm co-defendant, settlements increase by more than two-thirds, controlling for all other characteristics of the case.

Cases with accounting allegations result in higher settlements for several additional reasons. The presence of any one of three accounting factors—accounting issues, accounting irregularities or restatements—will raise average settlement values by approximately 20%. More often, two or more of these accounting variables will apply to the same case, further increasing the likely settlement.

One of Congress's major goals for the PSLRA was to involve institutional investors as lead plaintiffs, with the intention that institutional investor plaintiffs play a more active role in litigation and generate better outcomes for plaintiffs. Controlling for other case characteristics, cases with an institutional investor lead plaintiff settle for a statistically significant one-third more on average. Possible reasons for higher settlements in cases with institutional investors as lead plaintiffs include the retention of more effective plaintiffs' counsel in those cases, the lead plaintiff's more effective supervision of counsel and own contribution to strategy, or both. Alternatively, it may reflect a tendency for institutional investors to get involved in cases where the allegations have greater merit or the defendants' capacity to pay in relation to potential damages is greater.

Our model also indicates that settlements increase by approximately one-third if an IPO is involved. All such cases involve potential Section 11 claims, which have the potential to result in higher alleged damages than the accompanying 10b-5 claims.

While defendants' resources and the characteristics of a case affect settlements, only the health services sector pays markedly different settlements than other industries. Settlements involving companies in the health services sector are typically one-third higher than settlements involving any other industry, controlling for other case characteristics. This finding may relate to the existence of concurrent billing fraud allegations against health services companies brought under the federal False Claims Act.

H. THE PLAINTIFFS' BAR'S SHARE

As settlements rise, plaintiffs' counsel is taking home a smaller percentage of settlements, yet larger paychecks. The fee percentages requested by plaintiffs' counsel have fallen in recent years, although 33% is still the most frequent percentage, requested in over 40% of cases. We find that fee percentages are lower for cases with larger settlements.

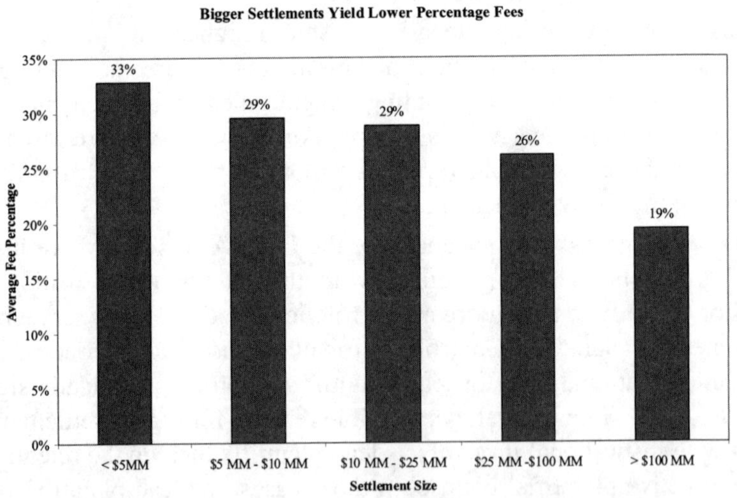

However, as median and mean settlements have climbed, so have plaintiffs' attorneys' total fees in the average shareholder class action. The average settlement in 2005 will yield over $6 million in fees to plaintiffs' counsel, as compared to $3.6 million in 2000.

I. CONCLUSION

Settlement of the WorldCom and Enron shareholder class actions will bring to an end two of the cases that epitomized the alleged mega-frauds that occurred during the stock market bubble and were revealed by its bursting. But these cases are part of a broader process in which shareholder class action cases with class periods ending during the bear market of 2000-2002 are reaching settlement. Large settlements in many of these cases are consistent with large losses. Indeed, we do not find a statistically significant change in the relationship between investor losses and settlement size, even when the WorldCom settlement is considered. Large settlements are likely to continue for several years as these bear market cases progress toward settlement.

NOTES

14

THREADING THE NEEDLE: OBSTACLES TO PARTIAL SETTLEMENTS IN SECURITIES CLASS ACTIONS

Alan Schulman

David Stickney

Timothy DeLange

Bernstein Litowitz Berger & Grossmann LLP

Alan Schulman is the Partner in Charge of the San Diego office of Bernstein Litowitz Berger & Grossmann LLP; David Stickney is a partner with the firm; and Timothy DeLange is an associate.

Table of Contents

Settling defendants, who are paying to obtain peace, logically insist that any settlement of a securities class action finally resolve the settling defendant's liability arising from the litigation. Just as defendants want peace, plaintiffs require a settlement that the district court will approve and that presents a low risk of reversal on appeal so that the recovery can be promptly distributed to the class. Partial settlements present unique challenges to the settling parties in achieving these objectives. Prior to the passage of the Private Securities Litigation Reform Act of 1995 (the "PSLRA"), a body of caselaw had developed to guide settling parties when faced with the complications of partial settlements.

When enacting the PSLRA, Congress codified certain aspects of the partial settlement caselaw. To protect a settling defendant from potential claims for contribution by non-settling defendants, the PSLRA requires, upon entry of the judgment, the entry of a mutual bar order discharging the settling defendant from all claims for contribution brought by or against any other person. 15 U.S.C. § 78u-4(f)(7)(A). To compensate non-settling defendants for the loss of such contribution claims, the PSLRA reduces the judgment or verdict against non-settling defendants by the *greater* of (1) the percentage of responsibility of the settling defendant; or (2) the amount paid to the plaintiff by that settling defendant. 15 U.S.C. § 78u-4(f)(7)(B).

In practice, uncertainty over application of these provisions has greatly complicated negotiations for partial settlements. Prior to passage of the PSLRA, settling parties would ask courts to enter orders barring future claims against the settling defendants for contribution *and indemnity.* Because the PSLRA's mandatory bar order discharges contribution claims, but not indemnity claims, non-settling defendants routinely object to any settlement that also bars indemnity claims on the grounds that Congress, by its silence, intended to prohibit bar orders broader than that expressly mandated by the PSLRA. While most district courts hold that the PSLRA did not limit the scope of permissible bar orders, such objections inject uncertainty and may cause delay.

The PSLRA's judgment credit provision further complicates negotiations. Not only does it increase plaintiffs' settlement risks by giving non-settling defendants a judgment reduction credit that is the "greater of" two alternate methodologies, but the "proportionate fault" method alone discourages settlement. By way of example, assume a securities class action against the chief executive officer of a bankrupt company and the solvent investment banks who advised the company. Damages are $1 billion, and the CEO is willing to pay $20 million—virtually his entire net worth—to get out of the case. While settlement would benefit both sides because the CEO wants out of the case and $20 million is the most plaintiffs would expect to recover from the CEO if plaintiffs prevailed at trial, settling with the CEO profoundly reduces the value of the case against the non-settling investment banks. If the jury assigns 50% fault to the settling CEO, a $1 billion verdict against the investment banks would be reduced to $500 million.

In this manner, the PSLRA erects obstacles to partial settlements.

I. BAR ORDERS UNDER THE PSLRA

While the scope of the bar order is important for a settling defendant, the bar order only concerns plaintiffs insofar as plaintiffs require a valid settlement agreement that the court will approve without undue delay. Prior to the passage of the PSLRA, courts uniformly approved orders barring claims for contribution *and indemnity* against settling defendants.[1] Barring indemnity claims is justified by the policy against indemnification for violations of the federal securities laws:

> The underlying goal of securities legislation is encouraging diligence and discouraging negligence in securities transactions . . . These goals are accomplished by 'exposing issuers and underwriters to the substantial hazard of liability for compensatory damages.'"

Eichenholtz, 52 F.3d at 483-84 (quoting *Globus v. Law Research Service, Inc.*, 418 F.2d 1276, 1289 (2d Cir. 1969)). *See also Franklin*, 884 F.2d at 1232 (invalidating indemnification provision in underwriting agreement); *Stewart*, 845 F.2d at 200; *Laventhol,* 637 F.2d at 676; *In re Wilshire Tech. Sec. Litig.*, 887 F. Supp. at 239 (indemnification claim by an underwriter previously dismissed from the action barred; indemnification provision of underwriting agreement held to be void as against public policy); *Globus*, 418 F.2d at 1288 (affirming district court's order setting aside verdict on cross claims for indemnification of Securities Act violation because "to tolerate indemnity under these circumstances would encourage flouting the policy of the common law and the Securities Act").

---

1. *See, e.g., Gerber v. MTC Elec. Tech. Co.*, 329 F.3d 297, 306 (2d Cir. 2003) (bar order may be issued in a partial settlement to preclude non-settling defendants from asserting contribution and indemnity claims); *Eichenholtz v. Brennan*, 52 F.3d 478, 487 (3d Cir. 1995); *Franklin v. Kaypro Corp.*, 884 F.2d 1222, 1232 (9th Cir. 1989); *Stewart v. American Int'l Oil & Gas Co.*, 845 F.2d 196, 200 (9th Cir. 1988); *Laventhol, Krekstein, Horwath & Horwath v. Horwitch,* 637 F.2d 672, 676 (9th Cir. 1980); *In re Wilshire Tech. Sec. Litig.*, 887 F. Supp. 236, 239 (S.D. Cal. 1995).

The PSLRA incorporates aspects of the existing caselaw. The statute expressly protects settling defendants from future contribution claims by mandating that a defendant "who settles any private action at any time before final verdict or judgment shall be discharged from all claims for contribution brought by other persons." 15 U.S.C. § 78u-4(f)(7)(A). The PSLRA also mandates mutuality, requiring the bar order to bar "all future claims for contribution arising out of the action—by the settling covered person against any person." 15 U.S.C. § 78u-4(f)(7)(A)(ii); *see In re MTC Elec. Tech. S'holder Litig.*, No. MDL 1059, 2005 U.S. Dist. LEXIS 10312, at *16 (E.D.N.Y. May 31, 2005) (concluding that a mutual bar order is appropriate); *In re Rite Aid Corp. Sec. Litig.*, 146 F. Supp. 2d 706, 726 (E.D. Pa. 2001) (the PSLRA "supports, and indeed *requires*, our entry of an order barring contribution claims both by and against 'settling covered persons'"); *Gerber*, 329 F.3d at 309 ("the PSLRA has resolved this dilemma in favor of mutual bar orders").

The PSLRA, however, makes no mention of indemnity, and the legislative history provides little guidance on what Congress had in mind.[2] Arguably, however, it was unnecessary for Congress to include indemnification claims in the PSLRA's bar order provision because, unlike the right to contribution, there is no right to indemnification under the federal securities laws. *See Lucas v. Hackett Assocs., Inc.,* 18 F. Supp. 2d 531, 535 (E.D. Pa. 1998) ("there is a logical explanation for Congress' omission. '[T]here is no express right to indemnification under the 1933 or 1934 [Securities] Acts.'") (*citing Eichenholtz,* 52 F.3d at 483).

Companies entering into partial settlements continue to insist upon bar orders broader than the contribution bar mandated by the PSLRA. Now, as before the PSLRA, barring contribution claims alone will not eliminate the threat to settling defendants of continued litigation arising from the underlying action.

Non-settling defendants predictably object to entry of such bar orders. With one exception, however, district courts overwhelmingly find the authority to enter bar orders that exceed the mandatory bar of the PSLRA. *See In re MTC Elec. Tech. S'holder Litig.*, 2005 U.S. Dist. LEXIS 10312,

2. *See Wisconsin Inv. Bd. v. Ruttenberg*, 300 F. Supp. 2d 1210, 1217 (N.D. Ala. 2004) (rejecting the non-settling defendants' "argument that the PSLRA's legislative history 'makes it evident that Congress consciously decided not to expand the scope of the bar order beyond contribution claims arising out of the action'"); *In re Cendant Corp. Sec. Litig.*, 166 F. Supp. 2d 1, 6 n.1 (D.N.J. 2001) (the "court's own review of testimony at various congressional hearings fails to uncover any discussion which would shed light on the specific purposes behind the contribution bar").

at *16 (approving order barring claims for contribution and indemnity); *In re Worldcom, Inc. Sec. Litig.*, No. 02 Civ. 3288, 2005 U.S. Dist. LEXIS 3791, at *37-*40 (S.D.N.Y. Mar. 15, 2005) (approving order barring claims for contribution, indemnity and contractual contribution); *Wisconsin Inv. Bd.*, 300 F. Supp. 2d at 1216-1217 (noting that prior to the enactment of the PSLRA courts routinely approved broad bar orders, and concluding that nothing in the statute or its legislative history indicated that Congress intended to divest courts of their power to impose bar orders extinguishing claims other than those for contribution); *In re Rite Aid*, 146 F. Supp. 2d at 726 (approving a bar order broader than the language of the PSLRA and holding that the statute does not limit the scope of a bar order); *Neuberger v. Shapiro*, 110 F. Supp. 2d 373, 381 (E.D. Pa. 2000) (approving settlement that proposed an order barring claims for indemnification among other claims); *Lucas*, 18 F. Supp. 2d at 535 (same).

In *Rite Aid,* the court explained that the PSLRA "does not include any explicit language stating that the order therein described is the *only* bar order that [courts] may entertain." 146 F. Supp. 2d at 726. Indeed, the PSLRA "was enacted against a background of prior decisional law under which orders barring indemnification claims had been entered" and neither the statute nor its legislative history addressed these cases. *Id.* at 726-27 (*citing Eichenholtz*, 52 F.3d at 487). The PSLRA left these pre-PSLRA cases barring indemnification claims untouched and did not negate the use of indemnification bar orders in federal securities cases. *Id.* at 727 n.32 (extending *Eichenholtz*, 52 F.3d at 483, to post-PSLRA cases).

In *Rite Aid*, the non-settling defendants argued that the original proposed language of Section 21D(f)(7)(A) included both a bar for contribution claims and a bar for indemnification claims. *Id.* at 726. The non-settling defendants contended that because the final text of the PSLRA mandated only a bar on contribution claims, Congress must have intended to prohibit orders barring claims other than contribution. *Id.* The court rejected this interpretation of the PSLRA and its legislative history, noting a proposed amendment adopted by the House, but which was not included in the final statute, which would have expressly *prohibited* courts from barring indemnification claims. *Id.* Although the court denied the bar order in question, it rejected the argument that "the text of the PSLRA prevents the entry of a bar order that precludes indemnification claims." *Id.* According to the *Rite Aid* court, since the PSLRA "contains no provision that explicitly limits [a court's] ability to enter a bar order that precludes indemnification claims," courts are free to consider the reasonableness of bar orders that deal with indemnification and other claims. *Id.* This approach is consistent with pre-PSLRA law and the federal policy of encouraging settlement.

One court, however, rejected a proposed bar order that was broader than that expressly mandated in the PSLRA. In *In re Initial Pub. Offering Sec. Litig.*, 226 F.R.D. 186 (S.D.N.Y. 2005), the court concluded that it had "no authority" to deviate from the express wording of the PSLRA in approving a bar order. *Id.* at 201. The settling parties submitted a proposed bar order seeking to allow the Lead Plaintiff to pursue the claims assigned by the settling defendant against the Underwriter, but barred any claim raised by the Underwriter. *Id.* The court granted preliminary approval of the proposed settlement, but ordered the settling parties to modify the proposed bar order to enjoin only claims for contribution. *Id.* Notably, the court did not cite any other decisions supporting its conclusion, nor did the court address any of the published decisions that had previously held that the PSLRA does *not* limit the scope of bar orders that may be approved by the court.

The decision in *IPO*, albeit in the distinct minority, shows the uncertainty of entering into a settlement that is contingent upon entry of a bar order that exceeds the PSLRA. At the very least, the non-settling defendants' objections can delay the approval of the settlement, especially given the possibility of appeal. Such uncertainty and delay are factors when negotiating partial settlements.

The non-settling defendants may be objecting solely in an attempt to improve their own bargaining position. To undercut such an attempt, plaintiffs can either refuse to agree upon a bar order that exceeds the PSLRA, or the settling parties can carve-out any appeals that are based solely on the scope of the bar order from the conditions to finality of the settlement.

II. THE PSLRA'S JUDGMENT REDUCTION CREDIT

When a settlement extinguishes the contribution rights of non-settling defendants, such non-settling defendants are entitled to a set-off against the judgment. *Franklin*, 884 F.2d at 1231; *In re Masters Mates & Pilots Pension Plan*, 957 F.2d 1020, 1031 (2d Cir. 1992). Put differently, the non-settling defendants must receive a judgment credit that "adequately compensates the non-settling defendants for their" lost claims. *Gerber*, 329 F.3d at 306; *Eichenholz*, 52 F.3d at 486 (non-settling defendants entitled to judgment set-off to "harmonize the equitable objectives of contribution with the encouragement of settlement").

Before passage of the PSLRA, courts employed various methods for reducing a judgment against a non-settling defendant. Courts were divided among three methods: the *pro rata* method; the *pro tanto* method; and the proportionate fault method.[3]

When enacting the PSLRA, Congress incorporated aspects of the two leading methods for providing judgment credit to non-settling defendants: the "proportionate share" approach employed by the Ninth Circuit in *Franklin v. Kaypro* prior to passage of the PSLRA, and the *pro tanto* approach favored by other circuits, such as the Second Circuit. *See, e.g., Singer*, 878 F.2d at 600. According to the PSLRA, "[i]f a covered person enters into a settlement with the plaintiff prior to final verdict or judgment, the verdict or judgment shall be reduced by the greater of—

(i) an amount that corresponds to the percentage of responsibility of that covered person; or

(ii) the amount paid to the plaintiff by that covered person."

15 U.S.C. § 78u-4(f)(7)(B).

This rule was designed to be pro-defendant by maximizing the amount of the judgment credit. One consequence of the rule, however, is its tendency to discourage settlements.

A. The Proportionate Fault Credit

The first of the PSLRA's alternative methods for calculating the size of the judgment credit, the "proportionate fault" method, is a significant factor when negotiating a partial settlement with a defendant facing potential liability for all or most of the damages. The claims against non-settling defendants will be discounted by the amount that corresponds to that settling defendant's percentage of responsibility.

---

3. Under the *pro rata* method, a plaintiff's damages would be allocated equally among all settling and non-settling defendants and any judgment against a non-settling defendant would be reduced by the settling defendant's *pro rata* share of the damages. *See, e.g., In re Masters Mates*, 957 F.2d at 1028. Under the *pro tanto* method, a judgment against a non-settling defendant is reduced by the amount paid in settlement by the settling defendant. *See, e.g., Singer v. Olympia Brewing Co.*, 878 F.2d 596, 600 (2d Cir. 1989). Under the proportionate fault method, a judgment against a non-settling defendant is reduced by the proportionate liability of the settling defendant. *See, e.g., Franklin*, 884 F.2d at 1231-1232.

The difficulty is illustrated by *In re Worldcom, Inc. Sec. Litig.*, No. 02 Civ. 3288, 2005 U.S. Dist. LEXIS 1805 (S.D.N.Y. Feb. 10, 2005). In *Worldcom*, the settlement with Worldcom's directors was contingent upon the entry of an order which would have altered the express language of the judgment credit of the PSLRA "to reflect any limitation on the financial capability of the [settling defendants] to pay their proportionate shares of liability" had a non-settling defendant obtained a contribution or equitable indemnification judgment against them. *Id.* at *29. Capping the reduction based on the net worth of the settling director defendants was clearly within the best interests of the plaintiffs, who had fought for the largest possible payment from the directors' own pockets, and the directors who faced ruinous liability.

Denying preliminary approval of the settlement, Judge Cote recognized the dilemma facing plaintiffs in attempting partial settlements of securities class actions: "the difference between the percentage of damages for which the [settling defendants] are deemed responsible and the amount they could actually pay could be immense." *Id.* at *31. The court further noted the inequities *to the defendants* who want to settle: "As a result, if the 'deep pockets' refuse to settle, it is likely that the plaintiff will refuse to settle with outside directors on terms they are able to meet." *Id.* at *50.

The reasoning in the *Worldcom* decision shows how the PSLRA can discourage settlements. The PSLRA creates "a destructive set of incentives [that] may deserve to be remedied, but because the statutory language is clear, the remedy must be legislative." *Id.* at *50-51.

B. The *Pro Tanto* Credit

The alternative to the PSLRA's proportionate fault credit—known as the *pro tanto* credit—can also complicate negotiations in certain partial settlements by inviting objections and exacerbating the plaintiffs' settlement risk. Under the PSLRA's *pro tanto* credit, non-settling defendants receive credit for "the amount paid to the plaintiff by [the settling defendant]." 15 U.S.C. § 78u-4(f)(7)(B)(ii). This alternative applies when the amount corresponding to the settling defendant's proportionate fault is less than the amount paid to the plaintiff in settlement.

In certain partial settlements, the exact monetary amount to be paid in the settlement is not fixed at the time the settling parties seek court approval of the settlement. This opens the door to objections by non-settling defendants who, relying on the PSLRA, will insist on knowing the size of the *pro tanto* credit. In *In re IPO*, for example, the exact amount that the settling defendants would pay in a partial settlement depended on the plaintiffs' total recovery from the non-settling defendants. 226 F.R.D. at 192. Objecting, the non-settling defendants contended that the PSLRA precluded such settlements and required certainty. *Id.* at 203. The court disagreed: "the [non-settling defendants'] argument is predicated on the baseless notion that, under the PSLRA, a partial settlement must predict the future—*i.e.*, it must tell any non-settling defendants precisely the value of a credit against their future liability, well before anybody knows the *extent* of that liability. Such a position makes little sense." *Id.; see also Gerber*, 329 F.3d at 304-305 ("We find no error in the district court's decision to leave the determination of the actual amount of the judgment credit for calculation at trial because the non-settling defendants will get at least the full settlement amount as a credit, unless the settlement damages are not common, an issue which is obviously contingent on the outcome of the trial.").

Even for partial settlements in which the amount being paid is certain, unresolved questions about how to apply the PSLRA's *pro tanto* credit can complicate partial settlements. The PSLRA is silent on how to apply the credit when "the amount paid to the plaintiff by [the settling defendant]" and the amount of the judgment against the non-settling defendant do not represent common damages. This may arise, for example, when investors in the class have different types of claims, and the non-settling defendant is liable for only one such claim. If, for instance, the class includes investors with § 10(b) claims and investors with § 14(a) claims, *and if* the settling defendant pays the class $1 billion to settle all claims, it would be absurd to give the non-settling defendant a credit for the full $1 billion if the judgment against the non-settling defendant is for only § 14(a) liability.

Such absurd results would discourage settlements. Given the PSLRA's silence on this situation, courts considering the amount of the credit following a partial settlement should look to guidance from analogous pre-PSLRA precedent.[4] Before passage of the PSLRA, courts employing the *pro tanto* method uniformly gave non-settling defendants a credit against the judgment for the amount paid in settlement that was *common* to damages in the judgment.[5] Accordingly, while there is no published decision on this point, non-settling defendants should still receive a credit only for the amount of the settlement that represents common damages. Nevertheless, uncertainty over application of the PSLRA's *pro tanto* credit provision can complicate negotiations and delay approval of the partial settlement.

III. CONCLUSION

Increasingly, Courts are sustaining securities complaints against issuers and additional participants in the fraud—such as auditors, financial advisors, underwriters and others. In the course of litigation, some of these defendants may seek to enter into partial settlements with plaintiffs, and such settlements may be advantageous for both sides. The PSLRA, however, complicates negotiations and can make it difficult for both sides to achieve their settlement goals.

---

4. "[C]ourts are inclined to interpret a statute in conformity to common-law concepts where the letter of the statute is silent in regard to certain consequences which are analogous to situations governed by common-law principles." 2B Singer, Sutherland Statutes and Statutory Construction § 56:3 (6th ed.) (citations omitted); *see also Cottage Sav. Ass'n v. Commissioner*, 499 U.S. 554, 562 (1991) ("Because these decisions were part of the 'contemporary legal context' in which Congress enacted [the statute] . . . we may presume that Congress intended to codify these principles"); *Lorillard v. Pons*, 434 U.S. 575, 581 (1978) ("[W]here, as here, Congress adopts a new law incorporating sections of a prior law, Congress normally can be presumed to have had knowledge of the interpretation given to the incorporated law, at least insofar as it affects the new statute.").
5. *See, e.g., Gerber*, 329 F.3d at 304 (affirming the district court's holding that the judgment reduction shall not necessarily be calculated by using the full amounts of the settlements, "as only the portion of the settlement attributable to common damages will be credited"); *U.S. Indus., Inc. v. Touche Ross & Co.*, 854 F.2d 1223, 1236 (10th Cir. 1988) ("where two or more defendants are responsible for separate injuries, an amount received in settlement from one defendant for one of the injuries may not be used to reduce the liability of the other defendant for the other injury"); *FDIC v. Geldermann, Inc.*, 763 F. Supp. 524, 530 (W.D. Okla. 1990) ("'[w]hen a plaintiff receives an amount from a settling defendant...it is normally applied as a credit against the amount recovered by the plaintiff from a non-settling defendant, provided both the settlement and the judgment represent common damages.'" (quoting *U.S. Indus., Inc.*, 854 F.2d at 1236)).

NOTES

SEC ENFORCEMENT INITIATIVES

15

RECENT SEC ENFORCEMENT CASES

Submitted by:

Joan McKown
Chief Counsel

Antonia Chion
Associate Director

Shannon A. Sullivan
Student Intern

Division of Enforcement
Securities and Exchange Commission
Washington, DC

Parts of this outline have been used in other publications.

The Securities and Exchange Commission, as a matter of policy, disclaims responsibility for any private publication or statement by any of its employees. The views expressed herein are those of the authors and do not necessarily reflect the views of the Commission or its staff.

Table of Contents

As our capital markets continue to experience unprecedented growth and expansion, the Securities and Exchange Commission's ("Commission" or "SEC") enforcement program has been challenged to keep apace of market developments. Violations involving broker-dealers, mutual funds and investment advisers, fraudulent securities offerings, issuer disclosure, financial fraud, and insider trading continue to form the core of the enforcement program.

This Outline will review some of the Division's significant recent activity. Copies of orders, administrative releases, and litigation releases concerning the cases discussed below can be accessed on the Commission's web site at <**www.sec.gov**>.

I. FINANCIAL FRAUD & OTHER DISCLOSURE AND REPORTING VIOLATIONS

SEC v. v. Joseph Nacchio, Robert S. Woodruff, Robin R. Szeliga, Afshin Mohebbi, Gregory M. Casey, James J. Koslowski, Frank T. Noyes,

SEC v. Roger B. Hoaglund

SEC v. William L. Eveleth

Litigation Release No. 19136 (March 15, 2005)
http://www.sec.gov/litigation/litreleases/lr19136.htm

On March 15, 2005, the Commission charged Joseph P. Nacchio, former co-chairman and chief executive officer of Qwest Communications International Inc., and eight other former Qwest officers and employees with fraud and other violations of the federal securities laws. In three separate but related civil actions, the Commission alleges that, between 1999 and 2002, the Qwest defendants engaged in a multi-faceted fraudulent scheme designed to mislead the investing public about the company's revenue and growth. According to the SEC's complaints, Nacchio and others made numerous false and misleading statements about Qwest's financial condition in annual, quarterly, and current reports, in registration statements that incorporated Qwest's financial statements, and in other public statements, including earnings releases and investor calls. As a result of that scheme, Qwest fraudulently recognized over $3 billion of revenue and excluded $71.3 million in expenses. The Commission, in October 2004, sued Qwest in a settled injunctive action in which the company agreed to pay a $250 million penalty for its misconduct. In addition to Nacchio, the Commission's complaints name former chief financial officers Robert S. Woodruff and Robin R. Szeliga, former chief operating officer Afshin Mohebbi, former executive vice president of wholesale markets Gregory M. Casey, former senior vice president of pricing and offer management Roger B. Hoaglund, former senior vice president of finance William L. Eveleth, former director of financial reporting James J. Kozlowski, and former senior manager of financial reporting Frank T. Noyes.

Hoaglund consented to the entry of a judgment enjoining him from violating the antifraud and internal control provisions of the federal securities laws and aiding and abetting reporting and books and records provisions, and directing him to pay a civil penalty of $100,000 and disgorgement of $200,000 plus prejudgment interest. Eveleth consented to entry of a judgment enjoining him from violating the antifraud and internal control provisions of the federal securities laws and aiding and abetting reporting and books and records provisions, and directing him to pay a civil penalty of $75,000 and disgorgement of $35,575 plus prejudgment interest, and prohibiting him from acting as an officer or director of any public company for five years. The actions against the other defendants are still pending.

On March 15, 2005, the Commission also instituted settled cease-and-desist proceedings and filed related civil actions for penalties against Mark A. Schumacher and Brian K. Treadway, former controllers at Qwest. (Litigation Release Nos. 19134 and 19135; Sec. Exch. Act. Rel. Nos. 34-51373 and 34-51375). The Commission also instituted a settled cease and desist proceeding against Jennifer J. Black, a former director of finance at Qwest. (Sec. Exch. Act. Rel. No. 34-51374).

SEC v. Qwest Communications International Inc.

Litigation Release No. 18936 (October 21, 2004)
http://www.sec.gov/litigation/litreleases/lr18936.htm

On October 21, 2004, the Commission charged Qwest Communications International Inc., one of the largest telecommunications companies in the United States, with securities fraud and other violations of the federal securities laws. The Commission's complaint alleged that, between 1999 and 2002, Qwest fraudulently recognized over $3.8 billion in revenue and excluded $231 million in expenses as part of a multi-faceted fraudulent scheme to meet optimistic and unsupportable revenue and earnings projections. Qwest consented to entry of a judgment enjoining it from violating the Securities Act and the Exchange Act and the Rules thereunder. The judgment also directed Qwest to pay a civil penalty of

$250 million and $1 disgorgement. The entire penalty amount will be distributed to defrauded investors. In addition, Qwest was required to maintain permanently a chief compliance officer ("CCO") reporting to a committee of outside directors and responsible for ensuring the company conducts its business in compliance with the federal securities laws.

The Commission's complaint alleged, among other things, that Qwest fraudulently characterized non-recurring revenue from IRU (Indefeasible Rights of Use) and equipment transactions as recurring "data and Internet service revenues," thereby masking its declining financial condition and artificially inflating its stock price; ignored generally accepted accounting principles ("GAAP") by recognizing upfront revenue from IRU transactions and equipment sales; failed to disclose in periodic filings with the Commission that it had committed to buy millions of dollars of equipment that it never intended to deploy in its network and entered into strategic relationships with, and invested in, many equipment and service vendors in part for the benefit of certain members of its senior management; and failed to disclose that it's executives received, as compensation, investment opportunities in some of it's vendors.

Previously, in February 2003, the Commission filed a civil injunctive action against former Qwest officers Joel M. Arnold, William L. Eveleth, Grant Graham, Thomas W. Hall, Douglas K. Hutchins, Bryan K. Treadway, John M. Walker, and Richard L. Weston (Litigation Release No. 17996). In September 2003, the Commission instituted a settled cease-and-desist proceeding and filed a related civil action for penalties against Loren D. Pfau, a former Qwest sales manager (Litigation Release No. 18374). In June 2004, the Commission instituted settled cease-and-desist proceedings and filed related civil actions for penalties against Augustine M. Cruciotti, a former Qwest executive vice president, and Steven L. Haggerty, a former Qwest senior vice president (Litigation Release Nos. 18754 and 18755). In July 2004, the Commission filed a civil injunctive action against Michael Felicissimo, the former CFO of Qwest's Wireless division (Litigation Release No. 18800). Also in July 2004, the Commission filed a subpoena enforcement action against Drake Tempest, Qwest's former general counsel (Litigation Release No. 18804).

SEC v. Elan Corporation, plc

Litigation Release No. 19066 (February 8, 2005)
http://www.sec.gov/litigation/litreleases/lr19066.htm

On February 8, 2005, the Securities and Exchange Commission announced the filing of a settled civil action against Elan Corporation, plc, a pharmaceutical company headquartered in Dublin, Ireland. The Commission charged Elan with violating the antifraud provisions of the federal securities laws for failing to disclose material information about the company's financial results in periodic reports filed with the Commission and in quarterly earnings press releases disseminated to investors in the United States.

According to the complaint, during 2000 and 2001, Elan represented in its public statements that it was generating record amounts of revenue, net income and operating cash flow from drug sales and licensing activities. Elan also claimed that it was making significant progress towards achieving its goal of transforming itself into a fully integrated pharmaceutical company and generating $5 billion of annual revenue by 2005. The complaint alleged that these statements were materially misleading because Elan failed to disclose, or inadequately disclosed, certain transactions that were critical to Elan's perceived success. As a result, investors were led to believe that Elan had achieved record results through improvements in the company's business, when in fact it had not.

Without admitting or denying the allegations in the complaint, Elan consented to the entry of a final judgment that permanently enjoins the company from violating the antifraud provisions of the federal securities laws as well as the reporting and internal controls provisions. The judgment also ordered Elan to pay $1 in disgorgement and a $15 million civil penalty, which is intended to be distributed to investors harmed by the alleged violations. The final judgment is subject to Court approval.

In the Matter of Google, Inc. and David C. Drummond

Admin. Proc. File No. 3-11795 (January 13, 2005)
http://www.sec.gov/litigation/admin/33-8523.htm

On January 13, 2005, the Commission charged Google, Inc. with failing to register the issuance of option grants to employees or provide required financial information to the option recipients. According to the Commission, the Silicon Valley search engine technology company issued over $80 million in stock options to its employees in the two years preceding its IPO, yet failed to register the securities or make financial disclosures mandated by federal securities law. The federal securities laws require companies issuing over $5 million in options during a 12-month period either to provide detailed financial information to the option recipients, or to register the securities offering with the Commission and thereby publicly disclose financial and other important information. According to the Commission, Google far exceeded the $5 million disclosure threshold, yet failed to register the options or provide the required financial information to employees. Google—which, at the time, was still a privately-held company—viewed the disclosure of the information to employees as strategically disadvantageous, fearing the information could leak to Google's competitors.

The Commission's Order charged Google with violating Section 5 of the Securities Act of 1933, which imposes registration and disclosure obligations in the offer or sale of securities, and further charges Drummond with causing Google's violation. Without admitting or denying the Commission's findings, Google and Drummond consented to an order that they cease and desist from violating or causing violations of Section 5. The Commission's Order also found that Google's General Counsel, David Drummond, was aware that the registration and related financial disclosure obligations had been triggered, but believed that Google could avoid providing the information to its employees by relying on an exemption from the law. According to the Commission, Drummond advised Google's Board that it could continue to issue options, but failed to inform the Board that the registration and disclosure obligations had been triggered or that there were risks in relying on the exemption, which was in fact inapplicable.

SEC v. Mark A. Bailin et al.

Litigation Release No. 19034 (January 13, 2005)
http://www.sec.gov/litigation/litreleases/lr19034.htm

SEC v. Koninklijke Ahold N.V. (Royal Ahold); SEC v. A. Michiel Meurs and Cees van der Hoeven; SEC v. Johannes Gerhardus Andreae; In the Matter of Ture Roland Fahlin

Litigation Release No. 18929 (October 13, 2004)
http://www.sec.gov/litigation/litreleases/lr18929.htm

SEC v. Peter O. Marion

Litigation Release No. 18796, (July 27, 2004)
http://www.sec.gov/litigation/litreleases/lr18796.htm

SEC v. Michael Resnick, Mark P. Kaiser, Timothy J. Lee, and William Carter

Litigation Release No. 18797, (July 27, 2004)
http://www.sec.gov/litigation/litreleases/lr18797.htm

On January 13, 2005, the Securities and Exchange Commission filed enforcement actions against nine individuals alleging they aided and abetted a massive financial fraud by signing and returning materially false audit confirmations sent to them by the auditors of the U.S. Foodservice, Inc. subsidiary of Royal Ahold (Koninklijke Ahold N.V.). The actions filed named as defendants Mark A. Bailin, Kenneth H. Bowman, Timothy Neal Daly, Michael J. Hannigan, Peter O. Marion, John Nettle, Gordon Redgate, Bruce Robinson and Michael Rogers. All of these individuals were employees of or agents for vendors which supplied U.S. Foodservice. The Commission's complaints alleged that U.S. Foodservice personnel contacted vendors and urged them to sign and return the false confirmation letters. Each of the individuals aided and abetted the fraud by signing and sending to the company's independent auditors confirmation letters that they knew materially overstated the amounts of promotional allowance income paid or owed to U.S. Foodservice. According to the Commission, U.S. Foodservice engaged in a scheme to report earnings equal to or greater than its targets, regardless of the company's true performance. Bailin, Hannigan, Nettle, Redgate, and Rogers each settled the Commission's action The U.S. Attorney's Office for the Southern District of New York announced criminal charges in this matter.

The Commission also filed a separate complaint against Bailin alleging that during February and March of 2000, after learning of material, nonpublic information about Ahold's intention to acquire U.S. Foodservice, he traded in the shares of U.S. Foodservice and recommended the purchase of U.S. Foodservice to six other traders. Bailin settled the Commission's action, by consenting to a permanent injunction, and payment of $2,224,446.51 disgorgement, $751,031.78 prejudgment interest and a $175,000 penalty.

On October 13, 2004, the Commission filed fraud and other charges in federal district court against Royal Ahold and three former top executives: Cees van der Hoeven A. Michiel Meurs, and Jan Andreae The Commission's complaints alleged that, as a result of the fraudulent inflation of promotional allowances at U.S. Foodservice the improper consolidation of joint ventures through fraudulent side letters, and other accounting errors and irregularities, Ahold's original SEC filings overstated net income, operating income and net sales. Ahold, Van der Hoeven, Meurs, and Fahlin settled settlements with the Commission. In a related matter, the Commission filed an administrative action charging Roland Fahlin, a former member of Ahold's supervisory board and audit committee, with causing violations of the reporting, books and records, and internal controls provisions of the securities laws.

Finally, on July 27, 2004, the Commission filed a complaint in federal district court alleging that Michael Resnick, Mark P. Kaiser, Timothy J. Lee and William Carter engaged in or substantially participated in the scheme to overstate the income of Royal Ahold by $700 million or more in SEC filings and other public announcements for at least fiscal years 2001 and 2002. Resnick, Kaiser, Lee, and Carter were top executives at U.S. Foodservice. The complaint alleged that they grossly inflated reported profits and induced numerous suppliers to submit false confirmations to the company's auditors in order to conceal their fraud.

SEC v. TV Azteca S.A. de TV Azteca S.A. de C.V., Azteca Holdings, S.A. de C.V., Ricardo Salinas Pliego, Pedro Padilla Longoria, and Luis Echarte Fernandez

Litigation Release No. 19022 (January 4, 2005)
http://www.sec.gov/litigation/litreleases/lr19022.htm

On January 4, 2005, the Commission filed civil fraud charges against TV Azteca S.A. de C.V., a Mexican issuer whose American depository receipts trade on the NYSE, its parent company, Azteca Holdings, S.A., de C.V. (Azteca Holdings), and three current and former TV Azteca officers and directors, Ricardo Salinas Pliego, Pedro Padilla Longoria, and Luis Echarte Fernandez. The Commission alleged in its complaint that the defendants engaged in an elaborate scheme to conceal Salinas's role in a series of transactions through which he personally profited by $109 million. The Commission's complaint also alleged that Salinas and Padilla sold millions of dollars of TV Azteca stock while Salinas's self-dealing remained undisclosed to the market place.

According to the Commission's complaint, Salinas and others caused TV Azteca or Azteca Holdings to file periodic reports that did not disclose Salinas's involvement in related party transactions between Unefon, a subsidiary of TV Azteca, and a private entity secretly co-owned by Salinas, called Codisco. The Commission also alleged that TV Azteca filed the false reports concealing Salinas' involvement in the Unefon debt transactions, despite receiving advice from its U.S. counsel that these transactions were material, reportable transactions under U.S. federal securities laws.

In a consent filed simultaneously with the complaint, Echarte settled the Commission's action against him by agreeing to the entry of a final judgment permanently enjoining him from violating, and aiding and abetting violations of the antifraud, reporting, books and records, and internal controls provisions of the federal securities laws and to pay a penalty of $200,000 and disgorgement of $1.

SEC v. The Walt Disney Company

Admin. Proc. File No. 3-11777 (December 20, 2004)
http://www.sec.gov/litigation/admin/34-50882.htm

On December 20, 2004, the Commission instituted settled enforcement proceedings against The Walt Disney Company (Disney). The Commission charged Disney for failing to disclose certain related party transactions between Disney and its directors, and for failing to disclose certain compensation paid to a Disney director. Under the settlement, Disney consented to the entry of an Order that it cease and desist from violating the proxy solicitation and periodic reporting provisions of the federal securities laws. The Commission found that between 1999 and 2001, Disney failed to disclose relationships between the company and its directors which were required to be disclosed in its proxy statements and annual reports filed with the Commission. In particular, Disney failed to disclose that the company employed three children of its directors, who received annual compensation ranging from $60,000 to more than $150,000. In addition, Disney did not disclose that the spouse of another director was employed by a subsidiary 50% owned by Disney and received compensation in excess of one million dollars annually. Further, Disney failed to disclose that it made regular payments to a corporation owned by a Disney director that provided air transportation to that director for Disney-related business purposes. Finally, Disney failed to disclose that it provided office space, secretarial services, a leased car, and a driver to another Disney director, services valued by the company at over $200,000 annually. Disney consented to the issuance of the Commission's Order, which requires Disney to cease and desist from committing or causing any violations and any future violations of Sections 13(a) and 14(a) of the Securities Exchange Act of 1934 and Rules 13a-1, 12b-20, and 14a-3(a) thereunder

SEC v. American International Group, Inc.

Litigation Release No. 18985 (November 30, 2004)
http://www.sec.gov/litigation/litreleases/lr18985.htm

On November 30, 2004, the Commission filed a civil action against American International Group, Inc. (AIG) for violating antifraud provisions of the federal securities laws and for aiding and abetting violations of reporting and record-keeping provisions of those laws. The Commission's action arises out of the conduct of AIG, primarily through its wholly owned subsidiary AIG Financial Products Corp. (AIG-FP), in developing, marketing, and entering into transactions that purported to enable a public company to remove certain assets from its balance sheet. AIG consented to the issuance of a final judgment (1) permanently enjoining it from violating, and from aiding and abetting violations of, certain provisions of the federal securities laws, (2) ordering it to comply with its undertaking to retain an independent consultant to examine certain prior transactions and to establish a transaction review committee to review future transactions, and (3) ordering itto disgorge the amount of fees that it received. In consenting to settle the Commission's action and related criminal charges, AIG and AIG-FP agreed to pay disgorgement, plus prejudgment interest, and penalties totaling $126,366,000.

In its complaint, the Commission alleged that from at least March 2001 through January 2002, AIG, primarily through AIG-FP, developed a product called a Contributed Guaranteed Alternative Investment Trust Security (C-GAITS), marketed that product to several public companies, and ultimately entered into three C-GAITS transactions with one such company, The PNC Financial Services Group, Inc. (PNC). For a fee, AIG and AIG-FP offered to establish a special purpose entity (SPE) to which the counter-party would transfer troubled or other potentially volatile assets. AIG and AIG-FP represented that, under generally accepted accounting principles (GAAP), the SPE would not be consolidated on the counter-party's financial statements. The counter-party thus would be able to avoid charges to its income statement resulting from declines in the value of the assets transferred to the SPE. The transaction that AIG and AIG-FP developed and marketed, however, did not satisfy the requirements of GAAP for non-consolidation of SPEs.

SEC v. Wachovia Corporation

Litigation Release No. 18958 (November 4, 2004)
http://www.sec.gov/litigation/litreleases/lr18958.htm

On November 4, 2004, the Commission filed settled civil action against Wachovia Corporation for violations of proxy disclosure laws and other reporting rules involving the 2001 merger between First Union Corporation (First Union) and Old Wachovia Corporation (Old Wachovia). The complaint alleges that Old Wachovia and First Union failed to disclose in quarterly reports and in a joint proxy statement-prospectus filed in connection with the merger the total number of shares of First Union common stock that Old Wachovia intended to and did purchase during the period when First Union and SunTrust Corporation (SunTrust) were engaged in a hostile takeover battle for Old Wachovia.

With respect to these purchases, neither First Union nor Old Wachovia disclosed in the quarterly or annual reports, or in their joint proxy sent to over two hundred thousand shareholders on June 29, 2001, that: (a) Old Wachovia authorized the purchase of First Union common stock; (b) subject to regulatory filings, Old Wachovia intended to purchase up to $500 million worth of First Union common stock; and (c) the total number of First Union common shares that Old Wachovia purchased in May and June 2001. This material information was not disclosed until August 2001, after the shareholders voted on the merger. Old Wachovia should have publicly disclosed more detailed information about its purchases of First Union common stock so that the market would be able to evaluate the effect of those purchases on First Union common stock price during that period.

Without admitting or denying the allegations in the complaint, Wachovia consented to entry of a judgment enjoining it from violating disclosure laws and reporting rules, and payment of a $37 million civil penalty.

In the Matter of Morgan Stanley

Admin. Proc. File No. 3-11725 (November 4, 2004)

http://www.sec.gov/litigation/admin-34-50632.htm

On November 4, 2004, the Commission instituted settled cease-and-desist proceedings against Morgan Stanley. According to the Commission, Morgan Stanley valued certain aircraft in its aircraft leasing business and certain bonds in its high-yield bond portfolio in a manner that violated financial reporting, recordkeeping, and internal controls provisions of the federal securities laws.

Regarding its impaired aircraft, the Commission alleged that Morgan Stanley used a valuation method not in compliance with Generally Accepted Accounting Principles (GAAP) to determine the value of certain impaired aircraft in its aircraft leasing portfolio. GAAP requires that the value for these aircraft be recorded at "fair value." Instead, during a slump in the aircraft leasing business brought on by the terrorist attacks of September 11, 2001, and for the third quarter of fiscal year 2002, the Commission alleged that Morgan Stanley obtained independent appraisers' estimates of "base value" and used the average of their estimates of base value to establish the recorded value of a number of its aircraft in violation of GAAP.

Regarding its high-yield bond portfolio, the Commission alleged that Morgan Stanley overvalued certain bonds in the portfolio in 2000 by taking a "longer view" as to their value, which entailed discounting current market conditions such as imbalances in supply and demand. By overvaluing those bonds, Morgan Stanley took less of a markdown than it would have had it complied with GAAP, thereby overstating its trading revenue for the fourth quarter of its fiscal year 2000.

Morgan Stanley agreed to cease and desist from committing or causing any violations of, and any future violations of the Exchange Act.

In the Matter of Hawaiian Airlines, Inc.

Admin Proc. File No. 3-11717 (October 22, 2004)
http://www.sec.gov/litigation/admin34-50584.htm

On October 22, 2004, the Securities and Exchange Commission instituted settled cease-and-desist proceedings against Hawaiian Airlines, Inc. (Hawaiian). This matter involved the failure to disclose material changes during the course of a $25,000,000 issuer tender offer by Hawaiian in mid-2002. The offer was intended to allow Hawaiian's majority stockholder, a partnership controlled by Hawaiian's then CEO, to cash out some of its Hawaiian holdings. Hawaiian failed to disclose to its shareholders that, prior to the closing of the tender offer, the company had experienced two months of financial results falling far short of Hawaiian's internal projections and casting doubt on Hawaiian's stated conclusion in the offering materials that the tender offer would not impair its future solvency. Had they disclosed the information, a higher proportion of Hawaiian's shareholders reasonably could have decided to tender their shares, reducing sales proceeds for Hawaiian's majority shareholder. Instead, non-tendering shareholders retained their shares, to their detriment. Nine months later, Hawaiian filed for bankruptcy. According to the Commission, Hawaiian failed to disclose to its shareholders that its financial results for April and May 2002, and the revised projections based on those results, materially undermined statements made by Hawaiian in the tender offer documents. As a result, Hawaiian violated and agreed to cease and desist from committing or causing any violations and any future violations of the Exchange Act and the Rules thereunder.

Previously, on September 23, 2004, the Commission instituted settled cease-and-desist proceedings against John W. Adams, Hawaiian's then-Chairman and CEO, and AIP, LLC, Hawaiian's majority shareholder, a partnership managed by Adams. The Commission ordered that Respondents cease and desist from causing any violations of the federal securities laws, and that Respondent AIP disgorge $2,229,193 and prejudgment interest in the amount of $237,094, for a total payment of $2,466,287. Adams was ordered to disgorge $3,782 and prejudgment interest in the amount of $402, for a total payment of $4,184 (In the Matter of John W. Adams and AIP, LLC, Administrative Proceeding File No. 3-11676 (September 23, 2004)).

In the Matter of General Electric Company

Admin Proc. File No. 3-11677 (September 23, 2004)
http://www.sec.gov/litigation/admin/34-50426.htm

On September 23, 2004, the Commission instituted settled cease-and-desist proceedings against General Electric Company (GE). The Commission charged that GE failed to fully describe the substantial benefits it had agreed to provide its former chairman and CEO John F. "Jack" Welch, Jr., under an "employment and post-retirement consulting agreement."

The Commission found that in proxy statements and annual reports filed with the Commission, GE failed to fully and accurately describe the retirement benefits Welch was entitled to receive from the company. In

December 1996, GE and Welch entered into an "employment and post-retirement consulting agreement" under which Welch agreed to continue as CEO until he was 65 and serve as a consultant thereafter. In the agreement, Welch received, as his principal form of compensation, lifetime access to the perquisites and benefits he had received as GE's chairman and CEO. GE's proxy statements only referred to Welch's entitlement to "...continued lifetime access to Company facilities and services comparable to those that are currently made available to him by the Company," but did not provide any other specific information about the "facilities and services" Welch would receive in retirement.

The agreement itself, which was appended as an exhibit to GE's 1996 annual report, stated that Welch was entitled to receive in retirement "continued access to Company facilities and services comparable to those provided to him prior to his retirement, including access to Company aircraft, cars, office, apartments, and financial planning services," but did not provide further meaningful and complete disclosure of those "facilities and services." Moreover, GE made no other disclosures in its SEC filings that allowed investors to understand the nature and scope of Welch's retirement benefits-specifically, investors could not learn from GE's previously filed proxy statements many of the most significant "facilities and services" Welch had been provided prior to his retirement, including personal use of GE-owned aircraft, personal use of chauffeured limousines and home security systems. The Commission further found that in the first year following Welch's retirement in September 2001, Welch received approximately $2.5 million in benefits under the agreement.

The Commission concluded that GE's inadequate disclosures violated the Exchange Act and the Rules thereunder. GE consented to the issuance of the Order, which orders GE to cease and desist from committing or causing any violations and any future violations of the foregoing statutory provisions and rules.

SEC v. Computer Associates International, Inc.; SEC v. Sanjay Kumar and Stephen Richards; SEC v. Steven Woghin

Litigation Release No. 18891 (September 22, 2004)
http://www.sec.gov/litigation/litreleases/lr18891.htm

On September 22, 2004, the Commission filed a partially settled securities fraud action in federal district court against Computer Associates International, Inc. and three of the company's former top executives – Sanjay Kumar, former CEO and Chairman; Stephen Richards, former Head of Sales; and Steven Woghin, former General Counsel. The Commission alleged that Computer Associates routinely kept its books open to record revenue from contracts executed after the quarter ended in order to meet Wall Street quarterly earnings estimates. In total, Computer Associates prematurely recognized $2.2 billion in revenue in FY2000 and FY2001 and more than $1.1 billion in premature revenue in prior quarters. In addition, the Commission alleged that Computer Associates, through former executives Kumar, Richards, Woghin and others, obstructed the Commission's 's investigation into the company's accounting practices.

According to the Commission, while the accounting fraud was occurring, defendants Kumar, Richards and Woghin received ill-gotten gains in the form of compensation they received from Computer Associates. In addition to committing securities fraud, the defendants interfered with the Commission's investigation by making materially false and misleading statements in a joint proffer session with the Commission and the United States Attorney's Office. During the same relevant period, Richards made materially false and misleading statements in sworn investigative testimony and Woghin encouraged several Computer Associates employees to make false and misleading statements to the SEC and/or Computer Associates' outside counsel.

In a joint settlement with the Commissin and the USAO, Computer Associates agreed to a permanent injunction against the future violations of the antifraud, reporting, books and records and internal control provision of the federal securities laws; to be subject to the review of an Independent Examiner, reporting to the Commission, the Justice Department and Computer Associates' Board of Directors; and to establish a comprehensive new ethics and compliance program, overseen by a new Chief Compliance Officer, and a new Compliance Committee of its Board of Directors. In addition, Computer Associates entered into a deferred prosecution agreement with the USAO requiring Computer Associates to pay $225 million to injured shareholders and directing Compute Associates to undertake the same remedial measures in the Commission's consent judgment. Woghin consented to a partial judgment imposing a permanent injunction prohibiting him from violating the antifraud reporting, books and records and internal control provisions of the federal securities laws and permanently barring him from serving as an officer or director of a public company. On November 10, 2004, the SEC instituted settled administrative proceedings against Steven Woghin, based on the entry of the permanent injunction, suspending him from appearing or practicing before the Commission as an attorney (In the Matter of Steven Woghin, Esq., Admin. Proc. File No. 3-11735 (November 10, 2004)).

SEC v. Royal Dutch Petroleum Company and The "Shell" Transport and Trading Company, P.L.C.

Litigation Release No. 18844 (August 24, 2004)
http://www.sec.gov/litigation/litreleases/lr18844.htm

On August 24, 2004, the Commission announced a settlement of an enforcement action against foreign-based oil companies Royal Dutch Petroleum Company ("Royal Dutch") and The "Shell" Transport and Trading Company, p.l.c. (together, Shell) in connection with their overstatement of 4.47 billion barrels of previously reported proved hydrocarbon reserves. Royal Dutch is a Dutch corporation headquartered in The Hague, while Shell Transport is an English corporation headquartered in London.

According to the Commission's order and complaint, Shell overstated proved reserves reported in its 2002 Form 20-F by 4.47 billion barrels of oil equivalent overstated the standardized measure of future cash flows reported in this filing by approximately $6.6 billion, and Shell materially misstated its reserves replacement ratio ("RRR"), a key performance indicator in the oil and gas industry. The Commission found that Shell's overstatement of proved reserves and its delay in correcting the overstatement, resulted from (i) its desire to create and maintain the appearance of a strong RRR, (ii) the failure of its internal reserves estimation and reporting guidelines to conform to SEC requirements, and (iii) the lack of effective internal controls over the reserves estimation and reporting process. These failures led Shell to record and maintain proved reserves it knew (or was reckless in not knowing) did not satisfy SEC requirements, and to report for certain years a stronger RRR than it actually had achieved.

Royal Dutch and Shell Transport settled these proceedings by consenting to a cease-and-desist order finding violations of the antifraud, internal controls, record-keeping and reporting provisions of the federal securities laws, and by paying $1 disgorgement and a $120 million penalty in a related civil action the Commission filed in federal district court. Shell has also undertaken to commit an additional $5 million to develop and implement a comprehensive internal compliance program under the direction and oversight of the Group's legal director. The companies settled without admitting or denying the Commission's substantive findings.

SEC v. Bristol-Myers Squibb Company

Litigation Release No. 18820 (August 4, 2004)
http://www.sec.gov/litigation/litreleases/lr18820.htm

SEC v. Bristol-Myers Squibb Company

Litigation Release No. 18867 (September 2, 2004)
http://www.sec.gov/litigation/litreleases/lr18867.htm

On August 4, 2004, the Commission filed a settled enforcement action against Bristol-Myers Squibb Company, a New York-based company whose largest division, the U.S. Medicines Group, is based in New Jersey. The Commission's complaint, filed in federal district court, alleged that Bristol-Myers perpetrated a fraudulent earnings management scheme by, among other things, selling excessive amounts of pharmaceutical products to its wholesalers ahead of demand, improperly recognizing revenue from $1.5 billion of such sales to its two largest wholesalers, and using "cookie jar" reserves to meet its internal sales and earnings targets and analysts' earnings estimates.

According to the Commission, Bristol-Myers inflated its results primarily by (1) stuffing its distribution channels with excess inventory near the end of every quarter in amounts sufficient to meet its targets by making pharmaceutical sales to its wholesalers ahead of demand; and (2) improperly recognizing $1.5 billion in revenue from such pharmaceutical sales to its two biggest wholesalers. When Bristol-Myers' results still fell short of the Street's earnings estimates, the company tapped improperly created divestiture reserves and reversed portions of those reserves into income to further inflate its earnings. As a result of its channel-stuffing, Bristol-Myers materially understated its accruals for rebates due to Medicaid and certain of its prime vendors, customers of its wholesalers that purchased large quantities of pharmaceutical products from those wholesalers.

Bristol-Myers agreed to the following relief: a permanent injunction against future violations of certain antifraud, reporting, books and records and internal controls provisions of the federal securities laws; disgorgement of $1; a civil penalty of $100 million; an additional $50 million payment into a fund for the benefit of shareholders; various remedial undertakings, including the appointment of an independent adviser to review, assess and monitor Bristol-Myers' accounting practices, financial reporting and disclosure processes and internal control systems. A final Judgment Order was entered against Bristol-Meyers in federal district court on August 6, 2004. (Litigation Release No. 18822).

In the Matter of Halliburton Company and Robert Charles Muchmore Jr.

Administrative Proceeding File No. 3-11574 (August 3, 2004)
http://www.sec.gov/litigation/admin/33-8452.htm

SEC v. Gary V. Morris

Litigation Release No. 18817 (August 3, 2004)
http://www.sec.gov/litigation/litreleases/lr18817.htm

SEC v. Halliburton Company and Robert Charles Muchmore Jr.

Litigation Release No. 18817 (August 3, 2004).
http://www.sec.gov/litigation/litreleases/lr18817.htm

On August 3, 2004 the SEC initiated enforcement proceedings against Halliburton Co., its former chief financial officer, Gary V. Morris, and its former controller, Robert C. Muchmore, Jr. The Commission's actions are in response to Halliburton's failure to disclose a 1998 change to its accounting practice. As a result of that undisclosed change, Halliburton's public statements regarding its income in 1998 and 1999 were materially misleading. Halliburton and Muchmore agreed to settle the enforcement actions by consenting to a Commission order to cease and desist from committing or causing future securities law violations and by agreeing to pay penalties of $7.5 million and $50,000 respectively, in a related civil action. Halliburton's penalty for the disclosure failure reflects lapses in the company's conduct during the course of the Commission investigation, which commenced in mid-2002.

Halliburton provides a wide range of industrial construction services. In providing those services, Halliburton, at times, incurs cost overruns; the overruns may be recovered from Halliburton's customer depending on the terms of the construction contract and the nature of the overruns. Historically, Halliburton recognized income arising from cost overrun claims only in the financial quarter in which the claim was finally resolved with the customer. From 1993 to 1997, Halliburton had set forth this practice in its periodic filings with the Commission. In the second quarter of 1998, Halliburton changed its historical accounting practice and began recognizing revenues by offsetting losses on certain projects with revenues based on estimated probable recoveries on claims that had not been resolved with customers.

Under the new practice, Halliburton recognized revenues on certain claims that the company believed were probable of collection rather than, pursuant to the prior practice, claims that had been finally resolved with its customers. Although both of Halliburton's claims recognition practices, the historical one and the revised one, are appropriate under Generally Accepted Accounting Principles, there was a significant difference in their respective effects on Halliburton's financial presentation: the new practice reduced losses on several large construction projects. As a result, Halliburton's reported income was higher under the revised practice than it would have been under the prior practice. Over six reporting periods, spanning approximately 18 months covering 1998 and 1999, Halliburton failed to disclose its change of accounting practice. In the absence of any disclosure, the investing public was deprived of a full opportunity to assess Halliburton's reported income—more particularly, the precise nature of that income, and its comparability to Halliburton's income in prior periods. It was not until March 2000 that Halliburton, in its 1999 Form 10-K, disclosed its change in accounting practice.

SEC v. Henry C. Yuen and Elsie M. Leung

Litigation Release No. 18199 (June 20, 2003)
http://www.sec.gov/litigation/litreleases/lr18199.htm

SEC v. Henry C. Yuen et al.

Litigation Release No. 18530 (January 6, 2004)
http://www.sec.gov/litigation/litreleases/lr18530.htm

SEC v. Gemstar-TV Guide International, Inc.

Litigation Release No. 18760 (June 23, 2004)
http://www.sec.gov/litigation/litreleases/lr18760.htm

SEC v. Peter C. Boylan

Litigation Release No. 18826 (August 10, 2004)
http://www.sec.gov/litigation/litreleases/lr18826.htm

In the Matter of Jonathan B. Orlick, Esq.

Admin. Proc. File No. 3-11801 (January 26, 2005)
http://www.sec.gov/litigation/admin/34-51081.htm

SEC v. Henry C. Yuen et al.

Litigation Release No. 19047 (January 21, 2005)
http://www.sec.gov/litigation/litreleases/lr19047.htm

During June of 2004, the Commission filed a complaint in federal district court charging Gemstar-TV Guide International, Inc. with improperly reporting its highly touted interactive program guide licensing and advertising revenues in its financial statements from 1999 through 2002. According to the Commission, during the relevant period, Gemstar generated revenues from the IPG by licensing the technology to third parties and selling advertising space on the IPG. The Commission's complaint alleged that Gemstar materially overstated its revenues by nearly $250 million by (1) recording revenue under expired, disputed, or non-existent agreements, and improperly reporting this as IPG licensing and advertising revenue; (2) recording and reporting revenue from a long-term agreement on an accelerated basis in contravention of GAAP and Gemstar's own stated and disclosed revenue recognition policy; (3) inflating its IPG advertising revenue by improperly recording and reporting revenue amounts from multiple-element transactions; (4) improperly recording and reporting IPG advertising revenue from non-monetary and barter transactions; and (5) improperly reporting certain revenues as IPG advertising revenues when in fact those revenues were derived from the sale of print advertising. The misstatements of revenue were reported in Forms 10-K, 10-Q, and 8-K filed with the Commission. The Commission alleged that these public statements misrepresented Gemstar's true financial performance and failed to disclose material information about that performance.

Gemstar agreed to settle the case by, among other things, paying a $10 million civil penalty and agreeing to a permanent injunction against further violations of the periodic reporting, recordkeeping, and internal controls provisions of the federal securities laws. In assessing the penalty amount, the Commission considered the scope and severity of Gemstar's misconduct, Gemstar's initial failure to cooperate in the Commission's investigation or undertake remedial actions, and Gemstar's significant cooperation and remediation following a change in senior management and restructuring of its corporate governance.

Previously, on January, 6, 2004, the Commission filed securities fraud charges against three former senior executives of Gemstar-TV Guide International, Inc., Peter Boylan, Johathan Orlick, and Craig Waggy representing its former co-president, general counsel, and chief financial officer of its wholly owned subsidiary, TV Guide, Inc. The complaint charged that these executives participated in Gemstar's widespread and complex scheme to inflate its licensing and advertising revenue and to mislead investors about the company's true financial performance. The January 6, 2004 action amended the Commission's complaint filed against Gemstar's former chief executive officer, Henry C. Yuen, and former chief financial officer, Elsie M. Leung, on June 19, 2003. The complaint sought permanent injunctions, civil money penalties, disgorgement of ill-gotten gains (including salaries, bonuses and any proceeds from the sale of stock during the fraud), and bars from service as an officer or director of a public company. Peter Boylan settled the federal district court action filed by the Commission. As part of the settlement Boylan consented to a fraud injunction and to pay a total of $600,000 in disgorgement and penalties.

On January 20, 2005, the court entered a consent judgment permanently enjoining Jonathan B. Orlick, a former Deputy General Counsel and Senior Vice President of Gemstar, from future violations or aiding and abetting violations of the Exchange Act. Orlick was also ordered to pay $150,000 in disgorgement, $5,510.62 in prejudgment interest, and a $150,000 penalty. Orlick was also prohibited from serving as an officer or director of a public company for ten years. In a related administrative action, Orlick agreed to be suspended from appearing or practicing before the SEC as an attorney. Orlick consented to the relief without admitting or denying the SEC's allegations.

The Commission's action is pending against three other former executives of Gemstar: Henry C. Yuen, former chief executive officer; Elsie M. Leung, former chief financial officer; and Craig Waggy, former CFO of TV Guide.

SEC v. Lucent Technologies Inc., Nina Aversano, Jay Carter, A. Leslie Dorn, William Plunkett, John Bratten, Deborah Harris, Charles Elliot, Vanessa Patrini, Michelle Hayes-Bullock, and David Ackerman

Litigation Release No. 18715 (May 17, 2004)
http://www.sec.gov/litigation/litreleases/lr18715.htm

In May of 2004, the Commission charged Lucent Technologies Inc. with securities fraud, and violations of the reporting, books and records and internal control provisions of the federal securities laws. The Commission also charged nine current and former Lucent officers, executives and employees, and one former Winstar Communications Inc. officer with securities fraud and aiding and abetting Lucent's violations of the federal securities laws.

The Commission's complaint alleged that Lucent fraudulently and improperly recognized approximately $1.148 billion of revenue and $470 million in pre-tax income during its fiscal year 2000. According to the Commission, the defendants, in their drive to realize revenue, meet internal sales targets and/or obtain sales bonuses, improperly granted, and/or failed to disclose, various side agreements, credits and other incentives (collectively "extra-contractual commitments") to induce Lucent's customers to purchase the company's products. These extra-contractual commitments were made in at least ten transactions in fiscal 2000, and Lucent violated GAAP by recognizing revenue on these transactions both in circumstances: (a) where it could not be recognized under GAAP; and (b) by recording the revenue earlier than was permitted under GAAP. The Commission also alleged that David Ackerman, at the time an officer of Winstar, engaged in a scheme with Plunkett that resulted in Lucent improperly recording a $125 million software purchase by Winstar at the end of Lucent's fourth quarter of fiscal year 2000.

Lucent agreed to pay a penalty for its failure to cooperate, based on, among other things, (1) incomplete document production, (2) failure to ensure that a relevant document was preserved and produced, (3) characterization by Lucent's counsel that Lucent's fraudulent booking of the $125 million software pool agreement between Lucent and Winstar was a "failure of communication" thus denying that an accounting fraud had occurred, (4) expanding the scope of employees that could be indemnified after reaching an agreement in principle to settle the case, and (5) failure to provide timely and full disclosure to the staff on a key issue concerning indemnification of employees. In addition, Lucent, Plunkett, Harris and Petrini have agreed to settle with the Commission, consenting to the entry of permanent injunctions against future violations of the anti-fraud, reporting, books and records and internal controls provisions of the federal securities laws. Lucent will pay a penalty of $25 million, while Plunkett will pay a penalty of $110,000 and be barred from acting as an officer or director of a public company; Harris will pay a penalty of $100,000 and be barred from acting as an officer or director of a public company for five years; and Petrini will pay a penalty of $60,000 and disgorge $109,505, representing profits gained as a result of the conduct alleged in the complaint, together with prejudgment interest thereon in the amount of $23,487. The Commission will litigate this case against the remaining seven defendants.

SEC v. Scott D. Sullivan (WorldCom)

Litigation Release No. 18605 (March 2, 2004)
http://www.sec.gov/litigation/litreleases/lr18605.htm

The Commission filed a civil enforcement action against Scott D. Sullivan, the former Chief Financial Officer of WorldCom, Inc. The Commission charged Sullivan with engaging in a fraudulent scheme to conceal

WorldCom's poor financial performance. The Commission alleged that Sullivan, with the consent and knowledge of WorldCom's former Chief Executive Officer, Bernard J. Ebbers, caused numerous improper adjustments and entries in WorldCom's books and records, often in the hundreds of millions of dollars, to make the company's quarterly and yearly financial results appear to meet Wall Street's expectations. In addition, the Commission alleged that Sullivan made numerous false and misleading public statements about WorldCom's financial condition and performance, and signed a number of SEC filings that contained false and misleading material information. In connection with the same conduct, Sullivan pleaded guilty to criminal charges filed by the U.S. Attorney's Office for the Southern District of New York. In addition, that office announced the related indictment of Bernard J. Ebbers.

Simultaneously with the filing of the complaint, Sullivan agreed, to the entry of an order permanently enjoining him from violating, directly or indirectly, provisions of the federal securities laws, including the antifraud, reporting, books and records, internal controls, and lying-to-auditors provisions. Sullivan also agreed to the entry of an order that would permanently bar him from serving as an officer or director of a public company. Monetary relief will be decided by the Court. In a separate administrative proceeding, Sullivan agreed to a Commission administrative order suspending him from appearing or practicing before the Commission as an accountant, under Rule 102(e) of the Commission's Rules of Practice.

The Commission's action against Sullivan is its fifth civil enforcement action related to the WorldCom fraud. The first was filed against WorldCom, Inc. on June 27, 2002, the day after WorldCom announced that it intended to restate its financial results for five quarters—all quarters in 2001 and the first quarter of 2002 (Litigation Release No. 17588). On Nov. 26, 2002, the Commission obtained a judgment against WorldCom that provided the full injunctive relief sought against the company. In addition, the judgment ordered WorldCom to undertake extensive reviews of its corporate governance and internal controls, as well as required the company to establish a training and education program for WorldCom officers and employees to minimize the possibility of future violations of the federal securities laws (Litigation Release No. 17866). Subsequently, the U.S. District Court ordered WorldCom to satisfy the Commission's 's civil monetary penalty judgment by paying $500 million in cash and transferring $250 million worth of common stock in the reorganized company when it emerges from bankruptcy into a fund for distribution to victims of the company's fraud, pursuant to Section 308 (Fair Funds for Investors) of the Sarbanes-Oxley Act of 2002 (Litigation Release Nos. 17829, 18219 and 18277). The Commission's plan for distributing the penalty to defrauded investors was approved July 19, 2004. (Litigation Release No. 18789). Previously, the Commission filed civil actions against former WorldCom Controller David F. Myers (Litigation Release No. 17753); former WorldCom Director of General Accounting Buford "Buddy" Yates, Jr. (Litigation Release No. 17771); and Betty L. Vinson and Troy M. Normand, former accountants in WorldCom's General Accounting Department (Litigation Release No. 17783). All of these actions are pending.

Enron Cases

The Commission brought the following actions against Enron's employees or employees of subsidiaries of Enron:

SEC v. Mark E. Koenig

Litigation Release No. 18849 (August 25, 2004)
http://www.sec.gov/litigation/litreleases/lr18849.htm

On August 25, 2004, the Commission charged Mark E. Koenig, a former Executive Vice-President and Director of Investor Relations at Enron Corp., with violating the antifraud provisions of the federal securities laws by participating in a scheme to defraud by disemminating and approving the dissemination of false and misleading information to the public about Enron's business in earnings releases and analyst calls. Koenig agreed to be enjoined permanently from violating the antifraud provisions of the federal securities laws, and to be barred from acting as an officer or director of a public company. As part of the settlement agreement, which is subject to the approval of the U.S. District Court, Koenig will pay disgorgement and a civil penalty totaling $1,493,572. The Commission brought this action in coordination with the U.S. Department of Justice Enron Task Force, which filed a related criminal charge with Koenig. Koenig agreed to enter into a guilty plea in connection with that charge and to cooperate with the government's continuing investigation.

SEC v. Paula H. Rieker

Litigation Release No. 18717 (May 19, 2004)
http://www.sec.gov/litigation/litreleases/lr18717.htm

On May 19, 2004, the Commission charged Paula H. Rieker (Rieker), a former Managing Director for Investor Relations and Corporate Secretary for Enron Corp., with violating federal securities laws by engaging in insider trading by trading on material inside information about significant losses in Enron Broadband Services (EBS) and by providing substantial assistance to Enron executives and senior managers in the dissemination of false and misleading information to the public about Enron business units in analyst calls and earnings releases. Rieker agreed to be permanently enjoined from violating and aiding and abetting the antifraud provisions, and to be barred from acting as an officer or director of a public company. As part of a settlement agreement, Rieker will pay disgorgement, prejudgment interest, and a civil penalty totaling $499,333. The Commission brought this action in coordination with the U.S. Department of Justice Enron Task Force, which filed a related criminal charge against Rieker. Rieker agreed to enter a guilty plea in connection with that charge and to cooperate with the government's continuing investigation.

SEC v. Richard A. Causey and Jeffrey K. Skilling

Litigation Release No. 18582 (February 19, 2004)
http://www.sec.gov/litigation/litreleases/lr18582.htm

SEC v. Andrew S. Fastow

Litigation Release No. 18543 (January 14, 2004)
http://www.sec.gov/litigation/litreleases/lr18543.htm

In January 2004, the Commission charged Richard A. Causey, the former Chief Accounting Officer of Enron Corp., with violating, and aiding and abetting the violation of, the antifraud, periodic reporting, books and records, and internal controls provisions of the federal securities laws. In February 2004, The Commission amended it's complaint to charge Jeffrey K. Skilling, Enron Corp.'s former President, Chief Executive Officer and Chief Operating Officer, with the same violations. The Amended Complaint further alleges that Skilling sold Enron stock while in possession of material, non-public information that generated unlawful proceeds of approximately $63 million. According to the Commission, Causey, Skilling, and others at Enron, engaged in a wide-ranging scheme to manipulate Enron's publicly reported earnings through a variety of devices designed to produce materially false and misleading financial results. The Commission also alleged that Causey, and others, made false and misleading statements concerning Enron's financial results and the performance of its businesses, and that these misrepresentations also were reflected in Enron's public filings with the Commission. The Commission is sought disgorgement of all ill-gotten gains, civil money penalties, a permanent bar from acting as a director or officer of a publicly held company, and an injunction against future violations of the federal securities laws. The Commission brought this action in coordination with the Justice Department's Enron Task Force, which filed related criminal charges against Causey and Skilling.

Also in January, the Commission settled civil fraud charges against Andrew S. Fastow, Enron's former chief financial officer. The complaint, filed on October 2, 2002 in federal district court alleged that Fastow defrauded Enron's shareholders and enriched himself and others by, among other things, entering into undisclosed side deals, manufacturing earnings for Enron through sham transactions, and inflating the value of Enron's investments. Fastow agreed to be enjoined permanently from violating the antifraud, periodic reporting, books and records, and internal control provisions of the federal securities laws, and to be barred permanently from acting as an officer or director of a public company. The Commission settled its action in coordination with the Justice Department's Enron Task Force, which entered into a guilty plea with Fastow on related criminal charges. In resolving the parallel civil and criminal proceedings, Fastow agreed to serve a ten-year sentence, disgorge more than $23 million and to cooperate with the government's continuing investigation.

SEC v. Richard A. Causey, Jeffrey K. Skilling and Kenneth L. Lay

Litigation Release No. 18776 (July 8, 2004)
http://www.sec.gov/litigation/litreleases/lr18776.htm

In July of 2004, the Commission initiated civil charges against Kenneth L. Lay, former Chairman and Chief Executive Officer of Enron Corp., for his role in a wide-ranging scheme to defraud by falsifying Enron's publicly reported financial results and making false and misleading public representations about Enron's business performance and financial condition. The Commission alleged, among other things, that Lay profited from the scheme to defraud by selling large amounts of Enron stock at prices that did not reflect its true value and that the sales occurred while Lay was in possession of material non-public information concerning Enron and generated unlawful proceeds in excess of $90 million during 2001. The Commission is seeking disgorgement of all ill-gotten gains, civil money penalties, a permanent bar from acting as a director or officer of a publicly held company, and an injunction against future violations of the federal securities laws.

SEC v. David W. Delainey

Litigation Release No. 18435 (October 30, 2003)
http://www.sec.gov/litigation/litreleases/lr18435.htm

On October 30, 2003, the Commission charged David W. Delainey (Delainey), the former Chief Executive Officer of Enron North America and Enron Energy Services, with violating the antifraud provisions of the federal securities laws by engaging in a wide-ranging scheme to manipulate Enron's publicly reported earnings through a variety of devices designed to produce materially false and misleading financial results. Delainey agreed, in part, to be enjoined permanently from violating the antifraud provisions, and to be barred from acting as an officer or director of a public company. As part of the settlement agreement, Delainey will pay nominal disgorgement of $100 and a civil penalty of approximately $3.74 million. The Commission brought this action in coordination with the U.S. Department of Justice Enron Task Force, which filed a related criminal charge against Delainey. Delainey agreed to enter a guilty plea in connection with that charge, forfeit approximately $4.26 million in unlawful proceeds, and cooperate with the government's continuing investigation.

SEC v. Wesley H. Colwell

Litigation Release No. 18403 (October 9, 2003)
http://www.sec.gov/litigation/litreleases/lr18403.htm

On October 9, 2003, the Commission charged Wesley H. Colwell (Colwell), the former Chief Accounting Officer of Enron North America, with violating the antifraud provisions of the federal securities laws by engaging in a wide ranging scheme to defraud by manipulating Enron's publicly reported earnings through a variety of devices designed to produce materially false and misleading financial results. The scheme included the misuse of reserve accounts, concealment of losses, inflation of asset values, and deliberate use of improper accounting treatment for transactions. Colwell agreed, in part, to be enjoined permanently from violating the antifraud provisions, be barred from acting as an officer or director of a public company, and pay $300,000 in disgorgement and prejudgment interest and a civil penalty of $200,000. As part of this settlement, Colwell will continue to cooperate with on-going investigations into Enron Corp. by the Commission and the U.S. Department of Justice Enron Task Force.

SEC v. Ben F. Glisan, Jr.

Litigation Release No. 18335 (September 10, 2003)
http://www.sec.gov/litigation/litreleases/lr18335.htm

On September 10, 2003, the Commission charged Ben F. Glisan, Jr. (Glisan), a former senior executive of Enron, with violations of antifraud, lying to auditors, periodic reporting, books and records, and internal controls provisions of the federal securities laws. The Commission alleged that Glisan participated in Enron's manipulation of its reported financial results through a series of fraudulent transactions designed to inflate Enron's earnings and operating cash flows, while at the same time concealing the full extent of its debt. Glisan agreed to file a consent and final judgment settling the Commission's action against him and to the entry of an officer and director bar against him.

SEC v. Kevin A. Howard, Michael W. Krautz, Kenneth D. Rice, Joseph Hirko, Kevin P. Hannon, Rex T. Shelby, and F. Scott Yeager

Litigation Release 18122 (May 1, 2003)
http://www.sec.gov/litigation/litreleases/lr18122.htm

SEC v. Kevin P. Hannon, et al.

Litigation Release 18862 (August 31, 2004)
http://www.sec.gov/litigation/litreleases/lr18862.htm

The Commission filed an Amended Complaint charging Kenneth D. Rice, former chief executive officer, Joseph Hirko, former chief executive officer, Kevin P. Hannon, former chief operating officer, Rex T. Shelby, a former senior vice president, and F. Scott Yeager, a former senior vice president, of Enron Broadband Services, Inc. ("EBS"), a wholly-owned subsidiary of Enron Corp., with violating the antifraud provisions of the federal securities laws by engaging in a wide-ranging fraudulent scheme to, among other things, inflate the value of Enron stock through a series of false and misleading statements and the omission of material information in such public statements about the technology, financial condition, performance and value of EBS. This action amended the Complaint filed against Kevin A. Howard and Michael W. Krautz, two former EBS executives, on March 12, 2003. In its Amended Complaint, the Commission sought disgorgement of the defendants' ill-gotten gains, civil money penalties, a permanent bar from acting as an officer or director of a publicly held company, and an injunction against future violations of the federal securities laws.

On August 31, 2004, the Commission settled civil fraud charges filed against Kevin P. Hannon. Hannon agreed to be enjoined permanently from violating antifraud provisions of the federal securities laws, and to be barred permanently from acting as an officer or director of a public company. The Commission settled its action in coordination with the Justice Department's Enron Task Force, which entered into a plea agreement with Hannon on related criminal charges. In resolving the parallel civil and criminal proceedings, Hannon agreed to pay disgorgement and a civil penalty totaling $3.2 million and to cooperate with the government's continuing investigation.

SEC v. Michael J. Kopper

Litigation Release No. 17692 (August 21, 2002)
http://www.sec.gov/litigation/litreleases/lr17692.htm

On August 21, 2002, the Commission charged Michael J. Kopper (Kopper), a former high-ranking Enron official, with violating the antifraud provisions of the federal securities laws by engaging in a scheme to create the appearance that certain entities that Kopper and others at Enron funded and controlled were independent of Enron to permit Enron's financial statements to not properly reflect Enron's interest in these entities, thereby enabling Enron to engage in various transactions with these entities that were designed to improve its apparent financial results. Kopper agreed to be enjoined permanently from violating the antifraud provisions, and to be barred permanently from acting as an officer or director of a public company. As part of the settlement agreement, Kopper will disgorge and forfeit a total of approximately $12 million. The Commission brought this action in coordination with the Justice Department's Enron Task Force, which filed related criminal charges against Kopper. Kopper agreed to enter a guilty plea in connection with those charges and to cooperate with the government's continuing investigation.

The Commission brought the following actions against entities that assisted or aided and abetted Enron in its fraudulent activity:

Canadian Imperial Bank of Commerce, Daniel Ferguson, Ian Schottlaender, Mark Wolf

Litigation Release No. 18517 (December 22, 2003)
http://www.sec.gov/litigation/litreleases/lr18517.htm

On December 22, 2003, the Commission charged Canadian Imperial Bank of Commerce ("CIBC") and three of its executives with aiding and abetting Enron's manipulation of its reported financial results through a series of complex structured finance transactions that were designed as "asset sales" for accounting purposes and allowed Enron to hide from investors and rating agencies the true extent of its borrowings. CIBC consented to entry of a final judgment settling the Commission's action against it and agreed to be permanently enjoined from future violations of the antifraud, books and records, and internal control provisions of the federal securities laws. CIBC also agreed to pay $80 million: $37.5 million in disgorgement, a $37.5 million civil penalty and $5 million in prejudgment interest. The Commission intends to have these funds paid into a court account pursuant to the Fair Fund provisions of Section 308(a) of the Sarbanes-Oxley Act of 2002 ("Fair Fund") for ultimate distribution to victims of the fraud.

Daniel Ferguson and Mark Wolf also consented to the entry of a final judgment that permanently enjoins each from violating the same antifraud, books and records, and internal control provisions of the federal securities laws. Ferguson has agreed to pay a total of $563,000: disgorgement of $265,000, a penalty of $265,000, and prejudgment interest of $33,000, and agreed to the entry of an order barring him from serving as an officer or director of a publicly traded company for a period of five years. Wolf, who is no longer employed by CIBC, agreed to pay a total of $60,000: $27,500 as disgorgement, a penalty of $27,500, and prejudgment interest of $5,000. The Commission will likewise direct those monies to Enron fraud victims pursuant to the Fair Fund provisions. Ian Schottlaender, a former managing director in CIBC's corporate leveraged finance group in New York City, is contesting the matter.

SEC v. J.P. Morgan Chase & Co.

Litigation Release No. 18252 (July 28, 2003)
http://www.sec.gov/litigation/litreleases/lr18252.htm

On July 28, 2003, the Commission charged J.P. Morgan Chase & Co. with aiding and abetting Enron's manipulation of its reported financial results through a series of complex structured finance transactions that were used by Enron to report loans from J.P. Morgan Chase as cash from operating activities and allowed Enron to hide the true extent of its borrowings from investors and rating agencies. J.P. Morgan Chase agreed to file a consent and final judgment settling the Commission's action against it and to be permanently enjoining it from future violations of the antifraud provisions of the federal securities laws. Morgan Chase also agreed to pay disgorgement, penalties and interest in the amount of $135 million.

In re Citigroup

Securities Exchange Act Release No. 48230 (July 28, 2003)
http://www.sec.gov/litigation/admin/34-48230.htm

On July 28, 2003, the Commission instituted and settled enforcement proceedings against Citigroup, Inc. for its role in assisting Enron and Dynegy to enhancing artificially their financial presentations through a series of complex structured transactions whose purpose and effect, among other things, was to allow those companies to report proceeds of financings as cash from operating activities on their statements of cash flows. Citigroup settled the matter with the Commission and agreed to disgorge $52,750,000 and pay a penalty of $48,500,000 in connection with its Enron-related conduct; to disgorge $9,750,000 and pay a penalty of $9,000,000 in connection with its Dynegy-related conduct; and to cease and desist from committing or causing any violation of, and any future violations of, federal securities laws.

SEC v. Merrill Lynch & Co., Inc., et al.

Litigation Release No. 18038 (March 17, 2003)
http://www.sec.gov/litigation/litreleases/lr18038.htm

On March 17, 2003 the Commission charged Merrill Lynch & Co. Inc. and four of its former senior executives with aiding and abetting Enron's earnings manipulation by engaging in two fraudulent year-end transactions which had the purpose and effect of overstating Enron's reported financial results. According to the Commission, Merrill Lynch believed that the two trades were essentially a wash, knew that the transaction would have a significant impact on Enron's reported results, bonuses, and stock price and demanded a multi-million dollar fee for entering into this transaction. The Commission agreed to accept Merrill Lynch's offer to settle this matter. Merrill Lynch agreed to pay $80 million dollars in disgorgement, penalties and interest and agreed to the entry of a permanent anti-fraud injunction prohibiting future violations of the federal securities laws. The four former Merrill Lynch executives named in the complaint, Robert S. Furst, Schuyler M. Tilney, Daniel H. Bayly and Thomas W. Davis, are contesting the matter.

<u>SEC v. Hollinger International, Inc.</u>

Litigation Release No. 18551, (January 21, 2004)
http://www.sec.gov/litigation/litreleases/lr18550.htm

<u>SEC v. Conrad M. Black, et al.</u>

Litigation Release No. 18969 (November 15, 2004)
http://www.sec.gov/litigation/litreleases/lr18969.htm

On November 15, 2004, the Commission filed an enforcement action in federal district court against Hollinger International's former Chairman and CEO Conrad M. Black (Black), former Deputy Chairman and COO F. David Radler (Radler), and Hollinger, Inc., a Canadian public holding company controlled by Black. The Commission's complaint alleged that Black, Radler and Hollinger, Inc. engaged in a fraudulent and deceptive scheme to divert cash and assets from Hollinger International, Inc., a U.S. public company and a subsidiary of Hollinger, Inc., and concealed their self-dealing from Hollinger International's public shareholders. According to the Commission, Black, Radler and Hollinger, Inc., among other things, defrauded Hollinger International shareholders through a series of related party transactions by which Black and Radler diverted to themselves, other corporate insiders and Hollinger, Inc. approximately $85 million of the proceeds from Hollinger International's sale of newspaper publications through purported "non-competition" payments. The Commission sought injunctions against the defendants from further violations of the securities laws, disgorgement of ill-gotten gains, pre-judgment interest, civil penalties, bars against Black and Radler from serving as officers or directors of a public company, and a voting trust upon the shares of Hollinger International held directly or indirectly by Black and Hollinger, Inc.

II. CASES INVOLVING ACCOUNTANTS AND AUDITORS

<u>In the Matter of KPMG LLP, Bryan E. Palbaum, CPA, John M. Wong, CPA, Kenneth B. Janeski, CPA, David A. Hori, CPA</u>

Admin. Proc. File No. 3-11714 (October 20, 2004)
http://www.sec.gov/litigation/admin/34-50564.htm

On October 20, 2004, the Commission instituted settled public administrative proceedings against KPMG LLP, Bryan E. Palbaum, John M. Wong, Kenneth B. Janeski, and David A. Hori, for engaging in improper professional conduct as auditors for Gemstar-TV Guide International, Inc.

As part of the settlement, KPMG was censured and agreed to pay $10 million to harmed Gemstar shareholders. (Gemstar, based in Hollywood, Calif., publishes TV Guide magazine and licenses and sells advertising on an interactive program guide (IPG) for television that enables consumers to navigate through and select television programs). KPMG has also agreed to conduct training for its partners and managers on qualitative materiality, accounting for multi-element transactions, and consideration of appropriate disclosure related to complex accounting issues. KPMG will adopt a policy that requires more effective consultation between audit engagement teams and its national office in connection with possible financial statement restatements. Additionally, Palbaum, Wong, Janeski, and Hori are denied the privilege of appearing or practicing before the Commission, with the right to reapply after periods of three years (Palbaum), one year (Wong and Janeski), and eighteen months (Hori).

The Commission's administrative order finds that from September 1999 through March 2002, the respondents' conduct resulted in repeated audit failures in connection with KPMG's audits of Gemstar's financial statements. The order also finds that the respondents reasonably should have known that Gemstar improperly recognized and reported in its public filings material amounts of licensing and advertising revenue. Despite indications of Gemstar's improper accounting and disclosure, the respondents issued unqualified audit reports representing that KPMG had conducted its audits in accordance with generally accepted auditing standards (GAAS) and that Gemstar's financial statements fairly presented its financial results in conformity with GAAP. In reaching these conclusions, the auditors unreasonably relied on representations by Gemstar's management and its inside or outside legal counsel or decided that the unsupported revenues were immaterial to Gemstar's financial statements.

The order also finds that in mid-August 2002, as part of Gemstar's audit committee's investigation into potential restatements of Gemstar's financial statements, certain information came to light that the local engagement team did not convey to KPMG's national office. KPMG did not have a policy that required that a local engagement team consult with the national office on all new significant issues that had come to the local engagement team's attention. Such a consultation should have led KPMG to consider the additional evidence that came to light during the audit committee's investigation and could have led KPMG to a more prompt decision to withdraw its previously issued audit report on Gemstar's 2001 financial statements. KPMG did not take that step until Nov. 22, 2002.

In the Matter of Grant Thornton LLP, Doeren Mayhew & Co. P.c., Peter M. Behrens, CPA, Marvin J. Morris, CPA, and Benedict P. Rybicki, CPA

Administrative Proceeding File No. 3-11377 (January 20, 2004)
http://www.sec.gov/litigation/admin/33-8355.htm

Grant Thornton and Doeren Mayhew Settle SEC Administrative Proceeding Relating to Audit of MCA Financial Corporation

Press Release No. 2004-106 (August 5, 2004)
http://www.sec.gov/news/press/2004-106.htm

On January 20, 2004, the Commission instituted public administrative proceedings pursuant to Commission Rule 102(e) and cease-and-desist proceedings against Grant Thornton LLP (a Chicago based accounting firm), Doeren Mayhew & Co. P.C. (a Michigan based accounting firm), Peter M. Behrens (a partner with Grant Thorton), and Marvin J. Morris and Benedict P. Rybicki (both directors at Doeren Mayhew) for misconduct in connection with their audit of MCA Financial Corporation's financial statements for the fiscal year ended January 31, 1998. At the time, MCA was a mortgage banking company based in Southfield, Michigan.

The Commission alleged that in connection with the 1998 MCA audit, the respondents caused and aided and abetted MCA's violations of the antifraud and reporting provisions of the federal securities laws, violated or caused and aided and abetted violations of the audit requirements of the Exchange Act and engaged in improper professional conduct. Specifically, among other things, the Commission alleged that despite knowing of MCA's failure to disclose several million dollars of material, related party transactions in its 1998 annual financial statements, Grant Thornton and Doeren Mayhew jointly issued a report containing an unqualified opinion on MCA's 1998 annual financial statements and consented to the inclusion of their report in MCA's debenture offering materials. The respondents failed to inform MCA's Board of Directors that MCA's 1998 annual financial statements did not disclose millions of dollars of material, related party transactions.

On August 5, 2004, the Commission accepted the offers of settlement of Grant Thornton LLP, Doeren Mayhew & Co. P.C., Peter M. Behrens, Marvin J. Morris and Benedict P. Rybicki. As part of the Order, Grant Thornton undertakes to: pay $1.5 million as a penalty; require its entire professional staff to undergo fraud-detection training and provide at least $1 million to fund such training; and suspend certain joint audits with other auditing firms for a period of five years. In addition, Grant Thornton is censured and required to pay disgorgement and prejudgment interest of $59,749.41. Additionally, pursuant to the Order, Doeren Mayhew, which voluntarily discontinued conducting public audits as of March 19, 2003, undertakes not to accept new public company auditing engagements for six months. In addition, if Doeren Mayhew engages in audits of public companies after the expiration of six months, Doeren Mayhew undertakes to establish and implement certain policies and procedures specifically designed to improve the quality of its public company audit practice for a period of three years. Doeren Mayhew also is censured and required to pay disgorgement and prejudgment interest of $115,126.86. Further, pursuant to the Order, Morris, Behrens and Rybicki are denied the privilege of appearing or practicing before the Commission for periods of five years, three years and one year, respectively, from the entry of the Order. Accordingly, by the entry of this Order, this matter is resolved as to all respondents in this proceeding.

III. FOREIGN PAYMENT CASES

SEC v. The Titan Corporation

Litigation Release No. 19107 (March 1, 2005)
http://www.sec.gov/litigation/litreleases/lr19107.htm

Report of Investigation Pursuant to Section 21(a) of the Securities Exchange Act of 1934 and the Commission Statement on potential Exchange Act Section 10(b) and Section 14(a) liability

Release No. 51283 (March 1, 2005)
http://www.sec.gov/litigation/investreport/34-51238.htm

On March 1, 2005, the Commission announced the filing of a settled enforcement action charging The Titan Corporation, a San Diego, Calif. based military intelligence and communications company, with violating the anti-bribery, internal controls and books and records provisions of the Foreign Corrupt Practices Act (FCPA). Titan consented to the entry of a final judgment permanently enjoining it from future violations of the FCPA and requiring it to pay approximately $15.5 million in disgorgement and prejudgment interest; pay a $13 million penalty, which will be deemed satisfied by Titan's payment of criminal fines of that amount in parallel proceedings brought by the U.S. Attorney's Office for the Southern District of California and the U.S. Department of Justice, Fraud Section; and retain an independent consultant to review the company's FCPA compliance and procedures and to adopt and implement the consultant's recommendations. The Commission also issued a Report of Investigation to provide guidance concerning potential liability under the antifraud and proxy provisions of the federal securities laws for publication of materially false or misleading disclosures regarding provisions in merger and other contractual agreements.

The Commission's complaint alleges, among other things, that from 1999 to 2001, Titan paid more than $3.5 million to its agent in Benin, Africa, who was known at the time by Titan to be the President of Benin's business advisor. In 2001, Titan funneled approximately $2 million, via its agent in Benin, towards the election campaign of Benin's then-incumbent President. Titan made these payments to assist the company in its development of a telecommunications project in Benin and to obtain an increase in the percentage of project management fees for it. A former senior Titan officer directed that these payments be falsely invoiced by the agent as consulting services and that actual payment of the money be broken into smaller increments and spread out over time. The complaint does not allege that the then-incumbent President knew of the payments.

The Report of Investigation states, among other things, that Titan affirmatively represented in a merger agreement with Lockheed Martin Corporation, dated September 15, 2003, that to its knowledge, neither the company "nor any of its Subsidiaries, nor any director, officer, agent or employee of the Company or any of its Subsidiaries, has ... taken any action which would cause the Company or any of its Subsidiaries to be in violation of the FCPA[,]" which was disclosed in the proxy statement and the merger agreement. As the Report highlights, when an issuer makes a public disclosure of information, the issuer is required to consider whether additional disclosure is necessary in order to put the information contained in, or otherwise incorporated into that publication, into context so that such information is not misleading. The issuer cannot avoid this disclosure obligation simply because the information published was contained in an agreement or other document not prepared as a disclosure document. The Report also states that the Commission will consider bringing an action if it determines that the subject matter of representations or other contractual provisions is materially misleading to shareholders because material facts necessary to make that disclosure not misleading are omitted.

<u>SEC v. GE In Vision, Inc.</u>

Litigation Release No. 19078 (February 14, 2005)
http://www.sec.gov/litigation/litreleases/lr19078.htm

On February 14, 2005, the Commission charged InVision Technologies, Inc. (InVision), a Newark, California-based manufacturer of explosive detection machines used in airports, with authorizing improper payments to foreign government officials in violation of the Foreign Corrupt Practices Act (FCPA). Simultaneous with the filing of the Commission's charges InVision agreed, without admitting or denying the charges, to disgorge $589,000 in profits from its FCPA violations plus prejudgment interest of approximately $28,700, and pay a $500,000 civil penalty. InVision also agreed to cease and desist from violations of the FCPA, and to comply with its undertakings to retain an independent consultant to ensure that InVision adheres to a corporate compliance program designed to detect and prevent violations of the FCPA. InVision was acquired in December 2004 by the General Electric Company, and now operates under the name GE InVision, Inc.; the conduct charged by the Commission occurred prior to the acquisition.

In both a federal court complaint and an administrative order, the Commission charged that from at least June 2002 through June 2004, InVision employees, sales agents and distributors pursued transactions to sell explosive detection machines to airports in China, the Philippines and Thailand. According to the Commission, in each of these transactions, InVision was aware of a high probability that its foreign sales agents or distributors made or offered to make improper payments to foreign government officials in order to obtain or retain business for InVision. Despite this, InVision allowed the agents or distributors to proceed on its behalf, in violation of the FCPA. The Commission also charged that InVision improperly accounted for certain payments to agents or distributors and failed to have an adequate system of internal controls to detect and prevent violations of the FCPA. The Commission's administrative order found that InVision violated the anti-bribery, books and records and internal controls provisions of the FCPA.

<u>SEC v. Monsanto Company</u>

Litigation Release No. 19023 (January 6, 2005)
http://www.sec.gov/litigation/litreleases/lr19023.htm

<u>In the Matter of Monsanto Company</u>

Admin. Proc. File No. 3-11789 (January 6, 2005)
http://www.sec.gov/litigation/admin/34-50978.htm

On January 6, 2005, the Commission filed two settled enforcement proceedings charging Monsanto Company, a global producer of technology-based solutions and agricultural products headquartered in St. Louis, Missouri, with making illicit payments in violation of the Foreign Corrupt Practices Act ("FCPA"). Without admitting or denying the Commission's charges, Monsanto consented to the entry of a final judgment in the federal lawsuit requiring it to pay a $500,000 civil penalty and consented to the Commission's issuance of its administrative order in which the Commission found that Monsanto violated the anti-bribery, books-and-records, and internal-controls provisions of the FCPA, ordered Monsanto to cease and desist from such violations, and required Monsanto to retain an independent consultant to review and make recommendations concerning the company's FCPA compliance policies and procedures. In determining to accept Monsanto's settlement offer, the Commission considered the cooperation that Monsanto provided the Commission staff during its investigation.

In both its federal court complaint and its administrative order, the Commission alleged that, in 2002, a senior Monsanto manager, based in the United States, authorized and directed an Indonesian consulting firm to make an illegal payment totaling $50,000 to a senior Indonesian Ministry of Environment official ("the senior Environment Official"). The bribe was made to influence the senior Environment Official to repeal an unfavorable decree that was likely to have an adverse effect on Monsanto's business. Although the payment was made, the unfavorable decree was not repealed. The Commission further charged that the senior Monsanto manager devised a scheme whereby false invoices were submitted to Monsanto and the senior Monsanto manager approved the invoices for payment. In addition, the Commission charged that, from 1997 to 2002, Monsanto inaccurately recorded, or failed to record, in its books and records approximately $700,000 of illegal or questionable payments made to at least 140 current and former Indonesian government officials and their family members. The Commission further charged that, in certain instances, entries were made in the books and records of the two Indonesian entities that concealed the source, use and true nature of these payments.

In a related proceeding, the United States Department of Justice entered into an agreement with Monsanto Company to defer prosecution on charges of violating the anti-bribery and books and records provisions of the FCPA. Under the Agreement, the Justice Department filed a criminal information charging the company; Monsanto will pay a $1 million monetary penalty; and Monsanto will retain for a period of three years an independent compliance expert to audit the company's compliance program and monitor its implementation of and compliance with new internal policies and procedures.

SEC v. ABB Ltd.

Litigation Release No. 18775, (July 6, 2004)
http://www.sec.gov/litigation/litreleases/lr18775.htm

On July 6, 2004, the Commission filed a settled enforcement action in the United States District Court for the District of Columbia charging ABB Ltd, a global provider of power and automation technologies headquartered in Zurich, Switzerland, with violating the anti-bribery, books-and-records, and internal-accounting-controls provisions of the Foreign Corrupt Practices Act (FCPA). Simultaneously with the filing of the complaint, and without admitting or denying its allegations, ABB consented to the entry of a final judgment enjoining it from future FCPA violations, and requiring it (i) to pay $5.9 million in disgorgement and prejudgment interest, (ii) to pay a $10.5 million penalty, which would be deemed satisfied by two of its affiliates' payments of criminal fines totaling the same amount in parallel criminal proceedings brought by the Department of Justice; and (iii) to retain an independent consultant to review the company's FCPA compliance policies and procedures.

In its complaint, the Commission charged that, from 1998 through early 2003, ABB's U.S. and foreign-based subsidiaries doing business in Nigeria, Angola and Kazakhstan, offered and made illicit payments totaling over $1.1 million to government officials in these countries. According to the complaint, all of the payments were made to influence acts and decisions by the foreign officials receiving the payments, in order to assist ABB's subsidiaries in obtaining and retaining business. The complaint further alleged that the payments were made with the knowledge and approval of certain management level personnel of the relevant ABB subsidiaries, and that at least $865,726 of the payments were made after ABB became a reporting company in the United States in April 2001. Finally, the complaint charged that ABB improperly recorded these payments in its accounting books and records, and lacked any meaningful internal controls to prevent or detect such illicit payments.

In determining to accept ABB's settlement offer, the Commission considered the full cooperation that ABB provided to the Commission staff during its investigation. The Commission also considered the fact that ABB brought this matter to the attention of the Commission's staff and the U.S. Department of Justice. Based in part upon ABB's cooperation, the Commission determined to allow ABB's $10.5 million civil penalty obligation to be deemed satisfied by two of its affiliates' payments of criminal fines totaling $10.5 million in a parallel criminal proceeding brought by the U.S. Department of Justice.

In that parallel proceeding, the U.S. Department of Justice filed criminal FCPA charges against two ABB subsidiaries, ABB Vetco Gray, Inc. and ABB Vetco Gray UK, Ltd. where each agreed to plead guilty to two felony counts of violating the anti-bribery provisions of the FCPA and to pay criminal fines that, between them, total $10.5 million.

IV. BROKER-DEALER CASES

SEC v. Frank Furino

Litigation Release No. 19126 (March 9, 2005)
http://www.sec.gov/litigation/litreleases/lr19126.html

On March 9, 2005, the Commission charged Frank J. Furino, a former clerk for a New York Stock Exchange floor broker, for his role in a fraudulent "trading ahead" scheme. Furino is charged with disclosing large, pending block orders from institutional customers to a day trader in return for cash payments between August 2000 and December 2001. The Commission alleges that the day trader traded ahead of the customer orders and profited on short-term price movements when the block order was filled. Until his recent termination, Furino was employed on the floor of the New York Stock Exchange as a clerk for a floor broker, Jefferies Execution Services, Inc. and its predecessor, Lawrence Helfant LLC.

The Commission alleges that between August 2000 and December 2001, Furino frequently alerted the day trader when institutional customers placed large orders with Helfant. Large orders can affect the market price of a stock by affecting the supply or demand for the stock. The day trader then "traded ahead" of the customer order – that is, bought or sold short the same security before Helfant executed the customer order. The day trader then closed his position as Helfant filled the customer's order, realizing a profit from the movement in the stock price caused by the large order. By means of this scheme, the day trader made over $300,000 in trading profits on at least 58 trades. Helfant's customers suffered losses because the scheme allowed the day trader to trade at more favorable prices than the customers were able to receive. Furino solicited and received from the day trader payments ranging from $2,500 to $10,000 per month over the course of the scheme. Furino's conduct breached duties of confidentiality and trust that he owed to his employer and to his employer's customers. Furino also violated his firm's written policies requiring confidential treatment of customer information, forbidding the use of confidential client information for personal benefit or for the benefit of another client, and forbidding acceptance of undisclosed compensation from clients.

The New York Stock Exchange, Inc. is also filing a separate action against Furino charging him with securities fraud and violation of NYSE rules

SEC v. David S. Davidson, et al.

Litigation Release No. 19090 (February 17, 2005)
http://www.sec.gov/litigation/litreleases/lr19090.htm

On February 17, 2005, the Commission filed a civil action against David S. Davidson, Lloyd S. Beirne and Brandon T. Bush, all of Boca Raton, Florida. Davidson is the former chairman and chief executive officer of D.L. Cromwell Investments, Inc. ("Cromwell"), a defunct broker-dealer formerly located in Boca Raton, Beirne is Cromwell's former president, and Bush was a Cromwell trader.

The Commission's Complaint alleges a short selling scheme in which, from late October 2002 through March 2003, defendants fraudulently used non-existent trades to hide a burgeoning short position in the stock of Expedia, Inc. ("Expedia"), held in Cromwell's proprietary account at its clearing broker, which is located in Philadelphia, Pennsylvania. Davidson, Beirne, and Bush used the access that Cromwell, as an introducing broker, had to the clearing broker's system to falsely place Expedia buy orders, which they knew they would cancel the next day, claiming the orders were placed in error. The Complaint alleges that defendants entered and cancelled these fictitious buys almost daily for five months, concealing the size of the short position from the clearing broker, and avoiding serious financial consequences, including margin calls. The Complaint further alleges that the scheme unraveled on March 19, 2003, when the announcement of a tender offer for Expedia by its majority shareholder lifted Expedia's price from $38 per share to more than $47. Shortly thereafter, the clearing broker discovered the fraud. Cromwell could not cover its short position in Expedia, which had grown to approximately 660,000 shares, and the clearing broker was forced to pay $18 million to cover the position.

SEC v. CIBC Mellon Trust Co.

Litigation Release No. 19081 (February 16, 2005)
http://www.sec.gov/litigation/litreleases/lr19081.htm

On February 16, 2005, the Commission filed settled enforcement proceedings against CIBC Mellon Trust Company, ("CIBC Mellon") headquartered in Toronto, Canada. In its complaint, the Commission charged that, between July 1998 and September 1999, CIBC Mellon participated in a fraudulent scheme to promote, distribute and sell the stock of Pay Pop, Inc. ("Pay Pop"), a now-defunct British Columbia-based telecommunications company. The complaint alleges that, during the period CIBC Mellon acted as Pay Pop's transfer agent, one of its senior managers was bribed by two of Pay Pop's officers and directors to assist them in obtaining a ready supply of Pay Pop stock for these officers and directors to illegally distribute to investors. By its failure to have sufficient policies, procedures and internal controls in place, CIBC Mellon failed to detect the bribes, and the illegal conduct, thereby allowing the scheme to succeed. The complaint further alleges that from 1998 through 2003, CIBC Mellon acted as a transfer agent for at least 113 companies whose securities were registered with the Commission and, from 1998 through the present, CIBC Mellon acted as a broker-dealer for at least 45 of those companies yet never registered with the Commission as a transfer agent, or as a broker-dealer as it was required to do. Subsequently, on February, 6, 2004, CIBC Mellon registered with the Commission as a transfer agent. CIBC Mellon Trust further requested that the Commission issue an order exempting it from the broker-dealer registration requirement of Section 15(a). The Commission has approved this request and will issue an order granting the exemption upon entry of the final judgment in these proceedings.

CIBC Mellon consented to the entry of a final judgment enjoining it from future violations of the antifraud, transfer agent registration, broker-dealer registration and securities registration provisions of the federal securities laws. CIBC Mellon has agreed to pay a $5 million civil penalty, $889,773 in disgorgement, and $140,270 in prejudgment interest. The civil penalty was assessed, in part, for CIBC Mellon's failure to cooperate in the investigation of this matter. In addition, based upon the court's anticipated entry of the final judgment, CIBC Mellon has agreed to the issuance of a settled administrative order finding that it violated the broker-dealer registration and transfer agent registration provisions of the Exchange Act for failing to register as a broker-dealer or as a transfer agent. The Commission Order will require CIBC Mellon to cease-and-desist from future violations of the broker-dealer and transfer agent provisions of the Exchange Act. In addition, CIBC Mellon will agree to maintain its registration as a transfer agent for as long as it continues to act as a transfer agent for any security registered with the Commission under Section 12 of the Exchange Act and, in anticipation of the entry of the Order requiring it to do so, CIBC Mellon has retained a qualified independent consultant to conduct a comprehensive review of all aspects of CIBC Mellon's business as a transfer agent and as a broker-dealer.

In the Matter of J.P. Morgan Securities, Inc.

Admin. Proc. File No. 3-11828 (February 14, 2005)
http://www.sec.gov/litigation/admin/34-51200.htm

On February 14, 2005 the Commission instituted and settled public administrative against J.P. Morgan Securities Inc. ("JPMSI"). The Commission found that JPMSI failed to preserve for three years, the first two of which in an easily accessible place, all electronic mail communications (including inter-office memoranda and communications) received and sent by its employees that related to its business as a member of an exchange, broker or dealer, and lacked adequate systems or procedures for the preservation of electronic mail communications. The Commission, NYSE, and NASD (collectively, "the regulators") discovered these deficiencies during an inquiry into the supervision of JPMSI's research and investment banking activities. In April 2003, the regulators initiated and settled enforcement actions against JPMSI and other broker-dealers for various violations involving their research and investment banking activities. In May 2003, the regulators focused their inquiry on the supervision of the research and investment banking activities of JPMSI and other broker-dealers. JPMSI produced certain e-mail in response to the regulators' request to produce email for various supervisory personnel and other employees and certified that e-mail productions for certain individuals were complete. In November 2003, the regulators requested that JPMSI provide information regarding its ability to locate and restore backup tapes containing e-mail responsive to the regulators' requests during the investigation. JPMSI subsequently advised the regulators that it had failed to retain or was unable to locate all responsive e-mail requested during those inquiries. Based on the foregoing and JPMSI's Offer of Settlement, the Commission found that JPMSI willfully violated Section 17(a) of the Exchange Act and Rule 17a-4 promulgated thereunder by failing to preserve electronic mail communications for three years, the first two of which in an easily accessible place.

In its Offer of Settlement, JPMSI agreed to pay penalties and fines totaling $2.1 million to resolve this proceeding and related actions by NYSE and NASD. In addition, JPMSI agreed to review its procedures regarding the preservation of electronic mail communications for compliance with the federal securities laws and regulations, and the rules of NYSE and NASD and establish systems and procedures reasonably designed to achieve such compliance.

SEC v. Morgan Stanley & Co., Incorporated

Litigation Release No. 19050 (January 25, 2005)
http://www.sec.gov/litigation/litreleases/lr19050.htm

On January 25, 2005, the Commission announced the filing in federal district court of a settled civil injunctive action against Morgan Stanley & Co. Incorporated (Morgan Stanley) relating to the firm's allocations of stock to institutional customers in initial public offerings (IPOs) underwritten by the firm during 1999 and 2000. In its complaint, the Commission alleged that Morgan Stanley violated Rule 101 of Regulation M under the Securities Exchange Act of 1934 by attempting to induce certain customers who received allocations of IPOs to place purchase orders for additional shares in the aftermarket.

In particular, the Commission alleged that during a restricted period, i.e., prior to Morgan's Stanley's completion of participation in the distribution of IPO shares, Morgan Stanley attempted to induce certain customers to make aftermarket purchases in violation of Rule 101 of Regulation M by engaging in the following activities. The Commission further alleged that Morgan Stanley communicated to certain customers that expressing an interest in buying shares in the immediate aftermarket and buying shares in the immediate aftermarket would help them obtain good allocations of over-subscribed, hot IPOs. In addition, Morgan Stanley solicited aftermarket interest from certain customers who Morgan Stanley knew had no interest in owning the stock of the IPO companies long-term. The Commission also alleged that Morgan Stanley proposed to certain customers the aftermarket price limits they should give to obtain a good IPO allocation. According to the Commission's complaint, in some instances, Morgan Stanley encouraged customers to increase the prices they had originally told Morgan Stanley they were willing to pay in the aftermarket. In addition the Commission alleges that Morgan Stanley accepted customers' aftermarket interest that they would buy "1 for 1" (or some other ratio) in the aftermarket, meaning that the customers intended to buy in the aftermarket an amount of shares equal to (or greater than) their IPO allocation. According to the Commission, Morgan Stanley's conduct after the distribution of IPO shares was complete, taken as a whole, demonstrates that when Morgan Stanley had solicited aftermarket interest from customers during the restricted period, it was attempting to induce them to place aftermarket orders in the first few days of trading. The Commission also asserted that Morgan Stanley violated Rule 101 of Regulation M in the Martha Stewart Living Omnimedia IPO by soliciting a 350,000 share aftermarket order from a customer before all the IPO shares had been distributed.

Under the terms of the settlement, a judgment will be entered against Morgan Stanley enjoining it from violating Rule 101 of the Commission's Regulation M and ordering it to pay a $40 million civil penalty. The settlement terms are subject to court approval.

SEC v. Goldman Sachs & Co.

Litigation Release No. 19051 (January 25, 2005)
http://www.sec.gov/litigation/litreleases/lr19051.htm

On January 25, 2005, the Commission announced the filing a settled civil injunctive action against Goldman, Sachs & Co. (Goldman Sachs) relating to the firm's allocation of stock to institutional customers in initial public offerings (IPOs) underwritten by the firms during 1999 and 2000. In its complaint, the Commission alleges that Goldman Sachs Goldman Sachs violated Rule 101 of Regulation M under the Securities Exchange Act of 1934 by attempting to induce certain customers who received allocations of IPOs to place purchase orders for additional shares in the aftermarket. The Commission's complaint, includes the following allegations. During the restricted period, Goldman Sachs attempted to induce, or induced, certain customers to make aftermarket purchases of IPO stock in violation of Rule 101 of Regulation M by engaging in the following activities: (1) Goldman Sachs communicated to certain customers that Goldman Sachs considered purchases in the immediate aftermarket to be significant in the determination of IPO allocations; (2) Goldman Sachs informed certain customers that it verified whether customers placed orders to purchase stock in the immediate aftermarket following an IPO; (3) Goldman Sachs sales representatives asked certain customers during restricted periods whether, and at what prices and in what quantities, they intended to place orders to purchase IPO stock in the immediate aftermarket; (4) Goldman Sachs encouraged certain customers that had provided "aftermarket interestto increase the prices they said that they would pay in the aftermarket; (5) Goldman Sachs sought and/or accepted aftermarket interest from customers based solely or in relevant part on the amount of their prospective allocations; and (6) through such questions and statements about aftermarket orders during restricted periods, Goldman Sachs communicated to certain customers hopeful of obtaining IPO allocations (including customers that did not have a genuine interest in long-term ownership of the stock being offered) that indications of intentions to place orders in the immediate aftermarket, and/or the aftermarket orders themselves, would increase their likelihood of receiving favorable allocations of IPO stock.

Under the terms of the settlement, a judgment will be entered against Goldman Sachs enjoining it from violating Rule 101 of the Commission's Regulation M and ordering each firm to pay a $40 million civil penalty. The settlement terms are subject to court approval.

In the Matter of Knight Securities, L.P.

Admin. Proc. File No. 3-11771 (December 16, 2004)
http://www.sec.gov/litigation/admin/34-50867.htm

On Dec. 16, 2004, the Commission instituted settled administrative and cease-and-desist proceedings against Knight Securities, L.P., finding that Knight defrauded its institutional customers by extracting excessive profits out of its customers' orders while failing to meet the firm's duty to provide "best execution" to the institutions that placed those orders.

According to the Commission, between January 1999 and November 2000, Knight earned over $41 million in illegal profits by failing to provide best execution to its institutional customers. Specifically, Knight defrauded its institutional customers by extracting excessive profits out of its customers' not-held orders while failing to meet the firm's duty to provide best execution to the institutions that placed those orders. By engaging in these trading practices, Knight extracted enormous profits—as high as $9.00 per share—by executing transactions that involved effectively no risk to Knight. Consequently, Knight improperly realized tens of millions of dollars in excessive per share profits from its institutional customers. The Commission also found that Knight failed reasonably to supervise

Knight's former leading sales trader and other institutional sales traders while they were systematically misusing Automated Confirmation Transaction Service (ACT) trade modifiers. Knight had no written procedures, no adequate systems in place and no supervisory personnel to prevent Knight's sales traders from consistently misusing the modifiers over a two-year period. Finally, the Commission found that Knight violated the books and records provisions of the federal securities laws by failing to (1) retain email communications relating to its business, (2) maintain a purchase and sales blotter that contained accurate information concerning the time of execution of certain trades, and (3) include required information on some order tickets and maintain certain order tickets for the time period required by the federal securities laws.

Knight, now known as Knight Equity Markets, L.P., agreed to pay more than $41 million in disgorgement of illegal profits, over $13 million in prejudgment interest and $12.5 million in civil penalties. Knight will also pay an additional $12.5 million in fines to settle a parallel NASD proceeding. Knight also voluntarily agreed to retain an Independent Compliance Consultant to conduct a comprehensive review of (1) Knight's policies and procedures with respect to best execution obligations, trade reporting requirements, limit order requirements and books and records requirements, and (2) Knight's supervisory and compliance structure. Knight also was required to cease and desist from committing or causing any future violations of the broker-dealer anti-fraud and books and records provisions of the Exchange Act, and was censured Knight for its failure to reasonably supervise its institutional sales traders.

<u>In the Matter of TD Waterhouse Investor Services, Inc.</u>

Admin. Proc. File No. 3-11669 (September 21, 2004)
http://www.sec.gov/litigation/admin/34-50415.htm

<u>In the Matter of Brandt, Kelly & Simmons, LLC and Kenneth G. Brandt</u>

Admin. Proc. File No. 3-11672 (September 21, 2004)
http://www.sec.gov/litigation/admin/ia-2302.htm

On September 21, 2004, the Commission filed settled civil charges against TD Waterhouse Investor Services, Inc., a national brokerage firm, for making undisclosed cash payments to three investment advisers to encourage them to use TD Waterhouse for their clients' brokerage business. TD Waterhouse made payments to the advisers from its profits on the advisory clients' brokerage business. The payments, however, did not directly benefit the advisers' clients. Instead, the advisers used the money for their own purposes. In settling the matter, TD Waterhouse agreed to pay a $2 million penalty, among other remedies. The Commission also announced related fraud actions against the three investment advisers and their principals for their failures to disclose the cash payments.

The Commission's Order found that TD Waterhouse knew its payments created potential conflicts of interest between the advisers and their clients. Each adviser that received compensation from TD Waterhouse compromised its ability to evaluate independently whether to recommend that its clients use TD Waterhouse to handle the clients' brokerage business. TD Waterhouse, which recognized that the advisers were required by law to disclose these conflicts to their clients, adopted written procedures that required TD Waterhouse personnel to ensure that the advisers made the proper disclosures, yet the firm failed to follow these procedures.

In agreeing to settle the charges, Kiely Financial and its principal, Joseph K. Kiely, agreed to disgorge the money they received from TD Waterhouse, plus interest, totaling $54,256 and pay a $100,000 civil penalty. Additionally, Rudney Associates and its principal, Eric A. Rudney, agreed to disgorge the money they received from TD Waterhouse, plus interest, totaling $22,331, and pay a $40,000 penalty. Kiely Financial, Kiely, Rudney Associates and Rudney also agreed to cease and desist from committing or causing violations of the federal securities laws.

The Commission also instituted litigated administrative and cease-and-desist proceedings against Brandt, Kelly & Simmons and its principal, Kenneth G. Brandt. The Order Instituting Proceedings alleges that the firm agreed to distribute a $7,500 cash payment from TD Waterhouse to its advisory clients to compensate them for fees they incurred when moving their accounts from another broker to TD Waterhouse. The Order alleges that the respondents did not inform their clients of the payment, but rather fraudulently misappropriated the money for their own uses.

SEC v. Thomas Weisel Partners LLC

Litigation Release No. 18855 (August 26, 2004)
http://www.sec.gov/litigation/litreleases/lr18855.htm

On August 26, 2004, the Commission announced that it settled charges against Thomas Weisel Partners LLC, a San Francisco, California-based brokerage firm and investment bank, arising from an investigation of research analyst conflicts of interest. This settlement is related to the global settlement that ten other firms reached with the Commission, NASD,

Inc. the New York Stock Exchange, Inc. (NYSE), and state regulators in April 2003. In connection with this matter, the Commission filed a Complaint against Thomas Weisel Partners in the U.S. District Court for the Southern District of New York, alleging violations of the federal securities laws and NASD and NYSE rules.

In the Commission action, Thomas Weisel Partners agreed to a federal court order that enjoins the firm from future violations of the federal securities laws and NASD and NYSE rules and requires the firm to make changes in the operations of its equity research and investment banking departments. As part of the settlement, Thomas Weisel Partners agreed to pay $5 million as disgorgement and an additional $5 million in penalties. $5 million of these payments will be placed into a distribution fund for the benefit of customers of the firm. The remainder will be paid to resolve related proceedings by state regulators. In addition, Thomas Weisel Partners will pay, over five years, $2.5 million to provide the firm's clients with independent research.

According to the Commission's Complaint, from July 1999 through 2001, research analysts at Thomas Weisel Partners were subject to inappropriate influence by investment banking at the firm. The Complaint also alleges that, on several occasions, Thomas Weisel Partners' analysts published research that contained exaggerated or unwarranted claims, and/or opinions for which there was no reasonable basis, and that Thomas Weisel Partners received payment from another investment bank for providing research coverage of that firm's investment banking client without disclosing that payment in research reports, as federal law requires. Further, the Complaint alleged that Thomas Weisel Partners made payments to other firms for those firms to publish research on Thomas Weisel Partners' underwriting clients without ensuring that such payments were disclosed. Finally, the Complaint alleged that Thomas Weisel Partners failed to supervise its research analysts adequately and to establish policies to ensure their proper conduct.

The final judgment, in part, orders Thomas Weisel Partners to implement structural reforms and provide enhanced disclosure to investors, including a broad range of changes relating to the operations of its equity research and investment banking operations.

SEC v. Deutsche Bank Securities Inc.

Litigation Release No. 18854 (August 26, 2004)
http://www.sec.gov/litigation/litreleases/lr18854.htm

The Commission settled charges against Deutsche Bank Securities Inc. (DBS), a brokerage firm and investment bank headquartered in New York, New York, arising from an investigation of research analyst conflicts of interest. This settlement is also related to the global settlement that ten other firms reached with the Commission, NASD, Inc., the New York Stock Exchange, Inc. (NYSE), and state securities regulators in April 2003.

The Commission filed a complaint against DBS in the U.S. District Court for the Southern District of New York, alleging violations of the federal securities laws and NASD and NYSE rules. In the SEC action, DBS has agreed to a federal court order that will enjoin the firm from future violations of the federal securities laws and NASD and NYSE rules and requires the firm to make changes in the operations of its equity research and investment banking departments. As part of the settlement, DBS has agreed to pay $25 million as disgorgement and $25 million in penalties for the conflicts of interest. DBS has agreed to pay an additional penalty of $7.5 million for failing to timely produce all e-mail during the investigation. One-half of the $57.5 million total of these payments—$28.75 million—will be paid in connection with the SEC action and related proceedings by the NASD and NYSE and will be placed into a distribution fund for the benefit of customers of the firm. The remainder will be paid to resolve related proceedings by state securities regulators. In addition, DBS will pay, over five years, $25 million to provide the firm's clients with independent research, and $5 million to be used for investor education.

According to the Commission's Complaint, from at least July 1999 through June 2001, DBS research analysts were subject to inappropriate influence by investment banking at the firm. The Complaint also alleged that DBS published exaggerated or unwarranted research or research that lacked a reasonable basis, received payments from other firms to publish research on certain companies without ensuring that such payments were disclosed, and made payments to other firms for those firms to publish research on DBS's underwriting clients. The firm also failed to maintain appropriate supervision over its research operations. Finally, during the investigation, DBS failed to timely produce all e-mail in response to regulatory requests and subpoenas.

In the Matter of Needham & Company, Inc.

Admin. Proc. File No. 3-11603 (August 25, 2004)
http://www.sec.gov/litigation/admin/33-8474.pdf

In the Matter of Janney Montgomery Scott LLC

Admin. Proc. File No. 3-11604 (August 25, 2004)
http://www.sec.gov/litigation/admin/33-8475.pdf

In the Matter of Morgan Keegan & Co., Inc.

Admin. Proc. File No. 3-11600 (August 25, 2004)
http://www.sec.gov/litigation/admin/33-8466.htm

In the Matter of Prudential Equity Group, LLC f/k/a Prudential Securities, Inc.

Admin. Proc. File No. 3-11601 (August 25, 2004)
http://www/sec.gov/litigation/admin/33-8469.htm

In the Matter of Adams Harkness, Inc. f/k/a Adams, Harkness & Hill, Inc.

Admin. Proc. File No. 3-11598 (August 25, 2004)
http://www.sec.gov/litigation/admin/33-8460.htm

In the Matter of Friedman, Billings, Ramsey & Co., Inc.

Admin. Proc. File No. 3-11599 (August 25, 2004)
http://www.sec.gov/litigation/admin/33-8461.htm

In the Matter of SG Cowen & Co., LLC f/k/a SG Cowen Securities Corporation

Admin. Proc. File No. 3-11602 (August 25, 2004)
http://www.sec.gov/litigation/admin/33-8472.pdf

On August 25, 2004, the Commission announced settled enforcement actions against seven broker-dealers for failing to disclose they had received payments for providing research coverage of certain public companies. The seven firms are: Needham & Company, Inc. (Needham), Janney Montgomery Scott LLC (Janney), Morgan Keegan & Co., Inc. (Morgan Keegan), Prudential Equity Group, LLC f/k/a Prudential Securities, Inc. (Prudential Equity), Adams Harkness & Hill, Inc. (Adams Harkness), Friedman, Billings, Ramsey & Co., Inc. (Friedman Billings), and SG Cowen & Co., LLC f/k/a SG Cowen Securities Corporation (SG Cowen). The Commission found that during the period 1999 through

2002, these firms received payments for research from other broker-dealers that were underwriting securities offerings for certain public, or soon-to-be public, companies. The underwriting broker-dealers paid the firms to issue research or "cover" their issuer clients. None of the firms disclosed in their published research reports the receipt and amount of the payments, as required.

The Commission fined four of the firms for violating the record-keeping requirements concerning business-related internal e-mail communications during the period July 1999 through June 2001. Each of the four firms – Adams Harkness, Janney, Morgan Keegan, and Needham – consented, without admitting or denying the findings, to a cease-and desist order. The firms also have consented to undertakings to ensure that they are in compliance with the record-keeping requirements. In addition, without admitting or denying the findings, the seven firms consented to orders that they cease-and-desist from committing any violations and any future violations and pay the following amounts: (1) Janney, $875,000; Morgan Keen, $875,000; Needham, $700,000; Adams Harkness, $575,000; Prudential Equity, $375,00; Friedman Billings, $125,000; and SG Cowen, $120,000 for a total of $3,650,000.

In re Bear Wagner Specialists LLC

Exchange Act Release No. 34-49498, (March 30, 2004)
http://www.sec.gov/litigation/admin/34-49498.htm

In re Fleet Specialists, Inc.

Exchange Act Release No. 34-49499, (March 30, 2004)
http://www.sec.gov/litigation/admin/34-49499.htm;

In re LaBranche & Co. LLC

Exchange Act Release No. 34-49500, (March 30, 2004)
http://www.sec.gov/litigation/admin/34-49500.htm;

In re Spear, Leeds & Kellogg Specialists LLC

Exchange Act Release No. 34-49501, (March 30, 2004)
http://www.sec.gov/litigation/admin/34-49501.htm

In re Van der Moolen Specialists USA, LLC

Exchange Act Release No. 34-49502, (March 30, 2004)
http://www.sec.gov/litigation/admin/34-49502.htm

In the Matter of SIG Specialists, Inc.

Exchange Act Release, (July 26, 2004)
http://www.sec.gov/news/press/2004-99.htm

In the Matter of Performance Specialist Group, LLC

Exchange Act Release, (July 26, 2004)
http://www.sec.gov/news/press/2004-99.htm

On March 30, 2004, the SEC and NYSE settled enforcement actions against five NYSE specialist firms: Bear Wagner Specialists LLC; Fleet Specialist, Inc.; LaBranche & Co., LLC; Spear, Leeds & Kellogg Specialists LLC; and Van der Moolen Specialists USA, LLC. The firms agreed to pay a total of $241,823,257 in penalties and disgorgement, consisting of $87,735,635 in civil money penalties and $154,087,622 in disgorgement, and implement steps to improve their compliance procedures and systems. On July 26, 2004, the SEC and NYSE settled enforcement actions against two NYSE specialist firms: SIG Specialists, Inc. and Performance Specialist Group LLC. The firms will pay a total of $5.2 million in penalties and disgorgement, consisting of $1.7 million in civil money penalties and $3.5 million in disgorgement, and implement steps to improve their compliance procedures and systems.

In a joint investigation, the NYSE and SEC found that the firms, through particular transactions by certain of their registered specialists, violated federal securities laws and Exchange rules by executing orders for their dealer accounts ahead of executable public customer or "agency" orders. Through these transactions, the firms violated their basic obligation to match executable public customer buy and sell orders and not to fill customer orders through trades from the firm's own account when those customer orders could be matched with other customer orders. Through this conduct, the firms improperly profited from trading opportunities; disadvantaged customer orders, which either received inferior prices or went unexecuted altogether; and breached their duty to serve as agents to public customer orders. In the settlements, the firms have neither admitted nor denied the allegations.

In the Matter of American Express Financial Advisors, Inc.

Admin. Proc. File No. 3-11395 (February 12, 2004)
http://www.sec.gov/litigation/admin/33-8365.htm

In the Matter of Legg Mason Wood Walker, Incorporated

Admin. ProFile No. 3-11398 (February 12, 2004)
http://www.seFile No. 3-11398 (February 12, 2004)

In the Matter of Linsco/Private Ledger Corp.

Admin. ProFile No. 3-11398 (February 12, 2004)
http://www.se.sec.gov/litigation/admin/33-8371.htm

In the Matter of Raymond James Financial Services, Inc.

Admin. ProFile No. 3-11398 (February 12, 2004)
http://www.sesec.gov/litigation/admin/33-8374.htm

In the Matter of UBS Financial Services Inc.

Admin. ProFile No. 3-11398 (February 12, 2004)
http://www.sesec.gov/litigation/admin/33-8377.htm

In the Matter of Wachovia Securities LLC

Admin. ProFile No. 3-11398 (February 12, 2004)
http://www.sesec.gov/litigatin/admin/33-8380.htm

In the Matter of H.D. Vest Investment Securities, Inc.

Admin. Proc. File No. 3-11398 (February 12, 2004)
http://www.seov/litigation/admin/33-8383.htm

The Commission and NASD brought enforcement and disciplinary actions against a total of 15 firms for failure to deliver mutual fund breakpoint discounts during 2001 and 2002. Breakpoint discounts are volume discounts applicable to front-end sales charges on Class A mutual fund shares (front-end loads). The Commission's orders found that the firms, by failing to disclose to certain customers that they were not receiving the benefit of applicable breakpoint discounts, violated antifraud provisions of the Securities Act. The Commission and NASD each brought cases against a group of 7 firms, and the NASD separately brought actions against the other 8 firms. The 15 firms agreed to compensate customers for the overcharges, pay fines in an amount equal to their projected overcharges that total over $21.5 million, and undertake other corrective measures.

In the Matter of Fidelity Brokerage Services LLC

Securities Exchange Act of 1934 Release No. 50138 (August 3, 2004) *http://www.sec.gov/litigation/admin/ 34-50138.htm*

The Commission and the New York Stock Exchange initiated and settled enforcement actions against Fidelity Brokerage Services, LLC as a result of the alteration or destruction of documents in numerous Fidelity Brokerage branch offices. In settlement of these actions, Fidelity Brokerage will pay a total of $2 million, consisting of a $1 million civil penalty imposed by the SEC and a $1 million fine imposed by the NYSE. In addition to these coordinated enforcement actions, the NYSE separately took disciplinary actions in related cases against seven individuals.

In a joint investigation, the SEC and the NYSE found that between January 2001 and July 2002, Fidelity Brokerage violated the broker-dealer record-keeping requirements of the federal securities laws because employees in at least 21 of its 88 branch offices altered or destroyed the firm's books and records. The violations related to Fidelity Brokerage's annual internal inspections, which were designed to determine whether branch offices were complying with the firm's policies and procedures, NYSE rules, and the federal securities laws. The firm's managers pressured branch office employees to obtain perfect inspections and gave advance notice of when the inspections would occur. Certain Fidelity employees took advantage of the advance notification and improperly prepared for the inspections.

In the Matter of Robertson Stephens, Inc.

Securities Exchange Act of 1934 Release No. 49077, (January 14, 2004) *http://www.sec.gov/litigation/admin/34-49077.htm*

On January 9, 2004, the Commission issued an Order in which it found that Respondent Robertson Stephens, Inc. ("RSI") willfully violated the broker-dealer antifraud, record keeping and reporting provisions of the securities laws. In the Order, the Commission found that RSI and certain senior executives of the firm had formed a series of investment limited partnerships referred to collectively as the "Bayview" partnerships. An entity controlled by RSI was the general partner of each of the limited partnerships. Two of the limited partnerships, Bayview 99 I and II, were formed to invest in a portfolio of companies that was chosen by an investment committee consisting of senior RSI executives. Another limited partnership, Bayview Corvis, also formed in 1999, invested solely in the securities of Corvis Corporation ("Corvis"), a telecommunications and

Internet equipment company that, at the time of the Bayview investment, was privately-held. Among other things, the Commission's order found that the Research Analyst's statements regarding Corvis during the January 23, 2001 investment committee meeting—that he would not buy Corvis stock at the market price, but would buy it if it was trading at $12 to $14 per share—were inconsistent with the buy rating on Corvis included in the January 16, 2001 research report, which had been issued when Corvis stock was trading at about $23 per share. On February 23, 2004, after no comments were received in response to the proposed distribution plan for disgorgement, the plan was approved.

SEC v. Daniel Calugar and Security Brokerage, Inc.

Litigation Release No. 18524, (December 24, 2003)
http://www.sec.gov/litigation/litreleases/lr18524.htm

On December 22, 2003, the Commission filed civil fraud charges against Security Brokerage, Inc. of Las Vegas and its president and majority owner, Daniel Calugar, for their participation in a scheme to defraud mutual fund shareholders through improper late trading and market timing. From at least 2001 to 2003, Calugar, trading through Security Brokerage, reaped profits of approximately $175 million from improper late trading and market timing, principally through mutual funds managed by Alliance Capital Management and Massachusetts Financial Services (MFS).

Based on the Commission's application, United States District Judge Robert Clive Jones of the District of Nevada issued a temporary restraining order freezing the assets of the defendants, prohibiting the destruction of documents, and granting expedited discovery. The Commission applied for the emergency relief after learning that on December 18, 2003, Calugar had transferred $50 million of proceeds from his scheme out of MFS. This transfer occurred on the same day that the Commission instituted an enforcement action against Alliance in connection with market timing activity. The Commission's action against Alliance identified Calugar as the largest market timer at Alliance.

Security Brokerage and Calugar are charged with violating the antifraud provisions of the federal securities laws. In addition to the emergency relief granted by the court, the Commission is seeking a judgment of permanent injunction, disgorgement of ill-gotten gains, and monetary penalties.

In the Matter of Raymond James Financial Services, Inc., J. Stephen Putnam and David Lee Ullom

Admin. Proc. File No. 3-11692 (September 30, 2004)
http://www.sec.gov/litigation/admin/33-8499.htm

On September 30, 2004, the Commission instituted enforcement proceedings against Raymond James Financial Services, Inc., a registered broker-dealer and investment adviser headquartered in St. Petersburg, Fla., based on the conduct of one of its former brokers, Dennis Herula. In the Order Instituting Proceedings, the Enforcement Division alleges that, in 1999 and 2000, Herula and others fraudulently solicited a number of investors to deposit approximately $44.5 million in a Raymond James brokerage account held in the name of Brite Business, promising them astronomical returns with no risk if they did so. The Division alleges that Herula, acting in his capacity as a Raymond James registered representative, used Raymond James' facilities and letterhead to carry out the scheme. As alleged in the Order, approximately $16.5 million of the investor funds raised—most of which were subsequently transferred to Herula's wife's brokerage account at Raymond James—were dissipated and never returned to investors, and Herula and his wife misappropriated approximately $8.7 million of those funds. The Order also alleges that Raymond James, J. Stephen Putnam, the firm's former president and chief operating officer, and David Ullom, Herula's former branch manager, failed reasonably to supervise Herula

The Commission previously brought fraud charges against Herula and others in connection with the Brite Business scheme on April 1, 2002. A Rhode Island federal court froze Herula's assets and subsequently granted the Commission's request for a default judgment against Herula on Oct. 17, 2002. See Commission Litigation Release Nos. 17461 (April 5, 2002) [emergency civil injunctive action filed and temporary restraining orders entered against Herula, Capalbo, and others]; 17800 (Oct. 23, 2002) [permanent injunction entered against Dennis Herula]; and 17957 (Jan. 29, 2003) [permanent injunction entered against Dennis Herula's wife, Mary Lee Capalbo].

Failure to Supervise Cases

In the Matter of Donaldson, Lufkin & Jenrette Securities Corp., Predecessor in Interest to Credit Suisse First Boston LLC

Exchange Act Release No. 50272 (August 26, 2004)
http://www.sec.gov/litigation/admin/34-50272.htm

On August 26, 2004, the Commission instituted settled administrative proceedings against Donaldson, Lufkin & Jenrette Securities Corp. (DLJ), predecessor in interest to Credit Suisse First Boston LLC (CFSB) (collectively, Respondent). The Commission's order found that Respondent failed reasonably to supervise R. Christopher Hanna (Hanna) with a view to preventing and detecting his violations of the federal securities laws during a portion of the twelve-year period that it employed him, from November 1989 to May 2001.

In order to perpetrate the misappropriations, Hanna created false letters of authorization (LOAs), purportedly by signed by the customers, directing transfers from customer accounts. Hanna also made unauthorized securities transactions in approximately sixty customer accounts.

The Commission's order found that Respondent failed reasonably to supervise Hanna with a view to preventing or detecting his violations. The Commission censured CSFB and ordered that CSFB pay a civil money penalty in the amount of $1,000,000. In addition, the Commission ordered CSFB to comply with certain undertakings, including retaining an independent consultant to review and evaluate the effectiveness of CSFB's supervisory and compliance systems, policies and procedures designed to detect and prevent violations of the federal securities laws.

V. MUTUAL FUNDS AND INVESTMENT ADVISERS

SEC v. K.L. Group, LLC, et al.

Litigation Release No. 19117 (March 3, 2005)
http://www.sec.gov/litigation/litreleases/lr19117.htm

On March 2, 2005, the Commission announced the filing of an emergency enforcement action to halt an ongoing hedge fund fraud concerning three related hedge fund investment advisers, multiple hedge funds, a registered broker-dealer and the principals that control these entities. The Commission's complaint names as defendants the hedge funds, KL Group Fund, LLC , KL Financial Group Florida, LLC, KL Financial Group DB Fund, LLC, KL Financial Group DC Fund, LLC, KL Financial Group IR Fund, LLC and KL Triangulum Group Fund, LLC (collectively "the Funds"), the unregistered hedge fund investment advisers, K.L. Group, LLC, KL Florida, LLC and KL Triangulum Management, LLC (collectively "the Advisers"), the principals of the investment advisers and hedge funds, Won Sok Lee (Lee), John Kim and Yung Bae Kim (Yung Kim) and Shoreland Trading, LLC (Shoreland), an Irvine, California based broker-dealer that defendant Lee controlled and that conducted all of the trading for the various hedge funds.

The Commission's complaint alleges that from approximately 1999 to the present, the Defendants have raised at least $81 million from investors nationwide by boasting annualized returns of 125 to 150% over the last several years and by sending false account statements to investors showing similar gains. According to the complaint, the hedge funds were suffering tremendous trading losses and only about $11 million remains of the more than $81 million that investors put into the hedge funds.

Acting on the Commission's request for emergency relief, Judge Kenneth L. Ryskamp of the United States District Court for the Southern District of Florida in West Palm Beach today issued temporary restraining orders, asset freezes and other relief against the defendants. The Court also appointed a receiver over all of the entities named in the Commission's action.

In the Matter of Brean Murray & Co, Inc.

Admin. Proc. File No. 3-11836 (February 17, 2005)
http://www.sec.gov/litigation/admin/34-51219.htm

On February 17, the Commission brought and settled an enforcement action against Brean Murray & Co., Inc., which is located in New York City and has been registered with the Commission as a broker-dealer since 1973.

The Order finds that, from August 2001 through September 2003, Brean Murray, on behalf of Canary Capital Partners LLC (Canary) and at least four other hedge fund customers, accepted and executed more than 3,500 trades in dozens of mutual funds after 4:00 p.m. Eastern Time, the time as of which those funds calculated their respective Net Asset Value (NAV). Brean Murray received and executed through its clearing broker the overwhelming majority of these trades after 5:00 p.m. This practice, also known as "late trading," violated Rule 22c-1 under the Investment Company Act. The Order also finds that in August 2001, at the request of Canary, Brean Murray began entering mutual fund trades directly into its clearing broker's platform as late as 5:45 p.m., but almost always after 4:00 p.m. ET. Shortly thereafter Brean Murray started entering late trades on behalf of its other hedge fund customers.

The Commission censured Brean Murray, and ordered Brean Murray to cease and desist from committing or causing any violations and any future violations of Rule 22c-1 under the Investment Company Act, to pay a civil penalty in the amount of $150,000, and to comply with certain specified undertakings.

SEC v. Northshore Asset Management et al.

Litigation Release No. 19084 (February 16, 2005)
http://www.sec.gov/litigation/litreleases/lr19084.htm

On February 16, 2005, the Commission announced that it filed an emergency enforcement action to halt fraudulent conduct concerning two hedge funds, Ardent Research Partners, L.P. ("Ardent Domestic") and Ardent Research Partners, Ltd. ("Ardent Offshore") (collectively, "the Ardent Funds"), against Northshore Asset Management, LLC ("Northshore"), Ardent Domestic, Ardent Offshore, Saldutti Capital Management, L.P. ("SCM"), Kevin Kelley ("Kelley"), Robert Wildeman ("Wildeman"), and Glenn Sherman ("Sherman") (collectively, the "Defendants").

The Complaint alleges that from April 2003 to the present, Northshore and its principals have diverted approximately $37 million of the Ardent Funds' assets to their control and invested them in illiquid securities of, and made loans to, entities in which Northshore and its principals have an interest. The Commission alleges that the Defendants did not disclose to the Ardent Funds' investors that Northshore had purchased SCM and that Northshore was managing a significant portion of the Ardent Funds' assets. Additionally, the Defendants made numerous misrepresentations concerning (i) the nature of the investments, (ii) the liquidity of the investments, and (iii) the use of investor funds for undisclosed loans. For the last several months, the Defendants have refused to honor valid redemption requests from Ardent Domestic investors.

In the Matter of Banc of America Capital Management, LLC, BACAP Distributors, LLC, and Bank of America Securities, LLC

Admin. Proc. File No. 3-11818 (February 9, 2005)
http://www.sec.gov/litigation/admin/33-8538.htm

On February 9, 2005, the Commission brought and settled an enforcement action against Banc of America Capital Management, LLC (BACAP), BACAP Distributors, LLC (BACAP Distributors) and Banc of America Securities, LLC (BAS) for entering into improper and undisclosed agreements that allowed favored large investors to engage in rapid short-term securities trading known as market timing in certain Nations Funds mutual funds and for fraudulently facilitating market timing and late trading in Nations Funds mutual funds as well as unaffiliated mutual funds. The Commission's Order detailed the conduct of Bank of America on three levels—as a mutual fund adviser, as a broker and as a clearing firm. As a fund adviser, BACAP permitted timing in its own funds. As a broker and clearing firm, BAS enabled late trading and market timing in many other mutual funds.

The Commission ordered BACAP, BACAP Distributors and BAS to pay $375 million, consisting of $250 million in disgorgement and $125 million in penalties. The money will be distributed to the mutual funds and their shareholders that were harmed as a result of market timing and late trading in Nations Funds and other mutual funds. The Commission also censured BACAP, BACAP Distributors and BAS, ordered them to undertake certain remedial actions to strengthen their oversight of compliance with the federal securities laws, and ordered that they cease and desist from further violations.

In the Matter of Columbia Management Advisors, Inc. and Columbia Funds Distributor, Inc.

Admin Proc. File No. 3-11814 (February 9, 2005)
http://www.sec.gov/litigation/admin/33-8534.htm

On February 9, 2005, the Commission brought and settled an enforcement action against Columbia Management Advisors, Inc. (Columbia Advisors) which during the relevant period was a wholly owned subsidiary of Fleet National Bank, Columbia Funds Distributor, Inc. (Columbia Distributor), and three former Columbia executives in connection with undisclosed market timing arrangements in the Columbia Funds. In settling the matter, the Columbia entities will pay $140 million, all of which will be distributed to investors harmed by the conduct. In separate orders, the SEC found that Peter Martin, former national sales manager, entered into several undisclosed timing arrangements that were inconsistent with the funds' prospectus disclosures, and that Erik Gustafson, formerly a Columbia portfolio manager, breached his fiduciary duty to the funds by approving four such arrangements. In addition, the SEC found that Joseph Palombo, formerly the chief operating officer of Columbia Advisors and chairman of the board of several Columbia funds, ignored indications of improper trading and failed to take appropriate action.

The Commission's administrative order against Columbia Advisors and Columbia Distributor found that, from at least 1998 through 2003, Columbia Distributor secretly entered into arrangements with at least nine companies and individuals allowing them to engage in frequent short-term trading in at least seven Columbia funds. In connection with certain of the arrangements, Columbia Distributor and Columbia Advisors accepted so-called "sticky assets"- long-term investments that were to remain in place in return for allowing the investors to actively trade in the funds. Columbia Advisors knew and approved of all but one of the arrangements and allowed them to continue despite knowing such short-term trading could be detrimental to long-term shareholders in the funds. The special arrangements were never disclosed to long-term shareholders or to the independent trustees of the Columbia funds. In addition to trading made pursuant to specific arrangements, the Commission's order found that Columbia allowed or failed to prevent hundreds of other accounts from engaging in a practice of short-term or excessive trading.

SEC v. James Tambone and Robert Hussey

Litigation Release. No. 19069 (February 9, 2005)
http://www.sec.gov/litigation/litreleases/lr19069.htm

On February 9, 2005, the Commission filed a civil fraud action in federal district court against two former executives of Columbia Funds Distributor Inc. in connection with undisclosed market timing arrangements in the Columbia complex of mutual funds. In its complaint, the Commission alleged that James Tambone, the former president of Columbia Funds Distributor, and Robert Hussey, a former senior sales executive, entered into or approved undisclosed timing arrangements with multiple investors that benefited the executives but were detrimental to long-term fund shareholders. According to the Commission, Tambone and Hussey acted improperly in entering and accepting the short-term trading arrangements, because the arrangements were never disclosed to long-term fund shareholders or the independent trustees of the funds and in most instances were directly contrary to the disclosures made in the prospectuses used to sell the mutual funds.

In the Matter of Southwest Securities, Inc., Daniel R. Leland, Kerry M. Rigdon and Kevin J. Marsh

Exchange Act Release No. 51002
http://www.sec.gov/litigation/admin/34-51002.htm

SEC v. Scott B. Gann and George B. Fasciano

Litigation Release No. 19027 (January 10, 2005)
http://www.sec.gov/litigation/litreleases/lr19027.htm

On January 10, 2005, the Commission and the NYSE brought settled enforcement proceedings against Southwest Securities, Inc., a Dallas, Texas based broker-dealer and investment adviser, and three of its managers. According to the Commission and NYSE, Southwest and the managers failed reasonably to supervise brokers in Southwest's downtown Dallas branch office who engaged in fraudulent mutual fund market timing schemes, late trading of mutual fund shares, or both. The Commission asserted that Southwest brokers used "masking activities," such as multiple customer accounts, multiple broker identification numbers, and multiple branch office numbers, to disguise their customers' market timing trades and trick the fund companies into accepting the trades. The Commission also filed a civil action in U.S. district court in Dallas against two former Southwest brokers, Scott B. Gann and George B. Fasciano, for allegedly engaging in a fraudulent market timing scheme.

Southwest agreed to pay a total of $10 million, consisting of $2 million in disgorgement and an $8 million civil money penalty, and to undertake a number of measures to prevent future misconduct.

In the Matter of Edward D. Jones & Co., L.P.

Securities Act Release No. 8520 (December 22, 2004)
http://www.sec.gov/litigation/admin/33-8520.htm

On December 22, 2004, the Commission, NASD and the New York Stock Exchange brought settled enforcement proceedings against Edward D. Jones & Co., L.P., a registered broker-dealer headquartered in St. Louis, Missouri, related to allegations that Edward Jones failed to adequately disclose revenue sharing payments that it received from a select group of mutual fund families that Edward Jones recommended to its customers. As part of the settlement of all three proceedings, Edward Jones will pay $75 million in disgorgement and civil penalties. All of that money will be placed in a Fair Fund for distribution to Edward Jones customers. Edward Jones also agreed to disclose on its public Web site information regarding revenue sharing payments and hire an independent consultant to review and make recommendations about the adequacy of Edward Jones' disclosures.

According to the Commission's Order, Edward Jones told the public and its clients that it was promoting the sale of certain mutual funds because of the funds' long-term investment objectives and performance. At the same time, Edward Jones failed to disclose that it received tens of millions of dollars from the funds or their affiliates each year, on top of commissions and other fees, for selling these mutual funds. Edward Jones also exclusively promoted the 529 college savings plans offered by its Preferred Families over all other 529 plans that it had available to sell.

In the Matter of Franklin Advisers, Inc. and Franklin/Templeton Distributors, Inc.

Exchange Act Release No. 50841 (December 13, 2004)
http://www.sec.gov/litigation/admin/34-50841.htm

On December 13, 2004, the Commission filed settled charges against Franklin Advisers, Inc. (FA) and Franklin Templeton Distributors, Inc. (FTDI) (collectively, Franklin), the investment adviser and principal underwriter and distributor affiliated with the Franklin Templeton mutual funds, alleging that Franklin, without proper disclosure, used fund assets to compensate brokerage firms for recommending the Franklin Templeton mutual funds over others to their clients. This practice is known as compensating brokerage firms for "shelf space." The Commission's order finds, and Franklin neither admits nor denies, that between 2001 and 2003, FTDI had shelf space agreements with 39 broker-dealers pursuant to which FTDI allocated $52 million from brokerage commissions related to trades of fund shares (which were fund assets) to the broker-dealers in exchange for shelf space. Franklin did not adequately disclose these agreements to the fund boards or the fund shareholders. Franklin agreed to pay $1 in disgorgement and a $20 million penalty as well as undergo certain compliance reforms.

In the Matter of Gary L. Pilgrim

Admin. Proc. File No. 3-11739 (November 17, 2004)
http://www.sec.gov/litigation/admin/33-8505.htm

In the Matter of Harold J. Baxter

Admin. Proc. File No. 3-11740 (November 17, 2004)
http://www.sec.gov/litigation/admin/33-8506.htm

SEC v. Gary L. Pilgrim, Harold J. Baxter, and Pilgrim Baxter & Associates, Ltd.

Litigation Release No. 18474 (November 20, 2003)
http://www.sec.gov/litigation/litreleases/lr18474.htm

In the Matter of Pilgrim Baxter & Associates, LTD

Administrative Proceeding File No. 3-11524 (June 21, 2004)
http://www.sec.gov/litigation/admin/ia-2251.htm

On November 20, 2003, the Commission ultimately settled in administrative proceedings an action that was filed in federal district court against

Gary L. Pilgrim, Harold J. Baxter, and Pilgrim Baxter & Associates, Ltd. (Pilgrim Baxter), a registered investment adviser. The Commission charged them with fraud and breach of fiduciary duty in connection with market timing of the PBHG Funds. Pilgrim was the President, Chief Investment Officer and Director of Pilgrim Baxter & Associates, and the President of the PBHG Funds. Baxter was the CEO and Chairman of Pilgrim Baxter & Associates, and the Chairman and trustee of the PBHG Funds and the PBHG Insurance Series Fund.

The Commission's complaint alleged that the defendants permitted a hedge fund in which Pilgrim and his wife had a substantial interest, Appalachian Trails, to engage in market timing of the high profile Growth Fund that Pilgrim himself managed. The complaint also alleges that Baxter provided non-public PBHG Fund portfolio information to a close friend at Wall Street Discount Corporation, who then passed this information to Wall Street Discount customers who used the portfolio information to market time the PBHG funds and to exercise hedging strategies through other financial and brokerage institutions. The Commission ordered Pilgrim Baxter to pay $90 million—$ 40 million in disgorgement and $50 million in civil penalties. Pilgrim Baxter further agreed to undertake a series of compliance and mutual fund governance reforms.

Under the terms of the Commission's order, Baxter and Pilgrim must each pay $80 million – $60 million in disgorgement and $20 million in civil penalties. This $160 million will be combined with the $90 million paid by Pilgrim, Baxter & Associates, Ltd. (PBA) in July 2004 and ultimately will be distributed to injured investors.

<u>In the Matter of Fremont Investment Advisors, Inc.</u>

Admin. Proc. File No. 3-11726 (November 4, 2004)
http://www.sec.gov/litigation/admin/ia-2317.htm

On November 4, 2004, the Commission charged San Francisco-based mutual fund adviser Fremont Investment Advisors with entering into improper and undisclosed agreements that allowed favored large investors to engage in rapid short-term securities trading known as market timing. Also charged by the Commission for their role in Fremont's improper market timing arrangements were former President and CEO Nancy Tengler, and former Vice President of Institutional Sales Larry Adams. In addition to the market timing charges, the Commission charged Fremont for allowing mutual fund trades to be placed after the 4:00 p.m. market close.

Fremont, agreed to pay $4.146 million to settle the Commission's fraud charges. Tengler has also agreed to settle the Commission's action, agreeing to pay $127,000 in disgorgement and penalties and to be suspended from the industry for six months. The Commission is litigating the action against Adams.

In the Matter of RS Investment, Inc., RS Investment Management, L.P., G. Randall Hecht and Steven M. Cohen

Admin. Proc. File No. 3-11696 (October 6, 2004)
http://www.sec.gov/litigation/admin/ia-2130.htm

On October 6, 2004, the Commission charged investment adviser RS Investment Management LP (RS), CEO G. Randall Hecht, and former CFO Steven M. Cohen with favoring certain mutual fund investors by allowing then to engage in frequent short-term trading (market timing). According to the Commission, RS entered into secret agreements that permitted select investors to generate millions of dollars in trading profits at the potential expense of other shareholders, and allowed RS to reap substantial advisory fees.

RS, a San Francisco-based investment adviser for ten mutual funds, has agreed to pay $25 million to settle the Commission's fraud charges, including disgorgement of $11.5 million and a civil penalty of $13.5 million. These amounts will be distributed to investors of mutual funds affected by the market timing. RS will also undertake significant compliance measures designed to protect against future violations. Hecht and Cohen have also agreed to pay monetary penalties and to other remedial actions.

In the Matter of PA Fund Management LLC, PEA Capital LLC, and PA Distributors LLC

Admin. Proc. File No. 3-11661 (September 15, 2004)
http://www.sec.gov/litigation/admin/34-50384.pdf

On September 15, 2004, the Commission instituted a settled enforcement action against the investment adviser, sub-adviser, and principal underwriter and distributor for the PIMCO Funds and Multi-Manager Series funds (the PIMCO MMS Funds). The suit charged the entities with failing to disclose to the PIMCO MMS Funds' Board of Trustees and shareholders material facts and conflicts of interest that arose from their use of directed brokerage on the PIMCO MMS Funds' portfolio transactions to pay for "shelf space" arrangements with selected broker-dealers.

The entities, PA Fund Management LLC (PAFM), PEA Capital LLC (PEA) and PA Distributors LLC (PAD), agreed to pay over $11.6 million in disgorgement and penalties and to undertake significant disclosure and compliance reforms.

In the Matter of Charles Schwab & Co., Inc.

Admin. Proc. File No. 3-11648 (September 14, 2004)
http://www.sec.gov/litigation/admin/34-50360.htm

On September 14, 2004, the Commission instituted settled public administrative and cease-and-desist proceedings against Charles Schwab & Co., Inc. The Commission charged that Schwab allowed investment adviser customers to change mutual fund orders after the 4:00 p.m. Eastern time market close, creating the risk that such customers could unfairly capitalize on late-breaking news at the expense of other mutual fund investors. Schwab consented to the entry of an order that it cease and desist from such violations and pay a $350,000 civil penalty, and is censured for its misconduct.

The Commission found that, since at least January 2001, Schwab engaged in a practice of allowing its investment adviser customers to change mutual fund orders after market close under certain circumstances and still receive that day's fund price. This occurred when a customer's original pre-4:00 p.m. mutual fund order was rejected by Schwab's computer system (such as when the customer had been banned from trading in a particular mutual fund or the mutual fund was closed to new investors). Schwab permitted the adviser to submit a substitute order in a different mutual fund. According to the Commission's Order, on hundreds of occasions since 2001, Schwab personnel contacted customers after the 4:00 p.m. market close and allowed the customer to submit a substitute order in a different fund while still receiving the current day's price. Schwab's practice of processing the substitute purchase order at the current day's price violated Rule 22c-1(a) under the Investment Company Act, which requires orders for mutual fund shares placed after 4:00 p.m. to receive the next day's fund price.

The Commission's Order does not find that Schwab personnel entered into any improper agreements with customers allowing the substitute orders, or that Schwab's customers engaged in any scheme to exploit Schwab's order entry process or circumvent its controls. However, Schwab's practice of allowing investment advisers to substitute mutual fund orders created a risk that investment advisers and their clients could capitalize on post-market close information by trading after hours based on stale fund prices. Schwab ceased the practice in October 2003, following an inquiry by the Commission staff and the initiation of an internal investigation by Schwab.

In the Matter of Bridgeway Capital Management, Inc. and John Noland Ryan Montgomery

Admin. Proc. File No. 3-11659 (September 15, 2004)
http://www.sec.gov/litigation/admin/ia-2294.htm

On September 15, 2004, the Commission instituted settled enforcement proceedings against Bridgeway Capital Management (Bridgeway), and its president, John Noland Ryan Montgomery, in connection with more than $4.4 million in illegal performance-based fees that Bridgeway charged to three of its mutual funds. The settlement requires that Bridgeway undertake certain compliance reforms and reimburse the affected fund shareholders $4,407,700, plus prejudgment interest of $458,764, and that Bridgeway and Montgomery pay penalties of $250,000 and $50,000, respectively.

In the Matter of Garrett Van Wagoner and Van Wagoner Capital Management, Inc.

Admin. Proc. File No. 3-11611 (August 26, 2004)
http://www.sec.gov/litigation/admin/ia-2281.htm

On August 26, 2004, the Commission instituted settled fraud proceedings against Van Wagoner Capital Management, Inc. (VWCM), the investment adviser to the Van Wagoner Funds, Inc. (the Funds), and Garrett Van Wagoner, the president of VWCM, relating to their misstatement of the valuations of certain securities held by the Funds. The Commission's Order found that Van Wagoner and VWCM misled the Funds' shareholders about the size and value of the Funds' investments in illiquid securities (securities that were not publicly traded or could not be sold readily), which obscured the fact that the Funds' holdings in those securities exceeded the limits promised in the Funds' shareholder disclosures. The settlement includes an $800,000 penalty from Van Wagoner and VWCM, a seven-year prohibition on Van Wagoner serving as an officer or director of a mutual fund, and a seven-year restriction on certain of Van Wagoner's activities with the investment adviser and compliance reforms by VWCM.

The Commission also announced actions against and settlements with: a former director of the Funds, Robert Colman, who purchased private equity securities in transactions at the same time as the Funds without first obtaining an order from the Commission permitting such joint investments; and a former private equity analyst of VWCM, Audrey L. Buchner, for prohibited, personal trading in the same public securities that the Funds also held or purchased, and omissions she made that concealed the overlap with the Funds' trading.

In the Matter of Janus Capital Management LLC

Admin. Proc. File No. 3-11590 (August 18, 2004)
http://www.sec.gov/litigation/admin/ia-2277.htm

On August 18, 2004, the Commission settled an enforcement action against Janus Capital Management LLC (JCM), a registered investment adviser based in Denver, Colorado, for entering into undisclosed market timing agreements with certain investors. JCM negotiated market timing agreements with 12 entities pursuant to which these entities were permitted to market time certain Janus mutual funds. At the same time JCM entered into these agreements, the prospectuses for the funds being timed stated, or at least strongly implied, that JCM did not permit frequent trading or market timing in these funds. Some of JCM's market timing agreements were entered into with the understanding that the market timer would make long term investments, so-called "sticky assets," in certain Janus mutual funds. In addition, JCM waived all redemption fees that would have otherwise been assessed against the market timers for their frequent trading activity.

The Commission ordered JCM to pay disgorgement of $50 million and civil penalties of $50 million, for a total payment of $100 million. JCM also consented to a cease-and-desist order and a censure, and agreed to undertake certain compliance and mutual-fund governance reforms.

SEC v. William A. DiBella and North Cove Ventures, LLC

Litigation Release No. 18829 (August 12, 2004)
http://www.sec.gov/litigation/lr18829.htm

In the Matter of Thayer Capital Partners, TC Equity Partners IV, LLC, TC Management Partners IV, LLC, and Frederic V. Malek

Admin. Proc. File No. 3-11585 (August 12, 2004)
http://www.sec.gov/litigation/admin/33-8457.htm

On August 12, 2004, the Commission filed a civil fraud action against William A. DiBella, the former Majority Leader of the Connecticut State Senate, and his consulting firm, North Cove Ventures, LLC., in Connecticut federal district court. The complaint alleged that, beginning in

November 1998, DiBella and North Cove participated in a fraudulent scheme with the then Treasurer of the State of Connecticut, Paul J. Silvester, concerning Silvester's investment of $75 million of the state pension funds with Thayer Capital Partners, a Washington, DC-based private equity firm. According to the complaint, Silvester used the investment to reward DiBella, his friend and political supporter, for past and anticipated future services. In connection with the investment, Silvester requested that Thayer, through its chairman, Frederic V. Malek, hire DiBella. Thayer agreed to retain DiBella and to pay him a percentage of the state pension fund's total investment with Thayer, even though DiBella had no prior involvement with the transaction and ultimately performed no meaningful work related to the investment. DiBella understood from Silvester that there was no work to be done on the deal.

The Commission also instituted separate, but related, settled administrative and cease-and-desist proceedings against Thayer, Malek, and two Thayer affiliates, TC Equity Partners IV, LLC and TC Management Partners IV, LLC, concerning their failure to disclose to the state pension fund that, at the request of Silvester, they retained and paid DiBella nearly $375,000 in connection with the state pension fund's investment with a Thayer private equity fund, Thayer Equity Investors IV, LP. Without admitting or denying the Commission's findings, Thayer, Malek, and the two Thayer affiliates consented to the issuance of an order censuring them and requiring them to cease and desist from violating certain provisions of the federal securities laws. The Commission also ordered Thayer to pay a civil penalty of $150,000 and Malek to pay a civil penalty of $100,000.

In the Matter of CIHC, Inc., Conseco Services, LLC, and Conseco Equity Sales, Inc.

Administrative Proceeding File No. 3-11578 (August 9, 2004)
http://www.sec.gov/litigation/admin/33-8455.pdf

In the Matter of Inviva Inc., and Jefferson National Life Insurance Company

Administrative Proceeding File No. 3-11579 (August 9, 2004)
http://www.sec.gov/litigation/admin/33-8456.pdf

On August 9, 2004, the Commission brought and settled the first enforcement action charging insurance companies with securities fraud for facilitating market timing of mutual funds through the sale of variable annuities. The insurance companies were subsidiaries of Conseco, Inc. (CIHC, Inc., Conseco Services, LLC, and Conseco Equity Sales, Inc.), and the company to which Conseco sold its variable annuity business in 2002, Inviva, Inc., and its subsidiary Jefferson National Life Insurance Company. The Commission's Orders found that the prospectuses through which the insurance companies sold the variable annuities misleadingly represented, among other things, that the annuities were "not designed for professional market timing organizations." In fact, the insurance companies affirmatively marketed and sold the annuities to professional market timers. Eventually, market timing assets constituted the majority of assets invested in the variable annuity products. The insurance companies profited by the fees earned from the sales of the annuities to the market timers.

Under the settlements, CIHC, Conseco Services, and CES agreed to pay $15 million, including disgorgement of $7.5 million and civil penalties of $7.5 million. Inviva and Jefferson National paid $5 million, including disgorgement of $3.5 million and a civil penalty of $1.5 million. These amounts were distributed to shareholders of mutual funds affected by the market timing. Inviva and Jefferson National also undertook compliance measures to protect against future violations.

In the Matter of Franklin Advisors Inc.

Administrative Proceeding File No. 3-11572 (August 2, 2004)
http://www.sec.gov/litigation/admin/ia-2271.pdf

On August 2, 2004, Franklin Advisers, Inc., an investment adviser firm in the fourth largest mutual fund complex in the U.S., agreed to pay $50 million dollars and undergo compliance reforms to settle charges by the Commission that it allowed rapid in-and-out trading, known as market timing, in mutual funds it managed, contrary to fund prospectus language. Franklin failed to disclose that over 30 identified market timers were allowed to freely market time for several months in 2000, contrary to prospectus language that indicated market timing would be monitored and restricted.

Under the settlement, Franklin paid $50 million, including disgorgement of $30 million and a civil penalty of $20 million. These amounts were distributed to shareholders of mutual funds affected by the market timing. Franklin also undertook compliance measures designed to protect against future violations.

In the Matter of Banc One Investment Advisors Corporation and Mark A. Beeson

Administrative Proceeding File No. 3-11530 (June 29, 2004)
http://www.sec.gov/litigation/admin/ia-2254.htm

In June of 2004, the Commission settled an enforcement action against Banc One Investment Advisors Corporation (BOIA), a registered investment adviser based in Columbus, Ohio, and Mark A. Beeson, former President and CEO of One Group Mutual Funds (One Group) and Senior Managing Director of BOIA. Among other things, the Commission found that BOIA violated, and Beeson aided and abetted and caused violations of, the federal securities laws by: (1) allowing excessive short-term trading in One Group funds by hedge-fund manager Edward J. Stern in the hope of attracting additional business, which created a conflict of interest because the trading increased BOIA's advisory fees but was potentially harmful to One Group funds; (2) failing to charge Stern redemption fees as required by One Group's international-fund prospectuses when other investors were charged the redemption fees; (3) having no written procedures in place to prevent the nonpublic disclosure of One Group portfolio holdings and improperly providing confidential portfolio holdings to Stern when other shareholders were not provided the same information; and (4) causing One Group funds to participate in joint transactions (a BOIA affiliate loaned money to Stern for the purpose of market-timing), raising a conflict of interest.

The Commission ordered BOIA to pay disgorgement of $10 million and a civil penalty of $40 million and ordered Beeson to pay a civil penalty of $100,000. BOIA also consented to a cease-and-desist order and a censure, and agreed to undertake certain compliance and mutual-fund governance reforms. In addition, Beeson consented to a two-year bar from the mutual-fund industry and a three-year prohibition on serving as an officer or director of a mutual fund or investment adviser.

In the Matter of Strong Capital Management, Inc., Strong Investor Services, Inc., Strong Investments, Inc., Richard S. Strong, Thomas A. Hooker, Jr. and Anthony J. D'Amato

Administrative Proceeding No. 3-11498 (May 20, 2004)
http://www.sec.gov/litigation/admin/34-49741.htm

In May of 2004, the Commission brought and settled an enforcement action against Strong Capital Management, Inc. (SCM), its founder and majority owner, Richard S. Strong, two affiliated entities and two other

SCM executives, for allowing and, in the case of Strong, engaging in undisclosed frequent trading in Strong mutual funds in violation of their fiduciary duties to the Strong funds and their investors. According to the Order, SCM entered into an express agreement with hedge fund manager Edward Stern allowing his hedge funds (the Canary hedge funds) to market time certain Strong funds, in order to obtain non-mutual fund business from Stern and his family. Under SCM's policies and procedures, other shareholders would have been ejected from the Strong funds for engaging in similar trading.

The Order further found that Richard Strong also engaged in frequent trading in several Strong funds, including one fund he managed. Between 1998 and 2003, he engaged in several hundred such trades, making gross profits of $4.1 million and net profits of $1.6 million. SCM failed to disclose the arrangement with Stern, and Strong and SCM failed to disclose Strong's personal trading, to the Strong funds' Boards of Directors or shareholders.

Based on these findings, the Commission ordered SCM to pay $40 million in disgorgement and $40 million in civil penalties and Strong to pay $30 million in disgorgement and $30 million in civil penalties. In addition, the Commission barred Strong from association with any investment adviser, investment company, broker, dealer, municipal securities dealer or transfer agent. The other two SCM executives also received sanctions.

SEC v. PIMCO Advisors Fund Management LLC, PIMCO Advisors Fund Management LLC, PEA Capital LLC f/k/a/ PIMCO Equity Advisors LLC, PIMCO Advisors Distributors LLC, Stephen J. Treadway, and Kenneth W. Corba

Litigation Release No. 18697 (May 6, 2004)
http://www.sec.gov/litigation/ litreleases/lr18697.htm

PIMCO Equity Mutual Funds' Adviser, Sub-Adviser, and Distributor to Pay $50 Million to Settle Fraud Charges for Undisclosed Market Timing

Press Release No. 2004-127 (September 13, 2004)
http://www.sec.gov/news/press/2004-127.htm

During May of 2004, the Commission ultimately settled certain aspects of an enforcement action it filed in federal district court against PIMCO Advisors Fund Management LLC (PAFM), PEA Capital LLC (PEA), PIMCO Advisors Distributors LLC (PAD), Stephen J. Treadway (the chief executive officer of PAFM and PAD as well as the chairman of the board of trustees for the PIMCO Funds: Multi-Manager Series), and Kenneth W. Corba (PEA's former CEO) for their defrauding of PIMCO mutual fund investors, in connection with an undisclosed market timing arrangement with Canary Capital Partners LLC. From February 2002 to April 2003, Canary engaged in approximately 108 round-trip exchanges in an aggregate amount of over $4 billion in several PIMCO Funds pursuant to its special market timing arrangement.

PAFM, PEA, and PAD (collectively, the PIMCO Entities) ultimately agreed to settle these charges. Under the settlement, the PIMCO Entities have been ordered to pay $50 million, consisting of $10 million in disgorgement and a civil penalty of $40 million. Without admitting or denying the Commission's findings, the PIMCO Entities also consented to cease-and-desist orders, censures, and to undertake certain compliance and mutual fund governance reforms. The Commission's litigation in federal court continues against Stephen J. Treadway and Kenneth W. Corba.

In the Matter of Putnam Investment Management, LLC

Administrative Proceeding File No. 3-11317 (April 8, 2004)
http://www.sec.gov/litigation/admin/ia-2226.htm

In April 2004, the Commission brought and settled an enforcement action against Putnam Investment Management LLC (Putnam), pursuant to which the Commission ordered Putnam to pay a $50 million civil penalty and $5 million in disgorgement for violating federal securities laws by failing to disclose improper market timing trading by Putnam portfolio managers. All of the money obtained by the Commission was distributed to investors harmed by the market timing trading.

The Commission's Order called for the appointment of an Independent Distribution Consultant who is charged with developing a plan for distributing the $55 million in disgorgement and penalties to harmed investors. The $55 million was to be distributed to investors in order of priority: first, as compensation to investors for losses attributable to excessive short-term trading and market timing trading activity by Putnam employees and, second, as compensation for advisory fees paid by mutual fund clients who suffered such losses. This Order supplemented a Commission Order entered on Nov. 13, 2003 pursuant to which Putnam agreed to undertake significant and far-reaching corporate governance, compliance, and ethics reforms.

The Commission's previously filed civil injunctive action charging two Putnam employees, portfolio managers Justin M. Scott and Omid Kamshad, with securities fraud for engaging in excessive short-term trading of Putnam funds in their personal accounts, is pending.

The Securities Division for the Commonwealth of Massachusetts has also settled related charges against Putnam calling for the payment of an additional $55 million.

<u>In the Matter of Massachusetts Financial Services Company</u>

Administrative Proceeding File No. 3-11450 (March 31, 2004) *http://www.sec.gov/litigation/admin/ia-2224.htm*

On March 31, 2004, the Commission brought and settled an enforcement action against Massachusetts Financial Services Company (MFS) related to the company's use of mutual fund assets—namely, brokerage commissions on mutual fund transactions—to pay for the marketing and distribution of mutual funds in the MFS Fund Complex (MFS Funds). The Commission issued an order that found MFS failed to adequately disclose to the Boards of Trustees and to shareholders of the MFS Funds the specifics of its "shelf-space" arrangements with brokerage firms and the conflicts created by those arrangements

The Commission found that from at least Jan. 1, 2000, through Nov. 7, 2003, MFS negotiated bilateral arrangements, known as "Strategic Alliances," with approximately 100 broker-dealers. Under these arrangements, MFS directed brokerage commissions on fund portfolio transactions to the brokerage firms in exchange for heightened visibility within the brokerage firms' distribution networks.

MFS agreed to settle this matter, without admitting or denying the Commission's findings. The Commission's Order censured MFS and ordered it to cease-and-desist from providing false reports and records and from engaging in prohibited transactions. MFS was to make a nominal disgorgement payment and will pay $50 million in civil penalties. MFS was to distribute the penalty to the MFS Funds in accordance with a distribution plan approved by the Commission. MFS has also undertaken to direct an independent consultant to conduct a review of, and to provide recommendations concerning, MFS's policies and procedures with respect to its Strategic Alliances including its disclosures to the Boards and shareholders, and to adopt the recommendations of the independent consultant.

In the Matter of Massachusetts Financial Services Co., John W. Ballen, and Kevin R. Parke

Investment Advisers Act of 1940 Release No. 2213 (Feb. 5, 2004)
http://www.sec.gov/litigation/admin/ia-2213.htm

On February 5, 2004, the Commission brought and settled an enforcement action against Massachusetts Financial Services Co. (MFS), its chief executive officer John W. Ballen, and its president and chief equity officer Kevin R. Parke, for violating federal securities laws by allowing widespread market timing trading in certain MFS mutual funds in contravention of those funds' public disclosures.

The Commission censured MFS and ordered it to pay $225 million, consisting of $175 million in disgorgement and $50 million in penalties. The Commission's Order further required MFS to undertake certain compliance and mutual fund governance reforms designed to enhance the independence of mutual fund boards of trustees and strengthen oversight of MFS's compliance with the federal securities laws. For their roles in the misconduct, the Commission prohibited Ballen and Parke from serving as an officer or director of any investment adviser and from serving as an employee, officer, or trustee of any registered investment company for three years. In addition, the Commission's Order placed certain restrictions on the duties Ballen and Parke can perform during that period. The Commission also suspended Ballen and Parke from association with any investment adviser or registered investment company for nine months and six months, respectively, and ordered each to pay a penalty of $250,000 and disgorge over $50,000 in ill-gotten gains derived from MFS's market timing practices. All of the money paid by MFS, Ballen, and Parke was to be distributed to harmed shareholders.

Invesco Cases

SEC v. Invesco Funds Group, Inc. and Raymond R. Cunningham

Litigation Release No. 18482 (December 2, 2003)
http://www.sec.gov/litigation/litreleases/lr18482.htm

In the Matter of Invesco Funds Group, Inc., AIM Advisors, Inc., and AIM Distributors, Inc.

Admin. Proc. File No. 3-11701 (October 8, 2004)
http://www.sec.gov/litigation/admin/34-50506.htm

In the Matter of Raymond Cunningham

Admin. Proc. File No. 3-11702 (October 8, 2004)
http://www.sec.gov/litigation/admin/34-50507.htm

On December 2, 2003, the Commission filed suit in the United States District Court for the District of Colorado against Invesco Funds Group, Inc. (IFG), and Raymond R. Cunningham, alleging that the defendants fraudulently accepted investments by market timers in Invesco mutual funds to enhance the management fees earned by IFG.

On October 8, 2004, the Commission instituted settled enforcement actions against IFG, AIM Advisors, Inc. (AIM Advisors), and AIM Distributors, Inc. (ADI). The Commission issued an order finding that IFG, AIM Advisors, and ADI violated the federal securities laws by facilitating widespread market timing trading in mutual funds with which each entity was affiliated The settlements required IFG to pay $215 million in disgorgement and $110 million in civil penalties, and require AIM Advisors and ADI to pay, jointly and severally, $20 million in disgorgement and an aggregate $30 million in civil penalties. By a separate order, the Commission also announced a settled enforcement action against Raymond R. Cunningham, the former president and chief executive officer of IFG and a former member of the Invesco funds' board of directors, for his role in IFG's market timing program. That settlement required Cunningham to pay $1 in disgorgement and $500,000 in civil penalties.

From at least 2001 through July 2003, IFG entered into undisclosed market timing agreements with over 40 individuals and entities, which allowed them to market time certain Invesco funds. Some of the timing agreements were entered into with the understanding that the market timer would maintain long-term investments, so-called "sticky assets," in certain non-timed Invesco funds. At their height, the market timers held over $1 billion of the assets invested in the Invesco funds and made excessive exchanges and redemptions totaling approximately $58 billion. In the aggregate, the market timing trades made under the agreements were detrimental to the Invesco funds' shareholders.

Between January 2001 and September 2003 AIM Advisors entered into 10 negotiated, but undisclosed, market timing agreements with individuals and entities, allowing the timers to exceed AIM Funds' per-year 10-exchange limit, and to make trades, valued collectively at tens of millions of dollars, within AIM Funds. One of the timing agreements was entered into with the understanding that the market timer would make a long-term investment, or invest so-called "sticky assets," in certain AIM Funds.

In the Matter of Timothy J. Miller

Admin. Proc. File No. 3-11619 (August 30, 2004)
http://www.sec.gov/litigation/admin/ia-2289.htm

In the Matter of Thomas A. Kolbe

Admin. Proc. File No. 3-11618 (August 30, 2004)
http://www.sec.gov/litigation/admin/ia-2288.htm

In the Matter of Michael D. Legoski

Admin. Proc. File No. 3-11620 (August 30, 2004)
http://www.sec.gov/litigation/admin/34-50289.htm

On August 31, 2004, the Commission announced settled enforcement actions against Timothy J. Miller, the former chief investment officer and a portfolio manager for Invesco Funds Group, Inc. (IFG); Thomas A. Kolbe, the former national sales manager of IFG; and Michael D. Legoski, a former assistant vice president in IFG's sales department. The Commission issued orders alleging that Miller, Kolbe and Legoski violated federal securities laws by facilitating widespread market timing trading in certain Invesco funds in contravention of those funds' public disclosures.

The Commission ordered Miller, Kolbe and Legoski to pay $1 in disgorgement each, and penalties in the amounts of $150,000, $150,000 and $40,000, respectively. In addition, for their roles in the misconduct, the Commission prohibited Miller, Kolbe and Legoski from associating with an investment adviser or investment company for a period of one year, and further prohibited Miller and Kolbe from serving as an officer or director of an investment adviser or an investment company for three years and two years, respectively. The Commission also barred Legoski from associating with any broker or dealer for a period of one year.

The Commission's Orders found that Miller, Kolbe and Legoski aided and abetted IFG's violations of the Investment Advisers Act of 1940, and that Miller caused IFG's violation of the Investment Company Act of 1940. The Orders required each of them to cease and desist from violating or causing future violations of these provisions.

•

VI. INSIDER TRADING

SEC v. Robert Goehring

Litigation Release No. 19105 (February 28, 2005)
http://www.sec.gov/litigation/litreleases/lr19105.htm

On February 28, 2005, announced the filing of a contested insider trading case in the United States District Court for the District of Connecticut against Robert Goehring. In its Complaint, the Commission alleged that Goehring, age 64, was the director of corporate communications of Gerber Scientific, Inc. ("Gerber"). Goehring's duties included helping prepare company press releases – including those announcing earnings and other material corporate developments – and serving as the company's investor relations contact. In this position, Goehring regularly obtained material, non-public information about Gerber. The Commission alleges that, between July 1998 and April 2000, Goehring traded in the Gerber stock nine times on the basis of material, nonpublic information he obtained in the course of his employment as Gerber's director of corporate communications. Goehring allegedly enjoyed profits and avoided losses from these illicit trades of $94,016. In addition, the Commission alleges that Goehring tipped his close friend, Armund Ek, who was not employed at Gerber, with material, non-public information about Gerber on three occasions. Ek allegedly bought and sold Gerber stock based on these tips and had profits and avoided losses totaling $11,453 as a result of his trading.

The Commission complaint alleges that because of his position with Gerber, Goehring owed a fiduciary duty, or other duty of trust or confidence owed directly, indirectly or derivatively to Gerber and its shareholders. This included a duty to not trade Gerber shares on the basis of material, non-public information and to not communicate such information improperly to others. By engaging in insider trading and by tipping his friend Ek with material non-public information about Gerber, Goehring violated Section 10(b) of the Securities Exchange Act of 1934 ("Exchange Act"). Also, on February 28, 2005, the Office of the United States Attorney for the Southern District of New York announced the unsealing of an indictment against Goehring on related insider trading charges.

SEC v. Armund Ek

Litigation Release No. 19104 (February 28, 2005)
http://www.sec.gov/litigation/litreleases/lr19104.htm

The Securities and Exchange Commission announced the filing of a settled insider trading case in the United States District Court for the Southern District of New York against Armund Ek ("Ek"). In its Complaint, the Commission alleged that Ek was a close friend of Robert Goehring ("Goehring"), Gerber's director of corporate communications. In his capacity as director of corporate communications, Goehring received material, nonpublic information about earnings results and other significant corporate developments at Gerber. Ek both bought and sold Gerber stock on three occasions based on tips of material, nonpublic information about Gerber that Goehring provided. Ek had profits and avoided losses totaling $11,438.

The Commission alleged that on each of the three occasions, Goehring knowingly or recklessly communicated the material, nonpublic information to Ek in breach of the duty of trust and confidence that he owed to Gerber and its shareholders. Ek knew or should have known that he was trading on the basis of material, nonpublic information that Goehring communicated to him in breach of that duty of trust and confidence.

As a result of his conduct, Ek violated Section 10(b) of the Securities Exchange Act of 1934 ("Exchange Act") and Exchange Act Rule 10b-5. Without admitting or denying the allegations in the Commission's Complaint, Ek consented to the entry of a judgment (i) permanently enjoining him from future violations of antifraud provisions of the federal securities laws, (ii) ordering disgorgement of profits and losses avoided of $11,438 plus prejudgment interest of $3,511, and (iii) imposing a civil penalty of $10,798.

SEC v. Patricia B. Rocklage, William M. Beaver and David G. Jones

Litigation Release No. 19032 (January 13, 2005)
http://www.sec.gov/litigation/litreleases/lr19032.htm

On January 12, 2005, the Commission filed an insider trading action involving trading in the common stock of Massachusetts-based Cubist Pharmaceuticals, Inc. against Patricia B. Rocklage, the wife of Scott M. Rocklage, Cubist's former Chairman and CEO, William M. Beaver, Patricia Rocklage's brother, and David G. Jones, Beaver's best friend and neighbor.

In its complaint, the Commission alleges that, on December 31, 2001, Scott Rocklage informed Patricia B. Rocklage of the negative results of a clinical trial involving one of Cubist's most important products, Cidecin. The complaint also alleges that, unbeknownst to her husband, Ms. Rocklage had a pre-existing understanding with her brother whereby she would give him "a wink and a nod" if she ever became aware of any bad news about Cubist that might affect its stock price. According to the complaint, shortly after learning about the trial results, Ms. Rocklage told her husband that she intended to signal Beaver to sell his Cubist stock. The complaint states that Scott Rocklage urged his wife not to take this action. The complaint asserts that, notwithstanding her husband's entreaties, by no later than the morning of January 2, 2002, Ms. Rocklage provided "a wink and a nod" to Beaver, who, at approximately 10 a.m. that day, sold all 5,583 shares of Cubist stock that he owned or controlled. The complaint further contends that, after receiving the signal from his sister, Beaver tipped his best friend and neighbor, Jones, who proceeded to sell all 7,500 shares of Cubist stock that he owned on the morning of January 3, 2002. Following the post market close announcement of the trial results on January 16, 2002, Cubist's stock price dropped by 46%, from a closing price of $31.75 that day to a closing price of $17.02 on January 17, 2002. By selling when they did, Beaver and Jones avoided losses of $99,527 and $133,222, respectively.

<u>SEC v. Eric I. Tsao</u>

Litigation Release No. 18889 (September 17, 2004)
http://www.sec.gov/litigation/litreleases/lr18889.htm

On September 17, 2004, the Commission announced that it has reached a settlement of its pending insider trading charges against Eric I. Tsao, a former executive at MedImmune, Inc., a biotechnology company based in Gaithersburg, Maryland. The Commission's complaint, originally filed on June 2, 2003, alleged that Tsao engaged in three separate episodes of insider trading between September 1999 and December 2001, from which he realized aggregate illicit profits of $146,850. The Commission's Complaint also alleged that when Tsao testified before the SEC staff during the investigation of this matter, he falsely denied having placed or authorized any of the relevant trades in two of the three separate instances of insider trading – and provided a false alternative explanation for the trading.

Without admitting or denying the allegations of the Complaint, Tsao consented to the entry of a Final Judgment against him that (1) permanently enjoins him from future violations of the federal securities laws; (2) bars him from acting as an officer or director of a public company; (3) requires him to disgorge $146,850 in illicit profits, and $24,758.30 in prejudgment interest thereon, and (4) orders him to pay civil money penalties in the amount of $220,275 and a Remedies Act penalty of $110,000. The Final Judgment allows Tsao to offset his payment of disgorgement and civil penalty by the corresponding amounts, if any, of restitution and criminal fine, respectively, he pays in connection with the parallel criminal proceeding, where Tsao has pled guilty to one felony count of criminal insider trading and one felony count of perjury arising from false statements that Tsao made to the SEC staff during the investigation.

SEC v. Derrick S. McKinley

Litigation Release No. 18832 (August 13, 2004)
http://www.sec.gov/litigation/litreleases/lr18832.htm

On August 13, 2004, the Commission announced that it filed a complaint against Derrick S. McKinley (McKinley), a former vice president and medical director of Gliatech, Inc. (Gliatech). Gliatech was a pharmaceutical company located in suburban Cleveland. The complaint alleges that McKinley sold Gliatech stock while in possession of material, nonpublic information concerning problems with Gliatech's primary product, Adcon-L Adhesion Barrier Gel (Adcon-L), a gel used to reduce scarring in patients following back surgery.

From August 1999 to August 2000, McKinley sold short 221,000 shares of Gliatech stock in a series of transactions, reaping profits of approximately $1.6 million. From the outset of his trading, McKinley was aware of three major problems involving Adcon-L. By August 1999, McKinley (1) knew that a study of Adcon-L clinical trials (Adcon-L Study) submitted by Gliatech to the U.S. Food and Drug Administration (FDA) suffered from defects that undermined its reliability; (2) knew of sterility problems resulting from defective packaging by the overseas contractor Gliatech hired to manufacture Adcon-L; and (3) knew of complaints of cerebral spinal fluid leaks (CSF leaks) in patients following surgeries in which Adcon-L had been used. In October 1999, the FDA issued an import ban that prevented shipments of Adcon-L from entering the U.S. The ban resulted from unresolved FDA concerns that included the defective packaging and sterility problems. In March 2000, news of complaints about the CSF leaks became public. In August 2000, news of an FDA investigation challenging the integrity and results of the Adcon-L Study became public. When each of these adverse developments became publicly known, the price of Gliatech stock dropped. McKinley profited from each of these three declines in the price of Gliatech stock.

SEC v. Guillermo Garcia Simon, et al.

Litigation Release No. 18763 (June 24, 2004)
http://www.sec.gov/litigation/litreleases/lr18763.htm

A Massachusetts federal court has entered a final judgment against Guillermo Garcia Simon, a former FleetBoston Financial Group employee residing in Buenes Aires, Argentina, in connection with his trading in the securities of FleetBoston in advance of the announcement of its acquisition by Bank of America Corporation. Under the terms of the final judgment, entered by consent, Simon was ordered to pay approximately $525,000 in disgorgement, interest, and a penalty. He was also enjoined from further violations of Section 10(b) of the Securities Exchange Act of 1934, and Rule 10b-5 thereunder.

The Commission filed an emergency enforcement action against Simon on Monday, October 28, 2003, only hours after Bank of America announced its acquisition of FleetBoston, and less than three days after Simon purchased FleetBoston securities. In its complaint, , the Commission alleged that Simon engaged in illegal insider trading when he bought FleetBoston securities late on Friday, October 24, while in possession of material, non-public information about the acquisition that was announced the next trading day. The day it filed its complaint, the Commission also sought, and was granted,a temporary restraining order and asset freeze against Simon. The Commission obtained the order before the transaction was concluded and as a result, was able to freeze Simon's trading account before any profits could be removed or dissipated.

VII. CASES INVOLVING MARKET MANIPULATION

SEC v. Concorde America, Inc., Absolute Health and Fitness, Inc., et al.,

Litigation Release No. 19085 (February 16, 2005)
http://www.sec.gov/litigation/litreleases/lr19085.htm

The Commission announced that on February 15, 2005, Judge William J. Zloch, U.S. District Judge for the Southern District of Florida, issued emergency asset freeze orders, among other relief, against Donald Oehmke, Bryan Kos, and five related relief defendants in connection with the manipulation of two small-cap companies traded nationwide on the Pink

Sheets, Boca Raton, Florida-based Concorde America, Inc. ("Concorde America"), and Greensboro, North Carolina-based Absolute Health and Fitness, Inc. ("Absolute Health"). The relief defendants are five off-shore entities: Da Silva, SA, Vanderlip Holdings, NV, Chiang Ze Capital, AVV, Ryzcek Investments, GMBH, and Barranquilla Holdings, SA. Concorde America claims to recruit Latin American workers for employment in Europe, and Absolute Health claims to own and operate several fitness centers. On February 14, 2005, the Commission filed a civil injunctive action, alleging that Oehmke, Kos, and others defrauded investors through two classic "pump and dump" schemes.

The Commission's Complaint alleges that Oehmke and Kos instigated both schemes, artificially creating demand for stock they owned in Concorde America and Absolute Health through unauthorized and false press releases, facsimile and e-mail spams, internet websites, promotional videos, and automatic voice-mail messages since approximately June 2004. According to the Commission's Complaint, Oehmke realized a net profit of over $11.3 million from his sales of Concorde America stock and more than $9.4 million from his sales of Absolute Health. The Commission's Complaint also alleges that Kos realized net profits of nearly $1.7 million from his sales of Concorde America stock, and more than $5 million from his sales of Absolute Health stock. The Commission also sued Concorde America and its president, Hartley Lord, alleging that they participated in the stock manipulation scheme, and sued Absolute Health alleging that it did not own any fitness centers. In addition, the Commission sued Thomas M. Heysek, Andrew M. Kline, and Paul A. Spreadbury alleging that they prepared false and misleading analyst reports, tout sheets, and press releases, among other things.

SEC v. Courtney D. Smith

Litigation Release No. 19064 (February 7, 2005)
http://www.sec.gov/litigation/litreleases/lr19064.htm

On February 7, 2005, the Commission filed a complaint in the United States District Court for the Central District of California charging Courtney D. Smith, a well-known financial commentator, for his role in an unlawful scheme to manipulate the stock price of GenesisIntermedia, Inc. (GENI), a now defunct public company that was based in Van Nuys, California. After the scheme collapsed in September 2001, GENI's stock price plunged to pennies per share, leading to the bankruptcy of three brokerage firms and the largest bailout in the history of the Securities Investor Protection Corporation.

The Commission alleged that Smith assisted GENI's Chief Executive Officer and his accomplice (a Saudi Arabian national reputed to be an international arms dealer and financier) in a fraudulent stock manipulation and lending scheme that occurred between September 1999 and September 2001. According to the complaint, GENI's CEO secretly paid Smith approximately $1.1 million in cash and GENI stock to tout GENI shares on television. Smith's public statements, many of which were false or misleading, artificially inflated the price of GENI shares and facilitated the misappropriation of approximately $130 million by GENI's CEO and his accomplice. Also according to the complaint, the manipulation of GENI's stock price began shortly after the company's June 1999 public offering. To benefit from the manipulation, GENI's CEO and his accomplice, with the assistance of Kenneth P. D'Angelo (a stock loan broker previously charged by the SEC and criminal authorities), developed a stock lending scheme in which they could profit from lending GENI shares (rather than selling them). The complaint alleged that the CEO and his accomplice, through an offshore entity called Ultimate Holdings, loaned approximately 15 million shares of GENI stock to more than a dozen broker-dealers in exchange for cash (based upon the market value of the shares). As the price of GENI shares increased from the efforts of Smith and others, Ultimate Holdings received additional funds when the GENI stock loans were marked-to-market by the broker-dealers involved. By lending the shares in this manner, Ultimate Holdings and GENI's CEO raised approximately $130 million without giving up control of the stock or depressing the market. GENI's CEO and his accomplice, however, defaulted on the stock loans and failed to repay the $130 million they had borrowed. As alleged in the complaint, the manipulation caused GENI's stock price to increase approximately 1,400%, from a low of $1.67 per share (split adjusted) on September 1, 1999 to a high of $25 per share on June 29, 2001

The Commission charged Smith with violating the antifraud provisions of the federal securities laws as well as the anti-touting provision. The United States Attorney's Office for the Central District of California announced related criminal charges against Smith.

<u>SEC v. Robert J. Cassandro, Michael C. Cardascia, and Stephen E. Apolant, Defendants, and Joan Cardascia, Relief Defendant</u>

Litigation Release No. 18909 (September 29, 2004)
http://www.sec.gov/litigation/litreleases/lr18909.htm

On September 29, 2004, the Commission filed a civil action against an attorney, Robert J. Cassandro, and two stock promoters, Michael C. Cardascia and Stephen E. Apolant, in a case that arose out of a fraudulent scheme to manipulate the price of Spectrum Brands Corporation's stock by exploiting the fear of bio-terrorism following September 11, 2001. Specifically, the complaint alleges that Spectrum Brands was secretly managed and controlled by a group of stock promoters in Hicksville, New York, some of whom were convicted felons. The complaint further alleges that to conceal its true ownership from the investing public, Spectrum Brands stated in a Form 8-K filed with the Commission on or about October 31, 2001, that a Michael J. Burns was the sole officer and director of the company and that the corporate address was in Hauppauge, New York. In truth, Burns had little or no management responsibility for Spectrum Brands and the Hauppauge address was a mail drop. The complaint alleges that Cassandro participated in drafting the false and misleading statements in the Form 8-K while knowing that the statements were false and misleading. Also, according to the complaint, Michael Cardascia and Apolant helped promote Spectrum Brands stock via Internet, radio, bulk e-mail, and fax while knowing that these communications contained false and misleading statements regarding the identity of the persons controlling and managing Spectrum Brands. The complaint also alleges that Michael Cardascia bought Spectrum Brands stock privately at a discount and that his wife Joan Cardascia, who was named as a relief defendant, was unjustly enriched when she sold it at inflated prices.

VIII. CASES INVOLVING SECURITIES OFFERINGS

<u>SEC v. Mobile Billboards of America, Inc., International Payphone Company, Reserve Guaranty Trust, Michael A. Lomas and Michael L. Young</u>

Litigation Release No. 18893 (September 23, 2004)
http://www.sec.gov/litigation/litreleases/lr18893.htm

On September 21, 2004, the Commission filed a complaint in the United States District Court for the Northern District of Georgia against Mobile Billboards of America, Inc. (Mobile Billboards), International

Payphone Company (International Payphone) itself and doing business as Outdoor Media Industries (Outdoor Media), Reserve Guaranty Trust (RGT), Michael A. Lomas (Lomas) and Michael L. Young (Young). Lomas, who resides in Long Beach, California, is the chairman of Mobile Billboards. Young is the president and a director of Mobile Billboards and resides in Bridgeton, Missouri.

The complaint alleged that from 2001 through the present, defendants Lomas, Young, Mobile Billboards, Outdoor Media, and RGT operated a Ponzi scheme involving the sale and leaseback of mobile billboards, selling more than $60.5 million of mobile billboard investments to more than 700 investors nationwide. The complaint charged the defendants with violations of the federal securities laws, and Lomas and Young with aiding and abetting the violations of federal securities laws. The complaint seeks, among other relief, injunctions against future violations, disgorgement of all ill-gotten gains with prejudgment interest, and the imposition of civil penalties against defendants. On the same day the complaint was filed, the defendants consented to orders permanently enjoining the defendants from future violations, freezing the assets of defendants, ordering accountings by Lomas and Young, and appointing a Receiver for the assets of Mobile Billboards, International Payphone, itself and doing business as Outdoor Media, and RGT.

SEC v. Colin Nathanson, Individually and Doing Business as Nathanson Investment Trust, Giant Golf Company, Play Big Enterprises, Inc., Starquest Management Inc., Whitehawk Consulting Group, Inc., Leafhead Consultants, Inc., Nettel Consulting Corp., YRMAC Consulting Services, Inc., and Millennium Technical Group, Inc.

Litigation Release No. 18861 (August 31, 2004)
http://www.sec.gov/litigation/litreleases/lr18861.htm

On August 26, 2004, the Honorable Gary L. Taylor, United States District Judge for the Central District of North Carolina, entered final consent judgments against defendants Colin Nathanson and eight of the business entities Nathanson founded. The Commission's complaint alleged that the defendants, based on Orange County, perpetrated a $29.5 million securities fraud. As part of the settlement, Nathanson and the defendant entities, controlled by a court-appointed receiver, consented to permanent injunctions, without admitting or denying the allegations in the Commission's complaint. Additionally, the defendant entities agreed to disgorge all of their funds and assets pursuant to one or more plans of distribution approved by the court, less any court-approved receivership fees and expenses. Nathanson consented to disgorge $4.7 million. In satisfaction of this debt, Nathanson agreed to disgorge to the receiver all of his real property, including three parcels of land he owns in Orange County, as well as certain personal property that he owns. Payment of the remainder of the $4.7 million is waived, based upon Nathanson's demonstrated inability to pay.

The Commission alleged that in four related schemes, the defendants lied to investors regarding how they would use the investor funds. The complaint alleged that without the investors' knowledge or consent, Nathanson commingled the investors' monies, and used the commingled funds to operate both the unprofitable defendant businesses and his other various unprofitable businesses. Additionally, the Commission's complaint alleged that since February 2001, Nathanson used at least $1 million of investor funds to support his extravagant lifestyle, including three homes and payment of $346,500 in gambling-related debts. Finally, the Commission alleged that, in Ponzi-like fashion, Nathanson caused over $5 million of the $29.5 million raised to be paid to certain investors either as purported "returns" on their investments when, in fact, their investments were not profitable, or as purported returns of their principal.

IX. SELF REGULATORY ORGANIZATIONS

Report of Investigation Regarding NASDAQ, as Overseen by Its Parent, NASD, Arising Out of Investigation of Suspicious Trading Activity and Net Capital Violations By MarketXT

Press Release 2005-14 (February 9, 2005)
http://www.sec.gov/news/press/2005-14.htm

In the Matter of MarketXT and Irfan Amanat

Admin Proc. File No. 3-11813 (February 9, 2005)
http://www.sec.gov/litigation/admin/33-8533.htm

The Commission issued a Report of Investigation concerning Nasdaq, as overseen by its parent, the NASD, in connection with an investigation and inspection of wash trades and net capital violations by MarketXT, an NASD member firm. The Report finds, among other things, that Nasdaq employees observed suspicious trading by MarketXT and did not communicate their observations to NASD Regulation, Inc. In response to the Commission's investigation and the inspection from which it stemmed, NASD and Nasdaq have implemented a number of remedial steps, all designed to strengthen the self-regulatory oversight of their market. NASD and Nasdaq have consented to the issuance of the report, but neither admit nor deny the findings or conclusions therein.

The Commission also instituted public administrative proceedings against MarketXT, Inc. (MarketXT), an Electronic Communications Network ("ECN") registered as a broker-dealer, and public administrative and cease-and-desist proceedings against Irfan Amanat (Amanat), MarketXT's de facto Chief Technology Officer. In the Order, the Division of Enforcement alleges that Amanat executed thousands of wash trades and matched orders over a three-day period in March 2002 in order improperly to qualify MarketXT for a tape revenue rebate program offered by Nasdaq. MarketXT improperly received approximately $50,000 in rebates from Nasdaq. In the Order, the Division also alleges that for the year ended December 31, 2001, and quarter ended June 30, 2002, MarketXT was operating without adequate net capital and did not maintain and preserve accurate books and records disclosing its true liabilities.

As a result of executing the fraudulent wash trades and matched orders, the Division alleged that MarketXT willfully violated Sections 10(b) and 15(c)(1)(A) of the Exchange Act, and Rule 10b-5 thereunder. The Division also alleged that Amanat willfully violated Section 10(b) of the Exchange Act and Rule 10b-5 thereunder, and willfully aided and abetted MarketXT's violation of Section 15(c)(1)(A) of the Exchange Act. The Division further alleged that MarketXT willfully violated Sections 15(c)(3) and 17(a)(1) of the Exchange Act, and Rules 15c3-1, 17a-3(a)(2), 17a-3(a)(11), and 17a-5 by failing to maintain adequate net capital and by failing to maintain and preserve adequate books and records. The Division sought disgorgement plus prejudgment interest and a civil penalty against MarketXT, and a cease-and-desist order and civil penalty against Amanat, in addition to any remedial sanctions appropriate in the public interest.

NOTES

NOTES

16

SEC & NASD ENFORCEMENT INITIATIVES: HOW TO DEAL EFFECTIVELY WITH THE SEC & NASD

Submitted by: Barry R. Goldsmith

NASD

- NASD News Release: *NASD Fines 20 Firms $1.65 Million for Municipal Trade Reporting Violations* (June 29, 2005)

  NASD censured and fined 20 securities firms a total of $1.65 million for late and/or inaccurate reporting of tens of thousands of municipal securities transactions to the Municipal Securities Rulemaking Board (MSRB). NASD is responsible for enforcing MSRB rules. These enforcement actions focused on misconduct that occurred from January 2003 through October 2004. During that period, 19 of the 20 firms failed to timely report at least five percent of their customer trades in municipal securities. Additionally, from January 2003 through May 2004, seven firms failed to timely report at least 12 percent of their inter-dealer municipal securities trades. NASD found that each firm failed to monitor its trade reporting to ensure compliance with MSRB reporting rules.

  http://www.nasd.com/web/idcplg?IdcService=SS_GET_PAGE&ssDocName=NASDW_014639

- NASD News Release: *Morgan Stanley to Pay $2.7 Million for IPO Lock-Up Violations/NASD Fines J.P. Morgan $150,000, Goldman Sachs $125,000 for Similar Violations* (June 9, 2005)

  NASD ordered three firms—Morgan Stanley & Co, J.P. Morgan Securities, Inc., and Goldman, Sachs & Co.—to pay more than $2.9 million following sales of restricted securities in violation of lock-up agreements as required by NASD rules. NASD censured the firms and ordered Morgan Stanley to pay a fine of $150,000 and disgorgement of more than $2.5 million in ill-gotten profits. J.P. Morgan was ordered to pay a fine $150,000 and Goldman Sachs was fined $125,000.

  http://www.nasd.com/web/idcplg?IdcService=SS_GET_PAGE&ssDocName=NASDW_014346

- NASD News Release: *NASD Charges 15 Firms With Directed Brokerage Violations, Imposes Fines Totaling More than $34 Million* (June 8, 2005)

  NASD imposed fines totaling more than $34 million on 15 broker-dealers in connection with the receipt of directed brokerage in exchange for preferential treatment for certain mutual fund companies. These cases are part of NASD's efforts to eliminate conflicts of interest in the sale of mutual funds and focus on brokerage firms involved in selling mutual funds to retail investors, as well as one mutual fund distributor. All of the cases involve violations of NASD's Anti-Reciprocal Rule, which prohibits firms from favoring the sale of shares of particular mutual funds on the basis of brokerage commissions received by the firm. Among other things, a firm may not recommend specific funds to sales personnel or establish preferred lists of funds in exchange for directed brokerage.

NASD found that the 14 retail firms, most of which sold funds offered by hundreds of different mutual fund complexes, operated "preferred partner" or "shelf space" programs that provided certain benefits to a relatively small number of mutual fund complexes in return for directed brokerage. NASD also censured and fined one mutual fund distributor, AllianceBernstein Investment Research and Management, Inc. AllianceBernstein paid for some of its shelf space obligations by having its affiliated investment adviser direct portfolio transactions to or for the benefit of firms to which the distributor owed revenue sharing fees.

http://www.nasd.com/web/idcplg?IdcService=SS_GET_PAGE&ssDocName=NASDW_014340

- NASD News Release: *Waddell & Reed, Inc. Agrees to Pay $5 Million Fine, Up To $11 Million in Restitution to Settle NASD Charges Relating to Variable Annuity Switching* (April 29, 2005)

NASD has resolved its action against Waddell & Reed, Inc., of Overland Park, KS, arising from thousands of variable annuity exchanges made as part of the firm's national switching campaign. In a complaint filed in January 2004, NASD charged Waddell & Reed with violating its obligations under NASD's suitability rule by failing to take reasonable steps to ensure that recommended variable annuity exchanges were in the best interests of customers.

Under the terms of the settlement with NASD and a separate agreement with a coalition of state regulatory authorities, Waddell & Reed will repay up to $11 million to more than 5,000 customers whose annuities were exchanged by the firm. The firm will pay a fine of $5 million to NASD and a fine of $2 million to state regulators.

http://www.nasd.com/web/idcplg?IdcService=SS_GET_PAGE&ssDocName=NASDW_013886&ssSourceNodeId=1091

- NASD News Release: *NASD Fines Raymond James $750,000 for Fee-Based Account Violations/Settlement Also Requires $138,000 in Restitution to Customers* (April 27, 2005)

  NASD censured and fined Raymond James & Associates, Inc. and Raymond James Financial Services, Inc. $750,000 for violations relating to the firms' fee-based brokerage business. The firms will also pay restitution totaling $138,000. NASD found that, from April 2001 through December 2004, the Raymond James firms failed to establish and maintain a supervisory system, including written procedures, reasonably designed to review and monitor their fee-based brokerage business. In addition, the firms also violated NASD rules by recommending and opening fee-based brokerage accounts for customers without first determining whether these accounts were appropriate and by allowing those accounts to remain open.

  http://www.nasd.com/web/idcplg?IdcService=SS_GET_PAGE&ssDocName=NASDW_013876&ssSourceNodeId=551

- NASD News Release: *Ladenburg Thalmann Agrees to Repay $1.2 Million to Customers Overcharged in Proceeds Transactions/NASD Fines Firm $275,000, Orders Review of Proceeds Rules Compliance Policies* (April 14, 2005)

  NASD announced that Ladenburg Thalmann & Co. of New York, NY agreed to refund $1.2 million, plus interest, to customers who were overcharged in "proceeds transactions"—transactions in which a customer sells securities through a broker and uses the proceeds to pay for other securities purchased at or about the same time.

  NASD also fined Ladenburg $275,000 and required the firm to retain an independent consultant to make recommendations for ensuring compliance with NASD's Proceeds Rule.

  http://www.nasd.com/web/idcplg?IdcService=SS_GET_PAGE&ssDocName=NASDW_013815&ssSourceNodeId=1177

- NASD News Release: *Florida Brokerage Firm LH Ross Expelled, Owner Franklyn Michelin Barred for Life to Settle NASD Charges of Widespread, Ongoing Fraud* (March 31, 2005)

  NASD expelled Boca Raton, FL-based brokerage firm LH Ross from the securities industry and barred its owner and president, Franklyn Michelin, for life to resolve charges of manipulation, fraud, excessive markups, sales of unregistered securities, books and records violations and supervisory violations in two pending enforcement actions against the firm. Both matters were scheduled to go before NASD hearing panels in coming weeks.

As part of the settlement, LH Ross and Michelin agreed to withdraw their appeals of three previous NASD hearing panel decisions that found, among other things, that LH Ross and Michelin had engaged in widespread fraud in the sales of unregistered self-offerings and had failed to cooperate with NASD investigators. Those previous decisions imposed sanctions that included expelling LH Ross (twice), barring Michelin, ordering the payment of more than $11.45 million in restitution and interest to harmed investors, and imposing $550,000 in fines. With the appeals dropped, those sanctions are now final.

In recent months, NASD has used two of its emergency powers for the first time to protect investors from LH Ross's ongoing fraudulent and illegal sales activities—by issuing its first temporary cease and desist order last August, and it first summary suspension of a securities firm in February.

http://www.nasd.com/web/idcplg?IdcService=SS_GET_PAGE&ssDocName=NASDW_013705&ssSourceNodeId=1177

- NASD News Release: *NASD Fines Citigroup Global Markets, American Express and Chase Investment Services More Than $21 Million for Improper Sales of Class B and C Shares of Mutual Funds/Firms to Offer Remediation on Over 275,000 Transactions to Over 50,000 Households* (March 23, 2005)

NASD censured and fined Citigroup Global Markets, Inc., American Express Financial Advisors and Chase Investment Services a total of $21.25 million for suitability and supervisory violations relating to mutual fund sales practices between January 2002 and July 2003. These cases are part of a larger, ongoing investigation into mutual fund sales practices.

The cases against Citigroup and Chase involve their recommendations and sales of Class B and Class C shares of mutual funds, while the action involving American Express relates only to Class B shares. In all three cases, the firms made recommendations and sales of mutual funds to their customers without considering or adequately disclosing, on a consistent basis, that an equal investment in Class A shares would generally have been more economically advantageous for their customers by providing a higher overall rate of return. The firms also had inadequate supervisory and compliance policies and procedures relating to these mutual fund sales.

In resolving these actions, the firms agreed to a remediation plan that includes over 50,000 households and more than 275,000 transactions in Class B shares, and to a lesser extent, Class C shares.

http://www.nasd.com/web/idcplg?IdcService=SS_GET_PAGE&ssDocName=NASDW_013648&ssSourceNodeId=1177

- NASD News Release: *NASD Fines Spear, Leeds & Kellog $1 Million for Concealing Sales of IPO Shares/Firm Implemented Internal System to Prevent Detection, Reporting of Sales by DTC* (March 22, 2005)

  NASD censured and fined Spear, Leeds & Kellogg, L.P. (now known as Goldman Sachs Execution & Clearing, L.P.) $1 million for creating and implementing an internal system to conceal sales of securities allocated in initial public offerings (IPOs) from the Depository Trust Corporation (DTC).

  In 1997, DTC—which provides clearance and settlement services to the securities industry—implemented a system approved by the Securities and Exchange Commission (SEC) to track sales of shares in initial public offerings.

  NASD found that around the time the system was implemented, some Spear Leeds customers objected to their sales of IPO shares being identified through the IPO tracking system, citing concerns about preserving the anonymity of their trading activity, and thereby preserving their ability to obtain future IPOs. In response, Spear Leeds developed and implemented a system designed to conceal sales of IPO shares from the IPO Tracking System.

  http://www.nasd.com/web/idcplg?IdcService=SS_GET_PAGE&ssDocName=NASDW_013628&ssSourceNodeId=1177

- NASD News Release: *NASD Fines Former Jesup & Lamont Research Analyst for Trading Contrary to His Own Recommendations* (February 23, 2005)

  NASD fined and suspended former Jesup & Lamont Securities Corporation research analyst Gary Davis for trading contrary to the recommendations in his research reports and for other violations relating to his activities as a research analyst. Davis was suspended from the industry for six months, fined $130,000 and prohibited from acting as a research analyst for 18 months. Nearly $117,000 of his fine represents profits Davis made through his unlawful trading.

NASD also charged Jesup & Lamont, a New York City broker-dealer, and its chief compliance officer, Robert Strong, with failing to adequately supervise Davis.

http://www.nasd.com/web/idcplg?IdcService=SS_GET_PAGE&ssDocName=NASDW_013410&ssSourceNodeId=1177

- NASD Press Release: *NASD Fines Quick & Reilly, Piper Jaffray $845,000 For Directed Brokerage Violations* (February 22, 2005)

  NASD fined Quick & Reilly, Inc. (now part of Banc of America Investment Services, Inc.) $570,000 and Piper Jaffray & Co. $275,000 for directed brokerage violations. In imposing sanctions against Piper Jaffray, NASD took into account the fact that the firm self-reported its violative conduct after conducting its own internal review.

  NASD found that both firms operated "preferred partner" or "shelf space" programs, giving favorable treatment to funds offered by certain mutual fund companies in return for brokerage commissions and other payments. That special treatment included higher visibility on the firms' internal websites, increased access to the firms' sales forces, participation in "top producer" or training meetings, and promotion of their funds on a broader basis than was available for other funds. That conduct violated NASD's "Anti-Reciprocal Rule" which prohibits firms from favoring the sale of shares of particular mutual funds on the basis of brokerage commissions.

  http://www.nasd.com/web/idcplg?IdcService=SS_GET_PAGE&ssDocName=NASDW_013402&ssSourceNodeId=1177

- NASD News Release: *NASD Charges American Funds Distributors, Inc. with Arranging $100 Million in Directed Brokerage Commissions for Top Sellers of American Funds* (February 16, 2005)

  NASD charged American Funds Distributors, Inc. (AFD) with violating NASD's Anti-Reciprocal Rule by directing approximately $100 million in brokerage commissions over a three-year period to about 50 brokerage firms that were the top sellers of American

Funds. The payments were made to reward the firms for past sales and to encourage future sales of American Funds' 29 mutual funds.

AFD is the principal underwriter and distributor of American Funds, the third largest mutual fund family in the U.S. with more than $450 billion in assets and approximately 25 million shareholder accounts. The commissions were payments for executing trades for the American Funds' portfolio that were directed to the brokerage firms as additional compensation for past sales of American Funds, and to ensure that American Funds would continue to receive preferential treatment at those firms.

NASD's "Anti-Reciprocal Rule," which first became effective in July 1973, is designed to prevent *quid pro quo* arrangements in which brokerage commissions, which are assets of the shareholders of the mutual funds, are used to compensate brokerage firms for selling the funds' shares. The rule also is designed to ensure that the execution of portfolio transactions by brokerage firms is guided by the principle of "best execution" and not by other considerations. In addition, the rule is meant to eliminate the danger that a brokerage firm, when recommending mutual funds to customers, will base its recommendations on the additional rewards the firm may receive in portfolio commissions from the funds rather than on the investment needs of the customer.

http://www.nasd.com/web/idcplg?IdcService=SS_GET_PAGE&ssDocName=NASDW_013358&ssSourceNodeId=1177

- NASD News Release: *NASD Bars Todd Eberhard, Former Park South Chairman and Once-Popular Television Personality/ Violations Include Fraudulent Trading, Improper Settlements with Customers, Failure to Make Required Regulatory Disclosures, Providing False and Misleading Testimony* (January 31, 2005)

  NASD barred Todd M. Eberhard, the former chairman of New York's Park South Securities, LLC, from the securities industry for federal securities fraud and other, multiple violations of NASD rules. Eberhard was known to millions as a guest analyst and commentator who appeared frequently on financial television programs on CNN, CNNfn, CNBC, Fox News Channel and on PBS' Nightly Business Report.

  The bar stems from NASD charges announced in October 2002 that Eberhard had committed securities fraud in connection with scores of mutual fund transactions. Park South was liquidated in 2003. In 2004, Eberhard pleaded guilty in federal court to mail and wire fraud, as well as conspiracy, investment adviser fraud and obstruction of justice.

http://www.nasd.com/web/idcplg?IdcService=SS_GET_PAGE&ssDocName=NASDW_013195&ssSourceNodeId=1177

- NASD News Release: *Banc One Securities Corporation Fined $400,000 for Supervisory Failures Relating to Late Trading—NASD Also Cites Banc One for Inaccurate Recording of Order Entry Times* (January 12, 2005)

  NASD censured and fined Banc One Securities Corporation $400,000 for failing to implement adequate supervisory systems and written procedures designed to detect and prevent "late trading" of mutual funds, and for inaccurately recording the entry time for customer orders.

  http://www.nasd.com/web/idcplg?IdcService=SS_GET_PAGE&ssDocName=NASDW_012983&ssSourceNodeId=1177

- NASD News Release: *NASD Fines H&R Block Financial Advisors $500,000 for Enabling Deceptive Market Timing, Orders Payment of $325,000 in Restitution—NASD Investigation of Individuals Involved in Scheme Continuing* (December 21, 2004)

  NASD censured and fined H&R Block Financial Advisors, Inc., $500,000 for enabling a hedge fund customer in its Orlando, FL branch office to engage in deceptive practices to market time mutual funds. NASD also ordered H&R Block to pay $325,000 to reimburse the affected funds. NASD's investigation into the activities of particular individuals involved in this market timing scheme is continuing.

  http://www.nasd.com/web/idcplg?IdcService=SS_GET_PAGE&ssDocName=NASDW_012819&ssSourceNodeId=553

- NASD News Release: *NASD Orders First Command to Pay $12 Million for Misleading Statements in Sales of Systematic Investment Plans to Military Personnel (Firm to Pay Restitution, Fund Investor Education Program for Military Community)* (December 15, 2004)

  NASD censured and fined First Command Financial Planning Inc., a Fort Worth, TX broker-dealer, $12 million for making misleading statements and omitting important information when selling mutual fund investments with up-front sales charges of up to 50 percent through a monthly installment method known as a "Systematic Investment Plan."

From that $12 million, First Command is ordered to pay restitution to thousands of customers who purchased a Systematic Investment Plan between Jan.1, 1999 and the present who terminated the plan and paid an effective sales charge greater than 5 percent. All money remaining will be payable to the NASD Investor Education Foundation, to be used for the investor education needs of members of the military and their families.

First Command also settled NASD charges of inappropriately confronting a customer who complained, failing to maintain e-mail, failing to maintain adequate supervisory systems and procedures and filing an inaccurate Form U-5 regulatory report. In a related action, NASD fined a First Command supervisor $25,000 and suspended him from acting in any supervisory capacity for 30 days.

The Securities and Exchange Commission also instituted settled enforcement proceedings against First Command based on similar allegations relating to the firm's sales of systematic investment plans.

http://www.nasd.com/web/idcplg?IdcService=SS_GET_PAGE&ssDocName=NASDW_012786&ssSourceNodeId=553

- NASD News Release: *NASD Fines Morgan Stanley $100,000 for Municipal Bond Disclosure Violations—Over $200,000 in Restitution Paid, Offer to Repurchase Bonds Required; Firm Fined Additional $25,000 for Slow Response to Investigators' Inquiries* (December 6, 2004)

NASD sanctioned Morgan Stanley DW Inc. for failing to disclose to purchasers of municipal bonds that those bonds could be called prior to their stated maturity dates, which could result in losses to the investors. Morgan Stanley's failure to disclose the call feature violates Municipal Securities Rulemaking Board (MSRB) Rule G-15. NASD censured the firm, imposed a fine of $100,000 and required the firm to offer to buy back bonds sold in up to 171 separate municipal bond transactions. Morgan Stanley has paid approximately $211,510 in restitution to customers since the NASD investigation began.

Early in NASD's investigation into this matter, Morgan Stanley failed to respond in a timely way to requests for information, resulting in a second disciplinary action that included a censure and a $25,000 fine.

http://www.nasd.com/web/idcplg?IdcService=SS_GET_PAGE&ssDocName=NASDW_012707&ssSourceNodeId=553

- NASD News Release: *NASD Fines 29 Firms Over $9.2 Million for Late Reporting—Failures Stall Disclosure of Potential Broker Misconduct to Public, Regulators, Brokerages* (November 30, 2004)

  NASD censured and fined 29 securities firms over $9.2 million for more than 8,000 late disclosures of reportable information about their brokers—including customer complaints, regulatory actions and criminal charges and convictions.

  NASD also prohibited two firms—Merrill Lynch and Wachovia—from registering new brokers for five business days, in view of the number of their reporting violations in this case and their previous regulatory filing histories. NASD imposed a similar prohibition and a $2.2 million fine against Morgan Stanley in July for late reporting violations.

  During the period January 2002 through March 2004, each of the 29 firms failed to timely report at least 25 percent of the required disclosures in the areas reviewed by NASD, and some firms failed to timely report over 70 percent. NASD also found that each firm failed to have supervisory systems and procedures in place reasonably designed to achieve compliance with these reporting requirements.

  To resolve these actions, each firm agreed to conduct internal audits to evaluate the effectiveness of its system for ensuring compliance with these reporting obligations. In addition, an officer of each firm must certify that such audits have occurred, that recommendations from the audits have been implemented and that the firm has established systems and procedures reasonably designed to achieve compliance with NASD reporting requirements.

  http://www.nasd.com/web/idcplg?IdcService=SS_GET_PAGE&ssDocName=NASDW_012595&ssSourceNodeId=553

- NASD News Release: *NASD Permanently Bars Frank Quattrone from the Securities Industry for Refusal to Testify in NASD Investigation—Quattrone's Misconduct Termed "Egregious"* (November 22, 2004)

  NASD's National Adjudicatory Council (NAC) permanently barred Frank Quattrone from working in the securities industry in any capacity for refusing to testify in an NASD investigation concerning his role in possible document destruction, obstruction of justice and other matters while at Credit Suisse First Boston (CSFB). The NAC overruled an earlier NASD hearing panel decision to fine Frank Quattrone $30,000 and suspend him for one year. In ordering the permanent bar, the NAC called Quattrone's conduct "egregious" and said it "impeded an NASD investigation and undermined the NASD's ability to carry out its regulatory mandate."

  http://www.nasd.com/web/idcplg?IdcService=SS_GET_PAGE&ssDocName=NASDW_012489&ssSourceNodeId=553

- NASD News Release: *NASD Charges H&R Block Financial Advisors With Fraud in Sale of Enron Bonds to Hundreds of Customers—Bond Sales Just Before Enron Collapse Cost Customers Millions of Dollars* (November 8, 2004)

  NASD charged H&R Block Financial Advisors, Inc., with fraud in the sale of millions of dollars worth of Enron Corporation bonds after Enron's finances, and its bond ratings, had begun to collapse. NASD charged that during the five-week period preceding the Enron bankruptcy filing—while Enron's financial crisis was unfolding publicly and official investigations were being launched—H&R Block's brokers made affirmative misrepresentations to customers, touted the supposed benefits of the Enron bonds, and failed to disclose the serious and significant risks associated with an investment in the bonds. From October 29, 2001 through November 27, 2001, approximately 200 H&R Block brokers recommended and sold over $16 million worth of Enron bonds to more than 800 customers in approximately 40 states. As an incentive, H&R Block paid its brokers sales credits significantly higher than those typically paid for similar bonds. NASD charged that H&R Block received profits of over $500,000.

http://www.nasd.com/web/idcplg?IdcService=SS_GET_PAGE&ssDocName=NASDW_012056&ssSourceNodeId=553

- NASD News Release: *NASD Fines Sentinel Financial Services $700,000 for Failing to Prevent Market Timing—Supervisory Inadequacies Cited; Over $650,000 in Restitution Paid to Affected Funds* (October 7, 2004)

  NASD censured and fined Sentinel Financial Services Company, of Montpelier, Vermont, $700,000 for failing to prevent market timing in three mutual funds offered by its affiliate, Sentinel Group Funds, Inc. Sentinel also failed to establish and maintain a reasonable supervisory system designed to detect and prevent market timing in violation of the funds' trading policies. After NASD completed its investigation, Sentinel paid $659,674 in restitution to the three affected funds—Sentinel International Equity Fund ($645,631), Sentinel Bond Fund ($10,098) and Sentinel High Yield Bond Fund ($3,945).

  http://www.nasd.com/web/idcplg?IdcService=SS_GET_PAGE&ssDocName=NASDW_011624&ssSourceNodeId=553

- NASD News Release: *NASD Orders First-Ever Suspension of Mutual Fund Business and $600,000 in Sanctions Against National Securities Corp. for Deceptive Market Timing Practices* (August 19, 2004)

  For the first time, NASD has prohibited a regulated firm from opening mutual fund accounts for new clients for 30 days—for facilitating deceptive market timing practices and for failing to have an adequate supervisory system to prevent deceptive market timing and late trading.

  National Securities Corp., based in Seattle, WA, was also fined $300,000 and ordered to pay almost $300,000 in restitution to the funds that were affected by the deceptive market timing. In addition, National was ordered to revise its supervisory systems to correct supervisory and email retention deficiencies. National's president, Michael A. Bresner, was fined $25,000 and received a one- month supervisory suspension for the firm's supervisory failures. David M. Williams, the firm's former chief operating officer, also was fined $25,000 and received a four-month supervisory suspension.

http://www.nasd.com/web/idcplg?IdcService=SS_GET_PAGE&ssDocName=NASDW_010888&ssSourceNodeId=553

- NASD News Release: *NASD Fines Morgan Stanley $2.2 Million for Late Reporting, Firm Temporarily Suspended from Registering New Brokers* (July 29, 2004)

  NASD censured and fined Morgan Stanley DW Inc. $2.2 million for more than 1,800 late disclosures of reportable information about its brokers. The late reports concerned, among other things, customer complaints and disciplinary actions by regulators. NASD also charged Morgan Stanley for supervisory failures relating to the late filings.

  In addition to ordering the fine, NASD prohibited Morgan Stanley from registering any new brokers for one week, required it to hire an independent consultant to assess the firm's supervisory systems and procedures in the reporting area, and imposed specific ongoing reporting obligations.

  NASD concluded that the late filings by Morgan Stanley had delayed several NASD investigations. The late filings also may have hampered the investing public's ability to accurately assess the background of certain brokers through NASD's public disclosure program, BrokerCheck, and compromised the ability of state securities regulators to review applications from brokers changing firms.

  http://www.nasd.com/web/idcplg?IdcService=SS_GET_PAGE&ssDocName=NASDW_010891&ssSourceNodeId=553

- NASD News Release: *NASD Fines Citigroup, Merrill Lynch and Morgan Stanley a Total of $750,000 for Failing to Comply with Discovery Obligations in Arbitrations* (July 19, 2004)

  NASD censured and fined Citigroup Global Markets, Inc., formerly Salomon Smith Barney, Merrill Lynch, Pierce, Fenner & Smith Incorporated, and Morgan Stanley DW Inc. $250,000 each for failing to comply with their discovery obligations in 20 arbitration cases during the period 2002 through 2004. All three firms must also implement written procedures designed to ensure that future discovery violations that lead to sanctions are elevated to senior officers for review and appropriate corrective action.

  These cases arise from arbitrations conducted before NASD Dispute Resolution, Inc. arbitration panels as well as arbitration panels sponsored by other regulatory forums. In these arbitrations, arbitration panels cited the firms for failing to produce documents to the claimants, as required by rules involving document discovery. After finding in each of the arbitrations that the firms failed to fully comply with their discovery obligations to produce documents—even after arbitration panels had issued orders compelling that production—the panels sanctioned the firms in amounts as high as $52,000.

http://www.nasd.com/web/idcplg?IdcService=SS_GET_PAGE&ssDocName=NASDW_009925&ssSourceNodeId=553

HOW TO DEAL EFFECTIVELY WITH THE SEC & NASD

17

CURRENT DEVELOPMENTS IN SEC ENFORCEMENT

Colleen P. Mahoney

Charles F. Walker

Erich T. Schwartz

Louis D. Greenstein

Andrew M. Lawrence

Skadden, Arps, Slate, Meagher& Flom LLP

About the Authors

Colleen P. Mahoney is a partner at Skadden, Arps, Slate, Meagher & Flom LLP. Ms. Mahoney and Skadden, Arps have represented and continue to represent some of the respondents in certain cases discussed in this outline. Prior to joining Skadden, Arps, Ms. Mahoney was the Acting General Counsel and Deputy Director of the Division of Enforcement at the Securities and Exchange Commission, during which time she was involved in certain of the matters and cases described herein.

Charles F. Walker is a partner at Skadden, Arps, Slate, Meagher & Flom LLP. Mr. Walker rejoined Skadden, Arps after serving as Securities Commissioner for the State of Delaware from 1996 to 1999. Previously, he served as Special Counsel in the Office of General Counsel of the Securities and Exchange Commission.

Erich T. Schwartz is a partner at Skadden, Arps, Slate, Meagher & Flom LLP. From 1994 through 2001, Mr. Schwartz was Assistant Director of the Division of Enforcement at the Securities and Exchange Commission, during which time he was involved in certain of the matters and cases described herein.

Louis D. Greenstein is an associate at Skadden, Arps, Slate, Meagher & Flom LLP. Mr. Greenstein was a Staff Attorney in the Division of Enforcement of the Securities and Exchange Commission from 1997 to 2000.

Andrew M. Lawrence is an associate at Skadden, Arps, Slate, Meagher & Flom LLP. Mr. Lawrence was a Senior Counsel from 2002 to 2004 and a Staff Attorney from 1999 to 2002 in the Division of Enforcement of the Securities and Exchange Commission.

This article is based on previous publications prepared by the authors.

Table of Contents

I. INTRODUCTION

The passage of the Sarbanes-Oxley Act of 2002 ("Sarbanes-Oxley" or "the Act") has ushered in a new era of enforcement by the Securities and Exchange Commission ("SEC" or "Commission"). The most significant provisions of the legislation are now familiar: (i) the establishment of a Public Company Accounting Oversight Board to regulate auditors of public companies; (ii) the grant of new authority to the SEC; and (iii) significant additions and enhancements to the timing and quality of information required to be publicly disclosed by public companies. The Act followed upon the Commission's new policy of "real time enforcement." Under that initiative, the staff was directed to "segment" its cases to quickly identify wrongdoing and seek interim relief where appropriate. In addition, the Commission continues to enhance enforcement by encouraging self-reporting. Under the Section 21(a) Report on cooperation issued on October 23, 2001, the Commission has provided guidance on compliance and self-policing, with the intent of incentivizing issuers to self-report and self-correct, while allowing the enforcement staff to harbor its limited resources.

This outline briefly discusses developments in legislation, Commission rulemaking and pronouncements, and noteworthy Commission enforcement actions that constitute the current SEC enforcement framework in the area of financial reporting and accounting.

II. THE SARBANES-OXLEY ACT OF 2002

On July 25, 2002, both houses of Congress passed the Sarbanes-Oxley Act of 2002 by overwhelming majorities. President Bush signed the Act into law on July 30, 2002.[1] Sarbanes-Oxley enacted a number of new corporate governance and accounting policies and directed the SEC to adopt additional regulations directed toward other areas of corporate reform. The Act also expanded the SEC's enforcement authority in significant respects and is intended to vastly increase its resources.

A. New Requirements for Public Companies

Public companies have many new obligations under Sarbanes-Oxley, including: (1) the duty of a company's CEO and CFO to certify the company's financial reports; (2) the duty of the audit committee of

---

1. Sarbanes-Oxley Act of 2002, Pub. L. No. 107-204, 116 Stat. 745 (2002) (hereinafter cited by section as the "Sarbanes-Oxley Act").

the board of directors to meet certain corporate governance criteria; (3) the duty of the company to report material changes in its financial condition or operations in "real time;" (4) the duty of management to create and disclose an internal controls report; (5) the duty of the company to make disclosures concerning all material off-balance-sheet transactions; and (6) the duty of the company to disclose whether it has adopted a code of ethics for senior financial officers. In addition, Sarbanes-Oxley prohibits a public company from making loans to its officers (subject to important exceptions) and prohibits officers from trading securities during pension fund blackout periods. Sarbanes-Oxley also requires executives to repay the company certain bonuses or other incentive-based compensation, as well as profits from the sale of the company's securities, if the company must later restate a financial report due to misconduct.

1. *Certification of Financial Reports*

Section 302 of the Act directs the SEC to require that each annual and periodic report filed with the SEC include a written certification by the Chief Executive Officer ("CEO") and Chief Financial Officer ("CFO") of each public company certifying that:

- The signing officer has reviewed the report;
- To the CEO/CFO's knowledge, the report does not contain any untrue statement of a material fact or omit to state a material fact necessary to make the statements made, in light of the circumstances which such statements were made, not misleading;
- The signing officers are responsible for establishing and maintaining internal controls, have designed such internal controls to ensure that material information relating to the public company and its subsidiaries is made known to such officers, have evaluated the effectiveness of the public company's internal controls within 90 days prior to the report, and have presented in their filing their conclusions as to the effectiveness of the internal controls based on that evaluation;
- The signing officers have disclosed to the auditors and the audit committee all significant deficiencies in internal controls and any fraud, whether or not material, involving management or employees who have significant roles in internal controls; and

- The signing officers have indicated in the report whether or not there were significant changes in internal controls subsequent to the date of their evaluation (together a "Section 302 certification").

On August 28, 2002, the Commission adopted new Exchange Act Rules 13a-14 and 15d-14 to implement Section 302 of the Act.[2]

Section 906 of the Act creates an independent CEO and CFO certification obligation additional to the Section 302 certification. Section 906 requires a certification that any periodic report containing financial statements fully complies with Section 13(a) or 15(d) of the Exchange Act and that the information contained in the periodic report fairly presents, in all material respects, the issuer's financial conditions and results of operations ("Section 906 certification"). A person who files a certification knowing the report does not comport with the requirements of Section

906 is subject to a fine of not more than $1 million or not more than 10 years in prison, or both.[3] A willful violation is punishable by a fine of not more than $5 million or not more than 20 years in prison, or both. There is no penalty specified in Section 906 for the failure to file the Section 906 certification.

The Section 302 and Section 906 certification requirements apply to non-U.S. companies filing annual reports on Form 20-F or Form 40-F. The SEC has made clear that reports furnished to the SEC on Form 6-K need not contain a Section 302 certification. The SEC has not provided similar guidance regarding whether Section 906 certifications are required on Form 6-K reports. Because Section 906 certifications are required only on "filed" reports and reports may be furnished on Form 6-K, by implication, a Section 906 certification may not be required in periodic filings submitted on Form 6-K.

2. *Public Company Audit Committees*

Sarbanes-Oxley mandates several new requirements for audit committees of public companies. In particular, audit committees must:

---

2. *See* Securities and Exchange Commission Final Rule: Certification of Disclosure in Companies' Quarterly and Annual Reports, Rel. No. 33-8124, 2002 WL 31720215 (Aug. 28, 2002).
3. Sarbanes-Oxley Act, Section 906(a).

- Be responsible for the appointment, compensation and oversight of auditors (including resolution of disagreements with company management);[4]
- Be composed of independent members of the board of directors;
- Establish procedures for the treatment of complaints received by the public company regarding accounting matters, including the confidential and anonymous submission of complaints by employees; and
- Have the authority and funding to engage independent counsel and other advisers to carry out its duties.[5]

Pursuant to Sarbanes-Oxley, the SEC adopted rules requiring the national securities exchanges and NASDAQ to prohibit the listing of any public company's securities if that issuer is not in compliance with the above-listed requirements.[6] The rules carve out limited exceptions for foreign private issuers to accommodate differences in certain home country legal requirements or corporate governance standards. The foreign private issuers exceptions within the rules permit:

- A non-management employee to sit on an audit committee if the employee is named to the foreign issuer's board pursuant to a home country legal requirement;
- One member of an audit committee of a foreign private issuer to be a representative of an affiliate of such an issuer as long as the representative receives no compensation, and does not serve as the chairperson of the audit committee, does not vote on audit committee matters, or serve as an executive officer of the issuer; and
- One member of an audit committee to be a representative of a foreign government if that representative does not serve as an executive officer of the issuer.

---

4. Sarbanes-Oxley Act, Section 301.
5. Id.
6. *See* Securities and Exchange Commission Final Rule: Standards Relating to Listed Company Audit Committees, Rel. No. 33-8220, 2003 WL 1833875 (Apr. 9, 2003).

The Commission has also adopted rules requiring public companies to disclose whether one member of their audit committee is a financial expert.[7] The Commission's rules require public companies to make specific disclosures in annual reports regarding whether there is a financial expert on their audit committee. Under the Commission's rules, a public company must disclose either that: (1) at least one member of its audit committee is a financial expert, provide his or her name, and state whether he or she is independent; or (2) the company does not have a financial expert on its audit committee and the reason why it does not.

The Commission's rules define the term “audit committee financial expert” to mean an individual possessing all of the following attributes:

- An understanding of generally accepted accounting principles and financial statements;
- An ability to assess the general application of such principles in connection with the accounting for estimates, accruals, and reserves;
- Experience preparing, auditing, analyzing, or evaluating financial statements that present a breadth and level of complexity of accounting issues generally comparable to the breadth and complexity of issues that can reasonably be expected to be raised by the company's financial statements, or experience actively supervising one or more persons engaged in such activities;
- An understanding of internal controls and procedures for financial reporting; and
- An understanding of audit committee functions.

In addition, to be considered an “audit committee financial expert” the individual must have acquired the above attributes through one or more of the following ways:

- Education and experience as a principal financial officer, principal accounting officer, controller, public accountant or audi-

---

7. *See* Securities and Exchange Commission Final Rule: Disclosure Required by Sections 406 and 407 of the Sarbanes-Oxley Act of 2002, Rel. No. 33-8177, 2003 WL 164269 (Jan. 23, 2003) (as amended by Rel. No. 33-8177A) (March 31, 2003) [hereinafter Release 33-8177].

tor or experience in one or more positions that involve the performance of similar functions;

- Experience actively supervising a principal financial officer, principal accounting officer, controller, public accountant, auditor or person performing similar functions;
- Experience overseeing or assessing the performance of companies or public accountants with respect to the preparation, auditing or evaluation of financial statements; or
- Other relevant experience.

3. Real Time Disclosure

The Act mandates that each public company disclose on a "rapid and current basis" any such additional information concerning material changes in its financial condition or operations as the SEC determines by rule is necessary or useful for the protection of investors and in the public interest. On March 16, 2004, the SEC adopted a rule requiring numerous additional Form 8-K disclosures to be made within a four-business day deadline for U.S. public companies.[8] This rule became effective on August 23, 2004.

4. Management Assessment of Internal Controls

Pursuant to the Act, the SEC has adopted rules[9] requiring that Forms 10-K and 10-KSB, and Forms 20-F and 40-F in the case of foreign private issuers, contain an "internal control report" which: (1) states the responsibility of management for establishing and maintaining an adequate internal control structure and procedures for financial reporting; and (2) contains an assessment of the effectiveness of the internal control structure and procedures for financial reporting as of the end of the most recent fiscal year of the public company.[10] In addition to the public company's certification, the company's public accounting firm is required to attest to and report

---

8. Securities and Exchange Commission Final Rule: Additional Form 8-K Disclosure Requirements and Acceleration of Filing Date, Rel. No. 33-8400, 2004 WL 536851 (Mar. 16, 2004).
9. *See* Securities and Exchange Commission Final Rule: Management's Report on Internal Control Over Financial Reporting and Certification of Disclosure in Exchange Act Periodic Reports, Rel. No. 33-8238, 2003 WL 21294970 (June 5, 2003).
10. Sarbanes-Oxley Act, Section 404(a); 17 CFR §§228.10 *et seq.*

on management's assessment in accordance with standards to be adopted by the Oversight Board.[11]

5. Disclosure of All Material Correcting Adjustments, Off-Balance Sheet, and Pro Forma Financial Information

Sarbanes-Oxley imposes three enhanced financial disclosure requirements. First, for every report that contains financial statements and is required to be prepared in accordance with generally accepted accounting principles, Sarbanes-Oxley requires that the report reflect all "material correcting adjustments" that have been identified by a registered public accounting firm in accordance with generally accepted accounting principles and SEC rules.[12]

Second, under the Act, the Commission adopted rules requiring the disclosure in periodic filings of all material off-balance sheet arrangements and other transactions or relationships that may have a material effect on the financial condition of a company or the significant components of a company's revenues or expenses.[13]

The Commission's rules define the term "off-balance sheet arrangements" to include, but not be limited to:

- Certain guarantee contracts;
- Retained or contingent interests in assets transferred to an unconsolidated entity;
- Derivative instruments classified as equity; or
- Material variable interests in unconsolidated entities that conduct certain activities.

Finally, Sarbanes-Oxley directs the SEC to issue rules regulating the presentation of "pro forma" financial information.[14] Pursuant to this mandate, the Commission adopted rules which require issuers that publish certain types of "non-GAAP financial measures" to assume additional disclosure responsibilities.[15] Part of this body of regulation, Regulation G, prohibits publicly-held companies from

11. Sarbanes-Oxley Act, Section 404(b); 17 CFR §§210.1-01 *et seq.*
12. Sarbanes-Oxley Act, Section 401(a).
13. Sarbanes-Oxley Act, Section 401(a). *See* Securities and Exchange Commission Final Rule: Disclosure in Management's Discussion and Analysis About Off-Balance Sheet Arrangements and Aggregate Contractual Obligations, Rel. No. 33-8182, 2003 WL 175446 (Jan. 28, 2003).
14. Sarbanes-Oxley Act, Section 401(b).

making non-GAAP financial disclosures that contain an untrue statement of a material fact or omit to state a material fact necessary in order to make the pro forma financial information, in light of the circumstances under which it was presented, not misleading. More notably, Regulation G mandates that when an issuer publicly discloses material non-public information that includes a non-GAAP financial measure, the issuer must include as part of the disclosure: (1) a presentation of the most directly comparable financial measure presented in accordance with GAAP and (2) a reconciliation of the differences between the non-GAAP presentation and the most directly comparable financial measure presented in accordance with GAAP. The Commission carved out a limited exception from Regulation G for certain foreign private issuers.

As part of its rules relating to the use of pro forma financial information, the Commission amended Form 8-K to require issuers to furnish to the Commission all public releases of earnings reports and similar announcements for quarterly or annual periods. In addition, the Commission amended Regulations S-K and S-B and Form 20-F to further regulate the use of non-GAAP financial data included in Commission filings.[16]

Regulation G and the amendments to the Commission's forms apply to disclosures made after March 28, 2003.

6. Code of Ethics

Acting pursuant to Section 406 of the Act, the SEC adopted rules directing public companies to adopt codes of ethics for their chief executive officer and senior financial officers.[17] Under the Commission's rules, public companies must disclose in their annual reports whether or not they have adopted a code of ethics and, if not, the reason why a code has not been adopted.

According to the release accompanying the Commission's rules, the codes of ethics are to be designed to deter wrongdoing and promote:

---

15. *See* Securities and Exchange Commission Final Rule: Conditions for Use of Non-GAAP Financial Measures, Rel. No. 33-8176, 2003 WL 161117 (Jan. 22, 2003). The SEC had previously issued a release cautioning issuers on the use of "pro forma" financial information. *See* Exch. Act Release No. 34-45124 (Dec. 4, 2001).
16. *Id.*
17. Sarbanes-Oxley Act, Section 406(a). *See* Release 33-8177, 2003 WL 164269.

- Honest and ethical conduct, including the ethical handling of actual or apparent conflicts of interest between personal and professional relationships;
- Full, fair, accurate, timely, and understandable disclosure in reports and documents that a company files with, or submits to, the SEC and in other public communications made by the company;
- Compliance with applicable governmental laws, rules, and regulations;
- The prompt internal reporting of violations of the code to an appropriate person or persons identified in the code; and
- Accountability for adherence to the code.

Disclosures relating to the adoption of codes of ethics are required in annual reports for fiscal years ending after July 15, 2003.

7. The Prohibition on Loans to Directors and Officers

Sarbanes-Oxley prohibits public companies from extending, maintaining, arranging for, or renewing credit, in the form of a personal loan, to any of its directors or executive officers.[18] Extensions of credit made before the enactment of Sarbanes-Oxley are permitted so long as there is no modification to any term of the credit and no renewal of the credit after Sarbanes-Oxley's enactment. However, Sarbanes-Oxley carves out exceptions to its general prohibition. For example, Sarbanes-Oxley does not prohibit home improvement and manufactured home loans (as defined in 12 U.S.C. § 1464), consumer credit (as defined by 15 U.S.C. § 1602), extension of credit under an open-end credit plan (as defined by 15 U.S.C. § 1602), a charge card (as defined by 15 U.S.C. § 1637(c)(4)(e)), or extension of credit in margin accounts of employees of brokers or dealers, provided that extension is made in the ordinary course of business on terms no more favorable than those made to the general public.[19]

8. Pension Fund Blackout Periods

Sarbanes-Oxley prohibits a director or executive officer from buying, selling, or acquiring the company's equity securities during a pension fund blackout period if the director or officer acquires the

18. Sarbanes-Oxley Act, Section 402(a).
19. *Id.*

security in connection with his or her service as a director or officer.[20] The company can recover any profits made by the director or officer, and if the company declines to do so, a shareholder may bring a derivative action.[21] Sarbanes-Oxley also ordered the SEC to issue rules to enforce these mandates. In response, the Commission adopted Regulation Blackout Trading Restriction ("Regulation BTR").[22] Regulation BTR prohibits purchases and sales of securities during a blackout period if the transaction is in connection with service as a director or executive officer and if the transaction involves equity securities acquired in connection with such service. The regulation defines a "blackout period" as a period of more than three consecutive business days during which the ability to purchase or sell any equity security of the company held in an individual account plan is temporarily suspended by a company. Regulation BTR exempts a number of transactions from its prohibitions.

9. Forfeiture of Bonuses

Sarbanes-Oxley requires the CEO and CFO of a public company to repay certain bonuses and other compensation if the company is required to restate its financial reports because it failed to comply with a financial reporting requirement under the securities laws as a result of "misconduct." In particular, the CEO and CFO are required to pay to the company: (1) any bonus or incentive-based or equity-based compensation received during the twelve month period following the initial issuance of the financial document which eventually required restatement and (2) any profits made from the sale of securities during that period.[23] The SEC has the ability to exempt individuals from this requirement.

B. Accounting Reforms

In one of its most significant provisions, Sarbanes-Oxley mandated the establishment of a Public Company Accounting Oversight Board (the "Oversight Board") to regulate auditors of public companies.[24] The Oversight Board is a private, non-profit corporate entity subject to

---

20. Sarbanes-Oxley Act, Section 306(a)(1).
21. Sarbanes-Oxley Act, Section 306(a)(2).
22. Securities and Exchange Commission Final Rule: Insider Trades During Pension Fund Blackout Periods, Rel. No. 34-47225, 2003 WL 152486 (Jan. 22, 2003).
23. Sarbanes-Oxley Act, Section 304(a).
24. Sarbanes-Oxley Act, Section 101(a).

oversight by the Commission.[25] It is composed of five members, initially appointed by the SEC, of whom two and only two members, must be current or former certified public accountants. The Oversight Board became operational on April 25, 2003.

The Oversight Board acts as the primary federal regulator for auditors of public companies, similar to the functions of the National Association of Securities Dealers and the stock exchanges with respect to broker-dealer firms. The Oversight Board is required to:

- Register public accounting firms that prepare audit reports;
- Establish or adopt auditing, quality control and ethics standards and rules that are proposed by a designated professional group(s) of accountants;
- Inspect registered public accounting firms;
- Conduct investigations and disciplinary proceedings and impose sanctions upon registered public accounting firms and their associated persons;
- Promote high professional standards of conduct among registered public accounting firms and their associated persons and improve the audit function; and
- Enforce compliance with the Act, Oversight Board rules, professional standards, and the securities laws relating to the preparation and issuance of audit reports.

All U.S. public accounting firms must register with the Oversight Board if such firms intend to prepare or issue audit reports after October 22, 2003.[26]

The Oversight Board has the authority to adopt auditing, quality control, and ethical standards proposed by a designated group of accountants and may modify, supplement, revise, or repeal any portion of such standards.[27] Among the standards the Oversight Board is in the process of adopting are requirements that each registered public accounting firm:

25. Sarbanes-Oxlcy Act, Section 101(a), Section 107(a).
26. Sarbanes-Oxley Act, Section 102(a); PCAOB Rel. No. 2003-007 (May 6, 2003).
27. Sarbanes-Oxley Act, Section 103(a)(1).

- Prepare, and maintain for at least seven years, audit work papers and other information related to any audit report, in sufficient detail to support the conclusions reached in such report;
- Provide a concurring or second partner review and approval of audit reports; and
- Describe in each audit report the auditor's testing of internal control structures and procedures of the issuer.[28]

The Act empowers the Oversight Board to conduct a continuing program of inspections of each registered public accounting firm to assess compliance with the Act, the rules of the Oversight Board, the rules of the SEC, and professional standards.[29]

The Oversight Board is also authorized to conduct investigations of registered accounting firms for violations of professional standards, the Oversight Board's rules or other laws or regulations relating to the preparation of audit reports, and the liability of accountants.[30] Significantly, the Act provides the Oversight Board the ability to impose sanctions on a registered accounting firm or the supervisory personnel at the firm if the firm failed reasonably to supervise an associated person for violations of the Oversight Board's rules, the federal securities laws or regulations relating to the preparation of audit reports, and the liability of accountants.[31]

C. Auditor Independence

Sarbanes-Oxley amends Section 10A of the Exchange Act, as well as other provisions of the federal securities law relating to auditors, and directs the Commission to issue regulations to carry out the amendments.[32] Acting on this congressional directive, the Commission adopted rules and amended existing rules focusing on auditor independence on January 28, 2003.[33] The Act and the Commission's new rules in this area place numerous restrictions upon auditors, including: (1) prohibiting accounting firms engaged in the audit of a public company from offering a number of non-audit services to the company contem-

---

28. Sarbanes-Oxley Act, Section 103(a)(2).
29. This inspection program will replace the American Institute of Certified Public Accountants' peer review program, where member accounting firms inspect each other to ensure compliance with all professional standards, *available at* http://www.aicpa.org/members/div/practmon/index.htm.
30. Sarbanes-Oxley Act, Section 105(b)(1).
31. Sarbanes-Oxley Act, Section 105(c)(6)(A).
32. Sarbanes-Oxley Act, Section 208(a).

poraneously with the audit; (2) prohibiting accounting firms from auditing a public company's financial statement if a firm previously employed the company's senior financial officers; (3) requiring the rotation of the lead audit partner every five years; (4) requiring the retention of audit papers for at least seven years; and (5) requiring the auditors to make certain timely reports to the audit committee. Each of these restrictions is described below.

1. Prohibited Non-Audit Services

The Act and the Commission's rules prohibit accounting firms from providing certain non-audit services to public companies contemporaneously with an audit. In order to maintain its independent status, an audit firm is prohibited from providing the following services concurrently with an audit:

- Bookkeeping and other services related to the accounting records or financial statements of the audit client;
- Financial information systems design and implementation;
- Appraisal or valuation services, fairness opinions, and contribution-in-kind reports;
- Actuarial services;
- Internal audit outsourcing services;
- Management functions or human resources;
- Broker or dealer, investment adviser, or investment banking services;
- Legal and expert services unrelated to the audit; and
- Any other service the Oversight Board determines is prohibited.[34]

The Commission's rules define the meaning and scope of the prohibited services. Auditors may provide non-audit services (including tax services) not expressly prohibited by the Act if the services are pre-approved by the audit committee.[35] In the discussion accompa-

33. *See* Securities and Exchange Commission Final Rule: Strengthening the Commission's Requirements Regarding Auditor Independence, Rel. No. 33-8183, 2003 WL 183801 (Jan. 28, 2003). The Commission reissued Rel. No. 33-8183 with minor changes on March 23, 2003.

34. Sarbanes-Oxley Act, Section 201(a).

nying the Commission's rules, the Commission cautions audit committee members to scrutinize the provision of prohibited services, which are reclassified as tax services to circumvent the purpose of the rules. The Oversight Board also may issue exemptions from the non-audit services prohibited on a case-by-case basis.[36]

2. Employment Restriction on Accountants

A registered public accounting firm may not participate in the audit of a public company if the CEO, controller, CFO, chief accounting officer or person holding an equivalent position was employed by the accounting firm and participated in the audit of such public company during the one-year period preceding the initiation of the audit.[37] The Commission's rules on this subject make clear that an accounting firm will not be considered independent with respect to an audit client if a former partner or professional employee of the accounting firm is in an accounting role or financial reporting oversight role at an audit client and has a continuing supervisor or financial interest in the accounting firm.

In addition, a firm will not be deemed independent if a former partner or professional employee is employed by the client in a financial reporting oversight role and he or she was a member of the audit engagement team for that client during the one-year period preceding the start date of the most recent audit that the employee served on the audit engagement team.

3. Audit Partner Rotation

Sarbanes-Oxley provides that a registered public accounting firm may not provide audit services to a public company if the lead audit partner or the partner responsible for reviewing the audit has performed audit services for that company in each of the five previous fiscal years.[38] The Commission's rules clarify and expand the rotation system required for audit partners. The Commission's rules provide that no audit partner may perform the services of lead partner or concurring partner for more than five consecutive years and, following the five-year rotation, such audit partners must wait five years before performing services again to that client. The rules also provide that no audit partner may, for more than seven consecutive years, (1) provide more

35. Id.
36. Sarbanes-Oxley Act, Section 201(b).
37. Sarbanes-Oxley Act, Section 206.
38. Sarbanes-Oxley Act, Section 203.

than ten hours of audit, review, or attest services in connection with a company's annual or interim financial statements, or (2) serve as the lead partner for any audit or review related to the annual or interim financial statements of a major subsidiary of the client. Following this seven-year rotation, such audit partners must wait two years before performing one or more of the foregoing services. The rules contain limited exceptions for accounting firms with less than five audit clients or less than ten partners.

4. Audit Record Retention

The Act requires auditors to retain all audit and review work papers for at least seven years.[39] Any knowing or willful failure to retain those papers for at least five years is punishable by a fine and up to ten years in prison.[40] On January 24, 2003, the Commission adopted rules defining the categories of documents to be retained.[41] According to the Commission's rules, auditors must maintain work papers, other documents that form the basis of the audit, and any other document that was: (1) created, sent, or received in connection with the audit and (2) contains conclusions, opinions, analyses, or financial data related to the audit. The rules also require retention of documents relating to a significant matter that are inconsistent with the final conclusions of the auditor. The Commission's rules relating to the audit records do not contain an exemption for audits of foreign issuers' financial statements. The rules apply to audits completed on or after October 31, 2003.

5. Auditor Reports to Audit Committees

The Act and the Commission's rules require the auditor to make timely reports to the audit committee of its public company client on matters including: (1) critical accounting policies and practices to be used; (2) alternative GAAP treatments of financial statements that have been discussed with management, the ramifications of these alternative treatments and the accounting firm's preferred method; and (3) all material written communication between the auditors and management, such as management letters or unadjusted difference schedules.[42]

---

39. Sarbanes-Oxley Act, Section 103(a)(2)(A)(i).
40. Sarbanes-Oxley Act, Section 802. The Act does not reconcile or otherwise explain the disparity between these two document retention time periods.
41. Securities and Exchange Commission Final Rule: Retention of Records Relevant to Audits and Reviews, Rel. No. 33-8180 (Jan. 24, 2003).

6. *Compensation*

The Commission's rules state that an accounting firm will not be deemed independent if, at any time during the audit or professional engagement period, any audit partner earns or receives compensation based on that audit partner procuring engagements to provide any products or non-audit services. This prohibition contains an exemption for small accounting firms.

The Commission's rules also require expanded disclosure in a company's proxy statement and annual report of fees paid to principal accounting firms. The disclosure must contain the amounts paid for services provided during the two most recent fiscal years in each of the following categories:

- Audit fees;
- Audit-related fees;
- Tax fees; and
- All other fees.

D. Increased Authority for the SEC

Sarbanes-Oxley increases the authority of, and imposes additional obligations upon, the SEC in regulating public companies by: (1) requiring that the SEC review the filings of public companies at least once every three years; (2) granting the SEC the additional power to bar individuals from serving as directors or officers; and (3) authorizing the SEC to seek new forms of equitable relief from federal courts.

1. *Increased Frequency of SEC Review*

The SEC periodically reviews filings by public companies, but previously had no requirement to review company filings according to a particular timetable. Sarbanes-Oxley requires the SEC to review the filings of a public company listed on a national securities exchange or traded on an automated quotation facility not less than once every three years.[43]

2. *Bars on Officers and Directors*

Sections 21(d)(2) of the Exchange Act and 20(e) of the Securities Act formerly authorized a court to prohibit a person from serving as

42. Sarbanes-Oxley Act, Section 204.
43. Sarbanes-Oxley Act, Section 408(c).

an officer and director if the person was found to have violated the antifraud provisions and the person's conduct demonstrated "substantial unfitness" to serve as an officer and director of a public company. The Act reduced the standard from "substantial unfitness" to "unfitness" and expands the SEC's authority to seek such a bar, allowing the agency to request the bar in an administrative cease and desist proceeding.[44] Previously, the SEC had to go to federal court to obtain an officer and director bar.

The "substantial unfitness" standard had resulted in many courts adopting a six-prong test[45] that had proven difficult for the Commission to satisfy.[46] The reduced standard may result in the Commission seeking such a remedy more frequently in the future, particularly in the areas of accounting and financial reporting.[47]

3. New Forms of Equitable Relief Available to the SEC

In any action brought by the SEC in federal court, Sarbanes-Oxley authorizes the SEC to request, and a federal court to grant, "any equitable relief that may be appropriate or necessary for the benefit of investors."[48] In addition, whenever the SEC investigates a public company for possible violations of the securities laws, and it appears that it is likely that the company will make "extraordinary payments" to the company's directors, officers, partners, controlling persons, agents, or employees, the SEC now has the ability to request that a federal court temporarily freeze those payments.[49] If a temporary order is entered, it can remain enforceable for up to ninety days.[50]

---

44. Sarbanes-Oxley Act, Section 305(a).

45. Pursuant to the six-prong test, courts had considered: (1) the egregiousness of the underlying securities law violation; (2) the defendant's repeat offender status; (3) the defendant's role or position when he or she engaged in the fraud; (4) the defendant's degree of scienter; (5) the defendant's economic stake in the violation; and (6) the likelihood that the misconduct will recur. *E.g., SEC v. Patel*, 61 F.3d 137, 141 (2d Cir. 1995).

46. *See, e.g., SEC v. Farrell*, 1996 WL 788367 (W.D.N.Y. Nov. 6, 1996) (court refused to impose bar against officer who was criminally convicted of insider trading).

47. *See* Stephen M. Cutler, Director, Division of Enforcement, *Remarks at the Glasser LegalWorks 20th Annual Federal Securities Institute*, Hallandale, Florida (Feb. 15, 2002) available at <http://www.sec.gov/news/speech/spch538.htm> (visited Dec. 30, 2002).

48. Sarbanes-Oxley Act, Section 305(b).

4. *Standards of Professional Conduct for Attorneys*

Following the directive of Section 307 of the Act, the Commission adopted rules setting standards of professional conduct for attorneys appearing and practicing before the Commission and setting forth procedures for attorneys that discover evidence of material violations in the clients they represent before the Commission.[51] The rules require an attorney to report the evidence to the chief legal counsel or the chief executive officer of a company. If the attorney determines that such officers failed to respond appropriately to the evidence, the rules require the attorney to report the evidence to the audit committee, another committee of independent directors, or the full board of directors. The rules also permit public companies to create a qualified legal compliance committee ("QLCC"). If a company has an established QLCC, the attorney may report evidence of a material violation to that committee in order to satisfy his or her requirements under the rules.

The Commission also published proposed rules requesting comment on an additional requirement for outside counsel that does not obtain a satisfactory resolution after he or she reports evidence of a violation to the audit committee of his or her client. Under the proposal, the attorney must withdraw from representation of the client for "professional considerations" and the issuer must then notify the SEC of such withdrawal through the filing of a Form 8-K.[52] This proposal is an alternative to the requirement that an attorney undertake a "noisy withdrawal" from the client if he or she does receive a satisfactory response from a reported violation that is ongoing or about to occur. Under the proposed "noisy withdrawal" requirement, the attorney's duty would be satisfied when the attorney notified the

---

49. Sarbanes-Oxley Act, Section 1103(a); *See SEC v. Gemstar-TV Guide International, Inc.*, 2004 WL 1058187 (9th Cir. 2004) (vacating district court ruling that termination payments to Gemstar's former CEO and its former CFO qualified as "extraordinary payments" subject to Section 1103 of Sarbanes-Oxley, where no evidence was introduced distinguishing payments from "usual" or "ordinary" payments); *SEC v. Vivendi Universal, S.A., et al.*, Litigation Release No. 18523 (December 24, 2003) (former Vivendi CEO relinquishing claim to $21 million severance package that SEC had sought to have placed in escrow pursuant to Section 1103 of Sarbanes-Oxley).

50. Id.

51. Securities and Exchange Commission Final Rule: Implementation of Standards of Professional Conduct for Attorneys, Rel. No. 33-8185, 2003 WL 193527 (Jan. 29, 2003).

52. *Id.*

Commission of the withdrawal and, in some circumstances, disaffirming documents filed with the Commission.

E. New Criminal Statutes and Enhanced Penalties

Sarbanes-Oxley creates several new criminal statutes and enhances the penalties for numerous other statutes. Two of the new criminal statutes are discussed above—the statutes prohibiting false CEO or CFO certifications of the company's financial statements and the destruction of accountants' work papers. The other new criminal statutes: (1) prohibit improper influence on the conduct of audits; (2) prohibit retaliation against whistleblowers; (3) revise current prohibitions on the destruction of documents with the intent to frustrate federal investigations; and (4) expand current prohibitions on securities fraud.

1. Improper Influence on Conduct of Audits

Sarbanes-Oxley prohibits any officer or director of a public company or person acting at their direction from fraudulently influencing, coercing, manipulating or misleading any independent public or certified accounting firm for the purpose of rendering the financial statements materially misleading.[53] The Commission adopted rules on this subject on May 20, 2003.[54] The Commission's rules were designed to ensure that management makes open and full disclosures to its independent auditors.

2. Retaliation Against Whistleblowers

Sarbanes-Oxley places criminal liability upon anyone who takes any harmful action against a person with the intent to retaliate against that person for providing truthful information to a federal law enforcement officer relating to the commission or possible commission of any federal crime.[55] The maximum penalty for violation of this section is ten years in prison and/or a fine.[56]

3. Document Destruction

Sarbanes-Oxley imposes criminal sanctions upon anyone who knowingly alters, destroys, mutilates, conceals, covers up, falsifies, or makes a false entry in any record or tangible object with the intent

53. Sarbanes-Oxley Act, Section 303(a).
54. *See* Securities and Exchange Commission: Final Rule: Improper Influence on Conduct of Audits, Rel. No. 34-47890, 2003 WL 21148349 (May 20, 2003).
55. Sarbanes-Oxley Act, Section 1107.
56. Id.

to impede, obstruct, or influence the investigation of a federal agency or any bankruptcy case under Chapter 11 of the Bankruptcy Code.[57] In order for the government to obtain a conviction under this statute, it need only prove that the destruction was "in relation to or contemplation of" a federal investigation or bankruptcy case, not that such an investigation or case was actually pending.[58] The maximum penalty for violation of this statute is twenty years and/or a fine.[59]

4. New Securities Fraud Statutes and Penalties

Sarbanes-Oxley creates a new securities fraud statute, which provides criminal liability for anyone who executes a scheme or artifice to: (1) defraud anyone in connection with any securities or (2) obtain any money or property in connection with the sale of securities by means of false or fraudulent pretenses, representations, or promises.[60] The maximum sentence under this provision is 25 years in prison and/or a fine. Sarbanes-Oxley also enhances the maximum penalties for willful violations of the securities laws by individuals by increasing the maximum term of imprisonment from ten to twenty years and increasing the maximum fines from $1 million to $5 million.[61] For anyone other than a natural person (e.g., corporations), Sarbanes-Oxley increased the maximum fine from $2.5 million to $25 million.[62] Sarbanes-Oxley also increases the maximum penalties for a number of other statutes. For the mail and wire fraud statutes, Sarbanes-Oxley increases the maximum sentence from five to twenty years. For violations of the Employee Retirement Income Security Act of 1974 ("ERISA"), Sarbanes-Oxley increases the maximum penalty of imprisonment from one year to ten years, the maximum fine for natural persons from $5,000 to $100,000, and the maximum fine for non-natural persons from $100,000 to $500,000.[63] Sarbanes-Oxley also directs the United States Sentencing Commission to re-evaluate the Sentencing Guidelines in order to ensure that the Guidelines sufficiently reflect the serious nature of the offenses and penalties set forth in Sarbanes-Oxley.[64]

---

57. Sarbanes-Oxley Act, Section 802.
58. *Id.*
59. *Id.*
60. Sarbanes-Oxley Act, Section 807.
61. Sarbanes-Oxley Act, Section 1106.
62. *Id.*
63. Sarbanes-Oxley Act, Section 904.

III. THE SEC'S SECTION 21(A) REPORT IN THE *LEON-MEREDITH* ACTION

The SEC provided significant guidance on cooperation and self-policing in its October 2001 Report of Investigation (the "Leon-Meredith Report") pursuant to Section 21(a) of the Exchange Act. The Leon-Meredith Report set forth the criteria the SEC will consider in determining whether, or how much, it will credit self-policing, self-reporting, remediation, and cooperation in making enforcement decisions.[65] This guidance was released simultaneously with the SEC announcing it had settled a proceeding against a company employee, alleging inaccurate books and records and misstated periodic reports, but was taking no action against the company.[66]

The Leon-Meredith Report identifies four broad measures to be considered by the staff in deciding whether and how to exercise its prosecutorial discretion: self-policing, self-reporting, remediation, and cooperation.

A. Self-Policing

The Leon-Meredith Report states the SEC will take into consideration policies and procedures a company has in place, prior to the discovery of misconduct, in its enforcement decisions. In this regard, the SEC will consider:

- Whether the company had procedures in place intended to prevent and detect the misconduct;
- The reasons the procedures failed to prevent the misconduct;
- The "tone at the top:" Whether the misconduct arose from pressure to achieve specific results, or there was a tone of lawlessness set by those in control of the company;
- The nature of the misconduct;
- The position of the wrongdoer;
- The actions or inactions of senior personnel;
- The pervasiveness of the misconduct; and

---

64. Sarbanes-Oxley Act, Section 905(b)(1).

65. *See* Exch. Act Rel. No. 34-44969; Accounting and Auditing Enforcement Rel. No. 1470 (October 23, 2001). The Report may be found at <http://www.sec.gov/news/litigation/investreport/34-44969.htm>.

66. *In the Matter of Gisela de Leon-Meredith*, Exch. Act Rel. No. 44970 (October 23, 2001). *See* Section L. below.

- How and by whom the misconduct was uncovered.

In the Leon-Meredith matter, the SEC found significant that the violative conduct was limited to three employees of a company subsidiary. Senior personnel acted promptly, utilizing the company's internal auditors to ascertain the nature and extent of Meredith's misconduct.

B. Self-Reporting

According to the Leon-Meredith Report, how and when the SEC and investors learn of wrongdoing, and a company's own actions after learning of potential wrongdoing, will influence whether and to what extent prosecutorial discretion will be exercised. The SEC will consider:

- Whether the company promptly disclosed on its own initiative the wrongdoing and its impact to the investing public, to the SEC and the relevant self-regulatory organization;
- Whether the company demonstrates a commitment to learn the truth, fully and expeditiously;
- Whether the company informs relevant persons, including its independent auditors, audit committee and Board of Directors; and
- Whether the company undertakes a thorough, expeditious, and comprehensive review of the nature, extent, origins and consequences of the conduct.

In deciding not to institute an enforcement action against Seaboard, the SEC found significant the Company's speed and candor in disclosing the wrongdoing. The audit committee and full board were notified in a timely fashion, and the company disclosed to both the SEC and the public that its financial statements would have to be restated. The SEC found relevant that the price of Seaboard's stock did not decline after disclosure of the need to restate its financial statements, or the restatement itself. The SEC also noted that Seaboard quickly engaged counsel to conduct an internal investigation.

C. Remediation

Once a company confirms that misconduct has occurred, the SEC will take into consideration what steps are taken. For example, the following steps may be viewed favorably by the staff in formulating an enforcement recommendation:

- Disciplining or terminating culpable employees;
- Changing or strengthening internal controls and procedures to prevent recurrence of the misconduct; and
- Identifying the extent of damage to investors and other corporate constituencies and compensating those affected by the misconduct.

In the Leon-Meredith matter, the staff looked favorably on Seaboard's swift and decisive actions. The Company terminated Meredith within 12 days of learning of the misconduct. Two employees responsible for supervising Meredith were also terminated. Seaboard strengthened its financial reporting processes to prevent a recurrence of such misconduct in the future. These steps included the development of a detailed closing process for the subsidiaries' accounting personnel, consolidating the subsidiaries' accounting functions under a Seaboard CPA, hiring additional qualified employees responsible for preparing the subsidiaries' financial statements, changing the subsidiaries' annual audit requirements, and vesting Seaboard's controller with supervisory responsibilities over the subsidiaries' reporting processes.

D. Cooperation

The fourth factor to be considered by the SEC in assessing an enforcement action against a company is the level of cooperation provided. The SEC will consider:

- Whether the results of the company's review, as well as all relevant documentation, is shared with the staff;
- Whether information is disclosed to the staff that was not requested and otherwise might not have been discovered;
- Whether the information shared is thorough and reliable so that it may be used by the staff to facilitate prompt enforcement action against those who may have violated the law;
- Whether results of internal investigations are memorialized in a writing and shared with the staff in a format that can be used by the staff in an enforcement proceeding; and
- Whether the company encouraged its employees to cooperate with the staff's investigation and whether efforts were made to secure such cooperation.

In the Leon-Meredith matter, the SEC found Seaboard's cooperation to be real and meaningful.[67] The company provided the Staff with all information relevant to the underlying violations, including details of the internal investigation and notes and transcripts of interviews conducted. In this regard, the SEC found it significant that Seaboard did not invoke the attorney-client privilege, work product protection, or other privileges or protections with respect to any information uncovered in the investigation.

IV. THE GENESIS OF THE CURRENT ENFORCEMENT FOCUS ON FINANCIAL REPORTI NG AND EARNINGS MANAGEMENT: FORMER CHAIRMAN LEVITT'S 1998 SPEECH

Former Chairman Levitt's 1998 speech, "The Numbers Game," at the New York University Center for Law and Business on September 28, 1998, remains the touchstone for the Commission's current enforcement focus on financial reporting and accounting. In that speech, the former Chairman discussed five practices companies engage in to smooth earnings and meet expectations that mask actual results and volatility from period to period:

- "Big bath charges" or overestimated one-time charges associated with restructuring. Companies hope these charges will be ignored in favor of future earnings. When the estimates fall short, the charges are "reborn" as income.
- "Merger magic" occurs when part of an acquisition price is classified as "in-process research and development." This can be written off as a one-time loss, eliminating any future earnings drag. The goal here is to enhance future earnings by concentrating losses in the acquisition period.
- "Cookie jar reserves" come into play when companies create large earnings reserves by making unrealistic assumptions in estimating

67. Importantly, the SEC has demonstrated an increased concern with companies that it believes have failed to cooperate fully with enforcement investigations. For example, in March 2004, the SEC imposed a $10 million penalty against Banc of America Securities for failure to promptly furnish documents requested by the SEC staff. *In the Matter of Banc of America Securities LLC*, Exch. Act Rel. No. 49386 (Mar. 10, 2004); *See also SEC v. Lucent Technologies, Inc.*, Litig. Rel. No. 18715 (May 17, 2004) (SEC imposing $25 million penalty for Lucent's alleged failure to cooperate with the staff's investigation and for actions the company took after the company reached a settlement in principle with the SEC).

their liabilities, *e.g.*, sales returns, loan losses or warranty costs. This creates a "cookie jar" that companies can reach into during subsequent periods of lagging earnings.

- Companies abuse the definition of "materiality," intentionally recording errors and then arguing that the bottom line effect is too small to matter.

- Finally, companies use inappropriate revenue recognition practices to boost earnings by recognizing sales before they are completed or when a customer can still terminate an order.

To remedy these and other accounting problems, former Chairman Levitt called for a three-part, coordinated approach including: (i) technical rule changes to improve the transparency of financial statements; (ii) enhanced oversight of financial reporting by those charged with the task; and (iii) a cultural change within corporate management and the wider financial community.

The former Chairman outlined several steps for improving the accounting framework, including:

- Instructing the staff to require detailed disclosures about changes in accounting assumptions to enable the market to understand better their effects.

- Asking the profession to clarify the ground rules for auditing purchased R&D.

- Charging the staff with the task of developing guidelines to stop the practice of manipulating "materiality" to excuse deliberate misstatements of performance.

- Developing interpretive guidelines for revenue recognition.

The former Chairman also announced steps aimed at financial reporting oversight including:

- Requesting private sector standard setters to update those current standards which are inadequate.

- Charging the staff with reinforcing existing regulatory initiatives by targeting for review companies announcing a restructuring of liability reserves, major write-offs or other practices that appear to manage or manipulate earnings.

- Convening a "blue ribbon" panel to review the role of the audit committee in corporate governance. In February 1999, that panel—the Blue Ribbon Committee on Improving the Effectiveness of Corporate Audit Committees (the "Blue Ribbon Committee")—announced a ten-point plan aimed at strengthening the role of audit committees. Suggestions ranged from revising the definition of "independent director" to mandating written charters detailing the duties and responsibilities of audit committees to requiring an annual audit committee letter to the shareholders. The panel's recommendations led to the new rules on audit committees and financial disclosure, discussed below.

V. STAFF ACCOUNTING BULLETIN NO. 99 - MATERIALITY

SAB 99 sets forth the SEC staff's view that materiality in the context of financial statements cannot be assessed solely by reliance upon "quantitative benchmarks." The first part of SAB 99 addresses the assessment of materiality by public reporting companies. The SAB notes that certain issuers and auditors have developed a "rule of thumb" for assessing materiality under which items that fall under a five percent threshold are deemed immaterial, absent extraordinary circumstances. SAB 99 pointedly rejects such a pure quantitative measure of materiality, noting that the courts, the Commission's regulations, and Commission enforcement actions all have historically and consistently considered "qualitative" factors in assessing materiality. The SAB notes a number of considerations that "may well render material a quantitatively small misstatement of a financial statement item," including:

- Whether the misstatement arises from an item capable of precise measurement or whether it arises from an estimate and, if so, the degree of imprecision inherent in the estimate.
- Whether the misstatement masks a change in earnings or other trends.
- Whether the misstatement hides a failure to meet analysts' consensus expectations for the enterprise.
- Whether the misstatement changes a loss into income or vice versa.
- Whether the misstatement concerns a segment or other portion of the registrant's business that has been identified as playing a significant role in the registrant's operations or profitability.

- Whether the misstatement affects the registrant's compliance with regulatory requirements.
- Whether the misstatement affects the registrant's compliance with loan covenants or other contractual requirements.
- Whether the misstatement has the effect of increasing management's compensation—for example, by satisfying requirements for the award of bonuses or other forms of incentive compensation.
- Whether the misstatement involves concealment of an unlawful transaction.

The staff specifically addressed the issue of managed earnings in this context, stating:

> . . . the staff believes that a registrant and the auditors of its financial statement should not assume that even small intentional misstatements in financial statements, for example those pursuant to actions to "manage" earnings, are immaterial. While the intent of management does not render a misstatement material, it may provide significant evidence of materiality. The evidence may be particularly compelling where management has intentionally misstated items in the financial statements to "manage" reported earnings. In that instance, it presumably has done so believing that the resulting amounts and trends would be significant to users of the registrant's financial statements. The staff believes that investors generally would regard as significant a management practice to over- or under-state earnings up to an amount just short of a percentage threshold in order to "manage" earnings. Investors presumably also would regard as significant an accounting practice that, in essence, rendered all earnings figures subject to a management-directed margin of misstatement.

The staff also condemned the practice of aggregating and netting misstatements. Each misstatement must be independently assessed for materiality, prior to netting or offset after combination with other misstatements. "If the misstatement of an individual amount causes the financial statement as a whole to be materially misstated, that effect cannot be eliminated by other misstatements whose effect may be to diminish the impact of the statement on other financial statement items."

The second part of SAB 99 addresses the earnings "management" practice of making intentional *immaterial* misstatements in a company's financial statements. The bulletin reiterates the requirements of the books and records provisions of the Exchange Act, which mandate that registrants:

> file reports pursuant to Section 15(d), make and keep books, records, and accounts, which, in reasonable detail, accurately and fairly reflect the transactions and dispo-

> sitions of assets of the registrant . . . and maintain internal accounting controls that are sufficient to provide reasonable assurances that, among other things, transactions are recorded as necessary to permit the preparation of financial statement in conformity with GAAP.

The Bulletin adds that a determination of "what constitutes 'reasonable assurance' and 'reasonable detail' [is] based not on a 'materiality' analysis but on the level of detail and degree of assurance that would satisfy prudent officials in the conduct of their own affairs." Based on these Exchange Act requirements, the staff concludes that "the failure to record accurately immaterial items, in some instances, may result in violations of the securities laws."

The staff clearly indicates that its concern with intentional material misstatements is directly related to the issue of managed earnings, stating:

> [i]t is unlikely that it is ever "reasonable" for registrants to record misstatements or not to correct known misstatements—even immaterial ones—as part of an ongoing effort directed by or known to senior management for the purposes of "managing" earnings. On the other hand, insignificant misstatements that arise from the operation of systems of recurring processes in the normal course of business generally will not cause a registrant's books to be inaccurate "in reasonable detail."

The staff also notes that Section 10A(b) of the Exchange Act—which , as discussed below, requires a registrant's auditor to take certain actions upon learning of an illegal act by the issuer or its personnel—may be triggered by an intentional immaterial misstatement in the registrant's financial statements. A violation of Section 13(b)(2) of the Exchange Act requires the auditors to "adequately inform" the audit committee of the issuer of the violation—regardless of a "netting" of the misstatement with other financial statement items.

The Second Circuit has stated that it found SAB 99 "persuasive guidance for evaluating the materiality of an alleged misrepresentation." *Ganino v. Citizens Utilities Co.*, 228 F.3d 154, 163 (2d Cir. 2000). The district court in that case had found that alleged misrepresentations regarding certain fees received by defendants were immaterial as a matter of law because they amounted to only 1.7% of defendants' annual revenue. Relying primarily on SAB 99, the Second Circuit held that reliance on a numerical benchmark was error. While noting that as a staff interpretation, SAB 99 "does not carry with it the force of law," the court nevertheless adopted its reasoning, stating:

> SEC staff accounting bulletins 'constitute a body of experience and informed judgment' . . . and SAB No. 99 is thoroughly reasoned and consistent with existing law - - its non-exhaustive list of factors is simply an application of the well-established

Basic [Inc. v. Levinson, 485 U.S. 244 (1988)] analysis to misrepresentations of financial results. . . .

Id. (*quoting Skidmore v. Swift & Co.*, 323 U.S. 134, 140 (1944)).

VI. STAFF ACCOUNTING BULLETIN NO. 100 - RESTRUCTURING AND IMPAIRMENT CHARGES

SAB 100 states the staff's views on the disclosure and accounting treatment of certain expenses commonly reported in connection with restructurings, business combinations and exit activities. The SAB notes that although the term "restructuring charge" is not defined in the accounting literature, and although triggering events for the recognition of such charges varies, restructuring charges "typically result from the consolidation and/or relocation of operations, or the disposition or abandonment of operations or productive assets."

The SAB notes that "exit costs," including, *e.g.*, involuntary employee termination benefits, cannot be accrued prior to the company's firm commitment to a detailed and specific exit plan, and that exit costs and accruals must be reversed if any accrued amount is no longer needed for its specific, intended purpose. In addition, the staff states it believes, "a rebuttable presumption exists that the exit plan should be completed and the exit costs and involuntary employee termination benefits incurred within one year from the commitment date."

Under SAB 100, exit costs must also meet the following conditions:

1. The cost is not associated with or does not benefit activities that will be continued.

2. The cost is not associated with or is not incurred to generate revenues after the commitment date.

3. The cost meets one of the following criteria:

   a. It is incremental to other costs incurred in the company's conduct of its activities prior to the commitment date and will be incurred as a direct result of the exit plan; or

   b. The cost will be incurred under a contractual obligation that existed prior to the commitment date and will either continue after the exit plan is completed with no economic benefit to the company or be a penalty to cancel the contractual obligation.

SAB 100 also addresses the type and quality of disclosure required in annual and quarterly reports regarding exit plans and restructuring charges; inventory valuation allowances; and standards for recognizing and measuring certain impairments.

VII. STAFF ACCOUNTING BULLETIN NO. 101 - REVENUE RECOGNITION

SAB 101 sets forth the staff's views on certain issues raised in connection with applying generally accepted accounting principles ("GAAP") to revenue recognition in financial statements. SAB 101 notes that, while many revenue recognition issues are specifically addressed in the accounting literature, others are not. In the latter case, the SAB states the staff will consider FASB guidance and other existing authoritative accounting standards. Under these standards and guidelines, SAB 101 states that "revenue should not be recognized until it is realized or realizable and earned." According to the staff, revenue is recognizable under this standard—that is, realized or realizable and earned—when all of the following criteria are met:

- Persuasive evidence of an arrangement exists.
- Delivery has occurred or services have been rendered.
- The seller's price to the buyer is fixed or determinable, and
- Collectibility is reasonably assured.

The SAB provides examples of "persuasive evidence of an arrangement," "delivery and performance" and "fixed or determinable sales price." SAB 101 also addresses the disclosures required with respect to the recognition of revenue, and states that "[b]ecause revenue recognition generally involves some level of judgment, the staff believes that a registrant should always disclose its revenue recognition policy." Examples of revenue transactions or events that the staff believes should be disclosed in Management's Discussion and Analysis ("MD&A") include:

- Shipments of product at the end of a reporting period that significantly reduce customer backlog and that reasonably might be expected to result in lower shipments and revenue in the next period.
- Granting of extended payment terms that will result in a longer collection period for accounts receivable (regardless of whether rev-

enue has been recognized) and slower cash inflows from operations, and the effect on liquidity and capital resources.

- Changing trends in shipments into, and sales from, a sales channel or separate class of customers that could be expected to have a significant effect on future sales or sales returns.[68]
- An increasing trend toward sales to a different class of customer, such as a reseller distribution channel that has a lower gross profit margin than existing sales that are principally made to end users. Also, increasing service revenue that has a higher profit margin than product sales.
- Seasonal trends or variations in sales.
- A gain or loss from the sale of an asset or assets.

On March 24, 2000, in SAB 101A, the staff delayed implementation (for one fiscal quarter) of SAB 101 for those issuers whose fiscal year begins between December 16, 1999 and March 15, 2000. On June 26, 2000, in SAB 101B, the staff further delayed implementation of SAB 101 until the fourth fiscal quarter for issuers with fiscal years beginning after December 15, 1999.

VIII. STAFF ACCOUNTING BULLETIN NO. 102—SELECTED LOAN LOSS ALLOWANCE METHODOLOGY AND DOCUMENTATION ISSUES

SAB 102 provides certain views of the staff on the development, documentation, and application of a systematic methodology for determining loan and lease losses in accordance with GAAP, while at the same time providing guidance to registrants to assist them in improving both their systematic methodologies for estimating loan loss allowances and their supporting documentation. The SAB applies to registrants that are credi-

---

68. Former Commissioner Isaac C. Hunt, Jr. has remarked that this practice, commonly known as "channel stuffing," may raise disclosure issues, even if it does not raise an issue of revenue recognition. Isaac C. Hunt, Jr., *Financial Reporting Challenges*, Remarks at the Financial Executives International Benchmarking the Quality of Earnings Program at 3, New York, New York (Apr. 26, 2001) <http://www.sec.gov/news/speech/spch483.htm>. *In the Matter of Sunbeam Corporation*, Exch. Act Rel. No. 44305 (May 15, 2001), discussed below, the Staff alleged that "channel stuffing" was part of a larger fraudulent accounting scheme.

tors in loan transactions that, individually or in the aggregate, have a material impact on the registrant's financial statements. The SAB is premised on the staff's view that loan loss estimates developed absent a disciplined methodology or adequate documentation can undermine the integrity and usefulness of an institution's financial statements.

While recognizing that a particular registrant's loss allowance is influenced by registrant-specific factors, SAB 102 sets forth the following specific elements that, in the staff's view, should be included in any effective loan loss allowance methodology:

- A detailed analysis of the loan portfolio, performed on a regular basis by competent and well-trained personnel in a consistent fashion, except taking into account, where appropriate, modifications for new factors affecting collectibility.
- Consideration of all loans and all known relevant internal and external factors that may affect collectibility.
- Identification of loans to be evaluated for impairment on an individual basis under SFAS No. 114 and segment the remainder of the portfolio into groups of loans with similar risk characteristics for evaluation and analysis under SFAS No. 5.
- Consideration of the particular risks in different kinds of lending and current collateral values, where applicable.
- Be based on current and reliable data.
- Be well documented.
- Include a systematic and logical method to consolidate the loss estimates and ensure the loan loss allowance balance is recorded in accordance with GAAP.

SAB 102 also sets forth that it is the staff's normal expectation with regard to what documentation a registrant should include in support of its loan loss allowance methodology. In particular, the staff would normally expect to find that registrants maintain written supporting documentation, including:

- Policies and procedures.
- Loan grading system or process.
- Summary or consolidation of the loan loss allowance balance.
- Validation of the loan loss allowance methodology.

- Periodic adjustments to the loan loss allowance process.

IX. STAFF ACCOUNTING BULLETIN NO. 103—UPDATE OF CODIFICATION OF STAFF ACCOUNTING BULLETINS

SAB 103, released on May 9, 2003, comprehensively updates the interpretive guidance included in the codification of staff accounting bulletins so as to insure that the interpretative guidance is consistent with current authoritative accounting and auditing guidance and SEC rules and regulations. SAB 103 represents the first comprehensive review of the SABs in more than 20 years, and was undertaken, in part, to make the entire SAB codification available on the SEC's website.[69]

X. STAFF ACCOUNTING BULLETIN NO. 104—REVENUE RECOGNITION

SAB 104, released on December 17, 2003, updates the guidance and integrates the related set of Frequently Asked Questions set forth in SAB 101 in order to make the SAB's interpretive guidance consistent with current authoritative accounting and auditing guidance and SEC rules and regulations. Like SAB 101, SAB 104 notes that, while many revenue recognition issues are specifically addressed in the accounting literature, others are not. In the latter case, the SAB states the staff will consider FASB guidance and other existing authoritative accounting standards. Under these standards and guidelines, SAB 104 states that "revenue should not be recognized until it is realized or realizable and earned." According to the staff, revenue is recognizable under this standard - - that is, realized or realizable and earned - - when all of the following criteria are met:

- Persuasive evidence of an arrangement exists.
- Delivery has occurred or services have been rendered.
- The seller's price to the buyer is fixed or determinable, and
- Collectibility is reasonably assured.

One significant addition to SAB 104 impacts revenue arrangements, such as bill and hold transactions, containing multiple revenue-generating activities. With regard to such transactions, the staff explicitly delineates its view that the determination of the units of accounting within an

69. *See* <http://www.sec.gov/interps/account/sabcode.htm>.

arrangement should be made prior to the application of SAB 104 by reference to the EITF Consensus.

XI. STAFF ACCOUNTING BULLETIN NO. 105—APPLICATION OF ACCOUNTING PRINCIPLES TO LOAN COMMITMENTS

SAB 105, released on March 9, 2004, summarizes the views of the staff regarding the application of generally accepted accounting principles to loan commitments accounted for as derivative instruments. The staff will not object if registrants that have not been applying the accounting described in this bulletin continue to use their existing accounting policies for loan commitments accounted for as derivatives entered into on or before March 31, 2004. For loan commitments accounted for as derivatives and entered into subsequent to that date, the staff expects all registrants to apply the accounting described in this bulletin.

XII. THE AUDITOR'S RESPONSIBILITY TO NOTIFY MANAGEMENT AND THE AUDIT COMMITTEE OF ILLEGAL ACTS UNDER EXCHANGE ACT SECTION 10A

Section 10A of the Exchange Act was enacted as part of the Private Securities Litigation Reform Act of 1995, and amended by the Sarbanes-Oxley Act of 2002. Under that statute, an independent public accountant who, during the course of an audit, becomes aware of information that an illegal act has or may have occurred, is required to determine whether it is "likely" that an illegal act has in fact occurred. If the accountant determines that it is "likely" that the illegal act occurred, he or she must (1) determine the possible effect of the illegal act on the issuer's financial statements; and (2) inform the appropriate level of management, and insure that the audit committee of the board of directors (or the full board in the absence of an audit committee) is adequately informed, as soon as practicable, unless the illegal act "is clearly inconsequential."

If, thereafter (i) the auditor concludes that the illegal act will have a material effect on the financial statements; (ii) the issuer has not taken "timely and appropriate remedial actions;" and (iii) the failure to take remedial actions is reasonably expected to warrant departure from a standard report of the auditor, or warrant resignation from the audit engagement, the accountant must, as soon as practicable, report his or her conclusion directly to the board of directors. Upon receiving such a report, the board of directors has one business day to inform the Commission that it has received the report and give the accountant notice that it so informed the Commission. An accountant who does not receive such notice must either resign from the engagement or furnish the Commission with a copy of its report.

It is important to note that an auditor's responsibility to inform senior management and the Audit Committee of an illegal act is not based on the familiar "materiality" standard, but rather a "clearly inconsequential standard" that appears to set a low threshold for triggering an auditor's responsibility.

The Sarbanes-Oxley Act amends Section 10A, adding prohibitions on the provision of non-audit services; requiring that the audit committee pre-approve services (both audit and non-audit) provided by the auditor; requiring audit partner rotation every five years; requiring the auditors to report to the issuer on critical accounting policies and on all material communications with management (including in particular, discussion of alternative treatments of financial information); restricting the auditor's employees from serving as CEO, CFO or Chief Accounting Officer in the year after leaving the firm; and imposing new requirements on audit committees. (*See* Section B. above.)

The Commission brought its first actions under Section 10A in October 2000. In *SEC v. Solucorp Indus. Ltd.,* 99 Civ. 11965 (WCC) (S.D.N.Y., filed Dec. 13, 1999), the Commission filed an amended complaint on October 31, 2000, charging an issuer's accountant with failure to take appropriate action after discovering possible illegal conduct during an audit. In that case, the accountant allegedly concluded that a license agreement was improperly backdated for revenue recognition purposes. Although the agreement was clearly material—constituting 40 percent of the company's revenues—the accountant is alleged not to have taken steps to determine the illegality of the conduct; its possible effect on the company's financial statements; or to inform the audit committee about the illegal action. On April 26, 2002, the Southern District of New York denied the defendant accountant's motion for summary judgment. The accountant argued that the Commission failed to allege that he had actual knowledge of or was reckless in disregarding the existence of the unlawful acts. In holding there is no scienter requirement, the court held that an auditor becomes subject to Section 10A upon acquiring knowledge of information indicating that an illegal act may have occurred. 2002 U.S. Dist. LEXIS 7438 (S.D.N.Y. Apr. 26, 2002).

The Commission also brought an unrelated administrative proceeding under Section 10A the same day it filed the amended complaint in *Solu-*

corp. That case—*In re Rossetti*, Admin. Proceeding No. 3-10354 (Oct. 31, 2000)—is discussed in Section M. below.

In September 2001, the Commission instituted and settled an administrative proceeding that included charges under Section 10A. That case—*In re Springer,* Admin. Proceeding No. 3-10589 (Sept. 27, 2001)—is discussed in Section M. below.

In January 2003, the Commission filed a complaint in the Southern District of New York against four senior partners of KPMG LLP alleging violations of Section 10A and securities fraud. *SEC v. KPMG LLP,* Litig. Release No. 17954 (Jan. 29, 2003), Litig. Release No. 18389 (Oct. 3, 2003). This pending case is discussed in Section M. below.

XIII. COMMISSION ENFORCEMENT ACTIONS AGAINST ISSUERS AND OFFICERS RELATING TO FINANCIAL REPORTING, EARNINGS MANAGEMENT AND IMPROPER ACCOUNTING PRACTICES

SEC v. John Houldsworth, Litig. Rel. No. 19248 (June 6, 2005); *SEC v. John Houldsworth and Richard Napier*, Litig. Rel. No. 19264 (June 10, 2005).

On June 6, 2005, the SEC filed an enforcement action against John Houldsworth, a former executive of General Re Corporation ("Gen Re") and former CEO of a Gen Re subsidiary, Cologne Re Dublin, for allegedly aiding and abetting a securities fraud committed by American International Group, Inc. ("AIG"). On June 10, 2005, the SEC announced that it had filed an amended complaint in which it added Richard Napier as a defendant in the action it instituted on June 6, 2005, against Houldsworth. According to the SEC's amended complaint, Napier was a Gen Re Senior Vice President and the executive responsible for Gen Re's relationship with AIG.

The amended complaint alleged that Napier, together with Houldsworth and others, helped AIG structure two sham reinsurance transactions that had as their only purpose to allow AIG to add a total of $500 million in phony loss reserves to its balance sheet in the fourth quarter of 2000 and the first quarter of 2001. According to the complaint, the transactions were initiated by AIG to quell criticism by analysts concerning a reduction in the company's loss reserves in the third quarter of 2000.

The Commission charged Houldsworth and Napier with aiding and abetting the violations by AIG and others of Sections 10(b), 13(a), 13(b)(2) and 13(b)(5) and Rules 10b-5, 12b-20, 13a-1, 13a-13 and 13b2-1 of the Exchange Act. In partial settlements of the Commission's claims, Houldsworth and Napier, in addition to undertaking to cooperate fully with the Commission, consented to the entry of partial final judgments permanently enjoining them from future violations of these provisions, barring each of them from serving as an officer or director of a public company, and deferring the determination of civil penalties and disgorgement to a later date.

In addition, Houldsworth, who is licensed as a Chartered Accountant in England, agreed to a Commission administrative order, based on the injunction, barring him from appearing or practicing before the Commission as an accountant, under Rule 102(e) of the Commission's Rules of Practice.

In connection with the same conduct, both Napier and Houldsworth entered guilty pleas to criminal charges filed by the U.S. Department of Justice, Fraud Section in a Virginia federal court. Under the respective plea agreements, each defendant agreed to cooperate fully with the DOJ's continuing investigation.

In the Matter of Tyson Foods, Inc.and Donald Tyson, Exch. Act. Rel. No. 34-51625 (Apr. 28, 2005); *SEC v. Tyson Foods, Inc. and Donald Tyson*, Litig. Rel. No. 19208 (Apr. 28, 2005).

On April 28, 2005, the SEC announced that it had instituted settled enforcement proceedings against Tyson Foods, Inc. ("Tyson Foods") and its former Chairman and CEO Donald Tyson ("Don Tyson"). The SEC alleged that in proxy statements filed with the Commission from 1997 to 2003, Tyson Foods made misleading disclosures of perquisites and personal benefits provided to Don Tyson both prior to and after his retirement as senior chairman in October 2001. The SEC also alleged that the company failed to maintain adequate internal controls over Don Tyson's personal use of company assets. The Commission separately charged Don Tyson with causing and aiding and abetting the company's disclosure violations.

Tyson Foods and Don Tyson agreed to settle the SEC's charges by consenting to the entry of a final judgment in a civil action filed in the U.S. District Court for the District of Columbia ordering Tyson Foods to pay a $1.5 million penalty and Don Tyson to pay a $700,000 penalty. In addition, both parties separately consented to the entry of an SEC Order ordering them to cease and desist from violating the proxy solicitation and periodic reporting provisions of the federal securities laws. The Order also required Tyson Foods to cease and desist from violating the internal controls provisions of the securities laws. The company and Don Tyson agreed to the settlements without admitting or denying the findings or allegations in the SEC's Order and complaint.

The SEC alleged that while Don Tyson was employed as senior chairman from 1997 to 2001, the company provided approximately $3 million of perquisites and personal benefits to him, his wife, his daughters and three individuals with whom he had close personal relationships. According to the Commission's Order, Don Tyson caused disclosure failures with respect to many of these perquisites because his responses to director and officer questionnaires were inadequate. The SEC also alleged that many of those perquisites had not been raised with or authorized by the company's compensation committee. According to the Order, the $3 million in perquisites included:

- $689,016 in personal expenses for him and two of his friends, including a $20,000 purchase for oriental rugs, an $18,000 purchase for antiques, a $15,000 vacation in London, an $8,000 horse and other substantial purchases of clothing, jewelry, artwork, vacations and theater tickets, which were paid through cash advances from the company's accounts, directly billed to the company or charged to three company credit cards that had been issued in the mid 1990s to Don Tyson and two of his friends;
- $464,132 in personal use by Don Tyson and his family and friends of company-owned homes in the English countryside and in Cabo San Lucas, Mexico, including use of the company-paid chauffeur, cook and housekeeper at the English home and the company's crewed boat in Cabo San Lucas;
- $426,086 of personal use of company-owned aircraft by him and his family and friends, including regular use by his family and friends with and without him on board;
- $203,675 in housekeeping provided at five different homes where Don Tyson and his family and friends lived and/or vacationed;
- $84,000 in lawn maintenance at five different homes where he and his family and friends lived;
- $46,110 to maintain nine automobiles owned and used by Don Tyson and his family and friends;
- $36,554 in telephone services for him and his family and friends;

- $15,000 in Christmas gift certificates that were provided to Don Tyson's family and friends; and
- $1,072,699 to cover Don Tyson's personal income tax liability associated with his receipt of these benefits.

The Order further found that in its proxy statements filed for 1997 to 2001, Tyson Foods:

- failed to disclose over $1 million of these perquisites, including $424,121 in housekeeping, lawn maintenance, automobile maintenance and telephone service that were not disclosed due to the company's internal control failures, and an additional $595,656 of perquisites (including gross-up payments for taxes thereon) that were mischaracterized in the company's 1998, 1999 and 2000 proxy statements as "performance-based bonuses," instead of as perquisites, due to a strategy to preserve the company's tax deduction for Don Tyson's compensation;
- used the misleading expression "travel and entertainment costs" to describe perquisites that could not be considered "travel" or "entertainment," such as over $372,539 in personal expenses received by Don Tyson and his friends;
- failed to separately identify by type and amount perquisites that exceeded 25 percent of Don Tyson's total perquisites, such as personal expenses, use of company homes, personal use of company aircraft and/or residential services.

In addition, according to the Order, the company's 2002 and 2003 proxy statements used the same misleading terms "travel and entertainment" to describe the continuation of Don Tyson's perquisites pursuant to an October 2001 retirement agreement with the company and failed to disclose fully the nature and scope of those benefits.

The SEC also alleged that due to internal control failures at Tyson Foods throughout most of 1997 to 2003, many of the perquisites described above (totaling approximately $1.5 million) were neither raised with nor authorized by the company's compensation committee or its board of directors.

As a result of these and other findings, the SEC's Order found that Tyson Foods violated Sections 13(a), 13(b)(2)(B) and 14(a) of the Exchange Act and Rules 13a-1, 14a-3 and 14a-9 thereunder, and ordered the company to cease and desist from committing any violations and any future violations of these statutory provisions and rules. The SEC's Order also found that Don Tyson caused the company's violations of Sections 13(a) and 14(a) of the Exchange Act and Rules 13a-1, 14a-3 and 14a-9 thereunder, and ordered Don Tyson to cease and desist from causing any violations and any future violations of the foregoing statutory provisions and rules.

In the Matter of the Coca-Cola Company, Exch. Act Rel. No. 51565 (Apr. 18, 2005).

On April 18, 2005, the SEC filed a settled administrative cease-and-desist proceeding against The Coca-Cola Company ("Coke"). The action related to Coke's alleged failure to disclose certain end-of-quarter sales practices in Japan used to meet earnings expectations, and misstatements in a Form 8-K concerning a subsequent inventory reduction.

According to the Commission, at or near the end of each reporting period between 1997 and 1999, Coke engaged in "channel stuffing" in Japan for the purpose of pulling sales forward into a current period. The channel stuffing, otherwise referred to as "gallon pushing", was accomplished by offering Japanese bottlers extended credit terms in order to induce them to purchase additional quantities of beverage concentrate. The Commission alleged that a bottler's inventory of concentrate purchased from Coke typically corresponds to the bottler's sales of finished product. Due to Coke's gallon pushing, however, Coke's Japanese bottlers' concentrate inventory levels increased at a rate more than five times greater than that of finished product sales. Coke's quarterly earnings per share increased approximately $0.01 to $0.02 as a result of the gallon pushing, and the practice made it likely that the bottlers would purchase less concentrate in future periods. Despite these effects, Coke did not disclose its gallon pushing practice in its periodic reports filed with the Commission.

The Commission also alleged that Coke's January 26, 2000 Form 8-K disclosing, among other things, a worldwide concentrate inventory reduction planned for the first half of 2000 was false and misleading because it failed to disclose that more than $0.05 of the estimated earnings impact resulting from the inventory reduction was attributable to an anticipated reduction of sales for Japan. The Commission also found the Form 8-K to be false and misleading because it improperly described: (1) the time period during which Coke reviewed inventory levels; (2) the Japanese bottlers' prior awareness of the inventory reduction; and (3) the inventory reduction as a joint effort between Coke and its bottlers, when the inventory reduction was in fact solely a Coke initiative.

Significantly, in announcing this action, the SEC noted that Coke's accounting treatment for sales made in connection with gallon pushing was proper. The SEC also commended Coke for taking substantial steps, both prior to and during the SEC's investigation, to strengthen its internal disclosure review process to prevent future violations.

Without admitting or denying the Commission's allegations, Coke agreed to cease-and-desist from committing or causing any violations and any future violations of Sections 17(a)(2) and 17(a)(3) of the Securities Act and Sections 13(a) of the Exchange Act and Rules 12b-20, 13a-1, 13a-11, and 13a-13 thereunder.

SEC v. Dollar General Corporation, et al., Litig. Rel. No. 19174 (April 7, 2005).

On April 7, 2005, the SEC filed a settled enforcement action against Dollar General Corporation ("Dollar General"), a Tennessee-based discount retailer. Without admitting or denying the SEC's allegations, Dollar General consented to the entry of a final judgment permanently enjoining it from future violations of the antifraud, books and records, internal controls, and periodic reporting provisions of the federal securities laws, specifically, Section 17(a) of the Securities Act, Sections 10(b), 13(a), 13(b)(2)(A) and 13(b)(2)(B) of the Exchange Act and Rules 10b-5, 12b-20, 13a-1, 13a-11 and 13a-13 thereunder. As part of the settlement, Dollar General agreed to pay $1 in disgorgement and a civil penalty of $10 million, which the Commission expects will be distributed pursuant to the Fair Fund provisions of Section 308(a) of the Sarbanes-Oxley Act of 2002.

The Commission alleged in its complaint that, during its fiscal years 1998 through 2001, Dollar General engaged in fraudulent or improper accounting practices in violation of GAAP which ultimately resulted in a restatement of Dollar General's financial statements in January 2002 reducing the Company's pre-tax income by approximately $143 million, or about 30 cents per share, over the restated period. The Commission alleged that Dollar General's misconduct included: (1) intentionally underreporting at least $10 million in import freight expenses for the Company's fiscal year 1999; (2) engaging in an $11 million sham sale of outdated, essentially worthless, cash registers in the Company's fiscal year 2000 fourth quarter; (3) overstating cash accounts; (4) manipulating the Company's reported earnings through the use of a general reserve or "rainy day" account; (5) failing to maintain accurate books and records and filing inaccurate financial reports with the Commission; and (6) failing to maintain adequate internal accounting controls.

The Commission alleged that some of the fraudulent or improper accounting practices were effected by, or known to, former senior executives and accounting personnel, and were motivated in part by their desire to report earnings that met or exceeded analysts' expectations and to maintain employee bonuses. The SEC also charged the company's former CEO, President, CFO, Controller, and Accounting Manager with accounting fraud.

SEC v. Time Warner, Inc., Litig. Rel. No. 19147 (Mar. 21, 2005); *In the Matter of James W. Barge, et al.*, Exch. Act Rel. No. 34-51400 (Mar. 21, 2005).

On March 21, 2005, the SEC charged Time Warner Inc. (formerly known as AOL Time Warner) with materially overstating online advertising revenue and the number of its Internet subscribers, and with aiding and abetting three other securities frauds. The Commission also charged that the Company violated a Commission cease-and-desist order issued against America Online, Inc. on May 15, 2000 by artificially inflating its online advertising revenue and the number of AOL subscribers, as well as its failure to consolidate AOL Europe's financial statements.

The Commission's complaint against Time Warner alleged, among other things, that beginning in mid-2000 and extending through 2002, the company employed fraudulent round-trip transactions that boosted its online advertising revenue to mask the fact that it also experienced a business slow-down. The SEC alleged that the round-trip transactions ranged in complexity and sophistication, but in each instance the company effectively funded its own online advertising revenue by giving the counterparties the means to pay for advertising that they would not otherwise have purchased. According to the SEC, to conceal the true nature of the transactions, the company typically structured and documented round-trips as if they were two or more separate, bona fide transactions, conducted at arm's length and reflecting each party's independent business purpose. Time Warner, however, delivered mostly untargeted, less desirable, remnant online advertising to the round-trip advertisers, and the round-trip advertisers often had little or no ability to control the quantity, quality, and sometimes even the content of the online advertising they received.

Several of the counterparties to the round-trip transactions were publicly traded companies. The SEC alleged that three of these counterparties improperly recognized revenue on the round-trip transactions and reported materially misstated financial results to their own investors. The Commission alleged that, as a consequence, the company aided and abetted the frauds of three public companies.

The SEC alleged that the company also artificially inflated the number of AOL subscribers in the second, third, and fourth quarters of 2001 so it could report to the investment community that it had met its new subscriber targets, an important metric the market used to evaluate AOL (both before and after its merger with Time Warner). According to the SEC, the company counted members from "bulk subscription sales" to corporate customers (for distribution to their employees) when the company knew that the memberships had not, and mostly would not, be activated.

In addition, the Commission alleged that, from March 2000 through January 2002, the company failed to properly consolidate the financial results of AOL Europe in its financial statements. AOL Europe was originally a 50/50 joint venture between AOL and Bertelsmann. In March 2000, AOL entered into a contingent purchase agreement relating to Bertelsmann's interest in AOL Europe. According to the Commission's complaint, the agreement gave AOL broad and direct powers enabling it to control the operations and assets of AOL Europe, a fact that the company acknowledged in a letter to the European Commission (in the context of satisfying EC merger regulations). The SEC alleged that the company's failure to properly consolidate AOL Europe, as required by GAAP when one entity has a controlling financial interest in another entity, resulted in material misstatements of its financial results, including overstatements of operating income and free cash flow in 2000 and 2001, overstatements of net income in 2000, understatements of net losses in 2001, and understatements of total debt in 2000 and 2001.

Without admitting or denying the allegations in the complaint, Time Warner consented to the entry of a judgment that, among other things, ordered it to pay $300 million in civil penalties. The judgment further ordered the company to comply with the Commission's May 15, 2000 cease-and-desist order against AOL; enjoined the company from violating antifraud, reporting, books-and-records, and internal control provisions of the federal securities laws; and enjoined the company from aiding and abetting securities fraud. As part of the settlement, Time Warner agreed to restate its historical financial results to reduce its reported online advertising revenues by approximately $500 million (in addition to the $190 million already restated) for the fourth quarter of 2000 through 2002 and to properly reflect the consolidation of AOL Europe in the company's 2000 and 2001 financial statements. The company also agreed to engage an independent examiner to determine whether the company's historical accounting for certain transactions was in conformity with GAAP.

In a separate administrative proceeding, Time Warner CFO Wayne H. Pace, Controller James W. Barge, and Deputy Controller Pascal Desroches consented to the entry of a Commission cease-and-desist order finding that they caused reporting violations by the company based on their roles in accounting for $400 million paid to the company by Bertelsmann AG in two sets of transactions. The SEC alleged that, in 2001 and 2002, the company inflated its online advertising revenue in connection with transactions in which Bertelsmann paid $400 million as consideration for amendments to a multi-billion-dollar contingent purchase agreement governing the company's purchase of Bertelsmann's interest in AOL Europe.

SEC v. Penthouse International, Inc., et al., Litig. Rel. No. 19048 (Jan. 24, 2005).

On January 24, 2005, the SEC filed a civil injunctive action against Penthouse International, Inc. ("Penthouse"), now known as PHSL Worldwide, Inc., a former officer of Penthouse, Charles Samel, and a Penthouse shareholder, Jason Galanis, charging them with accounting fraud, reporting violations and violations of the Sarbanes-Oxley certification rules. The Commission also instituted a settled cease-and-desist proceeding against Penthouse's former CEO, Robert C. Guccione.

The Commission alleged that Penthouse, Samel and Galanis engaged in accounting fraud and financial reporting violations at Penthouse in connection with the company's Form 10-Q for the quarter ended March 31, 2003. According to the complaint, Penthouse improperly included as revenue for that quarter $1 million received as an up-front payment in connection with a five-year website management agreement. The SEC allged that the payment should not have been recognized in that quarter because (1) the agreement was not actually signed until the following quarter, and (2) according to GAAP, the $1 million payment should have been recognized as deferred revenue and amortized into income over the five-year life of the agreement. The inclusion of the $1 million payment increased Penthouse's reported revenue by approximately 9%, from $11,072,000 to $12,072,000 and changed a quarterly net loss of $167,000 to a purported net profit of $828,000.

The Commission alleged that Penthouse's Form 10-Q was materially misleading in several other respects. For example, it bore an unauthorized electronic signature of Robert C. Guccione, Penthouse's principal executive officer and principal financial officer, and thus represented that Guccione had reviewed and signed it, and the accompanying Sarbanes-Oxley certification. According to the SEC, this representation was false, because Guccione had not seen or approved the filing of the Form 10-Q or the Sarbanes-Oxley certification. The SEC alleged that Penthouse's auditors and outside counsel also had not reviewed the filing, a fact that also was not disclosed in the filing.

The SEC also alleged that Samel and Galanis prepared and filed the false Form 10-Q, and they did so knowing or recklessly disregarding that Guccione had not seen or approved it, that Penthouse's auditor had not performed its required review of the Form 10-Q, and that it would be improper to include the $1 million payment as revenue for the quarter ended March 31, 2003. According to the SEC, in two subsequent filings on Form 8-K that purported to correct misstatements in the 10-Q, Penthouse failed to disclose that Guccione had not reviewed, approved or signed the 10-Q or the attached Sarbanes-Oxley certification. The SEC alleged that, in one of these filings, Penthouse also misrepresented that the company's disclosure controls and procedures were adequate.

The SEC's complaint alleged that Penthouse and Samel violated, and Galanis aided and abetted violations of, Section 10(b) of the Exchange Act, and Rule 10b-5 thereunder. Further, the complaint alleged that Penthouse violated Section 15(d) of the Exchange Act and Rules 12b-20, 15d-11, 15d-13 and 15d-14 thereunder, that Samel and Galanis aided and abetted violations of Section 15(d) of the Exchange Act and Rules 12b-20 and 15d-13 thereunder, and that Samel also aided and abetted violations of Rule 15d-14. In its complaint, the Commission seeks permanent injunctions and civil penalties as to all of the defendants; and officer and director bars against Samel and Galanis. The litigation against Samel and Galanis is pending.

SEC v. TV Azteca S.A. de C.V., et al., Litig. Rel. No. 19022 (Jan. 4, 2005).

The Commission filed civil fraud charges against TV Azteca S.A. de C.V. ("TV Azteca"), a Mexican issuer whose American Depositary Receipts trade on the NYSE. The SEC also filed civil charges against TV Azteca's parent company, Azteca Holdings S.A., de C.V., and three current and former TV Azteca officers and directors, including the company's chairman. The SEC's complaint alleges that the defendants engaged in a scheme to conceal the role of TV Azteca's chairman in a series of related party transactions through which he profited by $109 million. The complaint alleges that the chairman and others caused TV

Azteca to file periodic reports with the Commission that failed to disclose the chairman's involvement in the related party transaction and that, in several instances, TV Azteca and its management falsely denied the chairman's involvement in the transactions. The complaint further alleges that the chairman and a director, who formerly served as the company's CEO, sold millions of dollars of TV Azteca stock while the related party transactions remained undisclosed to investors.

In its action, the Commission is seeking a final judgment enjoining the defendants from future violations of the antifraud, internal controls, books and records, and reporting provisions of the federal securities laws. The Commission also seeks civil money penalties, disgorgement of ill-gotten gains plus prejudgment interest, and orders barring the chairman and the former CEO from serving as officers or directors of any publicly-held company with securities trading in the United States.

The Walt Disney Company, Exch. Act Rel. No. 50882 (Dec. 20, 2004).

On December 20, 2004, the Commission instituted settled enforcement proceedings against The Walt Disney Company ("Disney"), charging that, between 1999 and 2001, Disney failed to disclose certain related party transactions between the company and its directors which were required to be disclosed in its proxy statements and annual reports filed with the Commission. The Commission also charged that Disney failed to disclose certain compensation paid to a Disney director.

In particular, the Commission alleged that Disney failed to disclose that the company employed three children of its directors, paying them annual compensation ranging from $60,000 to $150,000, and that the spouse of another director was employed by a subsidiary 50% owned by Disney and received compensation in excess of $1 million annually. The Commission also alleged that Disney failed to disclose that it made regular payments to a corporation owned by a Disney director that provided air transportation to that director for Disney-related business purposes. The Commission further alleged that Disney failed to disclose that the company provided office and travel services valued at over $200,000 annually to another Disney director.

Without admitting or denying the Commission's findings, Disney consented to the issuance of a Commission order requiring the company to cease and desist from committing or causing any violations and any future violations of Sections 13(a) and 14(a) of the Exchange Act and Rules 13a-1, 12b-20, and 14a-3(a).

SEC v. American International Group, Inc., Litig. Rel. No. 18985 (Nov. 30, 2004).

On November 30, 2004, the Commission filed a settled enforcement action against American International Group, Inc. ("AIG") for violating the antifraud provisions and for aiding and abetting violations of the reporting and record-keeping provisions of the federal securities laws. The Commission action arose out of AIG's offer and sale of an alleged earnings management product. In its complaint, the Commission alleged that AIG developed, marketed, and, in the case of one public company—The PNC Financial Services Group, Inc. ("PNC")—entered into transactions designed to enable the buyer of its product to remove troubled or other potentially volatile assets from its balance sheet, thereby allowing the company to supposedly avoid charges to its reported earnings from declines in the value of these assets. The Commission alleged that AIG was reckless in not knowing that the product it developed did not satisfy the accounting standards for removing the assets from a company's balance sheet.

According to the Commission's complaint, from at least March 2001 through January 2002, AIG, primarily through its wholly-owned subsidiary, AIG-Financial Products Corp., marketed and sold to public companies a product known as C-GAITS. The Commission alleged this product consisted of AIG, for a fee, establishing a special purpose entity ("SPE") to which the counter-party would transfer troubled or other potentially volatile assets and, in return, receive preferred stock in the SPE. The Commission alleged that AIG represented to prospective counter-parties that, under applicable accounting standards, the SPE would not have to be consolidated on the counter-party's financial statements and the counter-party would not have to record declines in the value of the transferred assets or the preferred stock as charges to its earnings. According to the complaint, independent auditors for some potential counter-parties raised issues about whether certain features of AIG's product could violate the accounting requirements for nonconsolidation of SPEs. The Commission alleged that, with one exception, AIG did not inform other potential counter-parties of these issues.

In addition, the Commission's complaint alleged that AIG entered into three C-GAITS transactions through which PNC improperly sought to remove $762 million in loan and venture capital assets from its balance sheet and, therefore, avoid charges to its income statement from declines in the value of these assets. The Commission alleged that, as a result, PNC made materially false and misleading disclosures about its financial condition and performance in filings with the Commission and in press releases. The Commission alleged that AIG was reckless in not knowing that the transactions with PNC did not satisfy the standards for nonconsolidation by PNC.

In settling the Commission's action and related criminal charges by the Department of Justice, AIG agreed to pay $126 million, consisting of a penalty of $80 million, and disgorgement and prejudgment interest of $46 million. In addition, AIG consented, without admitting or denying the allegations in the Commission's complaint, to the entry of a permanent injunction against violating, and aiding and abetting violations of, certain provisions of the federal securities laws. AIG also agreed to the appointment of an independent consultant to examine certain AIG transactions going back to the year 2000, including any transaction that was effected with the primary purpose of enabling a public company to achieve an accounting or financial reporting result. Further, AIG agreed to establish a Transaction Review Committee to review certain future transactions involving heightened legal, reputational or regulatory risk.

SEC v. Conrad M. Black, F. David Radler and Hollinger, Inc., Litig. Rel. No. 18969 (Nov. 15, 2004).

On November 15, 2004, the Commission announced the filing of a complaint against Hollinger International Inc.'s ("Hollinger") former Chairman and CEO, Conrad Black, its former Deputy Chairman and COO, David Radler, and Hollinger, Inc., a Canadian public holding company controlled by Black (collectively, the "defendants").

The Commission's complaint alleged that from approximately 1999 through 2003, Black, Radler and Hollinger, Inc. diverted cash and assets from Hollinger, a U.S. public company and subsidiary of Hollinger, Inc., and concealed their self-dealing from Hollinger's shareholders. The Commission's complaint also alleged that the defendants engaged in a scheme to defraud Hollinger shareholders by diverting approximately $85 million of the proceeds from Hollinger's sale of newspaper publications, and further defrauded such shareholders by orchestrating the below-market sale of certain of Hollinger's assets to another privately-held company controlled and owned by Black. The complaint further alleged that Black authorized the investment of Hollinger's funds in a venture capital fund with which he was associated. Lastly, the Commission's complaint alleged that Black and Radler misled Hollinger's Board and Audit Committee and made materially false and misleading filings with the Commission, and that Black approved a materially false and misleading press release about his intentions with regard to the sale of Hollinger's assets.

The Commission requested that the court enjoin the defendants from violations of the securities laws, order the defendants to disgorge ill-gotten gains and pay pre-judgment interest, order the defendants to pay civil penalties, bar Black and Radler from serving as an officer or director of a public company, and impose a voting trust upon the shares of Hollinger held directly or indirectly by Black and Hollinger, Inc. The Commission's action against the defendants is pending.

In a related action, Hollinger previously consented to a federal court order, alleging that from at least 1999 through 2003, Hollinger's Commission filings contained material misstatements and omissions regarding transfers of certain corporate assets. The Commission also obtained a federal court order to ensure that the work of the Special Committee of Hollinger's board of directors continued under the jurisdiction and oversight of the court.

In re Wesley H. Colwell, Exch. Act. Rel. No. 50664 (Nov. 15, 2004).

Wesley Colwell, a certified public accountant, was Enron North America's Chief Accounting Officer from February 2000 until January 2002. On October 9, 2004, the SEC filed a complaint in district court in which it alleged that Colwell, in conjunction with other Enron employees, manipulated Enron's publicly reported earnings through a variety of devices, including misuse of reserve accounts, concealment of losses, inflation of asset values, and deliberate use of improper accounting treatment for transactions. Without admitting or denying the Commission's allegations, Colwell consented to the entry of an injunction from future violations of sections 10 (b), 13(a), 13b(2) and 13(b)(5) of the Exchange Act and Rules 10b-5, 12b-20, 13a-1, 13a-13, and 13b2-1. Colwell was also ordered to pay $275,000 in disgorgement, prejudgment interest of $25,000, and a civil penalty of $200,000.

On November 15, 2004, the Commission announced the filing of a settled administrative proceeding, pursuant to which Colwell was suspended from appearing or practicing before the SEC for four years.

SEC v. Qwest Communications International, Inc., Litig. Rel. No. 18936 (Oct. 21, 2004); *SEC v. Nacchio, et al.*, Litig. Rel. No. 19136 (Mar. 15, 2005).

On October 21, 2004, the Commission filed a settled enforcement action against Qwest Communications International, Inc. ("Qwest"), alleging that, between 1999 and 2002, Qwest fraudulently recognized over $3.8 billion in revenue and excluded $231 million in expenses as part of a scheme to meet optimistic and unsupportable revenue and earnings projections.

The Commission's complaint alleged that Qwest created the appearance of growth by engaging in one-time revenue generating transactions that the company publicly reported as recurring. The Commission's complaint also alleged that Qwest's accounting for such undisclosed one-time transactions was not in accordance with GAAP. The Commission's complaint further alleged that Qwest engaged in a variety of other conduct violative of the federal securities laws, including failing to disclose certain related party transactions, concealing the fact that the company improperly recognized $112 million of revenue between 2000 and 2002, understating expenses, and engaging in the sale of unregistered securities.

Without admitting or denying the Commission's allegations, Qwest consented to a permanent injunction from future violations of the federal securities and the imposition of a $250 million civil penalty to be distributed to defrauded investors pursuant to the Fair Funds provision of the Sarbanes-Oxley Act of 2002, and $1 disgorgement. The terms of the settlement also require Qwest to maintain permanently a chief compliance officer.

On March 15, 2005, the SEC charged Joseph P. Nacchio, former co-chairman and CEO of Qwest, and eight other former Qwest officers and employees with fraud and other violations of the federal securities laws. In three separate but related civil actions, the Commission alleged that, between 1999 and 2002, the Qwest defendants engaged in a multi-faceted fraudulent scheme designed to mislead the investing public about the company's revenue and growth.

According to the SEC's complaints, Nacchio and others made numerous false and misleading statements about Qwest's financial condition in annual, quarterly, and current reports, in registration statements that incorporated Qwest's financial statements, and in other public statements, including earnings releases and investor calls,. As a result of that scheme, Qwest fraudulently recognized over $3 billion of revenue and excluded $71.3 million in expenses.

In addition to Nacchio, the Commission's complaints named former CFOs Robert S. Woodruff and Robin R. Szeliga, former COO Afshin Mohebbi, former executive vice president of wholesale markets Gregory M. Casey, former senior vice president of pricing and offer management Roger B. Hoaglund, former senior vice president of finance William L. Eveleth, former director of financial reporting James J. Kozlowski, and former senior manager of financial reporting Frank T. Noyes. The SEC's complaints seek injunctions, disgorgement of ill-gotten gains plus prejudgment interest, and civil penalties against all of the defendants, and officer/director bars against Nacchio, Woodruff, Szeliga, Mohebbi, Casey, and Eveleth.

The Commission's complaints alleged that, in Commission filings and other public statements, Nacchio, Woodruff, and Szeliga fraudulently characterized nonrecurring revenue from the one-time sales of capacity in the form of indefeasible rights of use ("IRUs") and equipment as recurring "data and Internet service revenues," thereby masking Qwest's declining financial condition and artificially inflating its stock price. According to the SEC, Qwest used such nonrecurring revenue to fill the gap between actual and projected revenue. The SEC alleged in its complaint that, over time, Qwest's dependence on such one-time transactions grew to the point that it was likened internally to an "addiction" and the nonrecurring IRU and equipment sale transactions were likened to "heroin." Among other things, the Qwest executives' misrepresentations about Qwest's revenue sources allowed Qwest to maintain a stock price sufficiently high to complete its pending merger with US West, Inc. In addition, the Commission alleged that each of the defendants participated in the company's scheme to improperly recognize revenue on IRU transactions.

SEC v. Koninklijke Ahold N.V. (Royal Ahold), Litig. Rel. No. 18929 (Oct. 13, 2004).

On October 13, 2004, the Commission filed fraud and other charges against Royal Ahold ("Ahold") and former top executives of the company. The Commission also filed a related administrative action charging a former member of Ahold's supervisory board and audit committee with causing Ahold's violations of the federal securities laws.

According to the Commission's complaint, Ahold's filings with the Commission for fiscal years 2000, 2001 and the first three quarters of 2002 were materially false and misleading as a result of the fraudulent inflation of promotional allowances at U.S. Foodservice, Ahold's wholly-owned subsidiary, the improper consolidation of joint ventures through fraudulent side letters, and other accounting irregularities. The Commission previously filed a related action against U.S. Foodservice.

Ahold settled, without admitting or denying the Commission's allegations, by consenting to the entry of a judgment permanently enjoining the company from future violations of the federal securities laws. Ahold was not required to pay a penalty in the settlement in recognition of its extensive cooperation with the Commission's investigation.

In re General Electric Co., Exch. Act Rel. No. 50426 (Sept. 23, 2004).

On September 23, 2004, the SEC instituted a cease-and-desist proceeding against General Electric Company ("GE") for allegedly failing to fully disclose the terms of Jack Welch's—GE's former CEO—retirement package. The retirement package, which GE and Welch agreed to in 1996, included as a principal benefit continued access to GE "facilities and services" comparable to those Welch received as CEO, including access to GE aircraft, cars, offices, apartments, and financial planning services. In his first year of retirement, Welch received approximately $2.5 million in such benefits.

GE filed its agreement with Welch as an exhibit to its 1996 Form 10-K and incorporated it by reference as an exhibit in each subsequent Form 10-K until 2002, the year after Welch retired. However, neither these Forms 10-K, GE's other periodic reports filed during the years 1996-2002, nor GE's six proxy statements for the years 1997 through 2002 described or disclosed the type or nature of the benefits Welch would receive in retirement beyond stating that GE would provide him with lifetime access to GE facilities and services comparable to the access he enjoyed as CEO. As a result, according to the SEC, GE violated the proxy solicitation and periodic reporting provisions of the Exchange Act by filing annual reports and proxy statements that failed fully and accurately to disclose the "facilities and services" Welch would receive in retirement.

Without admitting or denying the Commission's findings, GE agreed to cease and desist from causing or committing any violations and any future violations of sections 13(a) and 14(a) of the Exchange Act and Rules 13a-1, 14a-3, and 14a-9.

SEC v. Computer Associates International, Inc., Litig. Rel. No. 18891 (Sept. 22, 2004).

On September 22, 2004, the Commission filed securities fraud charges against Computer Associates International, Inc. ("Computer Associates") and three former top executives—Sanjay Kumar, former Chairman and CEO, Steven Woghin, former General Counsel, and Stephen Richards, former Head of Sales. The Commission in its complaints alleged that from 1998 to 2000, Computer Associates' executives routinely held the company's books open for several days after the end of each quarter to improperly record revenue from contracts that were not executed until after the quarter ended. The Commission alleged that, as a result, Computer Associates prematurely recognized $2.2 billion in revenue in fiscal years 2000 and 2001, and more than $1.1 billion in revenue in prior quarters. Computer Associates was also charged with making material misrepresentations and omissions, through the individual defendants, about its revenue and earnings in SEC filings and other public statements.

Computer Associates reached a joint settlement with the Commission and the Justice Department. The settlement permanently enjoins Computer Associates from committing further violations of the antifraud, reporting, books and records, and internal control provisions of the federal securities laws, and requires the company to reform its corporate governance and financial controls and to appoint an independent examiner. Additionally, the settlement provides for a deferred prosecution agreement with the Justice Department, and requires Computer Associates to pay $225 million in restitution to injured shareholders.

This settlement is noteworthy because Computer Associates was not required to pay a penalty to the Commission, which could then be distributed to injured shareholders under the Fair Funds provision of the Sarbanes-Oxley Act. Instead, Computer Associates' penalty was paid directly to injured shareholders.

Woghin, the former General Counsel, consented to a partial judgment imposing a permanent injunction against future violations of the antifraud, reporting, books and records, and internal controls provisions of the federal securities laws, and barring him for serving as an officer or director of a public company. The Commission's claims for disgorgement and civil penalties against Woghin, and all of its claims against the other individual defendants, are pending.

SEC v. Aurora Foods, Inc., Litig. Rel. Nos. 18851 & 16866 (Aug. 25, 2004 & Jan. 23, 2001).

On January 23, 2001, the Commission filed civil charges against Aurora Foods, Inc. ("Aurora"), a producer and marketer of branded food products, three former senior officers of Aurora and four division level employees. According to the Commission's complaint, Ian Wilson, former Chairman of the Board and Chief Executive Officer; M. Laurie Cummings, former Chief Financial Officer; and Ray Chung, former Executive Vice President, engaged in a fraudulent scheme that caused Aurora to under-report trade marketing expenses by more than $43 million, thereby substantially inflating Aurora's reported earnings in 1998 and 1999 in order to meet analysts' expectations. The complaint further alleged that Wilson, Cummings and Chung repeatedly directed the division level defendants to (i) make inadequate or no accruals for known trade marketing expenses incurred in connection with sales already booked and (ii) conceal the inadequate accruals from the company's auditors by making false entries in various accounts on the Company's books.

Simultaneous with the filing of the complaint, Aurora consented, without admitting or denying the allegations in the complaint, to the entry of a permanent injunction from future violations of the reporting and internal control provisions of the Exchange Act. Two of the individual division level defendants also consented, without admitting or denying the allegations in the complaint, to the entry of a permanent injunction from future violations of the anti-fraud, reporting and internal control provisions of the Exchange Act and to pay civil penalties of $10,000 and $20,000, respectively.

Final judgments against Wilson, Cummings, Chung, and Timothy Andersen were entered on August 3, 2004, and against Dirk Grizzle on August 12, 2004. Each defendants consented, without admitting or denying the allegations in the complaint, to the entry of a permanent injunction from future violations of sections 10(b) and 13(b)(5) of the Exchange Act and Rules 10b-5 and 13b2-1. Wilson, Chung and Cummings, as "control persons" under section 20(a), were also enjoined from violations of sections 13(a) and 13(b)(2) of the Exchange Act and Rules 12b-20, 13a-1 and 13a-13. Wilson, Chung, Cummings, and Grizzle were ordered to disgorge their ill-gotten gains plus prejudgment interest in the amounts of $420,000, $142,000, $75,000, and $102,000, respectively. In addition, the district court imposed civil penalties against Chung, Cummings, Andersen and Grizzle of $125,000, $200,000, $125,000 and $75,000, respectively.

The Commission's action against the remaining individual defendant, one of Aurora's division controllers, is pending.

Royal Dutch Petroleum Company and the "Shell" Transport and Trading Company, P.L.C., Exchange Act Rel. No. 50233 (Aug. 24, 2004).

On August 24, 2004, the Commission announced the filing and settlement of an enforcement action against Royal Dutch Petroleum Company and The "Shell" Transport and Trading Company, p.l.c. (together, "Shell"), in connection with their alleged overstatement of 4.47 billion barrels of previously reported proved hydrocarbon reserves.

According to the Commission's order, Shell overstated proved reserves reported in its 2002 Form 20-F by 4.47 billion barrels of oil equivalent (boe), or approximately 23%. The order further concludes that Shell also overstated the standardized measure of future cash flows reported in this filing by approximately $6.6 billion. Shell corrected these overstatements in an amended filing on July 2, 2004, which reflected the degree of Shell's overstatements for the years 1997 to 2002.

The Commission's order also finds that, during this period, Shell materially misstated its reserves replacement ratio ("RRR"), a key performance indicator in the oil and gas industry. The Commission claimed that had Shell properly reported proved reserves, its RRR for the five-year period 1998 through 2002 would have been 80%, rather than the 100% Shell originally reported.

According to the Commission's order, Shell's overstatement of proved reserves, and its delay in correcting the overstatement, resulted from its desire to create and maintain the appearance of a strong RRR, the failure of its internal reserves estimation and reporting guidelines to conform to SEC requirements, and the lack of effective internal controls over the reserves estimation and reporting process. The Commission alleged that these failures led Shell to record and maintain proved reserves it knew or was reckless in not knowing did not satisfy SEC requirements, and to report for certain years a stronger RRR than it actually had achieved. The Commission order further alleged that Shell was warned on several occasions prior to the fall of 2003 that reported proved reserves potentially were overstated and, in such critical operating areas as Nigeria and Oman, depended upon unrealistic production forecasts. In each case, Shell either rejected the warnings as immaterial or unduly pessimistic, or attempted to "manage" the potential exposure by, for example, delaying de-booking of improperly recorded proved reserves until new, offsetting proved reserves bookings materialized.

Shell agreed to settle the matter, without admitting or denying the Commission's findings, by consenting to a cease-and-desist order finding violations of the antifraud and other provisions of the federal securities laws, and by paying $1 disgorgement and a $120 million penalty in a related civil action the Commission filed in U.S. District Court. Shell agreed to commit an additional $5 million to develop and implement a comprehensive internal compliance program under the direction and oversight of the company's legal director.

The Commission noted in its release announcing the settlement that in accepting Shell's settlement offer the Commission took into account Shell's cooperation with the staff's investigation and the remedial actions Shell had undertaken.

SEC v. Bristol-Myers Squibb Company, Litig. Rel. No. 18820 (Aug. 4, 2004).

On August 4, 2004, the Commission announced the filing and settlement of a civil action in the United States District Court for the District of New Jersey against Bristol-Myers Squibb Company ("Bristol-Myers"), a public company engaged in the manufacturing, distribution and sale of pharmaceuticals and other related health care products.

The Commission alleged that, from the first quarter of 2000 through the fourth quarter of 2001, Bristol-Myers engaged in a fraudulent scheme to inflate its sales and earnings in order to create the false appearance that the company had met or exceeded its internal sales and earnings targets and Wall Street analysts' earnings estimates.

The complaint alleged that Bristol-Myers inflated its results primarily by

(1) stuffing its distribution channels with excess inventory near the end of every quarter in amounts sufficient to meet its targets by making pharmaceutical sales to its wholesalers ahead of demand; and (2) improperly recognizing $1.5 billion in revenue from such pharmaceutical sales to its two biggest wholesalers. In connection with the $1.5 billion in revenue, Bristol-Myers covered these wholesalers' carrying costs and guaranteed them a return on investment until they sold the products. According to the complaint, Bristol-Myers recognized the $1.5 billion in revenue upon shipment, contrary to GAAP.

The complaint further alleged that the company tapped improperly created divestiture reserves and reversed portions of those reserves into income to further inflate its earnings. In addition, the complaint alleged that, as a result of the channel-stuffing, Bristol-Myers materially understated its accruals for rebates due to Medicaid and certain of its prime vendors, customers of its wholesalers that purchased large quantities of pharmaceutical products from those wholesalers.

Bristol-Myers, without admitting or denying the allegations, consented to a permanent injunction from future violations of certain anti-fraud, reporting, books and records and internal controls provisions of the federal securities laws. Bristol-Myers agreed to pay disgorgement of $1, a civil penalty of $100 million, and $50 million into a fund for the benefit of its shareholders. Bristol-Myers also agreed to various remedial undertakings, including the appointment of an independent advisor to review, assess and monitor the company's accounting practices, financial reporting and disclosure processes and internal control systems.

SEC v. Hallburton Company, Litig. Rel. No. 18817 (Aug. 3, 2004).

On August 3, 2004, the Commission announced the filing and settlement of civil enforcement proceedings against Halliburton Company ("Halliburton") and its former controller, Robert Muchmore ("Muchmore"), in the U.S. District Court for the Southern District of Texas. The Commission also instituted separately settled cease and desist proceedings against Halliburton and Muchmore. In addition, the Commission filed an enforcement action against Halliburton's former CFO, Gary Morris ("Morris"), in the Southern District of Texas. The SEC's action against Morris is pending.

The Commission alleged in its complaints against Halliburton, Muchmore, and Morris that over six financial reporting periods, spanning approximately 18 months covering 1998 and 1999, Halliburton failed to disclose that it had changed its accounting practice as to the recognition of revenue on certain cost overrun claims from its customers.

The Commission alleged that Morris and Muchmore were responsible for the company's failure to disclose the accounting change in Halliburton's Commission filings. Additionally, the Commission alleged that Morris and Muchmore played key roles in the preparation and review of quarterly earnings releases and analyst teleconference scripts that included the affected income figures. According to the Commission, Morris and Muchmore were, therefore, also responsible for the absence in the releases and scripts of any clarifying reference to the accounting change or its impact.

Halliburton, in settling with the Commission, agreed to: (1) consent to an order to cease and desist from committing or causing future securities law violations, and (2) pay a $7.5 million civil penalty. The Commission's order against Halliburton noted that the penalty, in part, reflects the Commission's view that there were unacceptable lapses in the company's conduct during the course of the investigation, which had the effect of delaying the production of information and documentation necessary to the staff's expeditious completion of its investigation.

Muchmore, in settling with the Commission, agreed to: (1) consent to an order to cease and desist from committing or causing future securities law violations, and (2) pay a civil penalty of $50,000.

SEC v. Michael Resnick, Mark P. Kaiser, Timothy J. Lee, and William Carter, Litig. Rel. No. 18797 (July 27, 2004).

On July 27, 2004, the Commission filed a complaint alleging that four former executives of wholesale food distributor U.S. Foodservice

("USF"), engaged in, or substantially participated in, a scheme to overstate the income of USF's parent company, Royal Ahold, by at least $700 million in fiscal 2001 and 2002. The SEC alleged that the following former USF officers participated in the scheme: Michael Resnick, the former CFO; Mark Kaiser, former Chief Marketing Officer; Timothy Lee, former Executive Vice President of Purchasing; and William Carter, former Vice President of Purchasing (collectively, the "Executives").

The Commission's complaint alleged that the Executives engaged in a scheme whereby USF "booked to budget"—reported earnings equal to or greater than the budgeted earnings targets set for USF, regardless of the company's true performance. The complaint alleged that the primary method used by the Executives to "book to budget" was to improperly inflate the amount of payments USF received from its vendors, otherwise known as promotional allowances. The Commission further alleged that Resnick, Kaiser, and Lee provided false and misleading justifications when questioned by Royal Ahold's independent directors about the promotional allowances recorded.

The Commission seeks a final judgment ordering the Executives to disgorge all ill-gotten gains, imposing civil money penalties, and enjoining the Executives from future violations of the federal securities laws. The Commission also seeks an order barring the executives from serving as officers and directors of any public company.

SEC v. Lay, Litig. Rel. No. 18776 (July 8, 2004).

On July 8, 2004, the Commission charged Kenneth Lay ("Lay") the former CEO and Chairman of the Board of Directors of Enron Corporation ("Enron"), with violating, and aiding and abetting the violation of, the antifraud, periodic reporting, books and records, and internal control provisions of the federal securities laws. Simultaneous with the filing of the Commission's complaint, Lay was charged criminally by the Department of Justice's Enron Task Force.

According to the Commission's complaint, Lay, along with others at Enron, engaged in a wide-ranging scheme to defraud investors. The Commission alleged that during 2001, Lay, with specific knowledge of rapidly deteriorating performances of Enron's business units, made numerous false and misleading public statements about Enron's financial condition. The Commission claimed that Lay, as Enron's Chairman and CEO, had oversight of Enron's business units and supervised the senior executives and managers of these units, reviewed drafts of public filings and draft press releases, and participated in conference calls with investment ana-

lysts.
The Commission's complaint further alleged that Lay profited from the scheme to defraud by selling large amounts of Enron stock at prices that did not reflect its true value. The SEC alleged that these sales also occurred while Lay was in possession of material non-public information concerning Enron and generated unlawful proceeds in excess of $90 million during 2001. Specifically, Lay sold over $70 million in Enron stock back to the company to repay cash advances on an unsecured Enron line of credit. The complaint stated that, in addition, while in possession of material non-public information, Lay amended two program trading plans to enable him to sell an additional $20 million in Enron stock in the open market. The Commission claimed that the proceeds from the sales constitute illegal gains resulting from his scheme to defraud. As a result of the alleged conduct, the Commission is seeking disgorgement of all ill-gotten gains, civil money penalties, a permanent bar from acting as a director or officer of a publicly held company, and an injunction against future violations of the federal securities laws.

SEC v. Skilling, Litig. Rel. No. 18582 (Feb. 19, 2004).

On February 19, 2004, the Commission charged Jeffrey K. Skilling ("Skilling"), the former President, CEO and COO of Enron, with violating, and aiding abetting the violation of, the antifraud, periodic reporting, books and records, and internal control provisions of the federal securities laws. Simultaneous with the filing of the Commission's complaint, Skilling was charged criminally by the Department of Justice's Enron Task Force.

According to the Commission's complaint, Skilling and others improperly used reserves within Enron's wholesale energy trading business, Enron Wholesale, to manufacture and manipulate reported earnings; manipulated Enron's "business segment reporting" to conceal losses at Enron's retail energy business, Enron Energy Services; manufactured earnings by fraudulently promoting Enron's broadband unit, Enron Broadband Services; and improperly used special purpose entities and the LJM partnerships to manipulate Enron's financial results. In addition, the SEC alleged that Skilling made false and misleading statements concerning Enron's financial results and the performance of its businesses, and that these misrepresentations were also contained in Enron's public filings with the Commission. The Commission further alleged in its complaint that Skilling sold Enron stock while in possession of material, non-public information that generated unlawful proceeds of approximately $63 million. As a result of the alleged conduct, the Commission's suit seeks disgorgement of ill-gotten gains, civil money penalties, a permanent bar from acting as a director or officer of a publicly held company, and an injunction against future violations of the federal securities laws.

SEC v. Causey, Litig. Rel. No. 18551 (Jan. 22, 2004).

On January 22, 2004, the Commission charged Richard A. Causey ("Causey"), the former Chief Accounting Officer of Enron, with violating, and aiding abetting the violation of, the antifraud, periodic reporting, books and records, and internal control provisions of the federal securities laws. Simultaneous with the filing of the Commission's complaint, Causey was charged criminally by the Department of Justice's Enron Task Force.

According to the Commission's complaint, Causey, and others, fraudulently manipulated Enron's merchant asset portfolio; improperly used "off-balance-sheet" special purpose entities; manipulated Enron's "business segment reporting" to conceal losses at Enron Energy Services; manipulated expenses to conceal losses at Enron Broadband services; and manipulated reserves in Enron's wholesale energy trading business to smooth earnings and conceal losses. The Commission's complaint further alleges that Causey, and others, made false and misleading statements concerning Enron's financial results and the performance of its businesses, which were also reflected in Enron's public filings. As a result of the alleged conduct, the Commission's suit seeks disgorgement of ill-gotten gains, civil money penalties, a permanent bar from acting as a director or officer of a publicly held company, and an injunction against future violations of the federal securities laws.

SEC v. Fastow, Litig. Rel. No. 18543 (Jan. 14, 2003).

On January 14, 2004, the Commission settled civil fraud charges against Andrew S. Fastow ("Fastow"), the former chief financial officer of Enron. The Commission's complaint, filed on October 2, 2002, alleges violations of the anti-fraud, periodic reporting, books and records, and internal control provisions of the federal securities laws. The Commission settled this action in coordination with the Department of Justice's Enron Task Force, which entered into a guilty plea with Fastow on related criminal charges. In resolving the parallel civil and criminal proceedings, Fastow agreed to serve a ten-year sentence, disgorge more than $23 million and to cooperate with the government's continuing investigation.

The allegations in the Commission’s complaint stems from Fastow’s conduct relating to six transactions. Three of the transactions, RADR, Chewco, and Southampton were part of an alleged scheme to hide Fastow's interest in and control of certain entities in order to keep those entities off Enron's balance sheet. The complaint alleges that Fastow secretly nominated certain of the owners of these entities, funded certain of their investments through undisclosed loans, collected undisclosed fees, and demanded and received under-the-table payments.

Two of the remaining three transactions, the Nigerian barges and the Cuiba transaction, are alleged to have been sham sales - best described as asset-parking arrangements. In one of these sales, a sale of an interest in certain Nigerian barges to a financial institution, Fastow is alleged to have promised that the financial institution would be taken out of the investment and later arranged for an entity that he controlled to buy the financial institution's interest at a pre-arranged rate of return. The last transaction included in the complaint relates to an instance of backdating documents to avoid diminution in Enron's investment in the stock of a technology company. Fastow and others allegedly created documents that purported to lock in the value of Enron's investment in the technology company back in August 2000, when that company's stock was trading at its all-time high price.

SEC v. Gemstar-TV Guide International, Inc. Litig. Rel. No. 18760 (June 23, 2004).

On June 23, 2004, the Commission filed a settled enforcement action against Gemstar-TV Guide International, Inc. ("Gemstar"), alleging that the company improperly reported its highly touted interactive program guide licensing and advertising revenues in its financial statements from 1999 through 2002.

The Commission's complaint alleged that Gemstar materially overstated its revenues by nearly $250 million through several means. First, Gemstar allegedly recorded revenue under expired, disputed, or non-existent agreements, and improperly reported this as interactive program guide ("IPG") licensing and advertising revenue. Second, the SEC alleged that Gemstar recorded and reported revenue from a long-term agreement on an accelerated basis in contravention of GAAP and Gemstar's own stated and disclosed revenue recognition policy, which required the recording and reporting of such revenue ratably over the terms of the agreement. Third, Gemstar allegedly inflated its IPG advertising revenue by improperly recording and reporting revenue amounts from multiple-element transactions. Gemstar's recording and reporting of this revenue was improper under GAAP because Gemstar could not determine the IPG advertising's fair value. Additionally, the SEC alleged that some of those improperly reported transactions included so-called "round-trip" transactions whereby Gemstar paid money to a third party that then used those funds to buy advertising from Gemstar. Fourth, the SEC alleged that Gemstar improperly recorded and reported IPG advertising revenue from non-monetary and barter transactions. Gemstar's recording and reporting of this revenue was not in accordance with GAAP because it did not meet the revenue recognition requirements for such transactions and because Gemstar could not properly establish the IPG advertising's fair value. Finally, the SEC's complaint alleged that Gemstar improperly reported certain revenues as IPG advertising revenues when in fact those revenues were derived from the sale of print advertising. Gemstar shifted revenues by invoicing advertisers for both IPG and print advertising, but recording the revenue only as IPG revenue.

Gemstar agreed to settle the case by, among other things, paying a $10 million civil penalty. The SEC stated that, in assessing the penalty amount, it considered the scope and severity of Gemstar's misconduct, Gemstar's initial failure to cooperate in the Commission's investigation or undertake remedial actions, and Gemstar's significant cooperation and remediation following a change in senior management and restructuring of its corporate governance.

SEC v. i2 Technologies, Inc., Litig. Rel. No. 18741 (June 9, 2004).

On June 9, 2004, the SEC announced a settled enforcement action against i2 Technologies, Inc. ("i2"). As part of the settlement, i2 agreed to pay a $10 million civil penalty and $1 disgorgement for allegedly misstating software license revenues. The Commission alleged that i2, in its periodic filings with the SEC, recognized software license revenues that required lengthy implementation or additional customization to be usable. Immediate recognition of long term sources of revenue was inappropriate, according to the SEC. The SEC alleged that i2 also improperly recorded revenue from barter transactions. These alleged transactions involved third party purchases of software licenses from i2, in exchange for i2's agreement to purchase a comparable amount of products or services in the future. Because i2 could not determine the fair value of items exchanged "within reasonable limits," the Commission claimed the up-front recognition of license revenue was improper and inflated reported revenues by $44 million. The penalty amount will become part of a fund for i2 investors.

SEC v. Symbol Technologies, Inc., Litig. Rel. No. 18734 (June 3, 2004).

On June 3, 2004, the SEC alleged in a settled enforcement action that Symbol Technologies, Inc. ("Symbol") and its senior managers inflated revenue, earnings and other measures of financial performance in order to create the appearance that Symbol had met or exceeded its financial projections. The complaint alleged baseless accounting entries, artificial reduction of operating expenses, improperly recognized revenue and manipulation of inventory levels and accounts receivable data. The allegedly fraudulent accounting practices had a cumulative net impact of $230 million on reported revenue and $530 million on pre-tax earnings. In addition, the Commission claimed that some of the senior managers interfered with two internal investigations into accounting practices by discarding, sanitizing, or withholding documents, and delayed the SEC staff's investigation.

As part of the settlement, Symbol agreed to pay $37 million to injured investors and appoint an independent examiner to review its accounting practices. In assessing the penalty amount, the Commission considered the scope and severity of the fraud, initial efforts to cover up the misconduct and impede investigations, and the company's eventual cooperation and remediation. Importantly, the SEC levied penalties against Symbol, and not just the alleged individual wrongdoers, for "having created and fostered the environment in which the wrongdoing took place."

SEC v. Lucent Technologies, Inc., Litig. Rel. No. 18715 (May 17, 2004).

On May 17, 2004, the SEC filed a settled accounting fraud action against Lucent Technologies, Inc. and nine former and current officers. The SEC complaint alleges that Lucent violated GAAP as a result of fraudulent and reckless actions by the individual defendants and deficient internal controls that led to numerous accounting errors by others. The SEC complaint also alleges that, in a drive to realize revenue, meet internal sales targets and/or obtain sales bonuses, the individual defendants improperly granted, and/or failed to disclose, various side agreements, credits and other incentives (collectively "extra-contractual commitments") to induce Lucent's customers to purchase the company's products. According to the SEC, these extra-contractual commitments were made in at least ten transactions in fiscal 2000, and Lucent violated GAAP by recognizing revenue on these transactions both in circumstances: (a) where it could not be recognized under GAAP; and (b) by recording the revenue earlier than was permitted under GAAP.

To settle the SEC charges, Lucent consented to a permanent injunction against future violations of the anti-fraud, reporting, books and records and internal controls provisions of the federal securities laws. As part of the settlement, Lucent also agreed to pay a $25 million penalty for failing to cooperate fully during the staff's investigation and for actions the company took after the company reached a settlement agreement in principle with the SEC. After the conclusion of the SEC investigation, Lucent's former Chairman/CEO and its outside attorney spoke to a reporter about a transaction that was a subject of the SEC investigation. Lucent's outside attorney characterized the transaction as a "failure of communication." The SEC found that Lucent's public statements undermined both the spirit and letter of its agreement in principle with the staff not to deny the SEC's allegations.

Three of the individual defendants reached settlements with the SEC. These defendants agreed to permanent injunctions against future violations of the anti-fraud, reporting, books and records and internal controls provisions of the federal securities laws, and to pay civil penalties ranging from $60,000 to $110,000. In addition, one of the settling defendants agreed to be barred from acting as an officer or director of a public company for five years and another agreed to a three year bar.

The Warnaco Group, Inc. Litig. Rel. No. 18701 (May 11, 2004).

In May 2004, the SEC brought a settled action against The Warnaco Group, Inc. ("Warnaco"), Warnaco's CFO, CEO, and general counsel, and former auditors, PricewaterhouseCoopers LLP ("PwC"), for allegedly issuing a false and misleading press release about its financial results and a misleading financial report. The SEC alleged that in 1999, Warnaco and PwC discovered inventory had been improperly recorded, resulting in a $145 million inventory restatement for the three years preceding. According to the complaint, in March 1999, Warnaco issued a press release, attributing the restatement to new accounting procedures, stating that the loss could be written off as start-up costs, and assuring investors of the company's financial health. The SEC alleged that the press release failed to inform investors that the write-offs were due to incorrect inventory accounting and would require the company to restate its financial results for the prior three years, resulting in $145 million less earnings for the three year period.

In April 1999, Warnaco filed its annual report, restating financial results for fiscal 1996-1998 to reduce inventory by $145 million and attributing the restatement to the adoption of new accounting procedures.

The SEC alleged in its complaint that senior management knew or should have known that the restatement "resulted from material flaws" in Warnaco's accounting and internal control systems and that the press release and annual report were misleading. Warnaco also agreed to settle additional alleged securities violations for what the SEC described as two misleading restatements the company made in April 2001 and July 2002.

Warnaco, its CEO and its general counsel were charged with fraud, reporting and internal control violations in the settled cease and desist order. The CEO agreed to pay $1,328,444 in disgorgement and prejudgment interest. The general counsel agreed to pay $165,722 in disgorgement and prejudgment interest. Warnaco paid no civil penalty.

The SEC also instituted and settled civil injunctive actions against Warnaco's former CFO and former auditors, PwC. Under the terms of the settlement, the former CFO agreed to pay $189,464 in disgorgement and prejudgment interest and a civil penalty of $75,000, and to a bar from serving as an officer or director of a public company for four years. PwC agreed to pay $2.4 million to settle the injunctive action. The SEC also filed a separate settled administrative proceeding, censuring PwC for aiding and abetting Warnaco's reporting violations.

Conseco, Inc., Exch. Act Rel. No. 49392 (Mar. 10, 2004); *SEC v. Dick*, Litig. Rel. No. 18621 (Mar. 11, 2004).

On March 10, 2004, the SEC filed a settled administrative proceeding against Conseco, Inc. ("Conseco"), alleging that Conseco's former CFO and former Treasurer and Chief Accounting Officer conducted a fraudulent scheme to avoid writing down the value of certain securities held by the company's subsidiary, Conseco Finance, and the resulting charges to earnings. According to the order, throughout fiscal 1999, Conseco and Conseco Finance made materially false and misleading statements about their earnings in SEC filings and in public statements announcing their earnings, overstating their results by hundreds of millions of dollars. Without admitting or denying the allegations, Conseco consented to the entry of an order requiring it to cease and desist from committing or causing any violations of the Exchange Act's books and records and internal control provisions. Conseco also consented to certain undertakings. No penalty was imposed against Conseco. The order notes that in determining to accept the settlement, the Commission considered certain remedial acts promptly undertaken by Conseco, and Conseco's cooperation with the Commission's staff.

The SEC also filed civil fraud charges against Conseco's former CFO and its former Treasurer and Chief Accounting Officer, alleging that they violated the anti-fraud provisions of the federal securities laws and aided and abetted Conseco and Conseco Finance's violations of the reporting, record keeping and internal control provisions of the federal securities laws. The complaint seeks an injunction against further violations of the above provisions, disgorgement of the salaries and bonuses earned during their fraudulent scheme, civil penalties and officer and director bars.

SEC v. Parmalat Finanziaria S.p.A., Litig. Rel. No. 18803 (July 28, 2004).

On December 30, 2003, the Commission filed a complaint in the United States District Court for the Southern District of New York alleging that the Italian Company Parmalat Finanziaria, S.p.A. ("Parmalat") engaged in "one of the largest and most brazen corporate financial frauds in history." The alleged fraud included the overstatement of cash reserves by approximately $4.9 billion and the understatement of Parmalat's liabilities by approximately $3.6 billion.

On July 28, 2004, the Commission announced that it had filed an amended complaint against Parmalat alleging that, among other things:

- Parmalat consistently overstated its level of cash and marketable securities. For example, at year-end 2002, Parmalat overstated its cash and marketable securities by at least 2.4 billion Euros ("_"). As of year-end 2003, Parmalat had overstated its assets by at least _3.95 billion (approximately $4.9 billion);
- As of September 30, 2003, Parmalat had understated its reported debt of _6.4 billion by at least _7.9 billion. Parmalat used various tactics to understate its debt, including: (a) eliminating approximately _3.3 billion of debt held by one of its nominee entities; (b) recording approximately _1 billion of debt as equity through fictitious loan participation agreements; (c) removing approximately _500 million of liabilities by falsely describing the sale of certain receivables as non-recourse, when in fact the company retained an obligation to ensure that the receivables were ultimately paid; (d) improperly eliminating approximately _300 million of debt associated with a Brazilian subsidiary during the sale of the subsidiary; (e) mischaracterizing approximately _300 million of bank debt as intercompany debt, thereby inappropriately eliminating it in consolidation; (f) eliminating approximately _200 million of Parmalat payables as though they had been paid when, in fact, they had not;

and (g) not recording a liability of approximately _400 million associated with a put option;

- Between 1997 and 2003, Parmalat transferred approximately _350 million to various businesses owned and operated by Tanzi family members;
- Parmalat transferred uncollectible and impaired receivables to "nominee" entities, where their diminished or nonexistent value was hidden. As a result, Parmalat carried assets at inflated values and avoided the negative impact on its income statement that would have been associated with a proper reserve or write-off of bad debt;
- Parmalat used these same nominee entities to fabricate non-existent financial operations intended to offset losses of its operating subsidiaries;
- Parmalat used the nominee entities to disguise intercompany loans from one subsidiary to another subsidiary that was experiencing operating losses; and
- Parmalat recorded fictional revenue through sales by its subsidiaries to controlled nominee entities at inflated or entirely fictitious amounts.

Simultaneous with the filing of the amended complaint, Parmalat consented, without admitting or denying the allegations in the Commission's complaint, to a permanent injunction against future violations of the antifraud provisions of the federal securities laws. Parmalat also agreed to adopt changes to its corporate governance to promote future compliance with the federal securities laws, including adopting by-laws providing for governance by a shareholder-elected board of directors, the majority of whom will be independent and serve finite terms; specifically delineating in the by-laws the duties of the board of directors; adopting a Code of Conduct governing the duties and activities of the board of directors; adopting an Insider Dealing Code of Conduct; and adopting a Code of Ethics. The by-laws will also require that the positions of chairman of the board of directors and managing director be held by two separate individuals. The settlement did not require Parmalat to pay a civil monetary penalty, because Parmalat's shareholders are being treated fairly in the bankruptcy process in which the company will be reorganized subject to approval by the Italian government.

SEC v. Vivendi Universal, S.A., Litig. Rel. No. 18523 (Dec. 24, 2003).

In this matter, the Commission filed a settled enforcement action in the United States District Court for the Southern District of New York. In its complaint, the Commission alleged that Vivendi Universal, S.A. ("Vivendi") and two of its senior executives had issued a misleading earnings release that falsely portrayed Vivendi's liquidity and cash flow positions as being more favorable than they actually were. In addition, the complaint alleged that Vivendi had inappropriately adjusted reserves and had taken part in other accounting practices in violation of GAAP in order to increase the company's EBITDA and meet ambitious earnings targets. The Commission's complaint also alleged that Vivendi failed to disclose various commitments and contingencies and failed to disclose its investment in a transaction to acquire shares of Elektrim Telekomunikacja Sp. zo.o, a Polish tele-communications company in which Vivendi already held a 49% stake. The Commission alleged that these actions violated the antifraud provisions of the Exchange Act and the Securities Act, the books and records provisions of the Exchange Act and the reporting provisions of the Exchange Act.

The defendants consented to the entry of orders permanently enjoining each of them from violating the securities laws. In addition, Vivendi consented to a civil money penalty of $50 million and disgorgement of $1. One of the executives consented to a civil money judgment of $1 million, and the other executive consented to a penalty of $120,000 and disgorgement of $148,149. The executives were also barred from serving as officers or directors of any public company for ten years and five years, respectively. The Commission intends for the funds to be paid to defrauded investors under the Fair Funds provisions of Sarbanes-Oxley.

SEC v. Canadian Imperial Bank of Commerce, Litig. Rel. No. 18517 (Dec. 22, 2003).

The Commission charged Canadian Imperial Bank of Commerce ("CIBC") and three of its executives with aiding and abetting Enron's accounting fraud through a series of complex structured finance transactions over a period of years preceding Enron's bankruptcy. Simultaneously with the filing of the complaint, CIBC settled the action, agreeing to consent to entry of a final judgment against the Company. CIBC agreed to pay $80 million in disgorgement, fees and penalties.

According to the complaint, the financings complained of involved purported transfers of assets from Enron to various off-balance sheet special purpose entities. Enron accounted for the asset transfers as sales in order to book earnings and operating cash flows, without reporting the associated debt on its financial statements. CIBC organized a syndicate of banks to provide the majority of the capitalization of the special purpose entities with debt financing. CIBC also provided outside "at risk" equity that was required to validate the financing of certain qualified special purpose entities. The complaint also alleged that the supposedly "at-risk" equity necessary to qualify these special purpose entities was not actually "at risk," due to various agreements between CIBC executives and Enron executives.

The Commission's complaint further alleges that CIBC took part in all of these actions, despite concerns that Enron had "financially engineered" a large portion of its profits. According to the complaint, CIBC nonetheless desired to be included in Enron's elite tier of banks. CIBC earned $18 million in fees from the fraudulent financing deals.

SEC v. Brightpoint, Inc, Litig. Rel. No. 18340 (Sept. 11, 2003).

The Commission filed a civil accounting fraud action against Brightpoint, Inc. ("Brightpoint"), American International Group, Inc. ("AIG"), two former officers of Brightpoint, and a former employee of Brightpoint. The Commission also instituted separately settled cease and desist proceedings against Brightpoint, AIG, one former Brightpoint employee and an AIG employee.

The Commission alleged that AIG, beginning in 1997, developed and marketed a "non-traditional" insurance product for the stated purpose of enabling public reporting companies to smooth earnings over a period of time, by creating the appearance of insurance, and an assumption of risk by AIG, when in fact AIG was simply accepting cash from the "insured" that would be refunded back. According to the complaint, AIG issued such a purported policy to Brightpoint, for the purpose of assisting Brightpoint to conceal $11.9 million in losses in 1998. The alleged policy allowed Brightpoint to recognize an insurance receivable of $11.9 million, when in fact all that occurred was a "round-trip" of cash.

The complaint further alleged that AIG and Brightpoint violated the antifraud provisions of the Exchange Act, as well as the reporting and books and records provisions, and that AIG aided and abetted Brightpoint's antifraud violation. Brightpoint and AIG consented to the entry of a final judgment in settlement of the civil matter enjoining the companies from further violations of the securities laws, as well as to a cease and desist order in the administrative proceeding. As part of the settlement,

AIG agreed to pay a $10 million civil penalty and $100,000 of disgorgement, and Brightpoint agreed to pay a $450,000 civil penalty.

SEC v. Rica Foods, Inc., Litig. Rel. No. 1844 (Aug. 18, 2003)

In this matter, the Commission filed a settled civil injunctive action against Rica Foods, Inc. ("Rica"), and its former CEO and CFO, for violations of the CEO and CFO certification requirements of the Sarbanes-Oxley Act of 2002. Rica consented to the entry of a final judgment enjoining Rica from future securities law violations and providing for other relief, including civil penalties against Rica's CEO.

In its complaint, the Commission alleged that Rica filed a Form 10-K with a purported unqualified audit opinion from Deloitte and Touche, LLP ("Deloitte"), despite the fact that Deloitte had not provided such an unqualified opinion. The financial statements filed by Rica also contained material classification errors, according to the Commission's complaint. Despite the lack of a signed audit report and the existence of the material classification errors, the CEO and CFO of Rica signed the certifications required by Section 302 of Sarbanes-Oxley. The Commission alleged that their actions violated the books and records provisions of the Exchange Act. The settlement resulted in the entry of a final judgment against the Company and the officers, permanently enjoining them from further violations of the books and records provisions of the Exchange Act, and required the former CEO to pay a $25,000 civil penalty.

SEC v. Peregrine Sys., Inc., Litig. Rel. No. 18920 (Aug. 14, 2003); *SEC v. Gardner*, Litig. Rel. No. 18919 (Oct. 6, 2004).

The Commission announced that, on July 23, 2003, the United States District Court for the Southern District of California entered a final judgment in the Commission's civil action against Peregrine Systems, Inc. ("Peregrine") related to charges stemming from an alleged securities fraud perpetrated over a three-year period. Specifically, the Commission alleged that Peregrine improperly recognized at least $259 million in revenue from "sham" sales of software licenses from 1999 through 2001. According to the complaint, Peregrine entered into non-binding sales agreements with customers to transfer software licenses. As part of the transactions, Peregrine and its customers executed secret side agreements which discharged the customers' obligation to pay for the licenses. Peregrine entered into these so-called "parking transactions" when the company needed revenue to meet earnings forecasts. In addition, the Commission alleged that Peregrine routinely held its books open after fiscal quarters ended when the company failed to close deals by the quarterly deadline.

Peregrine's officers allegedly undertook additional fraudulent measures to conceal the alleged revenue-inflating schemes. As explained in the complaint, Peregrine booked revenue from the "sham" transactions with corresponding additions to its accounts receivables. As customers did not pay and the receivables grew, Peregrine officials sold the receivables accounts to banks in exchange for cash. The company improperly accounted for these transactions as sales of receivables and removed the inflated accounts from its balance sheet.

Peregrine settled this matter by agreeing to be enjoined from violating the antifraud, reporting, books and records, and internal controls provisions of the federal securities laws. In addition, the company agreed to comply, on an accelerated basis, with the new rules requiring management to issue a report concerning the adequacy of the company's internal controls. *See* Section 404 of the Sarbanes-Oxley Act of 2002. Peregrine also consented to: (1) retain an Internal Auditor to ensure that its financial results are accurately reported, (2) appoint a Compliance Officer to perform a review of the company's corporate governance practices, (3) commence a training and education program for its officers and employees, to prevent future violations of the federal securities laws, and (4) disclose the current condition of its internal controls and financial reporting procedures, when a reorganization plan under Chapter 11 of the Bankruptcy Code became effective. The court also approved the Commission's decision not to require Peregrine to pay a civil money penalty or disgorgement. Related criminal proceedings also were instituted in this matter.

On October 6, 2004, the Commission filed civil fraud and related charges against six former senior officers of Peregrine, including the company's former CEO and its former President, for their roles in the alleged accounting fraud. The Commission's complaint alleged that the former officers orchestrated the alleged fraud at the company, while, at the same time, selling their personal holdings of Peregrine stock in the open market. The Commission's action against the former officers is pending.

In re Citigroup, Inc., Exch. Act Rel. No. 48-230 (July 28, 2003).

On July 28, 2003, the Commission filed a settled administrative proceeding against Citigroup, Inc. ("Citigroup") for its alleged role in causing the securities violations of Enron and Dynegy Inc. ("Dynegy"). The Commission's order states that Citigroup knew or should have known that the firm was assisting the energy companies in structuring financing transactions that were designed to mislead investors by overstating the energy companies' reported cash flow, net income, and tax savings.

Specifically, the order reported that Citigroup assisted Enron in executing transactions to create the appearance that Enron's cash flows were growing at a similar rate with the fair value of Enron's financial instrument assets. The order explains that the accounting method employed by Enron to account for these financial assets caused the widening of a gap between the fair value of the company's financial assets and its cash flows when the fair value of the financial assets increased. According to the Commission, Enron feared that the gap would cause the analyst community to question the sustainability of Enron's future earnings.

The order charges that in an effort to conceal this gap, Citigroup structured and stood as a counter-party to at least twelve different transactions that Enron used to facilitate its misreporting scheme. For example, in one of these transactions, known as Project Nahanni, Enron recognized $500 million in cash flow from operations that was, in the Commission's view, cash generated from a loan from Citigroup. The Commission charged that the disclosures relating to Project Nahanni and similar transactions were misleading because the disclosures duped investors into believing that Enron was generating the enhanced cash flows from ordinary investments and business activities.

The Commission's order also settled Citigroup's involvement in Dynegy's financing transactions. Similar to the findings related to Enron, the order reported that Citigroup assisted Dynegy in concealing a gap between Dynegy's current earnings and operating cash flows. Citigroup and Dynegy allegedly used a transaction known as Project Alpha to create the appearance that Dynegy had generated $300 million in cash flow and a related $79 million in tax savings from a complex natural gas contractual arrangement. In reality, according to the Commission, the earnings generated from Project Alpha were the proceeds of a Citigroup sponsored loan. The Commission explained that Citigroup knew or should have known that Dynegy was using Project Alpha to mislead analysts and investors about the true nature of the company's earnings.

Citigroup settled the matter by consenting to cease and desist from committing or causing any violations or future violations of Section 10(b) of the Exchange Act or Rule 10b-5. Citigroup also agreed to pay $120 million representing civil penalties, disgorgement, and prejudgment interests. Of that amount, $101 million was related to the Enron activities and $19 million was related to the Dynegy activities.

SEC v. J.P. Morgan Chase & Co., Litig. Rel. No. 18252 (July 28, 2003).

The Commission announced the filing and simultaneous settlement of aiding and abetting charges against J.P. Morgan Chase & Co. ("J.P. Morgan") on July 28, 2003. The Commission's action related to structured finance transactions entered into between J.P. Morgan and Enron during the years 1997 through 2001. In the complaint, the Commission alleged that, over the five year period, J.P. Morgan loaned Enron approximately $2.6 billion and, rather than account for these funds as loans, Enron reported the loan proceeds as cash flow from operating activities.

To carry out its alleged accounting scheme, Enron and J.P. Morgan executed seven structured finance transactions known as "prepays." According to the complaint, a typical prepay transaction for an energy commodity involves the purchaser of the commodity paying for a long-term energy supply at the time a contract is made. Under a typical agreement, the purchaser takes on the risk that energy prices may fall. The seller takes on the opposite risk.

The Commission asserted that the prepay transactions executed between Enron and J.P. Morgan were disguised loans from J.P. Morgan to Enron because an element of risk did not pass between the parties. According to the complaint, J.P. Morgan and Enron masked the risk-less feature of the transactions by executing a series of commodity trades among Enron, J.P. Morgan, and a J.P. Morgan special purpose entity. The Commission charged that J.P. Morgan knew the purpose behind the transactions was to allow Enron to mislead analysts and investors that the company was generating legitimate cash flows.

J.P. Morgan settled the matter by consenting to the entry of an injunction against future violations of Section 10(b) of the Exchange Act and Rule 10b-5. As part of the settlement, J.P. Morgan will pay $135 million representing a civil penalty, disgorgement, and prejudgment interest.

In re Reliant, Inc., Exch. Act Rel. No. 47-828 (May 12, 2003).

The Commission instituted a cease and desist proceeding against Reliant Resources, Inc. and Reliant Energy, Inc. (collectively referred to as "Reliant"), and simultaneously accepted Reliant's offer of settlement. Under the terms of the settlement, Reliant consented to entry of an order requiring Reliant to cease and desist from committing, or causing to be committed, further violations of the antifraud provisions, books and records provisions, and record keeping provisions of the securities laws.

The Commission found securities violations as a result of two distinct types of transaction. First, the Commission found that Reliant had violated the securities laws by taking part in "round trip" energy trades that were simultaneous buy and sell transactions that resulted in an equal amount of revenues and expenses for Reliant. The SEC found that these transactions were undertaken solely to increase volume at Reliant, and led to a material misstatement in Reliant's financial statements when accounted for on a gross basis. Second, the Commission found that Reliant took part in actions to shift earnings from the current period, where those earnings were coming in well above forecasted amounts, to future periods, where earnings were likely to come in below the forecasted amounts. These structured transactions created a smoothing effect on Reliant's earnings, which the Commission alleged created a material misstatement in Reliant's financial statements.

SEC v. HealthSouth Corp., Litig. Rel. No. 18044 (Mar. 20, 2003).

On March 20, 2003, the Commission announced that it filed a complaint in the Northern District of Alabama against HealthSouth Corporation ("HealthSouth") and Richard S. Scrushy ("Scrushy"), HealthSouth's Chairman and CEO.

The complaint alleges that between 1999 and 2002 Scrushy led a massive accounting fraud to meet or exceed analyst expectations by overstating HealthSouth's earnings by $1.4 billion. The complaint also asserts that Scrushy and HealthSouth's CFO certified the company's recent Commission periodic filings when they knew or were reckless in not knowing the filings misstated HealthSouth's earnings by 4,700%. An amended complaint filed on April 3, 2003, also alleges insider trading by Scrushy.

According to the Commission's complaint, HealthSouth's senior management met with Scrushy on a quarterly basis to present him with the company's actual earnings. When the actual earnings were under Wall Street's expectations, Scrushy directed his management to "fix" the shortfall. The Commission alleged that the shortfalls were "fixed" by the recording of false entries in HealthSouth's accounting books, including a contra revenue and expense accounts. The Commission asserted that Scrushy personally profited from his improper activities by selling almost eight million shares of HealthSouth stock between 1999 and 2002.

The Commission's complaint seeks injunctions against HealthSouth and Scrushy as well as civil penalties and disgorgement of all ill-gotten gains. The Commission is also seeking to permanently bar Scrushy from serving as a director or officer of a publicly held company.

The Commission's complaint was accompanied by a petition for emergency relief freezing the assets of Scrushy and requiring HealthSouth to escrow extraordinary payments.

On March 19, 2003, HealthSouth consented to the entry of emergency orders requiring the company to place in escrow all extraordinary payments to its directors, officers, partners, controlling person, agents, or employees; prohibiting the company from destroying documents; and providing expedited discovery for the Commission's case. The District Court also issued an order temporarily freezing Scrushy's assets pending a hearing on the Commission's petition.

On May 7, 2003, after an 11-day evidentiary hearing, the District Court granted Scrushy's motion to dismiss the SEC's petition for emergency relief and dissolved the asset freeze as to Scrushy. The District Court stayed the case pending resolution of any criminal charges against Scrushy.

SEC v. Merrill Lynch Co., Litig. Rel. No. 18038 (Mar. 17, 2003).

In this matter, the Commission filed suit against Merrill Lynch Co. ("Merrill Lynch") and four former executives of the firm alleging that the defendants aided and abetted Enron's securities fraud. The Commission's complaint was filed in the U.S. District Court in Houston. The complaint alleges that the defendants assisted Enron's accounting manipulation by engaging in two fraudulent transactions at the end of 1999. The transactions allegedly allowed Enron to overstate its earnings by more than $60 million, one third of Enron's reported fourth quarter 1999 earnings.

In the first transaction, executed on December 29, 1999, Merrill Lynch purchased an interest in a Nigerian shipping operation owned by Enron for $28 million. In the Commission's complaint, it asserted that there was an additional agreement between Enron and Merrill Lynch under which Enron agreed to relieve Merrill Lynch of its interest in the shipping operation within six months of the transaction. In the Commission's view, because risk in the transaction never passed to Merrill Lynch, the transaction was merely a loan, and Enron's recognition of revenue from the transaction was improper.

In the second transaction, Enron and Merrill Lynch entered an options agreement. The Commission stated that the defendants knew that the options were not going to be traded and that the intended purpose of the agreement was to create revenue for Enron and improperly inflate its earnings by $50 million. In the complaint, the Commission explained that

Merrill Lynch received $8.5 million from Enron for its involvement in the options transactions.

The complaint charges that Merrill Lynch and the individual defendants aided and abetted Enron's violations of the antifraud, reporting, books and records, and internal controls provisions of the federal securities laws. Merrill Lynch settled its involvement in the matter by agreeing to pay $80 million, representing a civil penalty, disgorgement, and prejudgment interest. Merrill Lynch also consented to the entry of an injunction against future violations of the antifraud and other provisions of the federal securities laws. On November 4, 2004, after a six week trial in Houston, Texas, a jury found the four former Merrill Lynch executives guilt of conspiracy and two counts of fraud for their roles in the transactions.

SEC v. Lernout & Hauspie Speech Products, N.V., Litig. Rel. No. 18014 (Mar. 4, 2003).

The Commission announced that, on February 28, 2003, the United States District Court for the District of Columbia entered a permanent injunction against Belgian-headquartered Lernout & Hauspie Speech Products, N.V. ("Lernout"). The order, which Lernout consented to without admitting or denying the allegations in the Commission's complaint, enjoins Lernout from violating the anti-fraud, reporting, books and records and internal controls provisions of the federal securities laws.

The Commission's complaint, which was filed in October 2002, alleged that Lernout engaged in a massive accounting fraud resulting in approximately $8.6 billion in lost market capitalization and the eventual liquidation of the company.

The Commission asserted that Lernout engaged in various forms of improper accounting conduct relating to the use of corporate entities that Lernout formed to fabricate revenue. According to the complaint, while listed on the NASDAQ National Market System, Lernout incorporated numerous shell companies in Belgium and Singapore for the purpose of creating trading partners. In the Commission's view, transactions with those trading partners—which Lernout reported as sales revenue—were disguised loans, rather than legitimate sales, and therefore Lernout's accounting for the transactions as revenue generating violated GAAP.

The Commission also stated that Lernout used other companies to create the appearance that Lernout was growing its customer base. With these fictitious customers, Lernout engaged in a series of cyclical transactions to fabricate more revenue. In a typical cyclical transaction, Lernout supplied or arranged for others to supply start-up financing to the shell companies. Lernout then sold software licenses to the shell companies. As part of the transaction, the shell company returned the start-up financing back to Lernout, which it accounted for as licensing revenue. The Commission asserted that the liabilities from the cyclical transactions were not reflected on Lernout's balance sheet.

In a related matter, on March 4, 2003, without admitting or denying the findings in the Commission's Order, Lernout consented to the entry of an order revoking the registration of its common stock.

SEC v. Safety-Kleen Corp., Litig. Rel. 17891 (Dec. 12, 2002).

On December 12, 2002, the Commission announced the filing of a complaint in the Southern District of New York against Safety-Kleen Corp. ("Safety-Kleen"), the company's CFO, and two senior accounting officials. In the complaint, the Commission alleged that Safety-Kleen's former CFO orchestrated a massive accounting scheme that caused Safety-Kleen to materially overstate its revenues and earnings in Commission filings and press releases.

According to the complaint, the former CFO, with the assistance of others, engaged in improper accounting practices including: 1) improper revenue recognition; 2) the capitalization of operating expenses; 3) improper treatment of reserves and accruals; and 4) improper recording of derivative transactions. The alleged purposes of these practices were to conceal the company's declining revenues, cause the company to meet analyst earnings projections, and create the illusion that Safety-Kleen's recent acquisitions achieved their predicted cost savings benefits. The complaint specifically asserts that the former CFO signed the company's Commission filings when he knew or was reckless in not knowing that the reports were materially false and misleading.

Safety-Kleen and two individuals settled that matter by consenting to the entry of an injunction against future violations of the antifraud and record keeping provisions of the federal securities laws. One of the settling individuals agreed to pay $28,476 in disgorgement and prejudgment interest. In a related matter, Safety-Kleen's former CFO and another individual were charged criminally by the U.S. Attorney's Office for the Southern District of New York.

SEC v. Kopper, Litig. Rel. No. 17692 (Aug. 21, 2002).

On August 21, 2002, the Commission charged Michael J. Kopper, a former high-ranking Enron official, with violating the anti-fraud provisions of the federal securities laws. Without admitting or denying the allegations of the complaint, Kopper agreed to be enjoined permanently from violating Section 10(b) of the Securities Exchange Act of 1934 and Exchange Act Rule 10b-5, and to be barred permanently from acting as an officer or director of a public company. As part of the settlement, Kopper will disgorge and forfeit a total of approximately $12 million. Simultaneous with the filing of the Commission's action, the Department of Justice's Enron Task Force filed related criminal charges against Kopper. Kopper agreed to enter a guilty plea in connection with those charges and to cooperate with the government's continuing investigation.

The allegations in the Commission's complaint stem from Kopper's conduct relating to three transactions, RADR, Chewco, and Southampton that were part of an alleged scheme to hide Kopper's interest in and control of certain entities in order to keep those entities off Enron's balance sheet. The complaint also alleges that Kopper exploited the fiction that these entities were independent of Enron to misappropriate millions of dollars representing undisclosed fees and other illegal profits.

SEC v. Dynegy Inc., Litig. Rel. No. 17744 (Sept. 25, 2002); *SEC v. Foster,* Litig. Rel. No. 18188 (June 12, 2003).

On September 25, 2002, the Commission filed a settled enforcement action against Dynegy Inc. ("Dynegy") in connection with alleged accounting improprieties and misleading statements by the Houston-based energy production, distribution and trading company. The Commission's case arose from (1) Dynegy's improper accounting for and misleading disclosures relating to a $300 million financing transaction involving special-purpose entities, and (2) Dynegy's overstatement of its energy-trading activity resulting from "round trip" or "wash" trades—simultaneous, pre-arranged buy-sell trades of energy with the same counter-party, at the same price and volume, and over the same term, resulting in neither profit nor loss to either party. The round-trip transactions were allegedly conducted to inflate reported revenues.

Dynegy, without admitting or denying the Commission's findings, consented to the entry of an administrative order to cease-and-desist from future violations of the anti-fraud, reporting, record keeping and internal control provisions of the federal securities laws. Dynegy also consented to the payment of a $3 million penalty in a related civil suit filed by the Commission in U.S. District Court for the Southern District of Texas.

The Commission also filed suit against three accounting professionals employed by Dynegy for behavior relating to the company's use of special purpose entities. The Commission asserted that, after receiving advice from Dynegy's outside auditors regarding the proper accounting treatment for the financing transaction, the individuals discarded the auditor's advice and affirmatively undertook improper accounting procedures. The complaint charges the individuals with securities fraud and aiding and abetting Dynegy's securities violations. The U.S. Attorney's Office for the Southern District of Texas charged three individuals for the same alleged accounting misconduct.

SEC v. Kozlowski, Litig. Rel. No. 1672 (Sept. 12, 2002); *SEC v. Walsh*, Litig. Rel. No. 17896 (Dec. 17, 2002).

On September 12, 2002, the Commission announced the filing of a civil action in the United States District Court for the Southern District of New York against three former top executives of Tyco International Ltd. ("Tyco") charging that they violated the federal securities laws by failing to disclose to investors the multi-million dollar low interest and interest-free loans they took from the company. The Commission's complaint alleged that L. Dennis Kozlowski, the former chief executive officer and chairman of the board of directors of Tyco, and Mark Swartz, the former chief financial officer and director, granted themselves hundreds of millions of dollars in secret low interest and interest-free loans from the company—loans which they used for personal expenses. They then allegedly covertly caused the company to forgive tens of millions of dollars of those outstanding loans, without disclosure to investors. The Commission's complaint further alleged that Mark A. Belnick, the former chief legal officer, failed to disclose the receipt of more than $14 million of interest-free loans from the company to acquire two residences, an apartment in New York City and a $10 million home in Park City, Utah, where he already owned another home. Finally, the Commission's complaint alleges that Kozlowski, Swartz and Belnick sold their shares of Tyco stock valued at millions of dollars while their alleged self-dealing remained undisclosed.

The Commission is seeking a final judgment ordering all defendants to disgorge all ill-gotten gains, imposing civil money penalties, enjoining the defendants from future violations of the federal securities laws, and an order barring the defendants from serving as officers or directors of a public company. In the cases of Kozlowski and Swartz, the Commission is seeking disgorgement of all compensation received from Tyco subsequent to their fraudulent acts and omissions, including salary, bonuses, stock options and grants and an order enjoining them from violating the antifraud, proxy, reporting, books and records and lying to auditor provisions of the federal securities laws. In the case of Belnick, the Commission is seeking all rent payments received from Tyco for the home office he retained in his Utah residence and an order enjoining him from violating the anti-fraud, proxy and reporting provisions of the federal securities laws. The Commission's complaint in this matter was filed simultaneously with related criminal charges against the defendants brought by the Manhattan District Attorney.

On December 17, 2002, the Commission filed a settled civil action in the United States District Court for the Southern District of New York alleging that Frank E. Walsh, Jr. violated the federal securities laws by signing a Tyco registration statement which Walsh knew contained materially misleading statements concerning fees or commissions payable in connection with Tyco's June 2001 $9.2 billion acquisition of The CIT Group, Inc. ("CIT"). The Commission's complaint in the Walsh matter alleges that in late 2000, Walsh, a director of Tyco from 1992 through February of 2002 recommended that Tyco consider acquiring CIT. After Walsh set up a meeting between Kozlowski and CIT's chief executive officer, Kozlowski proposed to pay Walsh a "finder's fee" for his services if the transaction was consummated. When the transaction was submitted to the Board, Walsh voted in favor of the transaction but did not disclose to the Board that he would receive a substantial fee. The agreement and plan of merger contained a representation by Tyco that, other than Tyco's investment bankers for the transaction, no other investment banking or finder's fees were to be paid in connection with the transaction. The agreement and plan of merger was incorporated by reference in, and attached to, a registration statement filed by Tyco with the Commission for the securities related to the contemplated merger between Tyco and CIT. As a director of Tyco, Walsh signed the registration statement knowing it contained a material misrepresentation regarding the payment of a "finder's fee." After the merger was consummated, Kozlowski caused Tyco to pay him a $20 million "finder's fee" in the form of $10 million in cash and a $10 million charitable contribution to a foundation chosen by Walsh.

Walsh, without admitting or denying the allegations in the Complaint, consented to the entry of a final judgment permanently enjoining him from violations of Section 17(a) of the Securities Act and Section 10(b) of the Exchange Act and Rule 10b-5 thereunder, permanently barring him from acting as an officer or director of a publicly-held company, and ordering him to pay restitution of $20 million; provided that restitution would be offset, in part or in whole, by any restitution paid by Walsh in the related criminal action brought by the Manhattan District Attorney.

SEC v. Adelphia Communications Corp., Litig. Rel. No. ______, (April 25, 2005); Litig. Rel. No. 17837 (Nov. 14, 2002); and Litig. Rel. No. 17627 (July 24, 2002).

On July 24, 2002, the Commission announced the filing of a civil action in the United States District Court for the Southern District of New York against Adelphia Communications Corporation ("Adelphia"); its founder John J. Rigas; his three sons Timothy J. Rigas, Michael J. Rigas, James R. Rigas; and two senior executives at Adelphia, James R. Brown and Michael C. Mulcahey, in one of the largest financial fraud cases brought by the Commission to date. In its complaint, the Commission charged that Adelphia, at the direction of the individual defendants: (1) fraudulently excluded billions of dollars in liabilities from its consolidated financial statements by hiding them in off-balance sheet affiliates; (2) falsified operations statistics and inflated Adelphia's earnings to meet analysts expectations; and (3) concealed rampant self-dealing by the Rigas family, including the undisclosed use of corporate funds to purchase company stock and luxury condominiums.

The Commission's complaint charged the defendants with violations of the antifraud, periodic reporting, record keeping, and internal control provisions of the federal securities laws. The Commission sought a judgment ordering the defendants to account for and disgorge all ill-gotten gains, including all compensation received by the individual defendants during the alleged fraud, all property unlawfully taken from Adelphia by the individual defendants through undisclosed related-party transactions, and any severance payments related to the individual defendants' resignation from the company. The Commission also sought civil penalties and orders barring each of the individual defendants from acting as an officer or director of a public company.

On November 14, 2002, the Commission announced that Brown, the former vice-president of Finance at Adelphia, without admitting or denying the allegations in the complaint, consented to the entry against him of a permanent injunction against violations of Section 17(a) of the Securities Act , Sections 10(b) and 13(b)(5) of the Exchange Act, and Rules 10b-5, 13b2-1, and 13b2-2, and, as a control person, of Sections 13(a) and 13(b)(2)(A) and 13(b)(2)(B) of the Exchange Act and Rules 12b-20, 13a-1 and 13a-13, and a permanent officer and director bar. Brown also agreed to provide the Court with an accounting. The Commission's claims against Brown for disgorgement of ill-gotten gains, plus prejudgment interest, and a civil penalty remain pending.

On April 25, 2005, the SEC announced that it and the United States Attorney's Office for the Southern District of New York ("USAO") reached an agreement to settle the SEC's civil enforcement action and resolve the criminal charges against Adelphia and the Rigas family defendants. The USAO also announced that it had entered into a non-prosecution agreement with Adelphia and had settled forfeiture claims against Rigas family members.

Under the settlement agreement, which is subject to the approval of the District and Bankruptcy Courts for the Southern District of New York, the Rigas family members will forfeit in excess of $1.5 billion in assets that they derived from the fraud, including the Rigas family's interests in certain cable properties. Upon the forfeiture of these assets, Adelphia will obtain title to those cable properties and will pay $715 million into a victim fund to be established in the District Court in accordance with the non-prosecution agreement. Under the non-prosecution agreement, payment to the victim fund must occur at or around the time of Adelphia's emergence from chapter 11 bankruptcy protection.

Also under the settlement agreement, Adelphia and the Rigas family members agreed to entry of permanent injunctions enjoining them from the antifraud, periodic reporting, and record keeping and internal control provisions of the federal securities laws. The individual Rigas family members further agreed to orders barring them from acting as officers or directors of a public company.

SEC v. WorldCom, Inc., Litig. Rel. No. 17588 (June 27, 2002); Litig. Rel. No. 18219 (July 7, 2003); *SEC v. Myers*, Litig. Rel. No. 17753 (Sept. 26, 2002); *SEC v. Yates*, Litig. Rel. No. 17771 (Oct. 7, 2002); *SEC v. Vinson*, Litig. Rel. No. 17783 (Oct. 10, 2002); *SEC v. Sullivan*, Litig. Rel. No. 18605 (Mar. 2, 2004).

On June 27, 2002, the Commission announced the filing of a civil action in the United States District Court for the Southern District of New York against WorldCom, Inc. ("WorldCom"), a major global communications provider. The Commission's complaint alleged that WorldCom fraudulently overstated its income, before income taxes and minority interests, by approximately $3.055 billion in 2001 and $797 million during the first quarter of 2002. The Commission's complaint further alleged that WorldCom falsely portrayed itself as a profitable business during 2001 and the first quarter of 2002 by reporting earnings it did not have. The Commission alleged that WorldCom did so by capitalizing (and deferring) rather than expensing (and immediately recognizing) approximately $3.8 billion of its costs. The company transferred these costs to capital accounts in violation of GAAP. The Commission alleged that these actions were intended to mislead investors and manipulate WorldCom's earnings to keep them in line with estimates by Wall Street analysts.

The Commission charged WorldCom with violations of Sections 10(b) and 13(a) of the Exchange Act and Rules 10b-5, 13a-1, 13a-13 and 12b-20. The Commission's complaint sought 1) a permanent injunction; 2) civil monetary penalties; 3) a court order prohibiting WorldCom and its directors, officers, employees, and agents from destroying, altering or hiding relevant documents; 4) a court order prohibiting WorldCom or its affiliates from making any extraordinary payments to any present or former officer, director or employee, including severance payments, bonus payments, or indemnification payments; and 5) the appointment of a corporate monitor to ensure that documents are not destroyed and extraordinary payments are not made.

On June 28, 2002, based upon a joint agreement between the Commission and WorldCom, U.S. District Court Judge Jed Rakoff entered an order:

- Directing WorldCom and its affiliates to preserve all items relating to WorldCom's financial reporting obligations, public disclosures required by the federal securities laws, or accounting matters.
- Providing for the Court to appoint a Corporate Monitor having oversight responsibility with respect to all compensation paid by WorldCom for the purposes of preventing unjust enrichment as a result of the conduct alleged in the Commission's complaint and to ensure that WorldCom assets are not dissipated by payments that are not necessary to the operation of WorldCom's business.[70]
- Forbidding, until the Corporate Monitor is in place, WorldCom from (1) paying more that $100,000 to any present or former officer, director or employee; or (2) making any extraordinary payment to any present or former director, present or former officers holding a position at or above the level of vice-president, or any person currently or formerly within financial reporting or accounting functions.
- Directing WorldCom to cooperate with the Corporate Monitor.

70. On July 3, U.S. District Court Judge Jed S. Rakoff appointed former Commission Chairman Richard Breeden as the Corporate Monitor.

The Commission also ordered WorldCom to file with the Commission, under oath, a detailed report of the circumstances and specifics relating to the Commission's complaint. WorldCom filed the report with the Commission on July 1, 2002.[71]

On November 1, 2002, the Commission filed an amended complaint against WorldCom adding claims that WorldCom violated the antifraud and books and records provisions of the federal securities laws in connection with several securities offerings. The amended complaint also broadened the time period relating to the Commission's charges by alleging that WorldCom misled investors from at least as early as 1999 through the first quarter of 2002, and further stated that the company had acknowledged that during that period, as a result of undisclosed and improper accounting, WorldCom materially overstated the income it reported on its financial statements by approximately $9 billion.

On November 26, 2002, the Commission announced that WorldCom consented, without admitting or denying the allegations in the Commission's complaint, to the entry of the judgment that settled the Commission's action against WorldCom. The judgment: (1) enjoined WorldCom from violating the antifraud, reporting, and the books and records and internal controls provisions of the federal securities laws, (2) ordered an extensive review of the company's corporate governance systems, policies, plans, and practices, (3) ordered an extensive review of the company's internal accounting control structure and policies, (4) ordered that WorldCom provide reasonable training and education to certain officers and employees to minimize the possibility of future violations of the federal securities laws, and (5) provided that civil money penalties, if any, will be decided by the court at a later date.

On July 7, 2003, Judge Rakoff approved the settlement of the Commission's claim for a civil penalty against WorldCom. Under the terms of the approved settlement, WorldCom was liable for a civil penalty of $2.25 billion, but once the U.S. Bankruptcy Court for the Southern District of New York approved WorldCom's reorganization plan, the company was only obligated to pay the reduced sum of $500 million in cash plus $250 million in common stock of the reorganized company. Pursuant to the Fair

71. *Re: WorldCom, Inc., HO-09440; Sworn Statement Pursuant to Section 21(a)(1) of the Securities Exchange Act of 1934* (July 1, 2002), *available at* http://www.sec.gov/news/wcresponse.htm. WorldCom filed a revised report on July 8, 2002. *Re: WorldCom, Inc., HO-09440; Revised Statement Pursuant to Section 21(a)(1) of the Securities Exchange Act of 1934* (July 8, 2002), *available at* http://www.sec.gov/news/wcresponserev.htm.

Funds provision of the Sarbanes-Oxley Act of 2002, the funds and stock paid as a result of the penalty will be returned to the shareholder victims of the company's fraud.

In addition to the charges against the company, the Commission has brought civil actions against five former employees of WorldCom: Controller David F. Myers on September 26, 2002; former WorldCom Director of General Accounting Buford "Buddy" Yates, Jr. on October 7, 2002; Betty L. Vinson and Troy M. Normand, former accountants in the WorldCom's General Accounting Department, on October 10, 2002; and Scott D. Sullivan, former WorldCom CFO. On November 14, 2002, Judge Rakoff entered consent judgments against Myers and Yates permanently enjoining each from violating the antifraud provisions, and aiding and abetting WorldCom's violations of the reporting, and the books and records and internal controls provisions of the federal securities laws. The consent judgment also imposed an officer and director bar and provided that any monetary relief will be decided by the Court at a later date. In addition, both Myers and Yates agreed to a follow-on Commission administrative order under Rule 102(e), based on the injunction, suspending each from appearing or practicing before the Commission as an accountant. On November 26, 2002, Judge Rakoff entered consent judgments against Vinson and Normand permanently enjoining them from violating the antifraud provisions, and aiding and abetting WorldCom's violations of the reporting, and the books and records and internal controls provisions of the federal securities laws. The consent judgments provide that any monetary relief will be determined by the Court at later date. Vinson and Normand also agreed to follow-on Commission administrative orders under Rule 102(e), based on the injunction, suspending them from appearing or practicing before the Commission as accountants.

On March 2, 2004, the SEC filed a civil enforcement action against Sullivan. Simultaneously with the filing of the complaint, Sullivan agreed, without admitting or denying the allegations in the complaint, to the entry of an order permanently enjoining him from violating, directly or indirectly, numerous provisions of the federal securities laws, including the anti-fraud, reporting, books and records, internal controls and lying-to-auditors provisions. The consent judgment also imposed an officer and director bar and provided that any monetary relief will be decided by the Court at a later date. In addition, Sullivan agreed to a follow-on Commission administrative order under Rule 102(e), based on the injunction, suspending him from appearing or practicing before the Commission as an accountant.

The Commission's action in WorldCom is significant for a number of reasons. First, the matter stands as the leading example of the Commission's new policy of "real time enforcement." WorldCom publicly announced its intentions to restate its financial results on June 25, 2002; the Commission filed its original complaint the next day. Second, it provides a glimpse into the Commission's efforts, in financial reporting matters, to quickly seek court intervention to prevent the destruction of documents and dissipation of corporate assets. Third, the Commission took the highly unusual step of ordering WorldCom to file a sworn statement under oath pursuant to Section 21(a) of the Exchange Act describing the events leading to the restatement.

Related criminal actions were brought by the U.S. Attorney for the Southern District of New York, the Mississippi Attorney General and the Oklahoma Attorney General.

SEC v. Bergonzi, Litig. Rel. No. 17577 (June 21, 2002); *In the Matter of Rite Aid Corp.*, Exch. Act Rel. No. 46099 (June 21, 2002); *In the Matter of Noonan*, Exch. Act Rel. No. 46100 (June 21, 2002).

On June 21, 2002, the Commission announced the filing of accounting fraud charges in the United States District Court in the Middle District of Pennsylvania against three former senior executives of Rite Aid Corporation ("Rite Aid"). The Commission's complaint charges former CEO Martin Grass, former CFO Frank Bergonzi and former Vice Chairman Franklin Brown with conducting a wide-ranging accounting fraud that resulted in Rite Aid overstating its income in every quarter from May 1997 to May 1999. When the wrongdoing was discovered by Rite Aid, the company was forced to restate its pre-tax income by $2.3 billion and net income by $1.6 billion, the largest restatement ever recorded at the time. The Commission's complaint also charged that Grass caused Rite Aid to fail to disclose several related-party transactions, in which Grass sought to enrich himself at the expense of Rite Aid's shareholders. Finally, the Commission alleged that Grass fabricated Finance Committee minutes for a meeting that never occurred, which purportedly authorized him to pledge Rite Aid's stock in an affiliated company as collateral on a bank line of credit.

Briefly, the Commission's complaint alleged the following fraudulent accounting practices, among others:

- Upcharges - Rite Aid systemically inflated the deductions it took against amounts owed to vendors for damaged and outdated products.

- Stock Appreciation Rights - Rite Aid failed to record an accrued expense for stock appreciation rights.
- Reversal of Actual Expenses - In certain quarters, Bergonzi, with no justification or support, directed that Rite Aid's accounting staff reverse amounts that had been recorded for various expenses incurred and already paid.
- "Gross Profit" Entries - Bergonzi directed Rite Aid's accounting staff to make improper adjusting entries to reduce cost of goods sold and accounts payable.
- Undisclosed Markdowns - Rite Aid overstated net income for fiscal year 1999 by overcharging vendors for undisclosed markdowns on those vendors' products.
- Vendor Rebates - On the last day of fiscal year 1999, Bergonzi directed Rite Aid to record entries to reduce accounts payable and cost of goods sold by $42 million, to reflect rebates purportedly due from two vendors. In addition, two weeks after the close of the fiscal year - Bergonzi directed the books be reopened to record an additional $33 million in credits. The entries are alleged to be improper as Rite Aid had not earned the vendor credits at the time of the entries.

The Commission charged Grass, Bergonzi and Brown with violations of the anti-fraud provisions of the federal securities laws, and as control persons, with violations of the reporting and internal control provisions. On May 26, 2004, the SEC submitted to the court a settlement with Bergonzi, pursuant to which he consented to the entry of a judgment permanently enjoining him from violating the antifraud, periodic reporting, books and records and internal controls provisions of the federal securities laws, and permanently barring him from acting as a director or officer of a publicly held company. Based on his financial condition, Bergonzi would not be ordered to pay civil penalties, and disgorgement of $299,747 plus prejudgment interest of $199,066.70 would be waived.

On May 27, 2004, the SEC submitted to the court a settlement with Grass, pursuant to which he consented to the entry of a judgment permanently enjoining him from violating the antifraud, periodic reporting, books and records and internal controls provisions of the federal securities laws, and permanently barring him from acting as a director or officer of a publicly held company. The judgment further provides that the Commission's claim for disgorgement of ill-gotten gains is satisfied by Grass's civil forfeiture of $3 million in connection with his criminal case, and that no civil penalty would be imposed in view of such forfeiture.

In a settled administrative action, Rite Aid, without admitting or denying the Commission's charges, consented to cease-and-desist from future violations of the reporting and internal control provisions of the securities laws. Significantly, the Commission, crediting the company's extensive cooperation, did not charge Rite Aid with violations of the anti-fraud provisions, nor did it seek any fine. Also, in an administrative action, Timothy Noonan, a former director and Chief Operating Officer of Rite Aid, without admitting or denying the Commission's charges, consented to cease-and-desist from future violations of the anti-fraud provisions, and from causing any future violation of the reporting and books and records provisions.

In related criminal matters, the United States Attorney for the Middle District of Pennsylvania filed charges against Grass, Bergonzi, Brown, Noonan and Eric Sorkin, Rite Aid's Executive Vice President for Pharmacy Services.

In re Microsoft Corp., Exch. Act Rel. No. 46017 (June 3, 2002).

On June 3, 2002, the Commission instituted and settled an administrative proceeding against Microsoft Corporation ("Microsoft"), a public company engaged in the business of providing software for personal computers, office systems and the Internet. The Commission alleged that Microsoft maintained undisclosed reserves, accruals, allowances and liability accounts (collectively "reserve accounts") that were (a) not in conformity with GAAP to a material extent, and/or (b) lacked properly documented support and substantiation. Moreover, Microsoft failed to maintain adequate internal controls in that it exempted certain reserve accounts from its company-wide requirement that every account be reconciled at least once each quarter and that the reconciliation include ascertaining if there existed adequate supporting documentation relating to activity in the account. The Commission alleged that between fiscal years 1995 and 1998, Microsoft maintained between approximately $200 million and $900 million in unsupported and undisclosed reserves, a significant portion of which did not comply with GAAP, which resulted in material inaccuracies in filings made by Microsoft with the Commission.

Microsoft, without admitting or denying the allegations, consented to cease-and-desist from committing or causing any violation of the reporting, internal controls and books and record provisions of the federal securities laws. This matter is significant for two reasons. First, the matter represents the alleged use of "cookie jar" reserves that did not result in fraud charges. This result may be at least partially attributable to the fact that the alleged misuse of the reserves involved both overstatements and understatements of earnings that may have clouded the picture in assessing investor losses, often a linchpin of any fraud charge. Second, despite the absence of a fraud charge, the matter sends a clear signal by the Commission that any change to reserve accounts must be accompanied by thorough documentation and support.

In re Edison Schools, Inc., Exch. Act Rel. No. 45925 (May 14, 2002).

On May 14, 2002, the Commission announced that it filed a settled administrative proceeding against Edison Schools Inc. ("Edison") for inaccurately describing certain aspects of its business in SEC filings. The Commission found that Edison failed to disclose that a substantial portion of its reported revenue consisted of payments that never reached Edison. These funds are instead expended by school districts (Edison's clients) to pay teacher salaries and other costs of operating schools that are managed by Edison.

Edison, without admitting or denying the Commission's findings, consented to the entry of an administrative order to cease-and-desist from future violations of the reporting provisions of the federal securities laws and to add a director of internal audit to its management team. The Commission's enforcement action in Edison is significant because the Commission, unlike most financial reporting cases, did not find that Edison's revenue recognition practices violated GAAP or that Edison's earnings were misstated. Rather, the Commission's enforcement action was based solely on Edison's failure to provide accurate disclosures.

SEC v. Xerox Corp., Litig. Rel. No. 17465 (Apr. 11, 2002); *SEC v. Allaire*, Litig. Rel. No. 18174 (June 5, 2003).

On April 11, 2002, the Commission announced the filing and settlement of a civil action filed in the United States District Court for the Southern District of New York against the Xerox Corporation ("Xerox"), a public company engaged in the document management business, offering an array of document products, services and solutions.

The complaint alleged that Xerox, from at least 1997 through 2000, employed a variety of undisclosed "accounting actions" to meet or exceed Wall Street's earnings expectations and disguise its true operating performance from investors. The complaint alleged that these actions, most of which allegedly violated GAAP, accelerated the company's recognition of equipment revenue into current periods at the expense of future periods.

The complaint alleged that many of the accounting actions related to Xerox's leasing arrangements. Under these arrangements, the revenue stream from Xerox's customer leases typically had three components: the value of the equipment; revenue that Xerox recognized for servicing the equipment over the life of the lease; and financing revenue that Xerox received on loans to its lessees. Under GAAP, Xerox was required to book revenue from the equipment at the beginning of the lease, but was required to book revenue from servicing and financing over the course of the entire lease. According to the complaint, Xerox relied on accounting actions to justify shifting more lease revenue to the equipment, so that a greater portion of that revenue could be recognized immediately.

Xerox, without admitting or denying the allegations, consented to the entry of a final judgment that permanently enjoins the company from future violations of the anti-fraud, reporting and record keeping provisions of the federal securities laws. Xerox agreed to restate its financials for the years 1997 to 2000, and to pay a civil penalty of $10 million, the largest in any SEC financial reporting matter to date. Xerox also agreed to have its Board of Directors appoint a committee composed entirely of outside directors to review the company's material internal accounting controls and policies. The SEC also announced that it was continuing its investigation of the matter as it relates to other parties.

On June 5, 2003, the Commission announced that it reached a settlement with six senior executives and accounting professionals employed by Xerox for conduct related to Xerox's accounting violations. The six defendants agreed to pay over $22 million in civil penalties, disgorgement and prejudgment interest. Four of the individuals agreed to be barred from serving as officers and directors of publicly-held companies for periods of up to five years.

SEC v. Buntrock, Litig. Rel. No. 17435 (Mar. 26, 2002).

On March 26, 2002, the Commission announced the filing of a civil complaint in the United States District court for the Northern District of Illinois charging the founder and five other former top officers of Waste Management, Inc. with perpetrating a massive financial fraud beginning in 1992 and continuing into 1997. The named defendants are: Dean Buntrock, Waste Management's founder, and former chairman of the Board of Directors, and Chief Executive Officer; Philip Rooney, former President and Chief Operating Officer, Director and Chief Executive Officer during a portion of the relevant period; James Koening, former Executive Vice President and Chief Financial Officer; Thomas Hau, former Vice President, Corporate Controller, and Chief Accounting Officer; Herbert Getz, former Senior Vice President, General Counsel, and Secretary; and Bruce Tobeckson, former Vice President of Finance.

In its complaint, the Commission alleges that the defendants fraudulently manipulated Waste Management's financial results to meet predetermined earnings targets. The company's revenues and profits were not growing fast enough to meet these targets, so defendants resorted to improperly eliminating and deferring current period expenses to inflate earnings. The Commission alleged that the defendants employed a multitude of accounting practices to achieve this objective including, among other things:

- avoiding depreciation expenses on their garbage trucks by both assigning unsupported and inflated salvage values and extending their useful lives,
- assigning arbitrary salvage values to other assets that previously had no salvage value,
- failing to record expenses for decreases in the value of landfills as they were filled with waste,
- refusing to record expenses necessary to write off the costs of unsuccessful and abandoned landfill development projects,
- establishing inflated environmental reserves in connection with acquisitions so that the excess reserve could be used to avoid recording unrelated operating expenses,
- improperly capitalizing a variety of expenses, and
- failing to establish sufficient reserves for income taxes and other expenses.

The Commission's complaint alleges that the defendants violated, and aided and abetted violations of, the anti-fraud, reporting and record keeping provisions of the federal securities laws. As relief, the Commission's complaint seeks permanent injunctions, disgorgement, civil penalties and prohibiting defendants from serving as officers or directors of public companies. The Commission's action is pending.

In re Trump Hotels & Casino Resorts, Inc., Exch. Act Rel. No. 45287 (Jan. 16, 2002).

This case was the Commission's first enforcement action charging that a company's use of "pro forma" earnings figures was misleading and violated Section 10(b) and Rule 10b-5.[72] The Trump Hotels & Casino Resorts, Inc.'s ("Trump Hotels") press release at issue had disclosed earnings in a manner that did not conform to generally accepted accounting principles ("GAAP"). The press release stated that net income and earnings-per-share figures excluded an $81.4 million one-time charge. The release failed to disclose, however, that net income included a one-time gain of $17.2 million. The SEC charged the undisclosed one-time gain was material because it represented the difference between positive and negative earnings, and between meeting analyst expectations or not meeting those expectations. The press release was alleged to be misleading because it implied that all one-time items were excluded (when in fact the one-time gain was included and only the one-time charge was excluded). Trump Hotels was ordered to cease-and-desist from committing or causing any violation, and any future violation, of Section 10(b) and Rule 10b-5.

In re Gisela de Leon-Meredith, Exch. Act Rel. No. 44970 (Oct. 23, 2001).

On October 23, 2001, the SEC instituted and settled an administrative proceeding against Gisela de Leon-Meredith ("Leon-Meredith"), the controller of Chestnut Hill Farms ("CHF"), a Seaboard Corporation ("Seaboard") subsidiary. According to the SEC, Leon-Meredith booked improper entries in CHF's books and records. Those improper entries, made over the course of five years, caused certain of CHF's assets on its balance sheet to be "substantially overstated" and its expenses to be understated. The SEC alleged that Leon-Meredith "deliberately undertook to conceal the errors through other improper entries and adjustments." Seaboard's internal auditing department questioned Leon-Meredith, after which she "confessed her wrongdoing."

After discovery of the wrongdoing, Seaboard launched an investigation, terminated Leon-Meredith and two of her supervisors, and restated five years of financial statements. Leon-Meredith was found by the SEC to have caused the misstatements in Seaboard's financial statements, and to have caused the company's books, records and accounts to be inaccurate and misleading. In settlement of the administrative proceeding, Leon-Meredith was ordered to cease and desist from committing or causing any violation of the Exchange Act's books and records provisions.

Seaboard was not charged by the SEC, based on its cooperation with and responses to the SEC staff. The Section 21(a) Report (discussed in

72. The Commission previously issued "cautionary advice" on the use of "pro forma" financial information in earnings releases. *See* Section B. above.

Section C. above) details the Commission's framework for crediting corporate behavior in *Leon-Meredith* and other cases.

SEC v. Messenger, Litig. Rel. No. 17042 (June 20, 2001).

On June 18, 2001, the Commission announced the filing and settlement of a civil action against former officers of Paracelsus Healthcare Corporation ("Paracelsus"), a former NYSE-listed company. The named defendants were the former Paracelsus Chief Executive Officer, Ron Messenger; the former Chief Financial Officer, James T. Rush; the former Controller, Scott Barton; and the former Vice President of Operations and Finance, Gary Hubschman.

The Commission's complaint alleged that the defendants violated GAAP by accumulating $16 million in "cookie jar" reserves, and then drawing upon those reserves to conceal a decline in the company's earnings. Defendants Messenger, Rush and Hubschman also failed to write off $15 million in uncollectible accounts receivable in violation of GAAP. The defendants were alleged to have concealed their conduct by providing false and misleading information on receivables and reserves to the company's auditors. As a result of defendant's actions and the deception of the auditors, Paracelsus was alleged to have overstated its income in amounts ranging from nine percent to 303 percent in the years 1993 to 1996.

All of the defendants consented to permanent injunctions against further violations of the anti-fraud, record keeping and reporting provisions of the federal securities laws. The individual defendants also consented to civil penalties in amounts ranging from $25,000 to $100,000, and Rush and Barton were barred under Rule 102(e) from practicing as accountants before the Commission for three years.

SEC v. Dunlap, Litig. Rel. No. 17001 (May 15, 2001); *In re Sunbeam Corp.*, Exch. Act Rel. No. 44305 (May 15, 2001); *In re David C. Fannin*, Sec. Act Rel. No. 7977 (May 15, 2001).

On May 15, 2001, the Commission filed civil charges against five former officers of Sunbeam Corporation ("Sunbeam") and the former engagement partner on the Arthur Anderson LLP audits of Sunbeam's financial statements. The named defendants are: Sunbeam's former Chairman and Chief Executive Officer Albert J. Dunlap; former principal financial officer Russell A. Kersh; former controller Robert J. Gluck; former vice-presidents Donald R. Uzzi and Lee B. Griffith; and Arthur Andersen LLP partner Philip Harlow.

According to the Commission's complaint, Dunlap and Kersh orchestrated a fraudulent scheme to create the illusion of a successful restructuring of Sunbeam and thus facilitate a sale of the Company at an inflated price. According to the complaint, the defendants employed a laundry list of fraudulent accounting techniques, including creating "cookie-jar" reserves and revenues, recording revenue on contingent sales, accelerating sales from later periods into the present quarter, and using improper bill and hold transactions. Specifically, the complaint alleges, among other things, that:

- The illegal conduct began at year-end 1996 with the creation of inappropriate "cookie-jar" reserves which increased Sunbeam's reported loss of 1996. These reserves were then used to inflate income in 1997, contributing to the false picture of a rapid turnaround. In addition, to further boost income in 1997, the charged Sunbeam officers caused the Company to recognize revenue for sales that did not meet applicable accounting rules. As a result, for fiscal year 1997, at least $60 million of Sunbeam's reported $189 million in earnings from continuing operations came from accounting fraud.
- Also in 1997, the charged Sunbeam officers failed to disclose that Sunbeam's 1997 revenue growth was, in part, achieved at the expense of future results. The Company had offered discounts and other inducements to customers to sell merchandise immediately that would otherwise have been sold in later periods, a practice known as "channel stuffing." The resulting revenue shift threatened to dilute Sunbeam's future earnings.
- The former engagement partner on the Arthur Anderson LLP audits of Sunbeam's financial statements authorized unqualified audit opinions on Sunbeam's 1996 and 1997 financial statements even though he was aware of many of the Company's accounting improprieties and disclosure failures.

The Commission charged that each defendant violated or aided and abetted violations of the antifraud, reporting, internal controls, and books and records provisions of the securities laws. The Commission's complaint seeks, as to each defendant, a permanent injunction against future violations and civil penalties. The Commission's complaint also seeks permanent bars against Dunlap, Kersh, Gluck and Uzzi from acting as an officer or director of a public company.

On September 4, 2002, the Commission announced that Dunlap and Kersh agreed to the entry of judgments permanently enjoining each from violating the antifraud, books and records, and internal control provisions of the federal securities laws; permanently barring each from serving as officers and directors of any public company; and requiring Dunlap to pay a civil penalty of $500,000 and Kersh to pay a civil penalty of $200,000. *See SEC v. Dunlap*, Litig. Rel. No. 17710 (Sept. 4, 2002). On November 4, 2002, the Commission announced that Griffith consented to the entry of a judgment permanently enjoining him from violating or aiding and abetting violations of the antifraud, reporting, books and records, and internal control provisions of the federal securities laws; and requiring him to pay a civil penalty of $75,000.

Gluck, Uzzi, and Harlow, the Andersen partner, entered into settlements with the Commission on January 27, 2003. *See SEC v. Dunlap*, Litig. Rel. No. 17952 (January 27, 2003). Gluck and Uzzi consented to the entry of judgments permanently enjoining them from future violations of the antifraud, reporting, and books and records provisions of the federal securities laws. They each agreed to pay a civil penalty in the amount of $100,000. Gluck also accepted a five-year bar from serving as an officer or director of a public company and from appearing or practicing before the Commission as an accountant. Harlow accepted a three-year bar from appearing or practicing before the Commission and in return, the Commission withdrew the allegations and charges in its complaint against Harlow.

These settlements resolved the remaining open matters related to the Sunbeam case.

In a related matter, the Commission filed and simultaneously settled an administrative proceeding against Sunbeam for filing false and misleading filings with the Commission from the fourth quarter of 1996 through the first quarter of 1998. Without admitting or denying the allegations in the Commission's Order, Sunbeam consented to the entry of a cease-and-desist order prohibiting future violations of the antifraud, reporting, internal controls, and books and records provisions of the securities laws.

The Commission also filed and simultaneously settled an administrative proceeding against David C. Fannin, the former Executive Vice President, General Counsel and Secretary of Sunbeam, based on allegations that Fannin was negligent in drafting certain Sunbeam press releases in early 1998 that presented a misleading picture of the Company's results of operation. Without admitting or denying the allegations in the Commission's Order, Fannin consented to the entry of a cease-and-desist order prohibiting future violations of Section 17(a)(3) of the Securities Act.

SEC v. Aurora Foods, Inc., Litig. Rel. No. 16866 (Jan. 23, 2001).

On January 23, 2001, the Commission filed civil charges against Aurora Foods, Inc. ("Aurora"), a producer and marketer of branded food products, three former senior officers of Aurora and four division level employees. According to the Commission's complaint, Ian Wilson, former Chairman of the Board and Chief Executive Officer; M. Laurie Cummings, former Chief Financial Officer; and Ray Chung, former Executive Vice President, engaged in a fraudulent scheme that caused Aurora to under-report trade marketing expenses by more than $43 million. The complaint charged that this scheme substantially inflated Aurora's reported earnings in 1998 and 1999 in order to meet analysts' expectations. The complaint further alleged that Wilson, Cummings and Chung repeatedly took active steps to perpetrate the fraud by directing the division level defendants to (i) make inadequate or no accruals for known trade marketing expenses incurred in connection with sales already booked and (ii) conceal the inadequate accruals from the company's auditors by making false entries in various accounts on the Company's books.

Although the individual defendants were charged with fraud, or aiding and abetting fraud, under Section 10(b) of the Exchange Act and Rules 10b-5 thereunder, the company itself was not. Rather, Aurora, along with the individual defendants, was charged with violating the reporting and internal control provisions under Section 13(a) and 13(b)(2) of the Exchange Act and Rules 12b-20, 13a-1 and 13a-3 thereunder. In addition, the Commission's complaint alleged that Wilson, Cummings and Chung, as control persons of Aurora, were liable for Aurora's violations of Sections 13(a) and 13(b)(2) of the Exchange Act and Rules 12b-20 and 13a-13 thereunder.

Simultaneous with the filing of the complaint, Aurora consented, without admitting or denying the allegations in the complaint, to the entry of a permanent injunction from future violations of the reporting and internal control provisions of the Exchange Act. Two of the individual division level defendants also consented, without admitting or denying the allegations in the complaint, to the entry of a permanent injunction from future violations of the anti-fraud, reporting and internal control provisions of the Exchange Act and to pay a civil penalty of $10,000 and $20,000 respectively.

The Commission's action against the remaining individual defendants is pending.

SEC v. Saylor, Litig. Rel. No. 16829 (Dec. 14, 2000); *In re MicroStrategy, Inc.*, Exch. Act Rel. No. 43724 (Dec. 14, 2000); *In re Parsons*, Exch. Act Rel. No. 43725 (Dec. 14, 2000).

On December 14, 2000, the Commission filed administrative reporting charges against MicroStrategy, Inc. ("MicroStrategy") and two of its employees, and filed civil accounting fraud charges against MicroStrategy's Chief Executive Officer, Chief Operating Officer and former Chief Financial Officer. The Commission charged in those actions that the company had violated GAAP by materially overstating its revenue and earnings from the sale of software and services.

In the administrative action against the company, the Commission alleged that the company recognized revenue prematurely on a number of occasions in contravention of AICPA Statement of Position 97-2 ("SOP 97-2"), which governs revenue recognition on the sale of software. As described in the complaint, under SOP 97-2, revenue is properly recognized where there is persuasive evidence of a sale agreement, delivery has occurred, the seller's fee is fixed and determinable, and collectibility is probable. Where the sale includes other elements—such as software upgrades, enhancements or consulting services—that are integral to the software's "functionality," contract accounting principles must be applied, and revenue recognition must be deferred until these services or products are provided. The Commission alleged that MicroStrategy improperly recognized material amounts of revenue up front in multiple element deals, where significant future services or products were not separable from the sale of the software license. The Commission also alleged that MicroStrategy improperly recognized revenue on contracts that were not executed until the reporting period subsequent to the period in which the revenue from the contract was recognized. According to the Commission's Complaint, as a result of these accounting practices, the company reported positive net income from the time of its initial public offering in June 1998 through March 2000, when it should have been reporting net losses.

Although the company's officers were charged under the anti-fraud provisions of the federal securities laws—including Section 17(a) of the Securities Act, Section 10(b) of the Exchange Act and Rule 10b-5—the company itself was not. Rather, MicroStrategy was charged only with violating or causing violations of the Exchange Act reporting provisions under Sections 13(a), 13(b)(2)(A), and 13(b)(2)(B) of the Exchange Act, and Rules 13a-1 and 13a-13. MicroStrategy agreed, without admitting or denying those allegations, to cease and desist from future violations of those statutes and regulations. The company also agreed to a number of undertakings in the areas of corporate governance, management and compliance, including the following:

- Adding one independent director to the Board who shall either have experience as (i) a CFO of a public company (or otherwise have been primarily responsible for external financial reporting), or (ii) as a member of an Audit Committee of a public company.
- Reporting to the Commission the departure of any non-management member of the Board.
- Adopting an updated charter for the Audit Committee consistent with the Blue Ribbon Committee recommendations.
- Creating an Internal Audit Department and adding a Director of Internal Audit to management.
- Adopting and implementing a Code of Conduct and Global Revenue Recognition Policy.
- Adopting and implementing a comprehensive policies and procedures manual governing accounting, finance and contracts matters, and providing training to officers, directors and employees on those policies and procedures.

The officers, without admitting or denying the allegations of the complaint against them, consented to injunctions against future securities law violations and were required to pay disgorgement of $10 million and each to pay a $350,000 civil penalty. The CFO also agreed to an administrative order barring him from practicing as an accountant before the SEC for three years. In addition, the company's corporate controller and accounting manager consented to administrative cease and desist orders prohibiting violations of the Exchange Act reporting and record keeping provisions.

SEC v. Gilbertson, Litig. Rel. No. 16743 (Oct. 2, 2000).

On October 2, 2000, the Commission filed civil charges against three former executives of HBO & Company, a vendor of healthcare software, charging that the executives directed a fraudulent scheme to inflate HBO & Company's revenues and net income from January 1998 through March 1999. In January 1999, McKesson Corporation merged with HBO & Company to form McKesson HBOC, a Fortune 100 company.

According to the Commission's complaint, Albert J. Bergonzi, Co-President, Co-Chief Operating Officer and Chief Financial Officer; Jay P. Gilbertson, Co-President and Co-Chief Operating Officer; and Dominick DeRosa, President of Enterprise Sales, engaged in a fraudulent scheme at HBO & Company to report falsely in press releases and periodic reports filed with the Commission that the company had met or exceeded analysts' quarterly earnings expectations. The March 1999 quarter was the first combined reporting period for McKesson HBOC. The complaint alleges that Bergonzi, Gilbertson and DeRosa repeatedly took active steps to perpetuate the fraud, including:

- Concealing contingencies related to software sales contracts in "side letters," which were hidden from HBO & Company's accounting staff responsible for revenue recognition. These side letter contingencies included such terms as rights to cancel, and even provided in some cases for continuing negotiations of the contract. Under generally accepted accounting principles, software sales cannot be recorded as revenue until contingencies are resolved.
- Fraudulently accounting for quarter- and year-end revenue by backdating contracts so they fell within the prior quarter.
- Making fraudulent entries designed to understate expenses and inflate HBO & Company's net income.
- Swapping product with other companies and creating misleading documentation in order to generate fraudulent software sales revenue.

The Commission's complaint alleges that the defendants violated the anti-fraud, internal controls, and books and records provisions, and also alleges that Gilbertson made false statements to HBO & Company's auditors in violation of Section 17(a) of the Securities Act, and Sections 10(b) and 13(b)(5) of the Exchange Act and Rules 13b2-1 and 13b2-2 thereunder. The complaint also alleges that each of the defendants was unjustly enriched through significant bonuses tied to meeting earnings expectations, or through sales of HBO & Company stock while the price was inflated due to their fraud, and seeks to compel disgorgement of these funds. Finally, the complaint seeks to suspend or bar the defendants from serving as officers or directors of public companies.

Simultaneous with the filing of the Commission's complaint, DeRosa consented, without admitting or denying the allegations in the complaint, to the entry of a permanent injunction on all of the alleged violations.

DeRosa agreed to disgorge $361,528 in ill-gotten gains and to pay a civil penalty of $50,000. DeRosa also agreed to be barred for five years from serving as an officer or director of a public company.

On July 1, 2003, the Commission announced it had reached a settlement with Gilbertson. Pursuant to the settlement, Gilbertson, without admitting or denying the allegations in the Commission's complaint, consented to an injunction from future violations of the federal securities laws and from serving as a director or officer of any public reporting company. Gilbertson was ordered to disgorge $733,360, plus prejudgment interest, and to pay a civil penalty of $1,000,000. As a result of his settlement in the civil action, on July 29, 2003, Gilbertson consented to an administrative order suspending him from appearing or practicing before the Commission as an accountant. In a related action, Gilbertson entered into a plea with U.S. Attorney for the Northern District of California to one count of conspiracy to commit securities fraud and one count of making false statements in a document filed with the SEC.

The Commission's action against Bergonzi is pending. In a separate action, the U.S. Attorney's Office for the Northern District of California brought criminal charges against Bergonzi.

In re Boston Scientific Corp., Exch. Act Rel. No. 43183 (Aug. 21, 2000).

On August 21, 2000, the Commission entered an order pursuant to which Boston Scientific Corp. ("Boston Scientific"), without admitting or denying the Commission's allegations, agreed to a cease and desist from committing or causing any violations of Sections 13(a), 13(b)(2)(A) and 13(b)(2)(B) of the Exchange Act and Rules 13a-1, 13a-13 and 12b-20 thereunder.

The Commission found that forty employees of Boston Scientific's Japanese subsidiary, and 143 independent distributors, participated in a scheme to inflate the subsidiary's sales figures. In 1997 and 1998 the Japanese subsidiary recorded thousands of false sales totaling more than $75 million. The Japanese subsidiary submitted its false sales and earnings data to Boston Scientific, which then incorporated those figures in its consolidated financial statements. The scheme was carried out by managers at the Japanese subsidiary who would store goods at leased warehouses and record sales to the cooperating distributors. To mask the fact that the distributors never paid for the goods, the managers would issue them credits and recorded false sales of the same goods to other distributors. The Japanese subsidiary also falsely confirmed the sales to Boston Scientific's independent auditors.

Boston Scientific uncovered the fraud in the fall of 1998, after the implementation of a new a management information system at the Japanese subsidiary. Boston Scientific promptly notified the SEC and went public with its discovery of the accounting irregularities. In its order, the Commission found that Boston Scientific failed to accurately track accounts receivable, cash receipts and product returns.

In accepting the offer of settlement, which did not include fraud charges, the Commission acknowledged the remedial acts promptly undertaken by Boston Scientific and the cooperation afforded the Commission staff.

In re Waste Mgmt, Inc., Exch. Act Rel. No. 42968 (June 21, 2000).

On June 21, 2000, the Commission entered an order pursuant to which Waste Management, Inc. ("WMI"), without admitting or denying the Commission's allegations, agreed to cease and desist from committing or causing any violations of Exchange Act Sections 10(b), 13(b)(2)(A) and 13(b)(2)(B), and Rule 10b-5.

The matter arose out of the merger of USA Waste Service, Inc. and Waste Management, Inc. in July 1998, creating WMI. Apparently as a result of that merger, WMI allegedly failed to implement and maintain effective and accurate accounting and management information systems in the year following the merger. As a result, the Commission alleged, WMI could not (and WMI management knew it could not, or was reckless in disregarding that it could not) generate information from which it could make responsible earnings forecasts. The company thereby projected materially inaccurate earnings forecasts for the second quarter of 1999 in violation of the Exchange Act anti-fraud provisions, according to the Commission.

In accepting the offer of settlement, the Commission acknowledged the company's prompt action in investigating the matter, and its cooperation in the Commission's investigation.

In re Cendant Corporation, Exch. Act Rel. No. 42933 (June 14, 2000); *SEC v. Corigliano*, Litig. Rel. No. 16587 (June 14, 2000); and related cases.

On June 14, 2000, the Commission filed administrative charges against Cendant Corporation ("Cendant"), charging that the company's books and records had been falsely altered, and that materially false periodic reports had been filed with the Commission in violation of Exchange Act Sections 13(a) and (b) and Rules 12b-20, 13a-1, 13a-13 and 13b2-g. Without admitting or denying the allegations, Cendant consented to an order requiring it to cease and desist from future violations of the Exchange Act provisions under which it had been charged. Significantly, Cendant was not charged under the anti-fraud provisions (although, as discussed below, several of its former officers and financial reporting managers were charged under those provisions).

Cendant had been formed in 1997 through the merger of HFS Incorporated ("HFS") and CUC International Inc. ("CUC"). The Commission alleged that for more than 12 years prior to the merger, CUC had been engaged in a scheme to manipulate earnings and mask CUC's true financial results. The Commission charged a number of CUC officers and employees with fraud, and/or with aiding and abetting fraud, in connection with that scheme, including Cosmo Corigliano, CUC's Chief Financial Officer; Anne Pember, CUC's Controller; Casper Sabatino, CUC's Vice President of Accounting and Financial Reporting; Kevin Kearney, CUC's Director of Financial Reporting; Steven Speaks, a CUC Division Controller; Mary Sattler Polverari, a CUC Supervisor of Financial Reporting; and Paul Hiznay, a CUC Division Accounting Manager.

The Commission's complaint alleged that Corigliano directed CUC's financial reporting managers to make unsupported alterations to the company's periodic financial results. Through improper use of company reserves, among other means, CUC management was alleged to have "manipulated" quarterly earnings to meet analyst expectations. Specifically, management was alleged to have intentionally overstated merger and purchase reserves and to have subsequently reversed those reserves directly into operating expenses and revenues. Books and records were falsified, and no system of internal accounting controls was implemented to prevent the scheme. The Commission's complaint alleged that in January 1998 alone Cendant's annual income was inflated by more than $100 million, primarily through improper use of reserves.

The Commission's actions against the CUC officers seeks an injunction against future violations of the anti-fraud, books and records, internal controls and reporting provisions and disgorgement of profits from the sale of company securities during the time of the alleged fraud. In addition, the Commission is seeking civil money penalties and an order permanently barring those individuals from acting as officers or directors of a public company.

Corigliano and Pember (CUC's CFO and Controller, respectively) are contesting the Commission's charges. Sabatino, the other officer charged in the case, consented to the entry of a judgment, without admitting or denying the allegations, pursuant to which he is permanently barred from acting as an officer or director of a public company and enjoined from future violations of the Exchange Act provisions under which he was charged. In addition, Corigliano, Pember and Sabatino pled guilty to criminal charges: Corigliano pled guilty to wire fraud, conspiracy to commit wire fraud, and causing false statements to be made in documents required to be filed with the Commission; Pember pled guilty to wire fraud and conspiracy to commit wire fraud; and Sabatino pled guilty to aiding and abetting wire fraud.

Kearney, CUC's Director of Financial Reporting, as well as the three other accused CUC financial reporting and accounting managers, settled the charges arising from the alleged fraud. Those four employees, all of whom are CPAs, consented to injunctions prohibiting them from future violations of the anti-fraud, periodic reporting and record-keeping provisions of the Exchange Act. Kearney was ordered to disgorge profits and interest from his sale of CUC and Cendant securities; to pay a civil money penalty of $35,000; and to consent to a five year bar from practice before the Commission under Rule 102(e). Speaks and Polverari also consented to an injunction against future violations; to pay civil money penalties of $25,000 each; and to a three year bar under Rule 102(e). Hiznay, the mid-level accounting manager, was charged only with causing the companies' violations of the reporting provisions under Exchange Act Section 13(a) and Rule 13a-1. He consented to an order requiring him to cease and desist from future violations of those provisions.

SEC v. Am. Online, Inc., Litig. Rel. No. 16552 (May 15, 2000); *In re Am. Online, Inc.*, Exch. Act Rel. No. 42781 (May 15, 2000).

On May 15, 2000, the Commission filed civil and administrative charges against America Online, Inc. ("AOL") for alleged financial reporting violations in connection with the company's accounting for certain advertising costs. Although not a fraud action, the case is significant. In the administrative action, the Commission found that in fiscal years 1995 and 1996, AOL had improperly capitalized certain costs incurred with acquiring new subscribers. Rather than expensing those costs as they were incurred, AOL reported them as assets on its balance sheet. Citing to Accounting Standards Executive Committee Statement of Position 93-7 ("SOP 93-7"), the Commission's order stated that such advertising costs must be expensed unless they fall under a narrow exception where persuasive historical evidence exists which permits a reliable prediction that future net revenues will be generated as a result of the advertising. AOL's model for estimating future membership retention did not meet the criteria set forth in SOP 93-7 because, in the Commission's view, "the unstable business environment [in which AOL operated] precluded reliable forecasts of future net revenues."

The Commission's order found that AOL would have incurred losses in six quarters of 1995 and 1996 rather than the profits it reported by not expensing the advertising costs as incurred. AOL was charged with violations of the reporting provisions under Exchange Act Section 13(a) and Rules 13a-1 and 13a-13, and of the books and records provisions of Exchange Act Section 13(b)(2)(A). AOL agreed, without admitting or denying the allegations, to cease and desist from future violations of those statutes and regulations. In the related federal court action, AOL consented to an order requiring that it pay a civil penalty of $3,500,000. This penalty was particularly significant because the case was not a fraud case and AOL, a public issuer, is not an otherwise regulated entity.

In re W.R. Grace & Co., Admin. Proceeding No. 3-9926 (June 30, 1999); *In re Scanlon*, Admin. Proceeding No. 3-9928 (June 30, 1999); *In re Gaughan*, Admin. Proceeding No. 3-9927 (June 30, 1999); *SEC v. W.R. Grace & Co.*, Litig. Rel. No. 16008 (Dec. 22, 1998).

On December 22, 1998, the Commission filed a complaint in federal court against W.R. Grace & Co. ("Grace") alleging accounting fraud and violations of Exchange Act Sections 10(b), 13(a) and 13(b)(2) and Rules 10b-5, 12b-20, 13a-1 and 13a-13. The complaint alleged that Grace falsely reported the results of operations for itself and its Health Care Group from 1991 through 1995, and that Grace deferred reporting income earned by its subsidiary, National Medical Care, Inc. ("NMC"), to "smooth" the earnings of the Health Care Group. It accomplished this income deferral by allegedly increasing or establishing reserves, in contravention of generally accepted accounting principles, and used the reserves to manipulate the quarterly and annual earnings of the Health Care Group. The primary goal was to bring the Group's earnings in line with Grace's earnings targets. Grace was also alleged to have released some of the excess reserves to increase its earnings per share.

On June 30, 1999, the Commission announced a settlement with Grace and two of the company's independent auditors, finding that Grace deceived investors from 1991 to 1995 by improperly inflating the reported income and growth rates of Grace and the Health Care Group. The Commission ordered Grace to cease and desist from further violations of the anti-fraud, reporting, record keeping, and internal control provisions of the Exchange Act. It also directed Grace to establish a $1 million education fund designed to improve awareness and education relating to proper financial reporting. Finally, the Commission voluntarily dismissed with prejudice the civil injunctive action pending against Grace in federal court.

Gaughan and Scanlon were partners of the independent auditor responsible for auditing Grace's consolidated financial statements during the relevant time period. The Commission found both partners failed to follow appropriate accounting standards and that they were a cause of Grace's violation of the Exchange Act. Pursuant to Exchange Act Section 21C, the Commission ordered the two auditors to cease and desist from further violations of Exchange Act Section 13(a) and 13(b) and Rules 12b-20, 13a-1 and 13a-13.

Without admitting or denying any of the findings, Grace and the two auditors consented to the orders.

This case was significant because it suggests that the Commission is shifting from traditional quantitative measures of materiality to a more a qualitative approach. In Grace, although the size of the reserves was relatively small, the Commission indicated that the conduct was qualitatively material because it made the difference between the company meeting or missing its earnings projections.

In re Livent Inc., Admin. Proceeding No. 3-9806 (Jan. 13, 1999); *In re Fiorino*, Admin. Proceeding No. 3-9814 (Jan. 21, 1999); *SEC v. Drabinsky*, 99 Civ. 0239 (TPG) (S.D.N.Y., filed Jan. 13, 1999); *SEC v. Banks*, 99 Civ. 8855 (TPG) (S.D.N.Y., filed Aug. 12, 1999).

On January 13, 1999, the SEC filed a federal court action, alleging that former officers, directors, and members of the accounting staff of Livent Inc., a Canadian-based theater owner and producer of live theatrical entertainment, engaged in a multi-faceted and pervasive fraud spanning eight years between 1990 and 1998. The fraud, allegedly orchestrated by Livent's former chairman and chief executive officer ("CEO"), and the company's former president and a director, had three main components: a multi-million dollar kickback scheme designed to misappropriate funds for personal use; the improper shifting of pre-production costs to fixed assets or other projects; and the improper recording of revenue for transactions that contained side agreements purposely concealed from Livent's outside auditors. The fraud involved multiple violations of the anti-fraud, books and records, and internal controls provisions of the federal securities laws, and resulted in at least seventeen false filings with the Commission which materially overstated the results of Livent's operations and its financial condition.

According to the complaint, Livent's former CEO manipulated income and operating cash flows with the active participation of several long-time associates, including Livent's former senior vice president of finance and administration, the company's former senior executive vice president and chief operating officer, several individuals in the company's accounting department, and Livent's former CFO and former Deloitte & Touche engagement partner for Livent's 1995 audit, among others.

The former CEO and president were also indicted for sixteen felony violations of the federal securities laws. Two other senior participants pleaded guilty to one felony count each, for violations of the federal securities laws.

The former senior vice president for finance and administration consented to a court order and administrative proceeding barring him from practicing before the Commission for five years. The Commission has entered three other administrative orders related to the conduct described in the complaint. Livent consented to an order directing the company to cease and desist from committing securities violations and to cooperate with the Commission; the former budgeting controller agreed to a cease and desist proceeding and a three-year bar from practicing before the Commission; and the former theater controller agreed to a three-year bar.

On August 12, 1999, the Commission filed a settled injunctive against Jerald Banks, Livent's former general counsel and secretary, alleging that Banks drafted and finalized certain side agreements which permitted the company to engage in improper revenue recognition. Banks consented to a permanent injunction enjoining him from violating the anti-fraud, books and records, and internal control provisions of the federal securities laws. Banks was also required to pay a civil penalty of $25,000, and was barred for five years under Rule 102(e) from appearing or practicing before the Commission as an attorney.

In re Sony Corporation and Sumio Sano, File No. 3-9666 (Aug. 5, 1998); *SEC v. Sony Corporation*, Litig. Rel. No. 15832 (D.D.C. Aug. 5, 1998).

On August 5, 1998, the Commission simultaneously instituted and settled public administrative and cease-and-desist proceedings against Sony Corporation ("Sony") and Sumio Sano, a Sony director and the General Manager of its Capital Market and Investor Relations Division. The same day, the Commission filed, and simultaneously settled, a related complaint against Sony in federal court. In both the administrative proceeding and the complaint, the Commission alleged that Sano caused Sony to violate the periodic reporting provisions applicable to foreign private issuers.

The Commission charged that Sony made inadequate disclosures about its Sony Pictures division both in its Form 6-K for the fiscal year ended March 31, 1994, which included copies of Sony's quarterly earnings, and in the annual report it filed with the Commission for the same fiscal year.

During fiscal year 1994, Sony made consolidated reports for its "entertainment" unit. It did not list Sony Pictures as a separate entity, but included its results with those of its music business. The losses of the motion picture business were, therefore, hidden behind the success and profitability of the music business. Further, in press releases and in the MD&A section of its public filings, Sony did not adequately describe the nature and extent of Sony Pictures' net losses, *i.e.*, there was no discussion of the fact that the downturn was mainly attributable to the interest and amortization costs of acquiring Sony Pictures, nor did it explain the impact of those losses on the consolidated statement. In fact, Sony noted certain positive developments in its motion picture industry, such as the success of certain films, box office share and Academy Award nominations.

Sano was the head of the department primarily responsible for drafting the press releases and the MD&A section of the annual report. As such, the Commission found that he should have been aware of the losses sustained by Sony Pictures as well as the effect of those losses on Sony's consolidated results.

The Commission issued an order pursuant to Exchange Act Section 21C requiring Sony and Sano to cease and desist from committing or causing any present or future violation of Exchange Act Section 13(a) and Rules 13a-1, 13a-16 and 12b-20. The Commission further ordered Sony (i) to engage an independent auditor to examine its MD&A presentation for the fiscal year ended March 31, 1999; (ii) to ensure that, going forward, Sony's Chief Financial Officer would be responsible for ensuring that Sony's public disclosures were accurate and in compliance with all legal and accounting requirements; and (iii) to adopt FAS 131, regarding segment reporting, and to provide separate segment reporting for, among other things, Sony Pictures.

In the settled civil action, Sony consented to the entry of a final judgment and was ordered to pay a $1 million civil penalty.

In this case, the Commission imposed on foreign issuers some of the same MD&A and other disclosure requirements that are imposed on domestic corporations. It also was significant that the Commission required an auditor review of Sony's MD&A. Finally, the penalty against Sony, an issuer, was unusual in a non-fraud case.

In the Matter of Sensormatic Electronics Corporation, File No. 3-9563 (Mar. 25, 1998); *SEC v. Assaf, et al.*, Civ. Act. No. 98-757 (EGS) (D.D.C., filed Mar. 25, 1998); and related cases.

On March 25, 1998, the Commission simultaneously instituted and settled public administrative and cease-and-desist proceedings against Sensormatic Electronics Corporation ("Sensormatic") and two former Sensormatic officers, Joy Lynn Schneider, former Controller of U.S. Operations and Thomas H. Pike, former Director of Management Information Systems. At the same time, the Commission filed a civil action in federal court seeking permanent injunctions and civil penalties against three former senior officers at Sensormatic: Ronald G. Assaf, former President and Chief Executive Office and then-current Chairman of the Board of Directors; Michael E. Pardue, former Chief Operating Officer, Chief Financial Officer, Executive Vice President and member of the Board of Directors; and Lawrence J. Simmons, former Vice President of Finance.

The Commission found that from the start of Sensormatic's 1994 fiscal year through July 10, 1995, the company manipulated its revenues and earnings in order to meet analysts' projections. Sensormatic accomplished its goal by improperly recognizing revenue in one quarter for products not shipped or not scheduled to arrive at the customer until the next quarter. At the end of each quarter, Sensormatic turned back the computer clocks that recorded and dated shipments so that out-of-period shipments and revenue would be recorded in the "correct" quarter. In total, Sensormatic recognized out-of-period revenue ranging from $4.6 million in one quarter to $30.2 million in another.

As a result of the scheme, Sensormatic filed materially false and misleading periodic reports and registration statements with the Commission.

The Commission charged Pardue and Simmons with participating in the fraudulent scheme detailed above from at least July 1, 1993 through mid-1995 and charged Assaf with knowing of the scheme. Further, Pardue and Simmons are alleged to have made false and misleading statements to auditors to keep them off the trail of this far-reaching scheme.

A cease-and-desist order was issued against Sensormatic in connection with the Commission's findings.

Assaf, Pardue and Simmons, without admitting or denying the allegations contained in the complaint, consented to the entry of a final judgment permanently enjoining them from violating the relevant provisions of the securities laws and requiring them to pay civil monetary penalties of $50,000, $40,000 and $50,000, respectively. Simmons also settled an administrative proceeding which barred him from practicing or appearing before the Commission for five years.

In settling the administrative proceeding instituted against Schneider, the Commission found that she knew that Sensormatic was improperly recognizing revenue, but failed to report the conduct to the audit committee. Further, Schneider knew that documents were withheld from the independent auditors and, in fact, hid a document in her own desk rather than give it to the auditors. A cease-and-desist order was issued against Schneider and she was barred from practice for three years.

In settling his administrative proceeding, the Commission found that Pike caused both the falsification of accounting records and Sensormatic's reporting violations by supervising the employees who falsified dates and turned back the computer clocks to carry out the scheme.

One month later, on April 27, 1998, the Commission instituted public administrative and cease-and-desist proceedings against Albert Glenn Yesner, a former Sensormatic Controller and Director of Business Controls who was also allegedly involved in the scheme. (That case is discussed in Section M. below.)

XIV. RULE 102(E) AND COMMISSION ENFORCEMENT ACTIONS AGAINST AUDITORS AND ACCOUNTANTS RELATING TO FINANCIAL REPORTING, AUDITOR INDEPENDENCE AND EARNINGS MANAGEMENT

The Commission's focus on financial reporting and earnings management has been directed at auditors and accountants as well as public companies and their employees. Although the Commission's primary enforcement weapon against auditors and accountants has historically been Rule 102(e), the anti-fraud action against Arthur Andersen LLP indicates the Commission will not hesitate to use other enforcement weapons in its arsenal. Rule 102(e) and some of the significant enforcement actions against major firms and their partners are discussed below.

A. Background of Rule 102(e)

Securities and Exchange Commission Rule 102(e), codified at 17 C.F.R. 201.102(e) allows the Commission to:

> censure a person or deny, temporarily or permanently, the privilege of appearing or practicing before it . . . any person who is found by the Commission after notice and opportunity for hearing in the matter not to possess the requisite

qualifications to represent others; or to be lacking in character or integrity or to have engaged in unethical or improper professional conduct; or to have willfully violated, or willfully aided and abetted the violation of any provision of the Federal securities laws or the rules and regulations thereunder.

This rule applies to all professionals practicing before the Commission, and while it is most often applied to accountants and lawyers, it has been applied, in one instance, to a geologist. *See In the Matter of Robert W. McDowell, Jr.*, Rel. No. 5903 (February 2, 1978).

B. Rule 102(e) Prior to Checkosky and Aldrich

Rule 102(e) was originally adopted shortly after the Securities Act of 1933 was enacted. It created admission requirements for attorneys practicing before the Commission if they engaged in unethical conduct or were found to lack the requisite character or integrity. *See In the Matter of William R. Carter and Charles J. Johnson*, Rel. No. 34-17597 (Feb. 28, 1981).

The rule was amended once in 1938 to remove admissions requirements and again in 1970 to allow for automatic suspension of persons (i) who had been convicted of felonies or certain misdemeanors; (ii) who had been suspended by state licensing boards; or (iii) who had violated federal securities laws.

C. The Checkosky & Aldrich Decisions

In 1987, the SEC initiated disciplinary proceedings against two accountants, Checkosky and Aldrich, who had been engaged to audit the financial statements of the Savin Corporation. The staff alleged that the auditors had improperly allowed the Company to defer certain start-up expenses in violation of GAAP. *See Checkosky v. SEC*, 23 F. 3d 452, 454-55 (D.C. Cir. 1994) ("Checkosky I"). According to the staff, the auditors failed to exercise due professional care in planning and performing the audits and preparing their audit reports. Checkosky and Aldrich offered the defense that they acted without scienter. The Administrative Law Judge found that Rule 2(e) does not require proof of scienter and that negligence was sufficient for a violation of the rule. The Judge thereby held that the auditors had engaged in improper professional conduct and suspended Checkosky and Aldrich from practicing before the Commission for five years. *See* id. at 455.

After extensive litigation, the U.S. Court of Appeals for the District of Columbia Circuit remanded the case to the Commission with instructions to dismiss. *See Checkosky v. SEC*, 139 F.3d 221 (D.C. Cir.

1998) ("Checkosky II"). The Court of Appeals decision was based on its view that Rule 102(e) lacked a clear standard for the mental state necessary for culpability under the rule. Id. at 223-225.

D. Revised Rule 102(e)

In response to *Checkosky II*, the Commission amended Rule 102(e) to define improper professional conduct as (i) "intentional or knowing conduct, including reckless conduct, that results in a violation of applicable professional standards"; or (ii) either of the following two types of negligent conduct: (a) "a single instance of highly unreasonable conduct that results in a violation of applicable professional standards in which an accountant knows, or should know, that heightened scrutiny is warranted"; or (b) "repeated instances of unreasonable conduct, each resulting in a violation of applicable professional standards, that indicate a lack of competence to practice before the Commission." *See Amendment to Rule 102(e) of the Commission's Rules of Practice*, Rel. No. 33-7593 (Oct. 19, 1998), 68 SEC Docket 489 (the "Adopting Release").[73]

Under the revised rule, "Professional standards" refers to "GAAP, GAAS, the AICPA Code of Professional Conduct, and Commission regulations" and may also apply to international standards when they are adopted. "Reckless" is defined to mean "an extreme departure from the standards of ordinary care . . . which presents a danger of misleading buyers or sellers that is either known to the actor or is so obvious that the actor must have been aware of it." "Highly unreasonable" is defined to mean an "intermediate standard, higher than ordinary negligence but lower than the traditional definition of recklessness used in cases brought under Section 10(b) and Rule 10b-5 of the Exchange Act." It is intended to be an objective standard.

As adopted, a single act of unreasonable conduct may form the basis for a disciplinary proceeding under the rule only if it occurs where the accountant, from an objective point of view, knew or should have known that heightened scrutiny was appropriate. Questions of auditor independence, for example, "always merit heightened scru-

---

73. The U.S. Court of Appeals for the District of Columbia Circuit has held that application of the amended Rule 102(e) to conduct occurring before its 1998 enactment is impermissibly retroactive. *Marrie v. SEC*, 2004 U.S. App. LEXIS 14663 (D.C. Cir. July 16, 2004) (reversing an SEC order barring two accountants from appearing or practicing before the Commission pursuant to Rule 102(e) for alleged conduct occurring in 1994).

tiny." "Negligence" is defined to mean "ordinary or simple negligence." "Repeated instances" is defined to mean more than once and "may encompass as few as two separate instances of unreasonable conduct occurring within one audit, or separate instances of unreasonable conduct within different audits."

E. Recent and Pending Proceedings Against Auditors and Accountants

In the Matter of KPMG, et al., Exch. Act Rel. No. 34- 51946 (June 30, 2005).

On June 30, 2005, the SEC announced a settled enforcement action against KPMG LLP ("KPMG Canada"), a Canadian audit firm, and two of its partners, Gary Bentham, the audit engagement partner, and John Gordon, the concurring and SEC reviewing partner, on the firm's audit of the financial statements of Southwestern Water Exploration Co. ("Southwestern"), a now-bankrupt Colorado corporation. The Commission Order found that KPMG Canada, Bentham and Gordon engaged in "improper professional conduct" within the meaning of Rule 102(e) of the SEC's Rules of Practice by virtue of their alleged violations of the auditor independence requirements imposed by the Commission's rules and guidance and by generally accepted auditing standards in the United States.

The SEC alleged that KPMG Canada, Bentham and Gordon lacked independence when they audited the 1999 through 2002 financial statements of Southwestern in that the firm had provided bookkeeping services to Southwestern and then audited its own work. According to the SEC Order, after KPMG Canada prepared certain of Southwestern's basic accounting records and financial statements, it issued purportedly independent audit reports on those financial statements.

KPMG Canada, without admitting or denying the Commission's findings, consented to the issuance of a Commission Order censuring the firm. KPMG Canada also agreed to a number of remedial undertakings, including adopting and implementing new auditor independence policies and procedures and paying $73,682 which represented its fees from the audit and bookkeeping services it performed for Southwestern plus prejudgment interest. The SEC stated that, in determining to accept KPMG Canada's offer of settlement, the SEC considered remedial acts promptly undertaken by KPMG Canada, cooperation afforded the SEC staff, and KPMG Canada's undertakings.

Bentham and Gordon, without admitting or denying the Commission's findings, also agreed to settle the matter. The SEC Order denied Bentham the privilege of appearing or practicing before the Commission as an accountant, with a right to apply to resume appearing or practicing before the Commission in two years. Additionally, the Order denied Gordon the privilege of appearing or practicing before the Commission as an accountant for nine months.

In the Matter of Deloitte & Touche LLP, Exch. Act. Rel. No. 51606 (April 26, 2005); *SEC v. Deloitte & Touche LLP,* Litig. Rel. No. 19202 (April 26, 2005).

On April 26, 2005, the SEC filed a settled enforcement action against Deloitte and Touche stemming from its audit of Adelphia Communications Corporation's fiscal year 2000 financial statements. The Commission issued an Order finding that Deloitte engaged in improper professional conduct and caused Adelphia's violations of the recordkeeping provisions of the securities laws because it failed to detect a fraud perpetrated by Adelphia and certain members of the Rigas family. In addition, the Commission filed a federal district court action alleging that Deloitte failed to implement audit procedures designed to detect the illegal acts at Adelphia.

The SEC alleged that Deloitte engaged in improper professional conduct and caused certain of Adelphia's books and records violations by failing to detect a fraud perpetrated by Adelphia and certain members of the Rigas family. According to the Commission, even though Deloitte identified Adelphia as one of its highest risk clients, Deloitte failed to design an audit appropriately tailored to address audit risk areas that Deloitte had explicitly identified. Specifically, the SEC alleged that Deloitte issued an audit report containing an unqualified opinion on Adelphia's financial statements for fiscal year 2000 while Deloitte knew or should have known that Adelphia: (a) failed to record all debt on its balance sheet or otherwise failed to disclose that it had improperly excluded $1.6 billion in debt from its balance sheet; (b) failed to disclose significant related party transactions; and (c) overstated its stockholders' equity by $375 million. In the federal court complaint, the SEC charged Deloitte with failing to implement audit procedures designed to detect illegal acts at Adelphia.

In settlement of the SEC's charges, Deloitte agreed to pay $50 million, consisting of a $25 million penalty in the federal court action, subject to court approval, and another $25 million in settlement of the administrative proceeding. The entire $50 million will be paid into a fund for compensation of victims of the Adelphia fraud. Deloitte also agreed to substantive undertakings designed to address its audit of high-risk clients in the future, including the involvement of Deloitte's forensic accounting specialists in planning high-risk audits, increased training of Deloitte's audit professionals in fraud detection, increased partner involvement in review of audit work papers, and the retention of an independent consultant to review Deloitte's compliance with the undertakings.

In the Matter of Deloitte & Touche LLP, et al., Exch. Act Rel. No. 51607 (Apr. 26, 2005).

On April 26, 2005, the Commission issued an Order instituting public administrative proceedings against Deloitte & Touche LLP related audit in 1999 of the fiscal 1998 financial statements of Just for Feet, Inc. ("Just for Feet"), formerly a shoe and sports apparel retailer. The engagement partner, Steven H. Barry ("Barry"), CPA, and the audit manager, Karen T. Baker ("Baker"), CPA, were also charged by the SEC.

The Commission Order found that Just for Feet falsified its 1998 financial statements by (1) improperly recognizing unearned and fictitious receivables and revenue from its vendors, (2) failing to properly account for excess, worthless and obsolete inventory and to disclose problems with excess inventory, and (3) improperly recording as income the value of display booths provided by its vendors. According to the SEC Order, these fraudulent financial statements were included in the company's annual report for fiscal 1998 and in two registration statements for the offering of securities filed with the Commission in 1999.

The SEC Order against Deloitte found that Deloitte, Barry and Baker reasonably should have known that Just for Feet's 1998 financial statements had not been prepared in accordance with generally accepted accounting principles. The Order further found that Deloitte, Barry and Baker did not comply with GAAS in the conduct of their audit and engaged in improper professional conduct within the meaning of Rule 102(e)(1)(ii) of the Commission's Rules of Practice through repeated instances of unreasonable conduct.

Specifically, the Order found that Deloitte, Barry and Baker did not respond adequately to indications that the company was recognizing unearned and fraudulent vendor allowances as income. The Order also cited Deloitte, Barry and Baker for failing to test adequately the company's reserve for obsolete or excess inventory and failing to respond adequately to indications that Just for Feet was fraudulently increasing its income through fictitious purchases of display booths from its vendors. In addition, the Order found that Deloitte's National Risk Management Program identified Just for Feet as a high-risk client, but Deloitte did not carry out the responsibilities required by such a designation.

Without admitting or denying the Order's findings, Deloitte agreed to accept a censure pursuant to Rule 102(e)(1)(ii) of the Commission's Rules of Practice and pay $375,000 to settle the charges. The SEC Order noted that, in determining to accept Deloitte's offer, the Commission considered Deloitte's willingness to undertake measures to address deficiencies in its National Risk Management Program as detailed in another order issued simultaneously concerning Deloitte's audit of the financial statements of Adelphia Communications Corporation. The Commission Order also denied Barry and Baker the privilege of appearing or practicing before the Commission as accountants with a right to apply for reinstatement, with respect to Barry, in two years, and, with respect to Baker, in one year.

SEC v. KPMG LLP, Litig. Rel. No. 17954 (January 29, 2003), Litig. Rel. No. 18389 (October 3, 2003); *In the Matter of KPMG LLP,* Exch. Act. Rel. No. 51574 (April 19, 2005); *SEC v. KPMG LLP, et al.,* Litig. Rel. No. 19191 (April 19, 2005).

On January 29, 2003, the Commission filed a complaint in the Southern District of New York charging that KPMG and four of the firm's senior partners engaged in securities fraud in connection with audit services provided to Xerox Corporation from 1997 to 2000. The Commission filed an amended complaint on October 3, 2003 to include a fifth senior audit partner.

On April 19, 2005, KPMG agreed to settle the federal court litigation by consenting to the entry of a final judgment finding that it violated Section 10A of the Exchange Act and ordering it to pay disgorgement of $9,800,000 (representing its audit fees for the 1997-2000 Xerox audits), prejudgment interest thereon in the amount of $2,675,000, and a $10,000,000 civil penalty, for a total payment of $22.475 million. KPMG also agreed to perform remedial undertakings designed to prevent future violations of the securities laws that arose from circumstances that were present in this case. As part of the settlement, the SEC agreed to dismiss the other claims asserted against KPMG in the federal court action.

In addition, KPMG, without admitting or denying the SEC's findings, consented to a Commission Order finding that it caused and willfully aided and abetted Xerox's violations of the anti-fraud, reporting, recordkeeping and internal controls provisions of the federal securities laws. The Order also found that KPMG violated its obligations to disclose to Xerox illegal acts that came to its attention during the Xerox audits. The Order censured KPMG and ordered it to cease and desist from committing or causing these violations. As a result of these findings, the SEC's Order found that KPMG willfully violated Section 10A of the Securities Exchange Act of 1934 (Exchange Act) and caused and willfully aided and abetted Xerox's violations of Section 17(a)(2) and (3) of the Securities Act of 1933 and Sections 13(a) and 13(b)(2)(A) and (B) of the Exchange Act and Rules 12b-20, 13a-1, 13a-13 and 13b2-1 promulgated thereunder. The SEC ordered KPMG to cease and desist from committing or causing these violations and censured the firm pursuant to Rule 102(e)(1)(iii) of the Commission's Rules of Practice.

The SEC's Order found that from 1997 through 2000, KPMG permitted Xerox to manipulate its accounting practices to close a $3 billion "gap" between actual operating results and results reported to the investing public. According to the Commission, during this period, Xerox used topside accounting actions at the end of financial reporting periods to increase equipment revenue and earnings through the improper acceleration of revenue from long term leases of Xerox copiers and through manipulation of excess or "cookie jar" reserves. The SEC alleged that these topside accounting actions violated GAAP and overstated Xerox's true equipment revenues by at least $3 billion and overstated its true earnings by approximately $1.5 billion during the four-year period.

According to the SEC Order, in each of the years 1997-2000, KPMG issued audit reports containing unqualified opinions stating that KPMG had applied generally accepted auditing standards ("GAAS") to its review of Xerox's accounting, that Xerox's financial reporting was consistent with GAAP and that Xerox's reported results fairly represented the financial condition of the company. However, Order found that throughout this period KPMG failed to comply with GAAS and allowed Xerox to utilize accounting actions that did not comply with GAAP. The SEC alleged that by doing so, KPMG allowed Xerox to manipulate its accounting practices to distort the company's financial results, failed to insist that Xerox disclose those practices and their financial impacts in the company's annual and quarterly reports, and allowed Xerox to falsify its books and records and to fail to maintain adequate internal controls over its accounting.

While this behavior was ongoing, as alleged by the Commission, KPMG auditors onsite at Xerox's domestic and international locations repeatedly cautioned the senior partnership at KPMG's headquarters about the improper revenue recognition practices pursued throughout Xerox. The Commission asserted that despite these warnings, the defendants only occasionally brought these practices to the attention of Xerox management and failed to take any action when Xerox continued the earnings manipulation. In the Commission's view, by issuing clean audits of Xerox's financial statements, with knowledge of the ongoing improper accounting at Xerox, the defendants violated the anti-fraud provisions of the federal securities laws and abdicated their professional duties as auditors.

The SEC's civil fraud injunctive action against the five KPMG audit partners involved in the Xerox audits during 1997 through 2000 is ongoing.

In the Matter of KPMG LLP, Exch. Act Rel. No. 50564 (Oct. 20, 2004).

On October 24, 2004, the Commission announced the filing of a settled administrative proceeding against accounting firm KPMG and four of its partners. The action arose from KPMG's alleged failure to identify and report a multitude of revenue recognition issues at KPMG client Gemstar-TV Guide International, Inc. ("Gemstar"). According to the SEC Order, KPMG, as Gemstar's independent auditor for the years 2000 through 2002 and contrary to GAAS, failed to exercise professional care and skepticism, failed to take appropriate action to correct disclosures that did not comply with GAAP and/or were inconsistent with Gemstar's financial statements, and ultimately failed to render accurate audit reports. The SEC also found that KPMG failed to take proper action when Gemstar disclosed information in 2002 tending to show that (1) its revenue recognition practices violated GAAP in certain respects and (2) that senior management may have intentionally violated GAAP to overstate Gemstar's financial performance.

According to the Commission, KPMG knew or should have known that Gemstar improperly recognized revenue in connection with at least seven transactions, including:

- Recognition of a $23.5 million upfront, nonrefundable payment from AOL as revenue over the 12 months ended April 2000, notwithstanding that the payment was for an eight-year licensing and technical support agreement.
- Recognition of $18.1 million in licensing revenue from Time Warner Cable ("TWC") in the last two quarters of 2001 and the first quarter of 2002 in connection with an agreement with AOL. Despite terms in the agreement to the contrary, Gemstar asserted that its agreement with AOL applied to TWC and that AOL Time Warner had agreed that it applied to TWC.
- Recognition of $17.5 million in revenue from Motorola, Inc. and $17 million in revenue from the Tribune Company during 2001 and the first quarter of 2002 for advertising on Gemstar's interactive program guide ("IPG") even though the revenue was part of multi-element transactions with Motorola and Tribune and Gemstar did not have sufficient stand-alone IPG advertising revenue to provide a basis on which to fair value the transactions' IPG advertising components.

The SEC further found that, in addition to failing to identify or report Gemstar's GAAP violations, KPMG also failed to identify or report Gemstar's improper disclosure of its revenue recognition policies relating to these transactions, policies of which KPMG knew or should have known.

Finally, the Commission found that KPMG did not have in place a policy that required an engagement team involved in potential restatements of financial statements upon which the firm had issued an audit report to consult with KPMG's Department of Professional Practice regarding all significant issues that had come to the attention of the engagement team subsequent to the issuance of the audit report on the financial statements in question. KPMG's policy only required consultation regarding the specific transaction being proposed for restatement. In August 2002, KPMG learned that Gemstar was considering restating its recognition of revenue from the Fantasy Sports transaction, and that Gemstar's Audit Committee was investigating the revenue recognition policies relating to other transactions. According to the Commission, consultation pursuant to a broader consultation policy would have led KPMG to become aware of and to consider the evidence that came to light during the Audit Committee investigation, and possibly have resulted in a more prompt withdrawal of KPMG's previously issued audit report on Gemstar's 2001 financial statements.

According to the Commission, these failures on the part of KPMG to exercise due care in its audits of Gemstar violated GAAS, and constituted repeated instances of unreasonable conduct sufficient to indicate a lack of competence to practice before the Commission pursuant to Rule 102(e)(1)(ii) and (iii)(B)(2). Without admitting or denying the Commission's findings, KPMG consented to be censured by the Commission, and the named-partners consented to bars from appearing or practicing before the Commission as accountants for between one and three years.

In the Matter of Ernst & Young LLP, Initial Decision No. 249
(April 16, 2004).

On November 13, 2002, the Commission instituted public administrative proceedings against Ernst & Young LLP ("E&Y") alleging that E&Y violated the auditor independence requirements in connection with E&Y's audit of PeopleSoft, Inc. from 1994 through 2000 by jointly developing and marketing a software product with PeopleSoft. The Commission alleged that E&Y agreed to pay PeopleSoft a guaranteed minimum royalty of 15% to 30% from each sale of the resulting product, with a guaranteed minimum royalty of $300,000. The Commission also alleged that E&Y earned hundreds of millions of dollars in consulting revenues from implementing PeopleSoft software for third parties pursuant to an "Implementation Partners Agreement" it had with PeopleSoft. The Commission further alleged that E&Y coordinated and jointly marketed its implementation services with PeopleSoft, including reciprocal endorsements of each other, links to each other's websites, holding themselves out as "business partners" of one another, sharing customer information, customer leads, and "target accounts." The Commission charged E&Y with violating Rule 2-02(b) of Regulation S-X and causing PeopleSoft to file reports with the Commission that failed to include independently audited financial statements as required.

This matter is significant because the Commission sought to enforce the auditor independence requirements in the absence of any allegations that the audit work itself was flawed.

Eleven days of public hearings were held on the matter in March and April 2003. On April 14, 2004, Chief Administrative Law Judge Murray issued an initial decision finding that E&Y's business and consulting relationships with PeopleSoft created an identity or mutuality of interests, so that E&Y was not independent in fact and appearance when it audited PeopleSoft's financial statements from 1994 to 1999. The initial decision requires E&Y to cease-and-desist from the practices in question and to pay approximately $1.7 million in disgorgement, the amount of the firm's fees for auditing PeopleSoft from 1994 through 1999, and $729,302.13 in prejudgment interest. The initial decision also requires E&Y to retain an independent consultant and prohibits E&Y from accepting audit engagements for public issuers for a period of six months.

In the Matter of Grant Thornton LLP, Doeren Mayhew & Co. P.C., Peter M. Behrens, CPA, Marvin J. Morris, CPA, and Benedict P. Rybicki, CPA, Securities Act Rel. 8355 (January 20, 2004).

On January 20, 2004, the Commission instituted public administrative proceedings pursuant to Rule 102(e) and cease-and-desist proceedings against Grant Thornton LLP ("Grant Thornton") Doeren Mayhew & Co. P.C. ("Doeren Mayhew"), a Grant Thornton partner and two Doeren Mayhew directors for alleged misconduct in connection with their audit of MCA Financial Corporation's ("MCA") financial statements for the fiscal year ended January 31, 1998. The Commission alleged that in connection with the 1998 MCA audit, the respondents caused and aided and abetted MCA's violations of the antifraud and reporting provisions of the federal securities laws, violated or caused and aided and abetted violations of Section 10A of the Exchange Act and engaged in improper professional conduct.

The Commission alleged that the respondents, notwithstanding knowledge that MCA failed to disclose several million dollars of material, related party transactions in its 1998 annual financial statements, jointly issued a report containing an unqualified opinion on MCA's 1998 annual financial statements and consented to the inclusion of their report in MCA's offering materials. The Commission also alleged that the respondents failed to inform MCA's Board of Directors that MCA's financial statements omitted the material, related party transactions. The Commission further alleged that the respondents engaged in improper professional conduct by failing to adequately plan the 1998 MCA audit, not acting with sufficient skepticism in conducting the audit, and not obtaining enough evidence to support their conclusions.

On August 5, 2004, the respondents consented to the Commission's entry of an Order Making Findings and Imposing Remedial Sanctions without admitting or denying the Commission's findings. As part of the Order, Grant Thornton agreed to (1) pay disgorgement and prejudgment interest of $59,749; (2) pay a penalty of $1.5 million; (3) be censured for its alleged conduct; (4) require its entire professional staff to undergo fraud-detection training and provide at least $1 million to fund such training; and (5) suspend certain joint audits with other auditing firms for a period of five years.

Pursuant to the Order, Doeren Mayhew, which voluntarily discontinued conducting public audits as of March 19, 2003, agreed not to accept new public company auditing engagements for six months. In addition, Doeren Mayhew agreed that if it engages in audits of public companies after the expiration of six months, it will establish and implement certain policies and procedures specifically designed to improve the quality of its public company audit practice for a period of three years. Doeren Mayhew also was censured and required to pay disgorgement and prejudgment interest of $115,126.86.

Pursuant to the Order, Morris, Behrens and Rybicki were denied the privilege of appearing or practicing before the Commission for periods of five years, three years and one year, respectively, from the entry of the Order.

In the Matter of PricewaterhouseCoopers LLP, Exch. Act Rel. No. 47900 (May 22, 2003).

The Commission instituted a settled administrative proceeding against PricewaterhouseCoopers LLP ("PwC") on May 22, 2003, for conduct relating to audit services provided to SmarTalk TeleServices Inc. ("SmarTalk"). SmarTalk disclosed a one-time charge for a $25 million restructuring reserve related to anticipated business combination expenses in its 1997 Form 10-K. In the Commission's view, the use of the reserve did not comply with GAAP, in part, because the company failed to establish a plan of restructuring detailing the costs pursuant to EITF No. 94-3. Phillip Hirsch, PwC's engagement partner for the SmarTalk audits, knew the company failed to finalize the restructuring plan by the end of 1997 as required by GAAP and that it continued to amend the plan through the first half of 1998. The Commission asserted that Hirsch's failures to bring this accounting violation to SmarTalk's management and to get SmarTalk to commit to a restructuring plan in 1997 violated his duty to maintain an attitude of professional skepticism towards his client.

In addition, the Commission's order states that in 1998, during PwC's review of the 1997 audit, the firm revised the 1997 work papers and removed documents from the complete set of work papers. These undocumented and improper revisions were made with the knowledge of several PwC partners.

PwC settled the administrative proceeding by agreeing 1) to pay a $1 million civil penalty; 2) create policies and procedures to preserve archived audit work papers; and 3) hire an independent consultant to confirm that such polices are instituted on a firm-wide basis.

SEC v. Kenneth Wilchfort and Marc Rabinowitz, Litig. Rel. No. 18102 (April 24, 2003).

On April 24, 2003, the Commission announced the filing of a complaint against Kenneth Wilchfort and Marc Rabinowitz, two partners of Ernst & Young LLP ("E&Y") for aiding and abetting the non-fraud based securities violations of Cendant Corporation ("Cendant") and a predecessor company, CUC International ("CUC"). The complaint alleges that Wilchfort and Rabinowitz, the E&Y partners responsible for providing audit services to Cendant and CUC, failed to detect, and take proper remedial actions against, Cendant and CUC's activities that caused their financial statements to violate GAAP. The complaint asserted that Wilchfort and Rabinowitz breached their duties as accountants when they failed to detect the improper accounting and issued unqualified audit opinions of Cendant and CUC's financial statements. The Commission explained that Wilchfort and Rabinowitz breached their duties despite the fact that Cendant and CUC provided them with false documents and lied to them.

Wilchfort and Rabinowitz settled the Commission's charges by consenting to the entry of injunctions against future violations of the reporting provisions of the federal securities laws. The defendants also consented to the entry of administrative orders suspending them from appearing and practicing before the Commission for at least four years.

*In the Matter of Moret Ernst & Young Accountant*s, Exch. Act Rel. No. 46130 (June 27, 2002).

On June 27, 2002, in the first-ever auditor independence case against a foreign audit firm, the Commission instituted and settled an administrative action against Moret Ernst & Young Accountants ("Moret"), a Dutch accounting firm known as Ernst & Young Accountants.

As alleged in the Commission's order, Moret audited the financial statements of Baan Company, N.V. ("Baan"), a business software company headquartered in the Netherlands and whose stock at the time was traded on the Nasdaq National Market for fiscal years 1995 through 1997. The Commission alleged that during the same period, Moret had joint business relationships with Baan that impaired Moret's independence as auditors. Most of the joint business relationships were established to allow Moret to assist Baan in implementing its software products for third companies. According to the Commission's order, Moret billed Baan approximately $1.9 million in connection with the joint business relationships.

The Commission also found that Moret improperly used and relied on audit work performed by its affiliated firm in the United States, Ernst & Young LLP. At the time, Ernst & Young also lacked independence from Baan due to joint business relationships it had with Baan.

Moret, without admitting or denying the Commission's order, consented to the Commission's entry of a censure pursuant to Rule 102(e)(1). Moret was also ordered to pay a civil penalty of $400,000 and to comply with a number of remedial undertakings to develop, enhance and implement auditor independence policies and practices.

In the Matter of KPMG LLP, Administrative Proceeding File No. 3-10676, Exch. Act Rel. No. 45272 (Jan. 14, 2002).

The Commission in this matter filed and simultaneously settled Rule 102(e) administrative proceedings against KPMG LLP ("KPMG"), alleging the accounting firm lacked independence from its client when it audited the client's financial statements at the same time it had substantial financial investments in the client. KPMG's audit client was AIM Funds ("AIM"), a family of mutual funds managed by AIM management. KPMG audited the financial statements of numerous AIM funds and portfolios.

In May 2000, KPMG invested $25 million through SunTrust Bank in an AIM government money market fund. Unbeknownst to KPMG at the time of the investment, that AIM fund was one of the funds audited by KPMG. KPMG made significant additional investments in that fund, reaching a point where its account balance represented approximately 35% of KPMG's total invested surplus cash and constituted approximately 15% of the fund portfolio's net assets.

KPMG remained unaware that it had invested in its audit client, and that the particular portfolio was one of those it audited, until an AIM employee notified AIM management, which in turn notified KPMG in December 2000. KPMG immediately liquidated its investment in the fund and resigned from all of its AIM fund audit engagements. AIM retained another audit firm to re-audit the financial statements of the relevant portfolios.

The SEC's order noted that KPMG not only issued audit reports while its independence was impaired, but it "repeatedly confirmed its putative independence from the AIM funds," including the portfolio in which it had invested, during the period in which it was invested in that portfolio. The order stated that "[t]his impairment of KPMG's independence occurred primarily because the firm lacked adequate policies or procedures to prevent or detect this independence problem and because the steps that KPMG personnel usually took before initiating similar firm investments were not taken here."

The SEC censured KPMG and demanded undertakings requiring the adoption and implementation of new policies and procedures, and additional training of relevant personnel.

The SEC's action in this matter is significant in that it censured the firm in a case where there were no showing of harm to investors, and no indication of any deliberate misconduct by the firm. The case highlights the importance of having adequate policies and procedures in place to prevent and detect violations.

In the Matter of Springer, Haugen and Haugen, Springer & Co., File No. 3-10589 (Sept. 27, 2001).

On September 27, 2001, the Commission simultaneously instituted and settled administrative proceedings against Charles Springer, CPA, Robert Haugen, CPA and Haugen, Springer & Co. pursuant to Rule 102(e). The Commission's order found that Vari-L Company, Inc. ("Vari-L") engaged in a financial reporting fraud to show consistently increasing revenue and earnings from at least 1996 through the first quarter of 2000. Vari-L's alleged fraudulent accounting practices, included, among other things (i) improperly recognizing revenue before goods were shipped to customers; (ii) recognizing false revenue; and (iii) overstating inventory by disregarding physical inventory counts. As a result of the fraud, Vari-L filed periodic reports with the Commission that overstated revenue, earnings and assets.

The Commission's order found that the auditors failed to conduct audits of Vari-L's financial statements in compliance with GAAS. Specifically, the Commission's order found, in part, that the auditors failed to obtain sufficient competent evidentiary matter in the area of revenue recognition. The auditors relied on management's representations and ignored information in audit work papers that suggested the representations were false. The Commission's order further found that Springer knew in 1998 that Vari-L had or may have improperly recognized $1.3 million of revenues in 1997 and failed to report the information to Vari-L's Audit Committee.

Springer, without admitting or denying the Commission's findings, consented to cease and desist from future violations of Section 10A, 10(b) and 13(a) of the Exchange Act, and Rules 10b-5, 12b-20 and 13a-1 thereunder. Pursuant to Rule 102(e), Springer consented to be barred from appearing or practicing before the Commission as an accountant with a right to re-apply after ten years. Also pursuant to Rule 102(e), Haugen, Springer & Co. and Haugen consented to be barred from appearing or practicing before the Commission as an accountant with a right to re-apply after three years.

Securities and Exchange Commission v. Arthur Andersen LLP, Litig. Rel. No. 17039 (JR) (D.D.C., June 19, 2001); *In the Matter of Arthur Andersen LLP*, File No. 3-10513 (June 19, 2001); *In the Matter of Robert E. Allgyer, CPA*, File No. 3-10515 (June 19, 2001); *In the Matter of Edward G. Maier, CPA*, File No. 3-10514 (June 19, 2001); *In the Matter of Walter Cercavschi, CPA*, File No. 3-10516 (June 19, 2001); *In the Matter of Robert G. Kutsenda, CPA*, File No. 3-10517 (June 19, 2001).

On June 19, 2001, the Commission filed and settled civil anti-fraud enforcement actions and Rule 102(e) proceedings against Arthur Andersen LLP ("Andersen") and three of its current or former partners in connection with the firm's audits of the annual financial statements of Waste Management, Inc. ("Waste Management") for the years 1992 through 1996. A fourth partner, a Regional Audit Practice Director, settled in a Rule 102(e) proceeding without a fraud charge.

The matter arose out of Andersen's issuance of unqualified audit opinions over a five year period. The Andersen partners were alleged to have identified a number of non-GAAP accounting practices engaged in by Waste Management as early as 1993 (and, in the case of the engagement partner, as early as 1992) that they initially concluded were not material. Andersen presented certain "Action Steps" to the company to bring Waste Management "to a minimum acceptable level of accounting." The company allegedly failed to implement the Action

Steps and continued to engage in non-GAAP accounting. In 1995, Waste Management engaged in a "non-GAAP netting of a $160 million one-time gain against unrelated expenses and prior period mis-statements. . ." The netted amount represented 10 percent of the company's pre-tax income that year. No disclosure was made of the netting. Two of the Andersen partners, as well as the Regional Audit Practice Director, allegedly concluded that the netting, as well as the non-disclosure of the mis-statements and of the unrelated gain, were not material—a conclusion with which the Commission disagreed.

Further non-GAAP netting, mis-classifications and mis-statements occurred in 1996. Nevertheless, according to the Commission's complaint, Andersen issued an unqualified opinion on the company's financial statements for that year as it did for the prior years. The Commission's order noted that Andersen received fees in excess of its audit fees for non-audit work during the years in question.

In the settlement, Andersen agreed to (i) the entry of a permanent injunction enjoining it from further violations of Section 10(b) or Rule 10b-5; (ii) payment of a civil penalty in the amount of $7 million; and (iii) a censure pursuant to Rule 102(e). The three Andersen partners on the engagement agreed to similar anti-fraud injunctions, fines and Rule 102(e) bars of five years (for the engagement partner) and three years (for the other two partners). The Regional Practice Director agreed to a one-year bar under Rule 102(e).

In the Matter of Barry Scutillo, CPA and Mark F. Jensen, CPA, File No. 3-9863 (May 4, 2001); File No. 3-10210 (May 4, 2001).

On April 1, 1999, the Commission filed an administrative action against two accountants, Barry Scutillo and Mark Jensen, pursuant to Rule 102(e). The Staff alleged that Scutillo and Jensen engaged in improper professional conduct in that they "intentionally, knowingly or recklessly" violated professional standards in connection with the audit of Sky Scientific, Inc.'s ("Sky") financial statements for the fiscal year ending 1994. The Staff alleged that the Respondents recklessly failed to observe that most of Sky's assets were fictitious or massively overvalued in violation of basic accounting standards and that million of dollars in expenses had not been recorded on Sky's books. Respondents asserted that their audit performance and conclusions were reasonable.

On May 3, 2001, in a lengthy initial decision, Administrative Law Judge James T. Kelly found that Scutillo violated Rule 102(e) because he was reckless in his audit of Sky's financial statements for the fiscal year ending 1994. This administrative action is significant because Judge Kelly retroactively applied the recklessness standard of amended Rule 102(e)(1)(ii). *In the Matter of Albert Glenn Yesner, CPA*, File No. 3-9586 (Oct. 19, 1999); *In the Matter of Russell Ponce, CPA*, File No. 3-8944 (Aug. 31, 2000) (both Commission opinions state that the "recklessness" standard is "not novel"). Judge Kelly found that the Commission opinions in *Yesner* and *Ponce* stand for the proposition that intentional, knowing or reckless conduct that did not comply with the applicable professional standards was "improper professional conduct" under Rule 102(e) before and after the rule amendment. Judge Kelly ordered that Scutillo be denied the privilege of appearing and practicing before the Commission as an accountant for three years.

On May 4, 2001, Jensen, without admitting or denying the Commission's finding, consented to an order denying him the privilege of appearing and practicing before the Commission as an accountant with the right to re-apply after three years.

In the Matter of Pat Rossetti and Jeffrey Yonkers, File No. 3-10354 (Oct. 31, 2000); *In the Matter of Pat Rossetti*, File No. 3-10354 (May 2, 2001); *In the Matter of Jeffrey Yonkers*, File No. 3-10354 (July 27, 2001).

On October 31, 2000, the Commission filed an administrative action against two accountants, Pat A. Rossetti and Jeffrey M. Yonkers, pursuant to Rule 102(e) and Section 21C of the Exchange Act. The Staff alleged that Rossetti and Yonkers violated Exchange Act Section 10A, and willfully aided and abetted violations of Exchange Act Section 13(a) and Rules 13a-1 and 13a-13, when they did not notify management or the company's board that the company's quarterly financial statements, as filed on Form 10-QSB, were prepared based on fractions of numbers from existing financial statements, rather than actual quarterly results. It is also alleged that Rossetti and Yonkers acted improperly in failing to require the company to record expenses related to certain options issued to consultants, causing the issuer's financial statements to be materially misleading.

Rossetti and Yonkers, on May 2, 2001 and July 27, 2001 respectively, without admitting or denying the Commission's findings, consented to cease-and-desist from future violations of Section 10A of the Exchange Act. Pursuant to Rule 102(e), Rossetti and Yonkers consented to be barred from appearing or practicing before the Commission as an accountant. Rossetti was granted a right to re-apply after three years, while Yonkers could re-apply after one year. The Commission found that Rossetti and Yonkers willfully violated Section 10A of the Exchange Act and aided and abetted violations of Section 13(a) of the Exchange Act and Rules 13a-1 and 13a-3 thereunder, and engaged in improper professional conduct.

In the Matter of YourBankOnline.com, Plastino and Butcher, File No. 3-10313 (Sept. 27, 2000).

On September 27, 2000, the Commission filed an administrative action against YourBankOnline.com (the "Company") and its president Pakie Plastino. The Commission also instituted administrative proceedings under Rule 102(e) against the Company's outside auditor, William Butcher. It is alleged that the Company overstated the purchase value of an internet banking software program in a March 1999 press release and fraudulently inflated the value of the software in its financial statements filed with the Commission.

According to the Commission's Order, Butcher, the Company's outside auditor, engaged in improper professional conduct in his audit of the financial statements. It is alleged that Butcher failed to take reasonable steps to determine the true value of the software, despite the fact that it was essentially the Company's only asset. This matter is significant because it alleges that a single act of highly unreasonable conduct may form the basis of a disciplinary proceeding under Rule 102(e).

On February 5, 2001, Secure Sign, Inc. (formerly YourBankOnline.com), without admitting or denying the Commission's findings, consented to cease and desist from future violations of Section 10(b) of the Exchange Act and Rule 10b-5 thereunder.

On February 27, 2001, the Commission granted the staff's motion to amend the order instituting proceedings. The staff asserted that, during its investigation, Plastino represented that he had not sold any YourBankOnline.com stock. However, after the proceedings were initiated, a business associate of Plastino's contacted the staff and stated that, in spring 1999, the associate had sold real estate to Plastino in exchange for YourBankOnline.com securities. The amended order instituting proceedings filed on the same day alleged that Plastino, in May 1999, following the dissemination of the misleading March 1999 press release agreed to purchase real estate for $600,000 in cash and 30,000 shares of YourBankOnline.com stock, valued at $11 per share.

On July 3, 2001, Plastino, without admitting or denying the Commission's findings, consented to cease and desist from future violations of Section 10(b) of the Exchange Act and Rule 10b-5 thereunder. Plastino also consented to pay disgorgement and prejudgment interest in the total amount of $72,750.

On July 3, 2001, Butcher, without admitting or denying the Commission's findings, consented to the entry of an order temporarily denying him the privilege of appearing or practicing before the Commission, with a right to reapply after one year.

In the Matter of KPMG Peat Marwick LLP, File No. 3-9500 (Mar. 8, 2001).

On December 4, 1997, the staff instituted cease-and-desist proceedings against KPMG Peat Marwick ("KPMG") alleging improper conduct and violations of the federal securities law in connection with its audit of a client from which it allegedly lacked the requisite independence.

The allegations stem from early 1995 when KPMG organized and funded KPMG BayMark ("BayMark") to engage in new lines of business, including the "corporate turnaround" business. BayMark was owned equally by four individuals, including Edward R. Olson. Late in 1995, as part of its corporate turnaround business, BayMark installed Olson as the President and Chief Operating Officer of Porta Systems, Corp. ("Porta"), a KPMG client with financial troubles.

The Order alleges that when KPMG audited Porta's 1995 financial statements, it lacked the independence required of an auditor because (i) KPMG had loaned Olson $100,000, giving KPMG a direct financial interest in Porta; (ii) KPMG had capitalized BayMark, 25% of which was owned by Olson, Porta's President and COO; (iii) KPMG had also capitalized two BayMark subsidiaries, one of which "controlled" Porta during the audit period as it had the authority to take any actions necessary to ensure Porta's survival; (iv) KPMG was entitled to a percentage of Porta's earnings; and (v) KPMG and BayMark should have been considered a single entity for independence purposes because of various contractual ties, including BayMark's use of "KPMG" in its name, KPMG's right to approve or reject BayMark's advertising material and the requirement that BayMark obtain KPMG's written consent before entering into any joint venture or partnership.

Despite warnings from the Office of the Chief Accountant ("OCA") about these very independence issues, KPMG audited Porta at the end of 1995 and issued an "Independent Auditor's Report," stating that it had "conducted [its] audits in accordance with generally accepted accounting standards."

The Staff alleged that issuing the audit opinion (i) rendered Porta's 1995 Form 10-K materially false because it had not been audited, as it represented, by independent accountants and (ii) violated Rule 2-02 of Commission Regulation S-X which requires that auditors be independent of their audit clients. Finally, it was alleged that KPMG violated Rule 102(e) by engaging in this improper professional practice.

After a hearing, Administrative Law Judge Mahony on January 21, 2000, in a lengthy initial decision, dismissed the administrative proceeding against KPMG. First, Judge Mahony found that after numerous meeting and negotiations between KPMG and the OCA, KPMG understood the changes required to resolve OCA's independence concerns between KPMG and BayMark were the (1) removal of the "KPMG" name; (ii) cancellation of any royalties due to KPMG; and (iii) the repayment of the loans to BayMark and Olson. However, KPMG had also negotiated with OCA that six ongoing engagements, including Porta, could be continued by KPMG while the changes were implemented. Judge Mahony concluded that KPMG did not engage in improper professional conduct in violation of Rule 102(e).

Judge Mahony also concluded that KPMG's loan to Olson, as an officer of KPMG's audit client, Porta, constituted an independence violation. KPMG conceded this violation.

Judge Mahony further concluded that since KPMG was not independent, KPMG caused Porta to file its 1995 annual report in violation of Section 13(a) of the Exchange Act and Rule 13a-1 thereunder which requires such report to be certified by an independent public accountant.

However, Judge Mahony found that it was unnecessary to impose a cease and desist order against KPMG, as sought by the staff, because KPMG had taken considerable steps to assure that the events that led to the administrative proceeding would not occur again, the audit of Porta was not challenged, the proceeding resulted from highly unusual circumstances and the violations had no adverse impact on investors.

The staff appealed Judge Mahony's opinion.

The Commission on January 19, 2001, in a lengthy opinion, found that KPMG had violated the independence requirement in two aspects. First, the Commission agreed with Judge Mahony that KPMG's loan to

Olson, as an officer of KPMG's audit client, Porta, constituted an independence violation. The Commission also found that KPMG's receipt of royalty fees from Baymark was a contingent fee that violated the independence requirements. The Commission found that Porta's turnaround agreement with Baymark required Porta to pay Baymark a "success fee" based on a percentage of Porta's quarterly earnings. Baymark, in turn, was obligated to pay KPMG, on a fiscal quarterly basis in arrears, a royalty fee of five percent of its quarterly consolidated income. The Commission rejected as irrelevant KPMG's argument that the fee was never received once OCA raised the issue, because AICPA rule 302 defines a contingent fee as received when "when the performance of the related services is complete and the fee . . . is determined." The Commission did agree with Judge Mahony's conclusion, however, that KPMG did not engage in improper professional conduct in violation of Rule 102(e).

The Commission agreed with Judge Mahony's conclusion that since KPMG was not independent, KPMG caused Porta to file its 1995 annual report in violation of Section 13(a) of the Exchange Act and Rule 13a-1 thereunder which requires such report to be certified by an independent public accountant. The Commission held that "negligence is sufficient to establish 'causing' liability under Exchange Act Section 21C(a), at least in cases in which a person is alleged to 'cause' a primary violation that does not require scienter."

Significantly, the Commission reversed Judge Mahony in ordering KPMG to cease and desist from causing violations of Section 13(a) of the Exchange Act and Rule 13a-1 thereunder, or from committing violations of the auditor independence requirements. In discussing the requirement that there be a likelihood of future violations to justify issuance of a cease and desist order, the Commission stated:

> Absent evidence to the contrary, a finding of past violation raises a sufficient risk of future violation. To put it another way, evidence showing that a respondent violated the law once probably also shows a risk of repetition that merits our ordering him to cease and desist.

In this case, the Commission reasoned that the seriousness of the violations, KPMG's failure to appreciate the seriousness of the violations, and the "forward-looking effect to be served by the cease and-desist order," warranted the order. The Commission noted in particular its conclusion that senior level employees at KPMG failed to undertake a reasonable inquiry that would have led them to discover the independence violations.

On January 30, 2001, KPMG filed a motion seeking reconsideration of the Commission's decision. In that motion KPMG contended that, in derogation of its due process rights, it was sanctioned for negligence based on the record of a hearing held under a scienter standard. KPMG also contended that the Commission disregarded its earlier adopted standard in deciding whether to issue a cease and desist order.

On March 8, 2001, the Commission denied KPMG's motion seeking reconsideration. The Commission found that KPMG was given fair notice that more than one culpability standard might be applied to the violations charged and was given a full and fair opportunity to litigate those standards. As to KPMG's second ground, the Commission found that unlike a civil injunction, the risk of future violation "need not be very great to warrant issuing a cease-and desist order." The Commission stated that "there was just not some risk but a serious risk of future violation, which, together with the traditional sanctioning factors we considered, fully warranted the cease-and-desist relief we issued."

KPMG appealed the Commission's decision to the United States Court of Appeals for the District of Columbia. KPMG contended, among other things, that (1) that the Commission lacked the authority to sanction accountants pursuant to Section 21C, and (2) that KPMG lacked fair notice of the Commission's interpretation of AICPA Rule 302 on contingent fees. The Court held that there is nothing in Rule 102(e) to indicate that it is the exclusive means for the Commission to sanction accountants. A proceeding under Section 21C is very different than one under Rule 102(e). The former is a law enforcement proceeding, while the latter is a professional disciplinary proceeding. However, the Court did hold that KPMG lacked fair notice that the Commission interpreted a "success fee" to constitute a prohibited contingent fee under AICPA Rule 302. AICPA Rule 302 does not cover all services to audit clients, only professional services. The success fee was paid to Baymark, with KPMG receiving a royalty fee from Baymark that was not contingent on the earnings or performance of an audit client. The Court reasoned that it was inappropriate to conglomerate these fees together to reach that conclusion that KPMG was provided fair notice. *See KPMG LLP v. SEC*, 289 F.3d 189 (D.C. Cir. May 14, 2002).

In the Matter of PricewaterhouseCoopers LLP, File No. 3-9809 (Jan. 14, 1999).

On January 14, 1999, the Commission simultaneously instituted and settled public administrative proceedings against Pricewaterhouse-

Coopers LLP ("PwC"), finding that PwC partners, managers and the PwC pension fund had engaged in improper professional conduct and had violated SEC rules by purchasing securities of PwC audit clients.

PwC is the entity that resulted from the merger of Coopers & Lybrand LLP ("C&L") and Price Waterhouse LLP in July, 1998. The Commission found that from 1996 through 1998, C&L procedures for ensuring compliance with independence standards with respect to publicly held audit clients failed to detect (i) four instances where professionals held securities of the companies to which they provided professional services; (ii) thirty-one instances where partners or managers owned securities of C&L clients to whom they did not provide professional services; and (iii) forty-five instances where C&L's retirement plan owned publicly traded securities of audit clients of C&L and PwC.

As a result, the Commission found that PwC failed to comply with the independence standards of Rule 2.01(b) of Regulation S-X and GAAS which prohibit, among other things, public accounting firms and their partners from having any direct or indirect financial interest in their audit clients.

Without admitting or denying the allegations, PwC agreed, in part, (i) to be censured; (ii) to establish a $2.5 million auditor independence education fund; (iii) to improve internal procedures to monitor adherence to auditor independence rules; (iv) to establish a database of publicly-held audit clients and of partners' securities transactions and to take action if any partner bought securities from a publicly-held audit client; (v) to prevent members and the pension plans from owning securities of PwC's publicly-held audit clients; and (vi) to conduct an internal investigation supervised by an outside person named by the SEC.

On January 7, 2000, the SEC made public the report of PwC's internal investigation. The report found that the violations were "widespread" and of 8,064 reported violations, 45.2 percent were by partners who audited public companies. Almost half of PwC partners, 1,301 out of a total of 2,698, reported violations (with an average of five each). Although the report concluded no audits were impaired and found excusable mistakes, the report also stated the violations were also attributed to laxity and insensitivity to the importance of independence compliance.

In the Matter of Jeffrey M. Steinberg and John Geron, File No. 3-9608 (May 22, 1998).

On May 22, 1998, the Commission instituted cease-and-desist proceedings against accountants Jeffrey Steinberg and John Geron alleging that the two Arthur Anderson & Co. partners caused Spectrum Information Technologies, Inc.'s ("Spectrum") violations of Section 13(a) of the Exchange Act and Rules 13a-13 and 12b-20 thereunder because they "advised and concurred in accounting which wrongfully allowed . . . [an auditing client] to recognize illusory revenues and profits" by concurring in an accounting treatment that "created the illusion of revenue and profits in the current period, even though the underlying transactions had no economic substance." Steinberg and Geron allegedly knew or should have known that the accounting treatment was improper.

The case is unusual for two reasons. First, it does not involve conduct by accountants in the context of an audit. Second, it was brought only as a cease-and-desist proceeding under Exchange Act Section 21C, and not as a proceeding under Rule 102(e). (The Commission has subsequently brought other 21C actions against auditors. *See, e.g., In the Matter of Eugene Gaughan*, CPA, File No. 3-9927 (June 30, 1999); *In the Matter of Thomas J. Scanlon*, CPA, File No. 3-9928 (June 30, 1999) (discussed above).)

Prior to a hearing on the charges, Steinberg and Geron moved for a more definite statement of the allegations against them, including the mental state that the Division believed sufficient for a cease-and-desist order under Section 21C. They argued, among other things, that proceeding under Section 21C instead of under Rule 102(e) was an "end run" around Checkosky II.

The Division responded that Section 21C allows the Commission to issue a cease-and-desist order against any person who "knew or should have known" that his act or omission would contribute to a violation of the Exchange Act and that accountants were not excluded from the definition of "any person" under the statute. Further, the Division argued, the "should have known" standard is classic negligence language.

Administrative Law Judge Mahony held that it was proper to apply the cease-and-desist provision to accountants. He concluded that liability under Section 21C "hinges on whether an accused 'knew or should have known' that [his/her] actions or omissions would contribute" to a violation of the federal securities laws or rules and regulations thereunder. *In the Matter of Jeffrey M. Steinberg and John Geron*, File No. 3-9608, 1998 SEC LEXIS 2079, Pre-hearing Order (Sept. 11, 1998).

Judge Mahony also reviewed the legislative history of the Remedies Act which, though sparse, indicated that Congress "intended the standard for a cease-and-desist order to be less than that for an injunction. Imposing a scienter standard . . . would subvert the whole purpose of providing the Commission with an 'alternative' remedy." Id.

On December 20, 2001, after the completion of a hearing, Judge Mahony held that the Division failed to prove that the respondents caused Spectrum's violations of Section 13(a) of the Exchange Act and Rules 13a-13 and 12b-20 thereunder. Accordingly, the order instituting proceedings was dismissed. Judge Mahony credited the testimony of the respondents' expert witnesses that Steinberg and Geron complied with applicable professional standards, considered the correct issues, and exhibited the appropriate degree of professional skepticism and judgment. Judge Mahony further noted that because the advice on the transactions at issue was given at an interim period, Steinberg and Geron were not required to verify management's representations regarding the transactions as they would have in the context of an audit. *See In the Matter of Jeffrey M. Steinberg and John Geron*, File No. 3-9608 (Dec. 20, 2001) (Initial Decision).

In the Matter of Albert Glenn Yesner, File No. 3-9586 (Apr. 27, 1998).

On April 27, 1998, the Commission issued an order instituting proceedings against Albert Glenn Yesner, Sensormatic's Controller, seeking, among other things, a determination of what if any remedial action is appropriate against Yesner under Rule 102(e). The Staff claimed that Yesner knew about the company's improper revenue recognition (discussed above) but failed to inform the audit committee. Further, in 1994, when Yesner learned that an employee had been told to withhold certain documents from the auditors, he allegedly told that employee to follow orders or quit.

On October 8, 1998, the Administrative Law Judge granted Yesner's motion for partial summary disposition "on the grounds that the holding in Checkosky controlled and required dismissal of the Rule 102(e)(1)(ii) charge." *In the Matter of Albert Glenn Yesner, CPA*, File No. 3-9586, Order Granting Motion to Reconsider Dismissal of the Rule 102(e)(1)(ii) Charge and Denying Requested Relief, 1998 SEC LEXIS 2692 (Dec. 3, 1998) (the "December 3, 1998 Order"). In the December 3, 1998 Order, the Administrative Law Judge declined to apply the revised Rule 102(e)(1)(ii) to Yesner's conduct. On December 11, 1998, the Judge certified to the Commission his December 3, 1998 order for interlocutory review. *In the Matter of Albert Glenn Yesner, CPA*, File No. 3-9586, 1998 SEC LEXIS 2859 (Dec. 11, 1998).

On October 19, 1999, the Commission accepted the certification, reversed the partial summary disposition and remanded for further proceedings. *In the Matter of Albert Glenn Yesner, CPA*, File No. 3-9586, 1999 SEC LEXIS 2229 (Oct. 19, 1999). The Commission opined that Yesner could be disciplined under Rule 102(e)(1)(ii) because Yesner had adequate notice of the standard of mental culpability against which his conduct was being weighed. The Commission noted that the Division of Enforcement told Yesner early in the administrative proceeding that it would attempt to prove that Yesner engaged in misconduct that was intentional, knowing or reckless; a standard which was not created by the amendment to Rule 102(e) following Checkosky.

Commissioner Johnson in his dissent opined that the Commission could not retroactively bring Rule 102(e) charges, even charges alleging recklessness, based on conduct before the effective date of the amendment to Rule 102(e). Commissioner Johnson stated that at the time the proceedings against Yesner were commenced, April 17, 1998, the Commission had failed to establish a consistent definition of the mental state necessary to establish a violation of Rule 102(e) until October 19, 1998, the date the Commission issued its release adopting the amendment to Rule 102(e).

On remand, Administrative Law Judge Mahony, with respect to the primary violations charged by the staff under Rule 102(e) alleging that Yesner acted with the requisite scienter, found that Yesner did not cause Sensormatic's primary violations of Sections 17(a)(1) of the Securities Act and 10(b) of the Exchange Act and Rule 10b-5 thereunder. Judge Mahony reasoned that although Yesner was aware of certain improperly recognized revenue he never attempted to quantify the amount because he was never led to believe it was a material amount. Yesner reasonably relied on people at more senior levels that were more knowledgeable of the company's revenue recognition practices. Accordingly, Judge Mahony dismissed the charges that Yesner violated Rule 102(e). *In the Matter of Albert Glenn Yesner, CPA*, File No. 3-9586 (June 19, 2001) (Final Decision).

With respect to the non-scienter primary violations charged by the staff, Judge Mahony applied a negligence standard. Judge Mahony found that Yesner's failure to report the improper revenue recognition practices to the audit committee was a cause of Sensormatic's primary violations of Section 17(a)(2) and 17(a)(3) of the Securities Act. Further, Judge Mahony found that Yesner was a cause of Sensormatic's violations of Section 13(a) and 13(b)(2)(A) of the Exchange Act and Rules 12b-20, 13a-1 and 13a-13 thereunder. Yesner was ordered to cease and desist from causing future violations of the same provisions.

XV. CONCLUSION

In the wake of the Sarbanes-Oxley Act of 2002, it is clear that financial fraud will remain front and center for the Commission and the staff over the next few years, and significant additional enforcement actions against auditors and public companies on these issues should be expected in the coming months. Accordingly, it is imperative that the corporate and public accounting communities keep these issues in mind in connection with financial reporting, disclosure and trading.

NOTES

NOTES

18

PARALLEL PROCEEDINGS UPDATE: ADDING MORE LINES

Robert C. Friese

Shartsis Friese LLP

Table of Contents

Until the recent past, when one spoke of "parallel proceedings" in the securities law context, the reference was to actions which might overlap involving the Securities and Exchange Commission, a state securities regulatory authority, a securities exchange, or the enforcement affiliate of the National Association of Securities Dealers, Inc. With the onset of what might be called the "Enron Era," the term parallel proceeding has come to mean joint prosecution, civil and criminal, of entities and individuals by the Commission and by one or more of the 94 United States Attorneys' Offices. (The exception had been United States Attorney's Office in the Southern District of New York, which more frequently prosecuted securities violations criminally, sometimes with and sometimes without the involvement of the Commission.)

Several years later, in September 2002, then Attorney General John Ashcroft called all United States Attorneys back to Washington to announce his intention that they pursue a corporate and investment fraud cases.

Still more recently we have seen the emergence not only of New York Attorney General Elliot Spitzer, but of other Attorneys General, including William Lockyer in California and Tom Reilly in Massachusetts, each commencing securities-related prosecutions. We also now see from time to time local District Attorneys' offices bringing related proceedings based on the conduct underlying the parallel securities enforcement actions. This type of proceeding, too, has extended beyond New York, most recently being observed in the San Diego District Attorney's indictment of six individuals in connection with the municipal pension fund scandal there which has dominated the news in that area. See, e.g., John M. Broder, San Diego Finds Itself Under Cloud of Inquiries, N.Y. Times, May 13, 2005; Mary Williams Walsh, 6 San Diego Officials Charged In Pension Case, N.Y. Times, May 18, 2005. These indictments parallel investigations being pursued by the Commission and the local U.S. Attorney's office.

Apart from the obvious difficulty for defense counsel, wondering from which direction(s) the punch(es) will come, the impact that these developments have on the approach and ability to defend one's clients is noteworthy. It is only within the last decade that it has become necessary to understand what have traditionally been two separate areas of practice – that of the white-collar criminal defense bar and that of traditional SEC defense counsel specializing in civil practice. While one could argue there has always been some potential overlap, in part since the Securities Exchange Act of 1934 is a criminal statute, though one which usually has been enforced only civilly, securities-related investigations only broadly commenced "going joint" within the last decade.

In bygone days of securities enforcement, what was known as a "criminal reference report" had to be submitted by SEC staff to and through its headquarters office in Washington for determining whether a case should be referred to the Department of Justice for criminal prosecution. In recent years, there is no such requirement. Now a phone call from Commission staff to a counterpart in the relevant U.S. Attorney's office suffices to commence the parallel proceeding process.

Before discussing the effect of all this, and the differences in approach of the traditional white-collar criminal defense bar and the securities defense bar on the civil side, one must look at the background which make this matter so complex.

The Seaboard/Thompson One-Two Punch

It is difficult to discuss parallel proceedings without mentioning two issuances by the federal agencies involved.

In October 2001 the Securities and Exchange Commission issued what is known as a Section 21(a) Report on "cooperation" (Exchange Act Release No. 34-44969, 77 SEC Docket (CCH) 220 (October 23, 2001)). This report has come to be called the "Seaboard Guidelines" owing to the fact that the Seaboard company's expansive cooperation with the Commission in its investigation led to its not being named in the enforcement action brought against the individual involved. While cooperation may not require total compliance with all 13 factors listed, it is clear that the term requires extreme compliance with many of the elements listed if the entity in question is to avoid being pursued. The factors weighed include whether the corporation turned over investigative information to Commission Staff, whether it distanced itself from individuals suspected or known to have acted wrongfully and, though not required, whether the corporation agreed to waive the attorney-client privilege concerning what it knows or will find out concerning the suspected wrongdoing.

On the criminal side former Deputy Attorney General Larry Thompson, on January 20, 2003, issued the Department of Justice's guidelines in the memorandum entitled "Principles of Federal Prosecutions of Business Organizations" (available at http://www.usdoj.gov/dag/cftf/business_organizations.pdf). This memorandum contains its own list of factors necessary for an entity to dodge criminal prosecution and, again, while not requiring waiver of attorney-client and work product protections, clearly reflects appreciation of waiver of both.

Adding to the complexity are various procedural requirements of the criminal enforcement process which can severely limit the ability of counsel and client to obtain access to the information and individuals necessary to put on an effective defense. This factor is nowhere more apparent than in the government's ability to seek a stay of discovery of related civil proceedings while the criminal investigation and enforcement process is going forward. When a grand jury is sitting concerning the matter, this adds another wall blocking access to information that could useful to prospective (or actual) defendants. See, e.g., Stanley Arkin and Charles Sullivan, DOJ Requests to Stay Civil Discovery: Recent Trends; Business Crimes, ALM Properties, Inc., September 11, 2004.

As has been noted in recent cases, the Martha Stewart and Frank Quattrone enforcement actions for example, conviction for obstruction of justice, perjury, or making a false statement to a federal officer (18 U.S. Code § 1001) may pose a greater threat of conviction than does an allegation of securities fraud, which often is more difficult to prove. As a consequence, it is usually the preference of the white-collar defense bar to assert an individual's privilege against self-incrimination rather than risk making a false or inaccurate statement that could be the basis for a separate charge.

While there may be compelling reasons for doing this in both securities-related prosecutions and more traditional criminal proceedings, the implications to an individual with a career to protect are extreme. The mere assertion of one's constitutional right in this regard will normally lead to one's dismissal or suspension from employment. Moreover, the assertion is invariably taken as a red flag by the enforcement authorities. Not only can asserting the privilege be commented on in a civil proceeding for damages, it can have major implications for one's right to indemnification, possible insurance coverage, and advancement of costs of defense. In the case brought by the NASD's enforcement arm against Frank Quattrone, the mere assertion of his Fifth Amendment privilege was taken as sufficient to bar him from the securities industry. Although this sanction is now under appeal, the risk that one's livelihood can be eliminated merely by asserting a constitutional right must be weighed in determining how to represent a prospective target.

Even an individual with an honest and compelling story to tell may find himself disbelieved owing to the fact that a primary malefactor may have rushed to be the first to plead. While it is no secret that the first to plead normally obtains the best plea bargain, it is offensive to contemplate the prospect of a guilty person successfully implicating an innocent one merely by virtue of "cooperating" with the prosecution by – perhaps falsely – implicating others less involved or not involved at all in the asserted crime. This risk is more than conjectural since cooperation is measured at the time of sentencing, with whatever prospect of obtaining a "downward departure" from the federal sentencing guidelines hinges largely on how effectively one implicates others. As will be briefly discussed below, the draconian nature of sentencing guidelines, even though declared unconstitutional and advisory only in U.S. v. Booker, 543 U.S. ___ (2005), in January of this year, these guidelines continue to be weighed heavily in the vast majority of sentences that have been meted out since then.

Limiting Access to Information

While the confluence of civil and criminal risk in parallel proceedings presents an immensely complicated series of judgment calls for defense counsel and client, one of the most serious complications lies in the increasing inability to gain access to the factual elements necessary to put on an effective defense, as well as to the resources necessary to fund that defense.

The main problem concerning access to information may be the constraints the criminal process places on gaining access to witnesses and information held by the prosecution. While it is true that cases are often stayed to allow criminal cases to be completed, given the length of time that can be required to construct and conclude complex criminal securities fraud actions, there has been a tendency in some courts to deny the government's requests to stay civil discovery, for example, relying on the need for individuals in class action proceedings to recover their losses sooner.

The Fundamental Fairness Issue

Apart from questions of fairness, one may ask whether multiple investigative and enforcement proceedings are necessary to achieve the ends sought – namely, decreasing fraudulent conduct in the corporate and securities areas. At present it is unusual for the civil and criminal enforcement agencies involved to disclose whether they will proceed together or whether they intend to leave the formal commencement of litigation to one agency or the other. The Commission's litigation releases sometimes thank other enforcement agencies, normally the United States Attorney's Office involved, for assistance even where no criminal proceeding is brought. Perhaps the agencies involved should advise those potentially involved of such decisions earlier.

Conclusion

The net effect of the criminalization of the securities laws that has resulted from the growth of parallel proceedings is certainly due praise in very many respects. Even a casual observer of the conduct that has led to the most egregious frauds must take comfort in seeing true criminals put behind bars.

Determining when extremes of carelessness or inadequate policing of the acts of others falls short of the intent traditionally required in criminal prosecutions remains a challenge for all involved in the enforcement process. When this challenge is complicated by having to deal with multiple agencies, multiple interrogations, and potentially multiple trials, one must question whether the balance has tipped too far toward the prosecution. Given the recent proceedings against the mutual fund and insurance industries by various enforcement agencies it is unlikely that we will soon see a shift away from the current environment (though the recent appointment of a new Chairman of the Commission may be the harbinger of such a shift). Nonetheless it is very important to keep an eye on whether individuals and entities are consenting, pleading, or merely being investigated, by too many people from too many angles.

NOTES

THE EXPANDING RESPONSIBILITIES AND LIABILITIES OF CORPORATE DIRECTORS

19

THE GOOD THE BAD AND THE UGLY: DIRECTOR RISK IN THE POST-ENRON WORLD

David J. Berger

Adrian Delmont

Wilson Sonsini Goodrich & Rosati, P.C.

David J. Berger is a partner and Adrian Delmont is an associate in the firm of Wilson Sonsini Goodrich & Rosati, P.C. Mr. Berger chairs the firm's M&A Litigation Group. Some of the views expressed in this article were first set forth in other publications written by Mr. Berger and others at WSGR, and the views expressed herein are solely those of the authors. The authors would like to thank Leila Ahlstrom Guerrero for her assistance with this article.

Table of Contents

I. INTRODUCTION

As we come together this year there are several interesting issues to consider. Perhaps the most obvious is whether the risks facing officers and directors in today's environment are any greater than they were a few years ago. While there have been a number of concerns raised by a variety of individuals and practitioners, there has also been some recent scholarly analysis questioning whether this concern has an empirical basis. In particular, with the notable exception of Van Gorkum many years ago, and more recently Enron and WorldCom, are directors and officers really that much more at risk than at any other time in the last 25 years? Or have we, as counselors to directors and officers overstated the changing environment, and in particular in the potential risk of liability that a director, officer, issuer, or underwriter faces today?

One way to think about it is to put you in a couple of different hypothetical situations. First, imagine you are the CEO of a leading company in an exciting growth industry. Your company prices its initial public offering ("IPO") at $18 per share, and by the close of the day the company is trading at $29 per share. Less than a year later the Company does another offering, raising an additional $100 million. Within three months of the secondary offering (and 15 months of the IPO) the Company misses its numbers, and within six months of the secondary offering (and 18 months of the IPO) your Company has filed for bankruptcy. The lawsuits, several of which have been filed after the initial miss, are filed again after the bankruptcy, naming you, several of the Company's other officers and directors, as well as the auditors and underwriters, for liability under various state and federal securities laws.

Not surprisingly, the specific claims in the case include numerous accounting allegations. One such allegation is that as CEO you personally agreed to give a large customer extended payment terms. These extended payment terms inflated revenues for particular periods and for the class period overall. In addition, plaintiffs allege that members of your management team agreed to take products back from customers for a full credit, and your chief financial officer severely inflated your accounts receivable. As a result of this "financial manipulation" the Company was able to significantly inflate revenues in periods right before the sale of securities. Finally, as CEO you sold some stock during this period while the market for the Company's stock was near its high.

Based upon these facts, what is the result? Criminal charges against you as CEO? Civil claims by the SEC against you and the other officers and directors? Is your insurance carrier going to move to rescind its policies on your behalf, putting all that you have ever worked for at risk? Should you accept having to pay a multi-million dollar settlement in lawsuits brought by shareholders against you and the other directors for your actions as an officer and director rather than risk taking the case to summary judgment and/or trial?

These facts are, of course, based on an actual case. Yet rather than settling, you—and the other "deep pocket" defendants—have decided to take this case to summary judgment. Having heard all the arguments, some of the conclusions reached by the court in ruling on your motion are as follows:

—the question as to whether revenue was properly recognized is "enormously complex", with the parties "generat[ing] well over 100 pages of conflicting expert testimony on these issues alone. It is absurd in these circumstances for Plaintiffs to suggest that the other defendants, who are not accountants, possibly could have known of any mistake by [the auditors]. Therefore, even if there are errors in the financial statements, no defendant except [the auditor] can be liable under Section 11 on that basis";

—with respect to the claim that the company took back product from customers for a full credit, "[g]iving an unsatisfied customer a refund is a normal business method of dealing with an unsatisfied customer. It is not a violation of the securities laws for [the company] to have failed to disclose such an obvious practice to potential investors."

—plaintiffs' argument that the company failed to adequately disclose the weakness in its internal controls "ignore[s] the fact the Prospectus included an express disclaimer that 'there can be no assurances' that [the company's] existing internal controls would continue to be adequate given the rapid pace at which the company was growing. The Prospectus made no predictions to the contrary. Thus, the Prospectus adequately bespoke caution regarding this potential risk…[and] [a]s a matter of law, [p]laintiffs cannot have been misled."

—in response to the Section 10(b) and Rule 10b-5 claims against you and the other officers, the court found that your "overall pattern of conduct…rebuts any inference of knowing or reckless conduct…[because] if [the company's] officers were bent on committing fraud, it is not likely that they would have provided such detailed risk disclosure in the prospectuses. Furthermore, if, as [p]laintiffs allege, the [o]fficers knew that [the company] was heading for financial disaster, they probably would have bailed out of their substantial stock holdings. Each of the [o]fficer

[d]efendants, by contrast, held onto most of their [ ] stock and incurred the same large losses as did the [p]laintiffs themselves."

—in conclusion, the court noted that plaintiffs have "submitted hundreds of pages to this court in an effort to create a genuine issue of fact. Using tortured reasoning, convolution of the issues, and the benefit of hindsight, they point to the most innocuous of optimistic language, and the most immaterial of omitted facts, and claim that they were somehow misled as to the nature of their investment. The court has thoroughly reviewed the record, and it concludes that there is no issue on [p]laintiffs' claims under the federal securities laws that can be submitted to the jury. For the reasons set forth above, no defendant is liable for any statement in, or omission from, either [prospectus]. Moreover, there is insufficient evidence, as a matter of law, for the jury to find intent to deceive or defraud on the part of any defendant in connection with [the company's] securities offerings."

The unfortunate company who suffered this fate was Worlds of Wonder (the company that brought us Teddy Ruxpin and Lazer Tag!). In the leading case titled <u>In re Worlds of Wonder Securities Litigation</u>, 814 F. Supp. 850 (N.D. Cal. 1993)—a case decided well before the PSLRA was passed—Judge Samuel Conti rejected all of plaintiffs' claims despite the undisputed fact that the company went bankrupt within 18 months of its IPO.[1]

The second situation for you to consider has somewhat similar facts. In this situation the company again had a successful IPO, at a price of $18.50 per share, and within a short period its stock rose to $23.50 per share. Unfortunately, and once again within six months of this offering, the company had a severe revenue shortfall and faced allegations of improper revenue recognition. As a result, the company's stock price fell dramatically, to a price of just over $2 per share after all of this information became public.

Not surprisingly, nearly a dozen cases were filed within days of the information becoming public. This time, you are a director (or general counsel) of one of the lead underwriters for the offering, trying to decide whether or not to settle the case. The choice you are facing is to settle now for tens of millions of dollars or to push forward to the summary judgment decision, with the promise that the settlement amount will increase substantially if your company loses its motion for summary judgment.

---

1. Wilson Sonsini Goodrich & Rosati represented several of the individual defendants in the <u>Worlds of Wonder Securities Litigation</u>.

Given these facts, one must wonder in today's environment how many of us would decide to take the risk and go forward to fight the case.

Once again this situation is taken from an actual case. In that case, in responding to the underwriters' motion for summary judgment solely on the basis that the underwriters performed adequate due diligence to meet their obligations under Section 11, the court held as follows:

—the "adequacy of due diligence may be decided on summary judgment when the underlying historical facts are undisputed." Otherwise, leaving the "question of what constitutes due diligence to the jury will lead to a battle of experts...who basically become paid advocates, ...express[ing] an opinion based on their own subjective viewpoints, which will be biased by their role. The jurors will then be forced to decide between these paid advocates. The resulting uncertainty will increase litigation against deep pocket defendants (such as underwriters) and encourage collusion between plaintiffs and the issuer, who will often be in a precarious financial situation already....[In contrast] treating due diligence as a question of law, once the historical facts are undisputed, will apportion the risk more appropriately, encourage settlement at early stages and lead to more equitable and consistent results."

—"Section 11 and 12(2) require a 'reasonable' investigation by the [u]nderwriters. This does not, as [p]laintiffs imply, require an audit on the part of the underwriters....[U]nderwriters may reasonably rely on SEC letters and documents as well as representations of management. That is not to say that underwriters may 'tacitly rely on management assertions'; rather, underwriters may rely on management's representations when it is reasonable to do so under the circumstances. It would be unreasonable, for example, to solely rely on management's representations when said representations could have been reasonably verified. It is not unreasonable, however, to rely on management's representations with regard to information that is solely in the possession of the issuer and cannot be reasonably verified by third parties. Underwriters cannot be expected to ferret out everything that management knows about the company; they only need to reasonably attempt to verify and believe the accuracy of the information in the prospectus. If the [u]nderwriter's overall investigation was reasonable under the circumstances, they are entitled to a due diligence defense."

—"The [p]rospectus sets out several risk factors" detailing potential problems the company may face. "These warnings, along with many others in the [p]rospectus, may, by themselves, entitle the [u]nderwriters to summary judgment."

—with respect to a claim that the underwriters failed to perform sufficient diligence on the company's policy on product returns and price protection, the court held that the underwriters not only interviewed several members of management but "then verified management's representations by contacting three major...customers, the [company's] distributors...subjected [the company's] budget to line-by-line scrutiny...reviewed its financial statements with [the company's auditor]...[and] obtained written representations from [the company] *and* selling stockholders that the [p]rospectus was accurate, as well as a comfort letter from [the company's auditor]."

—on the claim that the underwriters failed to uncover the company's improper revenue recognition policies, the court held that "[g]iven the complexity of the accounting issues, the [u]nderwriters were entitled to rely on [the expertise of the company's auditor]." Yet the underwriters went further, and reviewed confirmations from some of the company's customers and "confirmed [the company's] revenue recognition policy with other accounting firms." As a result, their investigation on this issue "was reasonable".

—"[p]laintiffs' contention that had the underwriters done more, they would have revealed problems, is not persuasive. The court cannot evaluate an underwriter's due diligence defense with the benefit of hindsight. The overall investigation performed here was reasonable under the circumstances at the time of the investigation."

—with respect to primary liability under Section 10(b) the court held that plaintiffs "offer no motive for the [u]nderwriters to participate in the alleged fraud, except to point to the fees that they earned from the [o]ffering. This court has previously stated that an allegation that professionals committed fraud in order to obtain professional fees is not a persuasive motive to establish scienter...In fact, the risk of monumental damages against underwriters if found liable for securities fraud more than balances the temptation of ill-gotten gains and makes such a motive implausible. An underwriter's greatest asset is its reputation for careful work. Fees for an offering could not approach the losses the underwriting firm would suffer from a perception that it would muffle a client's fraud."

— "Nor do the actions of the [u]nderwriters support a pattern consistent with scienter. The extensive risk warnings in the [p]rospectus, for example, negate any inference of scienter. If the [u]nderwriters had intended to mislead investors, they would not have included such warnings, which could have discouraged investors from purchasing [the company's] stock."

—Plaintiffs' claim that the underwriters knew that the company's business was declining. "Plaintiffs' evidence in support of these assertions, however, is not sufficient to infer scienter in this case. Plaintiffs' expert's opinion of what the [u]nderwriters likely did or did not know is far from what is required to infer scienter under the circumstances of this case."

Based upon these conclusions, the court in In re Software Toolworks Securites Litigation, 789 F. Supp. 1489 (N.D. Cal. 1992) granted summary judgment in favor of the underwriters against all claims brought by plaintiffs.[2]

Worlds of Wonder and Software Toolworks were both decided less than 15 years ago, and before the adoption of the PSLRA, which increased the burden on plaintiffs in securities class actions. Both decisions were authored by well respected judges, and were the subject of significant commentary at the time they were issued.

In today's environment, how many of the potential defendants in these situations would have chosen to proceed to summary judgment? A quick review of any newspaper these days shows very few, as the risks have so increased while the perceptions of the key actors involved—including management, outside directors, investment banks, auditors and anyone else affiliated in any way with a company which has been the victim of fraud—has reached such a point that it is virtually impossible for these individuals and entities to believe that they have any realistic chance of prevailing on a motion *regardless* of the merits of the situation.

The risk ratio seems to be better in Delaware on issues involving the scope of a director's fiduciary duties, although it may just be that the downside risk (i.e. the likelihood of personal liability, significant monetary damages and/or even criminal time) is less in Chancery Court than in district court. It is worth noting, however, that as this article goes to print there are several cases winding their way through the courts which could impact the standards applicable to directors, as well as the risk of liability to directors. Perhaps most notably the trial over Michael Ovitz's departure from the Walt Disney Company has been completed, and an opinion concerning the "good faith" standard applicable to directors coming out of that case should be issued in the near future. This opinion could have significant implications for directors of Delaware companies for many different reasons, including the fact directors can only be indemnified if they act in "good faith".

---

2. Wilson Sonsini Goodrich & Rosati represented the underwriters in the Software Toolworks Securities Litigation.

Yet one other point must be noted when considering the increased risks to officers and directors: the dramatic increase over the last several years in executive compensation, particularly CEO compensation. According to a recent New York Times article, the CEO of a major company in 2004 received on average a pay package of approximately $10 million, an increase of more than 12% from 2003. Further, this figure does not take into account the pay-out for some CEOs involved in extraordinary transactions, or gains on various forms of equity compensation.

The growth in CEO pay is not, of course, linked in any specific way to the increased risks faced by officers, but it may well be part of the reason why it is generally perceived to be more difficult to defend senior executives today than it was at the time Software Toolworks or Worlds of Wonder were decided. Certainly one factor that helped push Sarbannes-Oxley through Congress was the view that executives receiving such high compensation ought to be responsible for all aspects of their company's financial statements even when, as was recognized in Worlds of Wonder, complicated accounting questions are often the subject of much debate within the accounting profession, and asking a non-accountant to be an expert on these issues is neither realistic nor fair.

This outline briefly reviews some recent cases under Delaware law that discuss the issues facing directors in today's environment, as well as the broader issue of the evolving standards of review for corporate directors. These cases show how some courts are viewing director conduct in today's environment. Yet as discussed above, what is important is not just what these cases are saying but the overall environment for officers, directors and their advisers.

Perhaps the most important issue is whether we will return to an environment which existed less than 15 years ago, when "deep pocketed" defendants who believed they did not act improperly felt that they could afford to take their case to court and not be tarred with the fraud and/or bad judgment of the other parties to the case. A second such issue is whether the growth in executive (and particularly CEO) pay shall continue, and if so what implications that will have on the judicial system. Finally, it is worth considering whether the failures of Enron, WorldCom and the other notorious frauds of the last few years have been sufficiently removed from the front pages to allow a more level-headed discussion about such critical corporate governance issues as the scope of a director's liability, her responsibility to the corporation and what is an appropriate board for today's changing corporate environment.

II. RECENT DEVELOPMENTS IN DELAWARE CASE LAW

A. Director Independence

1. *In re Toys "R" Us, Inc. Shareholder Litigation,* No. Civ. A. 1212-N, 2005 WL 1497205 (Del. Ch. June 22, 2005)

This case arises out of the sale of Toys "R" Us ("TRU") to a buyout group led by Kohlberg Kravis Roberts & Co. (the "KKR Group"). The facts of the case are not particularly complicated. TRU is a specialty retailer of toys and baby products. The Plaintiffs moved to enjoin a vote of the TRU stockholders to consider approving a merger with an acquisition vehicle formed by the KKR group. *In re Toys "R" Us, Inc. Shareholder Litigation,* No. Civ. A. 1212-N, 2005 WL 1497205, at *1 (Del. Ch. June 22, 2005). The proposed merger provided that the TRU stockholders would receive $26.75 per share, a 123% premium over the $12.00 stock price that their stock was trading at in January 2004, when TRU began pursuing "strategic alternatives." Id.

The Plaintiffs claimed that TRU's board breached its fiduciary duties of care by failing to conduct a proper auction for the company, and more specifically by only seeking whole-company bids from a group of four bidders that had entered a final round of bidders for the primary toy division. As discussed in more detail below, the Court expressly found that the board acted reasonably and with due care in both its process and in accepting the final offer (and also noted that no other bidder had come forward after the final offer had been accepted by the board).

As part of their argument, plaintiffs' alleged that TRU's chief executive officer, John H. Eyler, Jr., and the company's financial advisor in the merger, Credit Suisse First Boston ("First Boston"), improperly dominated the board in favor of their own personal interests. In particular, plaintiffs alleged that Mr. Eyler was motivated by his stock options, while First Boston's primary interest was in the $7 million fee increase it would receive upon a sale of the whole company. Id. at *23. Plaintiffs then challenged the reasonableness of the board's deliberations in accepting the KKR Group's bid of $26.75 per share. Id. at *24.

With respect to the allegedly improper motives of Eyler and First Boston, the Court found that, "the plaintiffs sketch out a picture of a passive board who deferred too easily to the wishes of a CEO ... and financial advisor .... I am told that these agents of the board, who, on the surface, appeared to be making every effort to generate the highest value for Company stockholders, in reality were, consciously or subconsciously, driven by selfish motives antithetical to the stockholders' interests." Id. at *23. According to plaintiffs, Eyler was motivated to cause the sale of the whole company and trigger change of control provisions that were personally lucrative, and supposedly therefore hijacked the process to sell TRU's toys division. Id. He supposedly had additional incentive to sell TRU to the KKR Group because it offered the best, but not certain, prospects for Eyler's continued employment. Id.

The Court summarily rejected these arguments. First, the Court noted that "plaintiffs essentially accuse Eyler of the status crime of being a CEO. They tout the fact that he stands to gain over $60 million from the sale of the Company. They play up the fact that the KKR Group conditioned its original [bid]...on the retention of key (but unspecified) members of management." Id. "But they ignore [many] key realities, [including the fact that] Eyler's compensation from the merger results from the stock and options he holds—he therefore had more incentive than almost anyone to make sure that the board did the best risk-adjusted job it could of getting the best price." Id. As part of this analysis, the Court expressly noted that [c]ommentators on corporate governance have expressed the belief—and Delaware courts have concurred—that stock options, when used and designed prudently, can help align insiders' interests with those of public shareholders, because it gives insiders an incentive to increase the value of the company's shares." Id. at *25 n.42.

The Court concluded that "plaintiffs' challenge to Eyler's fidelity to the Company and its stockholders is not substantiated....A rational person could not, on this record, infer that Eyler's judgment was tainted by a personal desire to advantage himself at the expense of the Company's public stockholders. Indeed, the fact that Eyler was so heavily invested in the Company's equity no doubt encouraged him to take value-maximizing steps without regard for his future employment because he recognized that a good deal for Toys "R" Us stockholders would leave him very wealthy, too." Id. at *25.

The claim that First Boston had tilted negotiations to its own benefit likewise failed. First, the fact that First Boston stood to gain more from a large merger than a smaller acquisition was a function of the agreement it had with TRU, and was designed to provide First Boston with incentive to seek the highest possible value in the sale

TRU or its parts. See id. at *25. Second, over the course of the company's entire strategic investigation, First Boston had never advised TRU that a sale of the whole company was the best course of action until a bidder, in March 2005, came to First Boston with a whole-company bid. See id. at *26. And at that point, First Boston "if anything, urged the Company to stay the course and put the [toy division sale] to bed." Id.

The Court also refused to accept that when First Boston acted improperly just because its engagement letter paid it more for a sale of the whole company than if it had just sold a division. The court rejected the argument that when First Boston first learned of an opportunity to sell the entire company, "a light went off in First Boston's head. It was only then that First Boston, a very large investment bank with serious reputational interests at stake, suddenly realized, in an epiphanic blaze of financial acumen, that it might make a full $7 million more by tainting its advice to its client." Id. The Court went on, in typically quotable fashion: "Without indulging in the naive pretense that investment bankers are immune from financial temptation, one can confidently fail to embrace this implausible theory of advisorial disloyalty." Id.

The Court also rejected plaintiffs' claim of Eyler's and First Boston's allegedly pernicious sway over the TRU board. The Court noted that it found no evidence to conclude that the nine independent directors on TRU's ten person board had consciously abandoned a higher value alternative (e.g., selling only the toy division) for personal gains they stood to receive from a merger of the entire company. See id. at *27. Again, the Court noted that the TRU board's stock options helped to align them with the interest of TRU stockholders, and pursue the most lucrative end available. See id. "Put bluntly, if the [TRU] board failed to maximize shareholder value, it did so, not because it or its advisors were improperly motivated, but because it made errors in judgment." Id.

Finally, the Court concluded that "the bottom line is that the public stockholders will have an opportunity tomorrow to reject the merger if they do not think the price is high enough... .[As] the plaintiffs have dropped any claim that the merger vote ought to be enjoined because the proxy statement is materially misleading ... the vote of the stockholders, if affirmative, may well be a fully informed one that will have ratification effect, foreclosing as a practical matter, all claims of breach of fiduciary duty about the process leading to the merger." Id. at 42.

2. *In re Oracle Corp. Derivative Litig.,* 867 A.2d 904 (Del. Ch. 2004), aff'd 872 A.2d 960 (Del. 2005).

The action decided here involved claims that two of the top officers at Oracle Corporation ("Oracle") breached their fiduciary duty of loyalty to the corporation by selling stock in the company when they possessed material, adverse, non-public information that Oracle would not meet its projections for that quarter. See In re Oracle Corp. Deriv. Litig., 867 A.2d 904, 905 (Del. Ch. 2004), aff'd 872 A.2d 960 (Del. 2005). The facts of the case are well known, in part because of the court's earlier opinion denying defendants' Special Litigation Committee Defense on the basis that the Special Committee was not independent. In re Oracle Corp. Deriv. Litig., No. Civ. A. 18751, 2004 WL 2756278 (Del. Ch. Nov. 24, 2004).

The case arose out of the supposedly improper trading of Larry Ellison Oracle's founder and chairman and chief executive officer, and Jeff Henley, the company's chief financial officer. According to the Plaintiffs, both Ellison and Henley possessed material financial information before trades in Oracle stock in January 2001 that should have led them to recognize that Oracle would not meet the company's projections. Oracle Corp. Deriv. Litig., *supra*, 867 A.2d at 905. Plaintiffs contended that Ellison and Henley had thus reaped ill-gotten gains on their sales that should be returned to the company. Id. The Delaware Court of Chancery, on Ellison and Henley's motion for summary judgment, rejected the Plaintiffs' argument.

Initially the court considered the applicable standard to apply in an insider-trading case involving an alleged breach of fiduciary duty. As part of this analysis, and despite the Court's and the Defendants' skepticism as to whether Brophy v. Cities Service Co. (70 A.2d 5 (Del. Ch. 1949)), a Delaware common law proscription on insider trading, remains good law, the Court underwent a Brophy analysis, finding that even if Brophy standard applied, the Defendants were entitled to summary judgment. Oracle, supra, 867A.2d at 906-907, 929. The Brophy standard, as applied by the Court, demands that a plaintiff show:

> 1) the corporate fiduciary possessed material, nonpublic company information; and 2) the corporate fiduciary used that information improperly by making trades because she was motivated, in whole or in part, by the substance of that information.

Id. at 934. In resolving this case, the Court concluded that no rational fact finder could find that either condition applied to Ellison, Henley, or their trades. Id. at 906.

In coming to its conclusion, the Court placed reliance on a number of factors:

- The conservative bias of Oracle's financial projection system, resulting in estimates of earnings and license revenues that were more likely to be low than high, and the complete lack of evidence to cast doubt on the integrity of Oracle's estimation process.
- Oracle's estimates of its results at the time of Ellison and Henley's trades continued to predict that the company would either meet or exceed its projections for the quarter.
- The lack of record evidence that Ellison or Henley had received any information from subordinates at the time of their trades that would inform them the company was not in a position to make its numbers.
- The majority of Oracle's quarterly income is generated in the last month of any quarter, and most of the last month's revenue is generated in the last week of the quarter.
- Oracle's prospects for the quarter in question weakened substantially in the last month of that quarter—after the Defendants had made their trades—largely due to customers refusing to close deals in the final days of the quarter.
- The absence of any apparent exigency or rational motive that would lead Ellison or Henley—huge Oracle stockholders—to sell small portions of their Oracle holdings because of fears of a decline in Oracle's performance.

Id. at 906-907.

These factors led the Court to conclude that no one, not even Ellison or Henley, could have seen the drop in Oracle's quarterly numbers coming. See id. at 952. Rather, the Court found that "[i]n the end, the plaintiffs ask me to adopt a Monday-morning quarterback approach to materiality. Because Q3 01 went bad, it must have been reasonably foreseeable at the time. But there is no basis for a rational mind to accept that proposition." Id.

With respect to scienter, the Court held that both Henley and Ellison had reasonable, non-suspicious reasons for making their trades when they made them. See id. at 953-55. Henley made his trades early in the year, and "keeping with a pattern of diversification and his decision to trade in a new calendar (and therefore tax) year was motivated by proper, non-suspicious financial considerations. ... Henley sold 7% of his Oracle position, leaving him a huge stake in the company." Id. at 954.

Likewise, "[w]hat Ellison indicated was quite sensible: he had a number of expiring options that would, when exercised, trigger a huge tax liability and require him to sell shares. Because he would have to enter the market to sell in order to exercise his options, it was a prudent time to finally take his financial advisor's advice to diversity his holdings and to reduce some debt while he was in the market. Therefore, Ellison has advanced entirely reasonable, non-suspicious reasons for his trades. ... In sum, however wealthy Ellison is and however envious that may make some, the fact remains that Ellison sold only 2% of his Oracle holdings." Id. at 954-55.

Finally, in rejecting Plaintiffs' arguments with respect to the proper application of Brophy, the Court held that it would not accept a situation in which a corporate insider would be held strictly liable to return trading profits when the insider possesses information that casts some doubt on a company's ability to make its numbers, and the company then does not, in fact, make its numbers. See id. at 929-30. The Court specifically recognized the benefits of insider ownership: "the idea that many sophisticated commentators believe that it is a good idea that corporate insiders own company stock because having, as Ross Perot would say, 'skin in the game' will tend to align their interests with those of the public stockholders." Id. at 930. In short, "the use of equity as a compensation tool is a legitimate choice under our law and Delaware statutory law permits and its common law creates incentives for stockholders to serve as directors and officers." Id.

3. Beam v. Stewart, 845 A.2d 1040 (Del. 2004).

Beam v. Stewart challenged the independence of the directors of Martha Stewart Living Omnimedia, Inc. ("MSO"), claiming that the directors' friendships and personal relationships with Martha Stewart made them incapable of rendering an unbiased decision about whether or not to bring claims against her. The complaint alleged that Stewart's allegedly improper trading of shares of ImClone Systems, Inc. ("ImClone"), as well as other sales of MSO shares by Stewart, constituted a breach of fiduciary duty. The complaint further alleged that demand was futile based on the lack of independence of at least half of MSO's six-member board of directors.

The Court of Chancery dismissed the complaint for failing to make demand. The Court noted that while "some professional or personal friendships, which may border on or even exceed familial loyalty and closeness, may raise a reasonable doubt whether a director can appropriately consider demand . . . [n]ot all friendships, or even most of them, rise to this level. . .". Beam v. Stewart, 833 A.2d 961, 979 (Del. Ch. 2003), aff'd, 845 A.2d 1040 (Del. 2004). The Court held that in order to make a "reasonable inference" that a particular friendship rises to this level, the plaintiff must provide "specific factual allegations" concerning the "closeness or nature of the friendship, details of the business and social interactions between the two, or allegations raising additional considerations ... ." Id. at 979-80.

On appeal, the Delaware Supreme Court affirmed. In one of the last opinions written by former Chief Justice Veasey, the Supreme Court began by noting that "[i]ndependence is a fact-specific determination made in the context of a particular case. The [C]ourt must make that determination by answering the inquiries: independent from whom and independent for what purpose?" Beam, 845 A.2d at 1049-50. The Supreme Court agreed with the Court of Chancery that a director's independence may be questioned for any reason, including "financial ties, familial affinity, a particularly close or intimate personal or business affinity or because of evidence that in the past the relationship caused the director to act non-independently *vis á vis* an interested director." Id. at 1051. The Court held that allegations that directors moved "in the same business and social circles, or a characterization that they are close friends" is not enough to negate independence. Id. Rather:

> [t]o create a reasonable doubt about an outside director's independence, a plaintiff must plead facts that would support the inference that because of the nature of a relationship or additional circumstances other than the interested director's stock ownership or voting power, the non-interested director would be more willing to risk his or her reputation than risk the relationship with the interested director.

Id. at 1052. The Court found that none of the Plaintiff's allegations rose to this level.

In a final section of the opinion, titled "A Word About the Oracle Case," the Delaware Supreme Court advocated a relatively limited reading of the Court of Chancery's opinion in the first Oracle decision. The Supreme Court first noted that the Oracle case involved the creation of a Special Litigation Committee ("SLC"), and that unlike the demand-excusal context, where the board is presumed to be independent, the SLC has the initial burden of establishing its own independence that must be "like Caesar's wife—above reproach." Id. at 1055 (citation omitted). The Court also noted that "the Stanford connections in Oracle are factually distinct from the relationships present" in Beam. Id.

Beam is an example of a court conducting a searching inquiry about a director's independence, and demonstrates that this inquiry will go beyond financial or work relationships. All aspects of the relationship—be it personal, financial, business, or any other relationship—are open for inquiry and will be reviewed on a case-by-case basis to determine the specific nature of the relationship.

B. The Duties of Care and Good Faith

1. *Official Committee of Unsecured Creditors of Integrated Health Services, Inc. v. Elkins,* No. Civ. A. 20228-NC, 2004 WL 1949290 (Del. Ch. Aug. 24, 2004).

In the mid-1980s, defendant Robert N. Elkins ("Elkins") founded Integrated Health Services to operate a nation-wide chain of nursing homes. That chain, Integrated Health Services, Inc. ("IHS") operated successfully until February 2000, when IHS commenced a voluntary bankruptcy proceeding in the wake of certain federal legislation affecting IHS's profitability. The Official Committee of Unsecured Creditors (the "Creditors") soon commenced actions on behalf of the debtors of IHS, including an action against former and current IHS directors for allegedly breaching their fiduciary duties by approving certain compensation packages for Elkins. The United States Bankruptcy Court for the District of Delaware abstained from hearing the fiduciary duty claims, and the Creditors thus filed suit in the Delaware Court of Chancery. Official Committee of Unsecured Creditors of Integrated Health Services, Inc. v. Elkins, No. Civ. A. 20228-NC, 2004 WL 1949290, at **1, 3 (Del. Ch. Aug. 24, 2004).

In the first case after the Court of Chancery's opinion in In re Walt Disney Company Derivatives Litigation (825 A.2d 275 (Del. Ch. 2003)) to deal with executive compensation, the Creditors challenged eleven compensation agreements—loans, option grants, and loan forgiveness programs—the board had approved for Elkins. Id. at **1, 4-8. The Creditors alleged that the IHS directors, and Elkins, breached their fiduciary duties by "approving or ratifying certain compensation arrangements without adequate information, consideration, or deliberation[.]" Id. at *1. The Creditors also alleged that the Defendants wasted corporate assets by approving the compensation arrangements. Id. The defendant directors, joined by Elkins, filed a motion to dismiss on the grounds that the Creditors had failed to state a claim, and that the directors were entitled to the protection of an exculpatory clause contained in IHS's certificate of incorporation, in accordance with 8 Del. C. § 102(b)(7). Id. at *2.

The Court quickly determined that the challenged compensation arrangements had been approved by a majority of disinterested IHS directors (Id. at **2, 10-12), and moved on to the question of whether the defendants "consciously and intentionally disregarded [their] responsibilities," thus implicating a lack of good faith. Id. at *12. A lack of good faith would prevent the defendant directors from availing themselves of the exculpatory provisions of IHS's certificate of incorporation. Id.

In finding that the Creditors had stated a claim for breach of fiduciary duty with respect to some of the challenged transactions, but not all, the Court drew a distinction between allegations of non-deliberation and not enough deliberation. For example, the Court dismissed a claim that the defendants had breached their fiduciary duties by failing to consult a tax expert on the consequences of a compensation consultant's report on a 1997 loan program, and by failing to set up a monitoring mechanism with regard to that program, because despite such alleged failings, the complaint alleged that the directors engaged in discussion regarding the consultant's report and the loan program. Id. at *13. The court noted that while the directors' actions may or may not have been negligent "(or even grossly negligent), no inference can be drawn that this decision was made without good faith[,]" and therefore, the Section 102(b)(7) provision of IHS's certificate of incorporation precluded the imposition of monetary liability. Id.

In contrast, the Court found that the Creditors had stated a claim for breach of fiduciary duty with respect to a loan when the directors approved the loan without deliberation, and one director justified the action by stating that he knew Elkins would never "pull anything behind anyone's back." Id. at *15 (citation omitted). The court found that "[e]ven for an officer who founded a company and had been with that company for over 10 years, and even for a transaction as proportionately small as this, directors of a public corporation must exercise more than blind faith in approving loans." Id.

The Court also refused to dismiss fiduciary duty of loyalty claims against Elkins. See id. at **16-17. The Court noted that "employees negotiating employment agreements with their employers have the right to seek an agreement containing the best terms possible for themselves. However, once an employee becomes a fiduciary of an entity [(as Elkins was)], he has a duty to negotiate further compensation agreements 'honestly and in good faith so as not to advantage himself at the expense of the [entity's] stockholders.'" Id. at *16, quoting In re Walt Disney Co. Deriv. Litig., 825 A.2d at 290. The Court found:

> That Elkins set out agendas for Board and Compensation Committee meetings; that Elkins attended meetings; that he spoke with directors outside of the meetings; that he negotiated his compensation packages with the Board and Compensation Committee; or even that he spoke with the Board's compensation consultant are all, individually, not enough to show a breach of Elkins's duty of loyalty. But these, taken together, and coupled with the Complaint's allegations that Elkins reviewed and revised every draft of [the board's compensation consultant's] reports before they were submitted to the Board; that Elkins exerted pressure on [the board's compensation consultant] to justify Elkins's compensation; that Elkins's March 19, 1998 letter to the Board stated inaccurate facts as to what the Compensation Committee had previously approved in regard to forgiveness of previous loans; that Elkins caused IHS to disburse funds to him without corporate authority; that Elkins insisted on [a] 1999 Loan Program solely because he thought Citibank would seek to eliminate IHS's use of its credit agreement to provide loans to employees; and that Elkins insisted on extending a Five-Year Forgiveness Term to all of his loans, notwithstanding opposition by [the board's compensation consultant]; suggest Elkins "may have breached his fiduciary duties by engaging in a self-interested transaction."

Id. at *16 (citations omitted).

Finally, the Court dismissed the Creditors' waste claim, noting that "[w]aste is a standard rarely satisfied in Delaware courts." Id. at *17. "To succeed in proving waste, a plaintiff must plead facts showing 'an exchange that is so one sided that no business person of ordinary, sound judgment could conclude that the corporation has received adequate consideration.'" Id. (citations omitted). The Court further noted that a board's decision on executive compensation is entitled to great deference. Id. Hence, given that IHS's proxy materials had stated that the purpose of the compensation packages was to retain key employees, and Delaware's law recognizes this as a potential corporate benefit, the waste claim was dismissed because the compensation agreements subject to the waste claim could have induced Elkins to stay with IHS—a potential benefit to the company. Id. at **17-18.

2. *In re The Walt Disney Co. Deriv. Litig.,* No. Civ. A. 15452, 2004 WL 2050138 (Del. Ch. Sept. 10, 2004).

In *Disney*, plaintiffs filed a derivative action against The Walt Disney Company's ("Disney") board of directors in connection with the company's hiring and termination of Michael Ovitz, the former President of Disney. Plaintiffs alleged that the company's directors breached their duty of care by blindly approving Mr. Ovitz's employment agreement and non-fault termination benefits. Plaintiffs claimed that, as a result, Mr. Ovitz received approximately $140 million for just over one year of employment.

The Plaintiffs also claimed that Mr. Ovitz himself had violated his fiduciary duties as an officer of the company in negotiating, arranging, and finalizing the terms of his employment contract. On Ovitz' motion for summary judgment, the Delaware Court of Chancery dismissed the breach of fiduciary duty claims against Ovitz with respect to his actions before he was officially installed as Disney's President, on October 1, 1995. The Court did not dismiss the Plaintiffs' claims that Ovitz breached his fiduciary duties in receiving the non-fault termination benefits provided for in his termination agreement.

Ovitz officially became Disney's President on October 1, 1995 – the date he filled that position—even though at that time Ovitz did not have a finalized and duly executed employment agreement. In re The Walt Disney Co. Deriv. Litig., No. Civ A. 15452, 2004 WL 2050138, at *1 (Del. Ch. Sept. 10, 2004). His final agreement was signed on or about December 16, 1995, with an effective date of October 1, 1995. See id. Nevertheless, the Plaintiffs claimed that because a letter from Disney's CEO, Michael Eisner, outlining the key points of Ovitz' employment agreement was made public in

August 1995, Ovitz' eventual official installation as President, and status as a fiduciary, were foregone conclusions. Id. at *3.

The Court soundly rejected Plaintiffs' theory on a number of grounds. First, the Court set forth the simple conclusion that because Ovitz was not a fiduciary before October 1, 1995, he was free to negotiate the terms of his employment to his greatest advantage. Id. at *4. According to the Court, it was simply not within Ovitz' responsibility to ensure that Eisner had authority to extend an offer in the form it was presented to Ovitz, as Eisner was Disney's CEO at the time, vesting Eisner with apparent authority to take such actions. Id. The Court also held that finding Ovitz to be a fiduciary before he was actually installed as President would lead to uncertainty regarding when one becomes a fiduciary, while the bright-line rule the Court propounds (and upon which its decision ultimately turns) "is a more reasonable and desirable rule." Id.

The Court likewise rejected a Caremark claim against Ovitz. The Plaintiffs claimed that Ovitz, after being installed as Disney's President, should have conducted an investigation into his own hiring to make sure that Disney employed proper processes, and that the other directors and officer complied with their fiduciary duties to the company. Id. at *6. The Court, in rejecting this claim, noted that because Ovitz was not a fiduciary until October 1, 1995, and because no material changes to his employment agreement occurred after that date, as a matter of law Ovitz could not have breached a fiduciary duty he owed to the company by performing under his employment agreement and executing the document which conformed to the agreement. See id. Accordingly, "[b]ecause Ovitz did not breach his fiduciary duties, irrespective of whether other Disney directors and officers may have done so, Ovitz need not show the entire fairness of [his employment agreement], and he is entitled to summary judgment with respect to the claim that he breached his fiduciary duties by entering into [his employment agreement.]" Id.

In contrast, the Court declined to grant Ovitz' summary judgment motion with respect to whether he breached his fiduciary duties in accepting his no fault termination payments, when Ovitz was Disney's President and thus a fiduciary. The decision to offer Ovitz a no-fault termination, and the corresponding large payments, was arguably not mandated by Ovitz' employment agreement. Id. at *7. Plaintiffs alleged that Ovitz colluded with those on the other side of the bargaining process to secure his no fault termination, and in so doing allegedly manipulated corporate processes, thereby violating his duties to the company. See id.

Finally, the Court could not find record support that any group of disinterested members of Disney's board ever authorized the termination payments to Ovitz; and, no shareholder vote was ever taken on the issue. See id. The Court thus found that general issues of material fact remained with respect to whether Ovitz had used his position to obtain the no-fault termination payments in violation of his fiduciary duties. See id.

3. In re Emerging Communications, Inc. S'holders Litig., **No. Civ. A. 16415, 2004 WL 1305745 (Del. Ch. June 4, 2004).**

Emerging Communications addressed two related actions: an appraisal action and a class action for breach of fiduciary duty, both brought by minority shareholders of Emerging Communications, Inc. ("ECM"). In re Emerging Comms., Inc. S'holders Litig., No. Civ. A. 16415, 2004 WL 1305745, at *1 (Del. Ch. June 4, 2004). At issue in Emerging was the October 1998 two-step "going private" acquisition of ECM by Innovative Communications Corp. ("Innovative"), ECM's majority shareholder. Id. At the time of the acquisition, Jeffrey Prosser, ECM's Chairman and CEO, owned a controlling stake in both ECM and Innovative. Id.

Even before ECM became a publicly-traded company in December 1997, Prosser "indicated that he intended to merge Innovative into ECM, and he began exploring a combination of the two companies in January 1998." Id. at *4. In order to evaluate any potential merger with Innovative, ECM retained Prudential as its financial advisor and Cahill, Gordon and Reindel ("Cahill") as its legal advisor. Id. By the end of February 1998, ECM's board of directors had created a special committee for purposes of evaluating the draft merger agreement proposed by Prosser whereby Innovative would merge into a subsidiary of ECM. Id. at *5.

By May 1998, however, Prosser "began having significant reservations about the Proposed Merger, because the low market interest in ECM's common stock had caused that stock to be undervalued." Id. Prosser then met with Prudential, Cahill, and another member of ECM's board, John Raynor, to discuss the possibility of Innovative acquiring the remaining outstanding shares of ECM (the "Privatization"). Id. In effect, "Prosser switched from being a seller of ECM stock to becoming a buyer of that stock." Id. Significantly, Prosser retained Prudential and Cahill to represent Innovative in this proposed acquisition of ECM, which meant that "the advisors that initially were retained to work for the interests of ECM and its minority stockholders would now be working to serve the interests of Innovative, the party now bargaining against ECM." Id. at *6 (emphasis in original). Shortly thereafter, Prosser, Prudential, and Cahill presented to ECM's board a term sheet for the proposed acquisition of ECM, which valued ECM's shares at $9.125 per share. Id. Innovative's offer "was the first occasion that the ECM board and the First Special Committee (other than Raynor) learned of the abandonment of the Proposed Merger in favor of the Privatization." Id.

In response to Innovative's offer, ECM's board created another special committee to evaluate the fairness of the offer. Id. As part of its review process, the special committee retained Houlihan Lokey Howard & Zukin ("Houlihan") as its financial advisor. Id. Houlihan reviewed ECM's financial projections from March 1998, but was not provided with ECM's financial projections from June 1998, which were prepared at Prosser's request and distributed to Prudential, Cahill, and Innovative's lender, RTFC. Id. at *7. Significantly, these June 1998 projections forecast significantly higher growth than the March 1998 projections. Id. Indeed, based on these June 1998 projections, RTFC concluded that ECM was worth at least $28 per share. Id.

In August 1998, Houlihan presented its findings to ECM's board, and the special committee then rejected Innovative's offer of $9.125 per share. Id. In subsequent negotiations, however, Prosser raised his offer to $10.25 per share, which Houlihan concluded was a fair price, and ECM's board approved the acquisition on August 17, 1998. Id. at *9.

In both the appraisal and class actions, the plaintiffs alleged that the terms of the proposed acquisition were unfair to ECM's minority shareholders. Id. The court noted that the analyses of plaintiffs' two actions overlapped: "In a statutory appraisal action, the court must determine the 'fair value' of the corporation whose stock is being appraised," whereas the applicable standard for the class action breach of fiduciary duty claims was "entire fairness," which "has two aspects: fair dealing and fair price." Id. (citation omitted). In effect, the plaintiffs' "fiduciary 'fair price,' and statutory 'fair value,' contentions converge . . . ." Id. at *10.

In order to determine the "fair price" / "fair value" of ECM, the court discussed at length the relevant case authorities and the various approaches and methodologies proffered by each party's experts. Id. at **12-24. Ultimately, the court calculated 'the fair value of ECM on the merger date . . . to be $416,996,000, or $38.05 per share." Id. at *24. This conclusion, however, "did not address whether the unfairness was the product of a breach of fiduciary duty or if so, the nature or character of that duty. Accordingly, a 'fair dealing' analysis [was] required in this case, if only . . . for § 102(b)(7) exculpation purposes." Id. at *28. The court also noted that, because the acquisition was "a self-dealing transaction of which the majority stockholder [stood] on both sides, entire fairness is the standard of review *ab initio,*" and the "burden of proving fair dealing remains with the defendants." Id. at **30-32.

For purposes of examining "fair dealing," the court was required to address "'issues of when the transaction was timed, how it was initiated, structured, negotiated, and disclosed to the board, and how director and shareholder approval was obtained.'" Id. at *32 (quotation and citation omitted). In this case, the court held that the fact the "freeze-out merger [was] initiated by the majority stockholder . . . even though not dispositive, [was] evidence of unfair dealing." Id. The court also held that there was additional "evidence of unfair timing" because "Prosser abandoned [his] proposal [to merge Innovative into ECM] at the eleventh hour and 'flipped' the deal for his sole personal benefit to take advantage of the temporarily and artificially depressed stock price," which "benefited Prosser to the same extent that it disadvantaged the minority stockholders who were now being squeezed out of the enterprise." Id. Moreover, "the transaction was also unfairly structured, in that Prudential and Cahill, the firms that had been retained as advisors to ECM in the initially Proposed (but later abandoned) Merger, were co-opted by Prosser to serve as his advisors." Id.

The court also concluded that the minority shareholders were not represented adequately because "a majority of the full board of ECM ... were beholden to Prosser and, thus, were not independent of him," " a majority of the Special Committee ... were beholden to, and therefore not independent of, Prosser," and 'the only arguably independent Committee member" was "inadequate to represent the interests of ECM's minority shareholders effectively" because of "the severe information imbalance that existed between the two 'bargaining' sides." Id. at **33-36.

Accordingly, the court held that the "transaction, and the $10.25 per share merger price that has been adjudicated as unfair, were the product of unfair dealing." Id. at *38. However, "because ECM's §102(b)(7) charter provision exculpates those directors found to have violated *solely* their duty of care from liability for money damages," the court also addressed the nature of the fiduciary duty violated. Id. For Prosser and certain other defendants for whom there was evidence they "affirmatively colluded with Prosser to effectuate the Privatization, or that they otherwise deliberately engaged in conduct disloyal to the minority stockholders' interests . . . [and] knew or had reason to believe, that the merger price was unfair," the court held that these defendants were liable for breaching their fiduciary duty of loyalty. Id. at *41. As for the remaining director defendants, however, the court concluded that there was "no persuasive evidence that . . . [their] conduct [was] more egregious than breaches of their duty of care," particularly since there was no evidence that any of these defendants "intentionally conspired with Prosser . . . to obscure the true purpose of benefiting Prosser at the expense of the minority stockholders," or "acted with conscious and intentional disregard of their responsibilities, or made decisions with knowledge that they lacked material information." Id. at **42-43.

C. Corporate Control Transactions

1. *In re Cox Communications, Inc. Shareholders Litig.,* No. Civ. A. 613-N, 2005 WL 1355478 (Del. Ch. June 6, 2005).

The Cox decision addresses a request for fees that the Plaintiffs' attorneys allegedly earned in a suit attacking the Cox family's offer to take Cox Communications, Inc. ("Cox") private via merger. The Court, finding that the Plaintiffs took no appreciable risk, and lending no credence to the notion that the Plaintiffs' actions had a substantially important impact on the pricing of the transaction, awarded a substantially smaller fee than the $4.95 million the attorneys requested. In re Cox Comms., Inc. S'Holders Litig., No. Civ. A. 613-N, 2005 WL 1355478, at **1-2 (Del. Ch. June 6, 2005).

As of summer 2004, Cox was a publicly traded company listed on the New York Stock Exchange. Around that time, the Cox family, which controlled 74% of Cox's voting power, decided to take the company private, and on August 1, 2004, the family previewed its plans to buy-out the company's public shareholders for a price of $32 per share with Cox's board. Id. at *3. In a letter to the board following that meeting, the Cox family clarified that it expected Cox to form a Special Committee to respond to and negotiate the proposal, and the proposal itself specifically required approval by the Special Committee. Id.

A public announcement of the proposal the following morning, before the markets opened, set the Special Committee to work in negotiating the proposal, and sent Plaintiffs racing to the court house. By the end of the day, six complaints had been filed claiming that an offer of $32 per share was an unfair price for the public's shares in Cox. Id. at *4. Plaintiffs' counsel was selected after a "food fight" for lead counsel status. See id. at *5.

Over the course of the coming months, the negotiations of the transaction and the progression of the litigation took parallel paths to the same end. In what became a fairly established routine, the Special Committee's representatives dealt directly with the Cox family and its representatives, while Plaintiffs dealt almost exclusively with the Cox family's litigation counsel. See id. at *7. Eventually, negotiations between the Cox family and the Special Committee settled on an offer of $34.75 per share, which the Special Committee agreed to recommend to the Cox board as a whole. After learning of this development, the Cox family's litigation counsel called the Plaintiffs' counsel and relayed $34.75 per share as the family's "best and final offer" to settle the litigation. Id. The next day, Plaintiffs' counsel orally accepted the offer, subject to a Minority Approval Condition. Id. at *8. At the same time, the Special Committee's financial advisors were finalizing their analyses of whether they could provide a fairness opinion on the merger, and the Special Committee was negotiating the terms of a final merger agreement with the Cox family.

The merger agreement was finalized on October 18, 2004; the Special Committee got favorable fairness indications from its advisors that same day; the full Cox board voted to approve the deal that same day; and, the relevant lawyers entered into a memorandum of understanding settling the litigation. The Memorandum of Understanding stated that the Cox family acknowledged the desirability of settling the action, and acknowledged that the efforts of the Plaintiffs' counsel in the action were causal factors leading the Cox family to increase its bid to $34.75 per share. The family also agreed therein to a Minority Approval Condition. The next day, October 19, 2004, the Special Committee, on behalf of the company, and the Cox family signed the merger agreement. See id. at *8.

The parties to the litigation quickly entered into a stipulation of settlement, then negotiated the Plaintiffs' attorneys' fees of $4.95 million. See id. at *8. Upon presentation of the agreement to the Court for approval, no one objected to the terms of the merger, but an objection was interposed with respect to the Plaintiffs' attorneys' fees. See id. at *9.

The Court's analysis began by noting the procedural advantage a plaintiff has in this type of situation as a result of the Delaware Supreme Court's decision in Kahn v. Lynch Communications, Inc., 638 A.2d 1110 (Del. 1994). See Cox at *13. Pursuant to Lynch, and regardless of the procedural protections employed, a merger with a controlling stockholder is always subject to the "entire fairness" standard, even if it was negotiated and approved by a special committee of independent directors and subject to approval by a majority of disinterested shares. See id. at *12. Under such conditions, the best that a Lynch defendant, such as the Cox family, can hope for is a burden shift to the Plaintiffs (see id. at *12), as Lynch makes it impossible for a defendant to obtain dismissal of such claims on the pleadings. See id. at *15. The party filing a Lynch attack on the "entire fairness" of a proposed merger "can satisfy [the] Rule 11 [pleading standard] as to that [Lynch] allegation because financial fairness is a debatable issue and the plaintiff has at least a colorable positions." Id. This, the Objectors claimed and the Court acknowledged, creates an incentive for plaintiffs (or more accurately, Plaintiffs' attorneys) to nominally impede a going private merger transaction despite the safe guards in place. See id. In questioning the utility and motives underlying such suits, the Court twice emphasizes:

> In no instance has there been a situation when the [controlling stockholder's] lawyer told the plaintiffs' lawyer this is my best and final offer and received the answer "sign up your deal with the special committee, and we'll meet you in the Chancellor's office for the scheduling conference on our motion to expedite." Rather, in every instance, the plaintiffs' lawyers have concluded that the price obtained by the special committee was sufficiently attractive, and that the acceptance of a settlement at that price was warranted.

Id. at 17. What benefit, if any, such litigation brings to the merger process is thus seriously in doubt.

The Court's frustration with the procedural limitations enshrined in Lynch led the Court to add a final section to its opinion, titled "A Coda on the Jurisdictional Elephant in the Corner." Id. at *34. There, although not dispositive to the case at bar, the Court espouses "the need to adjust our common law of corporations to take appropriate account of the positive and negative consequences flowing from the standard of review governing going private transactions." Id. Lynch's purported failure to provide additional incentives for the use of Minority Settlement Conditions is "less than useful." Id. As the court noted, a defendant's inability to dismiss a Lynch claim on the pleadings "has generated perverse incentives for both defense and plaintiffs' counsel that cast doubt on the integrity of the representative litigation process." Id.

The Court added that "a relatively modest alteration of Lynch would do much to ensure this type of integrity, while continuing to provide important, and I would argue, enhanced, protections for minority stockholders." Id. at 35 (emphasis in original). In the Court's proposal, if a controller proposed a merger that was subject from its inception to negotiation and approval by an independent special committee and a Minority Approval Condition, the business judgment rule should presumptively apply. Id.

> In that situation, the controller and the directors of the affected company should be able to obtain dismissal of a complaint unless: 1) the plaintiffs plead particularized facts that the special committee was not independent or was not effective because of its own breach of fiduciary duty or wrongdoing by the controller (e.g., fraud on the committee); or 2) the approval of the minority stockholders was tainted by misdisclosure or actual or structural coercion.

Id. at 35. Nevertheless, despite the Court's proposal, the Court had to decide the instant case on the law and facts available.

Thus, the Court was "dragged into an academic debate of considerable complexity." Id. at *24. The Court, after examining the differences between going private via merger versus tender offer (which avoids Lynch litigation), largely to buttress its Coda on Lynch described above, settled on application of the standard for awarding attorneys fees set forth in Sugarland Indus., Inc. v. Thomas (420 A.2d 142, 147-50 (Del. 1980)).

In deciding to apply the Sugarland factors, which the Court labeled "the traditional factors that govern the size of the fee that should be awarded to the plaintiffs when they have been party to a settlement that the court found to be fair and reasonable to the class[,]" the Court declined to apply the attorneys' fees standards set forth in Chrysler Corp. v. Dann, 223 A.2d 384 (Del. 1966). Cox at **27-32.

Under the Dann standard, to receive their fees, the Plaintiffs would have had to establish that "the action in which they are sought must have had merit at the time it was filed. ... [And], a claim is meritorious within the meaning of the rule if it can withstand a motion to dismiss on the pleadings if, at the same time, the plaintiff possesses knowledge or provable facts which hold out some reasonable likelihood of ultimate success." Id. at *28. The Court then noted that it agreed with the Objectors "that there is no doubt that the plaintiffs' complaints were not meritorious when filed." Id. The Plaintiffs' complaint contained only conclusory allegations with respect to a moving target (the Cox family's offer, which was still being negotiated as the various complaints were filed), and the negotiations were being handled by a special committee who's integrity had not been attacked. Id. at **28-29. "The only purpose of their complaints was to act as a placeholder for a possible later attack on an actual fiduciary judgment of the Cox board to enter into a formal merger agreement with the Family. The complaints were therefore unripe and without merit." Id. at *29.

Despite its appeal, though, the Court notes that the Dann inquiry is usually applied in circumstances where the Court must decide to what extent a derivative suit actually caused a corporate defendant to act in a manner consistent with those plaintiffs' demands. Id. at *27. "The prior cases, therefore, all arise in the context of situations when the party objecting to the fee—most often, the corporation itself—denies that the plaintiffs' litigation efforts benefited them at all and that it would therefore be inequitable for them to be forced to contribute to a fee." Id. at 30. The court thus ultimately chooses the Sugarland test, refusing to hold "that the rigid Dann standard applies to an objection to a fee made by a party who does not object to the fairness of the settlement itself, will not be forced to bear any of the fee, and who does not contend that the defendants reduced any benefit they would have otherwise provided to the class by the amount of the fee they agreed to pay[.]" Id. at *32.

The "aptly named 'Sugarland' factors, which the Court ultimately applied, include: 1) the benefits achieved in the action; 2) the efforts of counsel and the time spent in connection with the case; 3) the contingent nature of the case; 4) the difficulty of the litigation; and 5) the standing and ability of counsel." Id.

In reference to the Sugarland factors, the Court stated, "I have absolutely no reason to believe that the plaintiffs are responsible for more than a very small amount of the difference between the original offer and the negotiated price." Id. at *32. The Court could discern no appreciable risk that the Plaintiffs' attorneys took in pressing their case when they knew the Cox family would almost certainly raise their bid to satisfy the Special Committee, and that the Cox family knew there was value in resolving the suit, as it could not be dismissed on the pleadings per Lynch. Id. at **32-33. Weighing these factors, the Court denied Plaintiffs' attorneys' the $4.95 million they sought, yet "awarded a fee larger than I otherwise would have. I do so by awarding a total award of fees and expenses of $1.275 million. That could be translated into an award of $500 per hour for 2000 hours worked, plus the full payment of expenses. Given the factors outlined above, that is a more than generous award." Id. at *34.

2. *Orman v. Cullman,* No. Civ. A. 18039, 2004 WL 2348395 (Del. Ch. Oct. 20, 2004).

Orman v. Cullman, No. Civ. A. 18039, 2004 WL 2348395 (Del. Ch. Oct. 20, 2004), revisits Delaware law interpreting voting lock-up agreements in the context of going private transactions. Orman is the first decision since the Delaware Supreme Court's ruling in Omnicare, Inc. v. NCS Healthcare Inc., 818 A.2d 914 (Del. 2003), to address the validity of deal protection devices.

Orman involved a claim against the board of General Cigar Holdings, Inc. ("General Cigar") for breach of their fiduciary duties in negotiating a merger transaction with Swedish Match AB ("Swedish Match"). Orman at *1. Swedish Match approached General Cigar in 1999 to propose the possibility of acquiring a significant stake in General Cigar, while leaving Cullman family members in management positions. Id. at *1. In response, the General Cigar board formed a special committee to evaluate the proposal and make recommendations to the full board. Id. at *2. The negotiations resulted in an agreement whereby General Cigar would merge with a Swedish Match subsidiary, and the public stockholders of General Cigar would receive $15.00 per share, a significant premium over the market price. Id.

As a condition to entering into the merger agreement, Swedish Match demanded that the Cullman family enter into a voting agreement in which they agreed to vote their shares against any alternative acquisition for 12 months following termination of the pending merger agreement. Id. at *2. In January 2000, the General Cigar special committee received word that Swedish Match was willing to increase its offer from $15.00 per share to $15.25, but the increase was contingent upon extension of the Cullman family lock-up from 12 months to 18. Id. at *3. General Cigar's investment advisor, Deutsche Bank, was on hand during that meeting, and opined that $15.25 was a fair price to the public shareholders. Id. Thus, on January 19, 2000, the special committee voted unanimously to recommend the merger to the full board, which subsequently met and approved the merger. Id. The merger agreement was announced on January 20, 2005. Id.

The merger agreement allowed General Cigar to entertain unsolicited bids for the business, if, upon recommendation of the special committee, the General Cigar board determined such proposals were *bona fides*, and would be more favorable to the public stockholder than the proposed merger with Swedish Match. Id. at *3. Likewise, the merger agreement permitted the General Cigar board to withdraw support for the merger agreement if they determined, upon consultation with outside counsel, that their fiduciary duties required them to do so. Id. Importantly, the merger agreement required that the merger be put to a vote of General Cigar's stockholders, and provided that the merger was conditioned upon approval by a majority of the public stockholders. Id.

General Cigar filed the proxy statement with respect to the shareholder vote on April 10, 2000, and on May 8, 2000, the public stockholders (i.e., "a majority of the minority") overwhelmingly approved the merger. Id. at *3.

Plaintiff, in reliance on Paramount Communications, Inc. v. QVC Network, Inc., 637 A.2d 34 (Del. 1994), and Omnicare, argued that the Cullmans had breached their fiduciary duties "by entering into the voting agreement" (i.e., the lock-up agreement). Orman at *5. In Paramount, the Delaware Supreme Court stated: "To the extent that a contract, or a provision thereof, purports to require a board to act or not act in such a fashion as to limit the exercise of fiduciary duties, it is invalid and unenforceable." Paramount, 637 A.2d at 51. The Court noted that Omnicare makes a similar observation.

The Court did not question the validity of this jurisprudence, but noted that such a statement did not apply to the case at bar. Id. at *5. In granting summary judgment in favor of the Defendants, the Court noted that in Paramount and Omnicare, the challenged action was the directors' entering into a contract as directors, while the Cullman family was entering into the voting agreement as shareholders. Id. "Nothing in the voting agreement prevented the Cullmans from exercising their duties as officers and directors." Id. Hence, the Cullmans could still have voted to withdraw their support of the merger agreement if they felt so inclined because of their fiduciary duties as officers and directors of the corporation.

The Court then turned to the question of whether the public shareholders' assent to the merger was "coerced." The Court, by reference to Omnicare, applied the two-step analysis in Unocal Corp. v. Mesa Petroleum Co., 493 A.2d 946 (Del. 1985), as dispositive. The court noted that deal protection devices, even when such devices protect a deal that does not result in a change of control, require enhanced scrutiny. Orman at *6. The Court thus framed the analysis as follows:

> The first stage of the Unocal analysis requires a board to demonstrate "that they have reasonable grounds for believing that a danger to corporate policy and effectiveness existed" without such measures. The second stage of Unocal proceeds in two steps: the board must establish that the deal protection devices are (1) not coercive or preclusive and (2) within a range of reasonable responses to the danger to corporate policy and effectiveness.

Id. at *6 (citations omitted).

In applying the first stage of the analysis (a task the Court labeled "simple") the Court found that during negotiations, Swedish Match required some form of deal protection. See id. at *7. If the General Cigar board had refused to meet Swedish Match's requirements, they would be left with no alternative deal. See id. This lack of alternatives, in and of itself, the Court holds as reasonable grounds to believe that a danger to corporate policy and effectiveness existed, "[a]s in Omnicare itself[,]" justifying some degree of deal protection. Id.

The Court also found application of Unocal's second stage of analysis to be "straightforward." The Court found the standard for determining whether a deal protection device is coercive was set forth in Williams v. Geier, 671 A.2d 1368 (Del. 1995). See Orman at *7 That is, "[t]he measures are improper if they 'have the effect of causing the stockholders to vote in favor of the proposed transaction for some reason other than the merits of that transaction.'" Orman at *7, quoting Williams, 671 A.2d at 1382-83.

The Court found that because the deal would not have occurred without inclusion of the deal protection devices, those devices were an integral part of the merits of the transaction. Orman at *7. As the deal protection devices were thus part of the merits of the transaction—necessary for the transaction to move forward, if at all—"General Cigar's public shareholders were not encouraged to vote in favor of the Swedish Match transaction for reasons unrelated to the transaction's merits. ... [N]othing in this record suggests that the lock-up had the effect of causing General Cigar's stockholders to vote in favor of the proposed transaction for some reason other than the merits of that transaction." Id. at *7. The Court concludes the first prong of the second stage of Unocol analysis as follows:

> Because General Cigar's public shareholders retained the power to reject the proposed transaction with Swedish Match, the fiduciary out negotiated by General Cigar's board was a meaningful and effective one, it gave the General Cigar board power to recommend that the shareholders veto the Swedish Match deal. That is to say, had the board determined that it needed to recommend that General Cigar's shareholders reject the transaction, the shareholders were fully empowered to act upon that recommendation because the public shareholders (those not "locked-up" in the voting agreement) retained the power to reject the proposed merger. For these reasons, I conclude as a matter of law that the deal protection mechanisms present here were not impermissibly coercive.

Id.

In the second prong of the second stage of the Unocal analysis, the Court turned to the question of whether the Cullman's voting agreement fell within a range of reasonable responses to the pending danger to corporate policy and effectiveness. Id. at *8. The Court found that without the lock-up, General Cigar would have lost the Swedish Match deal, the public stockholders would have lost the premium they stood to gain on their shares, and no other suitor was waiting in the wings with an equally attractive offer for the company. See id. Given such circumstances, the Court found that General Cigar's board "should therefore be afforded the maximum latitude regarding its decision to recommend the Swedish Match merger." Id.

3. ***Hollinger Inc. v. Hollinger Int'l, Inc.,* 858 A.2d 342 (Del. Ch. 2004).**

In Hollinger Inc. v. Hollinger Int'l, Inc., 858 A.2d 342 (Del. Ch. 2004), the Delaware Court of Chancery examines the bounds of section 271 of Delaware's General Corporations Law with respect to an asset sale by a subsidiary, and the parent corporation's attempt to force a shareholder vote with respect to that sale. Section 271 provides the directors of Delaware corporations with the right to sell "all or substantially all of its property and assets, including goodwill and corporate franchises" only upon approval by stockholder vote. Id. at 376.

In Hollinger, Plaintiff Hollinger Inc. ("Hollinger"), as controlling stockholder, sought to enjoin its subsidiary, Hollinger International, Inc. ("International") from selling the Telegraph Group, Ltd. (the "Telegraph Group"), an indirect subsidiary wholly owned by International that publishes London's Telegraph newspaper. Id. at 346. In addition to its section 271 argument, Hollinger also claimed that equity demanded a stockholder vote, lest Hollinger, as controlling stockholder, be relegated to the position of the average stockholder. The Court rejected both of Hollinger's arguments.

With respect to the section 271 argument, the Court held that selling the Telegraph Group was not tantamount to a sale of all, or substantially all, of International's assets. Under Delaware's jurisprudence, particularly "the seminal § 271 decision, Gimbel v. Signal Cos." (316 A.2d 599 (Del. Ch. 1974) aff'd, 316 A.2d 619 (Del. 1974)) the Court was not free to limit its discussion to balance sheets and economics, but was compelled to pursue the section 271 inquiry down two parallel lines of analysis: whether the Telegraph Group sale represented International selling all of its assets on (a) a quantitative basis, or (b) on a qualitative basis. The Court ultimately decided that the sale triggered neither aspect of section 271.

The Court's "quantitative" interpretation of section 271 with respect to the Telegraph Group sale turned on questions of economics. International, prior to the Telegraph Group sale, controlled four groups of newspapers, in Israel, Canada, Chicago, and the United Kingdom. See id. at 352-354. The Chicago group and the United Kingdom group (i.e., the Telegraph Group) were far and away International's most valuable assets, with 2003 EBITDAs of approximately $80 million and $57 million respectively, compared to slightly negative 2003 EBITDAs for the other two groups. See id.

The Court found, using bids that International had received for both the Chicago group and the Telegraph Group as its basis for comparison, that the Telegraph Group accounted for 56-57% of International's asset value, while the Chicago group accounted for 43-44%. Id. at 380.

Despite the Telegraph Group's significance as an asset by that measure, the Court held that by relative contribution to International's total revenues, the Telegraph Group accounted for less than 50% during the preceding three years. Id. at 380. Further, in terms of book value, neither the Telegraph Group nor the Chicago group approached 50% of International's asset value, because International's other operating groups and non-operating assets had value. Returning then to EBITDA, the Court determined, "[t]he picture that emerges is one of rough equality between the two [Chicago and Telegraph] Groups—with any edge tilting in the Chicago Group's direction." Id. at 382. After noting that the future financial prospects of both groups appeared substantially similar, the Court concluded its "quantitative" analysis as follows:

> The evidence therefore reveals that neither the Telegraph Group nor the Chicago group is quantitatively vital in the sense used in the Gimbel test. Although both Groups are profitable, valuable economic assets and although the Telegraph Group is somewhat more valuable than the Chicago Group, International can continue as a profitable entity without either one of them. International is not a human body, and the Telegraph and the Chicago group are not its heart and liver. International is a business. Neither one of the two groups is "vital"—i.e., "necessary to the continuation of [International's] life" or "necessary to [its] continued existence or effectiveness." Rather, a sale of either Group leaves International as a profitable entity, even if it chooses to distribute a good deal of the cash it receives from the Telegraph sale to its stockholders through a dividend or share repurchase.

Id. at 383 (citation omitted) (emphasis in original).

The Court then expressed its frustration with the "qualitative" aspects of the Gimbel test as "more than a tad unclear." Id. at 383. If the assets for sale are not "quantitatively" vital to a corporation's life, "it is not altogether apparent how they can 'substantially affect the existence and purpose of' the corporation within the meaning of Gimbel, suggesting either that the two elements of the test are actually not distinct or that they are redundant." Id. (citation omitted). Nevertheless, the Court endeavored to operate the Gimbel analysis under the following interpretation: "[The qualitative Gimbel] element is not satisfied if the court merely believes that the economic assets being sold are aesthetically superior to those being retained; rather, the qualitative element of Gimbel focuses on economic quality and, at most, on whether the transaction leaves the stockholders with an investment that in economic terms is qualitatively different than the one that they now possess." Id. at 384.

Hollinger's arguments stressed, with respect to Gimbel's qualitative element, the journalistic superiority of the Telegraph Group over International's other publications, and the social cachet associated with the Telegraph. Id at 383. Allegedly, to sell International's most prestigious possession would leave International owning the Chicago Sun-Times, the "Second Paper in the Second City", as its flagship publication. Id. at 384. Hollinger alleged that this would fundamentally, qualitatively transform International. Id. The Court rejected this aspect of Hollinger's argument, and after noting Gimbel's focus on the economic quality of planned asset sale, reminded the reader that "[e]ven with that focus, it must be remembered that the qualitative element is a gloss on the statutory language 'substantially all' and not on an attempt to identify qualitatively important transactions but ones that 'strike at the heart of the corporation's existence.'" Id. at 384, quoting Gimbel, 317 A.2d at 606.

The Court went on to note that when International went public, it did not own the Telegraph Group, and frequently bought and sold a variety of publications. Id. This, the Court notes, indicates that no International investor would assume that any of International's assets were "sacrosanct." Id. In fact, International had been so active in the M&A community that the Court observed the purchase or sale of any particular line of operations had become part of Internationals ordinary course of business. Id.

After noting that selling the Telegraph Group neither stuck at the heart of International, nor significantly deviated from International's common practices in the M&A market, the Court made the following observation: "Even more importantly, investors in public companies do not invest their money because they derive social status from owning shares in a corporation whose controlling manager can have dinner with the Queen. Whatever the social importance of the Telegraph in Great Britain, the economic value of that importance to International as an entity is what matters for the Gimbel test, not how cool it would be to be the Telegraph's publisher." Id. at 384.

The result of the Court's analysis concludes that because International's stockholders will remain, after the Telegraph sale, "investors in a publication company with profitable operating assets, a well-regarded tabloid newspaper of good reputation and large circulation [(i.e., the Chicago Sun-Times)], a prestigious newspaper in Israel, and other valuable assets[,]" the Telegraph sale was not "qualitatively" a sale of all, or substantially all, of International's assets. Id. In short, "[w]hile important, the sale of the Telegraph does not strike a blow to International's heart." Id.

Outside of the section 271 arguments discussed above, the Court also denied Hollinger's argument that principals of equity required a stockholder vote on the telegraph sale. Id at 386. This argument apparently went through a number of iterations over the course of briefing and argument, but can be summarized here in its two core assertions. First, Hollinger argued that because Hollinger's controlling stockholder, Conrad Black, and his affiliates on the International board had been excluded from the board committee reviewing International's options, equity demanded a stockholder vote. Id. at 387.

The Court, in rebuffing this assertion, noted that controlling stockholders have no inalienable right under the law to usurp the authority of the directors they elect. Id. Rather, like all other stockholders, a controlling stockholder must accept the informed, good faith business decisions of the directors unless the Delaware Corporations Law requires a vote. Id. Likewise, with respect to the equitable portion of such analysis, the Court noted that there is no reason why a controlling stockholder should hold veto power over asset sales when other, dispersed stockholders lack such rights. Id. After all, the controlling stockholder is often (and in this case was) able to participate directly in the identification and selection of the board. Id. The Court also notes that Hollinger apparently offered no means by which to resolve just when equity would demand recognition of a controlling stockholder's "special, natural law right to vote[.]" Id.

Further fatal to Hollinger's demand for a vote premised on equity was the fact that Hollinger was essentially trying to "undermine the decisions of independent directors its own controlling stockholder, Conrad Black, selected." Id. at 387-88. Hollinger, at the time, was suffering under an injunction and judicial orders that would have opened it to significant liability if it interfered with International's board or operations, so it was not as free as it otherwise would have been to influence the International board's actions. Id. Nevertheless, these restrictions on Hollinger's influence were brought about because it, along with and at the insistence of Black, "posed a legally cognizable threat to the rights and best interests of International and its public stockholders." Id. at 388. Hollinger thus "[had] only itself and its controlling stockholder, inside management, and directors to blame." Id.

Given the obvious tensions in Hollinger's first equitable argument, in its reply brief the argument had transformed into a Van Gorkum argument. See id. at 388, citing Smith v. Van Gorkum, 488 A.2d 858 (Del. 1985). Hollinger grounded this claim in the idea that the International board had acted in a grossly negligent manner in agreeing to sell the Telegraph Group rather than retain it and focus on improving returns from continuing operation. Hollinger at 388. The Court faulted Hollinger's position for slighting a "mountain" of evidence to the contrary. Id. In analyzing the evidence before it, the Court noted that Van Gorkum had involved "a finding that independent directors who accepted a large premium for selling an entire company were grossly negligent because they did not shop the company first, did not obtain a banker's opinion, and supposedly did not retain sufficient leeway to do a post-signing market check." Id. at 390. Noting that the Van Gorkum opinion stuck many commentators as "wrong-headed," the Court decided that enjoining the sale at issue "would represent a vigorous tightening of the Van Gorkum screw[,]" which the Court was not willing to tighten on the facts as it read them:

> By stark contract [to Van Gorkum], here, a group of independent directors worked with an interim CEO, who bears every indicium of independence ... , to fully expose International to the marketplace in a process designed by qualified investment bankers. The independent directors did not simply market the asset they ultimately sold; they marketed the whole company and every one of its assets. During that process, the investment banker did as it should have and tried to convince potential buyers to pay an even higher price for both the company and the Telegraph group than was finally approved. ... In the course of their process, the independent directors considered the risks facing the operations they were selling and a detailed financial analysis of the worth of those operations ... . Only after doing that and concluding that the price they were receiving ... was an attractive one when compared to the utility of retaining those assets did the [review committee] vote. I cannot call such a process irrational or grossly negligent without distorting the meaning of those concepts.

Hollinger, at 390-91.

D. Duty of Oversight

1. *Saito v. McCall,* No. Civ. A. 17132-NC, 2004 WL 3029876 (Del. Ch. Dec. 20, 2004).

In Saito v. McCall the Delaware Court of Chancery provided insight with respect to directors' duty of oversight by demonstrating a willingness to impute knowledge from individual directors to the board as a whole. This presumption of collective knowledge formed the basis of the Court's refusal do dismiss a claim that the Defendant board of directors failed to fulfill its oversight responsibilities, and further lays the foundation for the Plaintiffs' assertion of demand futility with respect to a board interconnected by the knowledge of accounting impropriety.

In January of 1999, McKesson Corporation ("McKesson"), a healthcare supply management company, merged with HBO & Company ("HBOC"), a provider of healthcare software. See Saito v. McCall, No. Civ. A. 17132-NC, 2004 WL 3029876, at *1, 2 (Del. Ch. Dec. 20, 2004). The transaction, whereby McKesson paid $14 billion in McKesson stock to acquire HBOC closed on January 12, 1999, following the approval of the HBOC and McKesson shareholders. Id. at **2, 3.

Upon acquiring HBOC, McKesson changed it's name to McKesson HBOC, Inc. ("McKesson-HBOC"), but the merged entity was soon forced to face accounting improprieties it inherited from HBOC. See id. at *2. The public learned of these alleged improprieties through a series of disclosures between April and July of 1999. See id. at *4. These improprieties included the following:

- On April 28, 1999, McKesson-HBOC announced that it would restate its earnings from previous quarters. Id. at *4.
- On May 25, 1999, McKesson-HBOC announced that it would further revise its results downward. Id.
- On June 21, 1999, McKesson-HBOC announced that Richard Hawkins, the CFO of McKesson-HBOC both before and after the merger, and Mark Pulido, the CEO of McKesson-HBOC both before and after the merger, had resigned from their positions; and, that Charles McCall, the former CEO of HBOC and chairman of McKesson-HBOC's board following the merger, had been stripped of his position. Id.

- On July 14, 1999, the Company announced that its previously reported restatements would be larger than originally revealed. Id.
- On July 16, 1999, McKesson-HBOC submitted an SEC filing concededing that HBOC's financial statements were inaccurate because of improper accounting. Id.

It took plaintiffs only two days from the first of these announcements to file the original complaint in Saito ("the product of a race to the courthouse[.]" Id. at **1, 4 n.25.). Following multiple attempts, plaintiffs ultimately filed a fourth amended complaint (the "Complaint"), which was the target of a variety of motions to dismiss. Id.

The central allegations of the Complaint were: "(1) that HBOC's directors and senior officers presided over a fraudulent accounting scheme; (2) that McKesson's officers, directors, and advisors learned of HBOC's fraudulent scheme during their due diligence into the proposed Merger, but nonetheless McKesson's board approved the Merger; and (3) that the McKesson-HBOC board acted too slowly in rectifying the accounting problems at HBOC after the Merger was completed." Id. at *1. Of the thirteen counts of alleged wrongdoing, the Court dismissed or stayed the majority (Counts I-IV, VI-VIII) on procedural grounds (generally lack of standing, ripeness, or failure to properly alleged demand futility), with the exception of Count V against McKesson-HMOC's directors, alleging violations of their Caremark duty of oversight. See Saito at **11, 6; see also, In re Caremark Int'l Inc. Deriv. Litig., 698 A.2d 959 (Del. Ch. 1996).

Count V of the Complaint sought redress against the McKesson-HBOC directors for "'failing to timely correct HBOC's false financial statements, monitor the accounting practices of McKesson-HBOC following the merger, implement sufficient internal controls to guard against the wrongful practices they knew about before the Merger and disclose HBOC's false financial statements.'" Saito at *6 (citation omitted). The Court had dismissed this claim before, without prejudice, encouraging the Plaintiffs to "'use the tools at hand' to 'develop additional particularized facts in order to allege properly an oversight claim that will meet the demand futility standard and to avoid the standing requirement of Delaware's continuing ownership rule.'" Id. at *1, quoting Ash v. McCall, No. Civ. A.

17132, 2000 WL 1370341, at *58 (Del. Ch. Sept. 15, 2000). The Court introduced its analysis of this claim by noting that "[h]ere, after using the 'tools at hand,' the complaint appears—barely—to state a claim under Caremark." Id. at *6 (citation omitted).

In framing its analysis, the Court noted Plaintiff's admission that in order for the Caremark claim to survive in the instant context, plaintiff had to show that the McKesson-HBOC board "(1) should have known that the unlawful accounting improprieties were occurring or had occurred; and (2) made no good faith effort to remedy the unlawful accounting improprieties." Id. at *6.

In resolving the first part of this inquiry, the court held that the following facts demonstrated sufficient knowledge on behalf of McKesson-HBOC's board to survive a motion to dismiss:

- The HBOC audit committee knew, through a 1998 meeting to discuss its 1997 audit with its auditor, Arthur Anderson ("Anderson"), that the 1997 audit was "high risk." The committee discussed the accounting-related risks inherent to the software industry, and specifically discussed risks arising from certain HBOC sales practices. Id. at **7, 2.

- At a July 10, 1998, meeting, the McKesson board came to learn that HBOC had some problems with its accounting practices. Id. at **7, 2.

- Later that fall, after a stall in negotiations, the McKesson board knew that the issues highlited in the July 10, 1998, board meeting had not been resolved, and that HBOC's accounting practices presented at least a $40 to $55 million problem. Id. at *7.

The Court reasoned that the knowledge of HBOC's accounting improprieties could be imputed to the board of the merged McKesson-HBOC through the following chain of relationships: at least four members of HBOC's board knew of the accounting improprieties. See id. at *7 n.68 And, "[a] reasonable inference, which the Court is entitled to draw at this procedural stage, is that that information [(i.e., knowledge of the audit committee about the accounting problems)] was communicated to the other HBOC board members who later served on McKesson-HBOC's board." Id. Likewise, approaching the question of McKesson-HBOC's board from the McKesson side of the merger, the Court notes that after the McKesson board had approved the merger on October 16, 1998, they learned the HBOC fired its CFO, Jay Gilbertson. See id at *7, 2.

Furthermore, shortly after the merger closed, the combined McKesson-HBOC audit committee met on January 27, 1999, with its advisers to discuss the transaction. Id. at *7. That discussion concerned accounting adjustments made to HBOC's financial statements in the same areas that had been highlighted to McKesson's board in a July 12, 1998, conference call among McKesson's CFO, Bear Stearns & Co., and Deloitte & Touche LLP (Bear Stearns rendered a fairness opinion on the merger to McKesson's directors, and Deloitte & Touche served as McKesson's auditor and also conducted due diligence on the merger for McKesson). See id. at *7, 2, 1.

As a result, the Court concluded the "knowledge" prong of its Caremark analysis, as it applied to the facts then at bar, as follows:

> Thus, viewing the above facts in a light most favorable to plaintiffs, it can be argued that the McKesson-HBOC board, a board comprised of directors from both sides of the transaction, knew or should have know that the HBOC accounting problems were unlawful. At a minimum, the new board's audit committee was comprised of directors from McKesson who should have known HBOC accounting practices were problematic. Those directors, regardless of their pre-Merger knowledge of the accounting problems, now had the benefit of serving with former HBOC directors who also should have known not only the existence of those problems but the extent of the problems.

Saito, at *7.

Having satisfied itself (for purposes of surviving a motion to dismiss) that the McKesson-HBOC board had knowledge of HBOC's accounting problems upon, or shortly following the merger, the Court turned to the several months that passed between gaining this knowledge and revealing it to the public in piecemeal fashion, from April through July of 1999. See id. While recognizing the tenuous nature of this claim, the court found that "[a]lthough the facts later adduced may prove otherwise, the procedural posture of the case requires [the Court] to focus of the plaintiffs' complaint and read it generously. Viewed in that manner, [the oversight count] survives defendants' motion to dismiss." Id.

Finally, with respect to demand futility, the Court proposed the following question: "[W]hether the plaintiffs can refute the presumption that McKesson-HBOC's board of directors could have properly exercised its independent and disinterested business judgment in responding to a demand." Id. at *7 n.71. Citing its conclusion that the combined McKesson-HBOC board had enough resources ("namely each other") to discover the extent of HBOC's accounting deficiencies once the merger was consummated, and concluding that a demand on the board in April 1999 would directly implicate the McKesson-HBOC audit committee's good faith, "[t]he substantial likelihood of liability these directors faced for a breach of their duty of good faith disabled the entire McKesson-HBOC board from mustering an independent and disinterested majority." Id. By imputing knowledge of HBOC's accounting improprieties from former HBOC board members to the April 1999 board of McKesson-HBOC, and finding a delay of three and a half months before public disclosure unacceptable, the Court concluded that the board's poor exercise of its duty of oversight carried with it the implicit presumption that the board could not exercise good faith in responding to a demand for action at that time. This conclusion validated Plaintiffs' claims of demand futility. Id.

NOTES

CORPORATE GOVERNANCE LITIGATION

20

THE NEW REGULATORY AND ENFORCEMENT ENVIRONMENT

Theodore N. Mirvis
Wachtell, Lipton, Rosen & Katz

Table of Contents

I. INTRODUCTION

In today's highly charged regulatory enforcement climate, investigative proceedings are a fact of life. Indeed, during the last two fiscal years, the SEC has brought more than 1,300 civil cases and the Justice Department has brought criminal cases alleging securities-related misconduct against more than 500 defendants. See Stephen M. Cutler, Second Annual General Counsel Roundtable: Tone at the Top: Getting it Right (Dec. 3, 2004).

The federal government is spending more time and resources than ever on corporate investigations and is conducting them in an increasingly aggressive way. No company is immune and the stakes are higher than they have ever been. The level of enforcement activity has increased dramatically, as has the size of the penalties that are assessed. It is therefore incumbent upon the boards and senior management of public companies to understand the government's new expectations and to ensure that the ethics and compliance programs at their firms are state-of-the-art.

To provide that background, this outline begins by describing the government's heightened expectations for companies that come under investigation. As Point II, below, notes, Department of Justice and SEC investigators are increasingly focusing on the nature and quality of a company's cooperation, including more frequent requests for companies to waive the protection of the attorney-client privilege and attorney work-product doctrine. Moreover, as Point III shows, the government has recently revised the standards it uses to evaluate a company's compliance program, and these evaluations weigh heavily in determinations about whether, and, if so, how aggressively, to proceed against companies. Point IV illustrates what can happen when things go wrong, with particular focus on some of the SEC's and the Justice Department's recent cases reflecting markedly increased penalties and more intrusive remedial measures, including the establishment of independent monitors, as well as board committee and management changes.

With these new government expectations as background, this outline turns to a discussion of some of the steps a prudent company should be taking to best position itself in this new regulatory and enforcement environment, including suggestions for designing a more effective compliance and control program, with particular focus on the board's role as set forth in Point V. Point VI offers guidance for managing the corporation's response when, despite all best efforts, a crisis does erupt. Finally, Point VII discusses the SEC's recent enforcement focus on "gatekeepers"—i.e., directors, lawyers, bankers, accountants—who fail to react appropriately when "red flags" warning of possible regulatory problems are waving, or who otherwise do not take sufficient action to avoid wrongdoing.

II. THE GOVERNMENT'S HEIGHTENED EXPECTATIONS FOR COMPANY COOPERATION

A. Justice Department

In 2003, then Deputy Attorney General Larry Thompson issued a memorandum, now known as the Thompson Memorandum, revising guidelines set forth in an earlier document for federal prosecutors to follow in considering the prosecution of a corporation. That memo puts special emphasis on the extent and nature of a company's cooperation as a factor to be weighed by the government in its charging decisions. The guidelines state that the "main focus of the revisions is increased emphasis on and scrutiny of the authenticity of a corporation's cooperation."

The General Principle set forth in Section VI specifies that:

> In determining whether to charge a corporation, that corporation's timely and voluntary disclosure of wrongdoing and its willingness to cooperate with the government's investigation may be relevant factors. In gauging the extent of the corporation's cooperation, the prosecutor may consider the corporation's willingness to identify the culprits within the corporation, including senior executives; to make witnesses available; to disclose the complete results of its internal investigation; and to waive attorney-client and work product protection.

Thus, identifying wrongdoers, encouraging employees to speak with government investigators, fully disclosing the results of any internal investigation and waiver of the attorney-client privilege and work-product protection seem to be expected elements of a company's cooperative efforts.

B. SEC

The extent of a company's cooperation is similarly important to the SEC in connection with its decisions on whether to bring an enforcement proceeding. The SEC has set forth specific criteria it will consider in determining whether, and how much, to credit self-policing, self-reporting, remediation and cooperation in deciding whether to take any enforcement action or bring reduced charges or seek lighter sanctions. See SEC Exchange Act Release No. 44969 (Oct. 23, 2001). The criteria include:

> Did the company promptly make available to our staff the results of its review and provide sufficient documentation reflecting its response to the situation? Did the company identify possible violative conduct and evidence with sufficient precision to facilitate prompt enforcement actions against those who violated the law? Did the company produce a thorough and probing written report detailing the findings of its review? Did the company voluntarily disclose information our staff did not directly request and otherwise might not have uncovered? Did the company ask its employees to cooperate with our staff and make all reasonable efforts to secure such cooperation?

SEC Enforcement Director Stephen Cutler stressed recently that the price of non-cooperation for companies under investigation is rising. Cutler explained that the Commission "is placing a greater emphasis then ever before on assessing and weighing cooperation when making charging and sanctions decisions." See Stephen M. Cutler, Remarks Before the D.C. Bar Assoc. (Feb. 11, 2004). Cutler went on to specify that the Commission is using a "more graduated scale" in assessing cooperation: "In other words, the Commission no longer begins and ends its assessment by asking, 'did this party cooperate, yes or no?' Now, it routinely goes on to consider, if the party did cooperate, how much? How often?" Id. Commentators now argue that the SEC has effectively altered its policy from rewarding cooperation to punishing non-cooperation. See, e.g., David Gourevitch and Seth T. Taube, The SEC Raises The Cost to Companies of Noncooperation, Prevention of Corporate Liability (Jan. 17, 2005).

III. THE GOVERNMENT'S NEW STANDARDS TO MEASURE CORPORATE COMPLIANCE PROGRAMS

A. The Thompson Memo

The Thompson memo also emphasizes that government prosecutors will look hard and critically at the depth and quality of a company's compliance program in connection with charging decisions. The memo states that:

> Compliance programs are established by corporate management to prevent and to detect misconduct and to ensure that corporate activities are conducted in accordance with all applicable criminal and civil laws, regulations, and rules. The Department encourages such corporate self policing, including voluntary disclosures to the government of any problems that a corporation discovers on its own.

However, the existence of a compliance program, without more, is not sufficient to avoid charges. Programs must be designed for "maximum effectiveness in preventing and detecting wrongdoing by employees" and corporate management must enforce the program without "tacitly encouraging" employees to engage in misconduct. Prosecutors are also instructed to determine whether the company's compliance program is merely a "paper program".

B. Sentencing Guidelines

In addition, the Federal Sentencing Commission, in April 2004, approved a set of amendments to the United States Sentencing Guidelines for Organizations, which became effective on November 2004. The amendments make significantly more stringent the guidelines' criteria for effective compliance programs and place greater responsibility on directors and officers for the oversight and management of compliance programs.

The revised Guidelines transform what was previously an application note on how to show "due diligence" into a new section entitled "Effective Compliance and Ethics Program." This new section incorporates both the well-known "seven steps" of an effective compliance program and a number of new requirements. The increased responsibilities of company directors in this process are at the heart of these new requirements. To truly understand the new responsibilities of company directors, one must read both the Guidelines and the accompanying application notes. As Paula Desio, deputy general counsel to the United States Sentencing Commission, recently noted at the annual Ethics Officers Association convention, the application notes tell readers "what the Commission meant." See Changes to Organizational Guidelines Expand Explanation of "Due Diligence", Prevention of Corporate Liability (Nov. 15, 2004).

The revised Guidelines require the following:

Directors Must be Knowledgeable. The revised Guidelines mandate that directors "be knowledgeable about the content and operation of the compliance and ethics program" and "exercise reasonable oversight" with respect to its implementation and effectiveness. Companies should have functioning information channels through which directors are kept abreast of the effectiveness of, and any changes to, compliance programs.

Directors Must be Informed. The revised Guidelines require that the person with "day-to-day" responsibility for overseeing the ethics and compliance function have "direct access to the governing authority" or a designated subgroup thereof. The application notes to the

Guidelines recommend that this person should update the board or its designated subgroup on the status of the program "no less than annually." Companies should therefore set aside a reasonable amount of time during at least one board meeting each year in order to allow substantive presentations and discussion related to the status of the ethics and compliance program.

Directors Must be Trained. The revised Guidelines also direct that all employees, including officers and directors, participate in compliance training programs. Companies should arrange for specialized training for their high-level officers and directors. Such training sessions might consist of dedicated presentations and question/answer periods at an annual board and senior management retreat that is designed, in part, to address these issues.

Annual Compliance Reviews Must be Substantive. When a company conducts its annual review of a company's compliance program, the review should cover all of the key elements of the revised Guidelines, including an assessment of whether:

- the company has adopted "standards and procedures to prevent and detect criminal conduct," including by determining whether appropriately documented ethics policies and procedures designed to assure compliance with these policies are in place;
- the board has adequate resources to meet its obligations to be knowledgeable about the content and operation of the compliance program, including an evaluation of whether the high-level personnel with day-to-day responsibility for the program have sufficient resources, authority and access to the board;
- discretionary authority has not been delegated to those who, based on past behavior, might engage in wrongdoing, including by assessing whether appropriate background checks are being conducted by the company;
- the company requires and provides periodic compliance training for all personnel, including officers and directors;
- the company has adequate "monitoring and auditing" systems and reporting systems in place that allow employees to report criminal or unethical conduct "without fear of retaliation," such as through an ethics hotline that permits anonymous reporting of ethical, legal or regulatory concerns;

- the company promotes incentives for employees to adhere to the compliance program and disincentives to deviate from it; and
- detected violations have been responded to with appropriate steps designed to prevent similar offenses in the future.

A company's ability to demonstrate that it has a well-documented and effective compliance program that is properly monitored by the board may be a significant consideration in a prosecutor's decision whether or not to charge a company if wrongdoing is uncovered and can be an important mitigating factor that reduces an organization's culpability score and fine range. Particularly in light of these recent amendments to the Organizational Guidelines, companies should devote sufficient time and resources to evaluating and improving their existing compliance programs, as failure to do so may expose a company to significant civil and even criminal liability.

C. Recent SEC Speeches

Consistent with these recent developments, the SEC also continues to emphasize the importance of a company's commitment to compliance. In a recent speech, Director of Enforcement Stephen Cutler spoke about the SEC's efforts to "induce" companies to address violations of "tone and culture" and to instill a culture of compliance. See Stephen M. Cutler, Second Annual General Counsel Roundtable: Tone at the Top: Getting It Right (Dec. 3, 2004). Cutler stressed that securities laws violations are often the product of both individual failings and "deficient" corporate culture. He explained that the large penalties imposed on the organizations themselves are part of the SEC's effort to improve the corporate culture and to impose financial penalties that significantly exceed the "cost of doing business."

In terms of maintaining the proper tone at the top, Cutler advised that senior corporate officers must "talk the talk" and "walk the walk". He explained that a company's ethical standards cannot just be contained in a manual that is distributed once or twice a year; they must "infuse the day-to-day lives" of company employees. He emphasized that it must be senior management rather than legal or compliance personnel doing the talking in order to convey the importance of ethics to the organization.

With respect to "walking the walk", Cutler cited eight ways in which a company can create the basis for an improved corporate culture:

- Managers themselves must comply with the letter and the spirit of the rules. If employees see managers bending the rules, they will do it too;
- Character must be made a key part of the firm's set of hiring criteria. The firm must be able to attract and retain people of good moral character;
- Integrity, ethics and compliance should be part of the promotion compensation and evaluation processes. The most effective way to show that "doing the right thing" is a priority is to reward it;
- Make clear that compliance risks won't be tolerated even if it means losing a lucrative piece of business or a transaction. Recent cases such as Enron and Arthur Anderson have demonstrated that the financial costs of non-compliance can be higher than ever imagined;
- When an ethical violation occurs, fix the problem and take appropriate action against the employee as soon as possible no matter how senior; setting the right tone means that employees understand that no one is above the law;
- All managers must be held accountable for setting the right tone;
- Monitor, follow-up and re-assess. Make sure on a regular basis that policies and procedures are being followed; and
- Don't fall victim to a checklist mentality. Any checklist or set of guidelines needs to be viewed in light of a company's unique culture and set of issues. One size does not fit all with respect to compliance programs.

SEC Chairman Donaldson has also emphasized that companies must "look beyond just conforming to the letter of the new laws and regulations. They must redefine corporate governance with practices that go beyond mere adherence to new rules and demonstrate ethics, integrity, honesty and transparency." See William H. Donaldson, Remarks at the 2003 Washington Economic Policy Conference (March 24, 2003).

IV. THE GOVERNMENT'S REACTION WHEN THINGS GO WRONG

A. Increased Enforcement by SEC

As noted above, in the past year, the SEC has significantly stepped up its enforcement efforts. Even companies with highly sophisticated compliance programs may find themselves confronting a government investigation. And these enforcement efforts are yielding fines in amounts that would have been unthinkable only a few years ago. As Cutler has observed: "We're clearly in the midst of an evolution, if not a revolution, in thinking. In only a decade we've gone from a regime in which monetary penalties were imposed only rarely to one in which large penalties seem to be part of virtually all significant settlements." See Stephen M. Cutler, 24th Annual Ray Garrett, Jr. Corporate & Securities Law Institute (April 29, 2004). Cutler has noted that in the last two fiscal years, the SEC has obtained orders for disgorgement and penalties in excess of $5 billion. Moreover, he has also made clear that a key, perhaps decisive factor in the size of the fine is the extent of the violator's cooperation: "If, for example, an entity—whether public company, accounting firm, or regulated entity—or its counsel is recalcitrant during an investigation, misleads the staff, or fails unreasonably to comply with Commission processes, the staff is very likely to seek a penalty in settlement." Id.

B. Recent Enforcement Proceedings

1. Royal Ahold

In a case which clearly shows the "credit" a company may receive if it conducts an internal investigation properly and shares its results with the SEC, the SEC settled accounting fraud charges against Netherlands-based Royal Ahold (Koninklijke Ahold N.V.) and three of its former executives. See Litigation Release No. 18929 (Oct. 13, 2004). In connection with the settlement, no penalty was assessed against Ahold. In part, this was because the Dutch Prosecutor's Office, conducting a parallel investigation, requested that the SEC not seek penalties against the individuals to avoid double jeopardy issues. However, the SEC made clear that no penalty was sought from the company because of its "extensive cooperation" with the Commission's investigation. According to the SEC press release:

> Ahold self-reported the misconduct and conducted an extensive internal investigation. On its own initiative, Ahold expanded its internal investiga-

tion beyond the fraud at U.S. Foodservice and the improper joint venture accounting to analyze accounting practices and internal controls at seventeen operating companies. Ahold promptly provided the staff with the internal investigative reports and the supporting information and waived the attorney-client privilege and work product protection with respect to its internal investigations. Ahold also made its current personnel available for interviews or testimony, significantly assisted the staff in arranging interviews with, or testimony from, former Ahold personnel located in the United States and abroad. Ahold promptly took remedial actions including, but not limited to, revising its internal controls and terminating employees responsible for the wrongdoing.

Associate Enforcement director Thomas C. Newkirk further stressed that the case is "an example of the clear corporate advantage to conducting a comprehensive internal investigation and fully cooperating with the SEC." See SEC Charges Royal Ahold and Three Former Top Executives with Fraud (Oct. 13, 2004).

2. *Halliburton*

In an example of the cost of non-cooperation, on August 3, 2004, in Securities and Exchange Commission v. Halliburton Co., Litigation Release No. 18817 (Aug. 3. 2004), the SEC announced a settlement following an SEC investigation focused on a 1998 change to Halliburton's revenue accounting practices.

As part of the settlement, Halliburton agreed to pay a $7.5 million civil penalty. The SEC noted that the $7.5 million fine, in part, reflected the SEC's view that "there were unacceptable lapses in the company's conduct during the course of the investigation, which had the effect of delaying the production of information and documentation necessary to the [SEC] staff's expeditious completion of its investigation." In addition, the SEC filed a civil action against Halliburton's former CFO who was not part of the company's settlement.

3. *Royal Dutch/Shell*

On August 24, 2004, foreign-based oil producer Royal Dutch/ Shell Group (comprised of operating companies owned by Royal Dutch Petroleum Company, headquartered in the Netherlands, and The "Shell" Transport and Trading Company, headquartered in the United Kingdom), agreed to pay a civil penalty of $120 million to settle an accounting fraud action arising out of oil reserve disclosures in periodic reports filed with the SEC. See Litigation Release No. 18844 (August 24, 2004). The settlement focused on Royal Dutch/Shell Group's overstatement of "proved" oil reserves, which resulted in the Group reporting an inflated Reserve Replacement Ratio ("RRR"), a key performance indicator in the oil and gas industry. The reserve overstatements stemmed from a 1998 change to the Group's reserve estimation guidelines that was intended to boost its RRR relative to its competitors.

The revised guidelines did not satisfy SEC oil reserve reporting requirements, however, which the SEC believed was known to the Group after the SEC staff issued interpretive guidance on the requirements in 2000 and 2001. The Group did not change its reserve estimation guidelines until 2003, and did not begin to publicly announce the recategorization of previously reported oil reserves until January 2004. The SEC was critical of the Group's delay in correcting the overstatement, attributing it to the Group's "desire to create and maintain the appearance of a strong RRR," it's "lack of effective internal controls over the reserves estimation and reporting process," and the Group's "attempt[] to 'manage' the potential exposure by, for example, delaying de-booking of improperly recorded reserves until new, offsetting proved reserves bookings materialized." These factors may account for the assessment of the $120 million penalty notwithstanding the SEC's acknowledgement of the Group's cooperation with the investigation. The SEC also cited the "substantial remedial efforts" already being undertaken by the Group, including, among others:

- the determination to self-report the need for the reserve recategorization prior to the involvement of any external governmental agency;
- an independent investigation ordered by the Group's audit committee, the results of which were provided to the SEC;
- enhancement of the Group's legal function; and
- board governance reforms, including the appointment of non-executive chairmen of two Group-related boards, as well as the creation of a committee of members of the Royal Dutch and Shell Transport boards to study issues relating to the structure and governance of the Group.

4. *Lucent Technologies, Inc.*

In connection with the settlement of an accounting fraud action, Lucent also agreed to pay a $25 million penalty as a result of its "failure to cooperate" with the SEC's investigation. See Lucent Settles SEC Enforcement Action Charging the Company With $1.1 Billion Accounting Fraud (May 17, 2004). The SEC cited the following conduct as evidence of its refusal to cooperate:

a. Through the investigation, Lucent provided "incomplete document production" and "failed to ensure that a relevant document was preserved and produced pursuant to subpoena";

b. After reaching an agreement in principle to settle, Lucent's former counsel characterized the accounting fraud as a "failure of communication", in a magazine interview effectively denying that a fraud had occurred;

c. After agreeing to settle, Lucent "expanded the scope of employees that could be indemnified" without being required to do so under state law or by its corporate charter; and

d. Lucent failed to provide adequate disclosure to the staff concerning its indemnification policies.

5. KPMG

The lengths companies may have to go in order to be viewed as cooperative may be best illustrated by reports of KPMG's actions in connection with a pending investigation. See Laurie P. Cohen, In the Crossfire: Prosecutors' Tough New Tactics Turn Firms Against Employees—As Sentencing Rules Stiffen, KPMG Axes Tax Partners, Won't Pay Their Legal Costs—What 'Cooperation' Entails, Wall Street Journal (June 4, 2004). According to published reports, KPMG has refused to advance legal costs to its partners and employees unless they agree to speak to prosecutors. It also apparently refused to enter into any joint defense arrangements. Moreover, the firm agreed to tell prosecutors which documents the individual employees were requesting to use in their defense and provided copies to prosecutors at the same time it provided them to the individuals' defense lawyers. However, the company refused to provide access to the individuals' lawyers to the documents it is sharing with the government. See id.; see also E. Lawrence Barcella Jr., Kirby D. Behre and James D. Wareham, Cooperation with Government is a Growing Trend; As Prosecutions Intensify, Companies and Executives are Learning to Play Ball, National Law Journal (July 19, 2004).

C. Deferred Prosecution Agreements

Over the past several years, numerous companies that have been the subject of criminal investigations have negotiated deferred prosecution agreements. See, generally, Steven R. Peikin, Deferred Prosecution Agreements: Standard for Corporate Probes, N.Y.L.J. (Jan. 31, 2005); Alan Vinegrad, Deferred Prosecution of Corporations, N.Y.L.J. (Oct. 9, 2003). The use of such agreements dramatically increased after the issuance of the Thompson Memo in 2003, and has been described as reflecting a trend toward rewarding corporations for cooperating with criminal investigations. See Peikin at p. 6. ("DPAs are a tangible reward for positive corporate behavior, particularly in the face of a criminal investigation.") A number of provisions seem to have become standard, including corporate acceptance of responsibility, cooperation with the continuing investigation, payment of fines and restitution, agreement to the imposition of an outside corporate monitor, institution of major corporate governance and compliance reforms and compliance with separate regulatory agreements.

D. Recent Examples of Deferred Prosecution Agreements

1. In a recent example, America Online, Inc. agreed on December 15, 2004 to pay $150 million to a compensation fund and $60 million in penalties and to comply with certain conditions in order to defer prosecution on charges of aiding and abetting securities fraud in connection with transactions between AOL and Purchase Pro.com. AOL agreed to, among other things, accept responsibility for the conduct of its employees in the transactions, adopt specific compliance measures and cooperate with the continuing criminal investigation. An independent monitor will also be appointed. In exchange, the Justice Department agreed to defer prosecution for a period of 24 months. Deputy Attorney General James Comey noted that one reason the Justice Department agreed to defer prosecution was to "minimize the collateral consequences of an indictment, which would have been borne by innocent employees and investors." See Prosecution Deferred as AOL Admits Facts in Federal Revenue Recognition Probe, 36 Sec. Reg. & L. Rep. (BNA) 2246 (Dec. 20, 2004).

2. Similarly, American International Group ("AIG") recently entered into a deferred prosecution agreement, and agreed to pay $126 million to settle criminal charges and a related SEC proceeding arising out of AIG's conduct in developing, marketing

and entering into transactions that purported to enable a public company to remove certain assets from its balance sheet. See Litigation Release No. 18985 (Nov. 30, 2004). AIG also agreed not to make any public statement denying any factual allegation contained in the SEC's complaint in the matter, although the agreement permits the company, consistent with that obligation, to take good faith positions in litigation involving any private party. AIG also agreed to cooperate fully with the continuing criminal investigation, including producing documents, recommending to its employees that they appear for interviews and testimony, providing access to AIG's accounting and legal consultants, and waving attorney-client and work product protection. In connection with the agreement, an independent consultant or monitor was retained and will provide information and report directly to the prosecutors.

3. On September 22, 2004, Computer Associates International, Inc. entered into a deferred prosecution agreement in connection with the resolution of a criminal investigation into accounting fraud and obstruction of justice. Under the terms of the agreement, Computer Associates accepted responsibility for its conduct and acknowledged that the conduct of certain former employees resulted in the company's filing false and misleading financial reports with the SEC and obstructing the government's investigation. The company also agreed to pay $225 million to create a fund to pay restitution to current and former shareholders. In addition, Computer Associates agreed to implement numerous remedial steps including the appointment of new management, the establishment of new compliance and disclosure committees, and adding a minimum of two new independent directors to the board.

4. In another recent example, Merrill, Lynch & Co., Inc. ("Merrill Lynch") executed a deferred prosecution agreement in September 2003 with the Department of Justice with respect to its activities in connection with the collapse of Enron. The agreement provided that: "Merrill Lynch acknowledges that the Department has developed evidence during its investigation that one or more Merrill Lynch employees may have violated Federal criminal law. Merrill Lynch accepts responsibility for the conduct of its employees giving rise to any violation in connection with the Year-End 1999 Transactions." The agree-

ment further provided that Merrill Lynch would not "make any public statement, in litigation or otherwise, contradicting Merrill Lynch's acceptance of responsibility set forth above."

V. WHAT COMPANIES CAN DO TO STAY OUT OF TROUBLE

In light of the amended Sentencing Guidelines, and the SEC's increasing focus on corporate culture, companies need to thoroughly review their existing compliance policies and programs to ensure that they will be viewed as "effective". Companies should also critically examine their training programs and any other ways in which the company's policies are communicated to its employees. Companies must also focus on the structure of compliance reporting within the company and how concerns about problems are reported up the ladder, to ensure that necessary information is promptly aired.

Set forth below are seven critical areas in which "best practices" can make a difference to the quality and effectiveness of a firm's compliance program and help foster a culture of compliance.

A. Establish An Appropriate Supervisory and Compliance Structure

The board and senior management must convey the clear message that responsibility for implementation of the compliance program rests with business unit leaders. Management must also make clear that compliance and legal departments are available to assist business unit leaders with implementing the system, but that such supporting departments are not primarily responsible for the implementation.

The company must establish a strong compliance leadership and structure. An independent, senior-level compliance officer position and compliance committee, or similar body, is often a helpful step, especially if given power to review compliance-related policies and structures created in business units. The compliance committee or task force personnel should include senior, highly regarded business people who will ensure that compliance function has real clout. The compliance officer and task force should have regular access to the board of directors and any appropriate board committee.

Clear lines of reporting should be established. "Supervisory accountability" must be clear in all lines of reporting; particular businesses or business heads must not be allowed to fall outside the lines.

There also should be a regularized system of compliance reviews. To implement that step, business unit leaders should meet periodically with the compliance officer and the compliance committee to report on each business unit's progress in ensuring that a complete and effective compliance program has been implemented and any gaps are addressed. Specialized compliance structures for foreign and new business operations may have to be developed.

Business units should periodically certify to the existence of an effective compliance system for the unit. In addition, companies must develop an effective mechanism to alert the board to significant compliance issues. The audit committee should review current compliance issues at every meeting. The company's legal counsel should give regular updates to the board relating to regulatory and legal proceedings and developments in compliance procedures.

B. Create a Sophisticated Inventory of Regulatory and Reputational Risks Faced by the Firm's Businesses

An effective compliance system is highly dependent on the identification of the compliance and control risks that are inherent in the company's businesses. Some are readily apparent; others are discernible only to those who know how the business is actually being done.

Experienced outside auditors and/or counsel familiar with how business is conducted and regulated should be used to carry out "business unit reviews" to assess areas of high reputational and regulatory risk.

A specialized "New Products/New Business" review process should be established that identifies new regulatory and reputational risks inherent in the proposed businesses, and ensures that an adequate legal and compliance infrastructure will be in place to support the new business, that additional training is adopted (especially when personnel unfamiliar with new product or market will be asked to "cross market"), and that necessary regulatory filings and reporting systems are in place.

C. Establish an "Early Warning" System to Identify Emerging Areas of Regulatory Focus

Regulators and prosecutors are constantly shifting areas of focus and finding new "hot" areas. These are often known to lawyers handling various investigations that have not yet become public. It is useful to establish a network of outside counsel, from various practice areas, who handle such investigations and who will see early signs of changes in regulatory standards and focus. Regulators and enforcement staff can be invited on a regular basis into the company for informal, non-adversarial sessions designed to gather additional information concerning these "hot" areas of regulatory interest and to showcase firm's improvements in its compliance program. The company's relationships with key regulatory bodies must be catalogued and properly managed. Business unit supervisors should be taught that these relationships are as important as those with key clients; key firm personnel should be identified who already are, or should be, serving on regulator's advisory boards, committee, and younger "stars" encouraged to include such service in their career goals.

D. Communicate the Board's and Senior Management's Compliance Message Throughout the Organization

Various communication tools can be used to set the proper "tone at the top"; for example, memos from senior management, training videos, etc.; periodic compliance presentations at meetings. "Business principles," ethical standards, compliance policies and procedure manuals should be disseminated. Employees should be required to certify annually that they have read and complied with the written policies applicable to their business. Periodically revise and republish all manuals to keep rules fresh in minds of both new hires and long-term personnel; keep such materials simple. Avoid sending mixed messages—e.g., conveying to personnel that meeting revenue targets must be achieved "at all costs"; rewarding "big producers" even when they evidence attitude that they are "exempt from compliance rules."

There should be a mandatory compliance component in year-end performance reviews, and compensation levels should reward ethical conduct and participation in implementing compliance systems. Stringent background checks must be done for new hires of employees and consultants; don't give business unit heads unfettered power to hire, especially laterals who will quickly assume authority or be given broad discretion. Train laterals promptly so they become "indoctrinated" with the firm's own compliance culture.

E. Conduct Specialized Training for Supervisors

Many supervisors and business unit managers do not fully understand what is expected of them or what tools and practices are available to manage regulatory and reputational risks effectively. "Supervisory training" should be provided so that all business unit supervisors understand their personal responsibility for supervision, the ways in which they can fail as supervisors, the tools available to them, and the "best practices" supervisors use to manage reputational risk. During training of supervisory personnel, senior management must visibly participate and drive home the message that each business unit leader has personal responsibility for supervision of his or her unit, and should look to legal and compliance personnel only for assistance and support, not as primary parties responsible for such supervision.

F. Ensure that Information Concerning Regulatory and Reputational Risks and Issues is Promptly Surfaced to Senior Management and Compliance Personnel

Training should be specifically designed to encourage immediate surfacing of employee and manager problems and concerns. Personnel must be taught to avoid "self-help"; use a "no surprises" approach, as opposed to a "zero-tolerance for violations" approach.

A comprehensive inventory of a company's existing surveillance systems and exception reporting should be taken; then, develop enhancements to fill identified gaps. Develop a highly sophisticated, adequately staffed internal audit group that fully understands how the business is done—not just financial auditors. All potential sources of compliance-related information should be reviewed including hotlines, ombudsmen, anonymous reporting, employee questionnaires and surveys to gather information to ensure that all genuine issues are actually investigated and corrected.

Companies can limit the risk of having "whistleblowers" going to the government unbeknownst to the firm by creating an environment that encourages employees to surface problems through established internal channels—Section 806 of Sarbanes-Oxley provides protection for employees who became aware of fraudulent activity and report it to someone inside or outside the company.

Personnel should be trained to forward all regulatory inquiries (subpoenas, CIDs, informal requests for trading information, etc.) to legal and compliance personnel for a centralized, considered response; in this area, especially, "self-help" must be forbidden; educate personnel that the consequences of creating even the appearance of obstructing an inquiry can be far worse than any other disciplinary action that might arise from the underlying conduct being investigated.

G. Use Internal Discipline Effectively to Reinforce the Compliance Message When Appropriate

Imposing internal disciplinary action can be an essential tool in a well-run compliance system, but such actions also carry with them special risks that require careful attention. Any disciplinary program must be applied in even-handed manner across the firm's businesses. If "big producers" are allowed to ignore internal compliance policies and procedures without suffering any internal discipline, this sends an obvious message to entire organization. Care must be given to internal and external dissemination of information concerning any internal disciplinary actions taken, in order to limit potential defamation/libel liability; in addition, sophisticated guidance is required in connection with possible regulatory filings arising from such disciplinary actions.

VI. WHAT TO DO IN RESPONSE TO A CRISIS

In this superheated enforcement environment, preparing effectively to deal with a crisis if it arises must be a top priority for corporate boards. Recent events demonstrate that one of the most critical determinants of whether a company is able to navigate successfully through a crisis is the government's perception of the board of directors. If the board is well prepared, actively involved in overseeing the company's response, and constructively engaged in devising solutions to the problems that are uncovered, the company is likely to achieve a faster and less onerous outcome.

Boards need to be proactive in taking the reins in the context of any governance, compliance or business crisis affecting the corporation. At the same time, boards need to be cautious not to overreact to any given situation and thereby create a crisis.

A thorough review should be undertaken of the company's degree of preparedness to appropriately respond to a crisis should one arise. Because it will be necessary to respond quickly and cohesively, companies must know in advance who to call when a crisis looms. A crisis management team should be put in place, including among others, corporate leadership, legal counsel and public relations advisors. Companies must keep in mind, however, that every crisis is unique and will have its own unexpected set of challenges.

Once a crisis becomes apparent, getting at the facts and finding out as much as possible about the situation is the first priority. If an industry-wide problem arises, the company must obtain an immediate report as to its involvement. The company will also want to promptly address whatever problem appears to be precipitating the crisis. If anything illegal is going on, it must be stopped immediately.

Depending on the issue, heightened involvement and supervision by the audit committee may be advisable. If warranted, the board may want to establish a special committee of independent directors for oversight of the internal investigation. However, it is important to stay focused: The internal investigation should be designed to uncover facts relevant to the crisis, and not as a preface to a full-scale compliance audit.

The company must focus on public relations and ensure that it speaks with a unified voice. A control group must be designated to assess and deliver the public message. It may be appropriate to make some disclosure of details regarding the matter, such as the existence of the investigation or that the company is conducting an internal inquiry. However, senior management and the board must be extremely careful about reflexively announcing that the company is "cooperating fully"; many executives (and inexperienced public relations gurus) automatically want to issue an announcement saying that the company is cooperating, but they fail to consider how those words will be interpreted by the government in this new environment.

Strategies should be developed with respect to involvement by the CEO. If the CEO is not a subject of an investigation but was knowledgeable about, or responsible for, the activity in question, then the matter should be handled by a management crisis team reporting to the general counsel and/or CEO and the board, or by a committee of the board. If the crisis team is being advised by outside advisors, the board or board committee should meet with these advisors in an executive session.

If the CEO is a subject of the investigation or supervised directly the subjects of the investigation, or instituted directly the practices being investigated or challenged, then the matter should be handled by officers designated by the independent directors (or by a special committee of independent directors) and by outside advisors retained by the independent directors (or by the special committee of independent directors created for this purpose). Both groups should report directly to the independent directors or their committee.

VII. THE SEC'S FOCUS ON GATEKEEPERS

In a recent speech, Cutler signaled the SEC's determination to focus on gatekeepers, including outside directors. See Stephen M. Cutler, The

Themes of Sarbanes-Oxley as Reflected in the Commission's Enforcement Program (Sept. 20, 2004). He stated that:

> Over the next year, we intend to continue following closely in our investigations on whether outside directors have lived up to their role as guardians of the shareholders they serve. As with the Chancellor case, we will exercise particular scrutiny in considering the role of directors in approving or acquiescing in transactions by company management.

In Chancellor, the SEC brought an action in the United States District Court for the District of Massachusetts against Chancellor Corporation, four of the company's former senior officers and a former outside director, among others, charging them with securities fraud. See SEC v. Adley et al, C.A. No. 03-10762. The former director, Rudolph Peselman, a member of the Chancellor Audit Committee, was alleged to have violated the antifraud provisions of the securities laws by signing a number of false financial statements and by ignoring clear warning signs that financial improprieties were occurring at the company. He was accused of failing to ensure that the company's public filings were accurate.

A second, former outside director was accused of "recklessly" ignoring "signs pointing to improper accounting treatment, thereby allowing management's fraud to continue." This director, Michael Marchese, settled with the SEC in April 2003. See Exchange Act Release No. 47732 (April 24, 2003).

The company was alleged to have improperly booked $19 million in revenue in 1998 from a Chancellor subsidiary it did not yet control. In addition, the company fired an audit firm that disagreed with its accounting decision and hired another auditor who approved the accounting treatment. There were also allegations that Chancellor improperly paid millions of dollars to entities controlled by its Chairman and CEO.

According to the SEC complaint, the outside director, Peselman knew that the auditors had been replaced as a result of the accounting dispute and knew that certain related-party payments had been written off. The complaint alleged that Peselman "recklessly signed a number of financial statements that were materially misleading and took no care to ensure their accuracy." Compl. ¶5. The SEC charged that by approving the company's financial statements, he had "completely neglected to fulfill his duties as a director and as an audit committee member." Compl. ¶60. The SEC further claimed that as an outside director, Peselman ignored "clear warning signs that financial improprieties were ongoing." See Litigation Release No. 18104 (April 24, 2003). The complaint alleged that:

Peselman signed Chancellor's Form 10-KSB for 1998 without taking any steps to ensure that it did not contain materially misleading statements. For example, Peselman made no inquiry into the reasons underlying Metcalf Davis's approval of the 1998 consolidation, even though that approval was completely contrary to Reznick Fedder's position on the issue. In addition, he knew that Chancellor had written off $1.14 million in related party payments in 1997. However, despite that knowledge, he signed off on 1998 financial statements reflecting millions of dollars in amounts owed to Adley's entities without checking whether there was adequate support for the amounts and whether the related party arrangements were adequately disclosed.

—Compl. 48.

The SEC has trumpeted this case as a model for enforcement actions against outside directors. Enforcement director Stephen Cutler has characterized the case as "the first salvo in this area." See SEC to Go After Directors Who Ignore Fraud, Chicago Sun-Times (Aug. 21, 2003). Cutler explained that the case "signifies the Commission's willingness to pursue cases against outside directors who were reckless in their oversight of management and asleep at the switch." Id. The case has been described as a "landmark case" by former enforcement director Stanley Sporkin, who noted that this is a case where "the person didn't profit, didn't buy and sell, but just fiddled while Rome burned." Id.

SEC Chairman William Donaldson also emphasized the role that the SEC envisions for outside directors in the context of mutual funds: "Independent directors, in particular, should serve as _independent watchdogs' guarding investors' interests - ...." See William H. Donaldson, America's Need for Vigilant Mutual Fund Directors (Jan. 7, 2004). Donaldson stressed that in pending investigations in the mutual fund area, the SEC was "carefully looking at the role that independent directors played, if any, in the problems at these firms. We are asking whether the directors were aware of these abuses, and whether there were red flags that were ignored." Id.

In keeping with the SEC's focus on gatekeepers, the SEC recently settled charges against John Isselman, the former general counsel of Electro Scientific Industries Inc. ("ESI"). While Isselman was not alleged to have known about the scheme to fraudulently boost the quarterly financials at ESI, he allegedly failed to communicate material information he learned about the scheme to the company's audit committee and outside auditors. See In re Isselman, Exchange Act Release No. 50428 (Sept. 23, 2004). According to an SEC enforcement lawyer, "Mr. Isselman failed in his gatekeeper role." See Tamara Loomis, SEC Gores GC in Sarbanes-Oxley Dust-Up, Legal Times (Jan. 24, 2005).

NOTES

21

SELECTED MEMORANDA

Submitted by:
Theodore N. Mirvis
Wachtell, Lipton, Rosen & Katz

Table of Contents

January 6, 2004

Planning for the Unexpected: Ten Commandments for Crisis Management

There can, of course, be no guarantees against unpleasant regulatory surprises in 2004. But prudence and fiduciary duty, as well as Sarbanes-Oxley and other ongoing regulatory initiatives, compel companies to establish effective corporate structures and processes designed to forestall or promptly and effectively address crises, including those that arise from violations of law. The following "ten commandments" can assist such efforts:

1. **The boy scouts knew it: be prepared**: Review the corporation's information and control systems, which when they function effectively should both reduce the occurrence of unplanned injurious events and facilitate the timely mitigation of the effects of those that do occur.

2. **Every situation is unique**: Establish core crisis teams in advance for each foreseeable type of crisis and work out goals, roles, and strategies in advance to the extent sensible.

3. **Beginnings are as important as endings**: After assembling the pertinent crisis team, think through the key opening issues (scope of inquiry, who to run it, goals, etc.). Assess management's grasp of relevant facts—use lawyers to investigate facts, if necessary (see Commandment #7). Events may require prompt action, but deliberate before acting; things are often not as time sensitive as the smell of smoke makes them seem. Provide timely and appropriate updates to board members.

4. **Stop any bad practices ASAP**: If there are on-going activities that are *clearly illegal, stop them as soon as you learn about them.*

5. **Speak with one voice, a trained one**: To law enforcement agencies and regulators; to lenders and institutional investors; and to suppliers, customers and the public. While the CEO may wish to appear quickly or immediately knowledgeable and in control, it may be better to leave communications in other hands, at least until all facts and a plan of action are clear.

6. **Try to make regulators your friend, but be careful of the first date**: Consider going to regulators at an early stage. Demonstrate

that the corporation and regulators are on the same side: both want to stop any bad practices that may exist, study causes, take corrective or preventive steps and develop appropriate remediation. Nonetheless, express reservation that the investigation of facts is ongoing. Do not provide beliefs until you have confidence.

7. **Guard attorney-client privilege, but realize it isn't what it used to be**: There is no inference of guilt that can correctly be drawn from careful preservation of this privilege. That said, the pressure to waive privilege in a variety of circumstances is increasing.

8. **Keep focused**: Design the internal investigation to uncover facts relevant to the crisis. After the fire is extinguished, consideration can be given to a broader scale compliance audit.

9. **Resist the urge to discipline too early**: Thoughtful judgment, not speed, is necessary.

10. **When the smoke clears, learn from the experience**: Review management information and control systems to prevent future similar problems. Rethink crisis response systems.

Theodore N. Mirvis
John F. Savarese
Adam O. Emmerich
Gregory N. Racz

January 19, 2004

Some Thoughts for Boards of Directors

The attached paper reflects advice I have been giving to directors and boards concerned about a growing overemphasis on process as a result of the post-Enron reforms embodied in Sarbanes-Oxley, new SEC regulations and new stock exchange rules. Compliance with the new regulations and rules is not that difficult. Process should not, and need not, overwhelm attention to the business of the company, and the new regulations and rules should not, and need not, deter the CEO and the directors from pursuing entrepreneurial opportunities. The business judgment rule is alive and well. The primary focus should be on performance of the business and maximizing shareholder value, not on process.

Martin Lipton

January 19, 2004

<u>Some Thoughts For Boards of Directors</u>

Martin Lipton

The post-Enron accounting and corporate governance reforms have imposed new responsibilities on corporate directors. At the same time, there is a continuing drumbeat of demands for limitations on director authority from activist shareholder groups, populist politicians and academic gadflies. Chief among the demands are a more stringent definition of director independence, more "shareholder power" and more restrictions on the amounts and form of executive compensation. These demands were backed up by 1100 shareholder proxy proposals in 2003, of which 172 were approved.

The response of accounting, consulting and legal advisors has been an almost endless parade of best practices, stylized agendas, checklists, director education programs and extra meetings. Some of these will undoubtedly contribute to improved governance and transparency. But the totality, unless judiciously applied, is more likely to make boards less, rather than more, effective, and in extreme cases will so overburden boards with process that they become dysfunctional. There is no legal reason for directors to be overly concerned about process. The business judgment rule is alive and well. It is not necessary for boards to overreact in order to establish entitlement to the protection of the rule.

In order to avoid an overemphasis on process and at the same time effectively discharge the board's fundamental duties to appropriately monitor and supervise the business of the corporation, it is necessary to identify the matters on which the board should focus and to create a reasonable program to deal with them. The following are recommendations for such a program in today's environment. Obviously, "one size does not fit all" and the board of each corporation can and should tailor procedures to its own circumstances. This memo assumes that the corporation has implemented all of the Sarbanes-Oxley, SEC and NYSE post-Enron reforms and this is not an "how to do it" memo about complying with those requirements.

<u>Tone at the top</u>. One of the single most important factors in ensuring that a board meets all of its duties is that there is the right "tone at the top" of the corporation. If the CEO and senior management are not personally committed to high ethical standards, full compliance with legal requirements and fair dealing, no amount of board process or corporate compli-

ance programs will ensure that the board avoids embarrassment. The board should periodically review with the CEO what the CEO is doing to set the right example and how it is being communicated to all employees and constituents of the corporation. The board's vision for the corporation, including its commitment to ethics and compliance, should be set out in the annual report.

CEO selection and succession planning. The single most important function of the board is selecting and evaluating the CEO and the senior executive leadership of the corporation and planning for their succession. There are no prescribed procedures for doing this and a board should fashion what it deems appropriate. The NYSE requirement for periodic executive sessions of the board is intended to facilitate CEO evaluation and selection. In fulfilling its CEO selection and succession function, the board should recognize that by itself competence is not enough. The integrity and dedication of the CEO is critical in enabling a board to meet all of its duties. In large measure the fate of each of the board and the CEO is in the hands of the other.

Independence. There is currently an overemphasis on board independence to the detriment of promoting the sort of board dynamic that can most effectively lead to a well-functioning board and an effective board partnership with senior management to the benefit of the corporation and its shareholders. The NYSE, after thoughtful consideration, decided to require only that a majority of the board be independent. Nevertheless many of the shareholder advisory services, institutional investors and academic gadflies are continuing to urge (in some cases, demand) that all directors other than the CEO be independent and that social and philanthropic ties among and between the directors and the CEO be considered as impugning, if not destroying, independence. The Breeden Report, which imposed new governance rules on MCI, goes so far as to prescribe rigid requirements for all director nominees and to mandate rotation of one director each year. The 2004 ISS Corporate Governance Policy defines independence as "no connection to the company other than a board seat." These types of requirements and restrictions are the antithesis of the kind of collegiality and relationship with the CEO that is necessary for the board and CEO together to promote the appropriate tone at the top, to agree on the corporate mission and work collectively to enhance the corporation's business. The concept of the board as remote strangers and as the agency for the discipline of management, rather than as partner with management in setting the strategic course of the corporation, is contrary to all prior experience and will not lead to better performance. The tension between the new norms of independence and the overarching objective of better performance, unless modulated and maintained in perspective, can cause the former to overwhelm the latter.

Monitoring performance. While the corporation laws literally say that the business of the corporation is to be managed by the board of directors, it is clear that the board's function is not to actually manage, but to ensure that the corporation is effectively managed by monitoring the performance of the CEO and senior officers. To meet its duty to monitor performance, the board and management together need to determine the information the board should receive. Here "more can be less." The board should not be overloaded with information. It is not necessary that the board receive all the information that the CEO and senior management receive. The board should receive financial information and ratios that enable it to readily understand results of operations, variations from budget and trends in the business, the corporation's performance relative to peers, and any other information that the board determines to be useful in its work. The board should receive copies of all security analysts' reports, press articles and other media reports on the corporation. If an article or report raises performance or other issues, the board should make sure it receives a satisfactory explanation of the issues raised in the publication including, if appropriate, of what is being done to correct the situation. By tracking these reports and articles, the board will avoid the possibility of being accused of ignoring problems that were known to others and which could have been known by the directors.

Monitoring compliance. As with performance, the board has a duty to monitor legal and regulatory compliance by the corporation. The board does not have a duty to ferret out compliance problems. It does, however, have a duty to take appropriate action when it is aware of a problem and management is not properly dealing with it. In normal situations it is sufficient for the board to review compliance matters and litigation semi-annually. This may be done directly by the board or through the audit committee. However it is done, it is a desirable practice for the board or the committee to have executive sessions with the general counsel of the corporation. Where there is a serious investigation or litigation that is being handled by outside counsel, direct reports by such counsel to the board or committee are desirable. In addition the board should annually receive a report as to the corporation's compliance programs and the views of the general counsel as to their adequacy.

The Enron directors have been criticized for not adequately performing their monitoring duties. The legal community, including prominent judges, have stated that Enron's short meetings are evidence of failure by the directors to fulfill their fiduciary duties. Some have suggested that a board's failure to allot adequate time to carry out its duties could call into question whether it had acted in good faith. In addition to scheduling regular board and committee meetings to provide ample time for the regular business of the board, boards should consider the desirability of an annual two-to-three-day board retreat with the senior executives at which there is a full review of the corporation's financial statements and disclosure policies, strategy and long-range plans, and current developments in corporate governance. Each retreat may be held at a location close to one of the corporation's operations so as to give the directors an opportunity to become acquainted with a number of the corporation's operations as the annual retreats are rotated among the corporation's various locations. During the retreat, meals and social activities may be arranged in a manner that encourages the directors to get to know the senior executives on a one-on-one basis. Corporations should also provide comprehensive orientation for new directors so as to acquaint them with the corporation's strategy, long-range plans, financial statements, properties and operations, corporate governance guidelines and senior executives. The annual retreat could satisfy a major portion of such an orientation.

Corporate strategy. Approval of the corporation's long-term strategy is a key board function. Strategy should be formulated initially by management and then developed finally by an interactive process with the board. Many companies find that as part of the strategy development process an annual strategy review that is part of a board retreat of the type referred to above is productive.

Crisis management. Perhaps the most important test of a board comes in times of crisis. Boards need to be proactive in taking the reins in the context of any governance, compliance or business crisis affecting the corporation. At the same time, boards need to be cautious not to overreact to any given situation and thereby create a crisis. There is a mixed record regarding how well boards have been handling recent crises. It appears that many boards have functioned quite well in taking a careful measure of the situation and putting in place the right procedures for obtaining the necessary information about the issues facing the corporation and developing the right strategies for responding to the situation and rectifying any management, disclosure or legal/compliance deficiencies. Others, however, appear to have either overreacted, or to have placed matters in the hands of lawyers, accountants and other outside experts, and thereby lost control of the situation to those outsiders. And, in some instances the crises themselves appear to have arisen in large part from the failure of management and the board to be proactive in reacting to earlier warning signs.

All crises are different and it is difficult to give generic advice that will be relevant to any particular crisis without knowing the facts involved. That said, in most instances when a crisis arises, the directors are best advised to manage through that crisis as a collegial body working in unison. While outside advisors (counsel, auditors, consultants and bankers) can play a very useful and often critical role in getting at all of the relevant facts of a given situation and in helping to shape the right result, the directors should maintain control and not cede the job of crisis management to the outside advisors. And, while there is often the impulse to resign from the board upon the discovery of a crisis, in most instances, directors are best served by staying on the board until the crisis has been fully vetted and brought under control.

Major transactions. Board consideration of major transactions, such as acquisitions, mergers, spinoffs, investments and financings, needs to be carefully structured so that the board receives the information necessary in order to make a reasoned decision. This does not mean that outside advisors are necessary, even for a very large transaction. If the corporation has the internal expertise to analyze the requisite data and present it in a manner that enables the board to consider the alternatives and assess the risks and rewards, the board is fully justified in relying on the management presentation without the advice of outside experts. There is no need for the board to create a special committee to deal with a major transaction, even a hostile takeover, and experience shows that a major transaction is best addressed by the full board. Management should build a strong foundation to support a major transaction, including an appropriate due diligence investigation. The board should have ample time to consider a major transaction, including in cases of complicated transactions and agreements a two-step process with the actual approval coming only after an initial presentation and the board having had time for reflection.

Related party transactions. There is nothing inherently improper about transactions between a corporation and its officers or directors; such transactions are often in the best interests of a corporation and its shareholders, offering efficiencies and other benefits that might not otherwise be available. It is entirely appropriate for an informed board, on a proper record, to approve such arrangements through its disinterested directors. As a matter of compliance and best practices, however, and particularly in the current governance and disclosure environment, the corporation should give careful attention to review and disclosure of all "related party" transactions. Full disclosure of all material related party transactions and full compliance with proxy, periodic reporting and financial footnote disclosure requirements is essential. Management should make sure that all related party transactions have been fully and carefully reviewed with the board. The board should reevaluate the corporation's policies and procedures for reviewing such transactions on both an initial and ongoing basis and for ensuring that all continuing related party transactions remain in the best interest of the corporation. The board should consider assigning to a committee consisting solely of directors who are both independent and disinterested with respect to the transaction under consideration (e.g., the audit or governance committee) the job of reviewing any newly proposed related party transactions. The committee should have the authority to hire such outside financial, legal and other advisors as it deems appropriate to assist it in its evaluation of such transactions. If a related party arrangement is of material significance to the corporation (either due to the nature of the service provided or by virtue of the identity of the related party), the board should consider whether additional steps are necessary to ensure that such transactions are properly monitored and evaluated. For example, the board should take active measures to ensure that the entities providing related party services are being held to the same standards the corporation would demand of unaffiliated third party service providers and that there is a clear reason for procuring the service from a related party.

Confidentiality and the role of directors outside the boardroom. A board should function as a collegial body, and directors should respect the confidentiality of all discussions that take place in the boardroom. Confidentiality is essential for an effective board process and for the protection of the corporation and its stockholders. Moreover, directors generally owe a broad legal duty of confidentiality to the corporation with respect to information they learn about the corporation in the course of their duties. Maintaining confidentiality is also essential for the protection of the individual directors, since directors can be responsible for any misleading statements that are attributable to them. Even when a director believes the subject matter of his or her statements is within the public domain, it is good practice for individual directors to avoid commenting on matters concerning the corporation. A director who receives an inquiry with respect to the corporation from outside the corporation may or may not have all of the relevant information and his or her response could involve the corporation, as well as the director, in a disclosure violation. Directors should also respect the role of the CEO as the chief spokesperson for the corporation. They should generally not engage in discussions with outsiders concerning corporate business unless specifically requested to do so by the CEO or the board. Where it is necessary for outside directors to speak on behalf of themselves or the corporation, here too it is best for one member of the board to be designated as the board's spokesperson. Where a board has a non-executive chairman or a lead director, under certain circumstances it may also be appropriate for the chairman or lead director to speak on behalf of the corporation, particularly within the ambit of those directors' special roles. In the ordinary course, all such matters should be handled in close consultation with the CEO so as to avoid confusion in the corporation's public statements and posture.

Board, committee and CEO evaluations. The NYSE requires annual evaluations. Many consulting firms have published their recommended forms and procedures for conducting these evaluations. Consultants have also established an advisory service in which they meet with the board and committee members to lead them through the evaluation process. Each board needs to decide how to conduct its evaluation. In making the decision, it should be noted that it is not required that the board receive outside assistance and it is not required that multiple-choice questionnaires and/or essays be the means of evaluation. If a board prefers to do the evaluation by discussion at meetings, that is acceptable. It should also be noted that documents and minutes created as part of the evaluation process are not privileged and care should be taken to not create ambiguous records that may be used in litigation against the corporation and the board.

Executive compensation. This is today's most high profile corporate issue. Everyone who has weighed in on this issue agrees that executive compensation should be aligned with long-term performance of the corporation and shareholder value. That said, there is a wide spectrum of views as to how to achieve the agreed objective. The only really useful advice is thoughtful process, full disclosure and recognition by the compensation committee that it should not be deterred by the current criticism of the level of executive compensation from doing what it feels is in the best interests of the corporation.

Charters, codes, guidelines and checklists. The audit, compensation and nominating-governance committees are required to have charters. The corporation is required to have a code of ethics. The board is required to have corporate governance guidelines and, as noted, there is no end to the number of recommended checklists designed to assist corporations in complying with Sarbanes-Oxley, SEC regulations and NYSE rules. All of these are to some extent useful in assisting the board and committees in performing their functions and in monitoring compliance. However, there is a tendency to expand the scope of charters and checklists to the point that they are counterproductive. If a charter or checklist requires review or other action and the board or committee has not taken that action, the failure can be considered evidence of lack of due care. The creation of charters and checklists is an art that requires experience and careful thought. It is a mistake to copy the published models. Each corporation should tailor its own charters and checklists, limiting them to what is truly necessary and what is feasible to accomplish in actual practice. In order to be "state of the art" it is not necessary that the corporation have everything someone else has. Charters and checklists should be carefully reviewed each year to prune unnecessary items and to add only those items that will in fact help directors in discharging their duties.

The audit committee. The post-Enron reforms have invested the audit committee with a special role in corporate governance. In large measure, the audit committee has become the principal means by which the board discharges its duty to monitor financial and disclosure compliance. Accordingly, boards should carefully select audit committee members and, to the greatest extent possible, be attuned to the quality of the audit committee's performance. In view of the audit committee's centrality to the board's duties of financial review, it is also important for the board as a whole to receive periodic reports from the audit committee and to be comfortable that the audit committee, the auditors and management are satisfied that the financial position and results of operations of the corporation are fairly presented.

Shareholder relations. One of the most significant products of the Enron-type scandals is the increase in shareholder-sponsored proxy resolutions and withhold-the-vote campaigns. In addition, the SEC has adopted a new rule with respect to disclosure of the director nominating process and is considering adopting a shareholder access rule that would enable shareholders to directly nominate a director through the corporation's own proxy. The board should regularly review the corporation's shareholder relations programs and consider whether it is appropriate for the board to have greater interaction with shareholders. Where the corporation has performance or compliance issues, direct board contact with shareholders may forestall a proxy initiative by shareholders. In addition, the corporation should weigh carefully opposition to shareholder proxy resolutions that can be accommodated without significant difficulty.

Today it is prudent to do a risk-reward analysis of shareholder resolutions, rather than to routinely oppose them.

Directors' duties and responsibilities. The basic responsibility of directors is to exercise their business judgment to act in a manner they reasonably believe to be in the best interests of the corporation and its shareholders. In discharging these obligations, directors are entitled to rely on management and the advice of the corporation's outside advisors. The board should make sure that the corporation's legal counsel, both internal and external, and auditors, both internal and external, know that they have direct access to the board, if ever needed.

Directors are not guarantors that nothing will go wrong on their watch. Directors are monitors and gatekeepers charged with the duty of installing competent managers and selecting competent advisors who they reasonably believe will serve the best interests of the corporation and diligently monitoring their conduct. They should inquire with due care to make sure that the corporation is operating in compliance with applicable laws and regulations, insist that management take the requisite responsibility for ensuring the accuracy and completeness of the corporation's financial statements and public disclosures and that management take all necessary corrective actions when compliance failures or deficiencies are noted. The courts continue to respect the directors' entitlement to rely on senior management's performance of their obligation to ensure the accuracy of information disseminated by the company.

Directors are expected to attend board meetings on a regular basis, as well as the meetings of the committees on which they serve, and to spend the time that is needed to properly discharge their functions. Directors should make sure that they are receiving from management and from the corporation's auditors and outside advisors all of the information and data they deem relevant to understanding the issues before them and reaching sound business judgments with respect thereto. Perhaps the clearest lesson so far from the accounting and compliance cases making headlines today is that, too often, boards did not have clear information as to what was going on.

When complex legal, governance or accounting issues arise it will be useful for a director to ask the following simple questions:

- Have I acted with undivided loyalty to the corporation and its shareholders and have all my personal interests in this matter been fully disclosed?

- Have I exercised due care in examining the issues underlying the proposed action, including receiving advice as to whether the action is in compliance with applicable rules and regulations?
- Will the proposed action and the relevant facts and circumstance be candidly disclosed to all effected parties?

If the answers to those questions are yes, a director will be fully protected in exercising his or her business judgment and, even if, with the benefit of hindsight, the judgments prove flawed, the director will not be faulted.

In the words of Norman Veasey, Chief Justice of Delaware:

> Although the law of fiduciary duty recognizes the evolving expectations of the standards of conduct of directors and officers, we must keep in mind that the business judgment rule continues unabated to protect directors' decisions made in good faith and to enable them to set strategic goals for prudent risk-taking. What has evolved in this new era is a sharper judicial focus on the processes employed by directors, but it is not a regulatory clamp on their business judgment.

February 2, 2004

The eBay Case and Corporate Opportunity

The Delaware Chancery Court recently considered the corporate opportunity doctrine in the context of investment opportunities offered to corporate insiders. The complaint in the eBay case alleges that certain officers and directors of eBay were allocated shares in hot IPOs by Goldman Sachs to show "appreciation for eBay's business and to enhance Goldman Sachs' chances of obtaining future eBay business" and amounted to the taking of a corporate opportunity by the defendant insiders. The insiders argued that the shares were offered because of the individuals' wealth, and were not opportunities within eBay's line of business or in which eBay had an interest or expectancy. The Court, reviewing a motion to dismiss, disagreed, finding that the allegations, if proven, would present a claim of usurped corporate opportunity.

eBay has not changed the legal standards of the corporate opportunity doctrine in Delaware. Indeed, the case reaffirms the rule devolving from Guth v. Loft that a corporate insider may not pursue an opportunity if:

> (1) the corporation is financially able to exploit the opportunity; (2) the opportunity is within the corporation's line of business; (3) the corporation has an interest or expectancy in the opportunity; and (4) by taking the opportunity for his own, the corporate fiduciary will thereby be placed in a position inimicable to his duties to the corporation.

Broz v. Cellular Information Systems, Inc., 673 A.2d 148, 154-55 (Del. 1996).

Establishing that an opportunity is corporate versus personal is always a fact-intensive inquiry. It is important to note that the procedural setting in eBay, a motion to dismiss, meant that the Court had to assume the truth of the plaintiffs' allegations for purposes of the decision. The complaint alleges that the opportunities were unique, that select insiders were chosen and that the allocations were essentially bribes to insiders for the purpose of obtaining the corporate investment banking business. Under these facts, the Court held that the defendants could be found to have wrongfully taken a corporate opportunity.

Whether an insider has usurped a corporate opportunity will always ultimately depend on the individual facts. eBay has not changed that, and it remains to be seen whether the plaintiffs will be able to prove their allegations at trial. eBay also has not addressed the issues presented when a corporate insider seeks approval for a transaction that the corporation could, but determines not to, pursue—a traditional safe-harbor for insiders. Broz, 673 A.2d at 157.

Steven A. Cohen

February 24, 2004

Delaware Court Orders Enhanced Disclosure on MONY Parachutes Leading to Delay in Proxy Vote

The Delaware Chancery Court last week issued a limited injunction requiring MONY to provide enhanced proxy statement disclosures concerning change in control arrangements that would be triggered in its pending cash merger with AXA. The Court's injunction will result in a delay of the scheduled shareholders meeting to approve the cash merger which had originally been scheduled for February 24, 2004. Importantly, the Court denied plaintiff's request for injunctive relief based on claims under the so-called Revlon doctrine, finding that the MONY Board had no affirmative duty to shop the AXA bid prior to entering into the cash merger agreement with AXA (see the accompanying memorandum on the separate Revlon findings).

The MONY/AXA transaction has been the subject of significant shareholder complaints. Highfields Management has been leading a campaign among dissident shareholders seeking to vote down the deal, claiming that the sale price is too low and that the transaction with AXA is poorly timed and driven by management's self interest. (A separate Federal court ruling supporting Highfields' proxy tactics is also discussed in the accompanying memorandum).

While the MONY ruling is noteworthy in several respects, it is important to note that the opinion does not establish significant new law on the topic of the materiality of proxy statement disclosures in the context of a merger vote. In determining to grant a limited injunction in the MONY matter, the Chancery Court relied on well established principles under Delaware law (which in turn rely on the standard for testing the materiality of a proxy statement disclosure established by the U.S. Supreme Court in 1976). Indeed, the Court dismissed several other claims raised by the plaintiffs relating to the adequacy of MONY's proxy statement disclosures, including claims challenging the adequacy of information provided concerning past indications of interest from a potential interested third party bidder. The Court's findings with respect to the sufficiency of disclosures relating to the MONY executive change in control agreements are specific to the facts at hand in MONY and do not suggest that companies in general need to approach change in control benefit disclosures, which are normally included in the "Interests of Certain Persons" section of a merger proxy, in any significantly different manner than they have in the past.

The MONY transaction involved a renegotiation of MONY's change in control benefits by the MONY Board to facilitate a sale of the company, and the Court's ruling relating to the disclosures on this subject must be understood in that context. In MONY, the executive CIC agreements were a leading, if not the main, element of the financial negotiations with AXA. An early all stock proposal from AXA had been turned down by the MONY Board in part due to the existence of executive CIC agreements with an aggregate cost equal to approximately 15.4% of the total equity value of MONY. The Board then negotiated with management and entered into new CIC agreements (the original agreements were set to expire in December 2003) that reduced the size of the CIC payments from $205 million (based on the analysis of the compensation consultants at Frederic W. Cook & Co.) to approximately $79 million in the aggregate. MONY then negotiated an all cash deal with AXA worth $1.5 billion in aggregate consideration and was able to obtain a dollar for dollar increase in the aggregate consideration offered by AXA as a result of the substantial reduction in CIC payment costs.

It was in the context of these facts that the Delaware Court found that the MONY proxy statement should be amended (as the plaintiffs had requested) to include more disclosure of the information that was presented to the Board concerning the CIC payments and their relative size compared to payments in "comparable" transactions. The Court placed significant weight on the fact that the Board had received an analysis from Frederic W. Cook & Co. showing that even at the reduced cost of $79 million, the CIC payments represented 6.37% of the total deal value and were still above the 75th percentile for comparable financial services transactions as analyzed by Cook. The Court noted in particular that the materiality of this comparative analysis disclosure was heightened by the Board's rejection of an initial offer by AXA for reasons relating, at least in part, to considerations associated with the "outsized CICs." The Court also reasoned that disclosure of the comparative information was necessary as a result of the extensive disclosure in the proxy statement about the steps the Board took to lower the payments under the CICs, which in the Court's view gave readers the impression that the amended agreements were in line with those in comparable transactions. The "Background of the Merger" section of the MONY proxy statement, for example, states "the amended CIC agreements would be more consistent with current market practices than the then existing agreement," without providing the details of the comparable transaction data that Cook had presented to the Board.

While the Chancery Court challenged the disclosure relating to the revised CIC agreements, the Court did not challenge the Board's actions in approving the revised arrangements. To the contrary, the Court specifically stated that the facts "seem to point to acceptable behavior in the approval of the CICs."

The treatment of change in control arrangements requires careful attention in any merger transaction, particularly one in which the payments represent an outsized level compared to the total deal value or the value that management is perceived by the market to have achieved for its shareholders. The MONY decision shows that Boards will be protected in their actions when they act with due care and loyalty on an informed basis. The decision also shows that companies should be careful with respect to, and understand the source of the data and the assumptions used in, the compensation analyses that are presented to them and any disclosure of the conclusions drawn from such analyses in their public SEC filings. In the end, the MONY decision mainly shows that bad facts (as perceived by the public and the Court) often produce adverse litigation results and that greater care in the manner in which these same facts were handled and presented could, with the benefit of hindsight, have potentially avoided an inopportune delay of an important merger vote.

Edward D. Herlihy
Craig M. Wasserman
Adam D. Chinn
Jeannemarie O'Brien

February 24, 2004

Delaware Court Affirms Sales Process with Post-Signing Market Check; Federal Court Affirms Use of Company Proxy Card By Dissidents

In connection with the proposed acquisition of The MONY Group by AXA Financial, the Delaware Chancery Court recently denied the shareholder plaintiffs' request for injunctive relief based upon allegations that the MONY board of directors, having decided to put the company up for sale, failed to fulfill their fiduciary duties by foregoing an auction in favor of entering into a merger agreement with a single bidder and allowing for a post-signing market check. In re The MONY Group Inc. Shareholder Litigation, C.A.20554 (Del. Ch. Feb. 17. 2004). However, the Chancery Court issued a limited injunction requiring MONY to provide enhanced proxy statement disclosures concerning change in control arrangements that would be triggered in its pending cash merger with AXA, delaying the scheduled shareholders meeting to approve the cash merger, but did not challenge the validity of the change in control arrangements (see the accompanying memorandum discussing the ruling on the change in control arrangements).

The Chancery Court denied the plaintiffs' request for injunctive relief based on claims under the so-called Revlon doctrine and reaffirmed existing Delaware law in the context of negotiating a change in control transaction, finding that the MONY board of directors had no affirmative duty to shop the AXA bid prior to entering into the merger agreement:

> "The consequences of a sale of control impose special obligations on the directors of a corporation. In particular, they have the obligation of acting reasonably to seek the transaction offering the best value reasonably available to the stockholders." As made clear in Revlon, this mandate requires a board to get the best short-term price for stockholders in a sale of control. This requirement, however, " does not demand that every change in the control of a Delaware corporation be preceded by a heated bidding contest." Rather, the basic teaching of Revlon and its progeny is that "the directors must act in accordance with their fundamental duties of care and loyalty." [footnotes omitted]

Recognizing that the reasonableness of the decisions made by the directors in the context of sale of control must be considered taking into account the complexities of the situation, the Chancery Court noted that a board can rely on its chief executive officer to conduct negotiations with a third party as long as there is active supervision by the board. The Chancery Court found that, on a number of occasions, the MONY board indicated its independence and control of the process. The Chancery Court noted that the MONY board had engaged an investment bank for advice in maximizing shareholder value and that the investment bank, which also provided a fairness opinion, was "itself incentivized to obtain the best available price due to a fee that was set at 1% of transaction value."

The well-reasoned opinion confirms existing Delaware law that, in the context of a sale of a company for cash, "a board can fulfill its duty to obtain the best transaction reasonably available by entering into a merger agreement with a single bidder, establishing a 'floor' for the transaction, and then testing the transaction with a post-agreement market check" — it is clear that no auction or pre-signing market check is required. The Chancery Court noted that "[s]ingle bidder approaches offer the benefits of protecting against the risk that an auction will be a failed one, and avoiding a premature disclosure to the detriment of the company's then-ongoing business." The Chancery Court found that an active solicitation process was not required but that a standard no-shop clause with a fiduciary out and a reasonable termination fee satisfied the requirement for a post-signing market check. The Chancery Court noted that most post-signing market checks reviewed by the Delaware courts last one to two months, and that the five months that had passed since the MONY/AXA merger agreement was signed was "adequate time for a competing bidder to emerge and complete its due diligence, notwithstanding the complexities of the business involved." In this specific case, citing case law regarding the reasonableness of a termination fee in the "one-to-five percent range of the proposed acquisition price," the Chancery Court found the fee "representing only 3.3% of MONY's total equity value and only 2.4% of the total transaction value" to be "well within the range of reasonableness."

In a separate federal District Court decision relating to a campaign being waged by dissident shareholders to vote down the MONY/AXA transaction, the District Court refused to enjoin the dissidents from mailing proxy solicitation materials that included a duplicate of the MONY proxy card that previously had been sent to shareholders by MONY. The MONY Group v. Highfields Capital Management, (S.D.N.Y. Feb. 11, 2004). The dissidents are seeking to block the MONY/AXA transaction, claiming that the price is too low and that the transaction with AXA is poorly timed and driven by MONY management's self interest.

In the District Court case, MONY had obtained a temporary restraining order against the dissident shareholders prohibiting them from including any proxy cards in their mailings to MONY shareholders. The dissidents, following consultation with the Staff of the Securities and Exchange Commission, had intended to include a duplicate version of the MONY proxy card originally mailed to shareholders by MONY. As part of the 1992 amendments to the proxy rules, the SEC adopted Rule 14a-2(b)(1), which exempts certain proxy solicitations from the proxy solicitation disclosure requirements. The District Court noted:

> The changes to the SEC's proxy rules in 1992 were specifically designed to correct a power imbalance between management and dissident shareholders arising out of the regulatory burdens created by the then-existing proxy rules. . . . Indeed, effectively foreclosing the mailing of a copy of the company's proxy card can be seen as frustrating the animating spirit that lies at the core of Rule 14a-2(b)(1). The 1992 amendments sought to remove impediments to shareholder communications and the "effective use of shareholder voting rights."

The SEC's Office of Mergers and Acquisitions previously has permitted dissident shareholders to use copies of management proxy cards, finding that providing management's proxy card would not create any proxy authority in the soliciting party "particularly where the party does not retain possession of the card" but asks for it to be sent to the third party tabulating the vote on behalf of the company. In refusing to enjoin the use by the dissident shareholders of MONY's own proxy card, the District Court found the SEC Staff's interpretation "persuasive and reasonable."

David A. Katz

March 25, 2004

Key Issues For Directors

The following is an updated list of key issues for directors, with my personal view as to each:

1. Understanding that the post-Enron reforms should not deter people from serving as directors and boards should not overreact to the new governance requirements and procedures by concentrating on process to the exclusion of the fundamental function of the board to advise on strategy and to monitor performance and risk management.

2. Creating the appropriate relationships between the board as a whole and the audit, compensation and nominating-governance committees so that the work of the committees is not duplicated by the board, but the significant actions of the committees are understood by the board as a whole and are integrated into the overall work of the board.

3. Organizing the executive sessions of the board so that they are meaningful reviews of management performance and management succession plans.

4. Making meaningful use of the annual evaluation process and the nominating committee with a view to achieving the best available board.

5. Regularly reviewing that the CEO and senior management are setting a "tone at top" that stresses professionalism, integrity, transparency, legal compliance and high ethical standards.

6. Cutting through the public and political gadflies' criticism of executive compensation and developing compensation programs specially tailored to each company that enables it to attract and retain the best available executives and reward outstanding performance.

7. Responding to poison pill, destaggering of staggered board, splitting role of Chairman and CEO and other corporate governance initiatives and to withhold the vote campaigns, which are increasingly being resorted to by labor unions and public pension funds and which are mainly for purposes other than improving the company's performance. Unless directors resist these actions, and the threats of these actions, we will have governance by referendum, or threat of referendum, rather than the board of directors.

8. Resisting the trend to establishing a special committee of independent directors to investigate almost all whistle-blower complaints, recognizing how disruptive such investigations are, and being judicious in deciding what really warrants investigation.

9. Resorting to outside advisors only when there is a real conflict or real need for special expertise, and continuing to obtain professional advice from the company's own general counsel and CFO.

Martin Lipton

April 7, 2004

Delaware Affirms that Directors can be Independent while Maintaining Social Ties and "Friendship" with Management

In recent months, the Delaware courts have decided a number of cases in which they appeared increasingly receptive to arguments that apparently independent directors were disqualified by alleged conflicts of interest. In its most recent opinion in this area, the Delaware Supreme Court has provided welcome guidance and has specifically addressed the persuasiveness of arguments that social connections and personal friendships can result in disqualification. Beam v. Martha Stewart, Del. Supr., March 31, 2004.

In Beam, a shareholder of Martha Stewart Living Omnimedia, Inc. ("MSLO") alleged that a pre-suit demand on the Board to pursue a derivative action against certain officers and directors of the company was futile because a majority of the Board was not independent. The plaintiff asserted that the personal friendships of certain non-management directors of MSLO with the CEO, and her ability, as the controlling stockholder of MSLO, to remove them from their directorships, rendered those directors "beholden" to her. Stressing the fact-specific nature of independence determinations and the presumption of independence applied in pre-suit demand cases, the Court rejected the allegations. Regarding social relationships, the Court said, "Allegations of a mere personal friendship or a mere outside business relationship, standing alone, are insufficient to raise a reasonable doubt about a director's independence."

The Court also reiterated its rejection of the concept of "structural bias," the supposition that "the professional and social relationships that naturally develop among members of a board impede independent decision-making." Here, the Court relied on the fact that most outside directors are individuals of high standing in the business community, and that they are unlikely to allow their "reputational capital" to be damaged by disregarding their obligations because of "friendship" with CEOs or controlling shareholders.

The Court also went out of its way to distinguish the recent Oracle case, in which the nexus of relationships among the members of the Special Litigation Committee and the defendants around Stanford University was deemed sufficient to taint the Committee's independence. The Court noted that directors are entitled to a more robust presumption of independence when a putative derivative plaintiff asserts excusal of his normal obligation to make pre-suit demand, as opposed to the Oracle situation, where a board committee exercises the extraordinary power of causing a derivative lawsuit to be dismissed.

No doubt, as the Beam opinion reminds us, each case of alleged directorial conflict of interest is different. Nonetheless, Beam represents an important restatement of the fundamental principle of corporate governance—the presumption that non-management directors are independent (even if they occasionally play golf with the CEO or attend his child's wedding) unless there is real evidence to the contrary.

Paul K. Rowe
Trevor S. Norwitz

June 10, 2004

Change-of-Control Employment Arrangements—What Directors Are Asking Today

Consistent with today's heightened emphasis on corporate governance matters, directors of public companies are inquiring about the appropriateness of adopting and maintaining change-of-control employment arrangements. Our responses to some commonly asked questions follow.

Does Sarbanes-Oxley affect change-of-control employment arrangements?

Sarbanes-Oxley does not address change-of-control arrangements and has no effect on the legality of such arrangements. Appropriately structured change-of-control protections continue to be legal, appropriate and in the best interests of companies and their shareholders.

While Section 1103 of Sarbanes-Oxley permits the SEC to petition a district court to require a company subject to an investigation of possible securities fraud to escrow "extraordinary payments" to directors, officers or employees for up to 90 days, this rule does not apply in the absence of fraud. Moreover, in a recent ruling, the United States Court of Appeals for the Ninth Circuit reversed a lower court decision granting the SEC's petition for the escrow of "extraordinary payments" to the former CEO and CFO of Gemstar-TV Guide (see our memorandum of May 28, 2004). The Ninth Circuit found that the SEC failed to establish that Gemstar's cash payments of approximately $38 million, in addition to significant stock-based remuneration, were of an extraordinary nature in the context of a severance arrangement.

Our company has received an unsolicited offer—is it too late to adopt or modify change-of-control arrangements?

We continue to recommend that, where possible, companies should adopt change-of-control arrangements prior to any actual or threatened change of control. If arrangements are adopted during a pending or threatened takeover, they will be subject to the heightened "enhanced scrutiny" standard in Delaware. However, uncertainty of executives regarding their future often is dramatically exacerbated by an unsolicited offer. Accordingly, companies often adopt new arrangements or augment existing arrangements in the context of a threatened takeover to retain and stabilize the employee base. In this context, appropriately structured arrangements adopted by fully informed boards of directors will be valid.

We already have change-of-control protections in place—is it necessary to review or change them?

Existing arrangements may be inadequate or otherwise out of date. For example, change-of-control definitions inadvertently may trigger when no change in ownership has occurred (*e.g.*, definition triggers if the company does not survive in a merger without regard to a change in board composition or shareholder base) or may not trigger when a change in ownership has actually occurred.

A clear understanding and expression of the events that cause change-of-control provisions to trigger is paramount. The Eighth Circuit recently dismissed a claim by former Honeywell employees who contended that their stock options should have vested upon shareholder approval of Honeywell's acquisition by General Electric which ultimately failed. Bohan v. Honeywell International Inc. (8th Cir. May 3, 2004). Under the Honeywell option plan, stock options vested upon a "merger in which [Honeywell does] not survive . . . , which is approved by the Company's shareowners." The court held that shareholder approval was a necessary, but insufficient, condition to acceleration. Similarly, litigation continues over the failed Sprint-MCI merger in which shareholder approval did trigger benefits although the merger never occurred.

What should change-of-control arrangements cost?

In light of the extensive discussion of the costs of change-of-control agreements in the recent MONY case (see our memorandum of February 24, 2004), directors have been asking focused questions about the appropriate potential cost of change-of-control packages. While the Delaware Chancery Court held that the proxy disclosure of MONY's change-of-control agreements was inadequate, the court did not disapprove of the board's actions in approving the change-of-control arrangements. In fact, the court specifically stated that the facts "seem to point to acceptable behavior in the approval of the CICs."

A board should determine, in its business judgment, the appropriateness of change-of-control packages to be provided to its employees taking into account the facts and circumstances that are relevant to the company. These may include: the importance of such arrangements in attracting and retaining key employees, the market cap of the adopting company and market practice in the company's industry. Most importantly, directors should have sufficient explanatory documentation, an understanding of the terms and potential costs of the change-of-control arrangements, and an opportunity for adequate discussion prior to approving such arrangements.

Do the New York Stock Exchange equity compensation rules require shareholder approval to enter into an agreement with an executive providing that all of the executive's unvested options automatically vest on a change of control?

No. Changes to the vesting schedule of options under a plan are not material revisions, whether or not the change requires an amendment to the plan under which the options were granted.

Michael S. Katzke
Jeremy L. Goldstein

October 25, 2004

Delaware Court Affirms Lockup of Majority Stockholder in Minority Squeeze-out

The Delaware Court of Chancery recently upheld an eighteen-month voting agreement granted by a controlling stockholder to a third party seeking to acquire a significant equity stake in a company by means of a merger in which shares held by the minority stockholders were cashed out. Orman v. Cullman, C.A. 18039 (Del.Ch. Oct. 20, 2004). The decision clarifies the type of deal protection that an acquiror can seek from a controlling stockholder after the Delaware Supreme Court's decision in Omnicare, Inc. v. NCS Healthcare striking a similar voting agreement. (See our memoranda of December 23, 2002 and April 10, 2003.)

The Cullman family controlled General Cigar Holdings, Inc. through its ownership of high vote shares. Swedish Match AB sought to acquire an equity stake in the company. The parties agreed to transaction in which the Cullmans would sell one-third of their equity to Swedish Match, followed by a cash merger in which the public minority (low vote) Class A shares would be acquired at the same price. As a result, Swedish Match would own 64% of the company, while the Cullmans (holding 36%) would remain in control of the board by agreement.

The merger was approved by a special committee of independent directors of the General Cigar board. As an essential part of the deal, Swedish Match insisted that the Cullmans enter into a voting agreement requiring them to vote for the proposed merger and to vote against, and not sell shares in connection with, any alternative transaction for a period of eighteen months after termination of the merger agreement.

The voting agreement specified that the Cullmans were bound only in their capacity as stockholders. The board retained the right to withdraw its recommendation in the face of a more favorable transaction, and to terminate the merger agreement if the stockholders failed to approve it. Most significantly, the merger agreement required approval by a majority of the Class A shares, with the Cullmans agreeing to vote their Class A shares pro rata in accordance with the public vote. The agreement provided no break-up or other termination fee.

The suit alleged that the voting agreement was unduly coercive of the stockholder vote. The Court disagreed, distinguishing Omnicare, a case in which the Board failed to retain the right to terminate the merger agreement and where the minority stockholders did not have the power to veto the deal to which the controlling stockholders had committed. These measures were found preclusive in Omnicare because they made the transaction a fait accompli. In Cullman, the Court—albeit applying Unocal scrutiny—found that the public stockholders were free to reject the deal, and were not illegally "coerced" to vote in favor, even though their vote may have been influenced by the blocking effect of the eighteen-month tail on the voting agreement.

Theodore N. Mirvis
Patricia A. Vlahakis
Marc Wolinsky

October 28, 2004

Director Liability Developments: Delaware Gets Dangerous?

A series of recent decisions in the Delaware courts, and the ongoing Disney trial, have once again raised questions about the level of personal risk that independent directors take on through service on corporate boards. The real danger posed by these developments has, in our view, been somewhat exaggerated in the media (for example, the Financial Times headlined its recent coverage of the Disney trial "Directors face a Disney doomsday"). But the fact remains that Delaware law is becoming more hospitable to plaintiffs seeking to reach the pocketbooks of individual directors.

The recent cases have raised questions in three areas: (1) Do directors now face personal liability for aggravated negligence, even where they do not profit personally from the alleged wrongdoing? (2) Are directors with special expertise in financial, accounting or other areas subject to a more stringent standard of conduct than others, and thus at higher risk of liability? (3) Are directors especially at risk in approving complex executive compensation packages?

1. Liability for negligent conduct without personal gain

In response to a crisis in the availability of D&O insurance in the mid-1980's, the Delaware legislature in 1987 enacted a statute (DGCL §102 (b)(7)) that permitted corporations to adopt charter provisions protecting directors from all personal liability for negligent or even grossly negligent conduct. The D&O crisis was caused by the Delaware Supreme Court's holding the directors of Trans Union personally liable for damages for their decision to sell the company at a significant cash premium to market in a friendly merger subject to a stockholder vote, which was found to have been grossly negligent (Smith v. Van Gorkom). For the nearly two decades since then it has been thought that, once the stockholders adopted a protective charter provision, independent directors could be held personally liable only for self-dealing-type transactions, in which they received some personal benefit, and not otherwise.

This bulwark of director protection adopted by the Delaware legislature was breached in 2003, when the Delaware Court of Chancery held that directors could be held personally liable if they committed aggravated negligence, even though they obtained no improper personal benefit and acted without any conflicting personal interest in the matter at issue. The court did this by characterizing aggravated negligence (not paying sufficient attention to corporate affairs) as a breach of the duty of "good faith" — that is, a breach not covered by the liability-protection provisions authorized by the legislature. The court thus created a back-door for plaintiffs to evade the legislature's statutory plan for protecting directors who lack a personal motive or interest to harm the corporation.

The "duty of good faith" decision concerned the Disney board's conduct at the time of the hiring and termination of employment of former Disney President Michael Ovitz. Essentially, the court ruled that plaintiffs could recover damages from the directors personally if they could prove at trial that the directors' lack of attention to the decision to hire and terminate, and to the financial terms of the discharge, amounted to a lack of "good faith." The court held, on a motion to dismiss, that the stockholders' complaint alleged sufficient facts (if proven) to show that the directors had not "exercised any business judgment or made any good faith attempt to fulfill" their fiduciary duties. Rather, the court held that the facts alleged suggested that the directors "consciously and intentionally disregarded their responsibilities, adopting a 'we don't care about the risks' attitude concerning a material corporate decision." That level of uncaring distinguished the case from one based on gross negligence, for which directors are not liable if the typical charter exculpation provision is in place:

> Knowing or deliberate indifference by a director to his or her duty to act faithfully and with appropriate care is conduct, in my opinion, that may not have been taken honestly and in good faith to advance the best interests of the company. Put differently, all of the alleged facts, if true, imply that the defendant directors knew that they were making material decisions without adequate information and without adequate deliberation, and that they simply did not care if the decisions caused the corporation and its stockholders to suffer injury or loss. Viewed in this light, plaintiffs' new complaint sufficiently alleges a breach of the directors' obligation to act honestly and in good faith in the corporation's best interests for a Court to conclude, if the facts are true, that the defendant directors' conduct fell outside the protection of the business judgment rule.

In re Walt Disney Co. Derivative Litigation, Del. Ch., 825 A.2d 275 (May 28, 2003).

How the new "good faith" exception will play out in practice remains to be seen. The actual trial of the Disney/Ovitz matter, which will determine whether any directors in fact breached any duties at all or are found liable, started last week in Delaware. Moreover, the Delaware Supreme Court has yet to address the interplay of the court's pretrial rulings with the Delaware statute and prior case law, and to weigh-in on the "good faith" liability theory in general. It is at least interesting to note in that regard that in an earlier decision in the Disney/Ovitz case itself, the Delaware Supreme Court—albeit writing before the 2002 post-Enron Sarbanes-Oxley reforms—had made the point that the fiduciary duty law is "distinct from the aspirational goals of ideal corporate governance practices" which are "*not* required by the corporation law and do not define standards of liability." Brehm v. Eisner, Del. Sup., 746 A.2d 244 (2000).

2. Expertise: the new risk factor

Earlier this year, the Delaware Court of Chancery entered a rare judgment, after a full trial, imposing personal liability on outside directors for voting to approve a going-private transaction at an unfair price, where the directors had no personal financial interest in the transaction itself. The transaction had been approved by a special committee of directors advised by independent legal counsel and an independent financial advisor which opined to the fairness of the merger's terms to the public minority, and had been conditioned on a majority-of-the-minority tendering into the first-step tender offer. In re Emerging Communications, Inc. Shareholders Litigation, Del. Ch., Cons. C.A. No. 16415 (May 3, 2004).

The Emerging Communications decision has provoked a great deal of public comment because the court relied, in part, on the fact that one of the directors held individually liable was a professional investment advisor, with significant experience in the business sector involved, and had previously been a financial analyst for a major investment banking firm and hedge fund focused in the same industry. The court reasoned that his "specialized financial expertise" put him in a position where he "knew, or at the very least had strong reasons to believe" that the price was unfair, and he was "in a unique position to know that." A second non-management director was held personally liable for a classic "loyalty" violation, since he was found "clearly conflicted" because he was an attorney whose firm received virtually all of its fees from the controlling stockholder and he was found to have "actively assisted" the controlling stockholder in carrying out the privatization transaction. Other non-management directors who voted to approve the same buy-out were not held individually liable.

The court's apparent willingness to embrace an analysis under which a certain category of non-management directors—those with specialized knowledge—might be found liable, while others without such expertise might be exonerated although they approved the same transaction and engaged in essentially the same conduct, is new and potentially troubling.

Such a doctrine would appear to violate the long-established Delaware view that all directors are equally responsible to shareholders and have the same fiduciary duties. If Emerging Communications in fact means that the Delaware courts will be quicker to impose liability on directors with financial, accounting, legal (or, for that matter, business) expertise, then the law will discourage the very individuals whose contributions might be greatest in the post-Sarbanes-Oxley environment. The directors most willing to serve will be persons without financial, accounting, legal or business expertise.

The court placed its holding on a basis that seems to expand the Disney "duty of good faith" exception to the statutory exculpation of Delaware directors. The court reasoned that while the other directors could argue that they relied on the fairness opinion of the independent financial advisor to the special committee, that argument was "implausible" in the case of the financially expert director whose expertise in the industry was "equivalent, if not superior" to that of the committee's financial advisor (Houlihan Lokey). Notwithstanding his lack of financial interest in the transaction, the court found that the director's vote to approve the transaction was "explainable in terms of only one of two possible mindsets"— either as a deliberate effort to further his personal interests (he was a consultant to a firm controlled by the controlling stockholder, receiving an annual $200,000 retainer for providing banking/financial advisory services, and had stood to receive a potential $2 million fee for other financial advisory work); or the director had "for whatever reason, 'consciously and intentionally disregarded his responsibility to safeguard the minority stockholders from the risk, of which he had unique knowledge, that the transaction was unfair." Either motivation, the court held, would render the director personally liable, notwithstanding the charter's exculpation provision, for conduct that "amounted to a violation of the duty of loyalty and/or good faith."

That latter prong of the court's analysis has attracted the most attention in that it seems to suggest a basis for personally liability based on personal expertise. While the court's language is broad, there is some reason to think that Emerging Communications does not presage that Delaware directors are to be classified by expertise level for purposes of assigning liability. As noted, the director in question, in addition to his expertise, was also distinguished from his fellow board members by the fact that he received a $200,000 annual retainer from the control shareholder. It is unclear whether a director who did not have such a financial relationship with the controlling shareholder would have been found liable for the same conduct. At the same time, however, other of the non-management directors were likewise held to have been not independent by reason of various financial ties to the controlling shareholder (the court referred pointedly to the level of their various consulting and/or director and committee fees, and their expectation of continued remuneration post-transaction) but escaped personal liability for their votes to approve the deal.

To be sure, the Emerging Communications court did find a number of bad facts: that the controlling stockholder had failed to provide an updated set of projections that forecasted substantially higher growth for the controlled subsidiary than the projections on which the special committee and its advisors relied; that the committee chair communicated with his fellow committee members by faxing confidential materials (including the financial analysis of the committee's financial advisor) to the secretary of the controlling stockholder with a request that they be faxed on to the committee members; that the actual fair value of the shares was over three times the transaction price ($38.05 v. $10.25); that the legal counsel and investment banking firm that had previously been engaged by the directors were "co-opted" by the controlling stockholder to serve as his advisors (although one might have thought that it was a good thing for the special committee not to be advised by firms previously selected by the controlling stockholder); that the controlling stockholder had "misled" the committee chair by "falsely representing" that the price of the deal strained the limits of his available financing; and that, as noted, a majority of the committee lacked true independence based on "lucrative" consultancy and directorship fees paid by the controlling stockholder and/or their expectation of continuing to serve as directors of that individual's controlled entities in the future). Perhaps it can reasonably be hoped that cases in which directors are held personally liable although they have no personal stake in the transaction, will be limited to egregious circumstances.

3. Executive compensation

Executive compensation has become the hot button issue that takeover defense and deal lock-ups once were. Traditionally, the Delaware courts took the view that they were ill-equipped to make qualitative judgments about the amount or structure of executive compensation, provided that the compensation was approved by independent directors (typically with advice from independent experts). Recent trends in Delaware decisions suggest that the courts are much more likely to try to find a way to overturn compensation arrangements they consider to be excessively generous or poorly structured.

The retreat from Delaware's prior approach has taken two forms. First, as has been widely publicized as a result of the Disney/Ovitz matter, the courts are creating new expectations of the level of director involvement in dealing with compensation. Boards or committees will be expected to be directly involved in negotiating new contracts, determining the structure of equity and incentive compensation, and supervising terminations and pay-out decisions. The compensation committee, in particular, seems likely to become the focus of extended scrutiny to the same degree as the audit committee has become as to accounting and related financial matters.

The Disney/Ovitz matter may represent a turning point here as well. The plaintiffs' allegations in Disney were that neither the board nor its compensation committee had sought to review the Ovitz agreement, and that neither the board, the compensation committee nor Disney CEO Michael Eisner had the benefit of any expert advice. Similar allegations—which the court called an "ostrich-like approach"—were made as to Ovitz's termination, with it being alleged that the board failed to seek to negotiate the departure terms or to inform itself on the conditions and terms of the Ovitz contract as it "allowed" the CEO to award Ovitz cash and options allegedly worth over $140 million for leaving a job that he had allegedly proven incapable of performing.

Second, the Delaware courts have announced a new and largely unexpected legal principle—that executives, since they owe fiduciary duties to shareholders in their capacity as officers and directors, owe a duty to shareholders when they negotiate their own employment contracts with the corporation or their severance payments upon exiting employment with the firm. Practitioners had believed that if negotiations with executives were handled on an arms-length basis, and approved by an independent compensation committee of the board (typically with advice from independent expert consultants), courts would not allow claims against the executive that the executive had breached a duty by obtaining "too much." But in recent cases the Delaware courts have announced that where a board is found to have awarded compensation in breach of its own duties, that liability may fall as well on the executive who obtained it.

In one case, the court held that Michael Ovitz, before becoming a Disney employee, was entitled "to seek the best employment agreement possible for himself" and indeed was even entitled to take advantage of any personal relationships he may have had with the company's negotiators (short of "aiding and abetting" a breach of their duties, a claim not asserted in the case). But once he was hired, and was negotiating separation from the company, Ovitz, (as a director and officer) was held to be under a fiduciary duty that may have obliged him to ensure that the process of his termination was "both impartial and fair." In re The Walt Disney Co. Derivative Litig., Del. Ch., Cons. C.A. No. 15452 (Sept. 10, 2004).

A second recent case from the Court of Chancery endorses both these new principles from the Disney/Ovitz litigation. Official Comm. Of Unsecured Creditors of Integrated Health Svcs. v. Elkins, Del. Ch., C.A. No. 20228-NC (Aug. 24, 2004). In this case, the Court held that an incumbent CEO was under a duty to see to it that his own employment arrangements were negotiated "in an adversarial and arms-length manner." The case also repeats Disney's holding that directors who "consciously and intentionally disregarded" their duties in relation to executive compensation matters could be held personally liable. At the same time, the Integrated Health Services opinion attempts to reassure directors by stating that "[t]he court does not look at the reasonableness of a Board's actions in this context [executive compensation], as long as the Board exercised some business judgment." The Integrated Health Svcs. opinion also notes that it is a fine line that separates personal liability from non-liability under the Disney standard: "a change in characterization from a total lack of deliberation (and for that matter, a difference between the meaning of discussion and deliberation, if there is one) to even a short conversation may change the outcome of a Disney analysis."

* * *

The full scope of the new liability risks outlined above await fleshing out in future decisions, trials and opinions of the Delaware courts, and, of course, the judgment of the Delaware Supreme Court. It remains fair to say that there has yet been no revolution in liability law in Delaware, and fundamental business judgment rule protections remain in place. Despite the journalistic headlines, "doomsday" for directors is still some way off. In terms of what directors should do as they perform their responsibilities, there is no fundamental change. Directors should exercise care in every decision they are called upon to make, and should be sensitive to anything that could be claimed to counter-indicate their disinterestedness. Business decisions made in compliance with the basic duties of care and loyalty will be protected from second-guessing, and cannot violate any "duty of good faith." The recent trend, however, reinforces what most directors already know: that it is more important than ever that they act diligently, avoid any spectre of conflicting interest, ask questions of management, make a record of their involvement, and ensure that they obtain adequate levels of advice and counsel from expert advisors.

Theodore N. Mirvis
Paul K. Rowe

November 29, 2004

Directors Have Enhanced Responsibilities Under Revised Organizational Sentencing Guidelines

In April 2004, the United States Sentencing Commission accepted the recommendations of an ad hoc advisory group to amend the Organizational Sentencing Guidelines in order to make the Guidelines' criteria for effective compliance programs more stringent and to place greater responsibility on officers and directors for the oversight and management of compliance programs. *See* our memorandum, "U.S. Sentencing Commission Toughens Requirements for Corporate Compliance Programs" (April 15, 2004). These first-ever amendments to the Organizational Guidelines were submitted to Congress on May 1, 2004, and became effective on November 1, 2004. The full text of the amended Guidelines is available at http://www.ussc.gov/2004guid/tabcon04_1.htm.

The revised Guidelines transform what was previously an application note on how to show "due diligence" into a new section entitled "Effective Compliance and Ethics Program." This new section incorporates both the well-known "seven steps" of an effective compliance program and a number of new requirements. The increased responsibilities of company directors in this process are at the heart of these new requirements. To truly understand the new responsibilities of company directors, one must read both the Guidelines and the accompanying application notes. As Paula Desio, deputy general counsel to the United States Sentencing Commission, recently noted at the annual Ethics Officers Association convention, the application notes tell readers "what the Commission meant."

The revised Guidelines require the following:

Directors Must be Knowledgeable. The revised Guidelines mandate that directors "be knowledgeable about the content and operation of the compliance and ethics program" and "exercise reasonable oversight" with respect to its implementation and effectiveness. Companies should have functioning information channels through which directors are kept abreast of the effectiveness of, and any changes to, compliance programs.

Directors Must be Informed. The revised Guidelines require that the person with "day-to-day" responsibility for overseeing the ethics and compliance function have "direct access to the governing authority" or a designated subgroup thereof. The application notes to the Guidelines recommend that this person should update the board or its designated subgroup on the status of the program "no less than annually." Companies should therefore set aside a reasonable amount of time during at least one board meeting each year in order to allow substantive presentations and discussion related to the status of the ethics and compliance program.

Directors Must be Trained. The revised Guidelines also direct that all employees, including officers and directors, participate in compliance training programs. Companies should arrange for specialized training for their high-level officers and directors. Such training sessions might consist of dedicated presentations and question/answer periods at an annual board and senior management retreat that is designed, in part, to address these issues.

Annual Compliance Reviews Must be Substantive. When the board conducts its annual review of a company's compliance program, the review should cover all of the key elements of the revised Guidelines, including an assessment of whether:

- the company has adopted "standards and procedures to prevent and deter criminal conduct," including by determining whether appropriately documented ethics policies and procedures designed to assure compliance with these policies are in place;
- the board has adequate resources to meet its obligations to be knowledgeable about the content and operation of the compliance program, including an evaluation of whether the high-level personnel with day-to-day responsibility for the program have sufficient resources, authority and access to the board;
- discretionary authority has not been delegated to those who, based on past behavior, might engage in wrongdoing, including by assessing whether appropriate background checks are being conducted by the company;
- the company requires and provides periodic compliance training for all personnel, including officers and directors;
- the company has adequate "monitoring and auditing" systems and reporting systems in place that allow employees to report criminal or unethical conduct "without fear of retaliation," such as through an ethics hotline that permits anonymous reporting of ethical, legal or regulatory concerns;
- the company promotes incentives for employees to adhere to the compliance program and disincentives to deviate from it; and

- detected violations have been responded to with appropriate steps designed to prevent similar offenses in the future.
- A company's ability to demonstrate that it has a well-documented and effective compliance program that is properly monitored by the board may be a significant consideration in a prosecutor's decision whether or not to charge a company if wrongdoing is uncovered and can be an important mitigating factor that reduces an organization's culpability score and fine range. Particularly in light of these recent amendments to the Organizational Guidelines, companies should devote sufficient time and resources to evaluating and improving their existing compliance programs, as failure to do so may expose a company to significant civil and even criminal liability.

John F. Savarese
Sarah Fern Meil

December 1, 2004

Delaware Speaks to Directors of Troubled Companies

In a welcome note of reassurance to directors of financially troubled companies, the Delaware Court of Chancery has held that director exculpation charter provisions adopted under Delaware's § 102(b)(7) protect directors from due care/mismanagement claims brought by creditors who are accorded standing to pursue fiduciary duty claims when the firm is insolvent. More broadly, the opinion is an important dilation on the same court's often-cited 1991 decision in Credit Lyonnais addressing the degree of discretion afforded directors when the firm is in the "zone of insolvency," and makes clear that there is no "new body of creditor's rights law." Production Resources Group, L.L.C. v. NCT Group, Inc., Del. Ch., C.A. No. 114-N (Nov. 17, 2004).

Vice Chancellor Strine's opinion makes several significant points concerning fiduciary duty claims asserted by creditors against directors of troubled firms:

- Credit Lyonnais is a "shield" for directors, not a sword for creditors. Most fundamentally, the opinion makes clear that directors of financially troubled firms are not exposed to a new set of fiduciary duty claims by creditors. In the Credit Lyonnais decision by then-Chancellor Allen, the Court of Chancery rebuffed the charge of a 98% stockholder that directors had disregarded its interests, famously stating that "at least where a corporation is operating in the vicinity of insolvency, a board of directors is not merely the agent of the residue risk bearers, but owes its duty to the corporate enterprise" — a statement some had interpreted as implying that directors in such circumstances owe a duty to creditors. The opinion in Production Resources explains that Credit Lyonnais recognizes that the protection of creditors lies in shielding directors from stockholder claims that directors are duty-bound to undertake extreme risk which might benefit stockholders so long as the company does not breach any legal obligations. At the same time, directors of troubled firms need not act solely in the interests of creditors. Rather, at bottom, the board of such a firm may chart a course with an eye to its duty to "the corporate enterprise" and thereby "to the community of interest that sustained the corporation." Credit Lyonnais thus provides a "shield" against stockholder claims that redounds to the benefit of creditors, but does not suggest that directors' duties change profoundly as the firm approaches insolvency or that there is some "magic dividing line" that signals the end to risk-taking that directors may lawfully undertake.

In this regard, the Production Resources opinion squarely, and forcefully, rejects the contention of some commentators and courts that directors of a company in the "zone of insolvency" are exposed to a new set of creditor challenges to their business judgment as violative of fiduciary duties to creditors, as well as the holdings of certain federal cases that a due care claim belonging to the corporation is transformed into something beyond the reach of charter exculpation provisions when the claim is asserted by a bankruptcy trustee. Undoubtedly, as the proportion of a firm's enterprise value comprised of debt increases, directors can and should bear that circumstance in mind as they exercise their business judgment. But the directors' duties do not profoundly change. Directors remain fully capable in the exercise of business judgment to chart a course that seeks to maximize the value of the firm, and are not required to choose a less risky alternative in order to protect the claims of creditors.

- Creditors of insolvent firms have standing to pursue fiduciary duty claims, but the claims remain derivative claims, not direct claims. In the case of an insolvent firm, creditors are granted standing to pursue fiduciary claims against directors, as the residual claimants to an inadequate pool of assets, but the claims continue to be derivative claims asserted in the right of the corporation as opposed to direct claims owned by the creditors. Whether the wrongful acts occur before or after insolvency, the claims of fiduciarily improper conduct continue to belong to the corporation, which is the recipient of any recovery that benefits the derivative plaintiffs — be they creditors or stockholders — only indirectly via their respective claims on the firm's assets. "[T]he fact of insolvency does not change the primary object of the director's duties, which is the firm itself. The firm's insolvency simply makes the creditors the principal constituency injured by any fiduciary breaches that diminish the firm's value and logically gives them standing to pursue these claims to rectify that injury."

- Directors of insolvent companies are protected from personal liability under charter exculpation provisions. Directors of insolvent firms are protected from personal liability for due care/mismanagement claims brought by creditors, including derivative claims, under charter exculpation provisions adopted pursuant to Delaware's

§ 102(b)(7). The decision notes that a primary purpose of the exculpation statute is "to encourage directors to undertake risky, but potentially value maximizing, business strategies, so long as they do so in good faith," and that when the firm has become insolvent, "the possibility of hindsight bias about the directors' prior ability to foresee that their business plans would not pan out is at its zenith and when the exculpatory charter provision is most useful." Accordingly, although § 102(b)(7) does not mention creditors, its protection extends to directors of insolvent firms even when creditors are accorded derivative standing, given the legislative purpose of "encouraging capable persons to serve as directors of corporations by providing them with the freedom to make risky, good faith business decisions without fear of personal liability." To withdraw exculpation merely because creditors are accorded standing to pursue fiduciary duty claims against the directors would "hollow § 102(b)(7) of much of its intended utility."

Directors of financially troubled companies often face incompatible demands by stockholder and creditor constituencies. Vice Chancellor Strine's opinion thoughtfully addresses that context and dispels the spectre that directors of troubled companies operate in a legal straitjacket obliging them to act solely in the interests of creditors. Directors' choices remain difficult ones, but under Production Resources it is clear that those choices, if made in the good faith exercise of business judgment as to the best interest of the firm itself, ought not give rise to any threat of personal liability at the behest of either stockholders or creditors.

Theodore N. Mirvis
Paul K. Rowe
Douglas K. Mayer

January 5, 2005

The Private Securities Litigation Reform Act: Ten Years After

This year marks the tenth anniversary of the Private Securities Litigation Reform Act of 1995 (the "PSLRA"). The PSLRA aimed to eliminate "abusive" securities fraud class actions by erecting "lead plaintiff" procedures designed to encourage institutional investors to take control of lawsuits from opportunistic plaintiffs' lawyers with nominal clients; tightening the rules for pleading fraud; providing a stay of discovery to assure that a fraud claim has a strong factual basis at the outset; creating a "safe harbor" for forward-looking statements accompanied by appropriate risk disclosure; imposing limitations on damages in cases where the stock price recovered after disclosure of the supposedly concealed or misrepresented information; directing the imposition of mandatory sanctions for violations of Fed. R. Civ. P. 11; and replacing joint and several responsibility for damages with proportionate liability for defendants who did not "knowingly" commit securities fraud.[1]

The PSLRA was passed on a rising tide of sentiment that the social costs of private securities litigation had come to outweigh its benefits. In the words of the House conference report, "[t]he private securities litigation system is too important to the integrity of American capital markets to allow this system to be undermined by those who seek to line their own pockets by bringing abusive and meritless suits."[2] The same sentiment led to passage, in 1998, of the Securities Litigation Uniform Standards Act ("SLUSA"), which sought to eliminate securities fraud class actions in state courts, the venue to which plaintiffs' lawyers had repaired to avoid the PSLRA.[3] It is safe to say that the tide crested that year.

Since passage of the PSLRA, we have seen the internet bubble, the wave of corporate scandals known eponymously as "Enron," the IPO scandals, the Wall Street research scandals, the mutual fund scandals, the executive compensation scandals, the explosion of accounting restatements[4] and, most recently, controversies embroiling the insurance and

---

1. 15 U.S.C. § 78u-4(a)-(f).
2. H.R. Conf. Rep. No. 104-369, at 31 (1995), *reprinted in* 1995 U.S.C.C.A.N. 730, 730.
3. *See, e.g.*, Mukesh Bajaj et al., *Securities Class Action Settlements*, 43 Santa Clara L. Rev. 1001, 1005-06 (2003) (discussing shift in filings from federal to state courts immediately after passage of the PSLRA, followed by reversal of that trend following enactment of SLUSA).

health care industries. The legal system has responded on all fronts: Congress, through the Sarbanes-Oxley Act, intervened in internal corporate governance; encouraged "whistle-blowing"; improved accounting oversight; extended the limitations period for securities fraud actions; mandated preservation of financial accounting documents; and heightened criminal and civil penalties for securities fraud.[5] The United States Sentencing Commission adopted new sentencing guidelines that encourage implementation of "effective compliance and ethics" programs and place greater responsibility on boards of directors to monitor internal controls.[6] The Delaware Chancery Court intensified scrutiny of outside directors' independence.[7] The stock exchanges imposed new governance requirements upon listed companies.[8] The Securities and Exchange Commission invigorated its enforcement efforts and adopted a "carrot and stick" approach to encourage internal investigation and self-reporting of securities violations.[9] The Department of Justice launched a Corporate Fraud Task Force and promulgated internal guidelines rewarding "cooperation."[10] And the New York Attorney General became a national figure by using obscure state statutes to force global enterprises to reform their business practices.

---

4. *See* HURON CONSULTING GROUP, 2003 ANNUAL REVIEW OF FINANCIAL REPORTING MATTERS 4 (2003) (showing increase in accounting restatements from 216 in 1999 to 330 in 2002 and 323 in 2003); U.S. GEN. ACCOUNTING OFFICE, PUB. NO. 03-138, FINANCIAL STATEMENT RESTATEMENTS: TRENDS, MARKET IMPACTS, REGULATORY RESPONSES, AND REMAINING CHALLENGES 5 (2002), available at http://www.gao.gov/new.items/d03138.pdf.
5. *See* Sarbanes-Oxley Act of 2002, Pub. L. 107-204, § 302 (codified at 15 U.S.C. § 7241) (requiring financial officers to certify in each annual or quarterly report that they have, *inter alia*, "designed . . . internal controls to ensure that material information relating to the issuer . . . is made known to such officers by others within those entities"); § 806 (codified at 15 U.S.C. § 1514A) (whistle-blower protection); §§ 101-109 (codified at 15 U.S.C. §§ 7211-7219) (accounting oversight); § 804 (amending 28 U.S.C. § 1658) (statute of limitations extension); §§ 103, 802 (codified at 15 U.S.C. § 7213, 18 U.S.C. §§ 1519-1520) (preservation of documents); § 1102 (amending 18 U.S.C. § 1512) (enhanced criminal penalty for destruction of documents); § 304 (codified at 15 U.S.C. § 7243) (providing for forfeiture of bonuses and profits); §§ 902-906 (enhancing penalties for white collar crime); § 805 (directing United States Sentencing Commission to review and amend the sentencing guidelines to ensure that the punishments for obstruction of justice are "sufficient to deter and punish that activity").
6. U.S. Sentencing Comm'n, Amendments to the Sentencing Guidelines 109-112 (2004), *available at* http://www.ussc.gov/2004guid/RFMay04.pdf; *see* U.S.S.G. § 8B2.1 (2004).
7. *See, e.g., In re Oracle Corp. Derivative Litig.*, 824 A.2d 917, 942 (Del. Ch. 2003).

The defense of securities law class actions has been complicated by this sea change in public perception of the social costs of corporate misconduct. Far from sounding the death knell for securities fraud class actions, the PSLRA has arguably revived a litigation device that was coming to be widely perceived as little more than a race-to-the-courthouse extortion racket. As intended, the lead plaintiff provisions have largely replaced figurehead plaintiffs with institutional investors in major cases.[11] In many cases, though, the institutions are public pension funds with decisionmakers perhaps motivated by politics rather than the shareholder interests envisioned by the framers of the PSLRA.[12] The plaintiffs' bar courts these funds intensively by touting large settlements. The consequence is upward pressure on settlement costs. In the process, a handful of large firms have emerged as the counsel of choice.[13] These firms have the capital and staff necessary to bear the costs of investigating and prosecuting complex claims over an extended period, and can resist the pressures for early settlement that characterized pre-PSLRA practice.[14] They employ squads of professional investigators to mine employment agency websites and identify former employees who can act as "confidential sources" for allegations that may have the appearance of sufficient detail to avoid dismissal under the PSLRA pleading standard. Courts have not stood in the way of this practice; rather, the few that have considered it have taken the view that neither the PSLRA's discovery stay nor employee confidentiality agreements preclude voluntary interviews with company employees about alleged wrongdoing within the company.[15]

---

8. *See, e.g.*, Self-Regulatory Organizations; Notice of Filing of Proposed Rule Change and Amendment No. 1 Thereto by the New York Stock Exchange, Inc. Relating to Corporate Governance, 68 Fed. Reg. 19051 (April 17, 2003) (proposed amendments to New York Stock Exchange Listed Company Manual); Self-Regulatory Organizations; Notice of Filing of Proposed Rule Change and Amendment No. 1 Thereto by the National Association of Securities Dealers, Inc. Relating to Proposed Amendments to NASD Rules 4200 and 4350 Regarding Board Independence and Independent Committees, 68 Fed. Reg. 14451 (March 25, 2003) (proposed amendments to NASDAQ rules governing listed companies).
9. *See, e.g.*, Report of Investigation Pursuant to Section 21(a) of the Securities Exchange Act of 1934 and Commission Statement on the Relationship of Cooperation to Agency Enforcement Decisions, Release No. 34-44969, 76 S.E.C. Docket 220, 2001 WL 1301408 (S.E.C. Oct. 23, 2001).
10. Memorandum from Deputy Attorney General Larry D. Thompson to Heads of Department Components, U.S. Attorneys, Principles of Federal Prosecution of Business Organizations (Jan. 20, 2003), *available at* http://www.usdoj.gov/dag/cftf/corporate_guidelines.htm.

Meanwhile, plaintiffs' lawyers at other firms have found other litigation devices. They have repackaged stock drop actions as class actions on behalf of employee benefit plan participants for breach of fiduciary and other duties under the Employee Retirement Income Security Act ("ERISA"). These actions may not be subject to heightened pleading requirements,[16] are not subject to mandatory discovery stays[17] and are often grounded in negligence, which is easier to prove than fraud.[18] The measure of damages is unclear,[19] but can arguably run to hundreds of millions of dollars in cases in which the ERISA plan was heavily invested in sponsor stock.[20] On top of the securities fraud class action, the ERISA action enormously increases the risks and hazards of litigation.

At the same time, the stringency of the PSLRA pleading standards has come under some pressure. Backing away from earlier decisions requiring plaintiffs to allege with great particularity that a defendant made a statement knowing it was false or consciously disregarding contrary information, some courts seem prepared to sustain a complaint on the basis of the "totality of the allegations" even if no particular allegation points to knowledge or recklessness.[21] One appeals court has even suggested

---

11. *See* STEVEN SHALAK & DANIEL DOOLEY, PRICEWATERHOUSECOOPERS LLP 2003, SECURITIES LITIGATION UPDATE—THE PENSION FUND FACTOR 1 (2003) (pension funds have acted as lead plaintiffs in 15 settlements of over $120 million); LAURA E. SIMMONS & ELLEN M. RYAN, CORNERSTONE RESEARCH, POST-REFORM ACT SECURITIES LAWSUITS: SETTLEMENTS REPORTED THROUGH DECEMBER 2003 9 (2003) (reporting that about 30% of all post-PSLRA settlements involved institutional lead plaintiffs); 2003 PRICEWATERHOUSECOOPERS LLP SECURITIES LITIGATION STUDY 6-7 (2003) (institutional investors and public pension funds comprised 51% of lead plaintiffs in securities class actions filed in 2002, and 42% of lead plaintiffs in actions filed in 2003).

12. Another post-PSLRA development is the increasing presence of foreign institutional investors as lead plaintiffs. *See* Stuart M. Grant & Diane Zilka, *The Role of Foreign Investors in Federal Securities Class Actions*, 1442 PLI/CORP. 91, 95 (2004).

13. *See* Richard A. Nagareda, *Administering Adequacy in Class Representation*, 82 TEX. L. REV. 287, 363 (2003).

14. *See* Tamara Loomis, *In Spite of Reform Law, Milberg Weiss Emerges as Winner in Securities Suits*, N.Y. L.J., April 22, 2003, at 1.

15. *See In re JDS Uniphase Corp. Sec. Litig.*, 238 F. Supp. 2d 1127, 1134, 1137 (N.D. Cal. 2002); *In re Tyco Int'l Ltd. Sec. Litig.*, No. 00-MD-1335-B, 2001 WL 34075721, at *3-*4 (D.N.H. Jan. 30, 2001); *In re Flir Sys. Inc., Sec. Litig.*, No. 00-360-HA, 2000 WL 33201904, at *3 (D. Or. Dec. 13, 2000). *But see, e.g.*, *Cal. Pub. Employees' Ret. Sys. v. Chubb Corp.*, --- F. 3d ---, 2004 WL 3015578, at *13-*20 (3d Cir. Dec. 30, 2004) (upholding dismissal of securities class action for failure to plead falsity with the requisite particularity, even though plaintiffs' allegations were based on information from a large number of former employees who acted as confidential sources).

(incorrectly, in our view) a theory of "corporate scienter" that would sustain a complaint in the absence of any facts showing that any individual who made a statement knew it was false or recklessly disregarded the truth.[22] Other courts, however, adhere more strictly to the PSLRA and continue to insist upon particularity in pleading both falsity and scienter.[23]

The stay of discovery, which was intended to protect defendants from actions in which the plaintiff sued first and then used discovery to raise a factual issue sufficient to overcome a motion to dismiss, has come under intense pressure. Some courts have lifted the stay to permit discovery of documents produced in parallel proceedings, such as governmental investigations or even ERISA class actions.[24] Given the rapid multiplication of SEC and DOJ investigations, these decisions, if generalized, could render the "filtering" function of the PSLRA meaningless in many instances. On top of this, a recent Seventh Circuit decision has weakened the forward-looking-statement "safe harbor" by holding that discovery should be permitted to determine whether accompanying "risk" cautions in fact disclosed the risks known to the corporation at the time the statement was made.[25]

Even the "bounceback" limitation on damages has come under pressure.[26] At least one Circuit—the Ninth—has held that a plaintiff may have suffered a loss even if, after the alleged fraud was disclosed, the stock price remained constant or climbed.[27] Other Circuits disagree,[28] and the issue is now before the Supreme Court.[29] But if the Court adopts the Ninth Circuit's view or some variant of it, the decision could have serious

16. *See, e.g., In re ADC Telecom., Inc. ERISA Litig.*, No. Master File, 03-2989 ADM/FLN, 2004 WL 1683144, at *2-*3 (D. Minn. Jul. 26, 2004) (refusing to apply Fed. R. Civ. P. 9(b) to claim that defendants imprudently invested pension funds); *In re Xcel Energy, Inc. Sec., Derivative and "ERISA" Litig.*, 312 F. Supp. 2d 1165, 1179 (D. Minn. 2004) ("In cases where a fraud, misrepresentation or omission is alleged to have occurred but is not itself the basis of the alleged [ERISA] breach, Rule 9(b) is not applied."); *In re Enron Corp. Sec., Derivative & ERISA Litig.*, 284 F. Supp. 2d 511, 652 (S.D. Tex. 2003) ("ERISA does not have heightened pleading requirements, but is subject to the notice pleading standard of Fed. R. of Civ. Procedure 8 . . . ."); *Rankin v. Rots*, 278 F. Supp. 2d 853, 866 (E.D. Mich. 2003) ("The heightened pleading requirement under Rule 9(b) will not be imposed where the claim is for a breach of fiduciary duty under ERISA."); *Stein v. Smith*, 270 F. Supp. 2d 157, 167 (D. Mass. 2003) (ERISA claims not sounding in fraud need not meet requirements of Fed. R. Civ. P. 9(b)). *Cf. In re Sears, Roebuck & Co. ERISA Litig.*, No. 02 C 8324, 2004 WL 407007, at *5-*6 (N.D. Ill. Mar. 3, 2004) (applying Fed. R. Civ. P. 9(b) to ERISA claim based on concealment allegations); *Vivien v. WorldCom, Inc.*, No. C 02-01329 WHA, 2002 WL 31640557, at *7 (N.D. Cal. Jul. 26, 2002) (applying Fed. R. Civ. P. 9(b) to ERISA claim that "clearly sound[ed] in fraud").

implications for the scope and applicability of the PSLRA's damages cap. The cap arguably "assumes that a corrective disclosure of the alleged misrepresentation or omission caused [a price] decline."[30] If the Court were to hold that no such decline must be alleged or proved, a plaintiff might argue that the PSLRA does not bar recovery of damages in cases where the stock price did not drop following disclosure of the fraud.[31]

There is one respect in which courts appear to be moving toward stricter enforcement of the PSLRA, and it is in the area of sanctions. The PSLRA mandates that, upon "final adjudication" of a securities action, the district court make sua sponte findings regarding the parties' compliance with Fed. R. Civ. P. 11(b).[32] That Rule generally permits—but does not require—district courts to impose sanctions on parties and/or their attorneys (depending on the situation) for submitting a pleading or motion for an improper purpose, or for filing a pleading or motion that is not supported by both the evidence and existing law (or a nonfrivolous argument for extension, modification or reversal of existing law). But in securities actions governed by the PSLRA, if a court concludes that a Rule 11 violation has occurred, it has no choice but to impose sanctions.[33] Moreover, the Act erects a rebuttable presumption that sanctions shall consist of either that portion of the opponent's attorneys' fees and costs that is attributable to the violation (in cases where the violation is in connection with a responsive pleading or motion) or all fees and costs incurred "in the action" (where the complaint failed substantially to comply with Rule 11(b)).[34] Although some courts appear not to have fully appreciated the mandatory nature of sanctions under the PSLRA,[35] the trend—particu-

---

17. *See, e.g.*, *In re Royal Ahold N.V. Sec. & ERISA Litig.*, 220 F.R.D. 246, 251 & n. 14 (D. Md. 2004) (acknowledging discretionary power to issue discovery stay in ERISA case, but noting that the PSLRA "does not cover ERISA claims"); *In re AOL Time Warner, Inc. Sec. and "ERISA" Litig.*, MDL No. 1500, 02 Civ. 8853 (SWK), 2003 WL 22227945, at *1 (S.D.N.Y. Sept. 26, 2003) (noting that the PSLRA mandatory discovery stay does not apply to ERISA actions, but using discretionary power to issue stay pending resolution of motion to dismiss in parallel securities litigation); *In re Tyco Int'l, Ltd. Multidistrict Litig. (MDL 1335)*, MDL No. 02-1335-B. 2003 WL 23830479, at *3 (D.N.H. Jan. 29, 2003) (refusing to stay discovery in ERISA case that had been consolidated with securities class action, even though plaintiffs in securities case admittedly would "derive an indirect benefit" from the discovery in the ERISA case).

18. *See, e.g.*, *Beach v. Commonwealth Edison Co.*, 382 F.3d 656, 668-69 (7th Cir. 2004) (holding that lack of proof of scienter did not defeat ERISA claim for breach of fiduciary duty); *Mathews v. Chevron Corp.*, 362 F.3d 1172, 1183 (9th Cir. 2004) (same); *In re AEP ERISA Litig.*, 327 F. Supp. 2d 812, 821-23, 825 (S.D. Ohio 2004) (no requirement that plaintiffs asserting ERISA claims plead scienter or meet the heightened pleading standard set forth in Fed. R. Civ. P. 9(b)).

larly in the Second Circuit—seems to be toward stricter enforcement. The Second Circuit has, in recent years, carefully policed district court's obligations to make Rule 11(b) findings,[36] and has held that a full award of fees and costs was required even when the complaint contained nonfrivolous claims.[37]

Courts have yet to consider in much depth the final major change effected by the PSLRA: the codification of a proportionate liability rule. The PSLRA replaces joint and several liability with proportionate liability for all defendants who engaged in non-knowing securities fraud under the 1934 Act and for outside directors' non-knowing violations of Section 11 of the 1933 Act.[38] The point of the provision was to protect outside directors and other peripheral actors from "coercive pressure . . . to settle meritless claims rather than risk exposing themselves to liability for a grossly disproportionate share of the damages in the case."[39] Logic would dictate that the existence of the provision results in fewer large judgments not only against outside directors, but also against auditors and analysts, since these "gatekeepers" will generally be less culpable than the issuer and its executives. What little data exists seems to support this hypothesis.[40]

More extensive research has been done on the effects of the PSLRA generally. The research shows that, on an annual basis, more cases have been filed after the Act than before[41] and issuers face a greater risk of being sued now than they did before 1995.[42] Although the rate of dismissal increased following passage of the PSLRA,[43] it has fallen off since 2002.[44] The length of time to disposition—whether by settlement or dismissal—has increased since passage of the PSLRA.[45] The settlement data

---

19. *See* ERISA § 409(a), 29 U.S.C. § 1009(a) (directing that defendants found liable for breach of fiduciary duty "shall be personally liable to make good to such plan any losses to the plan resulting from each such breach, and to restore to such plan any profits of such fiduciary which have been made through use of assets of the plan by the fiduciary, and shall be subject to such other equitable or remedial relief as the court may deem appropriate"). The kind and amount of relief awarded under this section is dictated in large part by the particular facts surrounding the alleged breach. *See, e.g., Cal. Ironworkers Field Pension Trust v. Loomis Sayles & Co.*, 259 F.3d 1036, 1046-47 (9th Cir. 2001) (tailoring damages award where plaintiffs complained that the *degree* of investment, rather than the "mere fact of investment in a particular security," constituted a breach); *Donovan v. Bierwirth*, 754 F.2d 1049, 1054-56 (2d Cir. 1985) (discussing different measures of loss applicable to, for example, breach by means of fraud or price manipulation and breach by means of improper investment).

20. The largest settlement to date in an ERISA class action is $85 million—the settlement reached, and tentatively approved, in the Enron litigation. *See* Ellen E. Schultz, *Enron Employees to Settle Retirement Suit for $85 Million*, WALL ST. J., May 13, 2004, at A2.

is mixed: median settlements have increased slightly,[46] but the number of "mega-settlements," i.e., settlements in excess of the once-unheard-of $100 million level, has increased significantly.[47] This is not surprising given the changes in bargaining power that have resulted from the ascendancy of public pension fund lead plaintiffs;[48] the financial and investigative resources of, and competition among, the leading plaintiffs' law firms; the increases in SEC and DOJ enforcement activities and the accompanying pressures to self-report (by means of submissions not necessarily immune from discovery in private actions[49]); the ongoing uncertainties about the measurement of damages; and the fear of litigating complex business and financial matters before a lay jury conditioned by the media to think the worst of corporate America.

We know of no study that would definitively show the extent to which the PSLRA has deterred "abusive" securities litigation. We do know that shareholder class actions—whether framed as securities fraud or ERISA suits—are more numerous than ever, and continue to pose risks and costs that can result in settlements disproportionate to the merits of the claims. Much remains to be done before the PSLRA can be finally assessed; the Circuits remain split on the proper pleading standard for scienter, the degree of protection afforded by the safe harbor, and the requirements for pleading loss causation. District courts are still grappling with the scope of the PSLRA's discovery stay and the proper interplay between securities

---

21. *See, e.g., Broudo v. Dura Pharm., Inc.*, 339 F.3d 933, 940 (9th Cir. 2003) (vacating district court's finding of no scienter because court failed to consider whether allegations taken as whole—rather than individually—gave rise to a strong inference of scienter); *see also PR Diamonds, Inc. v. Chandler*, 364 F.3d 671, 683 (6th Cir. 2004) (confirming that Sixth Circuit applies a "totality of the circumstances" test for scienter pleadings). *But see Fidel v. Farley*, --- F.3d ---, No. 02-6143, 2004 WL 2901274, at *11 (6th Cir. Dec. 16, 2004) (observing that "totality of the circumstances" test does not absolve plaintiffs of obligation to plead scienter with particularity). What is required to plead a "strong inference" of scienter varies somewhat from Circuit to Circuit. *Compare, e.g., In re Scholastic Corp. Sec. Litig.*, 252 F.3d 63, 76 (2d Cir. 2001) ("strong inference" can be pled by alleging "motive and opportunity" or "strong circumstantial evidence of . . . conscious misbehavior or recklessness"), *with In re Silicon Graphics Sec. Litig.*, 183 F.3d 970, 979 (9th Cir. 1999) (pleading "motive and opportunity" is not enough under the PSLRA; plaintiffs must plead facts showing intent or "*deliberate* recklessness" (emphasis added)).

22. *See City of Monroe Employees Ret. Sys .v. Bridgestone Corp.*, 387 F.3d 468, 506-08 & 508 n.35 (6th Cir. 2004) (attributing individual officer's knowledge of facts to corporate defendant for purposes of scienter pleading, but finding that plaintiffs had failed to plead a Section 10(b) case against that individual officer because he was not involved in making the supposedly fraudulent representations).

fraud and ERISA class actions premised on the same facts. How these issues are resolved in years to come will no doubt have an impact on the degree to which "abusive" securities class actions are—as Congress intended—curtailed.

Warren R. Stern
Sarah E. McCallum

23. *See, e.g., Southland Sec. Corp. v. INSpire Ins. Solutions, Inc.*, 365 F.3d 353, 366 (5th Cir. 2004) ("[f]or purposes of determining whether a statement made by the corporation was made by it with the requisite Rule 10(b) [sic] scienter" one must "look to the state of mind of the individual corporate official or officials who make or issue the statement" alleged to be false or misleading); *Chubb*, 2004 WL 3015578, at *13-*20 (applying rigorous particularity standard to uphold dismissal of complaint based largely on information from confidential sources).

24. *See, e.g., In re LaBranche Sec. Litig.*, 333 F. Supp. 2d 178, 182-83 (S.D.N.Y. 2004); *In re Royal Ahold N.V. Sec. & ERISA Litig.*, 220 F.R.D. 246, 250 (D. Md. 2004); *Singer v. Nicor, Inc.*, No. 02 C 5168, 2003 WL 22013905, at *2 (N.D. Ill. Apr. 23, 2003); *In re WorldCom, Inc. Sec. Litig.*, 234 F. Supp. 2d 301, 306 (S.D.N.Y. 2002); *In re Enron Corp. Sec., Derivative & ERISA Litig.*, Nos. MDL-1446, Civ.A. H-01-3624, 2002 WL 31845114, at *2 (S.D. Tex. Aug. 16, 2002). *But see, e.g., In re Lantronix, Inc. Sec. Litig.*, No. CV 02-03899 PA, 2003 WL 22462393, at *2 (C.D. Cal. Sept. 26, 2003) (refusing to lift stay even though documents had already been produced to governmental agencies); *Rampersad v. Deutsche Bank Sec. Inc.*, No. 02 Civ. 7311 (LTS), 2003 WL 21074094, at *2 (S.D.N.Y. May 9, 2003) (same); *In re Vivendi Universal, S.A., Sec. Litig.*, No. 02 Civ. 5571 (HB), 2003 WL 21035383, at *1 (S.D.N.Y. May 6, 2003) (same).

25. *See Asher v. Baxter Int'l Inc.*, 377 F.3d 727, 734 (7th Cir. 2004). *Compare Rombach v. Chang*, 355 F.3d 164, 176 (2d Cir. 2004) (safe harbor applied even though risk disclosures were "formulaic").

26. *See* 15 U.S.C. § 78*u*-4(e).

27. *See Broudo v. Dura Pharm., Inc.*, 339 F.3d 933, 938 (9th Cir. 2003) (holding that allegation of price inflation was sufficient to state a claim for securities fraud, even if price of securities did not fall following disclosure of fraud); *see also Gebhardt v. ConAgra Foods, Inc.*, 335 F.3d 824, 831-32 (8th Cir. 2003) ("[S]tockholders can be damaged in ways other than seeing their stocks decline. If a stock does not appreciate as it would have absent the fraudulent conduct, investors have suffered a harm.").

28. *See Semerenko v. Cendant Corp.*, 223 F.3d 165, 185 (3d Cir. 2000) ("Where the value of the security does not actually decline as a result of an alleged misrepresentation, it cannot be said that there is in fact an economic loss attributable to that misrepresentation); *Robbins v. Koger Properties, Inc.*, 116 F.3d 1441, 1447-48 (11th Cir. 1997) (a "showing of price inflation . . . does not satisfy the loss causation requirement").

29. *See Dura Pharm., Inc. v. Broudo*, 124 S. Ct. 2904 (2004) (granting cert.).

30. *See* Petition for Writ of Certiorari at 17, *Dura Pharm., Inc. v. Broudo*, 124 S. Ct. 2904 (2004) (No. 03-932).

31. *See* Respondents' Brief at 39-40, *Dura Pharm.* (No. 03-932) (noting that PSLRA only imposes damages cap where plaintiffs seek to "establish damages by reference to the market price of a security," 15 U.S.C. § 78*u*-4(e), and arguing that the cap would not apply where another measure is used); *see also Blackie v. Barrack*, 524 F.2d 891, 909 n.25 (9th Cir. 1975) (suggesting that measuring damages based on market price following disclosure is not the only measure available).

32. 15 U.S.C. 78*u*-4(c)(1).

33. 15 U.S.C. § 78*u*-4(c)(2).

34. 15 U.S.C. § 78*u*-4(c)(3)(A).

January 7, 2005

The WorldCom Settlement and Director Liability

Directors are asking themselves an important question this week in the aftermath of the recently announced WorldCom settlement: Is it still safe to sit on the Board of a public U.S. company in the aftermath of Enron, Sarbanes-Oxley and now the WorldCom directors' $18 million personal out-of-pocket settlement payments?

Our answer is "yes".

In support of this answer we offer the following observations:

- WorldCom represents an extreme case. It was the largest American company to ever file bankruptcy, with significant allegations of accounting fraud.
- The payments by the directors are part of a negotiated settlement. This is not a judicial decision that sets a new legal standard governing director duties.

---

35. *See, e.g.*, *Harding Univ. v. Consulting Servs. Group, L.P.*, 48 F. Supp. 2d 765, 772 (N.D. Ill. 1999) (denying motion for sanctions because court, in its "discretion," determined that "defendants suffered no damage" during the period between filing of complaint and its withdrawal; using "same reasons" to reject argument that PSLRA mandated sanctions); *see also Khan v. Park Capital Sec., LLC*, No. C 03 00574 RS, 2004 WL 1753385, at *6 (N.D. Cal. Aug. 5, 2004) (declining to impose sanctions under Rule 11 and the PSLRA even though claims against defendant "lack[ed] evidentiary support").
36. *See Rombach v. Chang*, 355 F.3d 164, 178 (2d Cir. 2004); *Gurary v. Winehouse*, 190 F.3d 37, 47 (2d Cir. 1999).
37. *See Gurary v. Nu-Tech Bio-Med, Inc.*, 303 F.3d 212, 223-25 (2d Cir. 2002) (vacating district court's award of half fees and costs; directing that defendants be awarded full fees and costs in connection with the action because the complaint failed substantially to comply with Rule 11(b)); *see also Gurary v. Winehouse*, 235 F.3d 792, 800 (2d Cir. 2000) (vacating district court's decision not to impose sanctions under Rule 11(b) and the PSLRA and holding that sanctions were mandated in connection with part of the complaint); *Inter-County Res., Inc. v. Med. Res., Inc.*, 49 F. Supp. 2d 682 (S.D.N.Y. 1999) (imposing sanctions for pleading Rule 10b-5 claims against people who were neither buyers nor sellers of securities).
38. 15 U.S.C. § 78*u*-4(f)(2), (10).
39. H.R. Conf. Rep. No. 104-369, at 37-38 (1995), *reprinted in* 1995 U.S.C.C.A.N. 730, 736-37.
40. *See* John C. Coffee, Jr., *What Caused Enron? A Capsule Social and Economic History of the 1990s*, 89 CORNELL L. REV. 269, 290 & n.94 (2004) (observing that "although auditors are still sued today, the settlement value of cases against auditors has significantly decreased").

- The payment of $18 million, while significant (purportedly roughly 20% of the directors combined net worth, excluding primary residences, retirement accounts and certain joint marital assets), pales in comparison to the personal financial costs suffered by the outside directors (as well as shareholders and employees) from the loss of value in their WorldCom shares.
- WorldCom is a very high profile case, on par with the likes of Penn Central and Lincoln Savings, and numerous other parties (including the banks) have or will contribute several billion dollars in aggregate to the settlement.
- Scathing reports by Special Investigative Counsel and Bankruptcy Monitor Richard Breeden painted a highly negative picture of the WorldCom directors (with significant focus on the Board's role in approving $400 million in loans to Bernard Ebbers).

Still, there remain some good reasons for concern:

- In the current environment, there is a huge and growing demand on the part of regulators, enforcement agencies and the public for "personal accountability" on the part of all corporate actors.

---

41. *See* Michael A. Perino, *Did the Private Securities Litigation Reform Act Work?*, 2003 U. ILL. L. REV. 913, 932 (2003) (observing a significant increase in the number of issuers sued since the passage of the PSLRA); Bajaj et al., *supra* note 3, at 1005-06 (noting short-lived decrease in filings immediately following passage of the PSLRA); ELAINE BUCKBERG ET AL., NERA ECONOMIC CONSULTING, RECENT TRENDS IN SECURITIES CLASS ACTION LITIGATION: 2003 EARLY UPDATE 2, 4 (2004) [hereinafter BUCKBERG ET AL. (I)] (statistics showing that, on average, annual post-PSLRA filings in federal court have exceeded annual pre-PSLRA filings); Jordan Eth & Daniel S. Drosman, *The Private Securities Litigation Reform Act: Five Years Young*, SEC. & COMMODITIES REG., Vol. 34, No. 13, at 155 (2001) (reporting data collected by Woodruff-Sawyer & Co.); *see also* CORNERSTONE RESEARCH, SECURITIES CLASS ACTION CASE FILINGS 2004: A YEAR IN REVIEW 2 (2004) (reporting a 17% increase in "traditional" securities class action filings from 2003 to 2004).
42. *See* BUCKBERG ET AL., NERA ECONOMIC CONSULTING, RECENT TRENDS IN SECURITIES CLASS ACTION LITIGATION: WILL ENRON AND SARBANES-OXLEY CHANGE THE TIDES? 4 (2003) [hereinafter BUCKBERG ET AL. (II)] (recording 40% increase in "probability of facing a securities class action" since 1995).
43. *See* Perino, *supra* note 41, at 937; RICHARD PAINTER ET AL., FEDERALIST SOCIETY FOR LAW AND PUBLIC POLICY STUDIES, PRIVATE SECURITIES LITIGATION REFORM ACT: A POST-ENRON ANALYSIS 8 (2002) (collecting data).
44. *See* BUCKBERG ET AL. (I), *supra* note 41, at 4 (observing sharp decrease in numbers of dismissals since passage of the Sarbanes-Oxley Act of 2002).

- Stephen Cutler, Director of the SEC's Division of Enforcement warned in a September 2004 speech that "Over the next year, we intend to continue focusing closely in our investigations on whether outside directors have lived up to their roles as guardians of the shareholders they serve."
- While the Commission recently rejected a settlement in Global Crossing (involving the non-executive chairman) and a provision of a recent Disney settlement (involving the CEO and then Chairman), due to their expansive notions of director and CEO duties, two Commissioners and the Staff were supportive of the settlements.
- We are witnessing an unfortunate trend in enforcement and private litigation, where each case (no matter what the specific facts of that case), tends to create a new precedent for the next action. There needs to be a strong effort to resist this trend.
- Few spokespeople today are standing up for the need for balance in the actions taken in response to the Enron and WorldCom scandals

---

45. *See* Bajaj et al., *supra* note 3, at 1010-11 (reporting increase in average time between filing and settlement or dismissal following passage of PSLRA); *see also* BUCKBERG ET AL. (II), *supra* note 42, at 5; PAINTER ET AL., *supra* note 43, at 8 (discussing NERA data showing increase in length of time to disposition following PSLRA).
46. *See* Bajaj et al., *supra* note 3, at 1022 (reporting "that the mean and median settlement amounts are higher for cases settled in the post-PSLRA period compared to those settled before 1996"); Perino, *supra* note 41, at 939-941 (collecting data and concluding that settlement size has increased slightly since passage of the PSLRA).
47. *See* 2003 PRICEWATERHOUSECOOPERS LLP SECURITIES LITIGATION STUDY 2 (2003) ("[T]he amounts of settlements, and the potency of cases, increased in 2003, continuing a trend that began in 1996—after passage of the [PSLRA]."); *see also* BUCKBERG ET AL. (II), *supra* note 42, at 7; Stanford Law School Securities Class Action Clearinghouse, Securities Fraud "Mega-Settlements" List, *available at* http://securities.stanford.edu. Another recent development in the settlement of securities class actions is the agreement of WorldCom and Enron directors to make major personal contributions toward settlement funds. *See* Kurt Eichenwald, *Ex-Directors at Enron Chip in on Settlement*, N.Y. TIMES, Jan. 8, 2005, at C1; Gretchen Morgenson, *10 Ex-Directors from WorldCom to Pay Millions*, N.Y. TIMES, Jan. 6, 2005, at A1.
48. *See* STEVEN SHALAK & DANIEL DOOLEY, PRICEWATERHOUSECOOPERS LLP 2003, SECURITIES LITIGATION UPDATE—THE PENSION FUND FACTOR 1 (2003) (observing correlation between presence of pension funds as lead plaintiffs and settlements of over $120 million); BUCKBERG ET AL. (II), *supra* note 42, at 10-11 ("Consistent with Congressional objectives, we find that settlements are about 20% higher in cases where the lead plaintiff is an institutional investor.").

and the aggressive enforcement calendar being pursued by the State A.G.s, the SEC and the DOJ.

- Thus, there remains a serious risk that the strong foundations of the business judgment rule and the traditional deference shown to corporate managers and outside directors are being slowly eroded. Some of the post-Enron, post-Sarbanes-Oxley expectations being placed on senior managers and outside directors, are both unrealistic and unfair.

What's a Board to do? We continue to offer the following core advice to all Boards and individual directors:

- If you serve on a board you must be active and attentive. You must put in the time and put in the effort (including by reading all Board materials carefully).
- You must have best-in-class governance practices. The New York Stock Exchange Governance Rules and related best-in-class charters and governance policies that have been adopted by most leading corporations provide a good solid roadmap for what is reasonable to be expected from a board and its committees.
- You must be exceedingly careful in the review of any transactions involving management participation.
- You must take the independence requirements set forth under the Stock Exchange Rules and Sarbanes-Oxley seriously, and avoid any appearance of impropriety. You must act solely in the interests of the company and its shareholders.
- You must do your diligence carefully before accepting a Board seat and associate yourself only with institutions and management teams of high integrity.
- You must take all regulatory/compliance and accounting deficiencies seriously and demand rapid corrective actions on the part of management.
- You should make sure there is adequate D&O insurance including, where practicable, separate "Side-A" insurance covering the direc-

---

49. *See, e.g.*, *In re Subpoenas Duces Tecum to Fulbright & Jaworski and Vinson & Elkins*, 99 F.R.D. 582, 585 (D.D.C. 1983) (law firm waived attorney-client privilege by producing documents to the SEC).

tors separate and apart from the corporation. This is particularly important in the context of a bankruptcy.

Martin Lipton
Edward D. Herlihy
Andrew R. Brownstein
Craig M. Wasserman

February 3, 2005

Corporate Governance: Shareholder Activism in 2004 and Implications for 2005

David A. Katz[50]

Shareholder activism continued to accelerate during the 2004 proxy season. The governance issues that drew the attention of shareholder activists were largely the same as those in the past, with an increased focus on executive compensation issues, while activist institutions such as CalPERS and other state pension plans and unions, with the support of leading proxy advisory firms such as Institutional Shareholder Services (ISS) and Glass Lewis, continued to promote their corporate governance agendas through a variety of tactics. These included organized "withhold vote" campaigns targeting members of the board of directors of such notable companies as Disney, Safeway, Coca-Cola and MBNA. Shareholder activism generally, and in particular the use of "withhold vote" campaigns, gained more significance in light of the Securities and Exchange Commission's proposed proxy access rules, which if adopted would mandate access under certain circumstances to a company's proxy statement for board nominees proposed by dissident shareholders.

Shareholder Proposals in 2004

Shareholder activism during the 2004 proxy season centered on the usual corporate governance topics, including issues such as:

- Executive compensation, with a particular focus on equity-based compensation and expensing of options,
- Eliminating shareholders rights plans, and
- Declassifying boards, so that all directors are elected annually.

One new topic was the use of shareholder proposals seeking to implement shareholder access to nominate candidates for election as directors on a company-by-company basis. As discussed below, this issue is likely to gain further prominence in 2005, particularly if the SEC's proposed proxy access rules are not adopted prior to or during the proxy season.

---

50. David A. Katz is a partner at Wachtell, Lipton, Rosen & Katz. Matthew M. Guest, an associate at Wachtell, Lipton, Rosen & Katz, assisted in the preparation of this article. The views expressed are the author's and do not necessarily represent the views of his colleagues or his firm

As in past proxy seasons, corporate governance issues were seized upon by activist shareholders, most frequently individuals or labor unions, who submitted proposals, often with the substantial support of significant shareholders such as state pension funds and influential proxy advisory firms. According to the recent Georgeson Shareholder review of the 2004 proxy season, the total number of corporate governance proposals that came to a vote declined by approximately 3 percent from 2003.[51] However, the number of these proposals that were submitted but subsequently omitted or withdrawn increased significantly by approximately 22 percent. This increase in withdrawn or omitted proposals is attributable at least in part to increased dialogue between companies targeted by these proposals and the shareholder proponents or proxy advisory firms, which led in some cases to the companies adopting governance changes which rendered the proposals moot, or at least satisfied the shareholder proponent sufficiently such that the proposal was withdrawn. Moreover, the possibility that proxy access rules could be adopted by the SEC provided an increased incentive to companies to discuss governance changes rather than face a shareholder proposal that would run the risk of being approved by either a majority of votes cast or a majority of outstanding shares.

Corporate governance proposals that were voted on in 2004 received on average a slightly higher level of shareholder support than in previous years; however, the total number of shareholder proposals receiving majority votes declined significantly in 2004 to just over 100, from over more than 170 in 2003. According to the Georgeson Shareholder review, once again this year shareholder proposals receiving on average the highest percentage votes were those relating to the repeal of takeover defense measures. Among these, proposals to repeal classified boards and supermajority voting requirements achieved on average a vote in excess of 50 percent of outstanding shares.[52]

"Withhold Vote" Campaigns

Traditional shareholder proposals took a back seat in 2004 to what was often a more potent tactic utilized by shareholder activists and proxy advisory firms to press for change in companies' governance policies—the threat of withhold votes with respect to some or all of the members of a company's board of directors who were up for election. Proxy advisors such as ISS have demonstrated a willingness to use this approach rou-

51. Georgeson Shareholder, *2004 Annual Corporate Governance Review* (available at http://www.georgesonshareholder.com/pdf/2004_corpgov.pdf).
52. *Id.*

tinely, according to established policies that dictate a withhold vote recommendation when, for instance, the board of a company has failed to implement a majority-approved shareholder proposal or fails to meet certain standards for board or committee independence. ISS's own assessment of the 2004 proxy season revealed that its use of withhold vote recommendations declined significantly in 2004, to 32 percent of the companies it covered versus 38 percent in 2003 and 54 percent in 2002.[53] As was the case with the decline in shareholder proposals coming to a vote, the reduction in withhold vote recommendations is likely .largely attributable to companies taking preemptive actions, again motivated at least in part by the possibility of proxy access rules, to address concerns of ISS and other proxy advisory firms.

Even with the decline in withhold vote recommendations, members of the board of directors of a substantial number of companies were the subject of withhold vote recommendations. Only five companies, however, ended up with withhold votes exceeding 30 percent this year. Indeed, for each of the withhold campaigns that resulted in high withhold vote, such as at Federated Department Stores (61 percent) and MBNA (47 percent), there were other high profile examples such as Safeway Stores where, despite a well-orchestrated and highly publicized withhold vote campaign by CalPERS (bolstered by an ISS withhold vote recommendation in the case of the company's Chairman and CEO), the percentage of withhold votes totaled less than 17 percent for each member of the board of directors standing for election.

Another widely reported withhold vote recommendation was ISS's withhold vote recommendation targeting Warren Buffett as a member of Coca-Cola's board of directors, based upon ISS deeming Mr. Buffett to be a non-independent member of the audit committee of the Coca-Cola board. Following reports of this withhold vote recommendation, and others targeting other highly regarded business leaders, there appeared to be a building sentiment that some withhold vote campaigns have gone too far—withhold vote recommendations were being made on the basis of agendas not of wide concern to all shareholders or narrow ideological litmus tests, rather than on the perceived value of a director candidate in building shareholder value or in contributing valuable business acumen and advice to the company. Despite this criticism, in its recently released Corporate Governance Policy Update for 2005, ISS made no change or

53. Institutional Shareholder Services, *2004 Postseason Report: A New Corporate Governance World: From Confrontation to Constructive Dialogue* (available at http://www.issproxy.com/pdf/2004ISSPSR.pdf).

exception to the policy that led to its withhold vote recommendation on Warren Buffett. In late 2004, the president of CalPERS was removed by the California state agency which oversees the management of the pension fund, a response that appeared to be in part driven by the criticism that CalPERS received over these recent actions.

Proposed Proxy Access Rules

The consistent view is that the decline in majority-approved shareholder proposals and withhold vote recommendations in 2004 are not attributable to any reduction in shareholder activism but instead appear to result from the fact that public companies increasingly are electing to adopt governance changes rather than facing dissident shareholder campaigns. The threat of dissident shareholder actions is of heightened concern, as successful director withhold vote campaigns and certain successful shareholder proposals may bring with them the possibility of shareholder access to the proxy to nominate directors under rules proposed by the SEC last year but not yet adopted.

The proposed access rules would generally provide access to the company's proxy statement for director nominees nominated by a shareholder or group holding at least 5 percent of a company's shares for at least two years if one or more of the company's board members received a withhold vote of 35 percent or greater at the last annual meeting, or if any shareholder proposal (made by a shareholder or group holding at least 1 percent of the company's shares for at least a year) to provide direct access to a company's proxy statement for shareholder director nominees had been approved by a majority of votes cast.[54] The proposed rules in general, and these low thresholds in particular, have been subject to significant criticism from a variety of sources.[55] Even if the proposed proxy access rules fail to be adopted by the SEC, it is possible that an increased number of shareholder proposals relating to access to the proxy statement for election of shareholder-nominated directors will be submitted for consideration.

Executive Compensation

A continued topic of interest for both the SEC and shareholder activists was executive compensation. Among the events of note this year were

54. Proposed Rule: Security Holder Director Nominations, Exchange Act Rel. No. 34-48626 (October 14, 2003).

55. *See, e.g.,* Comment letter of Wachtell, Lipton, Rosen & Katz (November 14, 2003).

the settlement between the SEC and General Electric regarding GE's disclosure of Jack Welch's retirement benefits,[56] and the late October speech by Alan Beller, the Director of the Division of Corporation Finance of the SEC, in which he expressed concern about the current level of disclosure by public companies of their executive compensation arrangements.[57] From both of these situations it is clear that the SEC maintains a heightened interest in executive compensation issues, and will insist on detailed disclosure of all compensation arrangements in order to fully comply with the proxy rules. Moreover, Mr. Beller mentioned in his speech several issues relating to executive compensation disclosure that are the subject of preliminary consideration by the SEC Staff for potential rule-making activity. Among these are

- More detailed requirements with respect to disclosure of perquisites and retirement benefits and deferred compensation,
- Enhanced disclosure of total compensation, and
- Possible expanded disclosure requirements for director compensation, additional executive officers beyond those currently required, compensation committee reports, and related party transactions as they relate to executive compensation.

It is likely that shareholder activists will continue to pursue their broad-based agendas relating to executive compensation issues in the 2005 proxy season. Also, based on its recent Corporate Governance Policy Update for 2005, it appears that ISS is continuing to refine its positions on executive compensation, and the application of these positions in the next proxy season may impact votes on compensation matters.[58] As an example, ISS indicated that it will recommend a vote against a company's equity plan with a three-year average "burn rate" (which means the ratio of annual equity awards made over outstanding shares) that is high relative to the relevant industry mean and is in excess of 2 percent of the company's outstanding shares.[59] This policy is entirely new and represents yet another area in which some companies can expect institutional shareholder resistance in the future.

---

56. *In the Matter of General Electric*, Exchange Act Rel. No. 34-50426 (September 23, 2004).
57. Alan Beller, *Remarks Before Conference of the NASPP, The Corporate Counsel and The Corporate Executive* (October 20, 2004).
58. Institutional Shareholder Services, *ISS U.S. Corporate Governance Policy: 2005 Updates*.
59. *Id.* at 15.

Other Developments

Another notable development in shareholder activism in 2004 was the very unusual dissident campaign involving MONY and its friendly merger transaction with AXA Financial. MONY's cash merger agreement with AXA was accompanied by renegotiation of executive change-in-control arrangements to lower the cost of these arrangements to the combined company. Certain dissident shareholders, including several investment firms, viewed the consideration to be received by the MONY shareholders in the merger as too low and contended that the transaction was driven by management's self-interest. The dissident MONY shareholders used a variety of tactics to oppose the merger including mailing proxy solicitation materials that included a duplicate of MONY's management's proxy card. A federal district court in New York initially agreed with the view of the SEC staff and refused to enjoin the inclusion of a duplicate of the company's proxy card in the dissident group's mailings which were claimed by the dissident group to be solicitations that were exempt from the proxy rules' disclosure requirements.[60] However, subsequently the U.S. Court of Appeals for the Second Circuit reversed the district court's decision, holding that the use of the duplicate proxy card should be enjoined on the grounds that it was being sent to facilitate revocation of shareholders' earlier proxies and thus the solicitation was not exempt from disclosure requirements under the proxy rules.[61] The Delaware Chancery Court, in a separate ruling, required MONY to provide additional disclosure concerning its executive compensation arrangements in its proxy statement.[62] In the end, the dissident campaign failed to achieve its objective but significantly impacted the voting process on the merger, resulting in a delayed approval of the merger by a small margin of votes. In addition, during the course of the dissident campaign, in order to provide additional incentive for its shareholder to approve the merger, MONY declared two special dividends totaling almost $0.35 per share that were payable contingent upon consummation of the merger. The MONY situation indicates that well-organized dissident shareholder actions can potentially jeopardize a vote even on a friendly merger, which is a risk that has not often been seen in the past.

---

60. *MONY Group, Inc. v. Highfields Capital Management, LP*, 2004 WL 253330, slip op. (S.D.N.Y., Feb. 11, 2004).
61. *MONY Group, Inc. v. Highfields Capital Management, LP*, 368 F.3d 138 (2d Cir. 2004).
62. *In re the MONY Group, Inc. Shareholders Litigation*, C.A. 20554 (Del. Ch. Feb. 17, 2004).

The recently completed merger between Anthem and WellPoint Health Networks was another notable deal that came under attack from an institutional shareholder this year. Citing what it deemed to be excessive change of control payments to WellPoint executives, CalPERS issued a press release announcing its opposition to the merger and indicating its intention to encourage other institutional shareholders to do the same. In a departure from some voting situations, ISS declared its disagreement with CalPERS by reaffirming its recommendation that shareholders of both companies vote in favor of the merger. In the end, CalPERS opposition had little or no effect on the voting results, as the merger was easily approved by each company's shareholders, including by more than 97 percent of the shares voting on the matter at each shareholder meeting.

A more recent example of institutional shareholder activism in merger votes can be seen in the pending vote on the proposed acquisition of King Pharmaceuticals by Mylan Laboratories. A hedge fund with a significant stake in King Pharmaceuticals obtained a voting stake in Mylan of almost ten percent, while taking on little or no additional economic risk, evidently by acquiring shares of Mylan (including their associated voting rights) and, through bank intermediaries, hedging by executing a short sale or derivative transaction on the same number of shares. This maneuver, evidently intended to increase the likelihood of the acquisition's approval by Mylan shareholders and eventual completion and the corresponding increase in the value of King Pharmaceuticals' shares, is presently the subject of a lawsuit by Carl Icahn challenging the tactic as improper under federal and state law.[63] Icahn, an almost 10 percent shareholder of Mylan, is separately waging a battle to block the merger on the basis that Mylan should be sold to a third party, and Icahn has himself submitted an acquisition proposal which he has reiterated in his solicitation materials opposing the issuance of Mylan shares in the acquisition of King Pharmaceuticals. Icahn also maintains a significant short position in King Pharmaceuticals and would therefore benefit from the decline in value of the King Pharmaceuticals shares if the merger were not approved. The ongoing contest in the Mylan/King Pharmaceuticals transaction, and the motivations underlying the respective shareholder groups' actions, illustrate the significant potential for sophisticated, well-capitalized institutional investors to wield considerable influence over the outcome of merger votes. This possibility should be carefully considered by

---

63. *High River Limited Partnership Plaintiff vs. Mylan Laboratories, Inc.,* Complaint (M.D. Pa., Dec. 10, 2004).

companies in determining their proxy solicitation strategies in the context of a deal or a contested situation.

* * * * **

It appears unlikely shareholder activism will subside markedly in the near future. High withhold votes at companies like Disney and MBNA—each approaching 50 percent—are still a recent memory. A lesson from recent years is that, at least with certain issues and certain companies, pressure from shareholder activists can have an impact, thus further encouraging continued activism in the near-term. This is particularly true in the current legal and regulatory climate of corporate scandals and Sarbanes-Oxley regulation where public companies have an additional incentive to lower their profile and to avoid unnecessary negative publicity. Boards of directors should continue to be guided by the principle of acting to protect the best interests of the company and all of its shareholders. Boards should be made aware of any potential shareholder activist campaigns targeting a particular industry or company, and consider acting proactively where appropriate. Directors should be cautious, however, not to overreact to the threat of these tactics at the expense of important longer-term shareholder interests.

February 22, 2005

Some Thoughts For Boards of Directors in 2005

Martin Lipton[64]

The post-Enron accounting and corporate governance reforms have imposed new responsibilities on corporate directors. At the same time, there is a continuing drumbeat of demands for limitations on director authority from activist shareholder groups, populist politicians and academic gadflies. Chief among the demands are a more stringent definition of director independence, more "shareholder power" and more restrictions on the amounts and form of executive compensation. These demands were backed up by more than 1100 shareholder proxy proposals in 2004, of which over 130 received majority shareholder votes. Increasingly, the pressures on today's directors are coming from a multitude of directions, with federal securities laws, federal sentencing guidelines, stock exchange governance requirements, shareholder activism and court decisions all competing to mandate or suggest new director responsibilities.

The decisions by the non-management directors of WorldCom and Enron to pay out of their own pockets $18 million and $13 million, respectively, to settle shareholder lawsuits has significantly increased the concerns of directors as to their exposure to liability. Although both WorldCom and Enron were extreme cases and neither involved any judicial determination of fault by the directors, the harsh language used by the lawyers representing the shareholder-plaintiffs and by Alan Hevesi, the Comptroller of the State of New York and the lead plaintiff in the WorldCom case, that the settlement "sends a strong message to the directors…that they must be vigilant guardians for the shareholders…[and] [w]e will hold them personally liable if they allow management…to commit fraud" has put additional pressure on directors.

The response to these pressures by the accounting, consulting and legal advisors to corporations has been an almost endless parade of best practices, stylized agendas, checklists, director education programs and extra meetings. Some of these will undoubtedly contribute to improved governance and transparency. But the totality, unless judiciously applied, is more likely to make boards less, rather than more, effective, and in

64. Partner, Wachtell, Lipton, Rosen & Katz. The author's colleagues, Igor Kirman and Umut Ergun, assisted in the preparation of this memorandum.

extreme cases will so overburden boards with process that they become dysfunctional.

Despite the WorldCom and Enron settlements, there is no legal reason for directors to be overly concerned about process. These two cases are among the most egregious of the series of scandals that followed the bursting of the Millennium Bubble, were the subject of scathing reports by the bankruptcy trustees critical of the directors, involved billions in fraudulent misstatements, and were brought under the strict liability provisions of the Federal Securities Laws, not the fiduciary duty requirements of state law. They do not establish a precedent for the future. The business judgment rule is alive and well. It is not necessary for boards to overreact in order to establish entitlement to the protection of the rule and freedom from the threat of personal liability. It is still safe to sit on the board of a public company in the U.S.

In order to avoid an overemphasis on process and at the same time effectively discharge the board's fundamental duties to appropriately monitor and supervise the business of the corporation, it is necessary to identify the matters on which the board should focus and to create a reasonable program to deal with them. The following are recommendations for such a program in today's environment. Obviously, "one size does not fit all" and the board of each corporation can and should tailor procedures to its own circumstances. This memo assumes that the corporation has implemented all of the Sarbanes-Oxley, SEC and NYSE post-Enron reforms and this is not an "how to do it" memo about complying with those requirements.

The role and duties of the board. The past twenty years have witnessed a transition from the advisory board to the monitoring board. While the board has always had a dual role as a resource and adviser for management, on the one hand, and as an independent agent of shareholders on the other, in recent years government regulators and activist shareholders, empowered by the reaction to the Enron-type scandals and often in competition with each other, have been tipping this balance with increasing force in favor of monitoring. But even today it is generally acknowledged that a combination of the two is necessary and that only a collegial board can function effectively. To be truly effective, each board must find the right balance between monitoring and advising as to strategy.

Tone at the top. One of the single most important factors in ensuring that a board meets all of its duties is having the right "tone at the top" of the corporation. The tone at the top will form the culture of the corporation and permeate the corporation's relationship not only with investors, but also with employees, customers, suppliers, local communities and other constituents. If the CEO and senior management are not personally committed to high ethical standards, principles of fair dealing, full compliance with legal requirements and resistance to Wall Street pressures for short term results, no amount of board process or corporate compliance programs will protect the board from embarrassment. The board should participate in creating the corporate culture and should periodically review with the CEO what the CEO and senior management are doing to set the right example and how it is being communicated to all employees and constituents of the corporation. Transparency is key: the board's vision for the corporation, including its commitment to ethics and zero tolerance to compliance failures, should be set out in the annual report and communicated effectively within the corporation.

CEO selection and succession planning. In addition to setting the tone at the top, the single most important function of the board is selecting and evaluating the CEO and the senior executive leadership of the corporation and planning for their succession. The critical importance of the CEO role is a function of the modern corporation itself. As Peter Drucker recently put it, "the Enterprise can be said to be the one invention that created the Modern Economy—far more so than any other invention, whether material or conceptual. With the invention of the Enterprise the Executive came into being as a distinct role and function, with one of his or her major tasks being the making of the decision between short-term yields and deferred expectations." As the central interface between the corporation and what stands outside it, e.g., society, the economy, technology, markets, customers and the media, the CEO plays the key role in the modern corporation.

There are no prescribed procedures for planning succession and selecting the CEO and a board should fashion the principles and procedures it deems appropriate. In fulfilling its CEO selection and succession function, the board should recognize that by itself competence is not enough. The integrity and dedication of the CEO is critical in enabling a board to meet all of its duties. In large measure, the fate of each of the board and the CEO is in the hands of the other.

Independence. There is an overemphasis on board independence that risks losing sight of the importance of promoting the sort of board dynamic that can most effectively lead to a well-functioning board and an effective partnership between the board and senior management. The NYSE, after thoughtful consideration, decided to require only that a majority of the board be independent. Today, most boards have only one or two directors that are not independent: the CEO and maybe one other current or former officer. Nevertheless, many of the shareholder advisory services, institutional investors and academic gadflies are continuing to urge (in some cases, demand) that all directors other than the CEO be independent and that social and philanthropic ties among and between the directors and the CEO be considered as impugning, if not destroying, independence. These types of requirements and restrictions are the antithesis of the kind of collegiality and relationship with the CEO that is necessary for the board and CEO together to promote the appropriate tone at the top, to agree on the corporate mission and work collectively to enhance the corporation's business. What companies need are directors who possess sufficient character and integrity to allow them to make judgments unaffected by considerations affecting themselves or those with whom they have relations. The concept of the board as remote strangers and as the agency for the discipline of management, rather than as partner with management in setting the strategic course of the corporation, is contrary to all prior experience and will not lead to better performance. The tension between the new norms of independence and the overarching objective of better performance, unless modulated and maintained in perspective, can cause the former to overwhelm the latter.

As a general rule, companies should be careful in the current environment to make full and complete disclosure of any relationships or transactions that could be deemed to affect the independence of a director. Many relationships that may have been considered commonplace in the past (such as a director's involvement with a nonprofit organization that is heavily supported by the company) may, in today's skeptical environment, cast doubt on the level of that director's independence when viewed with hindsight after a crisis has arisen. This is not to say that all such relationships should be prohibited, but rather that all should be considered in assessing a director's independence.

Executive compensation. This is today's most high-profile corporate issue and a major focus of shareholder activism. Virtually everyone who has weighed in on this issue agrees that executive compensation should be aligned with long-term performance of the corporation and shareholder value. In addition, most companies, including well-performing ones, need to engage in recruiting and retention efforts to attract, and prevent the loss of, qualified individuals serving as key employees. That said, there is a wide spectrum of views as to how to achieve the agreed objectives. The only really useful advice is thoughtful process, full disclosure and recognition by the compensation committee that it should not be deterred by the focus on levels of executive compensation from doing what it feels is in the best interests of the corporation. Executive compensation should directly link the interests of senior management and the long-term interests of shareholders. Some organizations, such as the Business Roundtable, have recommended the use of performance thresholds to achieve this. In order to ensure that compensation and severance packages are justifiable, members of the compensation committee should fully understand all the costs and benefits of the compensation arrangements that they are considering. Particular attention should be paid to severance arrangements and to all benefits provided to senior management in connection with termination of employment. Perquisites should be kept reasonable and a line should be drawn between business and personal expenses. Both the Business Roundtable and the Blue Ribbon Commission on Executive Compensation of the National Association of Corporate Directors have also emphasized the importance of transparency and full disclosure of compensation packages.

Director Compensation. Director compensation is one of the more difficult issues on the corporate governance agenda. On the one hand, more is being expected of directors today in terms of time commitment, responsibility and exposure to public scrutiny and potential liability. On the other hand, the higher the director's pay, the greater the chance it will raise an issue of independence. The compensation committee should determine the form and amount of director compensation with appropriate benchmarking against peer companies. It is legal and appropriate for basic directors' fees to be supplemented by additional amounts to chairs of committees and to members of committees that meet more frequently or for longer periods of time.

While there has been a current trend, encouraged by institutional shareholders, to establish stock-based compensation programs for directors, the form of such programs should be carefully considered to ensure that they do not create the wrong types of incentives for directors. In the current environment, restricted stock grants, for example, may be preferable to option grants, since stock grants will align director and shareholder interests more directly and avoid the perception that option grants may encourage directors to support more aggressive risk taking on the part of management to maximize option values. Perquisite programs and company charitable donations to organizations with which a director is affiliated should also be carefully scrutinized to make sure that they do not jeopardize a director's independence or create any potential appearance of impropriety. Where appropriate, such perquisites should be fully disclosed.

Nomination of director candidates. Under the existing corporate governance system, a company's nominating committee nominates candidates for membership on the company's board. Shareholders can propose potential director candidates to the company's nominating committee, which under the NYSE rules must be composed entirely of independent directors. The nominating committee has a duty to consider bona fide candidates and to nominate directors that it believes will best serve the interests of the company and its shareholders. In evaluating potential director candidates, whether they are proposed by management or shareholders, the nominating committee should use the same fundamental criteria. The foremost criterion is competence: boards should consist of well-qualified men and women with appropriate business and industry experience. The second important consideration is collegiality. A balkanized board is a dysfunctional board; a company's board works best when it works as a unified whole, without camps or factions and without internal divisions. The nominating committee should also try to ensure that the board consists of individuals who understand and are willing to shoulder the time commitment necessary for the board to effectively fulfill its responsibility to advise and monitor management. To this end, companies should consider including in their corporate governance guidelines policies limiting the number of boards on which a director may sit. Those guidelines should also address director tenure. Companies should consider whether it would be advisable for them to impose term and age limits on directors. There is no formula for the perfect board. Strong, independent directors are essential to proper board functioning, but so too are elusive qualities such as collegiality, sense of common purpose, energy, industry knowledge, business sense and trust. Each company, through its independent nominating committee, must have the flexibility to determine the mix of qualifications and attributes that is best suited to the specific needs of the corporation.

Monitoring performance. While the corporation laws literally say that the business of the corporation is to be managed by or under the direction of the board of directors, it is clear that the board's function is not to actually manage, but to ensure that the corporation is effectively managed by monitoring the performance of the CEO and senior officers. To meet its duty to monitor performance, the board and management together need to determine the information the board should receive. Here "more can be less." The board should not be overloaded with information. It is not necessary that the board receive all the information that the CEO and senior management receive. The board should receive financial information that enables it to readily understand results of operations, variations from budget and trends in the business, the corporation's performance relative to peers, and any other information that the board determines to be useful in its work. The board should receive copies of significant security analysts' reports, press articles and other media reports on the corporation. If an article or report raises compliance, performance or other issues, the board should make sure it receives a satisfactory explanation of the issues raised in the publication, including, if appropriate, what is being done to correct the situation. By tracking these reports and articles, the board will avoid the possibility of being accused of ignoring problems that were known to others and which could have been known by the directors.

Monitoring compliance. As with performance, the board has a duty to monitor legal and regulatory compliance by the corporation. The board does not have a duty to ferret out compliance problems. It does, however, have a duty to take appropriate action when it is aware of a problem and management is not properly dealing with it. In normal situations, it is sufficient for the board to review compliance matters and litigation semi-annually. This may be done directly by the board or through the audit committee. However it is done, it is a desirable practice for the board or the audit committee to have executive sessions with the general counsel of the corporation. Where there is a serious investigation or litigation that is being handled by outside counsel, direct reports by such counsel to the board or the audit committee are desirable. In addition the board should oversee an annual review of the corporation's compliance programs and its information and reporting systems and receive an opinion of the general counsel as to their adequacy.

In performing its monitoring function, the board should be sensitive to "red flags" and "yellow flags". When such flags are raised, the board should observe and investigate as appropriate and document its monitoring activities in minutes that accurately convey the time and effort directors devote to decisionmaking, even when the outcome is to take no action. In a few recent cases (Disney, Abbott and Caremark), influential courts have indicated that directors may be held liable for lack of good faith in situations where they utterly fail, in "ostrich-like" fashion, to exercise any oversight. However, none of these cases contemplate director liability where directors are using common sense and appropriate diligence in performing their oversight function. Directors remain fully protected by the business judgment rule when they make corporate decisions with the exercise of due care.

The federal sentencing guidelines also promote comprehensive compliance procedures and careful monitoring by requiring that directors be knowledgeable about compliance programs, be informed by those with day-to-day responsibility over compliance and participate in compliance training. The guidelines also provide that an effective compliance program monitored by the board may be a mitigating factor in a prosecutor's decision whether or not to charge a company with wrongdoing.

Review of controls and risk management. The board should also—whether directly, or through the audit committee—make sure that management has adopted and implemented proper risk assessment and management policies and procedures. The risks that a company might face include business risks (such as risks posed by defective products, violation of environmental requirements, accidents and political changes), financial risks (such as risks posed by financial asset composition, derivative securities, structured financing contingencies and guarantees), legal risks and reputation risks. The board should ensure that each category of risk is adequately addressed by the company's risk management procedures.

It is an important responsibility of management, and a key monitoring role for the board, to establish and maintain an adequate internal control structure and procedures for financial reporting and compliance with law, including applicable SEC disclosure requirements. The SEC rules implementing Section 404 of the Sarbanes-Oxley Act require management to prepare reports on internal controls and the independent auditor to attest to those reports as part of its audit, to be included in a company's annual report. The rules also call for a quarterly evaluation by management of a company's internal controls and procedures for financial reporting. Especially in the current environment, directors should pay careful attention to whether management has invested sufficient resources and energies in the company's control and risk monitoring and management infrastructure. The board should satisfy itself (by getting regular reports from the management and the internal auditor) that the company's existing internal control systems provide for the maintenance of financial records in a way that permits preparation of financial statements in accordance with GAAP and gives "reasonable assurance" of accuracy in financial reports, and that management designs and supervises processes that adequately identify, address and control compliance risks. That said, it should be borne in mind that while "reasonable assurance" is a high standard, it is not an absolute, and boards should avoid overreaction to the discovery of deficiencies.

Effectiveness of the board. The Enron directors have been criticized for not adequately performing their monitoring duties. The legal community, including prominent judges, have stated that Enron's short meetings are evidence of failure by the directors to fulfill their fiduciary duties. Some have suggested that a board's failure to allot adequate time to carry out its duties could call into question whether it had acted in good faith. In addition to scheduling regular board and committee meetings to provide ample time for the regular business of the board, boards should consider the desirability of an annual two-to-three-day board retreat with the senior executives at which there is a full review of the corporation's financial statements and disclosure policies, strategy and long-range plans, budget, the company's mission, succession planning and current developments in corporate governance. Each retreat may be held at a location close to one of the corporation's operations, so as to give the directors an opportunity to become acquainted with a number of the corporation's operations as the annual retreats are rotated among the corporation's various locations. During the retreat, meals and social activities may be arranged in a manner that encourages the directors to get to know the senior executives on a one-on-one basis. Corporations should also provide comprehensive orientation for new directors so as to acquaint them with the corporation's strategy, long-range plans, financial statements, properties and operations, corporate governance guidelines and senior executives. The annual retreat could satisfy a major portion of such an orientation. In addition to orientation, corporation's should consider education programs for continuing directors, both to enhance their skills as directors as well as to educate them on current regulatory and corporate governance developments.

Committees of the board. The NYSE requires a listed company to have an audit committee, a compensation committee and a nominating/governance committee, each comprised solely of independent directors. The requirement that a committee be composed of only independent directors does not mean that the CEO (and other employees) should be excluded from all the discussions or work of the committee. Indeed, it would be virtually impossible for the committee to function effectively without the participation of the CEO. All compensation matters, including the CEO's compensation, should be discussed with the CEO, and all governance and director nomination matters should be discussed with the CEO. The final determination is that of the committee. While the committees have the authority to retain consultants, there is no requirement that the compensation committee retain a compensation consultant or that the nominating/governance committee retain a search firm, if the committee believes that it does not need the assistance of a consultant.

All companies, as part of their broader governance reviews, should carefully consider which directors satisfy the requirements for independence. Questionnaires should be used to determine and document both independence and qualification for committee assignments. In addition to these core committees, boards may wish to establish a variety of additional standing committees to meet their ongoing governance needs, such as a risk management committee (if this function is not being performed by the audit committee), a compliance committee, or a committee on social responsibility. Boards also use special committees from time to time either to deal with conflict transactions (such as a management buyout) or other major corporate events (such as shareholder litigation or a hostile takeover bid) or to address particular special investigations or projects. While the use of special committees is perfectly appropriate and useful in many circumstances, such committees are also often used in situations where it might be best to keep the matter in question before the full board (or before all of the outside members of the full board). Special committees can sometimes become divisive in sensitive situations and there is a risk that the special committee and its chosen outside advisors may take a matter in a direction that would be different than that desired by the full board. Especially in matters of great sensitivity it is often preferable for all directors (or at least all outside directors) to remain active in monitoring the direction of the matter.

The work of the board will be facilitated by establishing the appropriate relationship between the board as a whole and each of these committees, so that the work of the committees is neither duplicated nor ignored by the board. The significant actions of the committees should be understood by the board as a whole and integrated into the overall work of the board. In order to enable both the board and its committees to deal with any special problems that may arise in the course of performing their duties, the board and its standing and special committees should be granted the authority to engage independent counsel where appropriate. That said, this authority should be used sparingly; as a general rule, a board or board committee should resort to it only when there is a real conflict or some other genuine need for independent or specialized advice. More often than not, a company's own general counsel or CFO can provide more pertinent advice and insight than that available from outside sources.

The audit committee. The post-Enron reforms have invested the audit committee with a special role in corporate governance. In large measure, the audit committee has become the principal means by which the board discharges its duty to monitor financial and disclosure compliance. Accordingly, boards should carefully select audit committee members and, to the greatest extent possible, be attuned to the quality of the audit committee's performance. In view of the audit committee's centrality to the board's duties of financial review, it is also important for the board as a whole to receive periodic reports from the audit committee and to be comfortable that the audit committee, the auditors and management are satisfied that the financial position and results of operations of the corporation are fairly presented.

Executive sessions. The NYSE requires the non-management directors to meet in regularly scheduled executive sessions of the board in which management is not present. Each board should determine the frequency and agenda for these meetings. These executive sessions should be viewed primarily as a safety valve to deal with problems and not a forum for revisiting matters already considered by the full board. The executive sessions should not usurp functions that are properly the province of the full board.

Board and committee agendas. The board and its committees should be proactive in working with senior management and the general counsel in setting their agendas for the year as well as for each board or committee meeting. While it is the management, not the board, that must set the strategic and business agenda for the company, including regulatory and compliance goals, directors should take a leadership role in defining the bounds of their oversight and responsibilities. The meeting and annual agendas should reflect an appropriate division of labor and should be distributed to the board or committee members in advance.

Separating roles of Chairman and CEO; lead director. Most American companies have traditionally had a single individual who carries the titles of both Chairman of the Board and CEO. While some shareholder activists have recently called for the separation of these roles, both ISS and TIAA-CREF leave this matter to the discretion of the board, provided that there is a lead director who presides over executive sessions of the board. While there is no formal requirement in the NYSE rules or in the Sarbanes-Oxley Act that a company have a lead director, the independent directors should have a leader who is not also the CEO. With such a leader, directors who have concerns about the company and its performance have a go-to person with whom they can discuss those concerns and have them relayed, where appropriate, to the full board. Whether he or she is called the lead director, the non-executive chair or the presiding director, this leader should have the following key roles: (1) be available to consult with the CEO about concerns of the board of directors; (2) be available to be consulted by any of the senior executives of the company as to any concerns the executive might have and (3) preside at executive sessions of the board—without the CEO being present—prior to or following certain of the regular meetings of the board. In order to be effective, he or she should be a senior person who is highly respected and regarded by the CEO and the other directors. The lead director is not an officer and would not have any of the formal duties of a chairman of the board, but he or she is the director who would assume leadership of the board if a need to do so should arise. A company might either have a single individual designated as a lead director or have a presiding directorship through which the committee chairs rotate. If a lead director is designated, the NYSE requires his or her name to be disclosed in the annual proxy statement. Alternatively, a company may disclose the procedure by which a presiding director is selected for each executive session.

Whistleblowers. Boards, and in particular audit committees, are required to establish procedures to enable employees to confidentially and anonymously submit concerns they might have regarding the company's accounting, internal controls or auditing matters. In addition, companies are subject to potential civil, and in some cases criminal, liability if they can be shown to have taken retaliatory action against a whistleblower who is an employee. In responding to these new constraints, there can be a temptation to establish a special committee of independent directors to investigate every single whistleblower complaint. This temptation should be resisted in favor of a procedure that filters whistleblower complaints, as such investigations can be extremely disruptive. SEC Enforcement Director Stephen Cutler recently urged companies to appoint a permanent ombudsman or business practices officer to receive and investigate complaints. Boards should ensure the establishment of an anonymous whistleblower hotline and a well-documented policy for evaluating whistleblower complaints, but they should also be judicious in deciding which complaints truly warrant further action.

Corporate strategy. Approval of the corporation's long-term strategy is a key board function. Strategy should be formulated initially by management and then developed finally by an interactive process with the board. Many companies find that as part of the strategy development process an annual strategy review that is part of a board retreat of the type referred to above is productive.

Crisis management. Perhaps the most important test of a board comes in times of crisis. Boards need to be proactive in taking the reins in the context of any governance, compliance or business crisis affecting the corporation. At the same time, boards need to be cautious not to overreact to any given situation and thereby create a crisis. There is a mixed record regarding how well boards have been handling recent crises. It appears that many boards have functioned quite well in taking a careful measure of the situation and putting in place the right procedures for obtaining the necessary information about the issues facing the corporation and developing the right strategies for responding to the situation and rectifying any management, disclosure or legal/compliance deficiencies. Others, however, appear to have either overreacted, or to have placed matters in the hands of lawyers, accountants and other outside experts, and thereby lost control of the situation to those outsiders. And, in some instances the crises themselves appear to have arisen in large part from the failure of management and the board to be proactive in reacting to earlier warning signs.

As the Blue Ribbon Commission on Board Leadership of the National Association of Corporate Directors recently recommended, the first decision a board must make during a crises is to decide whether the CEO should lead the corporation through the crises, noting that "if he or she is part of the problem or is otherwise compromised or conflicted, someone else — often one of the other directors — should take a leadership role." If the CEO is not compromised or conflicted, the CEO should lead the corporation's response to the crisis.

Each crisis is different and it is difficult to give generic advice that will be relevant to any particular crisis without knowing the facts involved. That said, in most instances when a crisis arises, the directors are best advised to manage through that crisis as a collegial body working in unison. While outside advisors (counsel, auditors, consultants and bankers) can play a very useful and often critical role in getting at all of the relevant facts of a given situation and in helping to shape the right result, the directors should maintain control and not cede the job of crisis management to the outside advisors. And, while there is often the impulse to resign from the board upon the discovery of a crisis, in most instances, directors are best served by staying on the board until the crisis has been fully vetted and brought under control.

Major transactions. Board consideration of major transactions, such as acquisitions, mergers, spinoffs, investments and financings, needs to be carefully structured so that the board receives the information necessary in order to make a reasoned decision. This does not mean that outside advisors are necessary, even for a very large transaction. If the corporation has the internal expertise to analyze the requisite data and present it in a manner that enables the board to consider the alternatives and assess the risks and rewards, the board is fully justified in relying on the management presentation without the advice of outside experts. There is no need for the board to create a special committee to deal with a major transaction, even a hostile takeover, and experience shows that a major transaction is best addressed by the full board. Management should build a strong foundation to support a major transaction, including an appropriate due diligence investigation. The board should have ample time to consider a major transaction, including in cases of complicated transactions and agreements a two-step process with the actual approval coming only after an initial presentation and the board having had time for reflection.

Related party transactions. There is nothing inherently improper about transactions between a corporation and its officers or directors; such transactions are often in the best interests of a corporation and its shareholders, offering efficiencies and other benefits that might not otherwise be available. It is entirely appropriate for an informed board, on a proper record, to approve such arrangements through its disinterested directors. As a matter of compliance and best practices, however, and particularly in the current environment, the corporation should give careful attention to all "related party" transactions. Full disclosure of all material related party transactions and full compliance with proxy, periodic reporting and financial footnote disclosure requirements is essential. Management should make sure that all related party transactions have been fully and carefully reviewed with the board. The board should reevaluate the corporation's policies and procedures for reviewing such transactions on both an initial and ongoing basis and for determining that all continuing related party transactions remain in the best interest of the corporation. The board should consider assigning to a committee consisting solely of directors who are both independent and disinterested with respect to the transaction under consideration the job of reviewing any newly proposed related party transactions. The committee should have the authority to hire such outside financial, legal and other advisors as it deems appropriate to assist it in its evaluation of such transactions. If a related party arrangement is of material significance to the corporation, the board should consider whether additional steps are necessary to ensure that such transactions are properly monitored and evaluated. For example, the board should take active measures to determine that the entities providing related party services are being held to the same standards the corporation would demand of unaffiliated third party service providers and that there is a clear reason for procuring the service from a related party.

Confidentiality and the role of directors outside the boardroom. A board should function as a collegial body, and directors should respect the confidentiality of all discussions that take place in the boardroom. Confidentiality is essential for an effective board process and for the protection of the corporation and its stockholders. Moreover, directors generally owe a broad legal duty of confidentiality to the corporation with respect to information they learn about the corporation in the course of their duties. Maintaining confidentiality is also essential for the protection of the individual directors, since directors can be responsible for any misleading statements that are attributable to them. Even when a director believes the subject matter of his or her statements is within the public domain, it is good practice for individual directors to avoid commenting on matters concerning the corporation. A director who receives an inquiry with respect to the corporation from outside the corporation may or may not have all of the relevant information and his or her response could involve the corporation, as well as the director, in a disclosure violation. Directors should also respect the role of the CEO as the chief spokesperson for the corporation. They should generally not engage in discussions with outsiders concerning corporate business unless specifically requested to do so by the CEO or the board. Where it is necessary for outside directors to speak on behalf of themselves or the corporation, here too it is best for one member of the board to be designated as the board's spokesperson. Where a board has a non-executive chairman or a lead director, under certain circumstances it may also be appropriate for the chairman or lead director to speak on behalf of the corporation, particularly within the ambit of those directors' special roles. In the ordinary course, all such matters should be handled in close consultation with the CEO so as to avoid confusion in the corporation's public statements and posture.

Board, committee and CEO evaluations. The NYSE requires annual evaluations. Many consulting firms have published their recommended forms and procedures for conducting these evaluations. Consultants have also established an advisory service in which they meet with the board and committee members to lead them through the evaluation process. Each board needs to decide how to conduct its evaluation. In making the decision, it should be noted that it is not required that the board receive outside assistance and it is not required that multiple-choice questionnaires and/or essays be the means of evaluation. If a board prefers to do the evaluation by discussion at meetings, that is acceptable. It should also be noted that documents and minutes created as part of the evaluation process are not privileged and care should be taken to avoid creating ambiguous records that may be used in litigation against the corporation and the board.

Charters, codes, guidelines and checklists. The audit, compensation and nominating-governance committees are required to have charters. The corporation is required to have a code of ethics. The board is required to have corporate governance guidelines and, as noted, there is no end to the number of recommended checklists designed to assist corporations in complying with Sarbanes-Oxley, SEC regulations and NYSE rules. All of these are to some extent useful in assisting the board and committees in performing their functions and in monitoring compliance. However, there is a tendency to expand the scope of charters and checklists to the point that they are counterproductive. If a charter or checklist requires review or other action and the board or committee has not taken that action, the failure can be considered evidence of lack of due care. The creation of charters and checklists is an art that requires experience and careful thought. It is a mistake to copy the published models. Each corporation should tailor its own charters and checklists, limiting them to what is truly necessary and what is feasible to accomplish in actual practice. In order to be "state of the art" it is not necessary that the corporation have everything someone else has. Charters and checklists should be carefully reviewed each year to prune unnecessary items and to add only those items that will in fact help directors in discharging their duties.

Shareholder activism; proxy advisors. One of the most visible byproducts of the Enron-type scandals is the increase in shareholder-sponsored precatory proxy resolutions and the high level of shareholder support that they are able to command. For the first time in 2003 and 2004, over 1,000 shareholder proposals were submitted to corporations (with over 400 on corporate governance alone in 2004), with record numbers of those resolutions achieving majority support among shareholders. On some issues, mostly related to antitakeover defenses, shareholder proposals now routinely receive majority support. One of the explanations for such shareholder support is the demise of "case-by-case" voting by institutional shareholders. Today, institutional shareholders, who control over 60% of stock in American corporations, typically subscribe to the services of proxy voting advisors, such as ISS, to provide analysis or advice with respect to shareholder votes. These proxy voting advisors publish proxy voting guides setting forth blanket voting policies on a variety of common issues that are frequent subjects of shareholder proposals. Institutional shareholders typically do not review individual shareholder proposals on a company-by-company basis. Instead, they rely heavily on these proxy voting guidelines, regardless of an individual company's performance or governance fundamentals. As a result, many shareholder votes are foreordained by a voting policy that is applied to all companies without reference to the particulars of a given company's credentials. The emergence of new proxy advisory services, such as Proxy Governance Inc., that promise to review issues on an "issue-by-company" basis is a recent development that should be welcomed.

A recent trend that has added significant pressure to boards that are considering majority vote resolutions is the growth of "withhold-vote" campaigns, as well as just-vote-no campaigns against single issues such as equity compensation plans. In recent years, shareholder activists have been increasingly willing to sponsor or support withhold vote campaigns against directors for a variety of perceived infractions, including issues of independence and the unwillingness of a board to implement shareholder resolutions that receive majority shareholder support. This year, in an effort to further increase the pressure of withhold-vote campaigns, a group of labor unions have submitted precatory proxy resolutions to more than 75 corporations urging amendments to governance documents to require that directors be elected by a majority rather than a plurality of the votes cast. Another factor that magnifies the power of shareholder proposals as an activist tool is the effect of corporate governance metrics on the rating and general public evaluation of companies, as organizations like ISS include responsiveness to shareholder proposals among the factors they consider in determining a corporate governance score.

In dealing with shareholder proposals, the board should regularly review the corporation's shareholder relations programs and consider whether it is appropriate for the board to have greater interaction with shareholders. Where the corporation has performance or compliance issues, direct contact between shareholders and non-management directors may forestall a proxy initiative by shareholders. In addition, the corporation should weigh carefully opposition to shareholder proxy resolutions that can be accommodated without significant difficulty. Today, it is prudent to do a risk-reward analysis of shareholder resolutions, rather than to routinely oppose them. As companies spend more time and effort to consider shareholder proposals, and especially majority vote resolutions, it might make sense to formalize the process by which this is done. By paying serious attention to shareholder proposals, and by being proactive in shareholder communications and disclosure, boards are most likely to create the right environment for acting on shareholder resolutions even when the ultimate determination may be to reject them.

Shareholder access. In 2003, the SEC proposed a new proxy rule that would enable shareholders to directly nominate a director through the corporation's own proxy. This proposed rule promises to magnify the problems associated with the voting power of institutional shareholders, creating the risk of an influx of special interest directors selected, in effect, by parties that have no legal duties or obligations to the public company or its shareholders at large and no special expertise in the company's industry. It also threatens to create annual election contests, which will cause significant disruption to management's operation of the company's business, and is likely to compromise, if not destroy, the collegiality of the board, creating an unproductive working environment. At this time, it appears that the SEC proposal will not be adopted and that the SEC will not require corporations to include precatory resolutions in their proxy statements seeking amendments to governance documents that would provide the same shareholder access as the proposed SEC rule.

Directors' duties and responsibilities. The basic responsibility of directors is to exercise their business judgment to act in a manner they reasonably believe to be in the best interests of the corporation and its shareholders. In discharging these obligations, directors are entitled to rely on management and the advice of the corporation's outside advisors. The board should make sure that the corporation's legal counsel, both internal and external, and auditors, both internal and external, know that they have direct access to the board, if ever needed.

Indemnification, D&O coverage. All directors should be fully indemnified by the company to the fullest extent permitted by law and the company should purchase a reasonable amount of D&O insurance to protect the directors against the risk of personal liability for their services to the company. Bylaws and indemnification agreements should be reviewed on a regular basis to ensure that they provide the fullest coverage permitted by law. Having in place governance procedures that are responsive to the recent legislative and regulatory initiatives and that reflect best practices, and having a robust record reflecting strong, good faith efforts to adhere to those procedures, will be helpful in assuring that a court respects the applicability of exculpatory charter provisions in any litigation that might arise.

D&O coverage provides a key protection to directors. While such coverage has become more expensive in recent years, it is still available in most instances and remains highly useful, despite some recent decisions construing the terms of D&O policies less favorably to the insured. In this regard, it is important to note that D&O policies are not strictly form documents and can be negotiated. Careful attention should be paid to retentions and exclusions, particularly those that seek to limit coverage based upon a lack of adequate insurance for other business matters, or based on assertions that a company's financial statements were inaccurate when the policy was issued. Care should also be given to the potential impact of a bankruptcy of the company on the availability of insurance, particularly the question of how rights are allocated between the company and the directors and officers who may be claiming entitlement to the same aggregate dollars of coverage. To avoid any ambiguity that might exist as to directors' and officers' rights to coverage and reimbursement of expenses in the case of a bankruptcy, many companies are purchasing separate supplemental insurance policies covering only directors and officers and not the company (so-called "side-A" coverage) in addition to their normal policies which cover both the company and the directors and officers individually.

The Business Judgment Rule. Directors are not guarantors that nothing will go wrong on their watch. Directors are monitors and gatekeepers charged with the duty of installing competent managers and selecting competent advisors who they reasonably believe will serve the best interests of the corporation and diligently monitoring their performance. Directors are expected to attend board meetings on a regular basis, as well as the meetings of the committees on which they serve, and to spend the time that is needed to properly discharge their functions. Directors should make sure that they are receiving from management and from the corporation's auditors and outside advisors all of the information and data they deem relevant to understanding the issues before them and reaching sound business judgments with respect thereto. They should inquire with due care to make sure that the corporation is operating in compliance with applicable laws and regulations and, insist that management take the requisite responsibility for ensuring the accuracy and completeness of the corporation's financial statements and public disclosures.

The courts continue to respect the directors' entitlement to rely on senior management's performance of their obligation to ensure the accuracy of information disseminated by the company and, more generally, management's obligation to take all necessary corrective actions when compliance failures or deficiencies are noted. That said, inroads on the Business Judgment Rule have doubtlessly been made—particularly in the change of control context and perhaps in connection with other high-profile issues such as executive compensation. Under today's dominant "monitoring" board concept greater engagement by directors is demanded. Yet while the change in social expectations from directors is quite real, ultimately the tool of director liability is too crude, too socially costly an implement to be deployed except very rarely, and the courts have to date exhibited a keen understanding of this fact. While it is true that courts and regulatory authorities have little tolerance today for directors who are simply sleeping at the wheel, it remains a verity of Delaware corporation law that the Delaware courts will not hold a director to be liable for a loss caused to the company if the court perceives that the director was actually trying to advance a legitimate corporate interest.

When complex legal, governance or accounting issues arise it will be useful for a director to ask the following simple questions:

- Have I acted with undivided loyalty to the corporation and its shareholders and have all my personal interests in this matter been fully disclosed?
- Have I exercised due care in examining the issues underlying the proposed action, including receiving advice as to whether the action is in compliance with applicable rules and regulations?
- Will the proposed action and the relevant facts and circumstance be candidly disclosed to all effected parties?

If the answers to those questions are yes, a director will be fully protected in exercising his or her business judgment and, even if, with the benefit of hindsight, the judgment prove flawed, the director will not be faulted.

In the words of Norman Veasey, former Chief Justice of Delaware:

> Although the law of fiduciary duty recognizes the evolving expectations of the standards of conduct of directors and officers, we must keep in mind that the business judgment rule continues unabated to protect directors' decisions made in good faith and to enable them to set strategic goals for prudent risk-taking. What has evolved in this new era is a sharper judicial focus on the processes employed by directors, but it is not a regulatory clamp on their business judgment.

March 13, 2005

Majority Vote to Elect Directors

The Model Business Corporation Act and Delaware corporation law provide for the election of directors by a plurality vote. Activist shareholders, led by union pension funds, have proposed precatory proxy resolutions to change the system. They want companies to adopt bylaws that provide for election of directors by a majority vote. The SEC has taken the position that companies may not exclude these proxy proposals and now ISS has adopted a policy supporting these proposals.

As is recognized by ISS, a requirement that directors be elected by a majority vote raises a number of technical and practical issues, and would almost certainly have unintended and unforeseen consequences. The committee of the American Bar Association that recommends changes to the Model Act is considering whether to amend the Act to require a majority vote and to deal with the technical and practical problems that would be created by abandoning a plurality vote. These problems can be dealt with in several ways, but all will result in increasing the ability of activist shareholders to accomplish their special interest objectives. Requiring a majority vote would give activists huge leverage by allowing them to threaten to withhold enough votes to defeat a nominee even though the withheld votes are substantially less than a majority of the outstanding shares. This shift in leverage to special interest activists would also be a further deterrent to competent people accepting nominations as directors.

While there is surface appeal to a majority vote requirement, it thus has the potential to cause serious disruption of the existing system. In contrast, there would be far less reason to object to a bylaw (a) that provides that if a majority of the outstanding shares vote to withhold against a nominee who has been nominated by the board, that nominee is not elected and (b) that deals with the technical and practical problems that that change entails. In light of the requirement that all members of the nominating committee be independent directors and the new SEC rules relating to the nomination process and its disclosure in the proxy statement, the burden to prove the will of the majority should be on the shareholders opposing the board's nominees, not on the nominees. This change would be far less disruptive and should not deter competent people from accepting nomination as directors. In weighing these issues, it should be kept in mind that activist shareholders have the ability to solicit shareholder proxies and elect their own nominees by a plurality vote. With the large percentage of the outstanding shares of most major companies held by institutional investors, this is a practical solution if in fact the majority of shareholders have lost confidence in management.

Martin Lipton

March 24, 2005

Corporate Governance: Majority Election of Directors

David A. Katz
and
Laura A. McIntosh[65]

The majority election of directors is one of the most significant issues of the 2005 proxy season. The idea gained momentum after the Securities and Exchange Commission apparently decided to postpone indefinitely any action on its proposed proxy access rule. This year, union pension funds have submitted precatory shareholder proposals under Exchange Act Rule 14a-8 to over 75 companies. Institutional Shareholder Services, a leading proxy voting and advisory firm whose recommendations are highly influential in determining institutional clients' votes, recently issued a policy of support for these precatory proposals, reversing its 2004 proxy season position.[66] Moreover, the California Public Employees' Retirement System (CalPERS), one of the more significant shareholder activists in the United States, recently announced that it would advocate majority voting for directors by seeking bylaw and charter amendments at individual companies; by pursuing changes to state laws; by advocating that new requirements be adopted by the SEC and major stock exchanges; and by amending the CalPERS corporate governance principles and guidelines.[67]

Proponents of majority voting cite American ideals of democracy, European examples of corporate elections and theoretical benefits of "meaningful" votes to support their cause. They view majority voting as investing "withhold vote" campaigns with the power to create board vacancies. Opponents argue that increased complexity of voting mechanics, negative impact on the functioning of boards and retrenchment towards classified board structures may be the unintended results of com-

---

65. David A. Katz is a partner at Wachtell, Lipton, Rosen & Katz. Laura A. McIntosh is a consulting attorney for Wachtell, Lipton, Rosen & Katz. The views expressed are the authors' and do not necessarily represent the views of the partners of Wachtell, Lipton, Rosen & Katz or the firm as a whole.
66. ISS US Corporate Governance Policy 2005 Updates: Policy Update Supplement: Majority Vote Standard (available at http://www.issproxy.com/pdf/MVPolicyUpdate.pdf) (hereinafter ISS Policy).
67. CalPERS Press Release, Mar. 14, 2005 (available at http://www.calpers.ca.gov/index.jsp?bc=/about/press/pr-2005/march/majority-vote.xml); *see also* Tiffany Kary, *Majority Voting Movement Gains Steam*, Dow Jones Corp. Governance Newsl., Mar. 16, 2005.

pulsory majority voting. Though majority voting could be viewed as a reasonable compromise between shareholder nominations of directors and the status quo, the potential negative consequences are substantial and must be very carefully considered.

Background

In the United States, the Revised Model Business Corporation Act (RMBCA), state corporate law and most public company organizational documents require a plurality vote for the election of directors. A typical proxy card for election of directors will offer the options of "yes" and "withhold," and theoretically a director can be elected with a single "yes" vote over the opposition of all other voting shares, if the votes are withheld or the shares are not voted. Majority voting is therefore seen by some as a way to transform "withhold" votes into meaningful "no" votes.[68] The United Kingdom, Germany and France, along with other European nations, require a majority vote in favor for the ratification of public company directors.[69]

Some advocates of the majority election of directors view majority voting as a possible compromise between the SEC's proposed proxy access rule and the status quo.[70] Joseph Grundfest, a former SEC Commissioner, suggested in a letter to the SEC that majority voting would be "a less confrontational mechanism that constructively engages shareholders in the process of nominating and electing directors."[71] It is worth noting that such a compromise is not currently favored by all proponents of proxy access. The American Federation of State, County and Municipal Employees (AFSCME), for example, has determined not to introduce any majority-voting resolutions this season so as not to dilute its focus on shareholder nomination of directors.[72]

---

68. *See, e.g.*, Letter from Ira M. Millstein to the United States Securities and Exchange Commission, Mar. 3, 2004, at 1 (hereinafter Millstein Letter); and Phyllis Plitch, *Majority Board Vote Push Gains Traction With Union Campaign*, Dow Jones News Newswires, Feb. 8, 2005.
69. *See, e.g.*, David F. Morrison, *Shareholder Proxy Access—America Should Not Go It Alone Again*, Insights, Aug. 2004, at 2.
70. *See, e.g.*, David Casserly, *Majority Director Elections Urged as Alternative to Shareholder Access*, ISS Friday Report, Apr. 16, 2004.
71. Letter from Professor Joseph A. Grundfest, et al. to the United States Securities and Exchange Commission, Apr. 7, 2004, at 3 (hereinafter Grundfest Letter).
72. *See* Ted Allen, *Majority Elections Proposal Gains Renewed Interest*, ISS Friday Report, Nov. 5, 2004 (quoting Richard Ferlauto, Director of Investment Policy, American Federation of State, County and Municipal Employees).

The Proposals

The most important majority voting proposals were set forth last spring in separate letters to the SEC from Grundfest and Ira Millstein.[73] Millstein proposed that any director in an uncontested election who did not receive the affirmative vote of a majority of votes cast would not be elected.[74] A director who had been nominated for re-election would remain in place only until his or her successor was elected. The means of electing a replacement director would be determined by the board as provided in the company's organizational documents. Under Millstein's proposal, if a majority of the board were not elected or re-elected, the company would be required to hold another shareholders' meeting within 120 days in order to elect directors.

Grundfest's proposal is designed to achieve a similar result, but it is specifically concerned with respecting the limits of SEC authority and avoiding direct conflict between the federal proxy rules and state corporate law. Under his proposal, a director who did not receive a majority of affirmative votes would be permitted to serve, but the "unratified" director and the entire board would be subject to extensive and intrusive disclosure obligations so long as the director were a member of the board. Required disclosure would include detailed descriptions of meeting agendas, voting records of every director and personal statements by the unratified director explaining all of his or her votes in terms of their impact on shareholder value and the interests of other potentially affected constituencies. The unratified director also would have to issue a public statement justifying his or her presence on the board. These disclosure requirements are designed to be a de facto requirement that every director be elected by a majority vote.

Grundfest and Millstein state that they intend their proposals to increase communication between a company and its shareholders so that

---

73. Grundfest Letter, *supra* note 6 (Grundfest was joined by the American Society of Corporate Secretaries and Barclays Global Investors, N.A.); Millstein Letter, *supra* note 3 (Millstein was joined by Robert L. Messineo, Holly J. Gregory and David Murgio). In addition, E. Norman Veasey, retired Chief Justice of the Delaware Supreme Court, has suggested an alternative: that any company that adopts a majority-voting requirement be exempt from any future SEC rulemaking regarding proxy access. Letter from Hon. E. Norman Veasey, Chief Justice of the Supreme Court of Delaware, to the United States Securities and Exchange Commission, Mar. 11, 2004.

74. Millstein's proposal applies only to uncontested elections; he notes that in a contested election, plurality voting rules would apply unless otherwise provided by law or the company's organizational documents.

nominated directors are likely to be elected. They suggest that majority voting is a way to give shareholders greater influence over director elections without some of the complexities and potential negative consequences of the SEC's proxy access proposal.

It is important to note that neither of these proposals would require that a majority of the outstanding shares be voted in favor of a director for him or her to be elected. Instead, the majority voting proposals now being considered implicitly recognize that a number of shareholders do not utilize the shareholder franchise and defer the decision to those shareholders actually casting a vote in the election of the directors.

Evaluating the Consequences

Majority voting proposals avoid some of the problems associated with the SEC's proposed proxy access rule. For example, majority voting would not, except in the extreme case of a majority of directors' receiving the affirmative votes of less than a majority of votes cast, result in additional election contests.[75] Nor would majority voting necessarily entail the election of dissident directors, as the replacement for a failed nominee most likely would be selected by the board, although dissidents clearly would be emboldened. Majority voting should not permit special interest groups to thwart an election unless they could win the support of enough shareholders to constitute a majority of voting shares.

Nonetheless, a majority voting requirement threatens significant negative consequences. Majority voting would give special-interest shareholder activists increased opportunity to pursue their particular objectives, in many cases to the detriment of other shareholders and the company as a whole. Activists would gain leverage from the ability to defeat a director nominee even if withheld votes constituted substantially less than a majority of the outstanding shares. Moreover, the functioning of the board would be disrupted if a key director did not win re-election; if the board had to function for a period of time without a full complement of members; or if top director candidates were deterred from participation by the potential embarrassment and reputational effects of "losing" an election.

In addition, any company that adopted majority voting would have to address numerous technical and practical issues of implementation.[76] Consider abstentions and broker non-votes, for example: Under the New York Business Corporation Law and under the RMBCA, abstentions and

75. This requirement appears in Millstein's proposal only. Grundfest's proposal limits the number of directors that may be considered "unratified" in order to avoid additional elections altogether.

non-votes are not considered votes cast and therefore do not affect the outcome of a shareholder vote.[77] In Delaware, by contrast, abstentions count as votes cast in the election; abstentions in such jurisdictions would increase the number of votes needed to constitute a majority and effectively would be votes against.[78] Companies would have to be very clear in explaining to their shareholders the mechanics of voting under a majority-vote rule. The role of broker votes also would take on heightened significance. And the question of voting thresholds in contested elections would require a thorough examination of its own.[79]

Some critics of majority voting fear that such a requirement would cause companies to retrench into classified board structures. The declassification of boards has been a significant topic in corporate governance in recent years and remains a popular issue with shareholders. In 2004, proposals to repeal classified boards received, on average, the affirmative vote of a majority of outstanding shares.[80] Certainly, if the threat of losing director elections becomes a real one, companies will want to minimize the number of board seats open in each election. The question then would be whether, given the current corporate governance climate and escalating shareholder pressure tactics, companies would be able to maintain or implement a classified board structure.[81]

Responding to the Proposals

It might be tempting to imagine that majority voting is a relatively harmless proposal, if only in contrast to the SEC's proposed proxy access rule and because current voting trends imply that the success of a director nominee in an uncontested election is virtually a sure thing. After all, in more than 12,000 individual director elections tracked last year by Glass,

---

76. ISS explicitly acknowledged this in indicating that its revised policy applies only to precatory shareholder proposals on majority voting: "We recognize that the arguments against a Majority Vote requirement raise numerous issues. Therefore, we support the majority vote principle but we believe that boards should have wide latitude in designing a workable standard. If this proposal were presented as a binding agenda item, we would carefully consider the ramifications of implementation." ISS Policy.
77. N.Y. Bus. Corp. § 614; Model Bus. Corp. Act § 7.25(c).
78. Del. Gen. Corp. § 215(2).
79. See note 9, *supra*.
80. Georgeson Shareholder, *2004 Annual Corporate Governance Review* (available at http://www.georgesonshareholder.com/pdf/2004_corpgov.pdf), Fig. 8 (hereinafter Georgeson Data).
81. *See generally* Andrew R. Brownstein & Igor Kirman, *Can a Board Say No When Shareholders Say Yes? Responding to Majority Vote Resolutions*, 60 Bus. Law. 23 (Nov. 2004).

Lewis & Co., over 99.9 percent of directors were elected with a majority of affirmative votes.[82] Furthermore, the results of recent "withhold vote" or "Vote No" campaigns, which gained new prominence in 2004, suggest that even concerted efforts by shareholders to defeat a board nominee are very unlikely to succeed.[83] Of the substantial number of companies in the S&P 1500 that were the subject of withhold vote campaigns, only five received withhold votes exceeding 30 percent, and only one of the five received withhold votes in excess of 50 percent.[84]

But history advises caution. Just 20 years ago, the idea that shareholder proxy proposals would become a major issue for public companies would have seemed laughable. In 1981, only two shareholder proposals not supported by management had ever been approved by shareholders.[85] Yet in each of the last two years, well over 100 shareholder proposals received majority votes in favor, and proposals to eliminate antitakeover measures such as classified boards and shareholder rights plans (poison pills) regularly garner majority approval.[86] Majority voting, too, could well be a weapon that will meaningfully empower shareholder activists down the line.

If majority voting is implemented on a large scale, it likely will occur via SEC rulemaking rather than amendments to state laws. Nonetheless, the American Bar Association recently formed the Majority/Plurality Voting Task Force, chaired by former Delaware Supreme Court Chief Justice E. Norman Veasey. The goal of the task force is to examine the possibility of modifying the RMBCA away from the default of plurality voting. A change to the RMBCA could have a significant impact, as it is currently the basis for corporate law in over half of the fifty states (Delaware being a notable exception). The ABA initiative has received support from insti-

---

82. *See* Steven Syre, *Not-so-free Elections*, Boston Globe, Feb. 24, 2005 ("Glass, Lewis & Co. tracked about 12,600 director elections last year and identified just 11 candidates who failed to win support from a majority of shares. (Four were candidates at Federated Department Stores Inc.)").
83. *See* David A. Katz, *Corporate Governance: Shareholder Activism in 2004 and Implications for 2005*, N.Y.L.J., Feb. 3, 2005, at 5.
84. Institutional Shareholder Services, *2004 Postseason Report: A New Corporate Governance World: From Confrontation to Constructive Dialogue* (available at http://www.issproxy.com/pdf/2004ISSPSR.pdf), at 6.
85. *See* Susan W. Liebeler, *A Proposal to Rescind the Shareholder Proposal Rule*, 18 Ga. L. Rev. 425, 426 (1984) (arguing for the rescission of Rule 14a-8, and citing SEC Commissioner Bevis Longstreth, Address Before the National Association of Manufacturers (Dec. 11, 1981), *reprinted in* Mut. Funds Guide (CCH) P11,348, at 14,031 (1982)).
86. *See* Investor Responsibility Research Center (IRRC) Online Analyst System (166 in 2003 and 139 in 2004); Georgeson Data.

tutional investor organizations such as the International Corporate Governance Network, which supports increased proxy access and has discussed the advantages of modifying state laws to require majority voting.

In the aftermath of the Sarbanes-Oxley Act of 2002, significantly strengthened NYSE and NASDAQ listing standards and the proposed SEC proxy access rule, companies are justifiably wary of further intrusions into their corporate governance, particularly at the level of board composition. Some commentators suggest that recent regulations have done enough to ensure that board nominees will be acceptable and accountable to shareholders. Martin Lipton has recently argued that "[i]n light of the requirement that all members of the nominating committee be independent directors and the new SEC rules relating to the nomination process and its disclosure in the proxy statement, the burden to prove the will of the majority should be on the shareholders opposing the board's nominees, not on the nominees."[87] He therefore suggests that requiring a majority of outstanding shares to cast withhold votes in order to defeat a board nominee would be less disruptive and likely would not deter top director candidates from standing for election. This reform, implemented with bylaws addressing logistical issues in a carefully considered way, would be an acceptable alternative to the majority voting proposals currently under discussion.

The trend toward increased corporate accountability is growing and manifesting itself in new forms every year. There are signs that companies are reacting by engaging in meaningful dialogue with their shareholders and reaching satisfactory compromises.[88] In responding to the issue of majority voting, companies would be well-advised to continue enhancing communication with shareholders, to undertake regular review of shareholder relations programs and to consider adopting a transparent process for considering shareholder proposals that receive a majority vote in favor.[89] Indeed, some prominent companies already are engaged in negotiations with union fund activists regarding majority voting: Ten major corporations have agreed to participate with four building trades unions in a working group formed "to promote informed shareholder and corporate consideration of a director-majority vote standard."[90] In exchange, the

---

87. Martin Lipton, *Majority Vote To Elect Directors*, Wachtell, Lipton, Rosen & Katz Client Memorandum, Mar. 13, 2005.

88. *See, e.g.*, Georgeson Data (noting a significant increase in 2004 in the number of corporate governance proposals submitted by shareholders for inclusion in a proxy statement that were subsequently omitted or withdrawn). *See also infra* text accompanying note 25.

89. *See* Brownstein & Kirman, *supra* note 16.

unions have agreed to withdraw the majority-vote resolutions previously submitted to these companies.

Conclusion

Majority election of directors is an idea that resonates deeply with the American democratic ethos. It purports to extend popular representation into the boardroom and appeals to shareholder activists who wish to have a greater impact on the governance and oversight of the corporation. Many proponents believe that it will be difficult, from a public relations standpoint, for companies to resist pressure toward majority voting, and they may be right. But no one should underestimate the potentially harmful consequences of ill-considered implementation of a majority-voting proposal.

Advocates of majority voting should consider whether, given the current regulatory environment, the increasingly interactive relationship between companies and shareholders and the numerous other options available to shareholders, a change of this magnitude is truly necessary or desirable. To the extent that any change is required, Lipton's proposal would enhance the shareholder franchise by enabling an action by a majority of the outstanding shares to block a director's election. This would be consistent with the minimum shareholder voting requirement for amending corporate charters, a standard that appropriately reflects the significance of the matter.

---

90. ISS Weekly Report, Mar. 7, 2005 (quoting Ed Durkin, Director of Corporate Affairs, United Brotherhood of Carpenters and Joiners of America (UBCJA)); *see also* Kary, *supra* note 2, at 3. The four unions are the UBCJA, the Sheet Metal Workers International Association, the Laborers' International Union of North America and the United Association. The companies include, among others, Merrill Lynch & Co., Intel Corp., Gap Inc., Chevron-Texaco Corp., JPMorgan Chase & Co. and Time Warner Inc.

March 24, 2005

No Substitute for Good Judgment

The agency theory of corporations always has been an oversimplification. Recently, it has become a dangerous one. Proponents of this theory take the view that science and statistics can explain management behavior; they combine this view with a general pessimism about human nature. The net result is a belief that self-interested opportunistic behavior by managers is to be expected and must be controlled with suspicion and supervision. The late Sumantra Ghoshal, of the Advanced Institute of Management Research (UK) and the London Business School, in a recently released article,[91] provides numerous compelling reasons for rejecting the negative view of management behavior that has become unquestioned doctrine over the last several decades in business schools around the world.

Ghoshal attributes the prevalence of the agency theory to a desire by academics to turn management studies into a science such as physics, complete with elegant mathematical models and accurate predictions of events. But as Ghoshal points out, theories in the social sciences, unlike theories in the physical sciences, can affect the behavior of their subjects. Treating people as untrustworthy makes them less trustworthy, not more so; assuming that people will behave opportunistically to maximize only their own enrichment often results in them doing so. Academics have preferred to ignore human nature in all its complexity and variety — including morality, common sense, judgment, effectiveness, leadership and experience — in favor of neat mathematical models. To the extent this view results in corporate governance regimes that emphasize suspicion, surveillance and liability for corporate actors, at the expense of the authority and autonomy necessary to manage effectively, the consequences for our corporations and the broader economy will be increasingly negative.

Even the "agency" aspect of agency theory is based on questionable assumptions. Whence the certainty, asks Ghoshal, that the job of managers is solely to maximize shareholder value? Shareholders have chosen a limited liability form in which to invest their capital, entitling them to the residual cash flows of the corporation but not to its actual assets or

---

91. Bad Management Practices are Destroying Good Management Practices (Academy of Management Learning & Education, 2005, Vol. 4, No. 1, 75-91; available at http://aom.pace.edu/AMLE/AMLEVolume4Issue1pp75-91.pdf)

resources, which are owned by the legal entity of the corporation itself. They are not the only investors in a company; management and employees generally have much more invested in terms of personal and financial risk than the average shareholder. Ghoshal posits that the only advantage of the agency model — of shareholders as "principals" whose interest is paramount and managers as "agents" who are trying to use company resources for their own benefit — is that it is a simple one for academics to structure and solve.

In recent months, the agency theory has been pushed to its logical limits and beyond. Some prominent commentators are now arguing for the extreme version: that shareholders should have the right to govern a company virtually by referendum. Activist shareholders are pushing proposals such as majority election of directors, proxy access for shareholder nominations of directors, limits on the form and amount of executive compensation and shareholder votes on key corporate events. They intend to turn directors, and to some extent management, into passive executors of shareholder will. This would be a grave mistake.

The prosperity of the American corporation long has been the envy of the world. We owe this success in no small measure to the institution of the board of directors and to the common sense, integrity and good judgment of corporate officers and directors. Though there have been scandals in recent years, they are the exception and not the rule. Treating them as the rule risks imposing impractical and onerous restraints that stifle entrepreneurial activity and hobble our competitiveness.

If agency theory began with the notion that shareholders take risks and are entitled to rewards, it is becoming the idea that shareholders are entitled to reap rewards while management and the board shoulder the risks. After the upheaval caused by the large-scale corporate crises of the past few years, some activist shareholders now seem to believe that they are entitled to as close to all of the financial gains of a company as possible in exchange for a minimal amount of risk, yet they expect directors to assume daunting personal liability for almost no reward. In the current corporate governance climate, board members are reluctant to accept meaningful payment for their efforts for fear of creating a "conflict." At the same time, the efforts of activist shareholders — frequently motivated by political considerations — to punish directors who did not benefit from corporate misfeasance but only failed to ferret it out, such as in the recent WorldCom settlement, cause even the most steadfast and reliable directors to fear for their personal assets. In the end, however, it is the shareholders who may be the losers if the current trend in risk-reward division continues. As Treasury Secretary John Snow recently observed, directors and management are growing less willing to take business risks that, on the whole, would produce benefits for investors and society, for fear of personal liability if something goes wrong. The irony is that in trying to eliminate all possible conflicts for directors, the regulators and activist shareholders may be creating the most substantial conflict of all.

Recent laws and regulations have done much that is good. Legislators and regulators have succeeded in improving communications between companies and their shareholders and in reminding directors of their responsibility to be active, engaged participants in the life of the corporation. Ultimately, though, the success of an enterprise depends not on the stringency of applicable laws and constraints, but on human competence, experience, integrity and many other qualities that the agency model ignores. Studies have shown time and again that the proportion of independent directors on the board has no significant effect on corporate performance. Neither does the separation of the roles of chairman of the board and CEO. It may well be time to accept the limitations of the agency theory, rein in our regulatory impulses and consider an alternative.

Ghoshal urges us to acknowledge that companies prosper when they simultaneously consider the interests of their customers, employees and shareholders and perhaps even the local community. Interestingly, after long study and debate, this principle has been adopted in the Company Law Reform legislation submitted this month by the English government to Parliament: "the basic goal for directors should be the success of the company for its members as a whole; but to reach this goal, directors would need to take a properly balanced view of the implications of decisions over time and foster effective relationships with employees, customers and suppliers and in the community more widely." In the United States, we have recognized this in the past. Beginning in the 1980s, over half of the states adopted statutory provisions specifically allowing or requiring boards to consider factors other than shareholder profit — e.g., the interests of customers, suppliers and local communities and the long-term interests of the company — when facing a takeover bid. At that time, courts rejected the idea of board passivity and indeed expanded the arena in which boards were urged to exercise their business judgment. This understanding of the vital role of the board of directors is threatened now by advocates of shareholder "empowerment" and expanded director liability. It is crucial that we preserve the basic principles underlying the American corporation. There is no substitute for sound judgment, common sense and a fundamental faith that American business, when invested with responsibility and trust, will continue to do great things.

Martin Lipton

April 20, 2005

The New Enforcement Environment

We are experiencing a period of rapid change in the environment when dealing with the SEC and the SROs. Regulators are employing aggressive new investigative techniques and the threshold for conduct to be deemed enforcement-worthy seems lower than ever before. While turnover in senior personnel has begun at the SEC, we do not expect these changes to lessen the intensity of the enforcement atmosphere.

As a result of the paradigm shift in the enforcement and regulatory environment, investment banks and other regulated entities in particular should be mindful of the following new realities:

- There is great danger in thinking that a course of conduct can be safely followed merely because it is not "expressly prohibited"—the regulators do not view the scope of their enforcement powers so narrowly. There may be a significant risk of enforcement action even in the absence of a law or regulation that is directly on point. Even in the absence of clear legal risk, the course of conduct may pose unacceptable reputational risk.

- Little comfort can be derived from the assertion that "everyone does it"—the defense of market practice will be ineffective if regulators find the practice unacceptable. Firms should hold themselves to a "best practices" standard, aspiring to lead the market, rather than follow it.

- Management must understand the new environment and the resulting demands placed upon the legal and compliance functions. There must be a genuine buy-in from senior management committing the firm to the approach—and the dedication of resources—needed to succeed in the new environment.

- Firms should be proactive and vigilant in assessing their businesses. Enhanced processes should be adopted for vetting new business products and services. On a regular basis, compliance or internal audit should review every business area and control function.

- Technology is a powerful tool. Firms should make greater use of available technology to monitor and surveil business activities.

- More than ever before, regulatory examinations are a first step down the road to enforcement action. Regulators are much more frequently dispatching examination staff in sweeps or targeted exams to prospect for conduct warranting enforcement action. Firms should manage the exam process accordingly. Personnel dealing with examiners should have the background, expertise and judgment skills required to ensure that the firm is responsive to the requests of the examiners and to recognize the significance of issues that emerge during the exam. Sufficient resources must be devoted to responding in a timely and accurate manner to exam requests.

- When issues are discovered internally, there can be great value in timely self-reporting to regulators so as to maximize the firm's credit for cooperation. At the same time, reporting too hastily and without a sufficient grasp of the facts can backfire. Early representations to the regulators that later turn out to be inaccurate or incomplete can lead to heightened skepticism, rather than extra credit.

- Firms should take every opportunity to enhance dialogue with regulators. It is in every firm's interest to maintain lines of communication and opportunities for interaction. These contacts should reinforce with regulators that the firm is committed to a strong compliance culture, takes a thoughtful approach to regulatory issues and genuinely seeks to maintain best practices.

- It is essential to remain attuned to regulatory developments, so as to recognize the regulatory significance of day-to-day business practices, as well as longer range trends. A wealth of material is available on regulators' websites, and senior regulatory officials frequently use public speaking engagements to highlight current priorities and concerns.

- Disclose, disclose, disclose—One lesson of recent years is the power of disclosure as a protective measure. Even in the new environment, we can expect the quality of disclosure to continue to tip the balance on whether or not enforcement action is taken at all.

Theodore A. Levine
Wayne M. Carlin

April 20, 2005

Court Upholds Attorney Work Product Protection for Audit Committee Report Provided Pursuant to Confidentiality Agreement with Government

As boards of directors are increasingly called upon to conduct internal investigations into suspected wrongdoing, one of the most difficult issues that companies face is whether they can provide the results of such investigations to government investigators without waiving the protections of the attorney work product doctrine. In an effort to address that concern, such reports are often provided pursuant to a confidentiality agreement with the government setting forth the parties' mutual position that the company's cooperative sharing of its report with government investigators is not intended to waive attorney-client and attorney work product protections. However, as our prior memoranda have noted, courts have disagreed about the effectiveness of these confidentiality agreements in protecting corporate privileges. See our memo dated February 26, 2004, "Reports to Government Investigators of Audit Committee Findings May Be Discoverable by Plaintiffs in Shareholder Lawsuits."

That judicial debate continues. In an important decision, the U.S. District Court for the Northern District of California recently ruled that because McKesson HBOC, Inc. had entered into confidentiality agreements with both the Securities and Exchange Commission and the United States Attorney's Office — pursuant to which it provided the results of an Audit Committee investigation — the company had not waived attorney work product protections. In re McKesson HBOC, Inc. Securities Litigation, No. C-99-20743 (Mar. 31, 2005). The court thus denied shareholder plaintiffs' effort to obtain discovery of those investigative materials. In its opinion, the court took into consideration "the benefit to the public of permitting disclosure of work product to the government" as support for the preservation of work product protections when materials are produced under a confidentiality agreement negotiated with government investigators.

In so holding, however, the court bluntly disagreed with the reasoning in prior decisions in California, see McKesson HBOC, Inc. v. Superior Court, 115 Cal. App. 4th 1229 (2004), and a recent decision by the Georgia Supreme Court, in McKesson Corp. v. Green, 610 S.E.2d 54 (Ga. 2005), finding that the very same McKesson investigative reports were discoverable by plaintiffs, notwithstanding the confidentiality agreements with the government.

Congressional efforts to resolve this judicial impasse — through H.R. 2179, which would have established that the production of investigative materials pursuant to a confidentiality agreement would not constitute a waiver — appear to have stalled. Despite the SEC's support for this bill, it does not appear likely at this time that this legislation will be passed. The SEC has continued, however, to support the enforceability of confidentiality agreements by filing amicus briefs, as it did in the In re McKesson HBOC Securities Litigation case.

Given this continuing uncertainty, the prudent course for companies is to weigh carefully the benefits and risks of producing internal investigative materials to the government and, if deemed appropriate to do so, to negotiate the strongest possible confidentiality agreement with the government. These decisions must be guided by the best interests of the company, with the recognition that there can be no certainty at this point whether such a disclosure will later be found to have waived the company's privilege.

John F. Savarese

May 2, 2005

Executive Compensation—Perquisites

In the Tyson Foods case, which was settled last week, the SEC finds that it is an internal controls failure for perquisites not to have been authorized by the company's compensation committee or board of directors.

The lesson is clear: The nature and amount of any substantial perquisites for named executive officers should be reported to and authorized by the compensation committee or the board of directors. Item 402(b) of SEC Regulation S-K requires disclosure when perquisites exceed the lesser of $50,000 or 10% of the total annual salary and bonus reported for the named executive. Two types of disclosures are required for each named executive: (1) the total dollar amount of the perquisites must be included in the summary compensation table; and (2) an additional footnote disclosure is required to specifically identify by type and amount each perquisite that exceeds 25% of the total perquisites reported for the named executive.

Martin Lipton

May 25, 2005

Delaware Court Dismisses Shareholder Suit Arising Out of JPMorganChase Acquisition of Bank One

Following last year's acquisition of Bank One by JPMorganChase ("JPMC"), rumors appeared in the press concerning the details of the negotiations between the parties. Shareholder plaintiffs filed suit in Delaware alleging that JPMC unnecessarily paid a premium in stock for Bank One, on the basis of media reports that a no-premium transaction was available.

The Court of Chancery dismissed the complaint. In re JPMorganChase Shareholder Litig., C.A. No. 531-N (Apr. 29, 2005). The Court held that a claim that an acquirer "overpaid" for a target states a derivative and not a direct claim — that is, the harm is to the acquiring corporation, and not to the shareholders of the acquirer. This is so even if, as here, the plaintiff argues that each shareholder of the acquiring corporation is improperly "diluted" by an overpayment.

Since the claim was derivative, it could not survive if a majority of the board was independent. Therefore, the Court examined the allegations made by plaintiffs that the JPMC board consisted of directors who were not independent, and concluded that the overwhelming majority of the directors were in fact independent, despite various business relationships with JPMC and despite (in some cases) leadership of charitable institutions which were alleged to be major recipients of JPMC's corporate giving. These rulings represent further assurance from Delaware that, despite last year's widely-reported finding with respect to certain Oracle directors who were professors at Stanford and found to lack independence with respect to a major Stanford donor, Delaware will not be quick to find that customary charitable relationships taint independence. The Court further found that nothing in the pleaded record of the negotiations called into question the board's exercise of business judgment in approving the transaction.

The JPMorganChase decision should help assure boards involved in merger transactions that the Delaware courts will not permit stockholder plaintiffs to rely on press and media speculation in framing non-meritorious legal claims.

Edward D. Herlihy
Paul K. Rowe

May 26, 2005

Corporate Governance: Executive Compensation, Disclosure and Board Oversight

David A. Katz
and
Laura A. McIntosh[92]

Executive compensation and related public disclosure are among the most high-profile topics in corporate governance today. Recent Securities and Exchange Commission settlements with General Electric[93] and Tyson Foods[94] and the recent Delaware lawsuit involving Abercrombie & Fitch[95] have drawn public attention to the details of executive compensation and the quality and significance of company disclosure. This article highlights some of the lessons to be learned from recent examples and offers suggestions to directors for best practices going forward.

Recent Cases

Examples of executive compensation-related controversies, lawsuits and settlements are, unfortunately, all too numerous at the moment. Three recent, highly-publicized situations offer cautionary tales for boards of directors and senior management.

General Electric: Pursuant to former General Electric Chief Executive Officer Jack Welch's retirement agreement, he was given permanent access to many perquisites and benefits that he had enjoyed as chief executive. The publicly-filed agreement did not detail these items, and the proxy statement disclosure made only the general statement that Welch would be entitled to "continued lifetime access to Company facilities and services comparable to those that are currently made available to him by the Company."[96] Proxy statements issued during Welch's tenure did not disclose some of the more expensive benefits he received, such as personal use of company aircraft and limousines. These perquisites came to

92. David A. Katz is a partner at Wachtell, Lipton, Rosen & Katz. Laura A. McIntosh is a consulting attorney for the firm. The views expressed are the authors' own.

93. In the Matter of General Electric Company, SEC Administrative Proceeding File No. 3-11677, Sept. 23, 2004 ("GE Settlement").

94. In the Matter of Tyson Foods, Inc. and Donald Tyson, SEC Administrative Proceeding File No. 3-11917, Apr. 28, 2005 ("Tyson Complaint").

95. Derivative Complaint, O'Malley ex rel. Abercrombie & Fitch Co. v. Jeffries, No. CA1077-N (Del. Ch. filed Feb. 8, 2005) ("Abercrombie Complaint").

96. *See* GE Settlement, *supra* note 1.

light in the course of Welch's divorce proceeding. In September 2004, the SEC stated in the settlement of its enforcement action against GE that the company's disclosure had not fully and accurately described Welch's retirement benefits.[97]

Tyson Foods: In March 2004, the SEC began an inquiry into allegedly excessive and undisclosed benefits involving former Tyson Foods Chairman Don Tyson. Only a few months later, during negotiations with the SEC regarding the company's failure to disclose Tyson's bonuses, the directors approved a contract with Tyson that in exchange for up to 20 hours of consulting per week—and over and above his existing retirement benefits—awarded him $1.2 million annually and access to expensive perquisites such as extensive use of the company jet.[98] The matter finally settled in April 2005, with the SEC finding that Tyson Foods made misleading disclosures of perquisites and personal benefits provided to Tyson both before and after his retirement as chairman. The SEC also found that, due to failures of internal controls, many of the more substantial perquisites were not known to or authorized by the board of directors or compensation committee.[99] Though the 2004 consulting contract was not mentioned in the SEC settlement, it contributed to the public impression of excess and waste in executive compensation and benefits.

Abercrombie & Fitch: A derivative suit was brought in February 2005 by a shareholder who claimed that the Abercrombie & Fitch board breached its duties of good faith, loyalty and candor by awarding a "grossly excessive and wasteful" pay package to the Chief Executive Officer, Michael Jeffries.[100] The suit also charged directors with waste of corporate assets by approving the payment of excessive compensation and the unjust enrichment of the chief executive.[101] The derivative complaint contrasted language from the company's proxy statement indicating that the Abercrombie & Fitch compensation committee's mandate was to pay bonuses that were commensurate with industry standards and the company's financial performance with a Bloomberg article stating that Jef-

97. *See id.*
98. *See* Mark Jaffe, U.S. Intensifies Efforts To Determine CEOs' Compensation, Bloomberg News Wire Services, The Record (Bergen County, NJ), Mar. 6, 2005.
99. *See* Tyson Complaint, *supra* note 2.
100. *See* Abercrombie Complaint, *supra* note 3.
101. *See id.* Similar allegations were made in a derivative complaint filed in November 2004 against the directors of The Fairchild Corporation in the Delaware Chancery Court. Derivative Complaint, Noto ex rel. Fairchild Corp. v. Steiner, No. CA871-N (Del. Ch. filed Nov. 18, 2004) ("Fairchild Complaint").

fries' salary was higher than those of eleven chief executives of comparable companies and that Abercrombie & Fitch's returns over the relevant period were low compared to peer retailers. In the April 2005 settlement, the company agreed to reduce by half a potential $12 million "stay" bonus to Jeffries, tie Jeffries' bonus to specific earnings targets and eliminate new stock options for Jeffries for two years.[102]

Internal Controls

The GE and Tyson settlements with the SEC illustrate the importance of board attention to all material aspects of executive compensation. GE failed to ensure that the details of Welch's retirement pay were properly disclosed, which potentially raises questions regarding the GE board's oversight. The Tyson Foods board was unaware that Don Tyson was receiving significant perquisites from the company and accordingly could not supervise appropriate disclosure. Moreover, when faced with an SEC investigation into compensation matters, the Tyson Foods board continued to approve benefits that could be viewed as disproportionate to the services provided by the former chairman.[103]

In addition, the SEC's conclusion that Tyson Foods failed to maintain adequate internal controls over Don Tyson's personal use of company assets raises important issues that would need to be considered in a Sarbanes-Oxley 404 review. It is clear that the SEC expects public companies to have compensation-related internal controls in place and that this would require both compensation committee and audit committee oversight. It would also appear to be an appropriate matter for public companies' internal audit functions to review to ensure that adequate internal controls exist and are effective.

The Abercrombie & Fitch settlement highlights the importance of board attention to company disclosure, but even more important, it may indicate a new development in the evolution of shareholder litigation alleging violations by directors of their duties under Delaware law. The plaintiff argued that the directors breached their fiduciary duties under Delaware law by failing to ensure that proxy disclosure accurately represented the company's policies regarding executive compensation. Though the lawsuit was not adjudicated, the threshold for liability in Delaware for

---

102. *See* Tiffany Kary, Abercrombie Settles Derivatives Suit on Compensation, Wall St. J., Apr. 12, 2005; Jeffrey Sheban, Investor Pressure Prompts Abercrombie & Fitch To Overhaul Executive Pay, Columbus Dispatch (Ohio), Apr. 12, 2005.

103. *See supra* text accompanying note 6.

disclosure violations under the so-called "duty of candor" may be lower than that under federal securities laws.[104]

Delaware Vice Chancellor Leo Strine recently rejected as inadequate a proposed settlement agreement in a derivative action involving The Fairchild Corporation. The complaint alleged breaches of fiduciary duty, corporate waste and unjust enrichment in challenging compensation paid to and other arrangements for the chairman and chief executive officer and his son, the chief operating officer and president.[105] Vice Chancellor Strine apparently indicated that, if the allegations in the complaint were true, the proposed settlement would not have provided adequate protection to shareholders from "a grotesque lack of controls in a company that also has no profits."[106] The Delaware courts continue to be focused on executive compensation matters and board oversight.

The lessons to be drawn from these examples is clear: Directors would be well-advised to obtain all relevant information regarding executive compensation prior to taking any action, to give careful consideration to approving appropriate compensation arrangements (including perquisites), and to pay close attention to the resulting disclosure to ensure that it is accurate, complete and transparent.

---

104. *See, e.g.*, Malone v. Brincat, 722 A.2d 5, 12, 14 (Del. 1998) (citations omitted):

> An action for a breach of fiduciary duty arising out of disclosure violations in connection with a request for stockholder action does not include the elements of reliance, causation and actual quantifiable monetary damages. Instead, such actions require the challenged disclosure to have a connection to the request for shareholder action. The essential inquiry in such an action is whether the alleged omission or misrepresentation is material.
>
> ....
>
> Delaware law also protects shareholders who receive false communications from directors even in the absence of a request for shareholder action. When the directors are ... deliberately misinforming shareholders about the business of the corporation, either directly or by a public statement, there is a violation of fiduciary duty. That violation may result in a derivative claim on behalf of the corporation or a cause of action for damages. There may also be a basis for equitable relief to remedy the violation.

See also generally Lawrence A. Hamermesh, Calling off the Lynch Mob: The Corporate Director's Fiduciary Disclosure Duty, 49 Vand. L. Rev. 1089 (1996).

105. *See* Fairchild Complaint, *supra* note 9.

Enhanced Responsibility

Historically, boards of directors and compensation committees generally have been content to approve the broad strokes of executive compensation: salary, bonus, retirement pay and perhaps severance and change-in-control arrangements. In some cases, perquisites appear to have been treated as "business expenses" that flew below the radar of the board of directors and were never addressed by the compensation committee. This approach, even if it was typical of past practices, no longer appears to be sufficient.

In the current environment, it is important for boards of directors and compensation committees in particular to be proactive in requesting detailed information about executive compensation packages before approving them. To assure themselves the protection of the business judgment rule, directors should take affirmative steps to make sure that they are fully informed on all compensation-related matters involving the key executives of the company. Directors should review and discuss, both in executive session and with the chief executive officer, the material components of the compensation package, including annual salary, incentive and performance-related pay, perquisites, retirement benefits, deferred compensation, tax gross-ups, supplemental executive retirement plans, severance payments and change-in-control agreements. Directors should consider how each aspect of executive compensation fits into the general picture of the company's compensation arrangements as well as the smaller picture of that executive's package.

In order to ascertain that compensation packages are appropriate and reasonable, directors should fully understand the costs and benefits of potential components of compensation. In this regard, directors are enti-

---

106. *See* David S. Hilzenrath, Fairchild Executives' Settlement Rejected, Wash. Post, May 19, 2005 at E1. Vice Chancellor Strine was also quoted as saying ""You've got a very poorly performing company over time that continually pays the CEO like he's a top slugger." *Id.* The total present value to the class of the rejected settlement was $2.9 million. The release in the rejected settlement covered a number of different claims because the original complaint was quite broad. In addition, the company had paid over $5 million to cover the Chairman's costs for defending criminal charges brought against him in France for acts not taken in his official capacity at the company, including paying a criminal fine for him. The Vice Chancellor appeared to be troubled that, in exchange for modest benefits, sweeping claims were going to be released where the complaint was broad and articulated troubling facts at a company that had been sued twice before and settled compensation claims, that the company is controlled by the Chairman, and that the company pays its managers well even when the company has poor results.

tled to rely on the advice of experts.[107] However, care should be taken in selecting these experts, and to the extent that compensation consultants are retained to advise the directors, prudence would dictate that these experts be retained by the compensation committee and not by management. It also would be beneficial for directors to review and discuss compensation policies to ensure that the compensation arrangements of the top executives are consistent with those policies as well as the corporation's goals generally.

Focus on Disclosure

The settlements described above illustrate the paramount importance of disclosure. Compensation committees should update their proxy disclosure annually instead of relying on generalized boilerplate from prior years. The Abercrombie & Fitch compensation committee likely never imagined that the broad description of their compensation goals set forth in the company proxy statement could form the basis of a lawsuit alleging misrepresentation. In this environment, proxy and other executive compensation disclosures should be carefully scrutinized for accuracy and completeness. Directors should consider reviewing the actual disclosure and discussing it with the counsel that prepared it prior to its submission to the SEC.

The compensation committee report currently is not considered "filed" under the Securities Exchange Act of 1934; however, the Abercrombie & Fitch settlement indicates the importance of treating the disclosure in the report as seriously as if it were legally part of a publicly-filed document. Alan Beller, Director of the Division of Corporation Finance at the SEC, noted in a widely-cited speech last October that the SEC may consider eliminating this "special treatment" for compensation committee reports unless companies and their advisors reciprocate with transparent disclosure.[108] Beller advocated for disclosure that focused on presenting complete descriptions of compensation arrangements in a clear and concise manner rather than on revealing the minimum amount of information that is required. For example, to the extent that it may be argued that certain elements of compensation may not be required to be disclosed under the line-item disclosure requirements, consideration should be given to mak-

---

107. *See, e.g.*, Delaware General Corporation Law Section 141(e).

108. Remarks Before Conference of the National Association of Stock Plan Professionals, The Corporate Counsel and the Corporate Executive by Alan Beller, Director, Division of Corporation Finance, U.S. Securities and Exchange Commission, Oct. 20, 2004 ("Beller Speech").

ing disclosure if it could be argued that shareholders will lack a complete understanding of an executive's compensation if these elements are not disclosed.[109] Moreover, to the extent that management makes decisions on what does and does not need to be disclosed, compensation committee members may wish to be informed as to these decisions so that their impact may be more fully considered before disclosure is made, rather than in hindsight.

Increasingly, boards of directors are hiring separate outside counsel for the board and for certain of its committees. Though companies should support the use of advisors and experts by boards and their committees (and should consider specifically delegating the power to retain such persons directly to board committees), boards should take care not to promote competing advisors or to bifurcate advice such that the board as a whole could be disadvantaged. It would make sense for the team that advises a compensation committee and assists in the drafting of its disclosure also to be involved in the drafting of any related board-level disclosure. Advisors will be more effective in drafting and reviewing company disclosure if they have been present at the deliberations and discussions held at both the board and committee levels. If, however, committees employ their own counsel, it is quite possible that the committee may receive different disclosure advice than the board (or management). In most cases, there is no need to retain separate committee counsel.

Conclusion

Two years ago, SEC Chairman William Donaldson famously alluded to a "disconnect between executive compensation and performance."[110] Increasing public disillusionment with executive compensation clearly relates to widespread concern that the compensation-related interests of executives are not aligned with those of shareholders. Beller recently identified a second, related concern: that inadequate or confusing disclosure is raising suspicions in the minds of shareholders that they are not receiving the full story.[111] Boards of directors should be vigilant in focus-

109. One example that the SEC staff appears to be focusing upon is comprehensive, understandable and consistent disclosure of the use of corporate aircraft by company executives.

110. Remarks Before the Economic Club of New York, by William H. Donaldson, Chairman, U.S. Securities and Exchange Commission, May 8, 2003.

111. *See* Beller Speech, supra note 16. Beller stated: "Too much executive compensation disclosure has become an example of the kind of disclosure companies should disavow—disclosure that says as little as possible while seeking to avoid liability, rather than disclosure that seeks to inform." *Id.*

ing on compensation and disclosure matters and taking steps to address these concerns in a proactive fashion.

Public company boards of directors should continue to work toward implementing best practices in the highly sensitive area of executive compensation. At a minimum, directors should ensure that they are fully informed as to the details and operation of executive compensation arrangements. Institutional investors continue to clamor for executive compensation to be tied to long-term corporate performance and increases in shareholder value. In addition, directors now need to consider whether perquisites provided to key executives would be viewed as reasonable; certainly, there should be a clear demarcation between business and personal expenses. Internal controls for compensation matters should be in place and actively used. Finally, directors and their advisors should take a fresh look at all disclosure regarding executive compensation matters and philosophy to ensure that it is clear, concise and sufficiently detailed.

June 24, 2005

Delaware Court Examines "Rules of the Road" in Auction Context

In a wide-ranging opinion touching on many aspects of the law governing the sale of public companies, the Delaware Court of Chancery has strongly endorsed the principle that well-advised boards have wide latitude in structuring sale processes. The opinion also provides express judicial guidance on a number of practices and issues that have arisen in the current deal climate and have not been recently addressed by the Delaware courts, including the legal status of deal-protection measures. In re Toys "r" Us, Inc. Shareholder Lit., Cons. C.A. No. 1212-N (Del. Ch. June 22, 2005).

The more noteworthy of the Court's holdings, from a practitioner's standpoint, include the following:

* The shareholder plaintiffs argued that by agreeing to give the KKR group a 3.75% break-up fee coupled with a "matching right", the board unreasonably deterred additional bids. The Court dismissed these challenges to the structure and amount of the provisions.

* The Court approved the board's decision to permit two of the private equity firms already in the bidding to "club" together, thus potentially reducing the number of competing bidders for future rounds. Indeed, the Court said that this "emerging practice among financial buyers" helps stockholders by permitting buyers "to make bids that would be imprudent, if pursued in isolation."

* When the Toys "r" Us board switched from a sale process focused on the company's most valuable division to one focused on sale of the whole company, the board also closed the process to all bidders except those who had engaged in due diligence and shown seriousness by submitting a bid. The court approved this decision, relying on the fact that it was widely reported that the process was being broadened, and yet no new buyers tried to enter the process.

* The Court found that allegations of conflict of interest on the part of the CEO, arising out of his holdings of options and equity, were groundless and that, in fact, such holdings aligned his interests with those of the public stockholders in a sale context.

* The financial advisor had an engagement letter which would earn it substantially greater fees for a sale of the whole company versus

some smaller transaction. The Court found that this fee structure did not taint the firm's work in advising the board what alternative to pursue.

* Although the board, prior to approving a final deal with one buyer, refused to permit its financial advisor to hold discussions with potential buyers with a view to the advisor providing financing to the bidders, after the transaction was approved and a fairness opinion rendered, the board then did permit the advisor to provide financing to the successful bidder. The Court said this chain of events "tends to raise eyebrows" but that the Court could not conclude that the advisor's work prior to approval of the transaction was tainted in any way. The opinion notes that a financial advisor's willingness to provide financing to bidders could benefit shareholders in some fact patterns, such as where the advisor's commitment to provide financing on the same terms to all comers has the effect of inducing "more bidders to take the risk of an acquisition." But the Court also uttered words of caution: "It is advisable that investment banks representing sellers not create the appearance that they desire buy-side work, especially when it might be that they are more likely to be selected by some buyers for that lucrative role than by others."

* The Court placed reliance on the fact that the company negotiated with KKR to cause KKR to remove a condition to its bid that company management be retained to run the business following the sale. In this regard the Court approved the practice of the CEO refusing to discuss his employment future with any of the potential buyers, a ban which was extended to other senior management.

These points are only some of the highlights of the decision, which deals with virtually every question that arises in the course of competitive bidding situations involving cash offers, and provides highly relevant guidance to buyers, advisors, and boards of directors involved in a competitive bidding situation. The Court's opinion, which explains the relationship between the financial, doctrinal and practical concepts relevant to the auction process, will bring much-needed clarity to a complex area of the law and provide comfort to directors that courts will not second-guess the decisions that need to be made to bring a sale process to successful conclusion.

Paul K. Rowe
Andrew J. Nussbaum

June 24, 2005

Majority Vote to Elect Directors

The effort by activist shareholders to get corporations to adopt majority voting for election of directors continues to pick up steam. The response to this effort also is picking up steam.

Within the week, the Council of Institutional Investors has written to 1,500 corporations requesting that they adopt majority voting, the Committee on Corporate Laws of the American Bar Association has released a discussion paper highlighting the issues involved in switching to majority voting and Pfizer has amended its corporate governance guidelines to require that any director who receives a majority of withheld votes must submit his or her resignation to the board, with the board to then decide what to do.

The new Pfizer policy is a variation of the proposal I made in my March 13 memo to the effect that if a majority of the outstanding shares vote to withhold against a director, then that director is not elected. My proposal and the Pfizer policy differ in that (1) Pfizer requires withholding of only a majority of the votes cast, while mine requires a majority of the outstanding shares and (2) Pfizer provides that the director submit a resignation to be considered by the board and I proposed that the director was not elected.

I continue to believe that whether the result is board consideration of resignation or non-election, the threshold should be a majority of the outstanding shares voting to withhold. I think the Pfizer approach of board consideration of resignation is preferable to non-election in that it solves or avoids many of the issues discussed in the ABA paper and our March 24 memo.

Adopting a corporate governance guideline now that provides for board consideration of a resignation if a majority of the outstanding shares are withheld may set a pattern that, if widely followed, should substantially address the concerns of the majority-voting movement.

Martin Lipton

June 28, 2005

Majority Vote to Elect Directors

The following are alternative model forms of corporate governance guidelines which may be adapted to implement the suggestion in our June 24, 2005 memo, Majority Vote to Elect Directors, *www.wlrk.com/docs/mved.pdf*.

Voting for Directors. Any nominee for Director who receives a number of votes "withheld" from or "against" his or her election greater than a majority of the outstanding shares entitled to vote in such election shall tender his or her resignation for consideration by the Corporate Governance and Nominating Committee. The Corporate Governance and Nominating Committee shall recommend to the Board the action to be taken with respect to such resignation.

Voting for Directors. Any nominee for Director in an uncontested election as to whom a majority of the shares of the Company that are outstanding and entitled to vote in such election are designated to be "withheld" from or are voted "against" his or her election shall tender his or her resignation for consideration by the Corporate Governance and Nominating Committee. The Corporate Governance and Nominating Committee shall evaluate the best interests of the Company and its shareholders and shall recommend to the Board the action to be taken with respect to such tendered resignation.

Martin Lipton
David A. Katz

NOTES

DEVELOPMENTS IN INTERNAL INVESTIGATIONS

22

INTERNAL INVESTIGATIONS: ESSENTIAL COMPONENTS TO COOPERATION IN AN SEC INQUIRY

Derek M. Meisner

Kirkpatrick & Lockhart Nicholson Graham LLP

Biographical Information

Derek M. Meisner is a member of Kirkpatrick & Lockhart Nicholson Graham LLP in Boston, Massachusetts. His practice focuses on representing clients in enforcement investigations conducted by the SEC, NASD and state securities regulators, litigating securities cases, conducting corporate internal investigations, and advising clients on related compliance and corporate governance issues. Prior to joining K&LNG, Mr. Meisner served as a Branch Chief in the SEC's Division of Enforcement in Washington, D.C., where he conducted and supervised prominent investigations relating to corporate financial reporting, broker-dealer/investment adviser practices, Regulation FD, market manipulation, hedge fund trading, offerings of unregistered securities, and insider trading, among others. Before joining the SEC, Mr. Meisner was associated with a Washington, D.C. law firm, where he successfully defended financial conglomerates in complex litigation arising out of the sale of securities, insurance and other financial products.

Judging from a recent string of high-profile settlements, the Securities and Exchange Commission is placing greater importance on corporate cooperation in its investigations, rewarding full cooperation in appropriate circumstances, and more importantly, penalizing the lack of it with steep penalties. *See, e.g. SEC v. Wachovia Corporation CA 04-1911* (D.D.C.), SEC Lit. Rel. No. 18958 (November 4, 2004) (imposing $37 million penalty against Wachovia for providing "incomplete and untimely document production" and failing to ensure "comprehensive and complete responses" to requests and subpoenas); *SEC v. Gemstar-TV Guide International, Inc.,* CV 04-04-4506 (C.D. Cal); SEC Lit. Rel. No. 18760 (June 23, 2004) (penalizing Gemstar $10 million due in part to its "initial lack of effective cooperation or remedial efforts"); *SEC v. Symbol Technologies et al.*, CV O4 2276 (E.D.N.Y), SEC Lit. Rel. No. 18734 (June 3, 2004) (imposing $37 million penalty against Symbol in part because of its "initial efforts to cover up the misconduct and impede two internal investigations and the SEC's investigation"); *SEC v. Lucent Technologies, Inc. et al.,* Civil Action No. 04-2315 (D.N.J.), SEC Lit. Rel. No. 18715 (May 17, 2004) (penalizing Lucent $25 million for its lack of cooperation). While no principle of law requires that a company cooperate in an SEC investigation, well-advised companies often determine that cooperation is in their best legal and financial interests.

Conducting an internal investigation is an essential predicate to establishing good faith cooperation in an SEC inquiry. An effective internal investigation can provide defense counsel with justification to persuade the SEC to reduce the contemplated charges, or to forego filing charges altogether. The SEC has set forth four broad criteria that it will consider in evaluating whether to charge a company with violations of the federal securities laws, including whether the company conducted a "thorough review of the nature, extent, origins and consequences of the misconduct." *See* Report of Investigation Pursuant to Section 21(a) of the Securities Exchange Act of 1934 and Commission Statement on the Relationship of Cooperation to Agency Enforcement Decisions, Release No. 34-44969, 76 S.E.C. Docket 220 (Oct. 23, 2001). The SEC also considers "the quality and propriety of the investigation into the misconduct, including the expedience and thoroughness of the review, whether the review was conducted by independent persons such as outside directors and legal counsel, and whether there were any limitations placed on those charged with the investigation." *Id.*

Six issues to consider in conducting an effective internal investigation are summarized below. The summaries are not meant to substitute for consultation with a qualified securities attorney.

1. Who Will Authorize and Supervise the Investigation

Typically, the company's board of directors or a committee of the board should authorize and supervise the investigation. This is particularly true if the "targets" of the investigation are company executives. Board members have a fiduciary duty to the company to ensure that it does not engage in unethical or illegal conduct, and must attempt to preserve shareholder value. However, if one of the board members is a suspected target, or if a targeted executive sits on the board, consideration should be given to allowing outside counsel to oversee the investigation and to shielding the particular board member or executive from *any* matters concerning the investigation.

In an accounting fraud settlement in 2004, *SEC v. Del Global Technologies et al.*, Case No. 04 CV 4092 (S.D.N.Y.), Lit. Release No. 18732 (June 1, 2004), the SEC highlighted the importance of precluding suspected wrongdoers from influencing an internal investigation or intimidating employees. In *Del Global*, the SEC imposed a significant civil penalty against Del Global Technologies, Inc. ("Del"), in part because Del, upon discovery of the fraudulent accounting scheme by its auditors, commissioned an internal investigation that sought to shield the alleged architect of the fraud, Del's CEO, from liability. In its litigation release accompanying its complaint, the SEC noted that Del's Audit Committee hired the CEO's close personal friend to conduct the investigation, and that during the investigation, the CEO and his associate were permitted to speak to (and intimidate) witnesses prior to their interviews.

2. Should the Company Retain Independent, Outside Counsel?

Absent unusual circumstances or significant financial constraints, it is preferable for a company to retain independent, outside counsel to conduct an investigation, as opposed to using in-house counsel. Outside counsel may bring certain advantages to the investigation, including specific knowledge of securities enforcement laws and white collar criminal laws, and recent investigative and litigation experience. Most importantly, SEC staff typically view independent, outside counsel as more cooperative than in-house counsel. This is particularly true with outside counsel who have formerly worked at the SEC, who may be viewed with less suspicion that an in-house lawyer employed exclusively by company management. This perception of fairness may allow outside counsel to develop a positive working relationship with the SEC staff at the inception of the investigation.

Conversely, SEC staff may view in-house counsel as business advisors rather than legal advisors and may try to obtain their investigative materials on the ground that they constitute business advice, and are not protected by the attorney-client privilege. In addition, in-house counsel may be viewed by company employees as an extension of management, which may cause the employees to be less than candid during interviews, particularly if the employees think their jobs may be at risk.

3. Should the Company Communicate with its Employees about the Investigation?

A company should take active steps to keep employees informed about the SEC's investigation to mitigate their fears and to prevent potentially damaging rumors from spreading. Employees should be instructed that they should not talk about the investigation to anyone unless counsel is present, and that they should inform counsel if they are contacted by anyone (including the press) for an interview. Furthermore, employees relevant to the investigation should be instructed to cooperate fully with the internal investigation.

4. How Should the Company Coordinate and Conduct Employee Interviews?

Generally, before interviewing senior employees, it may be useful for counsel to interview lower level employees and review background documents. However, when the SEC is conducting an expedited investigation, or when other exigent circumstances exist (i.e., deadlines to file quarterly or annual reports), sometimes there is no time for familiarization – counsel must go directly to the employees with the most knowledge of the pertinent facts.

In an interview, counsel should inform the employee of the general nature of the alleged misconduct under investigation and the status of the SEC's investigation. Counsel should also inform the employee that counsel represents the company, not the employee, and that the attorney-client privilege belongs solely to the company. In other words, the employee should not necessarily expect that the statements he or she makes during the interview will remain confidential, particularly when the company intends on disclosing the results of its investigation to the SEC.

Many attorneys make it a practice to advise company employees during interviews of their right to have their own counsel. In many instances, particularly for those employees who may be culpable or have interests adverse to the company, it is preferable for the employee to have his or her own counsel. However, in most instances, since the company is a private entity and is not acting as a government agent, the employee has no constitutional right to his or her own counsel during an investigation.

5. How are Documents and Computer Files Maintained?

Using an expansive definition of relevance, a written instruction must be given immediately to all affected employees to preserve all relevant documents and computer files. This is a crucial point: employees responsible for the wrongful conduct may attempt to destroy evidence of their involvement, which will impede the investigation and may raise criminal obstruction of justice concerns. Moreover, if the SEC learns that documents have been intentionally destroyed, the chances of an amicable resolution to the investigation decrease dramatically.

Counsel should immediately direct an employee to locate the most critical documents and files (which should be backed up and protected from viruses), to be placed under counsel's control. Furthermore, a detailed privilege log should be created and privileged documents should be segregated from other documents to prevent inadvertent disclosure and potential waiver. To preserve the protection of the work product doctrine, employees should also be discouraged from creating any new documents concerning the investigation. New documents should generally be created only by counsel or persons working as his or her agents. In addition, any document prepared during the investigation should note that it is privileged and confidential, protected by the attorney-client privilege and/or attorney work product doctrine, and distributed to the fewest possible people.

6. Should the Company Take Disciplinary and/or Remedial Action?

If an internal investigation reveals that employees have committed wrongdoing, the company should promptly suspend or terminate the responsible employees. The SEC made it clear in *Seaboard* that "remediation, including dismissing or appropriately disciplining wrongdoers" is a crucial step toward receiving credit for cooperation. Termination may also send a message to the SEC that the company is serious about rectifying past indiscretions.

A company seeking leniency from the SEC must also take remedial action. Remedial action may take several forms, including restating corporate financial statements, compensating investors, instituting new and improved internal controls and procedures, and disposing of members of management present during the wrongdoing, regardless if they are culpable. Of course, if the company's investigation reveals little or no wrongdoing, the company may rightfully decide to take no disciplinary or remedial action and mount a vigorous defense.

NOTES

23

THE ABCs OF AN SEC INVESTIGATION: 20 ESSENTIAL QUESTIONS AND ANSWERS

Derek M. Meisner

Kirkpatrick & Lockhart Nicholson Graham LLP

Biographical Information

Derek M. Meisner is a member of Kirkpatrick & Lockhart Nicholson Graham LLP in Boston, Massachusetts. His practice focuses on representing clients in enforcement investigations conducted by the SEC, NASD and state securities regulators, litigating securities cases, conducting corporate internal investigations, and advising clients on related compliance and corporate governance issues. Prior to joining K&LNG, Mr. Meisner served as a Branch Chief in the SEC's Division of Enforcement in Washington, D.C., where he conducted and supervised prominent investigations relating to corporate financial reporting, broker-dealer/investment adviser practices, Regulation FD, market manipulation, hedge fund trading, offerings of unregistered securities, and insider trading, among others. Before joining the SEC, Mr. Meisner was associated with a Washington, D.C. law firm, where he successfully defended financial conglomerates in complex litigation arising out of the sale of securities, insurance and other financial products.

The U.S. Securities and Exchange Commission ("Commission" or "SEC") is funded to take action; its budget for enforcement has increased exponentially in recent years, and as a result, it is opening more investigations and targeting new industries and companies. The mere existence of an SEC investigation, if revealed publicly, can damage business and personal reputations significantly.

Although each SEC investigation is unique, the following questions and answers are intended to provide the reader a basic familiarity with the SEC's investigative policies and procedures.

1) How does an SEC investigation begin?

An SEC investigation may result from complaints made by investors, referrals from state securities regulators or self-regulatory organizations (i.e., the New York Stock Exchange), press reports, or, as is more often the case, the initiative of the SEC staff. The SEC actively monitors unusual price movements on several securities markets, and conducts periodic inspections of investment advisers and broker-dealers, any of which can lead to an investigation.

The SEC does not need to demonstrate "probable" or "reasonable" cause to begin an investigation.[1]

2) How does the SEC conduct its investigations?

An SEC investigation is conducted by the Division of Enforcement and usually begins as an informal investigation. In informal investigations, the SEC does not have the power to issue subpoenas for documents or to compel testimony, and generally (except in the case of regulated entities such as broker-dealers and registered investment advisers) relies on companies and individuals to cooperate voluntarily with the investigation.[2] This sometimes puts defense counsel in a relatively good position to negotiate with the SEC regarding the volume and type of documents and/or testimony that will be provided. Defense counsel has every incentive to keep an investigation "informal" because the investigation is much more likely to be terminated quickly and without any adverse consequences to his or her client.

If the SEC staff feels that the investigation is progressing, or it is not receiving the level of cooperation it needs, the staff may request the Com-

---

1. Kenneth B. Winer et al., *SEC Enforcement*, RealCorporateLawyer.com (2003).
2. *Id.*

mission to enter a formal order. A formal order is necessary for the designated staff to issue subpoenas and compel testimony.

Formal investigations generally assume a higher profile at the SEC and require the commitment of additional staff resources. Compared to informal investigations, fewer formal investigations are terminated without adverse action being taken against the party being investigated.

3) What areas does the SEC generally investigate?

The majority of SEC investigations address alleged accounting deficiencies, insider trading, trading and/or sales practices of investment advisers, broker-dealers and mutual funds, regulatory failures to supervise, offerings of unregistered securities, "soft dollar" practices or disclosure problems. This list is by no means exhaustive, however.

4) Is it possible to predict the onset of an SEC investigation?

In the case of registered investment advisers and broker-dealers, an early warning sign of an SEC investigation includes the presence of an SEC enforcement staff attorney on a routine exam conducted by the SEC's Office of Compliance, Inspections and Examinations. In other instances, early warning signs are less obvious. For example, if a company receives adverse media attention relating to its securities or financial statements, or is named in a shareholder lawsuit pertaining to securities, the SEC may commence an investigation into the relevant activities. SEC counsel should carefully review all relevant company press releases and financial statements to ensure that they do not include material misrepresentations or omit to state material information.

5) If the SEC initiates an investigation, does that mean that violations of the federal securities laws have occurred?

No. The existence of an SEC investigation does not mean that any violation of law has occurred, nor does the SEC staff intend an investigation to be interpreted as an adverse reflection upon any person, entity or security.

6) Do SEC investigations have "targets"?

Tehnically, no. The SEC has instructed its staff to disclose only that it conducts non-public fact finding investigations which do not have "targets". Experienced defense counsel look past this routine disclosure, and attempt to ascertain the nature of the investigation and gage the disposition of the staff. With that information, counsel may be able to direct the investigation in a manner conducive to his or her client.

7) How long does an SEC investigation typically last?

The length of an SEC investigation depends upon its subject matter and scope. The average SEC investigation lasts anywhere between six months and one year. However, sometimes SEC investigations can last several years and put a tremendous strain on the resources of the party being investigated.

8) What are the SEC's enforcement remedies?

The SEC can bring enforcement actions either in the U.S. federal courts or before an independent administrative law judge. The factors considered by the SEC in deciding in which forum to proceed include: the seriousness of the wrongdoing, the technical nature of the matter, tactical considerations, and the type of sanction or relief to obtain. Often, if the conduct warrants it, the SEC will bring both proceedings.[3] In federal courts, the SEC files a complaint that alleges the misconduct and identifies the sanction or remedial action that is sought. Typically, the SEC asks the court to issue an injunction that prohibits the acts or practices that violate the federal securities laws or Commission rules. A court's order can also require various corporate actions, such as audits, accountings, or special supervisory arrangements. In addition, the SEC often seeks civil monetary penalties and disgorgement (the return of illicit profits). The courts may also bar or suspend an individual from serving as an officer or director of a publicly-traded company.

The SEC can also seek a variety of sanctions in an administrative proceeding. Administrative remedies can include cease and desist orders, suspension or revocation of broker-dealer and investment advisor registrations, censures, bars from serving as a corporate officer or director or associating with the securities industry, payment of civil monetary penalties, and disgorgement.

If not handled competently by defense counsel, either form of enforcement action has the potential to produce adverse collateral consequences for the defendant.

9) In what key areas has The Sarbanes-Oxley Act of 2002 expanded the SEC's authority?

The Sarbanes-Oxley Act of 2002 ("Sarbanes-Oxley") expands the SEC's authority in several important areas. Specifically, Sarbanes-Oxley reduces the standard for the SEC to obtain an officer or director bar in an

3. See http://www.sec.gov/about/whatwedo.shtml (official SEC Website).

injunctive action from "substantial unfitness" to simple "unfitness." Furthermore, Sarbanes-Oxley allows the SEC to obtain such a bar in an administrative proceeding pursuant to a cease-and-desist order without first instituting an enforcement action in federal court. In practice, this reduced standard has allowed to the SEC to seek officer and director bars for first time offenders, and in instances where the conduct at issue is relatively benign.

Prior to Sarbanes-Oxley, penalties sought by the SEC in an enforcement action were always paid to the U.S. Treasury. However, Sarbanes-Oxley provides that where a disgorgement fund has been created as a result of an SEC enforcement action against any person, civil penalties paid in the action may be placed in the disgorgement fund for the benefit of victims of the violation. This provision has motivated the SEC to seek penalties in types of cases where it was previously reluctant to do so.

Sarbanes-Oxley also allows the SEC, while investigating possible securities law violations, to request a federal court to impose a 45-day freeze on extraordinary payments (i.e., corporate bonuses) to corporate executives or employees. The order may be extended for an additional 45 days upon a showing of good cause. And, if a company or an executive is then charged with a violation of federal securities laws, the Commission may obtain a freeze for the duration of the action (or extend a freeze already in place). To date, the SEC has used this provision sparingly and with limited success.

Sarbanes-Oxley also amends federal bankruptcy law to make non-dischargeable in bankruptcy certain debts that result from violations of the antifraud provisions of the federal securities laws. This amendment effectively makes it easier for the SEC to enforce a monetary judgment in obtains against an individual.[4]

10) Can the SEC seek criminal penalties and sanctions?

No. However, at any time during an investigation, the SEC may refer the matter to the Department of Justice ("DOJ") with a recommendation that certain persons or entities be indicted and prosecuted. If the DOJ concurs in the recommendation (which is occurring more frequently), the matter will be referred to a grand jury and, assuming indictment, prosecuted by the U.S. Attorney.

---

4. David B. Bayless, *The New World of SEC Enforcement,* MoFo Update (November 2003).

11) Does lying to the SEC during an investigation constitute a criminal offense?

Yes. Under 18 U.S.C. § 1001, anyone who, "makes any materially false, fictitious or fraudulent statement or representation" to the SEC can be imprisoned for up to five years, and fined. In addition, a witness testifying falsely under oath before the SEC staff may be subject to a perjury conviction, whether the testimony is given in response to a direct question from the staff or is offered voluntarily by the witness.[5] The SEC has increasingly had success in convincing the DOJ to prosecute perjury cases based on false testimony before the staff.

12) Should a company utilize in-house counsel or retain outside counsel to help it in responding to an SEC investigation?

Absent unusual circumstances or significant financial constraints, it is vastly preferable for a company to retain independent, outside counsel experienced in SEC investigations.

Experienced defense counsel have specific knowledge of securities enforcement laws and white collar criminal laws, and understand the mechanics of an SEC investigation and type of information that the SEC is interested in. In addition, SEC staff may view independent, outside counsel as more cooperative and objective (particularly those lawyers with previous SEC experience) than in-house counsel, who are typically considered by SEC staff to be "aligned" with the company.

Given the need to retain outside counsel, it makes sense a company to conduct its due diligence on SEC defense counsel *before* the company experiences a problem. If a company waits until it receives an actual inquiry from the SEC, the company may not have enough time to select qualified counsel.

13) Should a company notify its employees of the SEC's investigation?

Generally, a company (with the assistance of outside counsel) should take active steps to keep employees informed about the SEC's investigation to mitigate their fears and to prevent potentially damaging internal and external rumors from spreading. If nothing else, if a company's employees are aware of (and understand the scope of) the SEC's investigation, they may be willing to help the company bring it to a successful conclusion. Employees should be instructed that they should not talk about the

---

5. *See* 18 U.S.C. § 1621.

investigation to anyone unless counsel is present, and that they should inform counsel if they are contacted by anyone (including the press) for an interview. Furthermore, employees relevant to the investigation should be instructed to cooperate fully with any internal investigation that is being conducted by outside counsel, particularly those employees who may be called by the SEC to testify as witnesses.

For employees that may have interests adverse to the company, it is preferable to retain them separate counsel. In fact, the SEC has recently taken the position that a company's failure to do so may be seen as a lack of cooperation.

14) Should a company publicly disclose the existence of an SEC investigation?

In the post Sarbanes-Oxley world, many companies should and do opt in favor of disclosing an SEC investigation. That being said, a number of factors should be considered when making the decision whether to disclose. A company should determine, among other things, whether the investigation will: (1) materially affect the company's financial results, business dealings or reputation; (2) lead to the dismissal of senior employees or board members; or (3) lead to private litigation against the company, including class action lawsuits.[6]

Generally, the greater the likelihood of any of these factors occurring, the more likely it is that disclosure will be warranted. If the company decides to disclose the investigation, it is essential to consult with SEC counsel regarding the specific wording of the disclosure, and the timing of the disclosure. In addition, the company should consult with counsel about how the company will respond to press and investor inquiries, and who should speak on behalf of the company about the issue.

On the other hand, if the company decides not to disclose the investigation, it is imperative that company employees not deny the existence of the investigation in response to any press or investor inquiries.[7]

15) Should a company take any remedial action in response an SEC investigation?

A company seeking leniency from the SEC must consider taking appropriate remedial action. Prompt remedial action taken will strengthen the SEC's view of the company as eager to do the right thing. Remedial

---

6. *See* Winer et al., *supra* note 2.
7. *Id.*

action may take several forms, including compensating investors, instituting new and improved internal controls and procedures, and disposing of members of management present during the wrongdoing, regardless of their culpability. If an internal investigation reveals that employees have committed wrongdoing, the company should consider suspending or terminate the responsible employees. The SEC has made it clear that remediation, including dismissing or appropriately disciplining wrongdoers, is a crucial step toward receiving credit for cooperation. Termination may also send a message to the SEC that the company is serious about rectifying past indiscretions.

16) Should a company retain documents an SEC investigation?

Yes. Document retention is of the utmost importance. Immediately upon becoming aware that the SEC is conducting an investigation, counsel should direct a senior employee to immediately send a written instruction to all affected employees to preserve all relevant documents and computer files. Employees responsible for the wrongful conduct may attempt to destroy evidence of their involvement, which will impede the investigation and may raise criminal obstruction of justice concerns. Moreover, if the SEC learns that documents have been intentionally destroyed, the chances of an amicable resolution to the investigation decrease dramatically.

Counsel should immediately direct an employee to locate the most critical documents and files to be placed under counsel's control. The company's IT department should be engaged to ensure that proper backups of documents exist, and that those backups are protected. Once it is in possession of documents, outside counsel should create a detailed privilege log and ensure that privileged documents are segregated from other documents in order to prevent inadvertent disclosure and potential waiver of the attorney-client and work product privileges.

17) How do I know if the SEC investigation has ended?

If the investigation is completed without recommendation for an enforcement action, the staff generally will give the target notice that the investigation has been terminated. If sufficient time has passed without any communication from the SEC staff, defense counsel (after consulting with his or her client) should consider contacting the staff to ascertain the status of the investigation.

18) What is a Wells submission?

If the SEC staff decides preliminarily to recommend an enforcement action, persons or entities that will be affected adversely by the recommendation are generally given an opportunity to make a Wells submission to the Commission. During a so-called "Wells call", the staff notifies a party that it has tentatively decided to recommend that the Commission bring an enforcement action for violations of various securities laws, and gives the party a specified period to make a written Wells submission. After receiving a Wells call, but prior to making any Wells submission, counsel for the affected party usually meets with the staff to learn more detail about the staff's recommendations. Experienced defense counsel use the meeting as an opportunity to convince the staff not to bring an action and/or to begin negotiating a favorable settlement.

If the staff ultimately decides to recommend an enforcement proceeding, the party's Wells submission (assuming it decides to submit one) is forwarded to the Commission in conjunction with the staff's enforcement memorandum. The Commission only authorizes proceedings after reviewing the staff's memorandum and any Wells submission, and considering any input from other SEC divisions.

In a Wells submission, counsel must be legally and factually persuasive and try to point out obvious weaknesses in the staff's case. Counsel must also avoid making statements that might be deemed an admission by their client or subsequently established to be false. In reality, while many Wells submissions convince the staff to recommend a less severe action, few Wells submissions actually succeed in convincing the staff not to recommend any action.

19) What percentage of SEC actions result in settlements?

The vast majority. The SEC simply does not have the resources to litigate and/or try all of the cases that it files. One benefit of settling with the SEC is that a party is not required to admit the underlying allegations in the SEC's complaint or administrative order. This "no admit or deny" policy allows many parties to avoid the consequences of admitting wrongful conduct, which can include an increased risk of private litigation, criminal exposure, and the loss of insurance coverage. However, SEC settlements do mandate that a party agree not to take any action or to make (or to permit to be made) any public statement denying, directly or indirectly, any allegations in the SEC's complaint or administrative order.

20) Should a company settle or litigate with the SEC?

The answer to this question depends on the specific facts and issues involved, including whether a settlement is in a party's best legal or financial interest. Many parties choose to litigate with the SEC, despite the risk of damage to their business or personal reputations and for publicly traded companies, shareholder flight. As the SEC staff continues to be stubborn and aggressive in its settlement demands and assertion of legal theories, this trend will probably increase.[8]

For these reasons, companies and individuals must have defense counsel experienced both in SEC enforcement matters and in SEC litigation.

8. *See* Baylcss, *supra* note 4.

NOTES

24

THE SEVENTH CIRCUIT'S *ABBOTT DERIVATIVE* DECISION—WHAT WENT WRONG?

David H. Kistenbroker

Pamela G. Smith

Alyx S. Pattison

Katten Muchin Rosenman LLP

Mr. Kistenbroker is National Chairman of Katten Muchin Rosenman's Litigation Department and National Chairman of the Firm's Securities Litigation Practice Group and Co-Chair of the Firm's Corporate Governance Practice Group.

Ms. Smith is a partner of the Firm whose practice is devoted to the defense of public companies, directors, and officers in securities cases, derivative actions, governmental and regulatory investigations and litigation, corporate governance disputes and related matters. Her practice also includes anti-fraud counseling and serving as counsel to board committees in internal investigations.

Ms. Pattison is an associate of the Firm. All are members of Katten Muchin Rosenman's Securities Litigation Practice Group.

The views expressed herein are solely those of the authors and do not necessarily reflect the views of Katten Muchin Rosenman LLP or its clients.

Biographical Information

David H. Kistenbroker is Chairman of the Firm's National Litigation Department, Chairman of the Securities Litigation Practice Group and Co-Chair of the Corporate Governance Practice Group.

Mr. Kistenbroker's practice is focused on the defense of publicly traded companies and their directors and officers in securities class actions, derivative actions, SEC investigations and corporate governance disputes. He has been selected by his peers as one of Illinois' leading trial lawyers, and in 1997 was featured in The National Law Journal for having one of the top ten defense verdicts in the nation. Mr. Kistenbroker is also a frequent lecturer on securities litigation and directors and officers insurance matters.

Table of Contents

Earlier this year, Bill Lerach commented "[v]irtually all the big class-action cases—Enron, WorldCom, AOL-Time Warner, Qwest, and Adelphia—have companion individual actions [filed] that involve billions of dollars of claims; claims that...are firmly rooted in favorable state court venues."[1] Lerach's comment was an unmistakable reference to derivative suits. Whether these actions are filed as a companion to federal securities cases or on a stand-alone basis, the number and settlement value of derivative suits are on the rise. The plaintiff's bar has been emboldened to file these suits by decisions like *In re The Walt Disney Company Derivative Litigation*[2] and *In re Abbott Laboratories Derivative Litigation.*[3]

While the *Disney* derivative decision grabbed headlines, a careful reading of the decision evidences no change in Delaware law.[4] After conducting a § 220 books and records inspection, the *Disney* shareholders cobbled together a complaint that alleged enough facts to support their allegation the Board "rubber-stamped" a stunningly lucrative employment contract for Eisner's friend Ovitz in violation of their duty of good faith.[5] While the facts recited in the opinion made for tantalizing headlines, the law was not new. Directors have always been required to act in good faith.

The same, however, cannot be said for the Seventh Circuit's error-laden decision in *Abbott.* The Seventh Circuit took a run-of-the-mill demand futility case, nullified the demand futility requirement and arguably created strict liability for employee misconduct. Although the *Abbott* complaint alleged a *Caremark* claim, the Seventh Circuit held that because the company had established and maintained corporate governance procedures *Caremark* did not apply. This error was compounded by the Court's ruling that it could: (i) *presume* the entire Board's knowledge of the company's failure to comply with certain federal regulations, and (ii) *presume* the entire Board's decision to not act in response to non-compliance notices. Once a board action was assumed, the demand futility analysis was a *fait accompli* – the Seventh Circuit used the *Aronson* business judgment rule test and concluded the Board's decision to not act was not in good faith – dismissal reversed.

In light of well-established Delaware law and Sarbanes-Oxley requirements, the Seventh Circuit has created a classic Catch 22 for directors. If

---

1. "*Lawyer Warns D&O Insurers Of New Legal Threat,*" Susanne Sclafane, National Underwriter (February 8, 2005), available at http://www.nationalunderwriter.com.
2. 825 A.2d 275 (Del. Ch. 2003).
3. 325 F. 3d 795 (7th Cir. 2001).
4. 825 A.2d 275 (Del. Ch. 2003).
5. *Id.*

directors do not establish and maintain adequate corporate governance procedures, *i.e.*, information and reporting systems, they risk liability under both *Caremark* and Sarbanes-Oxley. If they do establish and maintain such procedures, under *Abbott*, the court will presume both their knowledge of wrongdoing and their decision to not act, deny a motion to dismiss for to plead demand, and make a defense of the merits virtually, if not actually, impossible. Indeed, *Abbott* not only nullifies the demand futility requirement, it creates strict liability for corporate employee misconduct. The *Abbott* decision has undoubtedly made Illinois one of the most plaintiff-friendly derivate suit venues.

The Delaware courts have not yet adequately addressed *Abbott.* Shortly after *Abbott* was decided, Vice Chancellor Lamb decided *In re Citigroup Inc. Shareholders Litigation*,[6] and he seized the opportunity to address *Abbott.* Vice Chancellor Lamb was, however, subtle – he explained Abbott as merely representing a case in which the Seventh Circuit held that the complaint adequately pled a *Caremark* claim.[7] This "explanation" of *Abbott* is inviting and certainly indicates Vice Chancellor Lamb was unwilling to adopt the Seventh Circuit's Catch 22. But, the explanation is not accurate. The Seventh Circuit could have chosen to hold that the *Abbott* complaint had adequately pled a Caremark claim, but that is not what the Seventh Circuit did. Because it is unlikely that a different panel of the Seventh Circuit will be addressing this issue soon, the Delaware courts should critically analyze the *Abbott* decision and explicitly reject the *Abbott* presumptions.

The Abbott Procedural Posture

In *Abbott*, the Seventh Circuit reversed the district court's dismissal of a derivative complaint for failure to plead demand futility with particularity.[8] Because the complaint alleged a *Caremark* claim and did not challenge a Board decision, the district court had applied the *Rales v. Blasband*[9] test for demand futility.[10] The *Rales* test is used to determine demand futility when the complaint at-issue does not challenge board action.[11] To establish demand futility under *Rales*, the shareholder must plead particular facts demonstrating a majority of the directors "faced a

6. No. 19827, 2003 WL 21384599 (Del. Ch. June 5, 2003).
7. *Id.* at *2, n.8. *See also Beam ex rel. Martha Stewart Living Omnimedia, Inc. v. Stewart,* 833 A.2d 961, 971 n. 17 (Del. Ch. Sep 30, 2003) (Chancellor Chandler, collecting *Caremark* cases in which court held shareholders overcame demand futility inquiry and citing *Abbott* as chief among them), *aff'd* 845 A.2d 1040 (Del. 2004).
8. 325 F.3d at 798.

substantial likelihood of liability for their actions."[12] The district court had applied the *Rales v. Blasband* test for demand futility which is applicable to cases in which shareholders are not challenging board action.[13] In reversing, the Seventh Circuit applied the *Aronson v. Lewis*, "business judgment rule" test.[14] The *Aronson* test, however, is used to determine demand futility when the at-issue complaint challenges Board action. The complaint in *Abbott* not only failed to allege Board action, it expressly disclaimed any such action.

Applicable Legal Standards

Under Delaware law, before a shareholder can file a derivative suit, the shareholder must first serve the corporation with a demand specifying the action the shareholder believes should be taken to correct the alleged wrongs.[15] Rule 23.1 reflects the board of director's fundamental right and responsibility to govern a corporation, which includes the right to decide whether a lawsuit should be filed.[16] The purpose of the demand requirement is "to give the corporation the opportunity to rectify an alleged wrong without litigation through intracorporate dispute resolution and to control any litigation which does arise."[17] The demand requirement also reflects the substantive presumption that directors are disinterested and independent and capable of exercising their business judgment to consider impartially a shareholder's demand.[18]

---

9. *Rales v. Blasband*, 634 A.2d 927, 933-34 (Del. 1993) (holding the two-step test announced by the Delaware Supreme court in *Aronson v. Lewis*, 473 A.2d 805, 811 (Del. 1984) does not apply "where the board that would be considering the demand did not make a business decision which is being challenged in the derivative suit.").
10. *Abbott* 325 F.3d at 803 (district court dismissed the complaint for failure to plead demand futility with particularity under Fed. R. Civ. P. 23., stating that the complaint did not plead facts to show Abbott's directors faced a substantial likelihood of liability for their actions.).
11. *Rales*, 634 A.2d at 933-34.
12. 325 F.3d at 803.
13. *Rales v. Blasband,* 634 A.2d 927, 933-34 (Del. 1993) (holding the two-step test announced by the Delaware Supreme court in Aronson v. Lewis, 473 A.2d 805, 811 (Del. 1984) does not apply "where the board that would be considering the demand did not make a business decision which is being challenged in the derivative suit.")
14. *Aronson v. Lewis*, 473 A.2d 805 (Del. 1984).
15. Del. Ch. Ct. R. 23.1; Fed. R. Civ. Pro. 23.1; *see also Spillyards*, 278 Ill. App. 3d at 663, 675 (1st. Dist. 1996).
16. *Abbott*, 325 F.3d at 803; *Spiegel v. Buntrock*, 571 A.2d 767, 773 (Del. 1990).
17. *Spillyards* 278 Ill. App. 3d at 675.

While the demand requirement protects directors from frivolous litigation, it also protects the interests of all shareholders and the corporation by ensuring that the board of directors, rather than an individual shareholder or her counsel, makes an initial decision relating to potential litigation.[19] Therefore, if no demand has been made, the shareholder bears the burden of demonstrating that demand should be excused.[20] Because a board is presumed to be capable of considering a shareholder's demand, demand cannot be excused unless shareholders allege *particular facts* establishing a reasonable doubt about a majority of a board's ability to consider the demand impartially.[21] If the shareholder fails to meet the stringent requirements of Rule 23.1, his right to bring the company's claim is defeated and the complaint is dismissed.[22]

The Delaware Supreme Court has articulated two separate tests for determining whether demand should be excused—one is applicable only to cases in which the shareholders are challenging board action, the other inaction. If the shareholder is challenging action, i.e. a *decision* of the board, the court must apply the business judgment rule test established in *Aronson v. Lewis*.[23] The *Aronson* business judgment test is two-pronged and provides that demand futility is established if, accepting the well-pleaded facts as true, the alleged particularized facts raise a reasonable doubt that either (1) the directors are disinterested or independent or (2) the challenged transaction was the product of a valid business judgment.

If "the subject of the derivative suit is *not* a business decision of the board," the courts "should not apply the *Aronson* test for demand futility."[24] Where a complaint fails to specify and challenge a board "decision," the test announced in *Rales v. Blasband* applies.[25] Under this test, demand is futile only if the complaint alleges "particularized facts" demonstrating a "substantial likelihood" of a majority of the board's liability.[26]

---

18. *Beam v. Martha Stewart*, 845 A.2d 1040, 1048-49 (Del. 2004); *see also Spillyards*, 278 Ill. App. 3d at 675; *Miller v. Thomas*, 275 Ill. App. 3d 779, 788 (1st Dist. 1995) ("'In the absence of factual allegations to the contrary in the complaint, we must presume that defendants acted in good faith and with due care.'" (quotation omitted)).
19. *Spillyards* 278 Ill. App. 3d at 676 (citing *Pogostin v. Rice*, 480 A.2d 619, 624 (Del. 1984) and *Aronson v. Lewis*, 473 A.2d 805, 811 (Del. 1984)).
20. *Abbott* 325 F.3d at 804.
21. *Spillyards*, 278 Ill. App. 3d at 675 (quoting Del. Ch. Ct. R. 23.1); *see also Brehm v. Eisner*, 746 A.2d 244, 254 (Del. 2000) (complaint "must comply with stringent requirements of factual particularity").
22. Del. Ch. Ct. R. 23.1; Fed. R. Civ. Pro. 23.1.
23. 473 A.2d 805 (Del. 1984).

To avoid rendering the substantive presumption in favor of directors a nullity, Delaware courts have insisted that the "mere threat of personal liability" is insufficient to challenge directors' impartiality.[27] Therefore, when Rales applies, the pleading standard is heightened even further: the complaint must allege "particularized facts," demonstrating a "substantial likelihood" of a majority of the board's liability.[28] In considering whether a complaint meets this standard, the court must reject conclusions unsupported by specific facts and it may construe in the shareholders' favor only the reasonable inferences based on the facts alleged.[29] When the reasons proffered for excusing demand are not alleged with factual particularity, the complaint must be dismissed.[30]

As discussed below, in *Abbott* the Seventh Circuit erred by the corporate governance imputing knowledge based systems and controls and presuming that board decided is action applying the *Aronson* test to the complaint which challenged *no* decision by the board. The *Rales* test should have been used. Apparently, the Seventh Circuit was confused by the complexity involved in applying the *Rales* test. The test, by its terms, requires the courts to examine the substantive cause of action being pled

---

24. *Rales v. Blasband*, 634 A.2d 927, 933 (Del. 1993) (holding, "[t]he essential predicate for the *Aronson* test is the fact that a *decision* of the board of directors is being challenged in the derivative suit.") (emphasis added). *See also In re Oxford Health Plans, Inc.*, 192 F.R.D. 111, 117 (S.D.N.Y. 2000) (noting *Rales* applied to cases of nonfeasance and *Aronson* applied to board decisions, noting to extent director violated his duties by allowing others to make materially false statements, "the rule of *Rales* applies."); *Brehm v. Eisner*, 746 A.2d 244, 259 (Del. 2000) (applying *Aronson* test where plaintiffs challenged *decision* by The Walt Disney Company's Board to approve employment agreement.)
25. 634 A.2d at 933-34.
26. *See id.* at 937.
27. *Id.* at 936.
28. *Id.*
29. *White v. Panic*, 783 A.2d 543, 549 (Del. 2001) ("conclusory allegations are not considered as expressly pleaded facts or factual inferences"; court may "'not blindly accept as true all allegations, nor must [it] draw all inferences from them in plaintiffs' favor unless they are *reasonable* inferences.'") (quotation omitted) (emphasis added); *Brehm*, 746 A.2d at 254 (Complaint "must comply with stringent requirements of factual particularity.") (footnote omitted). Because the demand requirement is substantive, the heightened pleading requirement applies no matter what jurisdiction the case is filed in. *Spillyards,* 278 Ill. App. 3d at 675 (affirming dismissal, applying Rule 23.1 and heightened pleading standard). Conclusions of law as well as conclusions of fact unsupported by specific facts must be disregarded. *Rattner v. Bidzos*, No. Civ. A. 19700, 2003 WL 22284323, at *7 (Del. Ch. Sept. 30, 2003) (Court may not "accept cursory contentions of wrongdoing in light of the obligation to plead facts with particularity.").

against the directors. In *Abbott*, the shareholders' cause of action was one based on the directors' failure to monitor the corporation's compliance with the law – commonly known as a *Caremark* claim.[31]

As stated by the *Caremark* court, the elements of a failure to monitor claim are "(1) that the directors knew or (2) should have known that violations of law were occurring and, in either event, (3) that the directors took no steps in a good faith effort to prevent or remedy that situation, and (4) that such failure proximately resulted in the losses complained . . . ."[32] The court in *Caremark* explained that where the shareholder's theory is that the directors "should have known," i.e. ignorance of liability creating activities, liability can only be shown by facts demonstrating the directors failed to attempt in good faith to establish a reasonable information and reporting system.[33]

In considering the facts pled, the Seventh Circuit erred in holding that the shareholders had not pled a *Caremark* claim because the shareholders had not alleged that the company's information and control systems were inadequate.[34] *Caremark,* however, is not limited to cases in which systems are alleged to be inadequate.[35] On its face and as applied by subsequent Delaware courts, under *Caremark,* if systems are adequate, shareholders must plead facts showing that the directors either: (i) culpably participated in the wrongdoing, (ii) possessed actual knowledge of it, or (iii) consciously disregarded red flags of wrongdoing ("severe recklessness"), and took no action to remedy the wrongdoing.[36]

The Seventh Circuit never bothered to consider whether the complaint adequately pled particularized facts demonstrating any director's culpability, actual knowledge or severe recklessness. Based on the facts set forth in the *Abbott* decision, if this analysis had been conducted, it is unlikely that the Court could have held that a majority of the board's substantial

30. *Guttman v. Huang*, 823 A.2d 492, 507 (Del. Ch. 2003).
31. *In re Caremark Int'l Deriv. Litig.*, 698 A.2d 959 (Del. 1996).
32. 698 A.2d 971.
33. *Id.* at 971.
34. *Abbott* 325 F.3d 795 at 806.
35. *See e.g. McCall v. Scott*, 239 F. 3d 808 (6th Cir. 2001) (holding that Plaintiffs had stated a *Caremark* type claim where they alleged that the board failed to act in the face of numerous "red flags" that warned of systematic fraudulent practices and failed to act to rectify the situation despite its being brought to the attention of the board through adequate corporate control systems.) *See also Caremark* 698 A.2d at 971; *Rattner v. Bidzos,* No. 19700, 2003 WL 22284323 (Del.Ch. Oct. 7, 2003); *Citigroup*, 2003 WL 21384599, at *2; *Ash v. McCall,* No. 17132, 2000 WL 1370341, at *5, *9 (Del.Ch. Sept. 15, 2000)
36. *Caremark* 698 A.2d at 971; *Citigroup*, *2-3.

liability had been pled. By applying the *Aronson* test to an inaction case, the directors' fate was sealed.

The *Abbott* Facts

Abbott shareholders sued the Company's directors for breach of fiduciary duty after Abbott announced it had entered into a consent decree with the FDA pursuant to which it agreed to pay a $100 million civil fine, withdraw 125 types of in vitro diagnostic kits from the market, destroy inventory, and make a number of corrective changes in its manufacturing process.[37] The consent decree was the result of a six-year, federal investigation of two Abbott facilities.[38]

The complaint alleged that the six-year investigation of regulatory violations included thirteen separate inspections occurring in the *same* two plants and related to the *same* products and the *same* employees.[39] The inspections "were conducted under a program designed not only to ensure that data and information concerning in vitro diagnostic products were scientifically valid and accurate, but also to ensure that the human subjects were protected from undue hazard or risk during the course of the scientific investigations."[40] During this six-year period, the FDA sent *four* "formal certified Warning Letters" to the Company, detailing the violations and warning of penalties (ultimately imposed) that would result from a failure to correct the violations.[41] Three of these letters were sent to Abbott's CEO and Chairman of the Board.[42]

Each of the Company's annual 10K filings with the SEC during the six-year period, which were signed by the directors, disclosed that the Company's products were subject to substantial FDA regulation and the Company was involved in various claims and proceedings with the FDA.[43] However, the same SEC filings also asserted that in management's opinion the outcome of the claims and proceedings would not have

37. *Abbott* 325 F.3d at 798.
38. *Id.* at 801.
39. *Id.* at 799.
40. *Id.*
41. *Id.* Each of the letters stated: "'Failure to correct these deviations may result in regulatory action being initiated by the Food and Drug Administration without further notice. These actions include, but are not limited to seizure, injunction, and/or civil penalties.'"
42. *Id.* at 799-800. Letters dated March 28, 1994 and October 11, 1994 were copied to Abbott's then CEO and Chairman of the Board. On March 17, 1999, a the final letter was sent by certified mail directly to Abbott's then CEO and Chairman.
43. *Id.* at 802.

a material adverse impact upon the Company's financials. Most significantly, despite the Warning letters, each of these annual SEC filings asserted that the Company's facilities were "deemed suitable."[44]

On January 11, 1995, the WSJ published an article reporting that the FDA had found a "wide range of flaws" with Abbott's quality-assurance procedures.[45] In July 1995, Abbott entered into a comprehensive Voluntary Compliance Plan ("Plan") which provided Abbott and the FDA would work "'together to achieve compliance in areas recognized by FDA and Abbott to be problematic.'"[46] Nearly three years later, on February 26, 1998, the FDA sent another letter to Abbott in which the FDA explicitly recognized Abbott Laboratories' efforts to meet all of the Plan's requirements, but which nonetheless notified Abbott that the FDA was terminating the Plan because it had found continued "deviations" from the regulations.[47]

On April 13, 1999, less than one month after the FDA sent its final Warning Letter to Abbott's CEO and Chairman of the Board, the CEO sold 30% of his Abbott stock.[48] On June 15, 1999, Bloomberg reported the Company's receipt of the March 1999 Warning Letter and that Abbott was working with the FDA to resolve the problems.[49] Notwithstanding its receipt of Warning Letters dating back to October 1993, Abbott did not issue a press release disclosing the FDA's notifications of noncompliance until September 28, 1999.[50]

Abbott's press release stated the Company disagreed with the FDA's allegations of substantial noncompliance, but Abbott also warned that if its discussions with the FDA were unsuccessful, the FDA intended to file for an injunction against the production and sale of products at issue.[51] Two days later, Abbott disclosed the same facts in an SEC filing.[52] On November 2, 1999, the FDA filed for injunctive relief and the parties signed a consent decree that prohibited Abbott from manufacturing certain in vitro products until certain conditions were met, required the destruction of certain inventory, and required Abbott to pay a $100 mil-

---

44. *Id.*
45. *Id.* at 800.
46. *Id.*
47. *Id.*
48. *Id.*
49. *Id.*
50. *Id.*
51. *Id.*
52. *Id.*

lion fine, "the largest penalty ever imposed for a civil violation of FDA regulations at that time."[53]

The shareholders claimed that the Abbott directors were aware of the Company's six-year history of noncompliance with FDA regulations and their failure to take corrective action caused the Company's stock to decline in value, a $168 million charge against earnings in third quarter 1999, a $250 million loss in annual revenue, and the collapse of a planned acquisition worth $7 billion.[54] The complaint sought to recover all of these losses from Abbott's thirteen directors, eleven of whom were independent.[55]

The Seventh Circuit's Erroneous Ruling

In determining whether demand on the board would have been futile, the Seventh Circuit ruled that *Rales* did not apply because the directors in *Abbott* had made a conscious choice, a business decision, not to act with regard to the FDA investigations. Thus the court applied *Aronson.* The Court's ruling that *Aronson* applied was flatly contradicted by an explicit allegation in the complaint, which the Court quoted:

> 'Plaintiffs maintain that the facts as alleged in the complaint demonstrate that the directors knew of the continuing pattern of noncompliance with FDA regulations and knew that the continued failure to comply with FDA regulations would result in severe penalties and yet ignored repeated red flags raised by the FDA and in media reports and chose not to bring a prompt halt to the improper conduct causing the noncompliance, nor to reprimand those persons involved, nor to seek redress for Abbott for the serious damages it has sustained ....'[56]

The Court distinguished *Caremark* by noting that in that case, "there were no facts to indicate the directors "'conscientiously permitted a known violation of law by the corporation to occur."[57] In *Abbott,* the Court concluded, the facts did not "support the conclusion that the directors were 'blamelessly unaware of the conduct leading to the corporate liability.'"[58] The Court held that unlike the liability in *Caremark* which was "predicated on ignorance of liability creating activities" the directors in *Abbott* were fully informed of the wrongdoing and the shareholders

53. *Id.* at 801.
54. *Id* at 801-02.
55. *Id.* at 801.
56. *Id.* at 802-03.
57. *Id.* at 806 (citing *Caremark*, 698 A.2d at 972)
58. *Id.* (citing *Caremark,* 698 A.2d at 969 (quoting *Graham v. Allis Chalmers Mfg. Co.,* 188 A.2d 125, 130 (Del. 1963)).

alleged facts which seemed to indicate that the directors permitted a known violation of the law to occur.[59]

The Seventh Circuit's legal conclusions were not, however, based on facts pled in the shareholder complaint. Rather the conclusions were based on erroneous presumptions that flatly contradict the Delaware substantive presumption that directors act in good faith. The Court's conclusion that Abbott's directors were fully informed of the wrongdoing was premised exclusively on the fact that Abbott had in place a reasonable information and reporting system.

> Where there is a corporate governance structure in place, *we must then assume* the corporate governance procedures were followed *and that the board knew* of the problems *and decided no action was required.* Therefore, we cannot agree that the *Rales* test is applicable in this particular factual situation.[60]

Each of the Seventh Circuit's assumptions are unknown and contrary to Delaware law. Delaware law presumes that directors act in good faith.[61] Moreover, a *Caremark* claim is not defeated by the existence of corporate governance procedures. When such procedures are in place, i.e., the board has established a reasonable information and reporting system, a *Caremark* claim is stated by showing the directors' *knowledge* and inaction. Under *Caremark* and its progeny, directors' knowledge can be shown by facts demonstrating: (a) culpable participation, (b) actual knowledge, or (c) conscious disregard of "red flags."[62] The Seventh Circuit simply ignored this aspect of *Caremark* and its progeny was wrong in holding that *Caremark* did not apply to the complaint before it.

The Court's error was not, however, limited to its disregard of *Caremark.* That error is minor compared to the Seventh Circuit's tacit rejection of Delaware's presumptions that directors are faithful to their fiduciary duties. When the Seventh Circuit used the adequacy of the governance structures to *impute* knowledge to all Abbott directors, it rejected a decade of Delaware precedent and nullified the demand futility requirement. If

---

59. *Id.*
60. *Id.*
61. *Beam v. Martha Stewart*, 845 A.2d 1040, 1048-49 (Del. 2004) (Delaware law presumes directors *acted in good faith* and "were faithful to their fiduciary duties."). *See also Spillyards*, 278 Ill. App. 3d at 675; *Miller v. Thomas*, 275 Ill. App. 3d 779, 788 (1st Dist. 1995) ("'In the absence of factual allegations to the contrary in the complaint, we must presume that defendants acted in good faith and with due care.'" (quotation omitted)).
62. 698 A.2d at 971; *Rattner v. Bidzos*, No. 19700, 2003 WL 22284323 (Del.Ch. Oct. 7, 2003); *Citigroup*, 2003 WL 21384599, at *2; *Ash v. McCall*, No. 17132, 2000 WL 1370341, at *5, *9 (Del.Ch. Sept. 15, 2000)

taken seriously, the Seventh Circuit's *Abbott* ruling can only be understood as creating an unrebuttable presumption of director knowledge. Moreover, an element of all *Caremark* claims is director inaction. Because the *Abbott* complaint pled that the directors did not take action, the Seventh Circuit created a further presumption that the directors *chose* to not act. Based on its erroneous assumptions, the Seventh Circuit ruled that the shareholders had pled facts to indicate not only that the entire board had made a decision, but also that the board's decision to not take corrective actions was not in good faith.[63]

By applying the *Aronson* business judgment rule test for demand futility in a case which demanded the *Rales* inaction test, the Abbott directors' fate was sealed. When one assumes that the directors chose to not act in the face of six years of noncompliance, inspections, warning letters, and notice in the press, all of which then resulted in the largest civil fine ever imposed by the FDA and the destruction and suspension of products which accounted for approximately $250 million in corporate assets, the conclusion is preordained. No one would dispute that a decision to not act under such circumstances evidences bad faith. Determining whether the shareholders had pled demand futility by overcoming the business judgment rule was an equally predestined event and denial of the motion to dismiss followed.

If in fact, the shareholders had pled a board action, then the Seventh Circuit's analysis certainly would have been correct. This, however, was not what the shareholders did. Based on the facts recited in the *Abbott* opinion, if the Seventh Circuit had faithfully followed Delaware law and undertaken the *Rales* analysis, the motion to dismiss would arguably have been granted.

What Would the Outcome Have Been if the Seventh Circuit Had Followed Delaware Law Faithfully?

While the *Abbott* decision is not fulsome on facts relevant to determining whether a majority of Abbott's board were aware of legal violations, the opinion contains some clues. Only two of Abbott's *thirteen* board members were insiders and only the CEO sold stock during the relevant time period.[64] While the Court stated that "several" board members sat on Abbott's Audit Committee during the six-year period and the Audit Committee was required to meet with members of management responsible for compliance regulations, the court did not state that a majority of indepen-

63. 325 F.3d at 809.
64. *Id.* at 800.

dent directors had sat on the Audit Committee throughout the relevant six-year period.[65]

Even if, however, one assumes that a majority of Abbott's directors were aware of regulatory compliance issues, the *Abbott* case recites a number of facts pled in the complaint that indicate the company did take action. In July 1995, Abbott entered into a comprehensive Voluntary Compliance Plan ("Plan") which provided Abbott and the FDA would work "'together to achieve compliance in areas recognized by FDA and Abbott to be problematic.'"[66] Although three years later, the FDA sent a letter to Abbott terminating the Plan due to continued deviations, the letter explicitly "recognize[d] Abbott Laboratories' efforts to meet all of the Compliance Plan's commitments."[67] Finally, when Abbott did finally issue a press release regarding the FDA's allegations, it referenced Abbott's continued "discussions" with the FDA, which certainly indicate some effort on Abbott's part to negotiate a resolution with the FDA.[68]

These facts are critical for two reasons. First, they undermine the Seventh Circuit's conclusion that the directors decided to take no action in response to notice of legal violations. Second, under Delaware law, the content of the directors' action should not be second-guessed by the courts. As Chancellor Allen explained in *Caremark*:

> What should be understood, but may not widely be understood by courts or commentators who are not often required to face such questions, is that compliance with a director's duty of care can never appropriately be judicially determined by reference to *the content of the board decision* that leads to a corporate loss, apart from consideration of the good faith *or* rationality of the process employed. That is, whether a judge or jury considering the matter after the fact, believes a decision substantively wrong, or degrees of wrong extending through 'stupid' to 'egregious' or 'irrational," provides no ground for director liability, so long as the court determines that the process employed was either rational or employed in *a good faith* effort to advance corporate interests. To employ a different rule—one that permitted an 'objective' evaluation of the decision—would expose directors to substantive second guessing by ill-equipped judges or juries, which would, in the long-run, be injurious to investor interests.[69]

The Seventh Circuit studiously ignored this caution, and the *Abbott* case is now over. According to the Company's March 3, 2005 10-K:

---

65. *Id.* at 802.
66. *Id.* at 800.
67. *Id.*
68. *Id.*
69. 698 A.2d 967.

> On December 28, 2004, the trial court preliminarily approved a settlement of this matter pending a final approval hearing date, which is expected to occur in the first half of 2005. Under the terms of the settlement, a charter for the board's public policy committee has been adopted, Abbott will fund regulatory/compliance activities in the amount of $27 million, and the plaintiffs' attorneys fees will be paid from proceeds of insurance maintained by Abbott for its directors.

The Seventh Circuit's errors were rather costly for Abbott. If, however, the Seventh Circuit's errors are not roundly rejected, they will be even more expensive for other corporate boards and investors. Shortly after *Abbott* was decided, Vice Chancellor Lamb granted a motion to dismiss a *Caremark* claim against Citigroup's board in *In re Citigroup Inc. Shareholders Litigation.*[70] Vice Chancellor Lamb distinguished *Abbott* by noting that the Seventh Circuit held the complaint stated a *Caremark* claim.[71] While Vice Chancellor Lamb's "distinction" is appealing and certainly harmonizes *Abbott* with long-standing Delaware law, the distinction is not supportable. Nor is it sufficient to protect corporate boards and investors alike.

Conclusion

Given the passage of Sarbanes-Oxley, reasonable information and reporting systems are now a given. If *Abbott* is not explicitly rejected as wrongly decided, directors may find themselves exposed to liability every time a corporate employee breaks the law and causes the company to suffer a loss. Under *Abbott*, to withstand dismissal, a shareholder needs only to plead that corporate misconduct occurred, the misconduct caused losses and corporate governance procedures were adequate. Thereafter, the court will presume governance procedures worked, the entire corporate board was informed of the illegal activity, and the entire board chose not to act. This is strict liability. In other words, the *Caremark* claim formerly known as one of the most difficult to plead under Delaware law, has, under *Abbott*, become the easiest to plead. Bill Lerach's predictions about the filing of parallel cases in favorable state courts will be fulfilled, and as directors become strictly liable for corporate losses, fewer and fewer qualified individuals will be willing to sit on corporate boards.

---

70. No. 19827, 2003 WL 21384599 (Del. Ch. June 5, 2003)
71. *Id.* at *2, n.8.

NOTES

CRIMINAL INVESTIGATION & PROSECUTION OF SECURITIES VIOLATIONS

25

RECENT DEVELOPMENTS IN SECURITIES CASES AND INVESTIGATIONS

Andrew J. Levander

Dechert LLP

Andrew J. Levander is a partner in the New York office of Dechert LLP. He was trial counsel for Michael Rigas in the Adelphia criminal securities fraud trial, led the internal investigation of Symbol Technologies Inc., which resulted in a non-prosecution agreement for Symbol and the indictment and/or guilty pleas of thirteen former senior officers of Symbol in 2004, and is criminal counsel for a former executive of U.S. Foodservice in the Ahold investigation. The author thanks Phillip M. Meyer, an associate with the New York office of Dechert LLP, for his assistance in the preparation of this article.

Table of Contents

4. Agreement Between Symbol Technologies, Inc. and The U.S. Attorney's Office for the Eastern District of New York, dated June 3, 2004

5. Press Release: Robert Nardoza, United States Attorney's Office, June 3, 2004

6. U.S. Securities and Exchange Commission, Litigation Release No. 18929 / October 13, 2004; Accounting and Auditing Enforcement Release No. 2124 / October 13, 2004

7. News Release-06-15-05 -Bristol-Myers Squibb Agreement

8. Bristol-Myers Squibb Deferred Prosecution Agreement, June 2005

9. In Re Steinhardt Partners, L.P., 9 F.3d 230 (1993); 1993 U.S. App. LEXIS 28979

10. Maruzen Co., Ltd. V. HSBC USA, Inc., Memorandum and Order, 00 Civ. 1079 (RO), 00 Civ. 1512 (RO), (2002)

11. Merrill Lynch & Co., Inc. v. Allegheny Energy, Inc., 2004 U.S. Dist. LEXIS 21543 (2004)

12. In Re Natural Gas Commodity Litigation, 03 Civ. 61686; 2005 U.S. Dist. LEXIS 11950

I. INTRODUCTION

The continuing prosecution of high-profile white collar cases, particularly in the area of securities fraud, continues at a breathtaking pace. Led by zealous prosecutors at both the state and federal levels, hardly a day goes by without a new headline trumpeting an investigation or prosecution of corporate America (and beyond). We have become immune to the spectacle of corporate officials being sentenced to 15, 20, or even 25 years in jail for white collar crime.[1]

Perhaps recent events portend an ebbing of the prosecutorial tide. But the acquittals of former HealthSouth CEO Richard M. Scrushy[2] and former Bank of America broker Theodore C. Sihpol III[3] are probably attributable to jury nullification in the peculiar facts and circumstances of those cases.[4] And while Arthur Andersen[5] was a resounding defeat of the Department of Justice (and a pyrrhic victory for Arthur Andersen), the authorities will undoubtedly continue to pursue aggressive tactics under Sarbanes-Oxley, the Martin Act, and a host of other statutes at their disposal.

Thus, on the assumption that internal investigations and securities charges will remain an extremely visible and important part of the legal landscape, we touch upon various developments in this area in the discussion that follows.

---

1. See, e.g., Farzad, Roben, Jail Terms For 2 at Top Of Adelphia, The New York Times (June 20, 2005); see, e.g., Jennifer Bayot, Ebbers Sentenced to 25 Years in Prison for $11 Billion Fraud, The New York Times (July 13, 2005).
2. See Simon Romero and Kyle Whitmire, Former Chief of HealthSouth Acquitted in $2.7 Billion Fraud, The New York Times (June 29, 2005).
3. See Update 6: Ex-Broker Sihpol Is Acquitted on 29 Counts, The Associated Press (June 9, 2005).
4. Inexplicably, Scrushy was prosecuted in his hometown of Birmingham, Alabama, where he was extremely popular and politically savvy, while Sihpol was a middle-level executive who was the only person charged criminally when the higher ups and the hedge fund managers who made money on the late and rapid trading of mutual funds that Sihpol facilitated were not.
5. See Court Overturns Arthur Andersen Conviction, The Associated Press (May 31, 2005); see Arthur Andersen LLP v. United States, 125 S.Ct. 2129 (May 31, 2005) (a copy of this decision is included with the materials accompanying this article).

II. PROSECUTORIAL DEVELOPMENTS REGARDING INVESTIGATIONS

A. Prosecutorial Pronouncements On Cooperation

On January 20, 2003, the United States Department of Justice (the "DOJ"), issued guidelines entitled "Principles of Federal Prosecution of Business Organizations." This so-called Thompson Memorandum[6] outlined the criteria to be considered by federal prosecutors in determining whether or not to indict a corporation. These guidelines elaborated upon the guidelines previously issued by the DOJ in 1999.[7]

The Thompson Memorandum sets forth nine factors to be considered by federal prosecutors when deciding whether to bring criminal charges against a business entity: (1) the nature and seriousness of the offense; (2) the pervasiveness of wrongdoing within the corporation, including any complicity in the wrongdoing by senior management; (3) the corporation's history of similar conduct; (4) the timely and voluntary disclosure of wrongdoing by the corporation; (5) the adequacy and effectiveness of the corporation's compliance program; (6) remedial actions taken by the corporation; (7) collateral consequences of prosecuting the corporation; (8) the adequacy of prosecuting only responsible individuals; and (9) the adequacy of non-criminal prosecutorial alternatives. These nine factors are to be considered in addition to the general factors normally considered by prosecutors (i.e., sufficiency of evidence, likelihood of prevailing at trial, adequacy of non-criminal approaches, etc.). The Thompson Memorandum made explicit that the extent of a corporation's genuine cooperation with the government's investigation(s) and the remedial steps taken by the corporation will be critical aspects of the decision regarding whether a corporation will be indicted.

The United States Securities and Exchange Commission (the "SEC") has outlined a similar list of some of the criteria it will consider in deciding whether to bring an enforcement action, pursue reduced charges, seek lighter sanctions, or include mitigating language in any

---

6. The Thompson Memorandum, so named for former Deputy Attorney General Larry D. Thompson, is available on the DOJ's website, at http://www.usdoj.gov/dag/cftf/corporate_guidelines.htm. (A copy of this Memorandum is included with the materials accompanying this article.)

7. The previous guidelines are set forth in a memorandum entitled "Federal Prosecution of Corporations," issued by then U. S. Deputy Attorney General Eric Holder, Jr., on June 16, 1999. The memorandum has become known as the "Holder Memorandum."

SEC release and/or resolution of enforcement actions.[8] The Seaboard Report, like the Thompson Memorandum, emphasizes the importance of cooperation. The Seaboard factors include: (1) the nature of the misconduct (i.e., whether it was due to mistake, negligence, recklessness/deliberate indifference, or "unadorned venality"); (2) the cause of the misconduct—whether it stemmed from pressure to achieve certain results or a tone of lawlessness at the top; (3) the extent of senior-level involvement, and the extent to which the misconduct was systemic; (4) the duration of the misconduct; (5) the extent of the harm to investors and others; (6) how the misconduct was detected; (7) the amount of time that elapsed from discovery to effective response by the company; (8) whether timely remedial steps were taken, including disciplinary action against wrongdoers, and the extent and timeliness of disclosure to the public and regulators; (9) the processes followed by the company to resolve issues and ferret out needed information, including the timeliness of disclosure to the company's audit committee and board of directors; (10) whether the company was committed to learning the complete truth on an expedited basis, including the thoroughness of its review, and the independence of the reviewer; (11) whether the company fully, promptly and voluntarily shared the results of its review with the SEC, including possible waiver of the attorney-client privilege and work-product protection, and encouraged employees to cooperate; (12) whether there are assurances that the misconduct is unlikely to recur; and (13) any change of corporate control, such as through merger or bankruptcy.

The increasing focus of prosecutors and regulators on the thoroughness of a corporation's cooperation and remedial actions has provided a roadmap, albeit one not without significant costs and risks, for defense counsel representing corporations under investigation. In certain cases, the two most important factors in seeking a favorable outcome for the corporation may be (1) extensive and timely cooperation, including the production of materials and information otherwise protected by the attorney-client privilege and work-product doctrine, and (2) strong remedial actions, including steps to hold the culpable individuals accountable and to ensure that misconduct will not re-occur. On the

---

8. See Report of Investigation On The Relationship of Cooperation To Agency Enforcement Decisions, Exchange Act Release No. 44969, 76 S.E.C. Docket 220, 2001 WL1301408 (Oct. 23, 2001) (available at http://www.sec.gov/litigation/investreport/34-44969.htm) (known as the "Seaboard Report"). (A copy of this Report is included with the materials accompanying this article.)

other hand, failure to cooperate, in and of itself, can lead to criminal prosecution and/or severe financial penalties.

Three of the factors detailed in the Thompson Memorandum provide particular opportunity for counsel for the willing corporation in appropriate circumstances to alter the equation regarding potential indictment by creating a new, positive factual record regarding the corporation's conduct. Those three factors are: (1) the corporation's timely and voluntary disclosure of wrongdoing, and its willingness to cooperate; (2) the corporation's remedial actions; and (3) the existence and adequacy of the corporation's compliance program. Although there is considerable overlap among these factors, as the commentary provided in the Thompson Memorandum regarding these factors suggests, each of the three factors is addressed separately below.

1. Corporations' Timely and Voluntary Disclosure of Wrongdoing and its Willingness to Cooperate

The Thompson Memorandum measures cooperation and timely disclosure principally by the corporation's willingness to (1) "identify the culprits within the corporation, including senior executives"; (2) "make witnesses available"; (3) "disclose the complete results of its internal investigation"; and (4) "waive attorney-client and work product protection." Thompson Memorandum § VI-A.

a) Waiver of the privilege

In particular, the Thompson Memorandum states that while the waiver of the attorney-client privilege and work product doctrine are not "absolute requirements," those waivers are important in "obtain[ing] statements of possible witnesses, subjects, and targets, without having to negotiate individual cooperation or immunity agreements," and in providing a means to measure the adequacy and completeness of the corporation's disclosure and cooperation. Id. § VI-B. The Thompson Memorandum notes the salutary public purpose served by cooperation, in that it eases the burden on the government's investigation by identifying culpable individuals, providing information on the corporate hierarchy, and locating relevant evidence. Id.

In practice, prosecutors have tended to take a more absolutist approach to the question of privilege waiver—whether explicitly or implicitly, the privilege waiver is now an expected, and often required, part of any cooperation with the government; frequently a waiver is agreed to in order to demonstrate good faith to prosecutors. The downsides of such a wavier include the long and short term harm done to the attorney-client relationship by the disclosure of information originally meant to be shared only with counsel, the very significant risk that material and information produced to the government pursuant to the waiver will later be subject to discovery by third parties, including plaintiffs in civil litigation against the company and the downside of disclosing potentially negative information to the prosecutors. Hence, before making such an important decision, counsel should carefully weigh all of the facts and circumstances including: What is the strength of the government's case now, what is the likely strength at the end of the investigation, how helpful or harmful is the privileged information, and what is the company's likely ultimate posture in the matter.

If counsel and the client conclude that waiver is the appropriate course of action, counsel can seek to reduce the risk that providing the government with information as part of the company's cooperation will be deemed a waiver of privilege with respect to third parties. However, these methods are imperfect and cannot guarantee that the materials provided to the government, and possibly other materials concerning the same subject matter, will not ultimately be deemed discoverable in separate civil litigation. (We address this important issue in more detail in the section below entitled, "Providing Privileged Materials to the Government," and examine several recent cases bearing on this issue.)

b) Treatment of culpable employees

The Thompson Memorandum also provides that a prosecutor should analyze the corporation's apparent willingness to protect "culpable employees and agents." Among the determining factors in this analysis are the voluntary advancement of legal fees to non-cooperating individuals, the retention without sanction of employees who committed misconduct, and the use of joint defense agreements to communicate information about the government investigation to employees. The Thompson Memorandum suggests that prosecutors be "wary" of any attempt by the corporation to plead guilty itself in order to protect officers and employees from liability. Thompson Memorandum § VI-B.

Counsel would do well to tread carefully in this area as well. Any indemnity obligations under Delaware law and/or company by-laws should be disclosed and explained to prosecutors and regulators, lest a company's legal commitments to former officers or directors be misconstrued as "protection."[9] Similarly, the decision concerning whether to share information with counsel for employees under investigation, and whether to enter into joint defense agreements, is a delicate one. While counsel for individual employees understandably may seek information about the investigation in advance of, for example, an interview of their client by internal investigators, counsel for the company must carefully balance a desire to be helpful against both the integrity of its own investigation and the maintenance and development of trust in an important and sensitive relationship with prosecutors. Particularly where the evidence of wrongdoing is ambiguous or the theory of prosecution strained, counsel and the client must also take into account the long term morale of employees who will closely follow the company's response.

It is clear that, under the guidance of the Thompson Memorandum, prosecutors will be carefully watching to see how the company handles evidence of wrongdoing by any of its employees. The most clear-cut way to demonstrate that the company is not interested in protecting culpable individuals is to sanction those found to have committed wrongdoing. In some instances, this is straight-forward: clear evidence emerges of wrongdoing, it is presented to the appropriate decision-makers at the company, and action is taken to reprimand or punish the employee by means up to and including termination of his or her employment. It may behoove the company to communicate the actions it takes in this regard to the general population of employees in order to demonstrate its commitment to integrity and its intolerance of misconduct.

Yet this area too is not without complications. In some cases, the evidence is not clear-cut, or the investigation, for example, has yielded conflicting responses from interviewed employees.[10] In

9. The Thompson Memorandum notes that state law in some circumstances requires corporations to advance fees to officers prior to a determination of their guilt, and states that a corporation's "compliance with governing law should not be considered a failure to cooperate." Thompson Memorandum n.4.

10. While the Thompson Memorandum acknowledges that companies must "be fair to their employees," it emphasizes that they must be "unequivocally committed, at all levels of the corporation, to the highest standards of legal and ethical behavior." Thompson Memorandum § VIII.

some instances, ambiguous evidence surfaces concerning possible wrong-doing by a very senior officer. How counsel evaluates that evidence, to whom at the company counsel communicates concerns of this type, and the timing and nature of the disclosure to the government—which will be pressing for full and timely disclosure of the investigation's findings and will be particularly interested in how the company handles accusations of misconduct against senior officials—are all delicate and high-stakes decisions that must be carefully made.

Unfortunately, certain prosecutors have taken to going beyond the dictates of the Thompson Memorandum in extracting draconian cooperation terms. Thus, it was recently reported that certain white collar investigators were taking extreme views of cooperation: that the subject company not provide access to documents to its current and former employees, and not advance legal fees to any current or former employee who has invoked his constitutional rights.[11] Such demands, which can amount to thinly veiled attempts to coerce individual cooperation and to thwart the legitimate defense function, are not justified, much less compelled, by the Thompson Memorandum.

2. *Remedial Actions by the Corporation*

The Thompson Memorandum states that prosecutors should examine whether the corporation has taken steps to ensure that misconduct will not recur, such as making full restitution, strengthening its corporate compliance program, disciplining employees who have engaged in misconduct (no matter their rank), and disclosing employees' illegal conduct to the government. Id. § VIII.

The first example—whether the company has voluntarily made restitution to the victims of the wrongdoing—may be difficult to achieve quickly in a standard securities fraud matter. In such a case, it typically is the shareholders who have been harmed, and companies may be loath to move quickly to satisfy the often exorbitant monetary demands made by class plaintiffs' counsel. Nonetheless, the fact that restitution is viewed by the government as an example of the company's commitment to taking remedial steps suggests that the impact a settlement with the class will have on the investigation

---

11. See Laurie P. Cohen, In the Crossfire: Prosecutor's Tough New Tactics Turn Firms Against Employees, WALL STREET JOURNAL, June 4, 2004.

must be a factor that companies ponder in making their litigation decisions.

The second of those examples presents possibly the most significant opportunity for a willing corporation to establish its commitment to being a good corporate citizen. It is critical that the corporation evaluate the flaws in its corporate compliance program, and take the short-term and long-term steps to correct them. This is an area in which the corporation can create a positive factual record for itself by doing the right thing, and ensuring that appropriate controls are in place to minimize the chances of reoccurrence.

Finally, the remaining two examples of measures of remedial conduct—disciplining bad actors and disclosing illegality to the government—also are treated as evidence of cooperation, as discussed above.

3. Existence and Adequacy of the Corporation's Compliance Program

The Thompson Memorandum reminds prosecutors that the Department encourages self-policing through corporate compliance programs and notes that this guideline measures whether the corporation's compliance program is effective, or merely a paper tiger. Id. § VII. According to the Memorandum,

> the critical factors in evaluating any program are whether the program is adequately designed for maximum effectiveness in preventing and detecting wrongdoing by employees and whether corporate management is enforcing the program or is tacitly encouraging or pressuring employees to engage in misconduct to achieve business objectives.

Id.

As part of the determination whether the compliance program is well-designed and effective, the Memorandum asks prosecutors to consider a number of factors, including the program's comprehensiveness, the independence of the company's directors and whether the company has provided sufficient staff and resources to ensure that the program operates effectively. Id. In addition, two of the articulated factors can be demonstrated by the corporation even after the discovery of wrongdoing and misconduct, including some that have been discussed above. These include whether the corporation has taken remedial steps (i.e., restitution, disciplinary actions against wrongdoers, revision of the corporation's compliance program, etc.), and the extent of the company's cooperation with, and prompt disclosure to, the government. Id.

Here, again, the Thompson Memorandum emphasizes the critical importance of the company's cooperation with regulators. Such cooperation can be viewed, under the guidelines, as evidence of management's commitment to its compliance program, even when the existing compliance program failed to detect or stop the past misconduct.

B. The Impact Of Cooperation: Examples of "Rewarded" Targets

1. *Symbol Technologies, Inc.*

The travails at Symbol Technologies, Inc. ("Symbol") and Computer Associates, Inc., two major public companies in the New York area, have received a lot of coverage over the last couple of years. In the case of Symbol, the criminal and civil inquiries into Symbol ended with a non-prosecution agreement between Symbol and the United States Attorney's Office for the Eastern District of New York (the "Eastern District")[12] and a settlement with the SEC, and provides a very good illustration of the benefits of full cooperation and a commitment to extensive remedial actions by a corporation under investigation, particularly when viewed again in light of many recent investigation resolutions, including Corporate Associates.

Symbol, located in Long Island, New York, is a leader in the field of bar code scanning technology and enterprise mobility solutions. On June 3, 2004, the Eastern District announced the indictment and/or guilty pleas of thirteen former Symbol officers. Among the former executives indicted were the Company's former President and Chief Executive Officer, Chief Financial Officer, Chief Accounting Officer, Senior Vice President of Finance and General Counsel.

The Eastern District, in announcing its indictment, detailed a "massive corporate fraud scheme" in which Symbol's reported revenue was inflated by more than $200 million by means of "a stunning array of fraudulent accounting manipulations."[13] The misconduct described included false and prematurely recognized revenue, manipulation of accounting entries to achieve revenue and earnings

---

12. A copy of this Agreement is included with the materials accompanying this article.

targets, the use of "cookie jar" reserves, the misuse of the company's stock option program, and instances of obstruction of the company's internal investigations. Id. Postal Inspector-in-Charge William Kezer described the misconduct as

> a textbook case of a company 'cooking the books' to meet or exceed analysts' expectations. It is also unique in that virtually the entire former executive hierarchy was in the kitchen stirring the pot.

Id. Ultimately, the Company restated its financial statements for a five-year period, reversing cumulative net revenue in excess of $200 million and cumulative net earnings in excess of $300 million.

Given these circumstances, the company faced a substantial risk of indictment. An evaluation of the company under several of the Thompson Memorandum factors—including the nature and seriousness of the offense; the pervasiveness of the wrongdoing and involvement of former senior management; initial attempts to obstruct justice; and the adequacy of the company's then compliance program—seemed to tip the scales toward a decision to indict.

However, the Company avoided indictment and was able to enter into a non-prosecution agreement with the Eastern District, in critical part due to its extensive cooperation with prosecutors and regulators through the course of a two-year internal investigation, and its far-reaching, and costly, remedial actions. As described by the Eastern District, Symbol agreed to continue its cooperation with the government; agreed to pay over $100 million to compensate victims of the fraud (including a payment of $37 million to the SEC, which was to be distributed to injured shareholders, and by settling the class actions claims brought against the Company); shared the substance of hundreds of interviews of employees and former employees, and hundreds of thousands of pages of documents and email messages, with the government, including documents otherwise protected by the attorney-client privilege; made numerous witnesses available for government interviews; and, in instances in which it discovered misconduct by its officers, executives and employees,

13. See Press Release, Former Senior Executives At Symbol Technologies Indicted In Massive Corporate Fraud Scheme (June 3, 2004) (U.S. DOJ United States Attorney, E.D.N.Y.) (available at http://www.usdoj.gov/usao/nye/pr/2004jun3.htm) (a copy of this press release is included with the materials accompanying this article).

terminated their employment and reported the misconduct to the government. Id.

In addition, Symbol adopted significant remedial steps to ensure that the fraud would not recur. The Eastern District made particular note of the termination of employment for employees who engaged in misconduct or refused to cooperate with Symbol's internal investigation; the appointment of a new management team, including a new president and chief executive officer, a new chief financial officer, a new general counsel, and new senior vice presidents of finance, sales, operations and customer service; the dismissal of its former auditing firm and retention of a new firm; the restructuring of its board of directors, including the separation of the chief executive officer and chairman of the board functions, and the appointment of a non-executive chairman; the appointment of an independent examiner to serve for three years to examine and report on Symbol's internal controls and financial reporting practices; the establishment of an annual training and education program for certain of its directors, officers and employees; and the commitment of significant resources to improve its internal controls and accounting systems. Id.

In sum, the sheer comprehensiveness of the Company's internal investigation, its timely communications to the government concerning developments and discoveries, and its effective and thorough responses to the problems uncovered, allowed Symbol to avoid indictment in the face of a far-reaching and pervasive accounting fraud.

2. Royal Dutch/Shell Group

Another more recent example of an investigated company's cooperation being rewarded by the Department of Justice is Royal Dutch/Shell Group, Europe's second-largest oil company, which U.S. Attorney David Kelley of the Southern District of New York announced would not be prosecuted for overstating its oil and gas reserves.[14] Royal Dutch Petroleum Company and Shell Transport and Trading Company had been under federal investigation since

14. See U.S. Won't Prosecute Shell for Overstating Reserves (Update 2), BLOOMBERG, June 29, 2005 (available at http://www.bloomberg.com/apps/news?pid=10000085&sid=aaZ59QhUU6UM&refer=Europe); see also Mark Milner and David Teather, US drops Shell criminal action, THE GUARDIAN, July 1, 2005 (available at http://www.guardian.co.uk/business/story/0,3604,1518650,00.html).

last year, when the company disclosed that it had overstated its proved reserves as of 2002 by approximately 23 percent. Kelley's statements made clear that Shell's cooperation had contributed to his decision not to prosecute, and that his decision was based on reasons spelled out in the Thompson memorandum. Kelley cited Shell's "full cooperation" in the probe, the $120 million settlement with the SEC, and the company's willingness "to take substantial remedial actions." Possibly with the demise of Arthur Andersen in mind, Kelly also cited the "negative effect" on Shell's innocent employees that criminal prosecution would cause: "The public interest has been sufficiently vindicated," Kelley said. "Criminal prosecution of Shell would not serve the public interest."_

3. Royal Ahold NV

Since the Seaboard Report was issued, only two public companies — Electro Scientific Industries Inc.[15] and Homestore Inc.[16]— have avoided both penalties and charges by the SEC. In the Homestore case, the Commission's decision was due to "swift, extensive and extraordinary cooperation in the Commission's investigation" and "reporting its discovery of possible misconduct to the Commission immediately upon the audit committee's learning of it, conducting a thorough and independent internal investigation, sharing the results of that investigation with the government (including not asserting any applicable privileges and protections with respect to written materials furnished to the Commission staff), terminating responsible wrongdoers, and implementing remedial actions designed to prevent the recurrence of fraudulent conduct." Id.

Royal Ahold became the third: in the SEC's October 13, 2004 settlement with Royal Ahold, the Commission imposed no monetary

---

15. See SEC Litigation Release, SEC Charges Former Executives Of Electro Scientific Industries, Inc. with Financial Reporting Fraud, Release No. 2109 (Sept. 24, 2004) (available at http://www.sec.gov/litigation/litreleases/lr18896.htm).
16. See SEC Press Release, SEC Files Financial Fraud Case Charging Three Former Homestore Executives; Defendants Agree to Repay $4.6 Million in Illegal Trading Profits, Release No. 2002-141 (September 25, 2002) (available at http://www.sec.gov/news/press/2002-141.htm); see also Tim Reason, The Limits of Mercy: The cost of cooperating with the SEC is high. The cost of not cooperating is even higher, CFO MAGAZINE, April 1, 2005 (available at http://www.cfo.com/article.cfm/3804652/2/c_3805512?f=archives).

fine after Ahold's board and management voluntarily disclosed accounting irregularities at the company. In addition to bringing to the authorities' attention that its subsidiary U.S. Foodservice had apparently overstated revenue by more than $800 million, the company also conducted a full review of all potential problems, shared the results of its investigations with the SEC, analyzed and reformed its accounting practices at its operating units, and dismissed employees—including high-ranking management—without prompting from the regulatory agency. In announcing its settlement with Ahold, the Commission cited the company's cooperation and extensive remediation as the reason why it decided not to fine the company[17]:

> The Commission also did not seek a penalty from Ahold, among other reasons, because of the company's extensive cooperation with the Commission's investigation. Ahold self-reported the misconduct and conducted an extensive internal investigation. On its own initiative, Ahold expanded its internal investigation beyond the fraud at U.S. Foodservice and the improper joint venture accounting to analyze accounting practices and internal controls at seventeen operating companies. Ahold promptly provided the staff with the internal investigative reports and the supporting information and waived the attorney-client privilege and work product protection with respect to its internal investigations. Ahold also made its current personnel available for interviews or testimony, significantly assisted the staff in arranging interviews with, or testimony from, former Ahold personnel located in the United States and abroad. Ahold promptly took remedial actions including, but not limited to, revising its internal controls and terminating employees responsible for the wrongdoing.

Id.

By imposing no monetary penalty on a company that acted responsibly and proactively to disclose and correct any wrongdoing, the SEC sent a clear signal that Royal Ahold should serve as a model for how the Commission expects boards and management to behave when wrongdoing is uncovered.[18] As one commentator as noted, "[t]he Ahold settlement is emblematic of the SEC's new agenda. By

---

17. See SEC Litigation Release, SEC Charges Royal Ahold and Three Former Top Executives with Fraud; Former Audit Committee Member Charged with Causing Violations of the Securities Laws, Release No. 18929 (Oct. 13, 2004) (available at http://www.sec.gov/litigation/litreleases/lr18929.htm) (a copy of this press release is included with the materials accompanying this article).
18. Lawrence Byrne & Joseph Armao, Carrot and Stick: Understanding the SEC's Agenda, COMPLIANCE WEEK, Nov. 30, 2004.

imposing increasingly massive fines, the Commission has been showing the stick for the past several years. Now the SEC is showing the carrot by demonstrating that companies that act promptly and responsibly are more likely to receive leniency even if serious wrongdoing occurs." Id.

C. Perils of Failure to Cooperate

Prosecutors and regulators recently also have made clear the perils involved in appearing to fail to cooperate with a government investigation, or of taking actions that appear to interfere with such an investigation. The Department of Justice has made clear its intolerance of activity that it believes has obstructed a government investigation, as illustrated most notably by the Arthur Andersen indictment in March 2002. (Whether the destruction of one of the world's largest accounting firms was appropriate, particularly in light of the Supreme Court's subsequent criticism of the Department of Justice, is worthy of a seminar in itself.) In addition, the Department has prosecuted and won convictions against Frank Quattrone and Martha Stewart in high profile obstruction cases against individuals. And three former executives of Computer Associates International Inc. pleaded guilty to obstruction of justice based on false statements they had made to the Company's internal investigators.

But even where the misconduct at issue does not rise to the level of criminal obstruction, corporations face significant sanctions for failing to cooperate fully with governmental regulators. First, such failure can result in an indictment on the underlying misconduct being investigated. And second, it can result in substantial monetary penalties. Indeed, the SEC has imposed millions of dollars of penalties against companies purely for their failure to cooperate during SEC investigations.

1. Lucent Technologies Inc.

On May 17, 2004, the SEC announced that, as part of a settlement with Lucent Technologies Inc. ("Lucent") and the announcement of enforcement actions against numerous Lucent employees and former employees, Lucent agreed to pay a $25 million penalty imposed due to its lack of cooperation.[19] In announcing the penalty, Paul Berger, the SEC's associate director of enforcement, stated that "[c]ompanies whose actions delay, hinder or undermine SEC investigations will not succeed. . . . Stiff sanctions and exposure of their conduct will serve as a reminder to companies that only genuine cooperation serves the best interests of investors."

Specifically, the SEC took Lucent to task for (1) providing incomplete document production, including the production of key documents only after the testimony of relevant witnesses, and failing to preserve and produce particular relevant documents; (2) the public statements of Lucent's counsel characterizing a particular transaction benignly, after Lucent had agreed in principle to a settlement with the staff of the SEC without admitting or denying certain allegations; (3) after reaching an agreement in principle with the staff of the SEC, expanding the scope of employees to be granted indemnification against the consequences of the SEC enforcement action; and (4) failing to provide timely and full disclosure to the SEC regarding its indemnification of employees. Id.

The Lucent case continues to be an excellent illustration of the importance of cooperation with the government, and the perils a company faces by failing to cooperate with an investigation.

2. Other Recent Examples of Failure to Cooperate

Four other recent examples of companies that have failed—in the SEC's eyes—to cooperate fully and satisfactorily serve as (explicit) reminders by the SEC that such failures will not be tolerated:

- **Banc of America Securities** (March 2004) - $10 million fine: "BAS repeatedly failed to promptly furnish documents ... provided misinformation concerning the availability ... of such documents, and engaged in dilatory tactics that delayed the investigation."[20]

- **Halliburton** (August 2004) - $7.5 million fine: "The penalty against Halliburton serves as yet another reminder that the [SEC] will not tolerate lapses by companies that serve to delay or hinder the [SEC's] investigative processes."[21]

---

19. See SEC Press Release, Lucent Settles SEC Enforcement Action Charging the Company with $1.1 Billion Accounting Fraud, Release No. 2004-67 (May 17, 2004) (available at http://www.sec.gov/news/press/2004-67.htm).

20. See SEC Press Release, SEC Brings Enforcement Action Against Banc of America Securities for Repeated Document Production Failures During a Pending Investigation, Release No. 2004-29 (March 10, 2004) (available at http://www.sec.gov/news/press/2004-29.htm).

- **Computer Associates** (September 2004) - $225 million in restitution to shareholders: "[The restitution fund] should send a clear message that public companies will pay a heavy price for obstructing the government's investigation." (The former CEO, CFO, and others were later criminally charged by the Department of Justice for lying to company lawyers during the course of the investigation).[22]
- **Wachovia Corp**. (November 2004) - $37 million fine: Wachovia's fine is levied after "Wachovia provided incomplete and untimely document production."[23]

The lessons of these prosecutorial decisions, as well as the recent civil decisions in the Morgan Stanley[24] and UBS matters[25] regarding electronic document retention and production failures, cannot be ignored.

---

21. See SEC Press Release, SEC Charges Halliburton and Two Former Officers for Failure to Disclose a 1998 Change in Accounting Practice, Release No. 2004-104 (Aug. 3, 2004) (available at http://www.sec.gov/news/press/2004-104.htm).
22. See SEC Press Release, SEC Files Securities Fraud Charges Against Computer Associates International, Inc., Former CEO Sanjay Kumar, and Two Other Former Company Executives, Release No. 2004-134 (Sept. 22, 2004) (available at http://www.sec.gov/news/press/2004-134.htm).
23. See SEC Press Release, SEC Settles Action Charging Wachovia Corporation with Proxy Disclosure and Other Reporting Violations Involving the 2001 Merger Between First Union Corporation and Old Wachovia Corporation, Release No. 2004-152 (Nov. 4, 2004) (available at http://www.sec.gov/news/press/2004-152.htm).
24. In Ronald Perelman's lawsuit against Morgan Stanley—Coleman Holdings Inc. v. Morgan Stanley & Co., 03-5045, 15th Judicial Cir., Palm Beach Co., Fla. (W.Palm Beach)—the judge became so dissatisfied with Morgan Stanley's electronic discovery production that she ruled that its actions were in "bad faith" and that the jury could simply assume that Morgan Stanley helped defraud Perelman, instructing the jury that: "Morgan Stanley participated in a scheme to mislead [Coleman] and others and cover up the massive fraud at Sunbeam until Morgan Stanley and Sunbeam could close the purchase of Coleman." See Jill Barton, Perelman Wins $1.4 Billion Total in Suit Against Morgan Stanley, The Associated Press (May 19, 2005); see also Jonathan D. Glater, Morgan Stanley Gets a Lesson On Lawyers And the Law, The New York Times (May 17, 2005).
25. See Zubulake v. UBS Warburg LLC, No. 02 Civ. 1243 (SAS), 2004 U.S. Dist. LEXIS 13574 (S.D.N.Y. July 20, 2004) (Scheindlin, J.) (finding that UBS had willfully destroyed potential e-mail evidence in a sex discrimination case brought by a former equity salesperson).

III. AN INCREASINGLY COMMON TOOL: DEFERRED PROSECUTION AGREEMENTS FOR COMPANIES WHO COOPERATE

In the past year, the Department of Justice has announced deferred prosecution agreements with at least six companies, including Bristol-Myers Squibb, Monsanto Co., Time Warner Inc., American International Group Inc., and Computer Associates International Inc.

A typical deferred prosecution agreement includes a formal information, indictment or criminal complaint, but the government agrees to put the prosecution on hold in exchange for the company's cooperation. Furthermore, the DOJ requires a company to accept responsibility for illegal conduct by its employees, step up internal compliance programs, and provide investigators with nearly unfettered access to company records. If the company fulfills its obligations under the agreement, the DOJ agrees to drop all charges at the end of a probationary-type period. Deferred prosecution agreements also increasingly require companies to provide restitution to injured shareholders.[26]

Some have suggested that in light of the increasing criticism faced by the Department of Justice as it aggressively prosecutes corporate crime—and in the process putting companies out of business—the government already may have taken some of the criticism regarding Arthur Andersen and other cases to heart. Id. Since Andersen's demise, prosecutors increasingly have employed deferred prosecution agreements with companies accused of wrongdoing.[27] Under the terms of those deals, companies will face increased financial penalties and other sanctions if they violate the terms of their corporate probation.

But perhaps, as at least one commentator as suggested, deferred prosecution agreements are a further way for the government to both extract full cooperation, while at the same time rewarding it.[28] The Thompson Memorandum focused in large part on cooperation, and, as described above, the Memorandum directs prosecutors to consider amnesty or pre-

---

26. See Vanessa Blum, Justice Deferred: DOJ Gets Companies to Turn Snitch, LEGAL TIMES, March 25, 2005 (available at http://www.law.com/jsp/article.jsp?id=1111658711645).
27. In fairness, it was reported that the government had offered Arthur Andersen a deferred prosecution. See Kurt Eichenwald, Andersen Is Said to Be Near Deal on Enron Charges, THE NEW YORK TIMES (April 11, 2002).
28. See, e.g., Thompson Memo Opens the Door for Pre-Trial Diversions for Corporations, 17 CORPORATE CRIME REPORTER 29(1), July 21, 2003 (available online at http://www.corporatecrimereporter.com /07_212_03_pressrelease.html).

trial diversion for corporations that completely and quickly cooperate with investigators. Id. Presumably in response, federal prosecutors appear to increasingly rely upon "deferred prosecution agreements"[29] as a form of "pre-trial diversion to exact corporate reforms, large-dollar restitution, and cooperation from companies under investigation."[30]

Deferred prosecution agreements have been used in corporate misconduct such as the Prudential case since the early 1990s.[31] Following the Andersen prosecution, which effectively destroyed the company, the government seems to have become more sensitive to "the risk of putting another large company into failure." Id. Recent comments by Timothy Coleman, senior counsel to Deputy Attorney General James Comey, Jr., would seem to suggest that this risk, as well as the guidance articulated in the Thompson Memorandum of rewarding companies for full cooperation, informs the government's decisions: "Deferred prosecutions give a company the chance to reform itself without creating a situation where a lot of people are going to lose their jobs and a lot of investors are going to lose more money." However, he insists that an increase in the use of such agreements does not mean the government is going soft on corporate offenders: "We have unleashed hundreds and hundreds of prosecutors to make corporate crime a major law enforcement priority … [and] [t]here's been a dramatic increase in the sheer number of investigations."[32]

And from the company's point of view, deferred prosecution is likely the next-best thing to non-prosecution. Some recent examples illustrate how deferred prosecution agreements can be tailored creatively for each company, and would appear to represent positive outcomes for the target company.

---

29. The Department of Justice Manual states that a major objective of the Pretrial Diversion Program is "[t]o save prosecutive and judicial resources for concentration on major, serious cases." DOJ Manual (Oct. 1997), § 9-22.000, "Pretrial Diversion Program," at § 9-22.000B (available at http://www.usdoj.gov/usao/eousa/
foia_reading_room/usam/title9/22mcrm.htm).

30. See Michael R. Sklaire and Joshua G. Berman, Deferred Prosecution Agreements: What Is The Cost Of Staying In Business?, Legal Opinion Letter, Washington Legal Foundation, Vol. 15, No. 11, June 3, 2005 (available at http://www.sonnenschein.com/
docs/Cost_of_Staying_in_B.pdf).

31. Paul J. Martinek, Case Highlights Use Of Deferred Prosecution Agreements, Compliance Week, June 28, 2005 (available at http://www.complianceweek.com/index.cfm?fuseaction=article.viewArticle&article_ID=1859).

32. See Blum, Justice Deferred: DOJ Gets Companies to Turn Snitch, supra, n. 26.

A. Bristol-Myers Squibb Company

On June 15, 2005, the U.S. Attorney for New Jersey Christopher J. Christie announced that his office had entered into a deferred prosecution agreement with Bristol-Myers Squibb in which the company would be charged with conspiring to commit securities fraud, but that prosecution would be deferred for two years.[33] The deferred prosecution agreement requires that Bristol-Myers Squibb:

- Pay $300 million to a shareholder compensation fund (in addition to a prior $389 million settle shareholder litigation settlement);
- Force the CEO to relinquish his post;
- Appoint a "non-executive chairman" of the board and an additional director "acceptable to" the prosecutor;
- Have a monitor report to the prosecutor on the company's implementation of enhanced internal controls and financial reporting reforms; and
- Institute mandatory training programs.

In return, the government agreed to defer pursuing a criminal complaint filed against Bristol-Myers Squibb, and agreed to drop the criminal matter entirely in two years if the company cooperates fully with authorities.[34]

This resolution, like other deferred prosecution agreements, avoids corporate prosecution at a price: heightened cooperation obligations and commitment to serious remedial efforts. Notably, this particular agreement reflects a significant ongoing involvement of the government in corporate governance. Not only does the agreement require a separation of the CEO and Chairman functions, but Bristol-Myers agreed to an ongoing Monitor inside the Company. In contrast, the Symbol non-prosecution agreement required a quarterly report from an outside examiner. Whether such an intrusive remedy becomes standard fare remains to be seen.

---

33. See Press Release, Bristol-Myers Squibb Charged with Conspiring to Commit Securities Fraud; Prosecution Deferred for Two Years, (June 15, 2005) (U.S. DOJ United States Attorney, N.J.) (available at http://www.usdoj.gov/usao/nj/publicaffairs/NJ_Press/files/bms0615_r.htm) (a copy of this press release—as well as a copy of the deferred prosecution agreement—is included with the materials accompanying this article).

B. Computer Associates International, Inc.

Computer Associates was investigated by the Department of Justice for fraudulent accounting practices, and the investigation has resulted in the guilty pleas of several former executives.[35] However, on September 22, 2004, the company announced that it had entered into a deferred prosecution agreement with the Department of Justice.[36] Moreover, Computer Associates explained the agreement to investors and the public on its website:

> Computer Associates' goal is to provide shareholders with progress on the deferred prosecution agreement. We will continue to update this site as we achieve further milestones.

---

34. The company, too, was quick to announce the resolution. The following is an excerpt from a Bristol-Myers press release issued the same day as the DOJ release:

> Bristol-Myers Squibb Company announced today that it has resolved the investigation by the U.S. Attorney's Office in New Jersey relating to wholesaler inventory and various accounting matters, in a Deferred Prosecution Agreement (Agreement) with the government. The government will not pursue its filed criminal complaint if it is satisfied after two years that the company has complied with all of the terms of the Agreement. Under the Agreement, the company will make an additional payment of $300 million to the shareholder fund previously established in connection with the company's settlement with the Securities and Exchange Commission (SEC) announced in August 2004. In connection with the Agreement, the company will record an additional reserve of $249 million in the second quarter....
>
> [CEO] Peter R. Dolan ... said: "The company is very pleased to have reached this resolution with the U.S. Attorney. We are determined that the mistakes of the past not be repeated and that the company's reputation for adhering to the highest standards of ethical business practices be fully restored. The company looks forward to continuing to build on our recent successes, including four new product approvals within the past two and one-half years. I will devote full focus to my CEO duties and leading the company in capitalizing on the multiple opportunities ahead."
>
> Also under the two-year Agreement, the company will maintain and continue to implement remedial measures pursuant to the settlement with the SEC, take certain additional remedial action and continue to cooperate with the U.S. Attorney's Office, including with respect to the ongoing investigation regarding individual current and former employees of the company

Bristol-Myers Squibb Company Press Release, Bristol-Myers Squibb Announces Agreement With The U.S. Attorney's Office In New Jersey, (June 15, 2005) (available at http://www.bms.com/news/press/data/fg_press_release_5670.html).

On September 22, 2004, CA announced the resolution of the government's investigations into CA's past accounting practices. This marked the end of a troubling period in CA's history, as well as the beginning of a new era of opportunity for the company.

The company has accepted full responsibility for the illegal conduct that occurred at CA, and has agreed to implement controls and governance measures to ensure that such past practices are never repeated. Our obligation to ensure the highest standards of integrity throughout CA is more important than any business objective or other consideration.

DPA Progress:

Below are a number of steps we have completed in our efforts towards meeting the terms of the deferred prosecution agreement:

- Lee Richards appointed by SEC to serve as Independent Examiner
- Patrick J. Gnazzo Appointed Senior Vice President, Business Practices and Chief Compliance Officer
- Kenneth Feinberg Appointed Restitution Fund Administrator
- Computer Associates Selects SAP and Accenture for Worldwide Enterprise Resource Planning Transformation
- Doug Robinson Appointed Corporate Controller
- Bob Cirabisi Appointed Chief Accounting Officer
- Jean Mahon Hired as Director of Records and Information Management
- Established a New Disclosure Committee

Restitution Fund Update:

September 22, 2004 the United States Attorney's Office for the Eastern District of New York and Computer Associates International, Inc. ("CA") entered into a Deferred Prosecution Agreement to resolve SEC and Department of Justice investigations into accounting fraud and obstruction of justice by certain former CA executives and employees. Under the terms of the Agreement, CA agreed to pay $225 million to create a Fund to pay restitution to eligible current and former CA shareholders.

---

35. See Press Release, Former Computer Associates Executive Indicted on Securities Fraud, Obstruction Charges, (Sept. 22, 2004) (DOJ Release No. 04-642) (available at http://www.usdoj.gov/opa/pr/2004/September/04_crm_642.htm).
36. See Computer Associates International Inc. website, Investor Relations "Corporate Governance" section, "Deferred Prosecution Agreement" (available at http://investor.ca.com/phoenix.zhtml?c=83100&p=irol-govdeferred).

Andrew Hruska, the Assistant U.S. Attorney in the Computer Associates case, has observed, "It takes a long time to investigate a company for this sort of criminal activity. By the time you're ready to indict, the company has probably already taken remedial measures on their own. When that company comes to the government and says, 'Don't destroy a great American company,' that's a very appealing argument."[37]

The Corporate Associates deferred prosecution agreement requires only an outside examiner, not a more intrusive internal monitor. And given the alternative of a corporate indictment, the overall agreement satisfied the basic corporate objection of survival.

C. America Online ("AOL")

America Online was recently investigated for allegedly aiding and abetting PurchasePro.com (a seller of Internet procurement software and services) in reporting at least $10 million in false revenue in the fourth quarter of 2000 and announcing at least $20 million in false revenue in the first quarter of 2001. As a result of allegedly aiding the PurchasePro fraud, AOL was able to report approximately $20 million in additional revenue in the fourth quarter of 2000 and about $15 million of additional revenue in the first quarter of 2001. On December 15, 2004, the Department of Justice announced that it had entered into a deferred prosecution agreement with AOL.[38] As part of the deferred prosecution agreement, AOL agreed to

- Accept and acknowledge responsibility for the conduct of AOL personnel in the PurchasePro transactions;
- Cooperate fully with the Department of Justice;
- Pay $150 million to a compensation fund and $60 million in penalties;
- Adopt internal controls designed to deter potential violations of company policies and procedures; and
- Cooperate with an independent monitor, mutually agreed upon by the Department of Justice and AOL, who will report to the Department on at least a semi-annual basis.

---

37. See Blum, Justice Deferred: DOJ Gets Companies to Turn Snitch, supra, n. 26.
38. See Press Release, America Online Charged With Aiding and Abetting Securities Fraud; Prosecution Deferred For Two Years, (DOJ Press Release No. 04-790) (Dec. 15, 2004) (available at http://www.fbi.gov/dojpressrel/pressrel04/aolrelease121504.htm) (last modified Jan. 6, 2005).

Based on AOL's acceptance of those conditions and others, the DOJ agreed to defer prosecution on the complaint for 24 months. A separate agreement also required AOL's parent company, Time Warner, Inc., to cooperate with the ongoing criminal investigation. In addition, four former PurchasePro executives pled guilty to criminal charges for conduct related to the AOL/PurchasePro transactions. Id.

In announcing the agreement, Deputy Attorney General Comey said that the "deferred prosecution agreement gives AOL a chance to make amends for its conduct and clean up its act, in return for a stiff penalty and far-reaching reforms... In this major corporate investigation, the government has achieved a result that minimizes the collateral damage to shareholders and employees while imposing appropriate punishment and protecting the rights of victims." Id. Assistant Attorney General Wray added that the DOJ "will take into account steps taken by corporations, particularly if they involve significant remedial actions to ensure that such conduct does not occur in the future." Id.

Few corporations have survived an indictment. Particularly in the financial arena, such charges have destroyed or led to the demise of many institutions including, Arthur Andersen, Drexel, E.F. Hutton, Bankers Trust and Republic Bank. And even if a corporation can survive an indictment, the collateral consequences in terms of reputation and competition disadvantages are enormous. Hence, the deferred prosecution resolution may offer an attractive alternative to both the government and the corporate client.[39] To the extent, however, the Department of Justice requires more onerous and intrusive terms, this option may become less appealing in the future.

IV. PROVIDING PRIVILEGED MATERIALS TO THE GOVERNMENT

As mentioned above, a critical issue under the Thompson Memorandum and the Seaboard Report is the waiver of privilege under the guise of cooperation. Increasingly, prosecutors and regulators demand such otherwise privileged materials as the price of cooperation. This tactic threatens to undermine the attorney-client privileged in the corporate context and is potentially bad policy in the long run. Nonetheless, there are no signs that prosecutors or the SEC are deemphasizing this "litmus test" of cooperation any time in the near future.

---

39. A deferred prosecution can still lead to devastating consequences, including debarment proceedings.

If the decision is made to turn over privileged materials to the government, counsel for the company under investigation is well-advised to enter into a non-waiver agreement with the government agencies involved. Such a non-waiver agreement serves to document both parties' intention that production to the government of documents otherwise protected by the attorney-client or work product privilege will not waive the privilege with respect to third parties. Although perhaps at odds with traditional views on privilege, there is some recent authority supporting the conclusion that production to the government of otherwise privileged materials pursuant to such non-waiver agreement does not constitute a waiver. In fact, these decisions rely on such agreements as a manifestation of a continued effort by the corporation to maintain the confidentiality of privileged matter. See, e.g., In re Steinhardt Partners, LP, 9 F.3d 230, 236 (2d Cir 1993) ("Establishing a rigid rule would fail to anticipate situations in which the disclosing party and the government may share a common interest in developing legal theories and analyzing information, or situations in which the SEC and the disclosing party have entered into an explicit agreement that the SEC will maintain the confidentiality of the disclosed materials."); Maruzen Co., Ltd. v. HSBC USA, Inc., No. 00 Civ. 1079 (RO), 2002 U.S. Dist. LEXIS 13288, 2002 WL 1628782 (S.D.N.Y. July 23, 2003) (no waiver because of company's explicit confidentiality agreements with the SEC and United States Attorney's Office);[40] In re Leslie Fay Cos. Inc. Sec. Litig., 161 F.R.D. 274, 284 (S.D.N.Y. 1995) (same). However, courts continue to be split on this issue, and ultimately the privilege issue would be decided by a court. See, e.g., United States v. Bergonzi, 216 F.R.D. 487 (N.D. Cal. 2003) (finding waiver despite confidentiality agreement). Two recent New York cases further develop this evolving area of law, and both certainly will impact how government agencies conduct their investigations, and serve to inform the myriad decisions that a company under investigation must make.

A. Merrill Lynch & Co. v. Allegheny Energy, Inc. (October 2004)

In Merrill Lynch & Co. v. Allegheny Energy, Inc., No. 02 Civ. 7689 (HB), 2004 U.S. Dist. LEXIS 21543 (S.D.N.Y. Oct. 26, 2004),[41] Judge Baer in the Southern District of New York upheld the continuing validity of the work product protection for an internal investigation report.

40. Copies of the Steinhardt and Maruzen decisions are included with the materials accompanying this article.

41. A copy of this decision is included with the materials accompanying this article.

However, the opinion demonstrates the difficulty corporations may face after Sarbanes-Oxley and the heightened pressure on them to cooperate in government investigations.

Specifically, in that case, Allegheny sought the production of two reports that were the result of a Merrill Lynch internal investigation into the circumstances surrounding the theft of approximately $43 million in connection with an energy trade. In the fall of 2002, the United States Attorney's Office for the Southern District of New York informed Merrill Lynch that it was investigating the trade, and Merrill Lynch therefore undertook its own internal investigation (conducted by in-house and outside counsel), which culminated in two reports. When Merrill Lynch's internal investigation was disclosed, the company's outside auditor, Deloitte & Touche, requested and received copies of the internal report. Allegheny based is discovery request for the report on the ground that disclosure to Deloitte & Touche constituted a waiver of the attorney-client privilege and the work product protection. Judge Baer rejected the claim, stating:

> Courts are split in their treatment of disclosures to a corporation's accountants or auditors. More precisely, courts differ in their conceptualization of two critical points that are often implicitly intertwined in their analysis: whether the "adversary" contemplated by the work product privilege is necessarily a litigation adversary and whether a corporation's auditor is such an adversary, to whom disclosure will waive the privilege. While admittedly there are good arguments on both sides, in this case, I answer both questions in the negative and conclude that Merrill Lynch's disclosure of the reports to Deloitte & Touche did not constitute a waiver of the applicable work product protection."

Id. at *15.

In rendering his conclusion, Judge Baer drew an analogy to waiver in the government investigation context:

> Indeed, in an analogous context, the Second Circuit has specifically eschewed a per se rule of waiver for work product [citing In re Steinhardt Partners, LP, 9 F.3d 230, 236 (2d Cir 1993)]. Instead, the Court must assess of what type of common interests the work product doctrine contemplates and whether a corporation and its outside auditors share any such interest.

Id. at **18-19. The Court applied the Second Circuit's "more expansive 'because of' test for work product, under which any document prepared 'because of' existing or expected litigation" is protected by the work product privilege. Id. Judge Baer first found that the fact that even if a business decision was influenced by the outcome of the litigation, any documents prepared in anticipation of that litigation maintain their privileged status. Id. The Court then turned to what Judge Baer considered the "critical inquiry" of "whether Deloitte & Touche should be conceived of as an adversary or a conduit to a potential adversary... [and] an independent auditor could be conceived of as an adversary because of its important public function to independently ensure the accuracy of a company's financial reports." Judge Baer reasoned—citing Sarbanes Oxley's aims "at strengthening the independence of auditors and eliminating conflicts of interest"—that although auditors must retain their independence, the need for "independence" did not rise to the level of a "tangible adversarial relationship," concluding that:

> [A]ny tension between an auditor and a corporation that arises from an auditor's need to scrutinize and investigate a corporation's records and book-keeping practices simply is not the equivalent of an adversarial relationship contemplated by the work product doctrine. Nor should it be. A business and its auditor can and should be aligned insofar as they both seek to prevent, detect, and root out corporate fraud. Indeed, this is precisely the type of limited alliance that courts should encourage. For example, here Merrill Lynch complied with Deloitte & Touche's request for copies of the internal investigation reports so that the auditors could further assess Merrill Lynch's internal controls, both to inform its audit work and to notify the corporation if there was a deficiency.

Id. at **20-22.

B. In Re Natural Gas Commodity Litigation (June 2005)

Even more recently, Chief Magistrate Judge Andrew J. Peck of the Southern District of New York addressed similar issues in In Re Natural Gas Commodity Litigation.[42] In this case, Judge Peck found that production of a report of an internal investigation to the Commodity Futures Trading Commission (CFTC) did not waive the work product protection attaching to the report.

In the In Re Natural Gas Commodity Litigation case, the companies, after conducting internal investigations of alleged inaccurate reporting of natural gas transactions to trade publications, fired several traders. The Federal Energy Regulatory Commission and the CFTC, in connection with their own investigation, requested to review certain data analyses prepared as part of the internal investigations. The companies secured confidentiality and non-waiver agreements from each agency with respect to all material produced. In the subsequent litiga-

---

42. In Re Natural Gas Commodity Litigation, No. 03 Civ. 6186 (VM) (AJP), 2005 U.S. Dist. LEXIS 11950 (S.D.N.Y. June 21, 2005) (Peck, J.). A copy of this decision is included with the materials accompanying this article.

tion with the traders, the companies provided the underlying documents and data on which the analyses were based but refused to provide the analyses, claiming that the documents were privileged.

Judge Peck began by noting that the Second Circuit in In re Steinhardt Partners had "declined to adopt a per se rule that all voluntary disclosures to the government waive work product protection,"[43] and he similarly declined to fashion any such per se rule. Instead, looking to the Second Circuit, he found that:

> Crafting rules relating to privilege in matters of governmental investigations must be done on a case-by-case basis. Establishing a rigid rule would fail to anticipate situations in which the disclosing party and the government may share a common interest in developing legal theories and analyzing information, or situations in which the SEC and the disclosing party have entered into an explicit agreement that the SEC will maintain the confidentiality of the disclosed materials.

The In Re Natural Gas Commodity Litigation decision contains an exhaustive review of the current law on selective waiver generally, noting the conflict between Circuits on the issue as it relates to the work product doctrine.[44] Ultimately, Judge Peck felt constrained to apply the more protective Second Circuit rule, and declined to order production to plaintiffs in collateral civil litigation. In denying the traders' motion to compel, Judge Peck held that voluntary production of analyses to government agencies as part of a governmental investigation did not constitute a waiver of any privilege both because the companies had explicit written confidentiality and non-waiver agreements with the

---

43. In re Steinhardt Partners, LP, 9 F.3d at 236.
44. Judge Peck cited, at **27-28, the following cases as examples of approaches in other Circuits that differ from that in the Second Circuit: In re Columbia/HCA Healthcare Corp. Billing Practices Litig., 293 F.3d 289, 302-07 (6th Cir. 2002) (adopting per se waiver approach for attorney-client and work product privilege), cert. denied, 539 U.S. 977, 124 S. Ct. 27 (2003); United States v. MIT, 129 F.3d 681, 686, 688 (1st Cir. 1997) (rejecting selective waiver approach, finding attorney-client and work product privileges waived by disclosure to government agency, but leaving open issue of whether waiver would apply to opinion work product documents); Westinghouse Elec. Corp. v. Republic of the Philippines, 951 F.2d 1414, 1418, 1426-30 (3d Cir. 1991) (finding attorney-client and work product privileges waived because of prior disclosure of privileged documents to governmental agency; even if government and disclosing party had entered into a confidentiality agreement, result would be the same.); In re Chrysler Motors Corp. Overnight Evaluation Program Litig., 860 F.2d 844, 846-47 (8th Cir. 1988) (defendant waived work product privilege for documents sought by government which defendant had disclosed to adversary in civil litigation, despite confidentiality agreement).

agencies, and because the companies provided to the traders the underlying documents on which the analyses were based.

At least until the Supreme Court gives definitive guidelines, the issue of selective waiver or non-waiver will continue to be a hot issue for counsel. If production of otherwise privileged materials cannot be avoided, the corporation should carefully negotiate the scope of that production to preserve as much material as possible. In addition, it is critical to document the non-waiver agreement with each of the government agencies involved. To the extent feasible, the agreement should confirm the continuing confidentiality of the documents and information in question and the joint interest of the government and the company in investigating potential wrongdoing without waiving the privilege.[45]

* * *

---

45. A "template" confidentiality agreement between an investigated company and the DOJ and SEC is included with the materials accompanying this article.

1 of 1 DOCUMENT

ARTHUR ANDERSEN LLP, PETITIONER v. UNITED STATES

No. 04-368

SUPREME COURT OF THE UNITED STATES

125 S. Ct. 2129; 161 L. Ed. 2d 1008; 2005 U.S. LEXIS 4348; 73 U.S.L.W. 4393; Fed. Sec. L. Rep. (CCH) P93,266; 18 Fla. L. Weekly Fed. S 324

April 27, 2005, Argued
May 31, 2005, Decided

NOTICE: [***1]
The LEXIS pagination of this document is subject to change pending release of the final published version.

PRIOR HISTORY: ON WRIT OF CERTIORARI TO THE UNITED STATES COURT OF APPEALS FOR THE FIFTH CIRCUIT. *United States v. Andersen, 374 F.3d 281, 2004 U.S. App. LEXIS 11814 (5th Cir. Tex., 2004)*

DISPOSITION: Reversed and remanded.

LexisNexis(R) Headnotes

SYLLABUS: As Enron Corporation's financial difficulties became public, petitioner, Enron's auditor, instructed its employees to destroy documents pursuant to its document retention policy. Petitioner was indicted under *18 U.S.C. §§ 1512(b)(2)(A)* and *(B)*, which make it a crime to "knowingly . . . corruptly persuade another person . . . with intent to . . . cause" that person to "withhold" documents from, or "alter" documents for use in, an "official proceeding." The jury returned a guilty verdict, and the Fifth Circuit affirmed, holding that the District Court's jury instructions properly conveyed the meaning [***2] of "corruptly persuades" and "official proceeding" in *§ 1512(b)*; that the jury need not find any consciousness of wrongdoing in order to convict; and that there was no reversible error.

Held: The jury instructions failed to convey properly the elements of a "corrupt persuasion" conviction under *§ 1512(b)*. Pp. 6-12.

(a) This Court's traditional restraint in assessing federal criminal statutes' reach, see, *e.g.*, *United States v. Aguilar, 515 U.S. 593, 600, 132 L. Ed. 2d 520, 115 S. Ct. 2357*, is particularly appropriate here, where the act underlying the conviction -- "persuasion" -- is by itself innocuous. Even "persuading" a person "with intent to . . . cause" that person to "withhold" testimony or documents from the Government is not inherently malign. Under ordinary circumstances, it is not wrongful for a manager to instruct his employees to comply with a valid document retention policy, even though the policy, in part, is created to keep certain information from others, including the Government. Thus, *§ 1512(b)*'s "knowingly . . . corruptly persuades" phrase is key to what may or may not lawfully be done in the situation presented here. The Government suggests that "knowingly" does [***3] not modify "corruptly persuades," but that is not how the statute most naturally reads. "Knowledge" and "knowingly" are normally associated with awareness, understanding, or consciousness, and "corrupt" and "corruptly" with wrongful, immoral, depraved, or evil. Joining these meanings together makes sense both linguistically and in the statutory scheme. Only persons conscious of wrongdoing can be said to "knowingly . . . corruptly persuade." And limiting criminality to persuaders conscious of their wrongdoing sensibly allows *§ 1512(b)* to reach only those with the level of culpability usually required to impose criminal liability. See *Aguilar, supra, at 602, 132 L. Ed 2d 520, 115 S. Ct. 2357*. Pp. 6-9.

(b) The jury instructions failed to convey the requisite consciousness of wrongdoing. Indeed, it is striking how little culpability the instructions required. For example, the jury was told that, even if petitioner honestly and sincerely believed its conduct was lawful, the jury could convict. The instructions also diluted the meaning of "corruptly" such that it covered innocent conduct. The District Court based its instruction on the Fifth Circuit Pattern Jury Instruction for *§ 1503*, which defined [***4] "corruptly" as "knowingly and dishonestly, with the specific intent to subvert or undermine the integrity" of a proceeding. However, the court agreed with the Government's insistence on excluding "dishonestly" and adding the term "impede" to the phrase "subvert or undermine," so the jury was told to convict if it found petitioner intended to "subvert, undermine, or impede" governmental factfinding by suggesting to its employees that they enforce the document retention policy. These changes were significant. "Dishonest[y]" was no longer necessary to a finding of guilt, and it was enough for petitioner to have simply "impeded" the Government's factfinding ability. "Impede" has broader connotations than "subvert" or even "undermine," and many of these connotations do not incorporate any "corruptness" at all. Under the dictionary definition of "impede," anyone who innocently persuades another to withhold information from the Government "gets in the way of the progress of" the Government. With regard to such innocent conduct, the "corruptly" instructions did no limiting work whatsoever. The instructions also led the jury to believe that it did not have to find *any* nexus between the [***5] "persuasion" to destroy documents and any particular proceeding. In resisting any nexus element, the Government relies on *§ 1512(e)(i)*, which states that an official proceeding "need not be pending or about to be instituted at the time of the offense." It is, however, quite another thing to say a proceeding need not even be foreseen. A "knowingly . . . corrupt persauder" cannot be someone who persuades others to shred documents under a document retention policy when he does not have in contemplation any particular official proceeding in which those documents might be material. Cf. *Aguilar, supra, at 599-600, 132 L. Ed. 2d 520, 115 S. Ct. 2357*. Pp. 9-12.

374 F.3d 281, reversed and remanded.

JUDGES: REHNQUIST, C. J., delivered the opinion for a unanimous Court.

OPINIONBY: REHNQUIST

OPINION:

[*2131] [**1013] CHIEF JUSTICE REHNQUIST delivered the opinion of the Court.

As Enron Corporation's financial difficulties became public in 2001, petitioner Arthur Andersen LLP, Enron's auditor, instructed its employees to destroy documents pursuant to its document retention policy. A jury found that this action made petitioner guilty of violating *18 U.S.C. § § 1512(b)(2)(A)* and *(B)*. These sections make it [***6] a crime to "knowingly use intimidation or physical force, threaten, or corruptly persuade another person . . . with intent to . . . cause" that person to "withhold" documents from, or "alter" documents for use in, an "official proceeding." n1 The Court of Appeals for the Fifth Circuit affirmed. We hold that the jury [*2132] instructions failed to convey properly the elements of a "corrupt persuasion" conviction under *§ 1512(b)*, and therefore reverse.

n1 *We refer to the 2000 version of the statute, which has since been amended by Congress.*

Enron Corporation, during the 1990's, switched its business from operation of natural gas pipelines to an energy conglomerate, a move that was accompanied by aggressive accounting practices and rapid growth. Petitioner audited Enron's publicly filed financial statements and provided internal audit and consulting services to it. Petitioner's "engagement team" for Enron was headed by David Duncan. Beginning in 2000, Enron's financial performance began [**1014] to suffer, and, as 2001 wore [***7] on, worsened. n2 On August 14, 2001, Jeffrey Skilling, Enron's Chief Executive Officer (CEO), unexpectedly resigned. Within days, Sherron Watkins, a senior accountant at Enron, warned Kenneth Lay, Enron's newly reappointed CEO, that Enron could "implode in a wave of accounting scandals." Brief for United States 2. She likewise informed Duncan and Michael Odom, one of petitioner's partners who had supervisory responsibility over Duncan, of the looming problems.

n2 During this time, petitioner faced problems of its own. In June 2001, petitioner entered into a settlement agreement with the Securities and Exchange Commission (SEC) related to its audit work of Waste Management, Inc. As part of the settlement, petitioner paid a massive fine. It also was censured and enjoined from committing further violations of the securities laws. In July 2001, the SEC filed an amended complaint alleging improprieties by Sunbeam Corporation, and petitioner's lead partner on the Sunbeam audit was named.

On August 28, an article [***8] in the Wall Street Journal suggested improprieties at Enron, and the SEC opened an informal investigation. By early September, petitioner had formed an Enron "crisis-response" team, which included Nancy Temple, an in-house counsel. n3 On October 8, petitioner retained outside counsel to represent it in any litigation that might arise from the Enron matter. The next day, Temple discussed Enron with other in-house counsel. Her notes from that meeting reflect that "some SEC investigation" is "highly probable." *Id.*, at 3.

n3 A key accounting problem involved Enron's use of "Raptors," which were special purpose entities used to engage in "off-balance-sheet" activities. Petitioner's engagement team had allowed Enron to "aggregate" the Raptors for accounting purposes so that they reflected a positive return. This was, in the words of petitioner's experts, a "black-and-white" violation of Generally Accepted Accounting Principles. Brief for United States 2.

On October 10, Odom spoke at a general training meeting [***9] attended by 89 employees, including 10 from the Enron engagement team. Odom urged everyone to comply with the firm's document retention policy. n4 He added: "'If it's destroyed in the course of [the] normal policy and litigation is filed the next day, that's great. . . . We've followed our own policy, and whatever there was that might [*2133] have been of interest to somebody is gone and irretrievable.'" *374 F.3d 281, 286 (CA5 2004)*. On October 12, Temple entered the Enron matter into her computer, designating the "Type of Potential Claim" as "Professional Practice -- Government/Regulatory Investigation." App. JA-127. Temple also e-mailed Odom, suggesting that he "'remind the engagement team of our documentation and retention policy.'" Brief for United States 6.

n4 The firm's policy called for a single central engagement file, which "should contain only that information which is relevant to supporting our work." App. JA-45. The policy stated that, "in cases of threatened litigation, . . . no related information will be destroyed." Id., at JA-44. It also separately provided that, if petitioner is "advised of litigation or subpoenas regarding a particular engagement, the related information should not be destroyed. See Policy Statement No. 780 -- Notification of Litigation." *Id.*, at JA-65 (emphasis deleted). Policy Statement No. 780 set forth "notification" procedures for whenever "professional practice litigation against [petitioner] or any of its personnel has been commenced, has been threatened or is judged likely to occur, or when governmental or professional investigations that may involve [petitioner] or any of its personnel have been commenced or are judged likely." *Id.*, at JA-29 to JA-30.

[***10]

On October 16, Enron announced its third quarter results. That release disclosed a $ 1.01 billion charge to [**1015] earnings. n5 The following day, the SEC notified Enron by letter that it had opened an investigation in August and requested certain information and documents. On October 19, Enron forwarded a copy of that letter to petitioner.

n5 The release characterized the charge to earnings as "non-recurring." Brief for United States 6, n. 4. Petitioner had expressed doubts about this characterization to Enron, but Enron refused to alter the release. Temple wrote an e-mail to Duncan that "suggested deleting some language that might suggest we have concluded the release is misleading." App. JA-95.

On the same day, Temple also sent an e-mail to a member of petitioner's internal team of accounting experts and attached a copy of the document policy. On October 20, the Enron crisis-response team held a conference call, during which Temple instructed everyone to "make sure to follow the [document] policy." Brief for United [***11] States 7 (brackets in original). On October 23, Enron CEO Lay declined to answer questions during a call with analysts because of "potential lawsuits, as well as the SEC inquiry." *Ibid.* After the call, Duncan met with other Andersen partners on the Enron engagement team and told them that they should ensure team members were complying with the document policy. Another meeting for all team members followed, during which Duncan distributed the policy and told everyone to comply. These, and other smaller meetings, were followed by substantial destruction of paper and electronic documents.

On October 26, one of petitioner's senior partners circulated a New York Times article discussing the SEC's response to Enron. His e-mail commented that "the problems are just beginning and we will be in the cross hairs. The marketplace is going to keep the pressure on this and is going to force the SEC to be tough." *Id.*, at 8. On October 30, the SEC opened a formal investigation and sent Enron a letter that requested accounting documents.

Throughout this time period, the document destruction continued, despite reservations by some of petitioner's managers. n6 On November 8, Enron announced [***12] that it would issue a comprehensive restatement of its earnings and assets. Also on November 8, the SEC served Enron and petitioner with subpoenas for records. On November 9, Duncan's secretary sent an e-mail that stated: "Per Dave -- No more shredding . . . . We have been officially served for our documents." *Id.*, at 10. Enron filed for bankruptcy less than a month later. Duncan was fired and later pleaded guilty to witness tampering.

n6 For example, on October 26, John Riley, another partner with petitioner, saw Duncan shredding documents and told him "this wouldn't be the best time in the world for you guys to be shredding a bunch of stuff." Brief for United States 9. On October 31, David Stulb, a forensics investigator for petitioner, met with Duncan. During the meeting, Duncan picked up a document with the words "smoking gun" written on it and began to destroy it, adding "we don't need this." *Ibid.* Stulb cautioned Duncan on the need to maintain documents and later informed Temple that Duncan needed advice on the document retention policy.

[***13]

[*2134] In March 2002, petitioner was indicted in the Southern District of Texas on one count of violating *§ § 1512(b)(2)(A)* and *(B)*. The indictment alleged that, between October 10 and November 9, 2001, petitioner "did knowingly, intentionally and corruptly persuade . . . other persons, to wit: [petitioner's] employees, with intent to cause" them to withhold documents from, and alter documents for use in, "official proceedings, [**1016] namely: regulatory and criminal proceedings and investigations." App. JA-139. A jury trial followed. When the case went to the jury, that body deliberated for seven days and then declared that it was deadlocked. The District Court delivered an "*Allen* charge," *Allen v. United States, 164 U.S. 492, 41 L. Ed. 528, 17 S. Ct. 154 (1896)*, and, after three more days of deliberation, the jury returned a guilty verdict. The District Court denied petitioner's motion for a judgment of acquittal.

The Court of Appeals for the Fifth Circuit affirmed. *374 F.3d at 284*. It held that the jury instructions properly conveyed the meaning of "corruptly persuades" and "official proceeding"; that the jury need not find any consciousness of wrongdoing; and that there was no reversible [***14] error. Because of a split of authority regarding the meaning of *§ 1512(b)*, we granted certiorari. n7 *543 U.S. --, 160 L. Ed. 2d 609, 125 S. Ct. 823 (2005)*.

n7 Compare, *e.g.*, *United States v. Shotts, 145 F.3d 1289, 1301 (CA11 1998)*, with *United States v. Farrell, 126 F.3d 484, 489-490 (CA3 1997)*.

Chapter 73 of Title 18 of the United States Code provides criminal sanctions for those who obstruct justice. *Sections 1512(b)(2)(A)* and *(B)*, part of the witness tampering provisions, provide in relevant part:

"Whoever knowingly uses intimidation or physical force, threatens, or corruptly persuades another person, or attempts to do so, or engages in misleading conduct toward another person, with intent to . . . cause or induce any person to . . . withhold testimony, or withhold a record, document, or other object, from an official proceeding [or] alter, destroy, mutilate, or conceal an object with intent to impair the object's integrity or availability for use in an official proceeding . . . shall be fined [***15] under this title or imprisoned not more than ten years, or both."

In this case, our attention is focused on what it means to "knowingly . . . corruptly persuade" another person "with intent to . . . cause" that person to "withhold" documents from, or "alter" documents for use in, an "official proceeding."

"We have traditionally exercised restraint in assessing the reach of a federal criminal statute, both out of deference to the prerogatives of Congress, *Dowling v. United States, 473 U.S. 207, 87 L. Ed. 2d 152, 105 S. Ct. 3127 (1985)*, and out of concern that 'a fair warning should be given to the world in language that the common world will understand, of what the law intends to do if a certain line is passed,' *McBoyle v. United States, 283 U.S. 25, 27, 75 L. Ed. 816, 51 S. Ct. 340 (1931)*." *United States v. Aguilar, 515 U.S. 593, 600, 132 L. Ed. 2d 520, 115 S. Ct. 2357 (1995)*.

Such restraint is particularly appropriate here, where the act underlying the conviction -- "persuasion" -- is by itself innocuous. Indeed, "persuading" a person "with intent to . . . cause" that person to "withhold" testimony or documents from a Government proceeding or Government official is not inherently malign. n8 Consider, [*2135] for instance, [***16] a mother who suggests to her son that he invoke his right against compelled [**1017] self-incrimination, see *U.S. Const., Amdt. 5*, or a wife who persuades her husband not to disclose marital confidences, see *Trammel v. United States, 445 U.S. 40, 63 L. Ed. 2d 186, 100 S. Ct. 906 (1980)*.

n8 *Section 1512(b)(2)* addresses testimony, as well as documents. *Section 1512(b)(1)* also addresses testimony. *Section 1512(b)(3)* addresses "persuaders" who intend to prevent "the communication to a law enforcement officer or judge of the United States of information" relating to a federal crime.

Nor is it necessarily corrupt for an attorney to "persuade" a client "with intent to . . . cause" that client to "withhold" documents from the Government. In *Upjohn Co. v. United States, 449 U.S. 383, 66 L. Ed. 2d 584, 101 S. Ct. 677 (1981)*, for example, we held that Upjohn was justified in withholding documents that were covered by the attorney-client privilege from the Internal Revenue Service (IRS). See *id., at 395, 66 L. Ed. 2d 584, 101 S. Ct. 677*. No one would suggest that an attorney [***17] who "persuaded" Upjohn to take that step acted wrongfully, even though he surely intended that his client keep those documents out of the IRS' hands.

"Document retention policies," which are created in part to keep certain information from getting into the hands of others, including the Government, are common in business. See generally Chase, To Shred or Not to Shred: Document Retention Policies and Federal Obstruction of Justice Statutes, 8 Ford. J. Corp. & Fin. L. 721 (2003). It is, of course, not wrongful for a manager to instruct his employees to comply with a valid document retention policy under ordinary circumstances.

Acknowledging this point, the parties have largely focused their attention on the word "corruptly" as the key to what may or may not lawfully be done in the situation presented here. *Section 1512(b)* punishes not just "corruptly persuading" another, but "*knowingly* . . . corruptly persuading" another. (Emphasis added.) The Government suggests that "knowingly" does not modify "corruptly persuades," but that is not how the statute most naturally reads. It provides the *mens rea* -- "knowingly" -- and then a list of acts -- "uses intimidation or physical force, [***18] threatens, or corruptly persuades." We have recognized with regard to similar statutory language that the *mens rea* at least applies to the acts that immediately follow, if not to *other* elements down the statutory chain. See *United States v. X-Citement Video, Inc., 513 U.S. 64, 68, 130 L. Ed. 2d 372, 115 S. Ct. 464 (1994)* (recognizing that the "most natural grammatical reading" of *18 U.S.C. § § 2252(a)(1)* and *(2)* "suggests that the term 'knowingly' modifies only the surrounding verbs: transports, ships, receives, distributes, or reproduces"); see also *Liparota v. United States, 471 U.S. 419, 85 L. Ed. 2d 434, 105 S. Ct. 2084 (1985)*. The Government suggests that it is "questionable whether Congress would employ such an inelegant formulation as 'knowingly . . . corruptly persuades.'" Brief for United States 35, n. 18. Long experience has not taught us to share the Government's doubts on this score, and we must simply interpret the statute as written.

[**1018] The parties have not pointed us to another interpretation of "knowingly . . . corruptly" to guide us here. n9 In any event, the natural meaning of these terms provides a clear answer. See *Bailey v. United States, 516 U.S. 137, 144-145, 133 L. Ed. 2d 472, 116 S. Ct. 501 (1995)*. [***19] "Knowledge" and "knowingly" are normally associated [*2136] with awareness, understanding, or consciousness. See Black's Law Dictionary 888 (8th ed. 2004) (hereinafter Black's); Webster's Third New International Dictionary 1252-1253 (1993) (hereinafter Webster's 3d); American Heritage Dictionary of the English Language 725 (1981) (hereinafter Am. Hert.). "Corrupt" and "corruptly" are normally associated with wrongful, immoral, depraved, or evil. See Black's 371; Webster's 3d 512; Am. Hert. 299-300. Joining these meanings together here makes sense both linguistically and in the statutory scheme. Only persons conscious of wrongdoing can be said to "knowingly . . . corruptly persuade." And limiting criminality to persuaders conscious of their wrongdoing sensibly allows *§ 1512(b)* to reach only those with the level of "culpability . . . we usually require in order to impose criminal liability." *United States v. Aguilar, 515 U.S., at 602, 132 L. Ed. 2d 520, 115 S. Ct. 2357*; see also *Liparota v. United States, supra, at 426, 85 L. Ed. 2d 434, 105 S. Ct. 2084*.

n9 The parties have pointed us to two other obstruction provisions, *18 U.S.C. § § 1503* and *1505*, which contain the word "corruptly." But these provisions lack the modifier "knowingly," making any analogy inexact.

[***20]

The outer limits of this element need not be explored here because the jury instructions at issue simply failed to convey the requisite consciousness of wrongdoing. Indeed, it is striking how little culpability the instructions required. For example, the jury was told that, "even if [petitioner] honestly and sincerely believed that its conduct was lawful, you may find [petitioner] guilty." App. JA-213. The instructions also diluted the meaning of "corruptly" so that it covered innocent conduct. *Id.*, at JA-212.

The parties vigorously disputed how the jury would be instructed on "corruptly." The District Court based its instruction on the definition of that term found in the

Fifth Circuit Pattern Jury Instruction for *§ 1503*. This pattern instruction defined "corruptly" as "'knowingly and dishonestly, with the specific intent to subvert or undermine the integrity'" of a proceeding. Brief for Petitioner 3, n. 3 (emphasis deleted). The Government, however, insisted on excluding "dishonestly" and adding the term "impede" to the phrase "subvert or undermine." *Ibid.* (internal quotation marks omitted). The District Court agreed over petitioner's objections, and the jury was told [***21] to convict if it found petitioner intended to "subvert, undermine, or impede" governmental factfinding by suggesting to its employees that they enforce the document retention policy. App. JA-212.

These changes were significant. No longer was any type of "dishonesty" necessary to a finding of guilt, and it was enough for petitioner to have simply "impeded" the Government's factfinding ability. As the Government conceded at oral argument, "'impede'" has broader connotations than "'subvert'" or even "'undermine,'" see Tr. of Oral Arg. 38, and many of these connotations do not incorporate any "corruptness" at [**1019] all. The dictionary defines "impede" as "to interfere with or get in the way of the progress of" or "hold up" or "detract from." Webster's 3d 1132. By definition, anyone who innocently persuades another to withhold information from the Government "gets in the way of the progress of" the Government. With regard to such innocent conduct, the "corruptly" instructions did no limiting work whatsoever.

The instructions also were infirm for another reason. They led the jury to believe that it did not have to find *any* nexus between the "persuasion" to destroy documents and any particular [***22] proceeding. n10 In resisting any type of nexus [*2137] element, the Government relies heavily on *§ 1512(e)(1)*, which states that an official proceeding "need not be pending or about to be instituted at the time of the offense." It is, however, one thing to say that a proceeding "need not be pending or about to be instituted at the time of the offense," and quite another to say a proceeding need not even be foreseen. A "knowingly . . . corrupt persuader" cannot be someone who persuades others to shred documents under a document retention policy when he does not have in contemplation any particular official proceeding in which those documents might be material.

n10 We disagree with the Government's suggestion that petitioner's "nexus" argument is not preserved or that it is only subject to plain-error review for failure to comply with *Federal Rule of Criminal Procedure 30(d)*. Petitioner plainly argued for, and objected to the instructions' lack of, a nexus requirement. See, *e.g.*, Record 425 (arguing for a "nexus" and explaining that "it is insufficient for the government to show the defendant intended to affect some hypothetical future federal proceeding"); Record 931-932, 938; Tr. 4339-4345 (May 25, 2002). In so doing, it reasonably relied on language in *United States v. Shively, 927 F.2d 804, 812-813 (CA5 1991)*. Although the instruction petitioner proposed, based on *Shively*, does not mirror the nexus requirement it now proposes, its actions were sufficient to satisfy *Rule 30(d)*. This argument also was preserved in the Court of Appeals, which recognized that petitioner was challenging "the concreteness of the defendant's expectations of a proceeding." *374 F.3d 281, 298 (CA5 2004)*; see *United States v. Williams, 504 U.S. 36, 41-42, 118 L. Ed. 2d 352, 112 S. Ct. 1735 (1992)*. However, the Court of Appeals did not address, and petitioner did not preserve, its argument that informal inquiries are not covered by the statute. See *ibid.*

[***23]

We faced a similar situation in *Aguilar, supra, 515 U.S. 593, 132 L. Ed. 2d 520, 115 S. Ct. 2357* Respondent Aguilar lied to a Federal Bureau of Investigation agent in the course of an investigation and was convicted of "'corruptly endeavoring to influence, obstruct, and impede [a] . . . grand jury investigation'" under *§ 1503. 515 U.S., at 599, 132 L. Ed. 2d 520, 115 S. Ct. 2357*. All the Government had shown was that Aguilar had uttered false statements to an investigating agent "who might or might not testify before a grand jury." *Id., at 600, 132 L. Ed. 2d 520, 115 S. Ct. 2357*. We held that *§ 1503* required something more -- specifically, a "nexus" between the obstructive act and the proceeding. *Id., at 599-600, 132 L. Ed. 2d 520, 115 S. Ct. 2357*. "If the defendant lacks knowledge that his actions are likely to affect the judicial proceeding," we explained, "he lacks the requisite intent to obstruct." *Id., at 599, 132 L. Ed. 2d 520, 115 S. Ct. 2357*.

For these reasons, the jury instructions here were flawed in important respects. The judgment of [***24] the Court of Appeals is reversed, and the case is remanded for further proceedings consistent with this opinion.

It is so ordered.

REFERENCES: Go To Full Text Opinion

Go To Supreme Court Brief(s)

Go To Supreme Court Transcripts

U.S. Department of Justice

Office of the Deputy Attorney General

The Deputy Attorney General

Washington, D.C. 20530

January 20, 2003

<u>MEMORANDUM</u>

TO: Heads of Department Components
United States Attorneys

FROM: Larry D. Thompson
Deputy Attorney General

SUBJECT: Principles of Federal Prosecution of Business Organizations

As the Corporate Fraud Task Force has advanced in its mission, we have confronted certain issues in the principles for the federal prosecution of business organizations that require revision in order to enhance our efforts against corporate fraud. While it will be a minority of cases in which a corporation or partnership is itself subjected to criminal charges, prosecutors and investigators in every matter involving business crimes must assess the merits of seeking the conviction of the business entity itself.

Attached to this memorandum are a revised set of principles to guide Department prosecutors as they make the decision whether to seek charges against a business organization. These revisions draw heavily on the combined efforts of the Corporate Fraud Task Force and the Attorney General's Advisory Committee to put the results of more than three years of experience with the principles into practice.

The main focus of the revisions is increased emphasis on and scrutiny of the authenticity of a corporation's cooperation. Too often business organizations, while purporting to cooperate with a Department investigation, in fact take steps to impede the quick and effective exposure of the complete scope of wrongdoing under investigation. The revisions make clear that such conduct should weigh in favor of a corporate prosecution. The revisions also address the efficacy of the corporate governance mechanisms in place within a corporation, to ensure that these measures are truly effective rather than mere paper programs.

Further experience with these principles may lead to additional adjustments. I look forward to hearing comments about their operation in practice. Please forward any comments to Christopher Wray, the Principal Associate Deputy Attorney General, or to Andrew Hruska, my Senior Counsel.

<u>Federal Prosecution of Business Organizations</u>[1]

I. Charging a Corporation: General

A. General Principle: Corporations should not be treated leniently because of their artificial nature nor should they be subject to harsher treatment. Vigorous enforcement of the criminal laws against corporate wrongdoers, where appropriate results in great benefits for law enforcement and the public, particularly in the area of white collar crime. Indicting corporations for wrongdoing enables the government to address and be a force for positive change of corporate culture, alter corporate behavior, and prevent, discover, and punish white collar crime.

B. Comment: In all cases involving corporate wrongdoing, prosecutors should consider the factors discussed herein. First and foremost, prosecutors should be aware of the important public benefits that may flow from indicting a corporation in appropriate cases. For instance, corporations are likely to take immediate remedial steps when one is indicted for criminal conduct that is pervasive throughout a particular industry, and thus an indictment often provides a unique opportunity for deterrence on a massive scale. In addition, a corporate indictment may result in specific deterrence by changing the culture of the indicted corporation and the behavior of its employees. Finally, certain crimes that carry with them a substantial risk of great public harm, e.g., environmental crimes or financial frauds, are by their nature most likely to be committed by businesses, and there may, therefore, be a substantial federal interest in indicting the corporation.

Charging a corporation, however, does not mean that individual directors, officers, employees, or shareholders should not also be charged. Prosecution of a corporation is not a substitute for the prosecution of criminally culpable individuals within or without the corporation. Because a corporation can act only through individuals, imposition of individual criminal liability may provide the strongest deterrent against future corporate wrongdoing. Only rarely should provable individual culpability not be pursued, even in the face of offers of corporate guilty pleas.

Corporations are "legal persons," capable of suing and being sued, and capable of committing crimes. Under the doctrine of *respondeat superior*, a corporation may be held criminally liable for the illegal acts of its directors, officers, employees, and agents. To hold a corporation liable for these actions, the government must establish that the corporate agent's actions (i) were within the scope of his duties and (ii) were intended, at least in part, to benefit the corporation. In all cases involving wrongdoing by corporate agents, prosecutors should consider the corporation, as well as the responsible individuals, as potential criminal targets.

Agents, however, may act for mixed reasons -- both for self-aggrandizement (both direct and indirect) and for the benefit of the corporation, and a corporation may be held liable as long as one motivation of its agent is to benefit the corporation. In *United States v. Automated Medical Laboratories*, 770 F.2d 399 (4th Cir. 1985), the court affirmed the corporation's conviction for the actions of a subsidiary's employee despite its claim that the employee was acting for his own benefit, namely his "ambitious nature and his desire to ascend the corporate ladder." The court stated, "*Partucci* was clearly acting in part to benefit AML since his advancement within the corporation depended on AML's well-being and its lack of difficulties with the FDA." Similarly, in *United States v. Cincotta*, 689 F.2d 238, 241-42 (1st Cir. 1982), the court held, "criminal liability may be imposed on the corporation only where the agent is acting within the scope of his employment. That, in turn, requires that the agent be performing acts of the kind which he is authorized to perform, and those acts must be motivated -- at least in part -- by an intent to benefit the corporation." Applying this test, the court upheld the corporation's conviction, notwithstanding the substantial personal benefit reaped by its miscreant agents, because the fraudulent scheme required money to pass through the corporation's treasury and the fraudulently obtained goods were resold to the corporation's customers in the corporation's name. As the court concluded, "Mystic--not the individual defendants--was making money by selling oil that it had not paid for."

Moreover, the corporation need not even necessarily profit from its agent's actions for it to be held liable. In *Automated Medical Laboratories*, the Fourth Circuit stated:

> [B]enefit is not a "touchstone of criminal corporate liability; benefit at best is an evidential, not an operative, fact." Thus, whether the agent's actions ultimately redounded to the benefit of the corporation is less significant than whether the agent acted with the intent to benefit the corporation. The basic purpose of requiring that an agent have acted with the intent to benefit the corporation, however, is to insulate the corporation from criminal liability for actions of its agents which be inimical to the interests of the corporation or which may have been undertaken solely to advance the interests of that agent or of a party other than the corporation.

770 F.2d at 407 (emphasis added; quoting *Old Monastery Co. v. United States*, 147 F.2d 905, 908 (4th Cir.), cert. denied, 326 U.S. 734 (1945)).

II. Charging a Corporation: Factors to Be Considered

A. General Principle: Generally, prosecutors should apply the same factors in determining whether to charge a corporation as they do with respect to individuals. *See* USAM § 9-27.220, *et seq*. Thus, the prosecutor should weigh all of the factors normally considered in the sound exercise of prosecutorial judgment: the sufficiency of the evidence; the likelihood of success at trial,; the probable deterrent, rehabilitative, and other consequences of conviction; and the adequacy of noncriminal approaches. *See* id. However, due to the nature of the corporate "person," some additional factors are present. In conducting an investigation, determining whether to bring charges, and negotiating plea agreements, prosecutors should consider the following factors in reaching a decision as to the proper treatment of a corporate target:

1. the nature and seriousness of the offense, including the risk of harm to the public, and applicable policies and priorities, if any, governing the prosecution of corporations for particular categories of crime (*see* section III, *infra*);

2. the pervasiveness of wrongdoing within the corporation, including the complicity in, or condonation of, the wrongdoing by corporate management (*see* section IV, *infra*);

3. the corporation's history of similar conduct, including prior criminal, civil, and regulatory enforcement actions against it (*see* section V, *infra*);

4. the corporation's timely and voluntary disclosure of wrongdoing and its willingness to cooperate in the investigation of its agents, including, if necessary, the waiver of corporate attorney-client and work product protection (*see* section VI, *infra*);

5. the existence and adequacy of the corporation's compliance program (see section VII, *infra*);

6. the corporation's remedial actions, including any efforts to implement an effective corporate compliance program or to improve an existing one, to replace responsible management, to discipline or terminate wrongdoers, to pay restitution, and to cooperate with the relevant government agencies (*see* section VIII, *infra*);

7. collateral consequences, including disproportionate harm to shareholders, pension holders and employees not proven personally culpable and impact on the public arising from the prosecution (*see* section IX, *infra*); and

8. the adequacy of the prosecution of individuals responsible for the corporation's malfeasance;

9. the adequacy of remedies such as civil or regulatory enforcement actions (*see section X, infra*).

B. Comment: As with the factors relevant to charging natural persons, the foregoing factors are intended to provide guidance rather than to mandate a particular result. The factors listed in this section are intended to be illustrative of those that should be considered and not a complete or exhaustive list. Some or all of these factors may or may not apply to specific cases, and in some cases one factor may override all others. The nature and seriousness of the offense may be such as to warrant prosecution regardless of the other factors. Further, national law enforcement policies in various enforcement areas may require that more or less weight be given to certain of these factors than to others.

In making a decision to charge a corporation, the prosecutor generally has wide latitude in determining when, whom, how, and even whether to prosecute for violations of Federal criminal law. In exercising that discretion, prosecutors should consider the following general statements of principles that summarize appropriate considerations to be weighed and desirable practices to be followed in discharging their prosecutorial responsibilities. In doing so, prosecutors should ensure that the general purposes of the criminal law -- assurance of warranted punishment, deterrence of further criminal conduct, protection of the public from dangerous and fraudulent conduct, rehabilitation of offenders, and restitution for victims and affected communities -- are adequately met, taking into account the special nature of the corporate "person."

III. Charging a Corporation: Special Policy Concerns

A. General Principle: The nature and seriousness of the crime, including the risk of harm to the public from the criminal conduct, are obviously primary factors in determining whether to charge a corporation. In addition, corporate conduct, particularly that of national and multi-national corporations, necessarily intersects with federal economic, taxation, and criminal law enforcement policies. In applying these principles, prosecutors must consider the practices and policies of the appropriate Division of the Department, and must comply with those policies to the extent required.

B. Comment: In determining whether to charge a corporation, prosecutors should take into account federal law enforcement priorities as discussed above. *See* USAM § 9-27-230. In addition, however, prosecutors must be aware of the specific policy goals and incentive programs established by the respective Divisions and regulatory agencies. Thus, whereas natural persons may be given incremental degrees of credit (ranging from immunity to lesser charges to sentencing considerations) for turning themselves in, making statements against their penal interest, and cooperating in the government's investigation of their own and others' wrongdoing, the same approach may not be appropriate in all circumstances with respect to corporations. As an example, it is entirely proper in many investigations for a prosecutor to consider the corporation's pre-indictment conduct, *e.g.*,voluntary disclosure, cooperation, remediation or restitution, in determining whether to seek an indictment. However, this would not necessarily be appropriate in an antitrust investigation, in which antitrust violations, by definition, go to the heart of the corporation's business and for which the Antitrust Division has therefore established a firm policy, understood in the business community, that credit should not be given at the charging stage for a compliance program and that amnesty is available only to the first corporation to make full disclosure to the government. As another example, the Tax Division has a strong preference for prosecuting responsible individuals, rather than entities, for corporate tax offenses. Thus, in determining whether or not to charge a corporation, prosecutors should consult with the Criminal, Antitrust, Tax, and Environmental and Natural Resources Divisions, if appropriate or required.

IV. Charging a Corporation: Pervasiveness of Wrongdoing Within the Corporation

A. General Principle: A corporation can only act through natural persons, and it is therefore held responsible for the acts of such persons fairly attributable to it. Charging a corporation for even minor misconduct may be appropriate where the wrongdoing was pervasive and was undertaken by a large number of employees or by all the employees in a particular role within the corporation, *e.g.*, salesmen or procurement officers, or was condoned by upper management. On the other hand, in certain limited circumstances, it may not be appropriate to impose liability upon a corporation, particularly one with a compliance program in place, under a strict *respondeat superior* theory for the single isolated act of a rogue employee. There is, of course, a wide spectrum between these two extremes, and a prosecutor should exercise sound discretion in evaluating the pervasiveness of wrongdoing within a corporation.

B. Comment: Of these factors, the most important is the role of management. Although acts of even low-level employees may result in criminal liability, a corporation is directed by its management and management is responsible for a corporate culture in which criminal conduct is either discouraged or tacitly encouraged. As stated in commentary to the Sentencing Guidelines:

> Pervasiveness [is] case specific and [will] depend on the number, and degree of responsibility, of individuals [with] substantial authority ... who participated in, condoned, or were willfully ignorant of the offense. Fewer individuals need to be involved for a finding of pervasiveness if those individuals exercised a relatively high degree of authority. Pervasiveness can occur either within an organization as a whole or within a unit of an organization.

USSG §8C2.5, comment. (n. 4).

V. Charging a Corporation: The Corporation's Past History

A. General Principle: Prosecutors may consider a corporation's history of similar conduct, including prior criminal, civil, and regulatory enforcement actions against it, in determining whether to bring criminal charges.

B. Comment: A corporation, like a natural person, is expected to learn from its mistakes. A history of similar conduct may be probative of a corporate culture that encouraged, or at least condoned, such conduct, regardless of any compliance programs. Criminal prosecution of a corporation may be particularly appropriate where the corporation previously had been subject to non-criminal guidance, warnings, or sanctions, or previous criminal charges, and yet it either had not taken adequate action to prevent future unlawful conduct or had continued to engage in the conduct in spite of the warnings or enforcement actions taken against it. In making this determination, the corporate structure itself, *e.g.*, subsidiaries or operating divisions, should be ignored, and enforcement actions taken against the corporation or any of its divisions, subsidiaries, and affiliates should be considered. *See* USSG § 8C2.5(c) & comment. (n. 6).

VI. Charging a Corporation: Cooperation and Voluntary Disclosure

A. General Principle: In determining whether to charge a corporation, that corporation's timely and voluntary disclosure of wrongdoing and its willingness to cooperate with the government's investigation may be relevant factors. In gauging the extent of the corporation's cooperation, the prosecutor may consider the corporation's willingness to identify the culprits within the corporation, including senior executives; to make witnesses available; to disclose the complete results of its internal investigation; and to waive attorney-client and work product protection.

B. Comment: In investigating wrongdoing by or within a corporation, a prosecutor is likely to encounter several obstacles resulting from the nature of the corporation itself. It will often be difficult to determine which individual took which action on behalf of the corporation. Lines of authority and responsibility may be shared among operating divisions or departments, and records and personnel may be spread throughout the United States or even among several countries. Where the criminal conduct continued over an extended period of time, the culpable or knowledgeable personnel may have been promoted, transferred, or fired, or they may have quit or retired. Accordingly, a corporation's cooperation may be critical in identifying the culprits and locating relevant evidence.

In some circumstances, therefore, granting a corporation immunity or amnesty or pretrial diversion may be considered in the course of the government's investigation. In such circumstances, prosecutors should refer to the principles governing non-prosecution agreements generally. *See* USAM § 9-27.600-650. These principles permit a non prosecution agreement in exchange for cooperation when a corporation's "timely cooperation appears to be necessary to the public interest and other means of obtaining the desired cooperation are unavailable or would not be effective." Prosecutors should note that in the case of national or multi-national corporations, multi-district or global agreements may be necessary. Such agreements may only be entered into with the approval of each affected district or the appropriate Department official. See USAM §9-27.641.

In addition, the Department, in conjunction with regulatory agencies and other executive branch departments, encourages corporations, as part of their compliance programs, to conduct internal investigations and to disclose their findings to the appropriate authorities. Some agencies, such as the SEC and the EPA, as well as the Department's Environmental and Natural Resources Division, have formal voluntary disclosure programs in which self-reporting, coupled with remediation and additional criteria, may qualify the corporation for amnesty or reduced sanctions.[2] Even in the absence of a formal program, prosecutors may consider a corporation's timely and voluntary disclosure in evaluating the adequacy of the corporation's compliance program and its management's commitment to the compliance program. However, prosecution and economic policies specific to the industry or statute may require prosecution notwithstanding a corporation's willingness to cooperate. For example, the Antitrust Division offers amnesty only to the first corporation to agree to cooperate. This creates a strong incentive for corporations participating in anti-competitive conduct to be the first to cooperate. In addition, amnesty, immunity, or reduced sanctions may not be appropriate where the corporation's business is permeated with fraud or other crimes.

One factor the prosecutor may weigh in assessing the adequacy of a corporation's cooperation is the completeness of its disclosure including, if necessary, a waiver of the attorney-client and work product protections, both with respect to its internal investigation and with respect to communications between specific officers, directors and employees and counsel. Such waivers permit the government to obtain statements of possible witnesses, subjects, and targets, without having to negotiate individual cooperation or immunity agreements. In addition, they are often critical in enabling the government to evaluate the completeness of a corporation's voluntary disclosure and cooperation. Prosecutors may, therefore, request a waiver in appropriate circumstances.[3] The Department does not, however, consider waiver of a corporation's attorney-client and work product protection an absolute requirement, and prosecutors should consider the willingness of a corporation to waive such protection when necessary to provide timely and complete information as one factor in evaluating the corporation's cooperation.

Another factor to be weighed by the prosecutor is whether the corporation appears to be protecting its culpable employees and agents. Thus, while cases will differ depending on the circumstances, a corporation's promise of support to culpable employees and agents, either through the advancing of attorneys fees,[4] through retaining the employees without sanction for their misconduct, or through providing information to the employees about the government's investigation pursuant to a joint defense agreement, may be considered by the prosecutor in weighing the extent and value of a corporation's cooperation. By the same token, the prosecutor should be wary of attempts to shield corporate officers and employees from liability by a willingness of the corporation to plead guilty.

Another factor to be weighed by the prosecutor is whether the corporation, while purporting to cooperate, has engaged in conduct that impedes the investigation (whether or not rising to the level of criminal obstruction). Examples of such conduct include: overly broad assertions of corporate representation of employees or former employees; inappropriate directions to employees or their counsel, such as directions not to cooperate openly and fully with the investigation including, for example, the direction to decline to be interviewed; making presentations or submissions that contain misleading assertions or omissions; incomplete or delayed production of records; and failure to promptly disclose illegal conduct known to the corporation.

Finally, a corporation's offer of cooperation does not automatically entitle it to immunity from prosecution. A corporation should not be able to escape liability merely by offering up its directors, officers, employees, or agents as in lieu of its own prosecution. Thus, a corporation's willingness to cooperate is merely one relevant factor, that needs to be considered in conjunction with the other factors, particularly those relating to the corporation's past history and the role of management in the wrongdoing.

VII. Charging a Corporation: Corporate Compliance Programs

A. General Principle: Compliance programs are established by corporate management to prevent and to detect misconduct and to ensure that corporate activities are conducted in accordance with all applicable criminal and civil laws, regulations, and rules. The Department encourages such corporate self-policing, including voluntary disclosures to the government of any problems that a corporation discovers on its own. However, the existence of a compliance program is not sufficient, in and of itself, to justify not charging a corporation for criminal conduct undertaken by its officers, directors, employees, or agents. Indeed, the commission of such crimes in the face of a compliance program may suggest that the corporate management is not adequately enforcing its program. In addition, the nature of some crimes, *e.g.*, antitrust violations, may be such that national law enforcement policies mandate prosecutions of corporations notwithstanding the existence of a compliance program.

B. Comment: A corporate compliance program, even one specifically prohibiting the very conduct in question, does not absolve the corporation from criminal liability under the doctrine of *respondeat superior*. *See United States v. Basic Construction Co.*, 711 F.2d 570 (4th Cir. 1983) ("a corporation may be held criminally responsible for antitrust violations committed by its employees if they were acting within the scope of their authority, or apparent authority, and for the benefit of the corporation, even if... such acts were against corporate policy or express instructions."). In *United States v. Hilton Hotels Corp.*, 467 F.2d 1000 (9th Cir. 1972), *cert. denied*, 409 U.S. 1125 (1973), the Ninth Circuit affirmed antitrust liability based upon a purchasing agent for a single hotel threatening a single supplier with a boycott unless it paid dues to a local marketing association, even though the agent's actions were contrary to corporate policy and directly against express instructions from his superiors. The court reasoned that Congress, in enacting the Sherman Antitrust Act, "intended to impose liability upon business entities for the acts of those to whom they choose to delegate the conduct of their affairs, thus stimulating a maximum effort by owners and managers to assure adherence by such agents to the requirements of the Act."[5] It concluded that "general policy statements" and even direct instructions from the agent's superiors were not sufficient; "Appellant could not gain exculpation by issuing general instructions without undertaking to enforce those instructions by means commensurate with the obvious risks." *See also United States v. Beusch*, 596 F.2d 871, 878 (9th Cir. 1979) ("[A] corporation may be liable for the acts of its employees done contrary to express instructions and policies, but ... the existence of such instructions and policies may be considered in determining whether the employee in fact acted to benefit the corporation."); *United States v. American Radiator & Standard Sanitary Corp.*, 433 F.2d 174 (3rd Cir. 1970) (affirming conviction of corporation based upon its officer's participation in price-fixing scheme, despite corporation's defense that officer's conduct violated its "rigid anti-fraternization policy" against any socialization (and exchange of price information) with its competitors; "When the act of the agent is within the scope of his employment or his apparent authority, the corporation is held legally responsible for it, although what he did may be contrary to his actual instructions and may be unlawful.").

While the Department recognizes that no compliance program can ever prevent all criminal activity by a corporation's employees, the critical factors in evaluating any program are whether the program is adequately designed for maximum effectiveness in preventing and detecting wrongdoing by employees and whether corporate management is enforcing the program or is tacitly encouraging or pressuring employees to engage in misconduct to achieve business objectives. The Department has no formal guidelines for corporate compliance programs. The fundamental questions any prosecutor should ask are: "Is the corporation's compliance program well designed?" and "Does the corporation's compliance program work?" In answering these questions, the prosecutor should consider the comprehensiveness of the compliance program; the extent and pervasiveness of the criminal conduct; the number and level of the corporate employees involved; the seriousness, duration, and frequency of the misconduct; and any remedial actions taken by the corporation, including restitution, disciplinary action, and revisions to corporate compliance programs.[6] Prosecutors should also consider the promptness of any disclosure of wrongdoing to the government and the corporation's cooperation in the government's investigation. In evaluating compliance programs, prosecutors may consider whether the corporation has established corporate governance mechanisms that can effectively detect and prevent misconduct. For example, do the corporation's directors exercise independent review over proposed corporate actions rather than unquestioningly ratifying officers' recommendations; are the directors provided with information sufficient to enable the exercise of independent judgment, are internal audit functions conducted at a level sufficient to ensure their independence and accuracy and have the directors established an information and reporting system in the organization reasonable designed to provide management and the board of directors with timely and accurate information sufficient to allow them to reach an informed decision regarding the organization's compliance with the law. *In re: Caremark*, 698 A.2d 959 (Del. Ct. Chan. 1996).

Prosecutors should therefore attempt to determine whether a corporation's compliance program is merely a "paper program" or whether it was designed and implemented in an effective manner. In addition, prosecutors should determine whether the corporation has provided for a staff sufficient to audit, document, analyze, and utilize the results of the corporation's compliance efforts. In addition, prosecutors should determine whether the corporation's employees are adequately informed about the compliance program and are convinced of the corporation's commitment to it. This will enable the prosecutor to make an informed decision as to whether the corporation has adopted and implemented a truly effective compliance program that, when consistent with other federal law enforcement policies, may result in a decision to charge only the corporation's employees and agents.

Compliance programs should be designed to detect the particular types of misconduct most likely to occur in a particular corporation's line of business. Many corporations operate in complex regulatory environments outside the normal experience of criminal prosecutors. Accordingly, prosecutors should consult with relevant federal and state agencies with the expertise to evaluate the adequacy of a program's design and implementation. For instance, state and federal banking, insurance, and medical boards, the Department of Defense, the Department of Health and Human Services, the Environmental Protection Agency, and the Securities and Exchange Commission have considerable experience with compliance programs and can be very helpful to a prosecutor in evaluating such programs. In addition, the Fraud Section of the Criminal Division, the Commercial Litigation Branch of the Civil Division, and the Environmental Crimes Section of the Environment and Natural Resources Division can assist U.S. Attorneys' Offices in finding the appropriate agency office and in providing copies of compliance programs that were developed in previous cases.

VIII. Charging a Corporation: Restitution and Remediation

A. General Principle: Although neither a corporation nor an individual target may avoid prosecution merely by paying a sum of money, a prosecutor may consider the corporation's willingness to make restitution and steps already taken to do so. A prosecutor may also consider other remedial actions, such as implementing an effective corporate compliance program, improving an existing compliance program, and disciplining wrongdoers, in determining whether to charge the corporation.

B. Comment: In determining whether or not a corporation should be prosecuted, a prosecutor may consider whether meaningful remedial measures have been taken, including employee discipline and full restitution.[7] A corporation's response to misconduct says much about its willingness to ensure that such misconduct does not recur. Thus, corporations that fully recognize the seriousness of their misconduct and accept responsibility for it should be taking steps to implement the personnel, operational, and organizational changes necessary to establish an awareness among employees that criminal conduct will not be tolerated. Among the factors prosecutors should consider and weigh are whether the corporation appropriately disciplined the wrongdoers and disclosed information concerning their illegal conduct to the government.

Employee discipline is a difficult task for many corporations because of the human element involved and sometimes because of the seniority of the employees concerned. While corporations need to be fair to their employees, they must also be unequivocally committed, at all levels of the corporation, to the highest standards of legal and ethical behavior. Effective internal discipline can be a powerful deterrent against improper behavior by a corporation's employees. In evaluating a corporation's response to wrongdoing, prosecutors may evaluate the willingness of the corporation to discipline culpable employees of all ranks and the adequacy of the discipline imposed. The prosecutor should be satisfied that the corporation's focus is on the integrity and credibility of its remedial and disciplinary measures rather than on the protection of the wrongdoers.

In addition to employee discipline, two other factors used in evaluating a corporation's remedial efforts are restitution and reform. As with natural persons, the decision whether or not to prosecute should not depend upon the target's ability to pay restitution. A corporation's efforts to pay restitution even in advance of any court order is, however, evidence of its "acceptance of responsibility" and, consistent with the practices and policies of the appropriate Division of the Department entrusted with enforcing specific criminal laws, may be considered in determining whether to bring criminal charges. Similarly, although the inadequacy of a corporate compliance program is a factor to consider when deciding whether to charge a corporation, that corporation's quick recognition of the flaws in the program and its efforts to improve the program are also factors to consider.

IX. Charging a Corporation: Collateral Consequences

A. General Principle: Prosecutors may consider the collateral consequences of a corporate criminal conviction in determining whether to charge the corporation with a criminal offense.

B. Comment: One of the factors in determining whether to charge a natural person or a corporation is whether the likely punishment is appropriate given the nature and seriousness of the crime. In the corporate context, prosecutors may take into account the possibly substantial consequences to a corporation's officers, directors, employees, and shareholders, many of whom may, depending on the size and nature (e.g., publicly vs. closely held) of the corporation and their role in its operations, have played no role in the criminal conduct, have been completely unaware of it, or have been wholly unable to prevent it. Prosecutors should also be aware of non-penal sanctions that may accompany a criminal charge, such as potential suspension or debarment from eligibility for government contracts or federal funded programs such as health care. Whether or not such non-penal sanctions are appropriate or required in a particular case is the responsibility of the relevant agency, a decision that will be made based on the applicable statutes, regulations, and policies.

Virtually every conviction of a corporation, like virtually every conviction of an individual, will have an impact on innocent third parties, and the mere existence of such an effect is not sufficient to preclude prosecution of the corporation. Therefore, in evaluating the severity of collateral consequences, various factors already discussed, such as the pervasiveness of the criminal conduct and the adequacy of the corporation's compliance programs, should be considered in determining the weight to be given to this factor. For instance, the balance may tip in favor of prosecuting corporations in situations where the scope of the misconduct in a case is widespread and sustained within a corporate division (or spread throughout pockets of the corporate organization). In such cases, the possible unfairness of visiting punishment for the corporation's crimes upon shareholders may be of much less concern where those shareholders have substantially profited, even unknowingly, from widespread or pervasive criminal activity. Similarly, where the top layers of the corporation's management or the shareholders of a closely-held corporation were engaged in or aware of the wrongdoing and the conduct at issue was accepted as a way of doing business for an extended period, debarment may be deemed not collateral, but a direct and entirely appropriate consequence of the corporation's wrongdoing.

The appropriateness of considering such collateral consequences and the weight to be given them may depend on the special policy concerns discussed in section III, *supra*.

X. Charging a Corporation: Non-Criminal Alternatives

A. General Principle: Although non-criminal alternatives to prosecution often exist, prosecutors may consider whether such sanctions would adequately deter, punish, and rehabilitate a corporation that has engaged in wrongful conduct. In evaluating the adequacy of non-criminal alternatives to prosecution, *e.g.*, civil or regulatory enforcement actions, the prosecutor may consider all relevant factors, including:

1. the sanctions available under the alternative means of disposition;

2. the likelihood that an effective sanction will be imposed; and

3. the effect of non-criminal disposition on Federal law enforcement interests.

B. Comment: The primary goals of criminal law are deterrence, punishment, and rehabilitation. Non-criminal sanctions may not be an appropriate response to an egregious violation, a pattern of wrongdoing, or a history of non-criminal sanctions without proper remediation. In other cases, however, these goals may be satisfied without the necessity of instituting criminal proceedings. In determining whether federal criminal charges are appropriate, the prosecutor should consider the same factors (modified appropriately for the regulatory context) considered when determining whether to leave prosecution of a natural person to another jurisdiction or to seek non-criminal alternatives to prosecution. These factors include: the strength of the regulatory authority's interest; the regulatory authority's ability and willingness to take effective enforcement action; the probable sanction if the regulatory authority's enforcement action is upheld; and the effect of a non-criminal disposition on Federal law enforcement interests. *See* USAM §§ 9-27.240, 9-27.250.

XI. Charging a Corporation: Selecting Charges

A. General Principle: Once a prosecutor has decided to charge a corporation, the prosecutor should charge, or should recommend that the grand jury charge, the most serious offense that is consistent with the nature of the defendant's conduct and that is likely to result in a sustainable conviction.

B. Comment: Once the decision to charge is made, the same rules as govern charging natural persons apply. These rules require "a faithful and honest application of the Sentencing Guidelines" and an "individualized assessment of the extent to which particular charges fit the specific circumstances of the case, are consistent with the purposes of the Federal criminal code, and maximize the impact of Federal resources on crime." *See* USAM § 9-27.300. In making this determination, "it is appropriate that the attorney for the government consider, *inter alia*, such factors as the sentencing guideline range yielded by the charge, whether the penalty yielded by such sentencing range ... is proportional to the seriousness of the defendant's conduct, and whether the charge achieves such purposes of the criminal law as punishment, protection of the public, specific and general deterrence, and rehabilitation." *See* Attorney General's Memorandum, dated October 12, 1993.

XII. Plea Agreements with Corporations

A. General Principle: In negotiating plea agreements with corporations, prosecutors should seek a plea to the most serious, readily provable offense charged. In addition, the terms of the plea agreement should contain appropriate provisions to ensure punishment, deterrence, rehabilitation, and compliance with the plea agreement in the corporate context. Although special circumstances may mandate a different conclusion, prosecutors generally should not agree to accept a corporate guilty plea in exchange for non-prosecution or dismissal of charges against individual officers and employees.

B. Comment: Prosecutors may enter into plea agreements with corporations for the same reasons and under the same constraints as apply to plea agreements with natural persons. *See* USAM §§ 9-27.400-500. This means, *inter alia*, that the corporation should be required to plead guilty to the most serious, readily provable offense charged. As is the case with individuals, the attorney making this determination should do so "on the basis of an individualized assessment of the extent to which particular charges fit the specific circumstances of the case, are consistent with the purposes of the federal criminal code, and maximize the impact of federal resources on crime. In making this determination, the attorney for the government considers, inter alia, such factors as the sentencing guideline range yielded by the charge, whether the penalty yielded by such sentencing range ... is proportional to the seriousness of the defendant's conduct, and whether the charge achieves such purposes of the criminal law as punishment, protection of the public, specific and general deterrence, and rehabilitation." *See* Attorney General's Memorandum, dated October 12, 1993. In addition, any negotiated departures from the Sentencing Guidelines must be justifiable under the Guidelines and must be disclosed to the sentencing court. A corporation should be made to realize that pleading guilty to criminal charges constitutes an admission of guilt and not merely a resolution of an inconvenient distraction from its business. As with natural persons, pleas should be structured so that the corporation may not later "proclaim lack of culpability or even complete innocence." *See* USAM §§ 9-27.420(b)(4), 9-27.440, 9-27.500. Thus, for instance, there should be placed upon the record a sufficient factual basis for the plea to prevent later corporate assertions of innocence.

A corporate plea agreement should also contain provisions that recognize the nature of the corporate "person" and ensure that the principles of punishment, deterrence, and rehabilitation are met. In the corporate context, punishment and deterrence are generally accomplished by substantial fines, mandatory restitution, and institution of appropriate compliance measures, including, if necessary, continued judicial oversight or the use of special masters. *See* USSG §§ 8B1.1, 8C2.1, *et seq.* In addition, where the corporation is a government contractor, permanent or temporary debarment may be appropriate. Where the corporation was engaged in government contracting fraud, a prosecutor may not negotiate away an agency's right to debar or to list the corporate defendant.

In negotiating a plea agreement, prosecutors should also consider the deterrent value of prosecutions of individuals within the corporation. Therefore, one factor that a prosecutor may consider in determining whether to enter into a plea agreement is whether the corporation is seeking immunity for its employees and officers or whether the corporation is willing to cooperate in the investigation of culpable individuals. Prosecutors should rarely negotiate away individual criminal liability in a corporate plea.

Rehabilitation, of course, requires that the corporation undertake to be law-abiding in the future. It is, therefore, appropriate to require the corporation, as a condition of probation, to implement a compliance program or to reform an existing one. As discussed above, prosecutors may consult with the appropriate state and federal agencies and components of the Justice Department to ensure that a proposed compliance program is adequate and meets industry standards and best practices. *See* section VII, *supra*.

In plea agreements in which the corporation agrees to cooperate, the prosecutor should ensure that the cooperation is complete and truthful. To do so, the prosecutor may request that the corporation waive attorney-client and work product protection, make employees and agents available for debriefing, disclose the results of its internal investigation, file appropriate certified financial statements, agree to governmental or third-party audits, and take whatever other steps are necessary to ensure that the full scope of the corporate wrongdoing is disclosed and that the responsible culprits are identified and, if appropriate, prosecuted. *See* generally section VIII, *supra*.

Footnotes:

1. While these guidelines refer to corporations, they apply to the consideration of the prosecution of all types of business organizations, including partnerships, sole proprietorships, government entities, and unincorporated associations.

2. In addition, the Sentencing Guidelines reward voluntary disclosure and cooperation with a reduction in the corporation's offense level. *See* USSG §8C2.5)g).

3. This waiver should ordinarily be limited to the factual internal investigation and any contemporaneous advice given to the corporation concerning the conduct at issue. Except in unusual circumstances, prosecutors should not seek a waiver with respect to communications and work product related to advice concerning the government's criminal investigation.

4. Some states require corporations to pay the legal fees of officers under investigation prior to a formal determination of their guilt. Obviously, a corporation's compliance with governing law should not be considered a failure to cooperate.

5. Although this case and *Basic Construction* are both antitrust cases, their reasoning applies to other criminal violations. In the Hilton case, for instance, the Ninth Circuit noted that Sherman Act violations are commercial offenses "usually motivated by a desire to enhance profits," thus, bringing the case within the normal rule that a "purpose to benefit the corporation is necessary to bring the agent's acts within the scope of his employment." 467 F.2d at 1006 & n4. In addition, in *United States v. Automated Medical Laboratories*, 770 F.2d 399, 406 n.5 (4th Cir. 1985), the Fourth Circuit stated "that Basic Construction states a generally applicable rule on corporate criminal liability despite the fact that it addresses violations of the antitrust laws."

6. For a detailed review of these and other factors concerning corporate compliance programs, see United States Sentencing Commission, GUIDELINES MANUAL, §8A1.2, comment. (n.3(k)) (Nov. 1997). *See* also USSG §8C2.5(f)

7. For example, the Antitrust Division's amnesty policy requires that "[w]here possible, the corporation [make] restitution to injured parties...."

SECURITIES AND EXCHANGE COMMISSION

SECURITIES EXCHANGE ACT OF 1934
Release No. 44969 / October 23, 2001

ACCOUNTING AND AUDITING ENFORCEMENT
Release No. 1470 / October 23, 2001

Report of Investigation Pursuant to Section 21(a) of the Securities Exchange Act of 1934 and Commission Statement on the Relationship of Cooperation to Agency Enforcement Decisions

Today, we commence and settle a cease-and-desist proceeding against Gisela de Leon-Meredith, former controller of a public company's subsidiary.[1] Our order finds that Meredith caused the parent company's books and records to be inaccurate and its periodic reports misstated, and then covered up those facts.

We are not taking action against the parent company, given the nature of the conduct and the company's responses. Within a week of learning about the apparent misconduct, the company's internal auditors had conducted a preliminary review and had advised company management who, in turn, advised the Board's audit committee, that Meredith had caused the company's books and records to be inaccurate and its financial reports to be misstated. The full Board was advised and authorized the company to hire an outside law firm to conduct a thorough inquiry. Four days later, Meredith was dismissed, as were two other employees who, in the company's view, had inadequately supervised Meredith; a day later, the company disclosed publicly and to us that its financial statements would be restated. The price of the company's shares did not decline after the announcement or after the restatement was published. The company pledged and gave complete cooperation to our staff. It provided the staff with all information relevant to the underlying violations. Among other things, the company produced the details of its internal investigation, including notes and transcripts of interviews of Meredith and others; and it did not invoke the attorney-client privilege, work product protection or other privileges or protections with respect to any facts uncovered in the investigation.

The company also strengthened its financial reporting processes to address Meredith's conduct -- developing a detailed closing process for the subsidiary's accounting personnel, consolidating subsidiary accounting functions under a parent company CPA, hiring three new CPAs for the accounting department responsible for preparing the subsidiary's financial statements, redesigning the subsidiary's minimum annual audit requirements, and requiring the parent company's controller to interview and approve all senior accounting personnel in its subsidiaries' reporting processes.

Our willingness to credit such behavior in deciding whether and how to take enforcement action benefits investors as well as our enforcement program.

When businesses seek out, self-report and rectify illegal conduct, and otherwise cooperate with Commission staff, large expenditures of government and shareholder resources can be avoided and investors can benefit more promptly.[2] In setting forth the criteria listed below, we think a few caveats are in order:

First, the paramount issue in every enforcement judgment is, and must be, what best protects investors. There is no single, or constant, answer to that question. Self-policing, self-reporting, remediation and cooperation with law enforcement authorities, among other things, are unquestionably important in promoting investors' best interests. But, so too are vigorous enforcement and the imposition of appropriate sanctions where the law has been violated. Indeed, there may be circumstances where conduct is so egregious, and harm so great, that no amount of cooperation or other mitigating conduct can justify a decision not to bring any enforcement action at all. In the end, no set of criteria can, or should, be strictly applied in every situation to which they may be applicable.

Second, we are not adopting any rule or making any commitment or promise about any specific case; nor are we in any way limiting our broad discretion to evaluate every case individually, on its own particular facts and circumstances. Conversely, we are not conferring any "rights" on any person or entity. We seek only to convey an understanding of the factors that may influence our decisions.

Third, we do not limit ourselves to the criteria we discuss below. By definition, enforcement judgments are just that -- judgments. Our failure to mention a specific criterion in one context does not preclude us from relying on that criterion in another. Further, the fact that a company has satisfied all the criteria we list below will not foreclose us from bringing enforcement proceedings that we believe are necessary or appropriate, for the benefit of investors.

In brief form, we set forth below some of the criteria we will consider in determining whether, and how much, to credit self-policing, self-reporting, remediation and cooperation -- from the extraordinary step of taking no enforcement action to bringing reduced charges, seeking lighter sanctions, or including mitigating language in documents we use to announce and resolve enforcement actions.

1. What is the nature of the misconduct involved? Did it result from inadvertence, honest mistake, simple negligence, reckless or deliberate indifference to indicia of wrongful conduct, willful misconduct or unadorned venality? Were the company's auditors misled?

2. How did the misconduct arise? Is it the result of pressure placed on employees to achieve specific results, or a tone of lawlessness set by those in control of the company? What compliance procedures were in place to prevent the misconduct now uncovered? Why did those procedures fail to stop or inhibit the wrongful conduct?

3. Where in the organization did the misconduct occur? How high up in the chain of command was knowledge of, or participation in, the misconduct? Did senior personnel participate in, or turn a blind eye toward, obvious indicia of misconduct? How systemic was the behavior? Is it symptomatic of the way the entity does business, or was it isolated?

4. How long did the misconduct last? Was it a one-quarter, or one-time, event, or did it last several years? In the case of a public company, did the misconduct occur before the company went public? Did it facilitate the company's ability to go public?

5. How much harm has the misconduct inflicted upon investors and other corporate constituencies? Did the share price of the company's stock drop significantly upon its discovery and disclosure?

6. How was the misconduct detected and who uncovered it?

7. How long after discovery of the misconduct did it take to implement an effective response?

8. What steps did the company take upon learning of the misconduct? Did the company immediately stop the misconduct? Are persons responsible for any misconduct still with the company? If so, are they still in the same positions? Did the company promptly, completely and effectively disclose the existence of the misconduct to the public, to regulators and to self-regulators? Did the company cooperate completely with appropriate regulatory and law enforcement bodies? Did the company identify what additional related misconduct is likely to have occurred? Did the company take steps to identify the extent of damage to investors and other corporate constituencies? Did the company appropriately recompense those adversely affected by the conduct?

9. What processes did the company follow to resolve many of these issues and ferret out necessary information? Were the Audit Committee and the Board of Directors fully informed? If so, when?

10. Did the company commit to learn the truth, fully and expeditiously? Did it do a thorough review of the nature, extent, origins and consequences of the conduct and related behavior? Did management, the Board or committees consisting solely of outside directors oversee the review? Did company employees or outside persons perform the review? If outside persons, had they done other work for the company? Where the review was conducted by outside counsel, had management previously engaged such counsel? Were scope limitations placed on the review? If so, what were they?

11. Did the company promptly make available to our staff the results of its review and provide sufficient documentation reflecting its response to the situation? Did the company identify possible violative conduct and evidence with sufficient precision to facilitate prompt enforcement actions against those who violated the law? Did the company produce a thorough and probing written report detailing the findings of its review? Did the company voluntarily disclose information our staff did not directly request and otherwise might not have uncovered? Did the company ask its employees to cooperate with our staff and make all reasonable efforts to secure such cooperation?[3]

12. What assurances are there that the conduct is unlikely to recur? Did the company adopt and ensure enforcement of new and more effective internal controls and procedures designed to prevent a recurrence of the misconduct? Did the company provide our staff with sufficient information for it to evaluate the company's measures to correct the situation and ensure that the conduct does not recur?

13. Is the company the same company in which the misconduct occurred, or has it changed through a merger or bankruptcy reorganization?

We hope that this Report of Investigation and Commission Statement will further encourage self-policing efforts and will promote more self-reporting, remediation and cooperation with the Commission staff. We welcome the constructive input of all interested persons. We urge those who have contributions to make to direct them to our Division of Enforcement. The public can be confident that all such communications will be fairly evaluated not only by our staff, but also by us. We continue to reassess our enforcement approaches with the aim of maximizing the benefits of our program to investors and the marketplace.

By the Commission (Chairman Pitt, Commissioner Hunt, Commissioner Unger).

Footnotes

1 *In the Matter of Gisela de Leon-Meredith*, Exchange Act Release No. 44970 (October 23, 2001).

2 We note that the federal securities laws and other legal requirements and guidance also promote and even require a certain measure of self-policing, self-reporting and remediation. *See, e.g.*, Section 10A of the Securities Exchange Act of 1934, 15 U.S.C. § 78j-1 (requiring issuers and auditors to report certain illegal conduct to the Commission); *In the Matter of W.R. Grace & Co.*, Exchange Act Release No. 39157 (Sept. 30, 1997) (emphasizing the affirmative responsibilities of corporate officers and directors to ensure that shareholders receive accurate and complete disclosure of information required by the proxy solicitation and periodic reporting provisions of the federal securities laws); *In the Matter of Cooper Companies, Inc.*, Exchange Act Release No. 35082 (Dec. 12, 1994) (emphasizing responsibility of corporate directors in safeguarding the integrity of a company's public statements and the interests of investors when evidence of fraudulent conduct by corporate management comes to their attention); *In the Matter of John Gutfreund*, Exchange Act Release No. 31554 (Dec. 3, 1992) (sanctions imposed against supervisors at broker-dealer for failing promptly to bring misconduct to attention of the government). *See also Federal Sentencing Guidelines* § 8C2.5(f) & (g) (organization's "culpability score" decreases if organization has an effective program to prevent and detect violations of law or if organization reports offense to governmental authorities prior to imminent threat of disclosure or government investigation and within reasonably prompt time after becoming aware of the offense); *New York Stock Exchange Rules* 342.21 & 351(e) (members and member organizations required to review certain trades for compliance with rules against insider trading and manipulation, to conduct prompt internal investigations of any potentially violative trades, and to report the status and/or results of such internal investigations).

3 In some cases, the desire to provide information to the Commission staff may cause companies to consider choosing not to assert the attorney-client privilege, the work product protection and other privileges, protections and exemptions with respect to the Commission. The Commission recognizes that these privileges, protections and exemptions serve important social interests. In this regard, the Commission does not view a company's waiver

of a privilege as an end in itself, but only as a means (where necessary) to provide relevant and sometimes critical information to the Commission staff. Thus, the Commission recently filed an *amicus* brief arguing that the provision of privileged information to the Commission staff pursuant to a confidentiality agreement did not necessarily waive the privilege as to third parties. *Brief of SEC as Amicus Curiae, McKesson HBOC, Inc.*, No. 99-C-7980-3 (Ga. Ct. App. Filed May 13, 2001). Moreover, in certain circumstances, the Commission staff has agreed that a witness' production of privileged information would not constitute a subject matter waiver that would entitle the staff to receive further privileged information.

http://www.sec.gov/litigation/investreport/34-44969.htm

AGREEMENT BETWEEN SYMBOL TECHNOLOGIES, INC. AND
THE U. S. ATTORNEY'S OFFICE FOR THE EASTERN DISTRICT OF NEW YORK

SYMBOL TECHNOLOGIES, INC. ("Symbol"), by its undersigned attorneys, pursuant to authority granted by its Board of Directors, and the UNITED STATES ATTORNEY'S OFFICE FOR THE EASTERN DISTRICT OF NEW YORK (the "Office"), hereby enter into this Agreement (the "Agreement"). Except as specifically provided below, the Agreement shall be in effect for a period of three years from the date it is fully signed and executed.

1. The Office has informed Symbol that it is a target of an investigation being conducted by a grand jury sitting in the Eastern District of New York, with the assistance of the United States Postal Inspection Service (the "Postal Inspection Service"), involving accounting and financial fraud at Symbol. Symbol also has been informed by the United States Securities and Exchange Commission (the "SEC") that the SEC also is conducting an investigation of Symbol's accounting practices (the "SEC Investigation").

2. Symbol acknowledges that, as set forth in detail in Exhibit A, in or about and between 1999 and 2002, as a result of the conduct of certain Symbol officers, executives and employees, Symbol (a) violated federal criminal law in connection with accounting practices involving fabricated and other improper sales transactions, unsupported and fictitious accounting entries and the manipulation of Symbol's accounting reserves and expenses; and (b) filed and caused to be filed materially false and misleading financial statements and other documents with the SEC (collectively, "the Unlawful Practices").

3. Symbol accepts responsibility for its conduct by entering into this Agreement and by, among other things, the remedial actions that it has taken to date, its continuing

commitment to full cooperation with the Office, the Postal Inspection Service and the SEC (collectively, the "Investigative Entities"), and the other undertakings it has made as set forth in this Agreement.

4. In March 2002, Symbol retained the law firm Swidler Berlin Shereff Friedman, LLP to conduct an internal investigation into Symbol's accounting and financial practices. The investigation was conducted with the assistance of an outside forensic accounting team and involved more than 200 interviews and the review of hundreds of thousands of pages of documents and emails. Pursuant to the agreement among the Office, the SEC and Symbol dated November 19, 2002 (the "Confidential Materials Agreement"), Symbol has shared the results of its investigation, including documents that could have otherwise been withheld under the attorney-client privilege and the work product doctrine, with the Investigative Entities. Symbol acknowledges that its prior, ongoing and future cooperation are important factors in the Office's decision to enter into the Agreement, and therefore, Symbol agrees to continue to cooperate fully with the Investigative Entities regarding any matter about which Symbol has knowledge.

5. Symbol agrees that its cooperation shall include, but is not limited to, the following:

(a) Completely and truthfully disclosing all information in its possession to the Investigative Entities about which the Investigative Entities may inquire;

(b) Assembling, organizing and providing all documents, records, or other tangible materials in Symbol's possession, custody, or control as reasonably may be requested by any of the Investigative Entities, including, without limitation, "Confidential Materials" as that term is defined in the Confidential Materials Agreement, which is incorporated by reference herein and attached hereto as Exhibit B;

(c) Providing any documents, records, information, or testimony requested by the Office, to the extent provided for and pursuant to the terms of the Confidential Materials Agreement;

(d) Using its reasonable best efforts to make available its present and former employees to provide information and/or testimony as requested by any of the Investigative Entities, including, without limitation, sworn testimony in court proceedings, as well as interviews with law enforcement authorities. Cooperation under this paragraph shall include identification of witnesses who, to Symbol's knowledge, may have material information regarding its conduct;

(e) Providing testimony and other information deemed necessary by any of the Investigative Entities or a court to establish the evidentiary foundation necessary to admit into evidence documents in any criminal or other proceeding; and

(f) With respect to any information, testimony, document, record or other tangible material provided by Symbol to the Office or a grand jury, other than the Confidential Materials, Symbol consents to any and all disclosures of such materials to any other governmental agency designated by the Office as the Office, in its sole discretion, deems appropriate. With respect to any such materials that constitute "matters occurring before the grand jury" within the meaning of Rule 6(e) of the Federal Rules of Criminal Procedure, Symbol further consents to (a) any order sought by the Office permitting such disclosures; and (b) the Office's ex parte or in camera application for such orders.

6. Symbol agrees to pay a total of $139 million in stock and cash for purposes of compensation of shareholders for losses arising out of and in connection with the Unlawful Practices ("the Compensation Fund"), including for the resolution of the SEC Investigation and the pending class action litigations before the United States District Court, Eastern District of New York, entitled In re Symbol Technologies Litigation, 02 CV 1383 (LDW), Hoyle v. Symbol Technologies, Inc., 03 CV 1394 (LDW) and Salerno v. Symbol Technologies, Inc., 03 CV 2208 (LDW) (the "Shareholder Litigation"). The Compensation Fund shall be distributed in accordance with the final orders of the District Court overseeing the Shareholder Litigation. As part of the Compensation Fund, Symbol agrees to pay $37 million in cash in accordance with the terms of a Final Consent Judgment of Permanent Injunction and Other Relief as to Defendant Symbol Technologies, Inc., which will be submitted to the Court in the civil action that the SEC will commence against Symbol with respect to the Unlawful Practices (the "Cash Fund Payment").

7. Symbol shall ensure that any settlement agreement in the Shareholder Litigation shall provide that no portion of the Cash Fund Payment shall be disbursed to pay any attorney's fee or expenses arising out of or in connection with the Shareholder Litigation. Symbol also agrees that any such settlement agreement shall provide that the amount of the Cash Fund Payment shall not be used in any way to calculate or determine the amount of attorney's fees or expenses to be paid to counsel for the plaintiffs in the Shareholder Litigation or to

counsel for any other private parties seeking distribution of any portion of the Cash Fund Payment. Symbol further agrees that any settlement agreement in the Shareholder Litigation shall contain provisions necessary to effectuate the provisions of this paragraph.

8. Symbol also agrees to pay $3 million by certified check or bank cashier's check to the United States Postal Inspection Service Consumer Fraud Fund immediately upon execution of this Agreement.

9. Symbol represents that its Board of Directors and current Senior Management have taken numerous remedial actions in response to the misconduct at Symbol that has been discovered by its internal investigation and the investigations conducted by the Investigative Entities. These remedial actions (collectively, the "Remedial Actions, Policies and Procedures") include:

a. the termination of employees at all levels of the company whose improper activities and/or lax supervision resulted in improper accounting and inaccurate financial reporting;

b. the termination of employees who refused to cooperate with the Symbol's internal investigation or who took steps to obstruct or impede that investigation;

c. the appointment of new management, including a new President and Chief Executive Officer, a new Chief Financial Officer, new Senior Vice Presidents of Finance, Sales, Operations, Global Products and Customer Service, a new General Counsel and Secretary and a new Chief Information Officer;

d. the dismissal of its former auditing firm and the retention of a new firm;

e. the formation of a new Disclosure Committee composed of the Chief Executive Officer, President and Chief Operating Officer, Chief Financial Officer, Senior Vice President - Finance and Business Controller, Chief Accounting Officer and General Counsel, that meets prior to significant filings with the SEC and the issuance of significant press releases;

f. the restructuring of the Board of Directors, including the splitting of the Chief Executive Officer and Chairman functions and the appointment of a non-executive Chairman;

g. the revision of the Board of Director's Audit Committee charter to grant the Audit Committee greater responsibility and authority to oversee financial matters;

h. the implementation of numerous new accounting and financial controls, including the centralization of Symbol's finance functions, the commitment to spend approximately $100 million to upgrade the company's accounting and data management processes, the establishment of a formal review process for all large-dollar transactions and for other non-standard transactions, and the strengthening of the internal audit and month-end review process; and,

i. the creation and maintenance of a confidential hotline to provide a means for employees anonymously to report any potential violations of law or other misconduct.

10. Symbol agrees that it will establish and maintain a training and education program for certain of its directors, officers and employees designed to minimize the possibility of future violations of the federal securities laws by Symbol. Completion of such training shall be mandatory for (a) members of the Audit Committee of Symbol's Board of Directors; (b) all

Symbol officers, executives and employees who are involved in accounting and financial reporting functions, whether at the corporate or the division level, including but not limited to each officer or employee responsible for closing the books within his or her area of responsibility at the end of a quarterly or annual reporting period; and (c) all senior operational officers and executives at Symbol, at both the corporate and division level (the "Mandatory Participants"). Such training and education program will cover, at a minimum, the following subjects: the obligations imposed by the federal securities laws; proper internal accounting controls and procedures; discovering and recognizing indications of fraud and accounting practices that do not conform to Generally Accepted Accounting Practices or that are otherwise improper; and the obligations assumed by, and responses expected of, Symbol's directors, officers and employees upon learning of improper, illegal or potentially illegal acts relating to Symbol's accounting and financial reporting. Symbol shall commence providing the training mandated by this paragraph within 60 days after the date of the execution of this Agreement and shall, at that time, submit to the Office a written description of the content and planned implementation of the training and education program. Following the completion of the required training and education for all Mandatory Participants, Symbol shall continue to provide such training and education on an annual basis for all those who become Mandatory Participants during the preceding twelve months.

11. Symbol agrees that during the term of this Agreement it will retain an independent examiner that is acceptable to the Office and the Staff of the SEC (the "Independent Examiner"), to monitor Symbol's internal controls and financial reporting

practices and its compliance with this Agreement. The Independent Examiner will, among other things, and without limitation on any other obligation imposed by law:

(a) annually review Symbol's revenue recognition and accounting practices;

(b) annually review Symbol's internal accounting control structure and systems (the Independent Examiner, in determining the scope of any subsequent annual internal control review, may in its discretion rely on the results of its prior annual review in this area);

(c) annually review Symbol's implementation of, and compliance with, the Remedial Actions, Policies and Procedures; and

(d) report on an annual basis to the General Counsel of Symbol, the Office and the Staff of the SEC as to the propriety of Symbol's revenue recognition and accounting practices, the effectiveness of its internal accounting control structure and systems, and the effectiveness of the Remedial Actions, Policies and Procedures (each such report being referred to as the "Report").

After receiving each Report, Symbol's General Counsel will present the Report to Symbol's Board of Directors, including its Audit Committee, for their review. Copies of the Report shall also be submitted to the Office and the Staff of the SEC on an annual basis. Symbol agrees that the Independent Examiner will have access to any and all materials relating to Symbol's business and that all Symbol employees will be directed to cooperate fully with the Independent Examiner.

12. In consideration of Symbol's (a) acceptance of responsibility for its conduct as acknowledged herein; (b) cooperation-to-date and agreement to continue to cooperate with

the Investigative Entities; (c) agreement to make the payments set forth in paragraphs 6-8 above; (d) implementation of the Remedial Actions, Policies and Procedures; and (e) agreement otherwise to comply with all of the terms of this Agreement, the Office agrees that, except as provided in paragraphs 13-16 below, Symbol will not be prosecuted for the Unlawful Practices.

13. Symbol understands and agrees that should the Office, in its sole discretion, determine that Symbol deliberately has given false, incomplete, or misleading information under this Agreement, has otherwise deliberately violated any provisions of the Agreement or has committed, or attempted to commit, any crimes other than crimes relating to the Unlawful Practices, Symbol shall thereafter be subject to prosecution for any federal criminal violation of which the Office has knowledge, including a prosecution relating to the Unlawful Practices. Moreover, Symbol agrees that any prosecution relating to the Unlawful Practices that is not time-barred by the applicable statute of limitations on the date of this Agreement may be commenced against Symbol in accordance with this Agreement, notwithstanding the expiration of any statute of limitations. By this Agreement, Symbol expressly intends to and does waive any rights in this respect. Such waiver is knowing, voluntary and in express reliance on the advice of Symbol's counsel.

14. Symbol further understands and agrees that in the event that the Office, in its sole discretion, determines that Symbol has knowingly violated any provision of this Agreement or has committed or attempted to commit any crimes other than crimes relating to the Unlawful Practices, (a) all statements made by or on behalf of Symbol to any of the Investigative Entities, including the acknowledgment and acceptance of responsibility set forth in this Agreement and

Exhibit A, and any testimony given by Symbol before a grand jury or elsewhere, whether before or after the date of this Agreement, and any leads derived from such statements or testimony, shall be admissible in evidence in any criminal proceeding brought by the Office against Symbol; and (b) Symbol shall not assert in any criminal proceeding brought by the Office against Symbol any claim under the United States Constitution, Rule 11(f) of the Federal Rules of Criminal Procedure, Rule 410 of the Federal Rules of Evidence, or any other federal rule or provision, that statements made by or on behalf of Symbol before or after the date of this Agreement, or any leads derived therefrom, should be suppressed.

15. Symbol agrees that the decision whether conduct and/or statements of any individual will be imputed to Symbol for purposes of determining whether Symbol has violated any provision of this Agreement shall be in the sole discretion of the Office, provided, however, that the statements of any former officer, director or employee of Symbol shall not be attributed to Symbol for the purposes of paragraphs 13-15. Should the Office determine that Symbol has committed a knowing breach of any provision of this Agreement, the Office will provide written notice to Symbol addressed to its General Counsel, Peter Lieb, Esq., One Symbol Plaza, Holtsville, New York 11742-1300, and to Symbol's counsel, Andrew J. Levander, Esq., Swidler Berlin Sheriff Friedman, LLP, The Chrysler Building, 405 Lexington Avenue, New York, New York 10174, or to any successor that Symbol may designate, and will provide Symbol with a two-week period from the date of receipt of such notice in which to make a presentation to the Office to demonstrate that no breach has occurred or, to the extent relevant, that the breach was not knowing or had been cured. Symbol understands and agrees that the exercise of discretion by the Office is not subject to review in any court or tribunal outside the Department of Justice.

16. Symbol agrees that it shall not, through its attorneys, Board of Directors,

agents, officers or employees, make any public statement, in litigation or otherwise, contradicting its acceptance of responsibility or Exhibit A. Any such contradictory statement by Symbol, its present or future attorneys, Board of Directors, agents, officers or employees shall constitute a breach of this Agreement and Symbol thereafter shall be subject to prosecution as set forth in paragraphs 13-15. The decision as to whether any such contradictory statement will be imputed to Symbol for the purpose of determining whether Symbol has breached this Agreement shall be at the sole discretion of the Office. Upon the Office's notifying Symbol of any such contradictory statement, Symbol may avoid a breach of this Agreement by publicly repudiating such statement within 72 hours after notification by the Office. This paragraph is not intended to apply to any statement made by any Symbol officer, director or employee or former officer, director or employee who has been charged with a crime or other wrongdoing by the government or an agency thereof.

17. Symbol agrees that, if it sells or merges all or substantially all of its business operations as they exist as of the date of this Agreement to or into a single purchaser or group of affiliated purchasers during the term of this Agreement, it shall include in any contract for sale or merger a provision binding the purchaser/successor to the obligations described in this Agreement.

18. Symbol agrees that, following expiration of this Agreement, Symbol will continue to cooperate with the Investigative Entities in connection with any proceeding relating to the Unlawful Practices. Symbol's obligation to cooperate is not intended to apply where Symbol is a defendant in any such proceeding.

19. It is understood that this Agreement is binding only on Symbol and the Office, and specifically does not bind any other federal agencies, any state or local law

enforcement agencies, any licensing authorities, or any regulatory authorities. However, the Office will bring the Agreement and Symbol's cooperation and the Remedial Actions, Policies and Procedures to the attention of other federal agencies, state or local law enforcement agencies, and any licensing or regulatory authorities if Symbol so requests. It is the intent of the parties to this Agreement that the Agreement does not confer or provide any benefits, privileges or rights to any individual or any entity other than the parties hereto, and that nothing in the Agreement shall be construed as acknowledging that the Agreement, including Exhibit A and the evidence underlying the Agreement and Exhibit A, shall be admissible in any proceeding other than a proceeding brought by the Office. No promises, agreements or conditions have been entered into other than those set forth in this Agreement, and none will be entered into unless memorialized in writing and signed by all parties. Apart from the Confidential Materials Agreement, this agreement supersedes any prior promises, agreements or conditions between the parties. To become effective, this agreement must be signed by all signatories listed below.

Dated: June 3, 2004
Brooklyn, New York

William Nuti
Chief Executive Officer
Symbol Technologies, Inc.

Salvatore Iannuzzi
Chairman of the Board of Directors
Symbol Technologies, Inc.

Andrew J. Levander, Esq.
Counsel to Symbol Technologies, Inc.

ROSLYNN R. MAUSKOPF
United States Attorney
Eastern District of New York

By:____________________
Eric Corngold
Chief, Business and Securities Fraud Unit

____
David B. Pitofsky
Principal Deputy Chief, Criminal Division

enforcement agencies, any licensing authorities, or any regulatory authorities. However, the Office will bring the Agreement and Symbol's cooperation and the Remedial Actions, Policies and Procedures to the attention of other federal agencies, state or local law enforcement agencies, and any licensing or regulatory authorities if Symbol so requests. It is the intent of the parties to this Agreement that the Agreement does not confer or provide any benefits, privileges or rights to any individual or any entity other than the parties hereto, and that nothing in the Agreement shall be construed as acknowledging that the Agreement, including Exhibit A and the evidence underlying the Agreement and Exhibit A, shall be admissible in any proceeding other than a proceeding brought by the Office. No promises, agreements or conditions have been entered into other than those set forth in this Agreement, and none will be entered into unless memorialized in writing and signed by all parties. Apart from the Confidential Materials Agreement, this agreement supersedes any prior promises, agreements or conditions between the parties. To become effective, this agreement must be signed by all signatories listed below.

Dated: June 3, 2004
Brooklyn, New York

William Nuti
Chief Executive Officer
Symbol Technologies, Inc.

Salvatore Iannuzzi
Chairman of the Board of Directors
Symbol Technologies, Inc.

Andrew J. Levander, Esq.
Counsel to Symbol Technologies, Inc.

ROSLYNN R. MAUSKOPF
United States Attorney
Eastern District of New York

By:
Eric Corngold
Chief, Business and Securities Fraud Unit

David B. Pitofsky
Principal Deputy Chief, Criminal Division

EXHIBIT A

In any criminal proceeding brought by the United States Attorney's Office for the Eastern District of New York, the following statement by Symbol Technologies, Inc. ("Symbol"), shall be admissible against Symbol pursuant to Rules 801(d)(2) and 804(b)(3) of the Federal Rules of Evidence:

Symbol

1. Symbol is a Delaware corporation headquartered and with its principal place of business in Holtsville, New York. Symbol is one of the world's leading manufactures and distributors of wireless and mobile computing and bar code reading devices as well as other networking systems.

2. Symbol sells its products and services directly to end-users, as well as to distributors and value-added resellers ("VARs") that resell Symbol's products to end-users. These distributors and VARs are sometimes referred to as "channel partners" because they provide a channel through which Symbol's products are distributed from Symbol to end-users.

3. Symbol is a publicly traded corporation, the common stock of which is traded on the New York Stock Exchange under the trading symbol "SBL." Symbol's shareholders were located throughout the United States, including in the Eastern District of New York.

4. From approximately 1999 to 2002, Symbol's former senior management engaged in fraudulent practices that inflated Symbol's reported earnings by hundreds of millions of dollars. The central goal of these practices was to ensure that Symbol consistently reported revenues and earnings that met or exceeded the public estimates issued by professional stock analysts who followed and reported on Symbol. These fraudulent practices included, among others: (1) the material misrepresentation and generation of false and prematurely recognized revenue; (2) the manipulation of Symbol's corporate books and records through top-side corporate journal entries, commonly referred to as "Tango Adjustments;" and (3) the fabrication and utilization of improper restructuring expenses and "cookie jar" reserves.

5. After allegations of Symbol's misconduct were reported to the United States Securities and Exchange Commission (the "SEC"), Symbol retained a law firm to conduct an internal investigation into Symbol's accounting and financial practices. However, despite Symbol's agreement to cooperate with the SEC's investigation into the allegations of Symbol's misconduct, for several months certain former Symbol executives engaged in conduct designed to interfere with and obstruct Symbol's internal investigation and the SEC's investigation.

10. Another fraudulent technique used by former members of Symbol's senior management to overstate Symbol's quarterly revenues and earnings involved transactions that certain Symbol executives commonly referred to as "Candy Deals." In these Candy Deals, Symbol solicited VARs to order from distributors Symbol products for which the VARs did not have any end-user customers for the products. To induce the VARs to make such orders, Symbol promised (a) to repurchase the products from the VARs at the price the VARs paid the distributors, and (b) to pay the VARs an additional one percent of the purchase price.

11. The Candy Deals generated no net income for Symbol. On the contrary, the Candy Deals resulted in a net loss to Symbol because (a) the price a VAR paid to the distributor for the products was higher than the price the distributor had paid Symbol for the products, which meant that Symbol had to repurchase the products at a price greater than the price at which it had sold the products, and (b) Symbol paid the VARs an additional one percent bonus to participate in the Candy Deals.

12. Another fraudulent technique used to overstate Symbol's quarterly revenues and earnings involved making improper accounting entries in customer service accounts. Under GAAP and Symbol's own revenue recognition policy, revenue for customer service should not have been recognized until after services were rendered. However, Symbol made phony journal entries in its customer service accounts that caused revenue to be recognized when, at the time, Symbol had not provided any services to the customer. In addition, Symbol invoiced and recognized revenue on customer service contracts that had either expired or been cancelled by its customer.

Unlawful "Top-Side" Accounting Entries

13. Another fraudulent technique used by former members of Symbol's senior management to overstate the company's quarterly revenues and earnings and understate the company's expenses involved the manipulation of financial results through bogus accounting journal entries. This technique was known by those involved as the "Tango" process. In the Tango process, Symbol's raw quarterly financial results, including expenses, revenues and earnings, were manipulated and fraudulently adjusted by accounting journal entries in order to create the false appearance that Symbol had met its projected quarterly revenues and earnings.

14. As part of the quarterly closing process at Symbol, the company's raw results from each of its divisions were collected and consolidated. Then, in the Tango process, the consolidated raw numbers were compared to quarterly forecasts that Symbol's former management had provided to the company's Board of Directors (the "Board forecasts"). The Board forecasts were typically consistent with the estimates of Wall Street analysts. The Tango process was summarized in what were known by former high-ranking corporate executives as "Tango sheets." The Tango sheets listed the raw results and the Board forecasts, as well as various proposed accounting journal adjustments, known as "Tango adjustments," which were designed to adjust Symbol's raw results to meet or

exceed the Board forecasts. Symbol reported the fraudulent adjusted results to the public in its Form 10-Qs and Form 10-Ks.

15. The Tango adjustments were made and approved by former members of Symbol's senior management for the purpose of manipulating Symbol's reported revenues and earnings and without regard to whether the adjustments accurately reflected Symbol's financial condition or were made in compliance with GAAP and Symbol's accounting policies. The nature, size and timing of the Tango adjustments depended on the variance between Symbol's raw results and the Board forecasts, as well as on the opportunities for manipulation that former members of Symbol's senior management were able to identify.

Unlawful Expense and Reserve Manipulation

16. Another fraudulent technique used by Symbol's former senior management to misrepresent Symbol's financial condition was the false characterization of routine operating expenses as non-recurring expenses. These mischaracterizations of expenses violated GAAP and allowed Symbol to understate its reported routine operating expenses, which, in turn, allowed Symbol to overstate its financial performance in the eyes of professional stock analysts and the investing public.

17. Another fraudulent technique used by Symbol's former senior management to misrepresent Symbol's financial condition was the creation of excessive reserves, often referred to as "cookie jar reserves." Symbol created these cookie jar reserves by recognizing and reporting certain non-recurring expenses that far exceeded the expenses that Symbol was likely to incur. These cookie jar reserves violated GAAP and were created in order to allow Symbol fraudulently to overstate its financial performance in future financial reporting periods by reversing part or all of the reserves in those periods.

William Nuti
Chief Executive Officer
Symbol Technologies, Inc.

Salvatore Iannuzzi
Chairman of the Board of Directors
Symbol Technologies, Inc.

Andrew Levander
Counsel to Symbol Technologies, Inc.

Dated: June 3, 2004

1120

June 3, 2004

Robert Nardoza
United States Attorney's Office
(718) 254-6323

PRESS RELEASE

Former Senior Executives at Symbol Technologies Indicted in Massive Corporate Fraud Scheme - Corporation Has Purged Executives Responsible for the Fraud, Implemented Significant Corporate Reforms, Agreed to Cooperate with the Government's Investigation and Pay $139 Million

ROSLYNN R. MAUSKOPF, United States Attorney for the Eastern District of New York and a member of the President's Corporate Fraud Task Force, WILLIAM E. KEZER, Inspector in Charge, New York Division, U.S. Postal Inspection Service, and MICHAEL J. THOMAS, Special Agent-in-Charge, Internal Revenue Service - Criminal Investigation, announced today the unsealing of an indictment against seven top-level former executives at Symbol Technologies, Inc., including TOMO RAZMILOVIC, former president and chief executive officer, KENNETH JAEGGI, former senior vice president and chief financial officer, BRIAN BURKE, former senior vice president (operations), MICHAEL DEGENNARO, former senior vice president (finance), FRANK BORGHESE, former senior vice president (worldwide sales and service), CHRISTOPHER DESANTIS, former vice president (finance) and JAMES HEUSCHNEIDER, former director (finance) for their participation in a long-lived, pervasive accounting fraud scheme designed to ensure that Symbol could consistently report that its quarterly revenues and earnings met the estimates issued by professional stock analysts when, in fact, Symbol's true financial performance often fell short of the estimates. The indictment also alleges that an eighth defendant, Symbol's former general counsel, LEONARD GOLDNER, orchestrated a scheme in which he and other senior executives at Symbol fraudulently exploited Symbol's stock option plans to enrich the executives and illegally minimize their tax obligation at the expense of Symbol.[(1)]

The defendants will be arraigned at 3:00 p.m. this afternoon by United States District Judge Leonard D. Wexler, at the U. S. Courthouse in Central Islip, New York.[(2)]

Ms. MAUSKOPF, Mr. KEZER, and Mr. THOMAS also announced that, in a written Agreement executed today, Symbol has accepted responsibility for the fraudulent conduct of its former executives, adopted significant corporate reforms to ensure that the fraud does not recur, agreed to continue its cooperation with the government's ongoing investigation of the fraud and agreed to pay $139 million to compensate victims of the fraud and to help fund the United States Postal Inspection Service's Consumer Fraud Fund. As long as Symbol abides by the terms of the Agreement, the United States Attorney's Office for the Eastern District of New York has agreed not to prosecute Symbol. The Agreement with Symbol does not protect any individuals from prosecution.

SYMBOL TECHNOLOGIES, INC.

Symbol is the eighth largest public company on Long Island, employing approximately 5,600 employees worldwide, and one of the world's leading manufacturers and distributors of wireless and mobile computing and bar code reading devices and other networking systems. Its customers include the Department of Defense, the Department of Homeland Security, the United States Postal Service, federal and local law enforcement agencies, Wal-Mart and Federal Express. Its stock is traded on the New York Stock Exchange.

THE INITIATION OF THE INVESTIGATION

As the indictment sets forth, the government's investigation of fraud at Symbol began with an anonymous letter sent to the SEC in April 2001 reporting fraudulent revenue recognition practices at the company with respect to two specific transactions and alleging that "these two transactions are just the tip of the iceberg of how Symbol management continues to manipulate and improperly handle their business accounting." Shortly thereafter, Symbol commenced an internal investigation of the allegations. The indictment alleges, however, that for several months Symbol executives including the defendant MICHAEL DEGENNARO engaged in conduct designed to interfere with and obstruct the internal investigations. When, in approximately September 2002, the internal investigation discovered DEGENNARO's conduct, the company fired him. From that point forward, Symbol's cooperation with the government has been full and complete. For example, Symbol has shared the substance of hundreds of interviews conducted with current and former Symbol employees, customers and others, as well as over one-half million pages of documents and hundreds of thousands of restored email and voice mail messages. Symbol has also waived attorney-client privilege to assist the investigation, and has made available numerous witnesses for government interviews. Finally, in instances in which Symbol discovered misconduct by its officers, executives and employees, Symbol reported the misconduct to the government and terminated the individuals.

THE ACCOUNTING FRAUD SCHEME

As a result of the government's investigation, aided by Symbol's cooperation, a widespread and pervasive accounting fraud scheme was uncovered. The indictment alleges that, from 1999 to 2002, former Symbol executives engaged in widespread fraudulent practices that inflated Symbol's reported revenue by more than $200 million. The central goal of these practices was to ensure that Symbol consistently reported revenues and earnings that met or exceeded the public estimates issued by professional stock analysts who followed and reported on Symbol. Indeed, through the first quarter of 2001, Symbol had reported revenues and earnings, excluding non-recurring charges, that met or exceeded the consensus estimates of analysts for 32 consecutive quarters. In order to maintain Symbol's record of meeting or exceeding the consensus estimate, the defendant TOMO RAZMILOVIC established ambitious, and often unrealistic, financial performance targets for every Symbol division, and aggressively enforced those targets, rewarding those executives who met their targets and punishing those who failed. The indictment charges that it was the responsibility of the Symbol executives below RAZMILOVIC, including JAEGGI, BURKE, DEGENNARO, BORGHESE, DESANTIS and HEUSCHNEIDER, to ensure that the divisions for which they had responsibility met RAZMILOVIC's targets, and many executives' salaries and bonuses were tied to achieving these targets.

The defendants used a stunning array of fraudulent accounting manipulations to allow them to claim to have met the targets. These fraudulent practices included, among others, false and prematurely recognized revenue, a complex dance of manipulation of accounting entries to fabricate higher revenues and lower costs, referred to by the conspirators as "tango adjustments," phony classification of expenses and the creation of "cookie jar" reserves.

Unlawful Revenue Recognition Practices

Among the fraudulent techniques that the indictment alleges were used by Symbol's senior management to overstate Symbol's quarterly revenue and earnings were systematic "channel stuffing" transactions entered into at or near the end of fiscal quarters. Through these transactions, Symbol purported to sell products to various value added resellers ("VARs") and distributors even though the VARs and distributors had no firm obligation to pay for the products they purportedly purchased, and often could not afford to pay for the products they had purportedly purchased. These VARs and distributors were known at the company as "Friends of Frank," because they were companies with whom the defendant FRANK BORGHESE had developed a special relationship that fostered the channel stuffing activity.

The indictment further alleges that Symbol entered into "candy deals," as the conspirators described them. In these deals, Symbol pushed VARs to order Symbol products from distributors without having any customers to buy those products. To sweeten the deal, Symbol promised to buy back those products at the same price the VARs paid the distributors, and to pay the VARs an additional 1% of the purchase price. The candy deals actually cost Symbol money because it paid more to buy back the products than it had sold them for in the first place, plus an additional 1% bonus.

The indictment also alleges that, in order to overstate Symbol's quarterly revenues and earnings, Symbol deliberately shipped customers the wrong Symbol products at or near the end of quarters when the Symbol products that the customers actually wanted were unavailable. Later, when the desired products became available, Symbol either canceled the prior shipment or accepted the return of the wrong product, and then shipped the correct product to the customers. In this way, Symbol prematurely recognized revenue for legitimate orders.

The indictment also alleges that Symbol overstated its quarterly revenues and earnings by recognizing revenue on sales of Symbol products that were ordered by customers but which were not actually shipped to customers within that quarter. Under Generally Accepted Accounting Principles ("GAAP") and Symbol's own revenue recognition policy, revenue resulting from such transactions should not have been recognized until the products were actually shipped. However, despite Symbol's failure to ship the products by the end of a quarter, Symbol improperly recognized revenue on the products in that quarter. Moreover, in an effort to disguise Symbol's contravention of GAAP and its own revenue recognition policy, Symbol obtained phony "bill-and-hold" or "ship-in-place" letters from its customers. These bogus letters stated, in substance, that the customer wanted Symbol to hold the products at Symbol rather than ship the products to the customer. In reality, these letters were obtained after-the-fact and were back-dated to create the false appearance that the customer had requested "ship-in-place" transactions when, in fact, they had not. In some instances, these letters were obtained months after the Symbol customer already had received and paid for the Symbol products.

Finally, the indictment alleges that Symbol engaged in similar improper conduct with respect to its customer service transactions. Under GAAP and Symbol's revenue recognition policy, revenue for customer service should not have been recognized until after services were rendered. However, Symbol made phony journal entries in its customer service accounts in order to recognize revenue before Symbol had provided any services to the customer. In addition, Symbol invoiced and recognized revenue on customer service contracts that had either expired or been canceled by its customer.

<u>Tango Sheets</u>

The indictment alleges that Symbol's senior management systematically overstated the company's quarterly revenues and earnings and understated the company's expenses through an elaborate "dance" designed to square analysts' projections with Symbol's inferior actual results. The conspirators called this the "tango" process. In this process, Symbol's raw quarterly financial results, including expenses, revenues and earnings, were fraudulently adjusted to create the false appearance that Symbol had met its projected quarterly revenues and earnings. The nature, size and timing of the tango adjustments was limited only by the gap between Symbol's raw results and the revenue forecasts, and the conspirators' creativity for manipulation opportunities.

Unlawful Expense and Reserve Manipulation

The indictment alleges that Symbol's senior management misrepresented the company's financial condition through the false characterization of routine operating expenses as non-recurring expenses. Non-recurring expenses, because they are one-time charges not characteristic of ordinary business expenses, are routinely discounted by the investing public in assessing a company's overall financial performance. Thus, Symbol's mischaracterizations of these ordinary expenses allowed the company to understate its reported routine operating expenses, which, in turn, allowed Symbol to overstate its financial performance in the eyes of professional stock analysts and the investing public.

The indictment also alleges that Symbol used "cookie jar" reserves to manipulate its financial reporting. Symbol created these reserves by recognizing and reporting non-recurring expenses that far exceeded the expenses that Symbol was likely to incur. By doing that, the conspirators created a reserve that they could dip into later when they needed to bolster their results. These cookie jar reserves violated GAAP and were created in order to allow Symbol fraudulently to overstate its financial performance in future financial reporting periods by reversing part or all of the reserves in those periods.

THE STOCK OPTIONS "LOOK-BACK" SCHEME

Finally, the indictment alleges that Symbol's former general counsel LEONARD GOLDNER orchestrated a stock option exercise scheme in which certain key executives, including GOLDNER and KENNETH JAEGGI, were afforded a "look-back" period of up to 30 days to choose an advantageous exercise price for their options. These executives effectively chose the price at which they exercised stock options in a manner that allowed them to minimize the tax paid or maximize the profit made upon the exercise of their stock options. This practice violated the terms of Symbol's publicly filed stock option plans, was not approved by the company's board of directors, and defrauded the government and Symbol itself.

PENALTIES AND FORFEITURE [(3)]

The securities fraud conspiracy count carries a maximum prison sentence of five years, and each substantive securities fraud charge carries a maximum prison sentence of 20 years. In addition, each conspiracy and substantive securities fraud count carries a maximum fine of $5,000,000. The conspiracy to commit mail and wire fraud count carries a maximum prison sentence of five years, and each substantive count of mail fraud and wire fraud carries a maximum prison sentence of 20 years. In addition, each conspiracy and substantive mail and wire fraud count carries a maximum fine of $250,000. Each conspiracy and substantive count of income tax evasion carries a maximum prison sentence of five years and a maximum fine of $250,000. Each count of making a false filing with the Internal Revenue Service carries a maximum prison sentence of three years and a maximum fine of $250,000.

In addition, the indictment seeks a forfeiture money judgment against all defendants in the total sum of approximately $74 million for which the defendants are jointly and severally liable. The indictment also seeks forfeiture of directly traceable assets of the defendants KENNETH JAEGGI and LEONARD GOLDNER including securities, cash and bonds with a total estimated value of approximately $10 million. Finally, the indictment seeks forfeiture of substitute assets consisting of 12 real properties and cooperative apartments located in New York, Nevada, California and Florida, worth several million dollars.

SYMBOL'S AGREEMENT WITH THE GOVERNMENT

In the Agreement executed today, Symbol has accepted responsibility for its conduct and acknowledged that, as a result of the conduct of its former officers, executives and employees, the company (a) violated federal criminal law in connection with accounting practices involving fabricated and other improper sales transactions, unsupported and fictitious accounting entries and the manipulation of Symbol's accounting reserves and expenses; and (b) filed materially false and misleading financial statements with the SEC.

In the Agreement, Symbol has also agreed to pay $139 million in stock and cash for purposes of compensating shareholders for losses arising out of the company's criminal conduct. Of this money, $37 million in cash is being paid to the SEC (who will pass it through to a court-ordered compensation fund); $3 million is being paid to the United States Postal Inspection Service Consumer Fraud Fund; and the balance is being paid in stock through class action litigation. Importantly, Symbol has agreed that no portion of the money being paid through the SEC and to the United States Postal Inspection Service Consumer Fraud Fund will be disbursed to pay attorneys' fees in the class action cases and that the cash payment will not be used in any way to calculate or determine the amount of attorneys' fees in the class action.

Also pursuant to the Agreement, Symbol has agreed to continue its cooperation and to continue its implementation of numerous important remedial steps undertaken to ensure that the fraud at Symbol does not recur. These remedial steps include:

the termination of employees at all levels of the company whose improper activities and/or lax supervision resulted in improper accounting and inaccurate financial reporting, or who refused to cooperate with Symbol's internal investigation;

the appointment of new management, including a new president and chief executive officer, a new chief financial officer, new senior vice presidents of finance, sales, operations, global products and customer service, a new general counsel and secretary and a new chief information officer;

the dismissal of its former auditing firm and the retention of a new firm;

the restructuring of the board of directors, including the division of the chief executive officer and chairman functions and the appointment of a non-executive chairman;

the appointment of an independent examiner to serve for three years to monitor and report to the government and Symbol's board of directors on, among other things, Symbol's internal controls and financial reporting practices.

the establishment of an ongoing training and education program for certain of its directors, officers and employees designed to minimize the possibility of future violations of the federal securities laws by Symbol.

In light of Symbol's acceptance of responsibility, continued cooperation, remedial measures, and agreement to compensate the victims of its fraud, the United States Attorney's Office for the Eastern

District of New York has agreed not to prosecute Symbol for the fraudulent conduct of its former officers, executives and employees. Should Symbol violate the terms of the Agreement executed today, or commit any other crimes, it shall be subject to prosecution, including for the fraud that is the subject of the indictment.

"These charges and the Agreement with Symbol mark the shared commitment of this Office and our partners in the President's Corporate Fraud Task Force to shining the bright light of investigation onto massive financial crimes in companies infected with corrupt corporate management," stated United States Attorney ROSLYNN R. MAUSKOPF. "The former executives indicted today used every trick in the very long book of fraud in a comprehensive and sustained scheme to victimize shareholders and enrich themselves by falsifying the financial records of the company. This prosecution stands as the government's symbol that we will root out corporate fraud and ensure that companies return to serving their owners. We are also pleased that Symbol has accepted responsibility, has cooperated with the government's investigation, and is enacting major reforms in its corporate structure that will substantially reduce the risk of future fraudulent conduct." Ms. MAUSKOPF thanked the Securities and Exchange Commission for its assistance in this matter.

Postal Inspector-in-Charge WILLIAM E. KEZER stated, "This corporate fraud investigation revealed a textbook case of a company 'cooking the books' to meet or exceed analysts' expectations. It is also unique in that virtually the entire former executive hierarchy was in the kitchen stirring the pot. The indictment is evidence of the strong commitment of this agency and our partners in the President's Corporate Fraud Task Force to work as one in the aggressive investigation and prosecution of corporate fraud schemes."

Internal Revenue Service Special-Agent-in-Charge MICHAEL J. THOMAS stated, "The heart of corporate America is right here in New York. Corporate officers who choose to do business here have to play by the rules IRS enforces or face the consequences."

The government's case is being prosecuted by Assistant United States Attorneys Eric Corngold, Geoffrey Kaiser, Matthew Levine, Richard Lunger and Special Assistant United States Attorney Craig Warkol of the United States Securities and Exchange Commission.

<u>The Defendants</u>

TOMO RAZMILOVIC
DOB: 5/13/42

KENNETH JAEGGI
DOB: 11/15/45

BRIAN BURKE
DOB: 7/24/46

MICHAEL DEGENNARO
DOB: 10/18/65

FRANK BORGHESE

DOB: 9/16/54

LEONARD GOLDNER
DOB: 6/18/47

CHRISTOPHER DESANTIS
DOB: 11/10/65

JAMES HEUSCHNEIDER
DOB: 12/20/56

1. Five individuals have previously pleaded guilty to conspiracy charges arising out of the accounting fraud scheme: Robert Korkuc, former chief accounting officer, Robert Asti, former vice president (finance), Gregory Mortenson, former senior director (finance), Robert Donlon, former director (sales operations) and James Dean, former director (finance).

2. The defendants have also been charged in a related civil action filed by the United States Securities and Exchange Commission today in the Eastern District of New York.

3. The charges in the indictment are merely allegations, and the defendants are presumed innocent unless and until proven guilty.

U.S. SECURITIES AND EXCHANGE COMMISSION

Litigation Release No. 18929 / October 13, 2004

Accounting and Auditing Enforcement
Release No. 2124 / October 13, 2004

Securities and Exchange Commission v. Koninklijke Ahold N.V. (Royal Ahold), **Civil Action No. 04-1742 (RMU) (D.D.C.) (October 13, 2004)**

Securities and Exchange Commission v. A. Michiel Meurs and Cees van der Hoeven, **Civil Action No. 04-1743 (RMU) (D.D.C.) (October 13, 2004)**

Securities and Exchange Commission v. Johannes Gerhardus Andreae, **Civil Action No. 04-1741 (RMU) (D.D.C.) (October 13, 2004)**

In the matter of Ture Roland Fahlin, **Administrative Proceeding File No. 3-11707**

SEC CHARGES ROYAL AHOLD AND THREE FORMER TOP EXECUTIVES WITH FRAUD; FORMER AUDIT COMMITTEE MEMBER CHARGED WITH CAUSING VIOLATIONS OF THE SECURITIES LAWS

On October 13, 2004, the Securities and Exchange Commission filed fraud and other charges in the United States District Court for the District of Columbia against Royal Ahold (Koninklijke Ahold N.V.) (Ahold) and three former top executives: Cees van der Hoeven, former CEO and chairman of the executive board; A. Michiel Meurs, former CFO and executive board member; and Jan Andreae, former executive vice president and executive board member. The Commission also filed a related administrative action charging Roland Fahlin, a former member of Ahold's supervisory board and audit committee, with causing violations of the reporting, books and records, and internal controls provisions of the securities laws. The SEC's complaints allege that, as a result of the fraudulent inflation of promotional allowances at U.S. Foodservice, Ahold's wholly-owned subsidiary, the improper consolidation of joint ventures through fraudulent side letters, and other accounting errors and irregularities, Ahold's original SEC filings overstated: (a) net income by approximately 17.6%, 32.6%, and 88.1% for the fiscal years 2000, 2001 and first three quarters of 2002, respectively; (b) operating income by approximately 28.1%, 29.4%, and 51.3% for the fiscal years 2000, 2001 and first three quarters of 2002, respectively; and (c) net sales by approximately 20.8%, 18.6%, and 13.8% for the fiscal years 2000, 2001 and 2002, respectively. Ahold and three of the individual defendants have agreed to settlements with the Commission.

The Earnings Fraud At U.S. Foodservice

With respect to the fraud at U.S. Foodservice ("USF"), Ahold's wholly-owned subsidiary based in Columbia, Maryland, the Commission's complaint against Ahold alleges as follows:

- A significant portion of USF's operating income was based on vendor payments known as promotional allowances. USF executives materially inflated the amount of promotional allowances recorded by USF and reflected in operating income on USF's financial statements, which were included in Ahold's Commission filings and other public statements.

- USF executives also provided, or assisted in providing, Ahold's independent auditors with false and misleading information by, for example, persuading personnel at many of USF's major vendors to falsely confirm overstated promotional allowances to the auditors in connection with year-end audits.

- The overstated promotional allowances aggregated at least $700 million for fiscal years 2001 and 2002 and caused Ahold to report materially false operating and net income for those and other periods.

The earnings inflation at USF, which began at least a year before Ahold's acquisition, is the subject of the SEC's complaint against four former USF executives filed July 27, 2004 in the United States District Court for the Southern District of New York

The Joint Venture Sales and Operating Income Fraud
Ahold and the Top Officers

With respect to the fraudulent consolidation of joint ventures, the Commission's complaints against Ahold, van der Hoeven, Meurs, and Andreae allege as follows:

- Ahold fully consolidated several joint ventures in its financial statements despite owning no more than fifty percent of the voting shares and despite shareholders' agreements that clearly provided for joint control by Ahold and its joint venture partners. To justify full consolidation of certain joint ventures, Ahold gave its independent auditors side letters to the joint venture agreements, signed by Ahold and its joint venture partners, which stated, in effect, that Ahold controlled the joint ventures ("control letters").

- However, at the time or soon after executing the control letters, Ahold and its joint venture partners executed side letters that rescinded the control letters - and thus the basis for full consolidation (the "rescinding letters").

- Meurs signed all but one of the control and rescinding letters on behalf of Ahold. He also knew that Ahold's auditors were relying on the control letters and were unaware of the existence of the rescinding letters.

- Van der Hoeven cosigned one of the rescinding letters and he was at least reckless in not knowing that the auditors were unaware of its existence.

- Andreae participated in the fraud by signing the control and rescinding letters for ICA, Ahold's Scandinavian joint venture, and by knowingly or recklessly concealing the existence of the ICA rescinding letter from the auditors.

- As a result of the fraud, Ahold materially overstated net sales by approximately EUR 4.8 billion ($5.1 billion) for fiscal year 1999, EUR 10.6 billion ($9.8 billion) for fiscal year 2000, and EUR 12.2 billion ($10.9 billion) for fiscal year 2001. Ahold materially overstated operating income by approximately EUR 222 million ($236 million) for fiscal year 1999, EUR 448 million ($413 million) for fiscal year 2000, and EUR 485 million ($434) for fiscal year 2001.

In its administrative action against Fahlin, the Commission alleges the following:

- Fahlin signed the ICA control and rescinding letters on behalf of ICA Förbundet, one of Ahold's partners in the ICA joint venture. He later left ICA Förbundet and became a member of Ahold's supervisory board and audit committee. In that capacity, he received a report indicating that the auditors were relying on a "control letter" to accept the consolidation of ICA. Fahlin's failure to determine whether this "control letter" was the same letter he had signed and then rescinded was a cause of Ahold's violations of the reporting, books and records, and internal controls provisions of the securities laws.

Settlements

Ahold has agreed to settle the Commission's action, without admitting or denying the allegations in the complaint, by consenting to the entry of a judgment permanently enjoining the company from violating the antifraud, reporting, books and records, and internal controls provisions of the federal securities laws (Section 17(a) of the Securities Act of 1933 (Securities Act); Sections 10(b), 13(a), 13(b)(2)(A) and 13(b)(2)(B) of the Securities Exchange Act of 1934 (Exchange Act); and Exchange Act Rules 10b-5, 12b-20, 13a-1, and 13a-16). The Commission noted in the complaint that Ahold cooperated fully in the SEC staff's investigation.

Van der Hoeven and Meurs have agreed to settle the Commission's action, without admitting or denying the allegations in the complaint, by consenting to the entry of judgments permanently enjoining each of them from violating Section 17(a) of the Securities Act, Sections 10(b) and 13(b)(5) of the Exchange Act, and Exchange Act Rules 10b-5, 13b2-1, and 13b2-2, and from aiding and abetting violations of Sections 13(a), 13(b)(2)(A) and 13(b)(2)(B) and Exchange Act Rules 13a-1 and 13a-16. Van der Hoeven and Meurs have also consented to orders barring each of them from serving as an officer or director of a public company.

Fahlin has agreed to settle the Commission's administrative action by consenting to the entry of an order, without admitting or denying the findings in the order, directing him to cease and desist from causing any violations and any future violations of Sections 13(a), 13(b)(2)(A) and 13 (b)(2)(B) of the Exchange Act and Rules 13a-1 and 13a-16 thereunder.

The Commission has not reached a settlement with Andreae. The Commission has charged Andreae with fraud (Section 17(a) of the Securities Act, Sections 10(b) of the Exchange Act, and Exchange Act Rule 10b-5), falsifying accounting records, and lying to auditors (Exchange Act Section 13(b)(5) and Exchange Act Rules 13b2-1 and 13b2-2) or, in the alternative, aiding and abetting violations of Sections 10(b) and 13(b)(5) of the Exchange Act and Exchange Act Rules 10b-5, 13b2-1, and 13b2-2. The Commission has also charged Andreae with aiding and abetting violations of the books and records and reporting requirements (Sections 13(a), 13(b)(2)(A) and 13(b)(2)(B) of the Exchange Act and Exchange Act Rules 13a-1 and 13a-16). The Commission seeks an injunction against future violations of the above provisions, an order prohibiting Andreae from acting as an officer or director of any public company, and disgorgement of ill-gotten gains with prejudgment interest.

The Commission has not sought penalties in the enforcement actions for several reasons. First, the Dutch Public Prosecutor's Office, which is conducting a parallel criminal investigation in The Netherlands, has requested that the Commission not seek penalties against the individuals because of potential double jeopardy issues under Dutch law. Because of the importance of this case in The Netherlands and the need for continued cooperation between the SEC and regulatory authorities in other countries, the Commission has agreed to the Dutch prosecutor's request.

The Commission also did not seek a penalty from Ahold, among other reasons, because of the company's extensive cooperation with the Commission's investigation. Ahold self-reported the misconduct and conducted an extensive internal investigation. On its own initiative, Ahold expanded its internal investigation beyond the fraud at U.S. Foodservice and the improper joint venture accounting to analyze accounting practices and internal controls at seventeen operating companies. Ahold promptly provided the staff with the internal investigative reports and the supporting information and waived the attorney-client privilege and work product protection with respect to its internal investigations. Ahold also made its current personnel available for interviews or testimony, significantly assisted the staff in arranging interviews with, or testimony from, former Ahold personnel located in the United States and abroad. Ahold promptly took remedial actions including, but not limited to, revising its internal controls and terminating employees responsible for the wrongdoing.

Related Actions

This is the second round of enforcement actions the Commission has filed in this investigation. On July 27, 2004, the Commission filed a complaint in the United States District Court for the Southern District of New York against Michael Resnick, Mark P. Kaiser, Timothy J. Lee, and William Carter in connection with the financial fraud at USF and (with respect to Lee) insider trading of USF securities (Litigation Release No. 18797). The Commission also filed a related complaint against Peter O. Marion in connection with insider trading of USF securities (Litigation Release No.

18796).

The Commission's investigation is continuing.

➤ SEC Complaint in this matter (Koninklijke Ahold N.V. (Royal Ahold))

➤ SEC Complaint in this matter (A.Michiel Meurs and Cees Van Der Hoeven)

➤ SEC Complaint in this matter (Johannes Gerhardus Andreae)

http://www.sec.gov/litigation/litreleases/lr18929.htm

06-15-05 -- Bristol-Myers Squibb -- Agreement -- News Release

Bristol-Myers Squibb Charged with Conspiring to Commit Securities Fraud; Prosecution Deferred for Two Years

- Two Former Company Execs Indicted -

NEWARK - Bristol-Myers Squibb Company (BMS) has agreed to pay an additional $300 million in restitution and undertake a series of corporate reforms as part of an agreement with the government to defer prosecution on a charge of conspiring to commit securities fraud for the company's failure to disclose its "channel-stuffing" activities in 2000 and 2001, U.S. Attorney Christopher J. Christie announced.

Also today, a two-count Indictment was unsealed against Frederick S. Schiff, 57, of Manhattan, a former senior vice president and the chief financial officer at BMS, and Richard J. Lane, 54, of Doylestown, Pa., a former executive vice president at BMS and president of its Worldwide Medicines Group. The Indictment charges Schiff and Lane with conspiracy and securities fraud for allegedly planning and concealing the channel-stuffing scheme to meet aggressive internal sales and earnings targets and Wall Street consensus earnings estimates. The two are expected to make initial appearances before a U.S. Magistrate Judge on Thursday.

Separately, a criminal Complaint filed today in the District of New Jersey charges New Jersey-based BMS with conspiring to commit securities fraud. As part of the Deferred Prosecution Agreement, BMS has agreed to accept responsibility for its conduct, adopt internal compliance measures and cooperate with the ongoing criminal investigation. An independent consultant has been chosen to ensure the company's compliance with the agreement.

Deferred Prosecution Agreement

Under the Deferred Prosecution Agreement, BMS has agreed to pay an additional $300 million in restitution to victims of the fraud scheme. That brings the total to $839 million that BMS has paid to shareholders harmed by the fraudulent conduct, including an earlier consent agreement with the Securities and Exchange Commission to pay a $100 million civil penalty and an additional $50 million Shareholder Fund payment - as well as monies paid by BMS in settlement of two class action proceedings. This represents the full restitution for the losses sustained for shares traded in the four days after BMS announced their restatement in 2001.

Based on acceptance by BMS of these conditions and others, the Department of Justice has agreed to defer prosecution on the Complaint for 24 months. If at the end of that period the company has fully complied and met all its obligations under the Deferred Prosecution Agreement, the criminal Complaint will be dismissed.

"We balanced the need for punishment with an acknowledgment that this company provides great value and that its work should continue," said Christie. "At the same time, we have compensated the victimized shareholders and are prosecuting individuals responsible for the fraud at BMS. This approach meets the needs of justice, sends a deterrent message to others and does not cause undue harm to an otherwise outstanding company, its shareholders and employees."

The BMS investigation was conducted by the U.S. Attorney's Office for the District of New Jersey, the Federal Bureau of Investigation and the United States Postal Inspection Service. The investigation was conducted under the auspices of President Bush's Corporate Fraud Task Force, created in July 2002 to investigate allegations of fraud and corruption at U.S. corporations. To date, the Task Force has charged more than 900 individuals in over 400 cases. More than 500 individuals have been convicted to date.

The case is being prosecuted by Assistant U.S. Attorneys Robert M. Hanna and Joshua Drew.

Throughout 2000 and 2001 BMS concealed from the investing public its persistent use of an earnings management technique commonly known as "channel stuffing." BMS's channel stuffing consisted of enticing its wholesalers through use of financial incentives to buy and hold greater quantities of prescription drugs than was warranted by the demand for those products. By the end of 2001, BMS's channel stuffing resulted in nearly $2 billion in "excess inventory" at the wholesalers.

The two years at issue in the investigation - 2000 and 2001 - were, respectively, the last year of BMS's "Double-Double" and the first year of its "Mega-Double" campaigns, publicly announced corporate goals to double sales and earnings, first in the seven years from 1994 to 2000, and then in the five years from 2001 to 2005. BMS's channel stuffing and other improper earnings management during 2000 and 2001 were part of an effort to report financial performance consistent with its Double-Double and Mega-Double public announcements. Without the channel stuffing, BMS also likely would have missed the Wall St. consensus estimates for its sales and earnings.

BMS failed to disclose and made false and misleading statements to the investing public regarding: the use of financial incentives to the wholesalers to generate sales in excess of demand; the use of sales in excess of demand to hit budget targets; the level of excess inventory at the wholesalers; the amount that excess inventory increased each quarter in 2000 and 2001. As a result, investors were misled regarding BMS's true sales and earnings, and did not have an accurate picture of the health of the company's business operations.

In exchange for an agreement by the Department of Justice to defer prosecution, BMS is required to:

• Accept and acknowledge responsibility for its conduct, as reflected in the factual statement accompanying the agreement;

• Appoint a current member of the Board of Directors, James Robinson III, as the Non-Executive Chairman of the Board, to ensure BMS emphasizes openness, accountability and integrity in corporate governance;

• Cooperate fully with the U.S. Attorney's Office in its ongoing investigation;

• Pay $300 million in additional restitution to shareholders;

• Adopt internal controls and other remedial measures designed to prevent and deter potential violations of the federal securities laws; and

• Engage an independent monitor, former U.S. Attorney and Federal Judge Frederick B. Lacey, as agreed upon by the Department of Justice and BMS, who will monitor BMS's ongoing remediation efforts and report to the Department on a regular basis.

Other components of the Deferred Prosecution Agreement include:

• Requiring BMS to endow a chair at Seton Hall University Law School dedicated to the teaching of business ethics and corporate governance, which position shall include conducting at least one seminar on business ethics and corporate governance annually that members of BMS' executive and management staff may attend, as well as other corporate executives.

• Holding a meeting within 30 days of this agreement, for BMS senior executives and senior financial personnel and other BMS employees, to be conducted by U.S. Attorney Christie and others from his office for the purpose of communicating the goals and expected effect of the agreement.

• The appointment of an additional non-executive director acceptable to the U.S. Attorney's Office and the BMS Board of Directors within 60 days.

The Indictment

The two-count Indictment against Schiff and Lane alleges that they and other co-conspirators at BMS supervised and perpetuated the channel-stuffing scheme. The two executives and their co-conspirators allegedly instructed BMS finance and operations staff to create packages of financial incentives for drug wholesalers to buy products beyond prescription demand to artificially inflate sales and earnings; signed 10-Q and 10-K forms filed with the Securities and Exchange Commission with omissions of material fact and misleading information regarding sales and earnings performance at BMS; gave consistently misleading information about earnings and inventory in press releases and conference calls with Wall Street analysts; and employed accounting and bookkeeping gimmicks to mask the increasing rise in drug inventory levels with wholesalers.

Both executives actively participated in conference calls in which they misled analysts who raised questions about the company's wholesaler inventories, according to the Indictment.

They also ignored concerns expressed by company employees about the use of financial incentives to wholesalers, at a cost of tens of millions of dollars.

In one example, in October 2001, Schiff and Lane gave written approval for a package of $47 million in sales incentives to wholesalers so BMS could hit its earnings numbers for the third quarter, according to the Indictment. A month later, Lane gave written approval for a package of $85 million in sales incentives for the fourth quarter of 2001.

Throughout the period described in the Indictment, Schiff, Lane and BMS failed to disclose to Wall Street investors how the channel stuffing was artificially inflating the company's sales and earnings numbers.

According to the Indictment, in October 2000 - when the undisclosed channel-stuffing and wholesaler incentives were well under way - an analyst questioned Lane about "wholesaler inventory actions," to which Lane responded: "I don't think there was any significant wholesaler inventory activity in the quarter."

In an April 2001 conference call, Schiff responded similarly to an analysts question about wholesaler inventory levels: "... There are no unusual items that we see at this quarter compared to year-end. Everything that we see is right on target .... So there are no unusual items that we see in the inventory levels."

Timed with those conference calls, BMS repeatedly issued misleading press releases that, like the conference calls, failed to disclose the effect that the channel stuffing had on BMS sales and earnings, according to the Indictment.

As the scheme unfolded, Schiff and Lane were adamant and demanding of finance and operations staff that they do whatever it took to reach earnings estimates.

On May 19, 2000, for example, Lane wrote an email to Worldwide Medicines personnel: "Sales continue to be concerningly weak," he said. "We need to make our May target! [W] hen will this start to happen.??"

The Indictment alleges that Schiff and Lane and their co-conspirators transferred or demoted certain employees who suggested that the company's budget targets were too aggressive or expressed doubts that they could make the numbers.

Despite indictment, the defendants are presumed innocent unless and until proven guilty beyond a reasonable doubt.

Christie credited the FBI, under the direction of Special Agent in Charge Leslie Wiser, Jr., in Newark, and the U.S. Postal Inspection Service, under the direction of Postal Inspector in Charge Thomas C. Van de Merlen. The investigation was conducted under the auspices of President Bush's Corporate Fraud Task Force, created in July 2002 to investigate allegations of fraud and corruption at U.S. corporations, and led by Deputy Attorney General James B. Comey.

-end-

Defense Counsel:

BMS: Mary Jo White, Esq. New York

Schiff: David Zarnow, Esq. New York

Lane: Richard Strassberg, Esq. New York

Deferred Prosecution Agreement

1. Bristol-Myers Squibb Company ("BMS" or the "Company") by its undersigned attorneys, pursuant to authority granted by its Board of Directors, and the United States Attorney's Office for the District of New Jersey (the "Office"), enter into this Deferred Prosecution Agreement (the "Agreement"). Except as specifically provided below, the Agreement shall be in effect for a period of two years from the date it is fully executed.

2. The Office has informed BMS that it will file, on or shortly after the date this Agreement is fully executed, a criminal complaint in the United States District Court for the District of New Jersey charging BMS with conspiracy to commit securities fraud, contrary to Title 15, United States Code, Sections 78j(b) & 78ff and Title 17, Code of Federal Regulations, Section 240.10b-5, in violation of Title 18, United States Code, Section 371, during the period of 2000 through 2001.

3. BMS and the Office agree that, upon filing of the criminal complaint in accordance with the preceding paragraph, this Agreement shall be publicly filed in the United States District Court for the District of New Jersey, and BMS agrees to post the Agreement prominently on its website.

4. In light of BMS's remedial actions to date and its willingness to (a) undertake additional remediation; (b) acknowledge responsibility for its behavior; (c) continue its cooperation with the Office and other governmental regulatory agencies; (d) demonstrate its future good conduct and full compliance with the securities laws and Generally Accepted Accounting Principles; and (e) consent to payment of additional restitution as set forth in paragraph 21, the Office shall recommend to the Court that prosecution of BMS on the criminal complaint filed pursuant to paragraph 2 be deferred for a period of twenty-four (24) months from the filing date of the criminal complaint. If the Court declines to defer prosecution for any reason, this Agreement shall be null and void, and the parties will revert to their pre-Agreement positions.

5. BMS has undertaken extensive reforms and remedial actions in response to the conduct at BMS that is and has been the subject of the investigation by the Office. These reforms and remedial actions have included:

(a) Retaining the Honorable Frederick B. Lacey as Independent Advisor, to conduct a comprehensive review of the implementation and effectiveness of the internal controls, financial reporting, disclosure, planning, budget and projection processes and related compliance functions of the Company, as well as to serve additional supervisory and monitoring functions described herein;

(b) Entering a Consent filed in the United States District Court for the District of New Jersey in United States Securities Exchange Commission v. Bristol-Myers Squibb Company, Civ. Action No. 04-3680 (FSH) (the "D.N.J. Action") providing for, among other things, the payment of a $100 million Civil Penalty and an additional $50 million Shareholder Fund payment, both of which amounts are to be distributed pursuant to the Fair Fund provisions of Section 308(a) of the Sarbanes-Oxley Act of 2002, as well as incorporating an array of remedial measures to be undertaken by BMS together with extensive supervisory and monitoring responsibilities to be carried out by the Independent Advisor during a review period extending through the filing of the Company's Form 10-K for the year ended 2005;

(c) Making a payment of an additional $300 million to compensate present and former BMS shareholders in connection with lawsuits filed and consolidated in In re Bristol-Myers Squibb Securities Litigation, Master File No. 02-CV-2251 (LAP) (S.D.N.Y.) (the "Consolidated Shareholder Litigation");

(d) Making significant personnel changes after April 2002 and after the Office commenced its investigation including:

(i) replacing the former Chief Financial Officer (CFO);

(ii) replacing the former President of the Worldwide Medicines Group;

(iii) replacing the former Controller;

(iv) establishing the position of Assistant Controller for Financial Compliance and Control;

(v) establishing the position of Chief Compliance Officer;

(vi) establishing a position for an experienced securities regulation and disclosure lawyer who has a significant role in all BMS disclosure responsibilities;

(e) Changing its budget process, to assure that appropriate consideration is given to input and analysis from the bottom to top, and not exclusively from top to bottom, and adequately documenting that process;

(f) Forming a business risk and disclosure group that includes senior management, the Independent Advisor and counsel to the Independent Advisor;

(g) Identifying and implementing actions to improve the effectiveness of its disclosure controls and procedures and internal controls, including enhancing its resources and training with respect to financial reporting and disclosure responsibilities, and reviewing such actions with its Audit Committee and independent auditors;

(h) Implementing a formal review and certification process of its annual and quarterly reports filed with the Securities and Exchange Commission (SEC); and

(i) Providing an effective mechanism in the form of a confidential hotline and e-mail address, of which BMS employees are informed and can use to notify BMS of any concerns about wholesaler inventory levels or the integrity of the financial disclosures, books and records of BMS.

6. BMS shall maintain and continue to implement any remedial measures already undertaken or mandated as part of agreements BMS has reached in the following matters: In re Bristol-Myers Squibb Derivative Litigation, Master File No. 02-CV-8571 (LAP) (S.D.N.Y.) (the "Shareholder Derivative Action"); the "D.N.J. Action"; and the "Consolidated Shareholder Litigation."

7. In addition to the extensive remedial actions that it has taken to date, BMS agrees to undertake additional remedial actions and corporate reforms as set forth herein.

8. BMS shall establish the position of non-executive Chairman of the BMS Board of Directors (the "Non-Executive Chairman"), to advance and underscore the Company's commitment to exemplary corporate citizenship, to best practices of effective corporate governance and the highest principles of integrity and professionalism, and to fostering a culture of openness, accountability and compliance throughout the Company. BMS shall retain the position of Non-Executive Chairman at least throughout the term of this Agreement.

9. BMS agrees to appoint an additional non-executive Director acceptable to the Office to the BMS Board of Directors within sixty (60) days of the execution of this Agreement.

10. The Company's CFO, General Counsel, and Chief Compliance Officer regularly shall brief and provide information to the Non-Executive Chairman, in a manner to be determined by the Non-Executive Chairman. In addition, the Non-Executive Chairman shall have the authority to meet with, and require reports on any subject from, any officer or employee of the Company.

11. BMS agrees that until at least the date of the filing of the Company's Form 10-K for the year ended 2006, it will retain an outside, independent individual or entity (the "Monitor"), selected by BMS and approved by the Office. BMS may employ as the Monitor the Honorable Frederick B. Lacey. It shall be a condition of the Monitor's retention that the Monitor is independent of BMS and that no attorney-client relationship shall be formed between the Monitor and BMS.

12. The Monitor shall:

(a) Monitor BMS's compliance with this Agreement, and have authority to require BMS to take any steps he believes are necessary to comply with the terms of this Agreement;

(b) Continue the review, reforms and other functions undertaken as the Independent Advisor;

(c) Report to the Office, on at least a quarterly basis and between thirty and forty-five calendar days after the filing of the Company's Form 10-K for the year ended 2006, as to BMS's compliance with this Agreement and the implementation and effectiveness of the internal controls, financial reporting, disclosure processes and related compliance functions of the Company. The first report to the Office shall be due within forty-five (45) days after the close of the second quarter 2005, and subsequent quarterly reports (other than the final report) shall be due by the close of the quarter. The reporting function of the Monitor shall extend until forty-five (45) days subsequent to the filing of the Company's Form 10-K for the year ended 2006 in order to facilitate the submission of the Monitor's final report to the Office;

(d) Cooperate with the SEC and provide information about BMS as requested by that agency;

(e) Monitor BMS's compliance with applicable federal securities laws, and in his quarterly reports make recommendations necessary to ensure that the Company complies with applicable federal securities laws;

(f) Monitor BMS's compliance with agreements BMS has reached in the Shareholder Derivative Action, the D.N.J. Action, and the Consolidated Shareholder Litigation; and

(g) Monitor the information received by the confidential hotline and e-mail address described in paragraph 5(i).

13. BMS agrees that the Chief Executive Officer (CEO), Non-Executive Chairman, and General Counsel will meet quarterly with the Office and the Monitor, in conjunction with the Monitor's quarterly reports.

14. BMS shall adopt all recommendations contained in each report submitted by the Monitor to the Office unless BMS objects to the recommendation and the Office agrees that adoption of the recommendation should not be required. The Monitor's reports to the Office shall not be received or reviewed by BMS prior to submission to the Office; such reports will be preliminary until senior management of BMS is given the opportunity, within ten (10) days after the submission of the report to the Office, to comment to the Monitor and the Office in writing upon such reports, and the Monitor has reviewed and provided to the Office responses to such comments, upon which such reports shall be considered final.

15. BMS agrees that the Monitor may also disclose his reports, as directed by the Office,

to any other federal, state or foreign law enforcement or regulatory agency in furtherance of an investigation of any other matters discovered by, or brought to the attention of, the Office in connection with the Office's investigation of BMS or the implementation of this Agreement.

16. BMS agrees that if the Monitor resigns or is unable to serve the balance of his term, a successor shall be selected by BMS and approved by the Office within forty-five (45) days. BMS agrees that all provisions in this Agreement that apply to the Monitor shall apply to any successor Monitor.

17. The Non-Executive Chairman and the Compensation Committee of the Board of Directors shall set goals and objectives relevant to compensation of the CEO, evaluate the CEO's performance in light of those goals and objectives, and recommend to the Board of Directors compensation based on this evaluation.

18. BMS agrees that it will establish and maintain a training and education program, which shall be reviewed and approved by the Board of Directors, designed to advance and underscore the Company's commitment to exemplary corporate citizenship, to best practices of effective corporate governance and the highest principles of integrity and professionalism, and to fostering a culture of openness, accountability and compliance throughout the Company. Completion of such training shall be mandatory for (a) all BMS officers, executives and employees who are involved in accounting and financial reporting functions, or the oversight thereof, whether at the corporate or the division level, including but not limited to each officer or employee responsible for closing the books within his or her area of responsibility at the end of a quarterly or annual reporting period; (b) all employees of the BMS legal division with responsibility for finance, business risk or disclosure issues; and (c) other senior officers and executives at BMS, at both the corporate and operating levels, as proposed by BMS and approved by the Office (collectively the "Mandatory Participants"). Such training and education program will cover, at a minimum, the following subjects: (a) the obligations imposed by the federal securities laws, including disclosure obligations; (b) proper internal accounting controls and procedures; (c) discovering and recognizing accounting practices that do not conform to Generally Accepted Accounting Principles or that are otherwise improper; and (d) the obligations assumed by, and responses expected of, the Mandatory Participants upon learning of improper, illegal or potentially illegal acts relating to BMS's accounting and financial reporting. The Board of Directors shall communicate to the Mandatory Participants, in writing or by video, its review and endorsement of the training and education program.

19. BMS shall commence providing the training mandated by paragraph 18 within ninety (90) days after the date of the execution of this Agreement and shall, at that time, submit to the Office a written description of the content and planned implementation of the training and education program. BMS shall thereafter provide such training and education on an annual basis for all those who become Mandatory Participants during the preceding twelve months.

20. BMS shall endow a chair at Seton Hall University School of Law dedicated to the teaching of business ethics and corporate governance, which position shall include conducting one or more seminars per year on business ethics and corporate governance at Seton Hall University School of Law that members of BMS's executive and management staff, along with representatives of the executive and management staffs of other companies in the New Jersey area, may attend.

21. BMS shall make an additional payment of $300 million into the shareholder compensation fund established pursuant to the consent judgment in the D.N.J. Action. This payment shall be administered according to the terms of such fund. Together with this payment, BMS will have paid a total of $839 million in compensation to its shareholders and former shareholders. This sum includes payments already made by BMS of $300 million in the Consolidated Shareholder Litigation, $150 million in the D.N.J. Action, and $89 million in actions by shareholders who requested to be excluded from the settlement in the Consolidated Shareholder Litigation, as well as the additional $300 million that BMS shall pay pursuant to this Agreement. BMS may make the additional payment of $300 million in a single payment at or before the close of the third quarter of 2005, or in four approximately equal quarterly installments, with the first installment due at the close of the third quarter of 2005. None of the proceeds of the payment required by this Agreement shall be payable as attorney's fees. Any costs of administering the distribution of the additional payment called for by this agreement shall be borne by BMS. To the extent that any money paid into the D.N.J. shareholder compensation fund pursuant to this Agreement is not claimed by shareholders or former shareholders within three years, the remaining amount shall be paid to the United States Treasury.

22. Within thirty (30) days of the execution of this Agreement, BMS agrees to call a meeting, on a date mutually agreed upon by BMS and the Office, of its senior executives and any senior financial personnel, and any other BMS employees who the Company desires to attend, such meeting to be attended by the United States Attorney and other representatives of the Office for the purpose of communicating the goals and expected effect of this Agreement.

23. For a period of one year from the execution of this Agreement, the Non-Executive Chairman, CEO, and General Counsel shall contemporaneously monitor either in person or telephonically BMS's quarterly conference calls for analysts ("analyst calls"), and the Non-Executive Chairman shall attend and participate in any preparatory meetings held among the CEO, the CFO, the General Counsel and other members of BMS senior management in anticipation of the analyst calls. The General Counsel shall ensure that representatives of the BMS legal division are informed and consulted regarding, at a minimum, issues relating to disclosure or securities law that may arise in the course of preparing for the analyst calls.

24. The CEO and CFO shall prepare and submit to the Non-Executive Chairman, Chief Compliance Officer and the Monitor described in paragraph 11 written reports on the following subjects:

(a) all non-standard transactions with major U.S. wholesalers, such written report to be submitted within fifteen (15) days of such transaction;

(b) an overview and analysis of BMS's annual budget process for its major business units, including description of significant instances of any top-down changes to business unit submissions, such written report to be submitted together with the proposed budget submitted for approval to the Board of Directors;

(c) sales and earnings forecasts or projections at the corporate or major business unit level which indicate a quarterly target will not be met, together with a description of steps subsequently taken, if any, to achieve the budget target, such written report to be submitted quarterly and at least ten (10) business days prior to the Company's scheduled quarterly analyst call;

(d) description of significant instances in which the preliminary quarterly closing of the books of any major business unit indicated that the business unit would not meet its budget target for any sales or earnings measure.

25. BMS agrees that it shall include in its quarterly and annual public filings with the SEC and its annual report to shareholders financial disclosures concerning the following: (a)(i) for the Company's U.S. Pharmaceuticals business, estimated wholesaler/direct-customer inventory levels of the top fifteen (15) products sold by such business and (ii) for major non-U.S. countries, estimated aggregate wholesaler/direct-customer inventory levels of the top fifteen (15) pharmaceutical products sold in such countries taken as a whole measured by aggregate annual sales in such countries; (b) arrangements with and policies concerning wholesalers/direct customers and other distributors of such products, including but not limited to efforts by BMS to control and monitor wholesaler/distributor inventory levels; (c) data concerning prescriptions or other measures of end-user demand for such top fifteen (15) BMS pharmaceutical products sold within the U.S. and in major non-U.S. countries; (d) acquisition, divestiture, and restructuring reserve policies and activity; and (e) rebate accrual policies and activity. The CEO shall, at the annual BMS shareholder meeting, report to the shareholders on these topics.

26. BMS agrees that it will continue to review and improve, where necessary, the content of its public financial and non-financial public disclosures, including periodic SEC filings, annual and other shareholder reports, press releases, and disclosures during analyst conference calls, as well as during meetings with investors and credit ratings agencies. BMS agrees that it will at all times strive for openness and transparency in its public reporting and disclosures.

27. BMS shall encourage the free flow of information between its employees and its external auditor, and encourage its CFO and senior finance personnel to seek advice from the external auditor. The CEO, CFO, General Counsel, and Chief Compliance Officer shall meet quarterly with the

Company's external auditors, such meeting to occur following the closing of the Company's books for the quarter and prior to the Company's scheduled quarterly analyst call. At the quarterly meeting, the BMS attendees shall discuss business and financial reporting developments, issues and trends with the external auditor, as well as provide information to the external auditor concerning the subjects described in paragraph 24 above, and shall respond to inquiries from the external auditor.

28. BMS accepts and acknowledges responsibility for the facts set forth in the Statement of Facts attached as Appendix A (the "Statement of Facts") and incorporated by reference herein by entering into this Agreement and by, among other things, (a) the extensive remedial actions that it has taken to date, (b) its continuing commitment to full cooperation with the Office and other governmental agencies, and (c) and the other undertakings it has made as set forth in this Agreement.

29. BMS agrees that in the event that future criminal proceedings are brought by the Office in accordance with paragraphs 4 and 36 through 39 of this Agreement, BMS will not contest the admissibility of the Statement of Facts in any such proceedings. Nothing in this Agreement shall be construed as an acknowledgment by BMS that the Agreement, including the Statement of Facts, is admissible or may be used in any proceeding other than in a proceeding brought by the Office.

30. BMS expressly agrees that it shall not, through its present or future attorneys, Board of Directors, agents, officers or employees, make any public statement contradicting any statement of fact contained in the Statement of Facts. Any such contradictory public statement by BMS, its present or future attorneys, Board of Directors, agents, officers or employees, shall constitute a breach of this Agreement as governed by paragraphs 36 and 37 of this Agreement, and BMS would thereafter be subject to prosecution pursuant to the terms of this Agreement. The decision of whether any public statement by any such person contradicting a fact contained in the Statement of Facts will be imputed to BMS for the purpose of determining whether BMS has committed a knowing and material breach of this Agreement shall be at the sole discretion of the Office. Should the Office notify BMS of a public statement by any such person that in whole or in part contradicts a statement of fact contained in the Statement of Facts, BMS may avoid breach of this Agreement by publicly repudiating such statement within forty-eight (48) hours after such notification. This paragraph is not intended to apply to any statement by any former BMS employee, officer or director, or any BMS employee, officer or director testifying in any proceeding in an individual capacity and not on behalf of BMS.

31. BMS agrees that its continuing cooperation during the term of this Agreement shall include, but shall not be not limited to, the following:

(a) Not engaging in or attempting to engage in any criminal conduct as defined in paragraph 34.

(b) Completely, truthfully and promptly disclosing all information concerning all matters about which the Office and other government agencies designated by the Office may inquire, and continuing to provide the Office, upon request, all documents and other materials relating to matters about which the Office inquires, and analysis or other work product as may be requested by the Office, as promptly as is practicable. Cooperation under this paragraph shall include identification of documents that may be relevant to the matters under investigation.

(c) Consenting to any order sought by the Office permitting disclosure of any materials that constitute "matters occurring before the grand jury" within the meaning of Rule 6(e) of the Federal Rules of Criminal Procedure.

(d) Not asserting, in relation to any request of the Office, any claims of attorney-client privilege or attorney work-product doctrine as to any documents, records, information or testimony requested by the Office related to: (i) factual internal investigations undertaken by the Company or its counsel relating to the matters under investigation by the Office; (ii) legal advice given contemporaneously with, and related to, such matters. Such materials are referred to hereinafter as the "Confidential Materials." By producing the Confidential Materials pursuant to this Agreement, BMS does not intend to waive the protection of the attorney-client privilege or the attorney work-product doctrine, or any other applicable privilege, as to third parties. The Office will maintain the confidentiality of the Confidential Materials pursuant to this Agreement and will not disclose them to any third party, except to the extent that the Office determines, in its sole discretion, that disclosure is otherwise required by law or would be in furtherance of the discharge of the duties and responsibilities of the Office.

(e) Making available BMS officers, directors, and employees and using its best efforts to make available former BMS officers, directors, and employees to provide information and/or testimony at all reasonable times as requested by the Office, including sworn testimony before a federal grand jury or in federal trials, as well as interviews with federal law enforcement authorities. Cooperation under this paragraph shall include identification of witnesses who, to BMS's knowledge, may have material information regarding the matters under investigation.

(f) Providing testimony, certifications, and other information deemed necessary by the Office or a court to identify or establish the original location, authenticity, or other evidentiary foundation necessary to admit into evidence documents in any criminal or other proceeding as requested by the Office.

32. BMS has provided extensive cooperation to the Office in connection with its investigation. BMS acknowledges and understands that its prior, ongoing and future cooperation are important factors in the decision of the Office to enter into this Agreement, and BMS agrees to continue to cooperate fully with the Office, and with any other governmental agency designated by the Office, regarding any issue about which BMS has knowledge or information.

33. BMS authorizes the Office and the SEC to share information from and about BMS with each other and hereby waives any confidentiality accorded to that information by law, agreement or otherwise that would, absent authorization by BMS, prohibit or limit such sharing. No other waivers of confidentiality shall be required in that regard.

34. BMS will inform the Office of any credible evidence of criminal conduct at BMS occurring after the date of the Agreement, including making available internal audit reports, letters threatening litigation, "whistleblower" complaints, civil complaints, and documents produced in civil litigation so evidencing such criminal conduct. For purposes of this Agreement, "criminal conduct" is defined as (a) any crime related to BMS's business activities committed by one or more BMS executive officers or directors; (b) securities fraud, accounting fraud, financial fraud or other business fraud materially affecting the books, records or publicly-filed reports of BMS; and (c) obstruction of justice.

35. The Office may continue to investigate current and former BMS employees. Nothing in this Agreement restricts in any way the ability of the Office to investigate and prosecute any BMS employee or former BMS employee.

36. Should the Office determine during the term of this Agreement that BMS has committed any criminal conduct as defined in paragraph 34 commenced subsequent to the date of this Agreement, or otherwise in any other respect knowingly and materially breached this Agreement, BMS shall, in the discretion of the Office, thereafter be subject to prosecution for any federal crimes of which the Office has knowledge, including crimes relating to the matters set forth in the Statement of Facts. Except in the event of a breach of this Agreement, it is the intention of the parties to this Agreement that all investigations of BMS relating to the matters set forth in the Statement of Facts that have been, or could have been, conducted by the Office prior to the date of this Agreement shall not be pursued further as to BMS.

37. Should the Office determine that BMS has knowingly and materially breached any provision of this Agreement, the Office shall provide written notice to BMS of the alleged breach and provide BMS with a two-week period in which to make a presentation to the Office to demonstrate that no breach occurred, or, to the extent applicable, that the breach was not material or knowingly committed or has been cured. The parties understand and agree that should BMS fail to make a presentation to the Office within a two-week period after receiving written notice of an alleged breach, it shall be conclusively presumed that BMS is in breach of this Agreement. The parties further understand and agree that the determination whether BMS has breached this Agreement rests solely in the discretion of the Office, and the exercise of discretion by the Office under this paragraph is not subject to review in any court or tribunal outside the Department of Justice. In the event of a breach of this Agreement that results in a prosecution of BMS, such prosecution may be premised upon any information provided by or on behalf of BMS to the Office at any time, unless otherwise agreed when the information was provided.

38. BMS shall expressly waive all rights to a speedy trial pursuant to the Sixth Amendment of the United States Constitution, Title 18, United States Code, Section 3161, Federal Rule of Criminal Procedure 48(b), and any applicable Local Rules of the United States District Court for the District of New Jersey, for the period that this Agreement is in effect.

39. In case of a knowing material breach of this Agreement, any prosecution of BMS relating to the facts set forth in Appendix A that are not time-barred by the applicable statute of limitations as of the execution of this Agreement may be commenced against BMS notwithstanding the expiration of any applicable statute of limitations during the deferred prosecution period. BMS agrees to waive the statute of limitations with respect to any crime that would otherwise expire during the two-year term of this Agreement, and this waiver is knowing and voluntary and in express reliance on the advice of counsel.

40. This agreement expires twenty-four (24) months after the date of its execution, except that, in the event that the Office is conducting an ongoing investigation, prosecution or proceeding related to the facts set forth in the Statement of Facts, the provisions of paragraph 31(b)-(f) regarding the Company's cooperation shall remain in effect until such investigation, prosecution or proceeding is concluded.

41. The Office agrees that if BMS is in full compliance with all of its obligations under this Agreement, the Office, within ten (10) days of the expiration of twenty-four (24) months from the execution of this Agreement, will seek dismissal with prejudice of the criminal complaint filed pursuant to paragraph 2. Except as otherwise provided herein, during and upon the conclusion of the term of this Agreement, the Office agrees that it will not prosecute BMS further for the matters that have been the subject of the Office's investigation relating to this Agreement.

42. BMS agrees that, if it sells or merges all or substantially all of its business operations as they exist as of the date of this Agreement to or into a single purchaser or group of affiliated purchasers during the term of this Agreement, it shall include in any contract for sale or merger a provision binding the purchaser/successor to the obligations described in this Agreement.

43. It is understood that this Agreement is limited to BMS and the Office on behalf of the U.S. Department of Justice and cannot bind other federal, state or local authorities. However, the Office will bring this Agreement and the cooperation of BMS and its compliance with its other obligations under this Agreement to the attention of other prosecuting offices, if requested to do so.

44. This Agreement constitutes the full and complete agreement between BMS and the Office and supersedes any previous agreement between them. No additional promises, agreements, or conditions have been entered into other than those set forth in this Agreement, and none will be entered into unless in writing and signed by the Office, BMS's counsel, and a duly authorized representative of BMS. It is understood that the Office may permit exceptions to or excuse particular requirements set forth in this Agreement at the written request of BMS or the Monitor, but any such permission shall be in writing.

AGREED TO:

Bristol-Myers Squibb Company

Date: June 15, 2005

Christopher J. Christie
United States Attorney
District of New Jersey

Date: June 15, 2005

APPENDIX A - STATEMENT OF FACTS

Bristol-Myers Squibb Company ("BMS" or the "Company") is a Delaware corporation with offices in New Jersey and one of the world's leading producers of pharmaceuticals and health care products. For 2000, BMS reported sales of $18.216 billion and net earnings of $4.711 billion. For 2001, BMS reported sales of $19.423 billion and net earnings of $5.245 billion. The great majority of BMS's sales and earnings in 2000 and 2001 were from sales of pharmaceutical products.

BMS is a publicly traded corporation, the common stock of which is listed on the New York Stock Exchange. BMS's shareholders are located throughout the United States, including in the District of New Jersey.

Wholesaler Sales & Channel Stuffing

BMS manufactures pharmaceutical products and distributes those products through wholesalers. In 2000 to 2001, four U.S. wholesalers handled the distribution of approximately 85% of BMS's U.S. pharmaceutical products. These wholesalers delivered BMS pharmaceutical products to thousands of independent pharmacies, retail chains, hospitals and other health care providers across the country. Wholesalers generally purchased product at least sufficient to meet the demand of these retail businesses.

In 2000 to 2001, BMS regularly used financial incentives to spur wholesalers to buy product in excess of prescription demand, so that BMS could report higher sales and earnings. This practice, which is commonly known as "channel stuffing," was also referred to as "sales acceleration" or "trade loading."

BMS used a variety of financial incentives to spur wholesalers to buy and hold additional product in excess of prescription demand. The financial incentives included:

(a) pre-price increase buy-ins - allowing wholesalers to purchase product in advance of a BMS price increase for the product;

(b) "extended datings" of invoices - extending the due date for the wholesaler's payment beyond the usual thirty days;

(c) additional early payment discounts - discounts beyond those customarily offered to wholesalers for paying early for product; and

(d) "future file" purchases - allowing wholesalers to buy at an old, lower price, even after a price increase had become effective.

Growth of Excess Inventory

Channel stuffing in 2000 to 2001 resulted in "excess inventory" at the wholesalers, because the wholesalers took on more inventory than the amount needed to meet anticipated demand. In the absence of sales incentives or investment purchases, a wholesaler's "normal" inventory level was generally in the approximate range of three weeks' to one month's supply of a mature prescription drug.

The process of reducing excess inventory to levels closer to normal was often called a "workdown," and generally involved selling less than demand during the workdown period. High levels of excess inventory were therefore likely to have an adverse effect on future sales.

Double-Double, Mega-Double and "Top Down" Budgeting

In 1994, BMS announced what became known as the "Double-Double" goal: to double BMS's sales, earnings and earnings per share ("EPS") in a seven year period. The Double-Double required average compound annual growth of approximately 10%. The last year of the Double-Double was 2000, and at the end of the year BMS announced that it had achieved the doubling of earnings and EPS, and that it "virtually" doubled its sales since 1993.

In September 2000 BMS announced the "Strategy for Growth," which incorporated what became known as the "Mega-Double" goal, a plan to double year-end 2000 sales and earnings by the end of 2005, a five-year period. Achievement of the Mega-Double required average compound annual growth of nearly 15%.

The Double-Double and Mega-Double goals were accompanied by what was known as a "top-down" budget process. BMS set aggressive sales and earnings budget targets for the Company and its business units, consistent with the Double-Double and Mega-Double goals.

Earnings Guidance and Estimates

The management of many public companies, including BMS, provided "guidance" to the investing public regarding the expected performance of the business, including EPS, for upcoming quarters and years. In 2000 and at least until December 13, 2001, BMS advised the investing public through its guidance that it expected performance consistent with the Double-Double and Mega-Double.

Relying in part on a company's guidance, professional securities analysts then made public their own estimates of the company's expected performance. These "earnings estimates" or "analyst expectations"--which when averaged were referred to as the "consensus estimates"--were closely followed by investors.

By 2000, BMS had met or exceeded analysts' consensus estimates for at least twenty-four

(24) straight quarters, and this consistency was part of the company's public image. BMS understood that its failure to meet or exceed the consensus estimates for a quarter likely would result in a decrease in the company's stock price.

SEC Reporting

As a public company, BMS was required to comply with the rules and regulations of the United States Securities and Exchange Commission (SEC). The SEC is an independent agency of the United States government which was charged by law with maintaining honest and efficient markets in securities. The SEC's rules and regulations were designed to protect members of the investing public by, among other things, ensuring that a company's financial information was accurately disclosed to the investing public.

Under the SEC's rules and regulations, BMS and its officers were required to submit quarterly reports on Form 10-Q and annual reports on Form 10-K which included financial statements that accurately presented BMS's financial condition and the results of its business operations. Federal law further required the data in these reports to be truthful and consistent with the underlying facts and required the accounting treatments employed in these reports to be consistent with generally accepted accounting principles ("GAAP").

Federal law also required that the Forms 10-Q and 10-K include a section entitled Management's Discussion and Analysis ("MD&A") containing additional information about the company's financial condition and operations. MD&A must contain any material information necessary to make the accompanying financial statements not misleading. The purpose of MD&A was to give investors an opportunity to look at the company through the eyes of management, and understand the company's prospects for the future. MD&A is required to focus on material events and uncertainties known to management that would cause reported financial information not to be necessarily indicative of future operating results or of future financial condition.

Press Releases and Conference Calls

After the end of each quarter, BMS made public announcements about its sales, earnings and business operations generally. The company issued press releases which described sales performance, overall and by product, and held conference calls for analysts regarding the performance of the business. In preparation for the conference calls, senior BMS executives met and discussed issues expected to arise and how to respond to those issues.

The Scheme to Defraud

"Making the Numbers"

BMS promoted a corporate culture in which meeting or exceeding company budget targets and the consensus estimates was considered mandatory. Achieving these goals was known as "making the numbers" or "hitting the numbers." Meeting internal BMS budget targets generally also resulted in sales and earnings that met or exceeded the consensus estimates.

To this end, BMS set aggressive internal sales and earnings targets for 2000, 2001 and earlier periods that would enable the company to hit the widely-touted Double-Double and Mega-Double goals. Every quarter, and at year-end, BMS pressured lower-level employees to meet their budget targets. Certain employees who suggested that the company's budget targets were too aggressive or expressed doubts that they could make the numbers were transferred or demoted.

In the late 1990s, BMS's use of channel stuffing and the accompanying build-up of excess inventory at the wholesalers caused concern among several BMS executives, and during 1999 the Company made some effort to reduce or slow the growth of excess inventory. At the end of 1999, however, senior management refused to accept a proposed BMS budget that would have missed the Double-Double goal, and reassigned the senior executive responsible for the budget proposal. No serious or systematic effort to work down inventory was adopted or undertaken by BMS during the period 2000 to 2001.

Throughout 2000 and 2001, BMS used channel stuffing to boost its sales and artificially inflate its earnings, which enabled BMS to make its numbers and report results consistent with the Double-Double and Mega-Double. This use of channel stuffing to boost sales and earnings, and the resulting steadily increasing levels of excess inventory at the wholesalers, was concealed from the investing public, and was not disclosed to BMS's external auditors and Board of Directors. Without channel stuffing, BMS would have missed its budget targets and the consensus estimates.

Manipulation of Corporate Reserves

BMS regularly set aside funds in "reserve" accounts, to be used for costs related to events such as corporate acquisitions, divestitures or restructuring. Under GAAP, reserves were to be based on good-faith estimates of costs that were reasonably likely to occur. BMS was not permitted to establish reserves that were not based on good-faith estimates of reasonably likely future costs, or to carry excess amounts in its reserve accounts for future use. BMS was not permitted to use reserves to increase revenue in the future or for expenses not related to the purpose for which the funds were originally set aside.

BMS maintained a "reserve schedule" showing available funds from BMS's improperly-established reserves, as well as excess amounts from other reserves. BMS used funds from the reserve schedule for improper purposes, in particular to boost BMS revenue when the company needed additional income to hit the consensus estimates.

Deliberate Rebate Under-Accrual

BMS expected, at the time it sold its products, that at a later time it would have to pay rebates in connection with a portion of those sales. These rebates included Medicaid, "prime vendor" and "managed health care" rebates. Because BMS sold its products to wholesalers, there was a period of time -- a "lag"-- between the time of sale and when BMS received and paid the rebate claims. In keeping with GAAP, BMS was required to set aside funds to pay for expected rebates at the time it booked revenue from its sales.

As BMS's excess inventory at the wholesalers grew in 2000 and 2001, BMS imposed accounting policies and procedures which caused BMS not to accrue for the rebate liabilities for excess inventory. These policies were inconsistent with GAAP and resulted in an under-accrual in BMS's rebate accounts.

Throughout 2000 and 2001 BMS finance staff used an artificially low lag period of six months to estimate accrual balances, even as the excess inventory at the wholesalers grew steadily. By deviating from GAAP and intentionally under-accruing in the Medicaid rebate account, BMS hid the growth of excess inventory and made BMS's sales figures look stronger than they actually were.

Closing Budget Gaps Through Channel Stuffing and Improper Accounting

In 2000 and 2001, BMS often approached the end of a quarter with a gap between actual sales and earnings and the level of sales necessary to hit the company's budget targets. BMS used channel stuffing to make up the company's sales and earnings shortfalls and close the gap. This practice led to a steady increase in excess inventory at the wholesalers.

At various times during a quarter or at quarter-end, in order to supplement the revenue from channel stuffing activity, BMS used funds from improperly-established reserves to bolster income and enable BMS to hit its earnings targets and the consensus estimates.

In every quarter in 2000 and 2001, BMS publicly announced that it had met or exceeded the consensus estimates. BMS would not have been able to make its numbers without channel stuffing and improper accounting measures. BMS did not disclose to the investing public that its success in makings its numbers was due to channel stuffing and improper accounting measures.

False and Misleading Disclosure

In 2000 and 2001, BMS did not disclose the nature or extent of the company's channel stuffing in its 10Ks and 10Qs or in its quarterly press releases and analyst conference calls. For example, BMS did not disclose:

(a) the use of financial incentives to the wholesalers to generate sales in excess of demand;

(b) the use of sales in excess of demand to close budget gaps and hit budget targets;

(c) the level of excess inventory at the wholesalers; and

(d) the amount that excess inventory increased each quarter in 2000 and 2001.

Items (a) through (d) above constituted information reasonably likely to have a material effect on BMS's financial condition or results of its business operations. Failure to disclose this information deprived the investing public of information regarding BMS's past performance and future prospects. Further, in addition to omitting material information, BMS made or caused others to make or permitted false and misleading statements of material fact on the quarterly analyst conference calls and in the company's SEC filings.

DIRECTOR'S CERTIFICATE

I have read this agreement and carefully reviewed every part of it with counsel for Bristol-Myers Squibb Company ("BMS"). I understand the terms of this Agreement and voluntarily agree, on behalf of BMS, to each of the terms. Before signing this Agreement, I consulted with the attorney for BMS. The attorney fully advised me of BMS's rights, of possible defenses, of the Sentencing Guidelines' provisions, and of the consequences of entering into this Agreement. No promises or inducements have been made other than those contained in this Agreement. Furthermore, no one has threatened or forced me, or to my knowledge any person authorizing this Agreement on behalf of BMS, in any way to enter into this Agreement. I am also satisfied with the attorney's representation in this matter. I certify that I am a director of BMS, and that I have been duly authorized by the Board of Directors of BMS to execute this certificate on behalf of BMS.

6/13/05
Date

James D. Robinson
Bristol-Myers Squibb Company

CERTIFICATE OF COUNSEL

I am counsel for Bristol-Myers Squibb Company ("BMS"). In connection with such representation, I have examined relevant BMS documents, and have discussed this Agreement with the authorized representative of BMS. Based on my review of the foregoing materials and discussions, I am of the opinion that:

1. The undersigned counsel is duly authorized to enter into this Agreement on behalf of BMS.

2. This Agreement has been duly and validly authorized, executed and delivered on behalf of BMS, and is a valid and binding obligation of BMS.

Further, I have carefully reviewed every part of this Agreement with directors of BMS. I have fully advised these directors of BMS's rights, of possible defenses, of the Sentencing Guidelines' provisions, and of the consequences of entering into this Agreement. To my knowledge, BMS's decision to enter into this Agreement is an informed and voluntary one.

____________________ 6/15/05 Date

____________________ 6/15/05 Date

Attorneys for Bristol-Myers Squibb Company

CERTIFIED COPY OF RESOLUTION

Upon motion duly made, seconded, and unanimously carried by the affirmative vote of all the Directors present, the following resolutions were adopted:

WHEREAS, Bristol-Myers Squibb Company ("BMS") has been engaged in discussions with the United States Attorney's Office for the District of New Jersey (the "Office") in connection with an investigation being conducted by the Office into activities of BMS relating to wholesaler inventory and certain accounting issues;

WHEREAS, the Board of Directors of BMS consents to resolution of these discussions by entering into a deferred prosecution agreement that the Board of Directors has reviewed with outside counsel representing BMS, relating to a criminal complaint to be filed in the U.S. District Court for the District of New Jersey charging BMS with conspiracy to commit securities fraud,

NOW THEREFORE, BE IT RESOLVED that outside counsel representing BMS from Debevoise & Plimpton LLP be, and they hereby are authorized to execute the Deferred Prosecution Agreement on behalf of BMS substantially in the same form as reviewed by the Board of Directors at this meeting and as attached hereto as Exhibit A, and that a Director of the Company is authorized to execute the Director's Certificate attached thereto.

SECRETARY'S CERTIFICATION

I, Sandra Leung, the duly elected Secretary of Bristol-Myers Squibb Company (the "Company") a corporation duly organized under the laws of the State of Delaware, hereby certify that the following is a true and exact copy of a resolution approved by the Board of Directors of the Company at a meeting held at New York, New York on June 12, 2005;

WHEREAS, Bristol-Myers Squibb Company ("BMS") has been engaged in discussions with the United States Attorney's Office for the District of New Jersey (the "Office") in connection with an investigation being conducted by the Office into activities of BMS relating to wholesaler inventory and certain accounting issues;

WHEREAS, the Board of Directors of BMS consents to resolution of these discussions by entering into a deferred prosecution agreement that the Board of Directors has reviewed with outside counsel representing BMS, relating to a criminal complaint to be filed in the U.S. District Court for the District of New Jersey charging BMS with conspiracy to commit securities fraud,

NOW THEREFORE, BE IT RESOLVED that outside counsel representing BMS from Debevoise & Plimpton LLP be, and they hereby are authorized to execute the Deferred Prosecution Agreement on behalf of BMS substantially in the same form as reviewed by the Board of Directors at this meeting and as attached hereto as Exhibit A, and that a Director of the Company is authorized to execute the Director's Certificate attached thereto.

IN WITNESS WHEREOF, I have hereunto signed my name as Secretary and affixed the Seal of said Corporation this 13th day of June, 2005.

Secretary

CORPORATE SEAL

In re STEINHARDT PARTNERS, L.P., STEINHARDT MANAGEMENT CO., INC., and MICHAEL STEINHARDT, Defendants-Petitioners. SALOMON BROTHERS TREASURY LITIGATION Plaintiff-Respondent, v. STEINHARDT PARTNERS, L.P., STEINHARDT MANAGEMENT CO., INC., and MICHAEL STEINHARDT, Defendants-Petitioners. SECURITIES AND EXCHANGE COMMISSION, Amicus Curiae.

Docket No. 93-3079

UNITED STATES COURT OF APPEALS FOR THE SECOND CIRCUIT

9 F.3d 230; 1993 U.S. App. LEXIS 28979; Fed. Sec. L. Rep. (CCH) P97,818; 27 Fed. R. Serv. 3d (Callaghan) 726

October 15, 1993, Argued
November 8, 1993, Decided

SUBSEQUENT HISTORY: [**1] As Amended November 22, 1993.

PRIOR HISTORY: Petition for a writ of mandamus to set aside an Opinion and Order of the United States District Court for the Southern District of New York, Patterson, J., dated June 30, 1993, granting plaintiff's motion to compel production of documents.

DISPOSITION: The petition is denied. $

CASE SUMMARY:

PROCEDURAL POSTURE: Defendant corporations petitioned for a writ of mandamus to set aside an order of the United States District Court for the Southern District of New York granting plaintiff investment broker's motion to compel the production of documents.

OVERVIEW: While being investigated by the Securities and Exchange Commission (SEC) for possible violations regarding the Treasury markets, defendant corporations voluntarily submitted a memorandum containing their legal theories to the SEC. Subsequently, plaintiff investment broker sued defendants, alleging fraud and manipulation in the Treasury markets. Plaintiff requested production of documents previously produced by defendants to any investigating government agency. Defendants refused to produce the legal memorandum on the basis that it was protected by the work product doctrine. The district court granted plaintiff's motion to compel production. Defendants petitioned for a writ of mandamus to set aside the order. The court denied the petition, holding that defendants' voluntary disclosure to the SEC, an adversary, waived the work product privilege as to plaintiff. The court noted that it was not adopting a per se rule and that determinations regarding voluntary disclosures to the government had to be made on a case by case basis.

OUTCOME: The court denied the petition and lifted the stay on the proceedings, since defendants waived the protections of the work product doctrine.

LexisNexis(R) Headnotes

Civil Procedure > Appeals > Reviewability > Adverse Determinations
Civil Procedure > Disclosure & Discovery
[HN1] The general rule is that pretrial discovery orders are not appealable.

Civil Procedure > Remedies > Extraordinary Writs
Civil Procedure > Disclosure & Discovery
[HN2] The Second Circuit will use mandamus to review discovery orders involving a claim of privilege only when: (i) an issue of importance and of first impression is raised; (ii) the privilege will be lost in the particular

case if review must await a final judgment; and (iii) immediate resolution will avoid the development of discovery practices or doctrine undermining the privilege.

Civil Procedure > Remedies > Extraordinary Writs
[HN3] On the merits, an appellate court applies a stringent standard of review to petitions for mandamus.

Civil Procedure > Remedies > Extraordinary Writs
[HN4] A petitioner seeking a writ of mandamus must show that he or she lacks an adequate alternative means to obtain the relief sought, and must demonstrate a clear and indisputable right to the issuance of the writ, amounting to a clear abuse of discretion or a usurpation of judicial power. This standard requires a showing of an extreme need for reversal. It is not enough that the court of appeals might disagree with the district judge's decision were it a conventional appeal from a final judgment. Even if the judge was wrong, indeed very wrong, that is not enough.

Civil Procedure > Disclosure & Discovery > Work Product
[HN5] An attorney's protected thought processes include preparing legal theories, planning litigation strategies and trial tactics, and sifting through information. At its core, the work-product doctrine shelters the mental processes of the attorney, providing a privileged area within which he can analyze and prepare his client's case. The doctrine grants counsel an opportunity to think or prepare a client's case without fear of intrusion by an adversary.

Civil Procedure > Disclosure & Discovery > Work Product
[HN6] The waiver doctrine provides that voluntary disclosure of attorney work product to an adversary waives the privilege as to other parties.

Civil Procedure > Disclosure & Discovery > Work Product
[HN7] A client cannot be permitted to pick and choose among his opponents, waiving the attorney-client privilege for some and resurrecting the claim of confidentiality to obstruct others, or to invoke the privilege as to communications whose confidentiality he has already compromised for his own benefit.

Civil Procedure > Disclosure & Discovery > Work Product
[HN8] An allegation that a party facing a federal investigation and the prospect of a civil fraud suit must make difficult choices is insufficient justification for carving a substantial exception to the waiver doctrine to the attorney-client privilege.

Civil Procedure > Disclosure & Discovery > Work Product
[HN9] Crafting rules relating to privilege in matters of governmental investigations must be done on a case-by-case basis.

COUNSEL: TFREDERICK P. SCHAFFER (Argued), Schulte Roth & Zabel, New York, NY, for Defendants-Petitioners Steinhardt Partners, L.P., Steinhardt Management Co., Inc. and Michael Steinhardt.

THEODORE V. WELLS, JR., Lowenstein, Sandler, Kohl, Fisher & Boylan, Roseland, NJ, for Defendant-Petitioner Michael Steinhardt. KAREN MORRIS (Argued), Morris & Morris, Wilmington, DE, for Plaintiff-Respondent Salomon Brothers Treasury Litigation. STANLEY M. GROSSMAN, Pomerantz Levy Haudek Block & Grossman, New York, NY, for Plaintiff-Respondent Salomon Brothers Treasury Litigation. JULES BRODY, Stull, Stull & Brody, New York, NY, for Plaintiff-Respondent Salomon Brothers Treasury Litigation.

PAUL GONSON, Solicitor, Securities and Exchange Commission, Washington, DC, for Amicus Curiae Securities and Exchange Commission.

JUDGES: Before: NEWMAN, Chief Judge, KEARSE, Circuit Judge, and TENNEY n1, District Judge.

n1 The Honorable Charles H. Tenney, Senior United States District Judge for the Southern District of New York, sitting by designation. [**2]

OPINIONBY: TENNEY

OPINION:

[*232] TENNEY, District Judge:

Defendants-petitioners Steinhardt Partners, L.P., Steinhardt Management Co. and Michael Steinhardt (collectively "Steinhardt") are codefendants with several other parties in a civil class action suit alleging manipulation of the market for two-year Treasury notes during the Spring and Summer of 1991. In answer to a discovery request in the class action suit, Steinhardt identified as responsive a memorandum prepared by its attorneys and previously submitted to the Securities and Exchange Commission (SEC). Steinhardt declined to produce the memorandum, claiming that the memorandum was attorney work product. Plaintiffs moved to compel production. The district court granted the motion to compel, holding that the prior disclosure of the memorandum to the SEC waived the claim for work product protection. Steinhardt filed this petition for a writ of mandamus to prevent discovery of the document. The court's jurisdiction arises under *28 U.S.C. § 1651* and the petition is denied.

Background

This petition for a writ of mandamus arises out of highly publicized allegations of wrongdoing in the market for Treasury notes. In [**3] June 1991, the SEC began an informal investigation of the Treasury markets. As part of this informal investigation, the SEC asked Steinhardt, among many others, to provide certain documents related to its trading activities. In August of 1991, the SEC began a formal investigation of the Treasury markets, and issued subpoenas to Steinhardt and others. Steinhardt complied with these subpoenas.

In the Spring of 1992, the SEC's Enforcement Division solicited Steinhardt's views regarding several issues in the investigation. The SEC explained to counsel that it had not yet decided whether to initiate enforcement proceedings against Steinhardt. Apparently, existing case law did not provide complete answers to some of the possible legal bases for an enforcement action in the Treasury markets. After two meetings between the SEC and Steinhardt, the Enforcement Division asked Steinhardt's counsel to submit a memorandum that would address the facts and issues involved in the case and discuss the relevant legal theories. Steinhardt claims that the SEC stated that this would not be a so-called Wells submission, although the SEC's amicus brief now characterizes the memorandum as a Wells [**4] submission. See *17 C.F.R. § 202.5(c)*. We do not address the question of whether the memorandum was in fact a Wells submission, since we do not believe that characterizing the memorandum as such alters our conclusion.

Counsel prepared and submitted a memorandum and accompanying exhibits to the SEC on June 26, 1992. A notice reading "FOIA Confidential Treatment Requested" appeared on the document. Steinhardt does not dispute the SEC's assertion that there was no agreement that the SEC would maintain the confidentiality of the memorandum. See Amicus Brief of SEC at 8. To date, the SEC has not brought any enforcement proceedings against Steinhardt related to its trading activities in the Treasury markets during 1991.

While the SEC investigated the Treasury markets, civil suits commenced against Steinhardt and numerous other defendants. Now consolidated as a class action, the suits allege various acts of fraud and manipulation in the Treasury markets, and have not reached a hearing on the merits. During discovery, plaintiffs requested all documents previously produced by defendants to any investigating government agency. Steinhardt identified the June 26, 1992 memorandum as [**5] responsive to the request, but declined to produce the document, citing the work product doctrine. On June 3, 1993, plaintiffs moved to compel production of the memorandum. After hearing the parties on June 17, 1993, the district court granted the motion to compel [*233] on June 30, 1993. Steinhardt promptly filed a petition for mandamus. This court entered a stay of the order compelling production, pending consideration of the petition for mandamus.

Discussion

I.

As a threshold matter, the court must determine whether it will use mandamus to review the district court's order compelling production of the memorandum. We have consistently expressed reluctance to use mandamus as a means to circumvent [HN1] the general rule that pretrial discovery orders are not appealable. *In re W.R. Grace & Co., 984 F.2d 587, 589 (2d Cir. 1993)*. "Unlike other circuits, we have rarely used the extraordinary writ of mandamus to overturn a discovery order involving a claim of privilege." *Chase Manhattan Bank, N.A. v. Turner & Newall, PLC, 964 F.2d 159, 163 (2d Cir. 1992)*. [HN2] The circuit will use mandamus to review discovery orders involving a claim of privilege [**6] only when:

> (i) an issue of importance and of first impression is raised; (ii) the privilege will be lost in the particular case if review must await a final judgment; and (iii) immediate resolution will avoid the development of discovery practices or doctrine undermining the privilege.

W.R. Grace, 984 F.2d at 589, quoting *Turner & Newall, 964 F.2d at 163*.

This dispute presents one of the very rare circumstances permitting the use of mandamus to review a district court order. The circuit has not previously resolved the important question of whether disclosure of attorney work product in connection with a government investigation waives the privilege in later civil discovery. The district courts of the circuit have addressed similar questions, arriving at different results. See *Enron Corp. v. Borget, 1990 U.S. Dist. LEXIS 12471, 1990 WL 144879* (S.D.N.Y. Sept. 22, 1990) (no waiver of work product protection); *Teachers Ins. & Annuity Ass'n v. Shamrock Broadcasting Co., 521 F. Supp. 638 (S.D.N.Y.*

1981) (disclosure to SEC waived attorney-client privilege); *Byrnes v. IDS Realty Trust, 85 F.R.D. 679 (S.D.N.Y. 1980)* [**7] (applying Eighth Circuit law and holding attorney-client privilege not waived); *GAF Corp. v. Eastman Kodak Co., 85 F.R.D. 46 (S.D.N.Y. 1979)* (no waiver of work product protection). The circuits have also split on this issue. Compare *Westinghouse Elec. Corp. v. Republic of the Philippines, 951 F.2d 1414 (3rd Cir. 1991)* (waiver of work product and attorney-client privilege upon voluntary disclosure of information to SEC and Department of Justice) and *In re Subpoenas Duces Tecum, 738 F.2d 1367, 238 U.S. App. D.C. 221,* (D.C. Cir. 1984) (waiver of work product and attorney-client privilege upon voluntary disclosure of information to SEC) with *Diversified Indus., Inc. v. Meredith, 572 F.2d 596, 606 (8th Cir. 1977)* (en banc) (no waiver of attorney-client privilege).

In addition, the alleged privilege will be lost if review must await final judgment. Disclosure of the memorandum will destroy the alleged privilege and moot the question. As to the final part of the Turner & Newall test, Steinhardt's argument that the district court's order will lead to discovery practices undermining the privilege [**8] is not a mere conclusory allegation, but is supported by the decisions of at least one circuit. See *Diversified, 572 F.2d at 611.* Given the fact that this court is yet to resolve this important issue, a decision from at least one circuit supporting petitioner's argument that the district court's order undermines the privilege, and the need for immediate resolution before the alleged privilege is lost, this petition satisfies the conditions of the Turner & Newall test.

II.

[HN3] On the merits, we apply a stringent standard of review to petitions for mandamus. [HN4] The petitioner must show that he or she lacks an adequate alternative means to obtain the relief sought, and must demonstrate a clear and indisputable right to the issuance of the writ, amounting to a clear abuse of discretion or a usurpation of judicial power. *Mallard v. United States District Court, 490 U.S. 296, 309, 104 L. Ed. 2d 318, 109 S. Ct. 1814 (1989).* This standard requires a showing of an "extreme need for reversal." *In re Weisman, 835 F.2d 23, 27* [*234] *(2d Cir. 1987).* It is not enough that the court of appeals might disagree with the district judge's decision were [**9] it a conventional appeal from a final judgment. Id. "'Even if the judge was wrong, indeed very wrong . . . that is not enough.'" Id., quoting *United States v. DiStefano, 464 F.2d 845, 850 (2d Cir. 1972).*

In considering the merits, we do not address the question of whether the memorandum actually constituted attorney work product. The record does not state that the district judge conducted an in camera review of the memorandum to determine whether it was indeed work product. Believing the question of waiver dispositive of the motion, the district court stated that "the present motion involves only whether the protection of the work-product doctrine has been waived as to the Memorandum, not whether the protection ever existed." A66. The record indicates that in the district court, plaintiffs did not dispute the fact that the memorandum constituted attorney work product. See id. Since the issue was not raised in the district court, we accept the district court's assumption that the memorandum includes the mental impressions, conclusions, opinions, or legal theories of an attorney within the meaning of *Fed. R. Civ. P. 26(3).*

The district [**10] court found that Steinhardt had disclosed the work product to an adversary, and that the disclosure was voluntary. A65. The district court then held, as a matter of law, that the voluntary disclosure waived the privilege in this subsequent civil suit. The district court followed the analysis of the Westinghouse and In re Subpoenas Duces Tecum opinions that the policy considerations behind the work product doctrine do not merit the creation of an exception to the waiver rule. A69.

The district court's finding that Steinhardt voluntarily disclosed the memorandum to an adversary was not erroneous. The court correctly concluded that Steinhardt disclosed the memorandum voluntarily. The declarations submitted by Steinhardt in connection with the motion to compel do not allege that the SEC coerced or required compliance in any way. This case is therefore distinguishable from situations in which disclosure to an adversary is only obtained through compulsory legal process. See generally, *In re Subpoenas Duces Tecum, 738 F.2d at 1373.*

We agree with the district court's conclusion that the SEC stood in an adversarial position to Steinhardt when it [**11] requested assistance. See e.g., *Westinghouse, 951 F.2d at 1428; In re Subpoenas Duces Tecum, 738 F.2d at 1372.* This was not a case in which a party complied with a benign request to assist the SEC in performing its routine regulatory duties. The determinative fact in analyzing the adversarial nature of the relationship is that Steinhardt knew that it was the subject of an SEC investigation, and that the memorandum was sought as part of this investigation. The fact that the request came from the SEC's Enforcement Division further supports the conclusion that this was an adversarial relationship. Even though the SEC's investigation has not resulted in any formal enforcement proceedings against Steinhardt, the presence of an adversarial relationship does not depend on the existence of litigation. Additionally, the fact that

Steinhardt cooperated voluntarily does not transform the relationship from adversarial to friendly.

Given these findings of fact by the district court, we now turn to its holding that voluntary disclosure to the SEC waived the privilege as a matter of law. The logic behind the work product doctrine [**12] is that opposing counsel should not enjoy free access to an attorney's thought processes. *Hickman v. Taylor, 329 U.S. 495, 511, 91 L. Ed. 451, 67 S. Ct. 385 (1947);* In the *Matter of Grand Jury Subpoenas, 959 F.2d 1158, 1166-67 (2nd Cir. 1992).* [HN5] An attorney's protected thought processes include preparing legal theories, planning litigation strategies and trial tactics, and sifting through information. See *Hickman, 329 U.S. at 511.* "At its core, the work-product doctrine shelters the mental processes of the attorney, providing a privileged area within which he can analyze and prepare his client's case." *United States v. Nobles, 422 U.S. 225, 238, 45 L. Ed. 2d 141, 95 S. Ct. 2160 (1975).* "The doctrine grants counsel an opportunity to think or prepare a client's case without fear of intrusion by an adversary." *In re Six Grand Jury Witnesses, 979 F.2d 939, 944 (2d* [*235] *Cir. 1992)*, cert. denied, *113 S. Ct. 2997 (1993).*

Common sense and the practicalities of litigation define the limits of the work product doctrine. *Nobles, 422 U.S. at 238.* [**13] Once a party allows an adversary to share the otherwise privileged thought processes of counsel, the need for the privilege disappears. Courts therefore accept the waiver doctrine as a limitation on work product protection. [HN6] The waiver doctrine provides that voluntary disclosure of work product to an adversary waives the privilege as to other parties. See *Nobles, 422 U.S. at 239; In re John Doe Corp., 675 F.2d 482, 489 (2d Cir. 1982).*

Steinhardt relies on the Eighth Circuit's opinion in Diversified for the proposition that voluntary disclosure of privileged material to an investigatory government agency does not waive the privilege as to subsequent private litigants. The en banc opinion in Diversified addressed this question in the context of the attorney-client privilege, rather than in the context of the work product doctrine. See *Diversified, 572 F.2d at 611 n.4.* This is not fatal to Steinhardt's argument, since much of the reasoning in Diversified has equal, if not greater, applicability in the context of the work product doctrine.

Examination of conflicting authority and of [**14] the purposes of the work product doctrine convinces us that Steinhardt waived any work product protection by voluntarily submitting the memorandum to the SEC. The Diversified opinion based its "selective waiver" theory on the policy consideration that if voluntary disclosure to the SEC waives privilege as to subsequent private litigants, parties might be discouraged from cooperating with governmental investigations. Id.; see also *Byrnes, 85 F.R.D. at 688-89.* Corporations might also hesitate before initiating an independent investigation of wrongdoing within the corporation when asked to by government authorities. *Diversified, 572 F.2d at 611.*

However, the Supreme Court has rejected attempts to use "the work-product doctrine to sustain a unilateral testimonial use of work-product materials . . . ." *Nobles, 422 U.S. at 239-40.* We have previously denied a claim of privilege after a claimant decided to selectively disclose confidential materials in order to achieve other beneficial purposes. *In re John Doe Corp., 675 F.2d at 489.* Similarly, we now reject [**15] Steinhardt's attempt to use the doctrine to sustain the unilateral use of a memorandum containing counsel's legal theories voluntarily submitted to an investigatory body.

The D.C. Circuit rejected the selective waiver theory, in part based on the perception that the selective waiver doctrine allows a party to manipulate use of the privilege through selective assertion. *Permian Corp. v. United States, 665 F.2d 1214, 1221, 214 U.S. App. D.C. 396 (D.C. Cir. 1981).* We agree that selective assertion of privilege should not be merely another brush on an attorney's palette, utilized and manipulated to gain tactical or strategic advantage. The Permian court noted that the basis for the attorney-client privilege is that frank communication between attorney and client will be fostered by confidentiality, and that the "privilege ceases when the client does not appear to have been desirous of secrecy. . . . Voluntary cooperation with government investigations may be a laudable activity, but it is hard to understand how such conduct improves the attorney-client relationship." *Id. at 1220-21.* [HN7] "The client cannot be permitted to pick and choose among his [**16] opponents, waiving the privilege for some and resurrecting the claim of confidentiality to obstruct others, or to invoke the privilege as to communications whose confidentiality he has already compromised for his own benefit." *Id. at 1221.* Although Permian was limited to a discussion of the attorney-client privilege, the D.C. and Third Circuits applied similar reasoning to work product in *In re Sealed Case, 676 F.2d 793, 219 U.S. App. D.C. 195*, (D.C. Cir. 1982), and *Westinghouse Elec. Corp. v. Republic of the Philippines, 951 F.2d 1414 (3rd Cir. 1991)*, respectively.

Voluntary disclosure is generally made because a corporation believes that there is some benefit to be gained from disclosure. See generally, James D. Cox, Insider Trading Regulation and the Production of Evidence, *64 Wash. U.L.Q. 421 (1986)* (analyzing market incentives for disclosure of positive [*236] and negative information). The SEC's amicus brief argues convincingly that the protection of privilege is not required to encourage compliance with SEC requests for cooperation with investigations. See Amicus Brief [**17] of SEC at 20-25. The SEC has continued to receive voluntary cooperation from subjects of investigations, notwithstanding the rejection of the selective waiver doctrine by two circuits and public statements from Directors of the Enforcement Division that the SEC considers voluntary disclosures to be discoverable and admissible. See id. at 3, 20-25; SEC Form 1662.

The D.C. Circuit recognizes that a corporation has substantial incentives to cooperate with SEC requests for assistance. Voluntary cooperation offers a corporation an opportunity to avoid extended formal investigation and enforcement litigation by the SEC, the possibility of leniency for prior misdeeds, and an opportunity to narrow the issues in any resulting litigation. *In re Subpoenas Duces Tecum, 738 F.2d at 1369; In re Sealed Case, 676 F.2d at 801;* see *In re Worlds of Wonder Securities Litigation, 147 F.R.D. 208, 213 (N.D. Cal. 1992).* These incentives exist regardless of whether private third party litigants have access to attorney work product disclosed to the SEC. "When a corporation elects to participate in a voluntary disclosure [**18] program like the SEC's, it necessarily decides that the benefits of participation outweigh the benefits of confidentiality . . . . It forgoes some of the traditional protections of the adversary system in order to avoid some of the traditional burdens that accompany adversary resolution of disputes, especially disputes with such formidable adversaries as the SEC." *In re Subpoenas Duces Tecum, 738 F.2d at 1372;* quoting *In re Sealed Case, 676 F.2d at 822-23.*

Petitioner alleges that a denial of the petition will present those in similar situations with a Hobson's choice between waiving work product protection through cooperation with investigatory authorities, or not cooperating with the authorities. Whether characterized as forcing a party in between a Scylla and Charybdis, a rock and a hard place, or some other tired but equally evocative metaphoric cliche, the "Hobson's choice" argument is unpersuasive given the facts of this case. [HN8] An allegation that a party facing a federal investigation and the prospect of a civil fraud suit must make difficult choices is insufficient justification for carving a substantial exception [**19] to the waiver doctrine.

In denying the petition, we decline to adopt a per se rule that all voluntary disclosures to the government waive work product protection. [HN9] Crafting rules relating to privilege in matters of governmental investigations must be done on a case-by-case basis. *Upjohn Co. v. United States, 449 U.S. 383, 396, 66 L. Ed. 2d 584, 101 S. Ct. 677 (1981);* see *In re Six Grand Jury Witnesses, 979 F.2d at 944* (work product doctrine to be applied in a common sense manner in light of reason and experience as determined on a case-by-case basis). Establishing a rigid rule would fail to anticipate situations in which the disclosing party and the government may share a common interest in developing legal theories and analyzing information, or situations in which the SEC and the disclosing party have entered into an explicit agreement that the SEC will maintain the confidentiality of the disclosed materials. See *In re Sealed Case, 676 F.2d at 817* (work product protection only waived if privileged material is disclosed to a party who doesn't share such common interests); *In re LTV Securities Litigation, 89 F.R.D. 595, 614-15 (N.D. Tex. 1981)* [**20] (SEC and corporation shared interest in analyzing facts and legal theories upon appointment of an independent special investigatory officer by consent decree).

Conclusion

At the time of the submission of the memorandum to the Enforcement Division, the SEC and Steinhardt stood in an adversarial position. Steinhardt's voluntary submission of the memorandum to the Enforcement Division waived the protections of the work product doctrine as to subsequent civil litigants seeking the memorandum from Steinhardt.

The petition is denied and the stay is lifted.

(20

UNITED STATES DISTRICT COURT
SOUTHERN DISTRICT OF NEW YORK

MARUZEN COMPANY, LTD.,

Plaintiff,

v.

HSBC USA, INC. (F/K/A REPUBLIC NEW YORK CORPORATION), HSBC BANK USA (F/K/A REPUBLIC NATIONAL BANK OF NEW YORK), REPUBLIC NEW YORK SECURITIES CORPORATION, JAMES E. SWEENEY, WILLIAM H. ROGERS, and MARTIN A. ARMSTRONG,

Defendants.

YAKULT HONSHA CO., LTD.,

Plaintiff,

v.

REPUBLIC NEW YORK SECURITIES CORPORATION, HSBC USA, INC. (F/K/A REPUBLIC NEW YORK CORPORATION), HSBC BANK USA (F/K/A REPUBLIC NATIONAL BANK OF NEW YORK), WILLIAM H. ROGERS, JAMES E. SWEENEY, and MARTIN A. ARMSTRONG,

Defendants.

MEMORANDUM AND ORDER
00 Civ. 1079 (RO) • FILE IN
00 Civ. 1512 (RO)

OWEN, District Judge:

Before me is a motion to compel by the two remaining plaintiffs in the Princeton Noteholder civil actions, Maruzen Company, Ltd. ("Maruzen") and Yakult Honsha Co., Ltd. ("Yakult"), who were not part of the settlement with the Republic Defendants (for reasons that are irrelevant to the instant motion) and who have not released their claims against the Republic

Defendants.[1] Maruzen and Yakult seek documents from the Republic Defendants' internal investigation that the Republic Defendants produced to certain regulatory and investigative authorities[2] in an effort to help those authorities uncover the full scope of the alleged Princeton Note scandal.

The main issue here is whether the Republic Defendants had confidentiality agreements with the various agencies, and if so whether such agreements affect work product protection waiver. The leading case in this circuit is In re Steinhardt Partners, L.P., 9 F.3d 230 (2d Cir. 1993). There, as here, the plaintiffs moved to compel the production of a memorandum that was prepared by defendants' attorneys and submitted to the SEC. There was no agreement between defendants and the SEC to keep the memorandum confidential. The Second Circuit found that the work product protection was waived because "the waiver doctrine provides that voluntary disclosure of work product to an adversary waives the privilege as to other parties." Id. at 235. The court noted that "[v]oluntary disclosure is generally made because a corporation believes that there is some benefit to be gained from disclosure" and that such cooperation "offers a corporation an opportunity to avoid extended formal investigation and enforcement litigation by the SEC, the possibility of leniency for prior misdeeds, and an opportunity to narrow the issues in any resulting litigation." Id. at 235-36. "These incentives exist regardless of whether private

[1]The Republic Defendants include Republic New York Securities Corporation ("RNYSC"), HSBC USA, Inc. (f/k/a Republic New York Corporation) and HSBC Bank USA (f/k/a Republic National Bank of New York).

[2]Those authorities are the U.S. Attorney's Office, Southern District of New York ("USAO"), the Securities and Exchange Commission ("SEC"), the Commodities Futures Trade Commission ("CFTC"), the Federal Reserve Bank of New York and the Board of Governors of the Federal Reserve (together, the "Fed"), the New York State Banking Department (the "NYSBD"), and Japan's Financial Supervisory Agency.

third party litigants have access to attorney work product disclosed to the SEC." Id. at 236.

While the motion to compel was granted in Steinhardt, the Second Circuit declined "to adopt a *per se* rule that all voluntary disclosures to the government waive work product protection" and insisted upon dealing with these issues on a "case-by-case basis." Id.

> Establishing a rigid rule would fail to anticipate situations in which the disclosing party and the government may share a common interest in developing legal theories and analyzing information, or *situations in which the SEC and the disclosing party have entered into an explicit agreement that the SEC will maintain the confidentiality of disclosed materials.*

Id. (emphasis added).

According to Anne T. Vitale, the Republic/HSBC lawyer with principal responsibility for the Princeton actions and who submitted a declaration in opposition to this motion, the Republic Defendants had confidentiality agreements with all of the authorities (Vitale Decl. ¶¶ 9-15). For example, Ms. Vitale states in her declaration that the Republic Defendants had an oral confidentiality agreement with the U.S. Attorney's Office, which was confirmed by AUSA Richard D. Owens at a meeting on August 13, 2001. (Vitale Decl. ¶ 9). Ms. Vitale claims that this agreement was subsequently honored when the USAO permitted Republic to seek a protective order governing the confidentiality of the documents in the criminal case against Mr. Armstrong prior to the USAO's production to Mr. Armstrong. (Vitale Decl. ¶¶ 11-12). Moreover, the Republic Defendants submitted a letter from AUSA Owens dated March 27, 2002, in which he states that "[t]he understanding between HSBC and the [USAO] at the time the Material was produced was that the [USAO] would maintain the Material in confidence and not disclose it to any third parties, other than Government agents and agencies, except as required by law." (Van Dyke Sur-Reply Decl., Exh. D).

Plaintiffs have failed to dispute the facts put forth by Ms. Vitale regarding the existence of confidentiality agreements with the various authorities, and conceded as such at the oral argument on this motion. (6/14/02 Tr. 29:21-32:11). Therefore, finding that the Republic Defendants had explicit confidentiality agreements with the authorities satisfying Steinhardt, In re Lesley Fay Companies, Inc. Securities Litigation, 161 F.R.D. 274 (S.D.N.Y. 1995), and Permian Corp. v. U.S., 665 F.2d 1214, 1218, 1222 (D.C. Cir. 1981), plaintiffs' motion to compel is hereby denied in all respects.

So ordered.

Dated: New York, New York
July 18, 2002

United States District Judge

MERRILL LYNCH & CO., INC., MERRILL LYNCH CAPITAL SERVICES INC., and ML IBK POSITIONS, INC., Plaintiffs, - against - ALLEGHENY ENERGY, INC., Defendant, ALLEGHENY ENERGY, INC., and ALLEGHENY ENERGY SUPPLY CO., LLC., Counterclaim-Plaintiffs, - against - MERRILL LYNCH & CO., INC., and MERRILL LYNCH CAPITAL SERVICES, INC., Counterclaim-Defendants.

02 Civ. 7689 (HB)

UNITED STATES DISTRICT COURT FOR THE SOUTHERN DISTRICT OF NEW YORK

2004 U.S. Dist. LEXIS 21543

October 22, 2004, Decided
October 26, 2004, Filed

SUBSEQUENT HISTORY: Partial summary judgment granted by, in part, Partial summary judgment denied by, in part *Merrill Lynch & Co. v. Allegheny Energy, Inc., 2005 U.S. Dist. LEXIS 6073 (S.D.N.Y., Apr. 12, 2005)*

PRIOR HISTORY: *Merrill Lynch & Co. v. Allegheny Energy, Inc., 2003 U.S. Dist. LEXIS 21122 (S.D.N.Y., Nov. 25, 2003)*

DISPOSITION: [*1] Defendant's motion for leave to amend granted in part. Defendant's application for production of reports denied.

LexisNexis(R) Headnotes

COUNSEL: For Merrill Lynch & Co., Inc., Merrill Lynch Capital Services, Inc., ML IBK Positions, Inc., Plaintiffs: John Gueli, Stuart J. Baskin, Shearman & Sterling, L.L.P., New York, NY.

For Allegheny Energy, Inc., Defendant: Alan Ross Arkin, Stanley S. Arkin, Arkin, Kaplan, LLP, New York, NY; Hyman L. Schaffer, Arkin, Schaffer & Kaplan L.L.P., New York, NY.

For Allegheny Energy, Inc., Counter Claimant: Alan Ross Arkin, Stanley S. Arkin, Arkin, Kaplan, LLP, New York, NY; Hyman L. Schaffer, Arkin, Schaffer & Kaplan L.L.P., New York, NY.

For Merrill Lynch & Co., Inc., Merrill Lynch Capital Services, Inc., Counter Defendants: John Gueli, Stuart J. Baskin, Shearman & Sterling, L.L.P., New York, NY.

JUDGES: Harold Baer, Jr., U.S.D.J.

OPINIONBY: Harold Baer, Jr.

OPINION:

MEMORANDUM & ORDER

Hon. HAROLD BAER, JR., District Judge:

Present before the Court are two outstanding issues. First, counterclaim plaintiffs Allegheny Engery, Inc. n1 and Allegheny Energy [*2] Supply Co., LLC (collectively, "Allegheny") move pursuant to Federal Rule of Civil Procedure *("Fed. R. Civ. P.") 15(a)* for leave to file Second Amended Counterclaims in the above-captioned matter. Second, Allegheny seeks discovery of two reports produced in connection with an internal investigation conducted by counterclaim defendants Merrill Lynch & Co., Inc. and Merrill Lynch Capital Services, Inc. n2 (collectively, "Merrill Lynch"). For the reasons discussed herein, Allegheny's motion for leave to amend is granted in part and denied in part and its request for production of the two reports is denied. For the purposes of the following discussion, familiarity with the facts of this case as set out in the Court's

November 24, 2003 Opinion and Order, *Merrill Lynch & Co., Inc. v. Allegheny Energy, Inc., 2003 U.S. Dist. LEXIS 21122, No. 02 Civ. 7689, 2003 WL 22795650 (S.D.N.Y. Nov. 25, 2003)*, n3 is presumed.

n1 Allegheny Energy, Inc. is also a defendant in this action.

n2 These two Merrill Lynch entities, together with ML IBK Positions, Inc., are the original plaintiffs.

n3 Although the Westlaw version of this decision is dated November 25, 2003, the Slip Opinion was signed on November 24, 2003.

[*3]

I. Motion for Leave to Amend

Fed. R. Civ. P. 15(a) provides that leave to amend "shall be freely given when justice so requires." Under this standard the decision to grant leave to amend is within the sound discretion of the Court. *Krumme v. WestPoint Stevens Inc., 143 F.3d 71, 88 (2d Cir. 1998)*. Leave should not be granted, however, if it would prejudice the opposing party, id., or where the proposed amendment would be futile, *Prudential Ins. Co. of Am. v. BMC Indus., Inc., 655 F. Supp. 710, 711 (S.D.N.Y. 1987)* (finding that "it is inappropriate to grant leave when the amendment would not survive a motion to dismiss"). Merrill Lynch does not claim it would be prejudiced by the proposed amendments or that it would be futile to amend. Indeed, Merrill Lynch only opposes Allegheny's motion to the extent that Allegheny seeks punitive damages and demands a jury trial in its proposed Second Amended Counterclaims. Where, as here, a party seeks to amend pleadings after the deadline set by the Court's scheduling order, n4 the Second Circuit has held that the stricter "good cause" standard applies. *Parker v. Columbia Pictures Indus., 204 F.3d 326, 340 (2d Cir. 2000)*. [*4] "Good cause" requires diligence, id., which Allegheny has shown, as it moved for leave to amend within three weeks of its receipt of documents produced during discovery, which, in part, formed the basis of its motion. n5 Allegheny therefore has met both of these standards and, accordingly, will be allowed to amend its counterclaims. Unfortunately, this does not end the inquiry.

n4 The last date for amended pleadings in the June 23, 2003 pre-trial scheduling order -- agreed to and signed off by the parties -- was August 29, 2003.

n5 Allegheny also bases its motion on Daniel Gordon's guilty plea, which was entered and accepted by Judge Lynch on December 19, 2003. United States v. Gordon, No. 03 Cr. 1494.

Allegheny's proposed amendments conflict with the Court's November 24, 2003 Opinion and Order in two important regards. First, Allegheny's proposed Second Amended Counterclaims seek punitive damages for Allegheny's first counterclaim for fraud. I previously decided that punitive damages were not available [*5] for Allegheny's fraudulent inducement claim. *Merrill Lynch & Co., Inc., 2003 U. S. Dist. LEXIS 21122, 2003 WL 22795650 at *8*. As I earlier explained, this claim arises from Allegheny's breach of contract claim, which requires Allegheny to establish that Merrill Lynch's conduct was directed at and worked a harm to the public in general. *Id. 2003 U.S. Dist. LEXIS 21122 at *8-9*. As Merrill Lynch points out, Allegheny did not move for reconsideration, and it is far too late for it to do so now. In any event, Allegheny has not presented additional allegations of the requisite public harm. It may be that Daniel Gordon's ("Gordon") plea allocution has implied a more far-reaching fraud, Letter from Stanley Arkin to the Court of 7/12/04 ("Arkin Letter"), Ex. A at 27:23-28-:1 (describing a decision by Gordon's "superiors" to alter financial data to make the Energy Trading Division look more profitable to potential buyers). This does not alter the harm alleged. As I have already noted, "the conduct for which Allegheny here seeks redress is not Merrill Lynch's role in assisting Enron [to] deceive and harm the public, but rather Merrill Lynch's alleged deception of Allegheny." *Id. 2003 U.S. Dist. LEXIS 21122 at *8*. Therefore, Allegheny's motion is denied [*6] to the extent that it seeks punitive damages on its fraud counterclaim.

Second, Allegheny's proposed Second Amended Counterclaims are at odds with my earlier decision in this matter to the extent that they make a jury demand. The plain language of Section 11.09(b) of the Asset Contribution and Purchase Agreement n6 provides that "the parties hereto hereby irrevocably waive any and all right to trial by jury in any legal proceeding arising out of or related to this Agreement or any of the transaction contemplated hereby." *Id. 2003 U.S. Dist. LEXIS 21122 at *10*. All of Allegheny's counterclaims either "arise out of" or are "related to" the agreement between the parties and I have already decided that the balance of the case law favors enforcement of this mutually agreed-upon and bargained for contractual term. There is nothing further to address and therefore Allegheny's motion is denied in this respect as well.

n6 The Asset Contribution and Purchase Agreement was the January 8, 2001 agreement between Allegheny and Merrill Lynch for the purchase of the Merrill Lynch's energy commodity trading business, Global Energy Markets for $ 490 million in cash and a 2% equity interest in Allegheny Supply. *Merrill Lynch & Co., Inc., 2003 U.S. Dist. LEXIS 21122, 2003 WL 22795650, at *2.*

[*7]

II. Discovery of Reports

A. Factual Background

Allegheny also seeks production of two reports, which are the results of Merrill Lynch's internal investigation into the circumstances surrounding Gordon's theft of some $ 43 million in connection with the Falcon Energy Trade. n7 In the Fall of 2002, shortly after this lawsuit was filed, the United States Attorney's Office for the Southern District of New York informed Merrill Lynch that it was investigating the Falcon Energy Trade. Merrill Lynch therefore undertook its own internal investigation (conducted by and under the supervision of in-house and outside counsel), which culminated in two reports: (1) the March 5, 2003 Report to James Mann, Office of the General Counsel of Merrill Lynch; and (2) the June 25, 2003 Special Review of Transaction Approval and Processing Controls.

n7 At his plea allocution, Gordon admitted that he created a fictitious entity called Falcon, which he presented to his colleagues as a company that would hedge the risk of other long-term energy transactions, including those of the Global Energy Markets purchased by Allegheny. Arkin Letter, Ex. A at 26:24-27:16. The parties disagree as to whether or not Gordon acted alone.

[*8]

In August 2003, there was widespread publicity concerning Gordon's theft in connection with the Falcon Energy Trade. As a result, Andrew McMaster ("McMaster"), the lead client services partner for Deloitte & Touche, Merrill Lynch's independent auditor, spoke with John McDermott ("McDermott"), the Director of Corporate Audit at Merrill Lynch, who works out of Merrill Lynch's Office of General Counsel, and inquired about Gordon's theft and Merrill Lynch's subsequent actions. McDermott informed McMaster that Merrill Lynch's counsel and corporate auditor had investigated the theft and produced the two reports at issue here, under the direction and supervision of counsel. McMaster requested and was provided with a copy of these reports. Both McMaster and McDermott attested that these reports were provided to assist McMaster to "identify any potential internal control, accounting or audit issues of which [he] was not already aware based on [his] routine and regular prior discussions with Merrill Lynch during the course of the audit...." Letter from John Gueli to the Court of 9/28/04 ("Gueli Letter"), Ex. B. P5; see also id., Ex. A P4. Further, both McMaster and McDermott declared [*9] that these reports were provided with the understanding that (1) they were prepared by counsel and were privileged; (2) Deloitte & Touche would keep these materials confidential; and (3) there would be no further disclosure. Id., Ex. A PP4-6; Ex. B PP5-7. According to McMaster, he read the reports and concluded that they presented no new issues and did not impact Deloitte & Touche's audit work or Merrill Lynch's financial statements. Ultimately, Deloitte & Touche issued an unqualified audit report with regard to Merrill Lynch's 2003 financial statements.

Allegheny now seeks to obtain both of these reports and argues that this disclosure to Deloitte & Touche constituted a waiver of any applicable privileges. Merrill Lynch apparently concedes that the attorney-client privilege has been waived and argues that the reports instead fall under the work product privilege. Merrill Lynch acknowledges that Deloitte & Touche's audit work and discussions with Merrill Lynch personnel regarding internal control and other issues are discoverable. However, Merrill Lynch argues that these two reports contain substantially more information, including the details of "Merrill Lynch's counsel's investigation, [*10] mental impressions, conclusions, and opinions regarding Gordon's theft...." Gueli Letter at 4 n.2. Merrill Lynch seeks to shield these intimate details from disclosure.

B. The Work Product Privilege

The work product privilege, as articulated by the Supreme Court in *Hickman v. Taylor, 329 U.S. 495, 91 L. Ed. 451, 67 S. Ct. 385 (1947)* and later codified by *Fed. R. Civ. P. 26(b)(3)*, provides that materials prepared in anticipation of litigation are not discoverable absent a showing that the party seeking discovery has a substantial need for the materials and cannot obtain the equivalent without undue hardship. This doctrine "is intended to preserve a zone of privacy in which a lawyer can prepare and develop legal theories and strategy 'with an eye toward litigation,' free from unnecessary intrusion by his adversaries." *United States v. Adlman, 134 F.3d 1194, 1196 (2d Cir. 1998)* (citing *Hickman, 329 U.S. at 510-11, 91 L. Ed. 451, 67 S. Ct. 385*). The policy underlying work product protection is "to promote the adversary system by safeguarding the fruits of an attorney's trial preparations from the discovery attempts of the opponent." *United States v. Am. Tel. & Tel. Co., 206 U.S. App. D.C. 317, 642 F.2d 1285, 1299 (D.C. Cir. 1980).* [*11] As counsel for Allegheny observed not too long ago,

> the American legal system takes as its axioms the importance of effective counsel, the need for a client to be able to confide in his or her (or, since Upjohn n8, its) attorney, and the advantages of zealous representation in an adversarial system. The attorney-client and work-product privileges were instituted to serve those important social ends, even at the cost of occasionally limiting the truth-seeking function in individual cases.
>
> Stanley S. Arkin and Charles Sullivan Attacking, Business Crime: Corporate Attorney-Client Privilege and Work Product, N.Y.L.J., May 5, 2004, at 3, (col. 1).

Thus, when weighing two fundamental components of our legal system -- the liberal rules of discovery outlined by the Federal Rules of Civil Procedure, e.g., *Ratliff v. Davis Polk & Wardwell, 354 F.3d 165, 170 (2d Cir. 2003)* ("Discovery rules 'are to be accorded a broad and liberal treatment [] to effectuate their purpose that civil trials in the federal courts no longer need be carried on in the dark.'") (alteration in original) (quoting *Schlagenhauf v. Holder, 379 U.S. 104, 115, 13 L. Ed. 2d 152, 85 S. Ct. 234 (1964)),* [*12] and the "adversary system's interest in maintaining the privacy of an attorney's thought processes and in ensuring that each side relies on its own wit in preparing their respective cases," *Sporck v. Peil, 759 F.2d 312, 316 (3d Cir. 1985)* -- the balance must sometimes tip towards a limitation on the free-flow of information so that a higher purpose is served. This is entirely consistent with a variety of other doctrines within our legal system, including the exclusionary rule, the prohibition against hearsay, and the application of evidentiary privileges. As the Supreme Court has observed, "there is no gainsaying that arriving at the truth is a fundamental goal of our legal system. But various constitutional rules limit the means by which government may conduct this search for truth in order to promote other values embraced by the Framers and cherished throughout our Nation's history." *James v. Illinois, 493 U.S. 307, 311, 107 L. Ed. 2d 676, 110 S. Ct. 648 (1990)* (internal quotation marks and citation omitted) (discussing the exclusionary rule).

n8 *Upjohn Co. v. United States, 449 U.S. 383, 66 L. Ed. 2d 584, 101 S. Ct. 677 (1981).*

[*13]

The parties here do not contest the applicability of the work product privilege to the two reports. Indeed, it is evident that the reports were at least initially protected by the privilege as they were the results of an internal investigation conducted under the guidance of counsel after Merrill Lynch was informed that it was the subject of a criminal investigation. Under these circumstances, it is safe to say that the reports were prepared in anticipation of litigation. See *In re LTV Sec. Litig., 89 F.R.D. 595, 612 (N.D. Tex. 1981)* ("Investigation by a federal agency presents more than a 'remote prospect' of future litigation and gives grounds for anticipating litigation sufficient for the work-product rule to apply."). Instead, the debate here centers on whether Merrill Lynch waived the applicable privilege when it provided the reports to Deloitte & Touche.

C. Waiver

Generally speaking, "the work product privilege should not be deemed waived unless disclosure is inconsistent with maintaining secrecy from possible adversaries." *Stix Prods. v. United Merchants & Mfrs., 47 F.R.D. 334, 338 (S.D.N.Y. 1969).* "The work product privilege is not [*14] automatically waived by any disclosure to third persons. Rather, the courts generally find a waiver of the work product privilege only if the disclosure 'substantially increases the opportunity for potential adversaries to obtain the information.'" *In re Pfizer Inc. Sec. Litig., 1993 U.S. Dist. LEXIS 18215, No. 90 Civ. 1260, 1993 WL 561125, at *6 (S.D.N.Y. Dec. 23, 1993)* (quoting *In re Grand Jury, 561 F. Supp. 1247, 1257 (E.D.N.Y. 1982))* (internal citation omitted). Implicit in this analysis is the question of whether the third party itself can or should be considered an adversary. Accordingly, courts have generally held that where the disclosing party and the third party share a common interest, there is no waiver of the work product privilege. E.g., id. ("Disclosure of work product to a party sharing common interests is not inconsistent with the policy of privacy protection underlying the doctrine."); see also *Viacom, Inc. v. Sumitomo Corp. (In* *re Copper Mkt. Antitrust Litig.), 200 F.R.D. 213, 221 n.6 (S.D.N.Y. 2001)* (same).

This much is settled. However, courts are split in their treatment of disclosures to a corporation's accountants or auditors. More precisely, courts differ in their [*15] conceptualization of two critical points that are often implicitly intertwined in their analysis: whether the "adversary" contemplated by the work product privilege is necessarily a litigation adversary and whether a corporation's auditor is such an adversary, to whom disclosure will waive the privilege. While admittedly there are good arguments on both sides, in this case, I answer both questions in the negative and conclude that Merrill Lynch's disclosure of the reports to Deloitte & Touche did not constitute a waiver of the applicable work product protection.

In a frequently cited case, In re Pfizer, Inc. Sec. Litig., Judge Buchwald held that Pfizer's disclosure of documents to its independent auditor, KPMG Peat Marwick ("Peat Marwick"), did not waive its work product privilege. *1993 U.S. Dist. LEXIS 18215, 1993 WL 561125, at *6*. Judge Buchwald's decision was based on her observation that "Pfizer and Peat Marwick obviously shared common interests in the information, and Peat Marwick is not reasonably viewed as a conduit to a potential adversary." Id. Other courts have adopted precisely this analysis. E.g., *Gutter v. E.I. Dupont de Nemours & Co., 1998 U.S. Dist. LEXIS 23207, No. 95 Civ. 2152, 1998 WL 2017926,at *5 (S.D. Fla. May 18, 1998)* [*16] (holding that disclosure to outside accountants did not waive the work product privilege "since the accountants are not considered a conduit to a potential adversary"); *Gramm v. Horsehead Indus., Inc., 1990 U.S. Dist. LEXIS 773, No. 87 Civ. 5122, 1990 WL 142404, at *5 (S.D.N.Y. Jan. 25, 1990)* (same). Still others have applied this approach, but scrutinized the precise role of the accountants. E.g., *Samuels v. Mitchell, 155 F.R.D. 195, 201 (N.D. Cal. 1994)* (deciding that disclosure did not constitute a waiver of the work product privilege because the accounting firm was acting as a consultant, not a "public accountant," at the relevant time).

Judge Hellerstein articulated another view in Medinol, Ltd. v. Boston Scientific Corp., where, in finding a waiver of the work product privilege, he emphasized the "public watchdog" role of independent auditors. *214 F.R.D. 113, 116 (S.D.N.Y. 2002)* (quoting *United States v. Arthur Young & Co., 465 U.S. 805, 817-18, 79 L. Ed. 2d 826, 104 S. Ct. 1495 (1984))*. Judge Hellerstein observed that it "has become crystal clear in the face of the many accounting scandals that have arisen as of late, in order for auditors [*17] to properly do their job, they *must* not share common interests with the company they audit." *Id. 214 F.R.D. at 116* (emphasis in original). While this is a valid policy consideration, the fact is that the determination in Medinol was based on a finding that the auditor's interests were not aligned with that of the corporation and that the disclosure of the documents at issue -- the Special Litigation Committee's minutes -- did not serve a pertinent litigation interest.

These cases turn on their facts. In Mass. Inst. of Tech., for example, the First Circuit noted that the Massachusetts Institute of Technology ("MIT") had a common interest with the Department of Defense's ("DOD") audit agency in "the proper performance of MIT's defense contracts and the proper auditing and payment of MIT's bills." *129 F.3d 681 at 686 (1st Cir. 1997)*. However, the First Circuit found that the audit agency -- which was responsible for preventing an overcharge for services -- was a potential adversary because a review of MIT's billing statements could result in a dispute or even litigation. *Id. at 683, 687*. Thus, MIT was found to have forfeited its work product protection, but only after an analysis of [*18] the parties' relationship. Similarly, in In re Raytheon Sec. Litig., the court recognized that "the pivotal question is whether disclosure of documents protected by the work product doctrine to an independent auditor substantially increases the opportunities for potential adversaries to obtain the information." *218 F.R.D. 354, 360 (D. Mass. 2003)*. After a discussion of the public responsibilities of independent auditors, the court noted that "there is no evidence that materials disclosed to an independent auditor are likely to be turned over to the company's adversaries except to the extent that the securities laws and/or accounting standards mandate public disclosure." Id.

As these cases make clear, the Court's inquiry must not end with the mere fact of a disclosure to the independent auditors. Indeed, in an analogous context, the Second Circuit has specifically eschewed a per se rule of waiver. *In re Steinhardt Partners, 9 F.3d 230, 236 (2d Cir.)* ("we decline to adopt a per se rule that all voluntary disclosures to the government waive work product protection"). Instead, the Court must assess of what type of common interests the work [*19] product doctrine contemplates and whether a corporation and its outside auditors share any such interest.

Courts in this District have ruled that it not necessary that the party to whom disclosure made share a "litigation" interest with the party that asserts the privilege. *Cellco P'ship d/b/a Verizon Wireless v. Nextel Communications, Inc., 2004 U.S. Dist. LEXIS 12717, No. M8-85, Civ.A. 03-725, 2004 WL 1542259, at *1 (S.D.N.Y. July 9, 2004)* (deciding that defendant and its advertising agency shared a common business interest and therefore disclosure of an e-mail with legal advice did not waive work product privilege); *In re Copper Mkt.*

Antitrust Litig., 200 F.R.D. at 221 n.6 (holding that there was no waiver of the work product protection because the business and public relations firm specializing in "litigation-related crisis management" shared a common interest). Thus, the fact that Merrill Lynch and Deloitte & Touche do not share a common litigation interest is of no moment. n9

> n9 This view of "common interests" may very well stem from this Circuit's approach to work product protection in general. Our Circuit has adopted the more expansive "because of" test for work product, under which any document prepared "'because of' existing or expected litigation" is sheltered under the protection of the work product privilege. *Adlman, 134 F.3d at 1198* (rejecting the narrower formulation that encompasses only those documents "prepared 'primarily or exclusively to assist in litigation'"). Under this formulation, work product protection extends to documents prepared in anticipation of litigation even if they are "intended to assist in the making of a business decision influenced by the likely outcome of the anticipated litigation." *Id. 134 F.3d at 1195.*

[*20]

Instead, the critical inquiry -- to me -- must be whether Deloitte & Touche should be conceived of as an adversary or a conduit to a potential adversary. As Judge Hellerstein and other courts have observed, an independent auditor could be conceived of as an adversary because of its important public function to independently ensure the accuracy of a company's financial reports. Clearly, outside auditors must maintain an independent role in this regard. Indeed, a good portion of the reforms embodied in the *Sarbanes-Oxley Act of 2002* ("Sarbanes Oxley"), *15 U.S.C. § 7201 et seq.*, are aimed at strengthening the independence of auditors and eliminating conflicts of interest (S.E.C. Release No. Jan 28, 2003). See, e.g., John C. Coffee, Jr., Gatekeeper Failure and Reform: The Challenge of Fashioning Relevant Reforms, *84 B.U. L. Rev. 301, 335, 336 (April 2004)*. I concur with the need for auditors to retain their independence. I conclude, however, that a waiver is not supported by the circumstances of this case or applicable case law and that such a holding will not impair auditor independence.

As I read them, the work product cases require a tangible adversarial relationship. [*21] The First Circuit, for example, found that the DOD's audit agency was an adversary because it could potentially dispute a billing charge and file suit against MIT, not because of its duty to review MIT's accounts. *Mass. Inst. of Tech., 129 F.3d at 687.* This requirement makes particular sense when one considers the importance of the work product doctrine in safeguarding our adversary system of litigation. *Hickman, 329 U.S. 495 at 511, 91 L. Ed. 451, 67 S. Ct. 385* (reasoning that without work product protection "an attorney's thoughts, heretofore inviolate, would not be his own. Inefficiency, unfairness and sharp practices would inevitably develop in the giving of legal advice and in the preparation of cases for trial. The effect on the legal profession would be demoralizing. And the interests of the clients and the cause of justice would be poorly served."). Further counseling for a more concrete approach is the Supreme Court's observation that the work product "doctrine is an intensely practical one, grounded in the realities of litigation in our adversary system." *United States v. Nobles, 422 U.S. 225 at 238, 45 L. Ed. 2d 141, 95 S. Ct. 2160.*

Thus, any tension between an auditor and a corporation that arises from an [*22] auditor's need to scrutinize and investigate a corporation's records and book-keeping practices simply is not the equivalent of an adversarial relationship contemplated by the work product doctrine. Nor should it be. A business and its auditor can and should be aligned insofar as they both seek to prevent, detect, and root out corporate fraud. Indeed, this is precisely the type of limited alliance that courts should encourage. For example, here Merrill Lynch complied with Deloitte & Touche's request for copies of the internal investigation reports so that the auditors could further assess Merrill Lynch's internal controls, both to inform its audit work and to notify the corporation if there was a deficiency. An internal control, as defined by the professional standards of the American Institute of Certified Public Accountants ("AICPA"), "is a process -- effected by an entity's board of directors, management, and other personnel -- designed to provide reasonable assurance regarding the achievement of objectives in the following categories: (a) reliability of financial reporting, (b) effectiveness and efficiency of operations, and (c) compliance with applicable laws and regulations. [*23] " AICPA AU § 319.06 (2001). As this definition indicates, information regarding internal controls directly relates to the reliability of financial information and legality of corporate behavior. n10 Without access to this information, auditors would likely fail in the fulfillment of their important public function. Consistent with this, Deloitte & Touche requested Merrill Lynch's investigative reports in August 2003 so that it could determine whether Gordon's theft and the surrounding circumstances impacted upon Merrill Lynch's financial statements, and, if necessary, report any conditions that could adversely affect the corporation's ability to record or report financial data to directors and officers, e.g., AICPA Statement on

Auditing Standards ("SAS") 60.02 -- both of which ultimately lead to the dissemination of more accurate information to the investing public.

n10 At the time of the disclosure in this case, auditors were not required to report separately on a corporation's internal controls. Compare AICPA AU § 319.05 ("The auditor uses the understanding of internal control and the assessed level of control risk in determining the nature, timing, and extent of substantive tests for financial statement assertions.") with Sarbanes-Oxley § 404, *15 U.S.C. § 7262* (requiring management to report annually on internal controls and auditors to report on management's assessment of such controls). Under current law, internal controls play a more direct role in the work of auditors.

[*24]

There was no further disclosure of the protected material in this case, nor could there have been, as Deloitte & Touche was under an ethical and professional obligation to maintain materials received from its client confidential, unless disclosure was required by law or accounting standards. Gueli Letter, Ex. B P7. The relevant standards at the time in question did not contemplate disclosure of documents or their specific contents to a third party. Instead, if an auditor learned of a "reportable condition," i.e., an internal control deficiency that "could adversely affect the organization's ability to record, process, summarize, and report financial data," AICPA SAS 60.02, the auditor was obligated to report this information to corporate management, the audit committee, and/or the board of directors. AICPA SAS 60.02, .09, .10, AICPA SAS 61. The applicable standard specifically provides that an auditor's report on a reportable condition should state that it is to be used only by personnel within the corporation, unless the auditor is required to furnish the report to government authorities. AICPA SAS 60.10. The only public revelation could have been, in the worst case scenario, a general [*25] statement by Deloitte & Touche regarding its inability to accurately evaluate Merrill Lynch's financial statements due to internal control deficiencies. In sum, the nature of the disclosure in this case and the obligations of Deloitte & Touche under the applicable accounting standards simply do not make out a waiver.

Moreover, to construe a company's auditor as an adversary and find a blanket rule of waiver of the applicable work product privilege under these circumstances could very well discourage corporations from conducting a critical self-analysis and sharing the fruits of such an inquiry with the appropriate actors. See *United States v. Arthur Young & Co., 677 F.2d 211, 220 (2d Cir. 1982)*, aff'd in part, rev'd in part, *465 U.S. 805, 79 L. Ed. 2d 826, 104 S. Ct. 1495 (1984)* (noting that "a prudent organization might not be perfectly candid with independent auditors once it knew that the information revealed would be reachable" by the Internal Revenue Service). Because this likelihood cannot be empirically documented, the Court's assessment "is thus intuitive and indeed visceral. With that caveat, the court is 'persuaded' that it is likely that corporations will be less willing [*26] to engage in this sort of self-investigation if the results of such an investigation can be discovered in parallel civil litigation." *In re LTV Sec. Litig., 89 F.R.D. at 612.*

This conclusion does not necessarily mean that auditors will be any less independent. In fact, the SEC rules implementing the Sarbanes-Oxley Act specifically contemplate a role for independent auditors in internal investigations that will not compromise their independence. *In re Strengthening the Commission's Requirements Regarding Auditor Independence, 2003 WL 183801* (S.E.C. Release No. Jan 28, 2003). Instead, the aim should be for corporations to share information with their auditors to facilitate a meaningful review and, ultimately, the availability of more accurate information for the investing public. It is also important to encourage complete disclosure between a company and its auditor, so that auditors are not inadvertently shielded from complete frankness by corporate management, so that they can later claim that they had no knowledge of alleged malfeasance. As one commentator has urged, public policy should seek to eliminate the "perverse incentives" for auditors not [*27] to inquire too closely into corporate wrongdoing lest they too be held liable in subsequent securities litigation. Coffee, *84 B.U. L. Rev. at 345.* Finally, a waiver of the work product privilege upon disclosure of a document to a company's outside auditor will not meaningfully prevent the situations that have arisen in recent scandals where auditors actively participated in corporate fraud and the ensuing cover-ups. Instead, lawmakers and professional organizations can and have acted to alter the legal, regulatory, and ethical framework in which corporate management and auditors operate. The work product privilege is a separate doctrine that exists to safeguard other values no less precious, those of our adversary system of litigation. We should not sacrifice one to save another, particularly when I believe no such savings will be made.

Thus, this Court must weigh, on the one hand, a litigant's right to "every man's evidence," *United States v. Bryan, 339 U.S. 323, 331, 94 L. Ed. 884, 70 S. Ct. 724 (1950)*, with the need to promote complete disclosure between a corporation and its auditors so that both parties can fulfill their necessary roles. When presented with a similar dilemma [*28] of competing policy concerns, the Second Circuit reasoned that "one policy has to bend a bit." *Arthur Young & Co., 677 F.2d at 220.* I therefore find that Allegheny is not entitled to the roadmap to Merrill Lynch's internal investigation and the mental impressions and opinions of its counsel. In this context, Merrill Lynch and Deloitte & Touche were not adversaries contemplated by the work product doctrine and there was no waiver.

It is hereby:

ORDERED that Allegheny's motion for leave to amend is granted, except to the extent that it seeks punitive damages on its fraud counterclaim and demands a jury trial; and it is further

ORDERED that Allegheny's application for production of the two reports discussed herein is denied; and it is further

ORDERED that the Clerk of the Court close this motion.

SO ORDERED.

New York, New York
October 22, 2004

Harold Baer, Jr.

U.S.D.J.

In Re NATURAL GAS COMMODITY LITIGATION

03 Civ. 6186 (VM) (AJP)

UNITED STATES DISTRICT COURT FOR THE SOUTHERN DISTRICT OF NEW YORK

2005 U.S. Dist. LEXIS 11950

June 21, 2005, Decided

PRIOR HISTORY: *In re Natural Gas Commodity Litig., 358 F. Supp. 2d 336, 2005 U.S. Dist. LEXIS 2870 (S.D.N.Y., 2005)*

LexisNexis(R) Headnotes

COUNSEL: [*1] For Conerstone Propane Partners, L.P., individually and on behalf of all others similarly situated, Plaintiff: Ali Oromchian, Finkelstein Thompson & Loughram, San Francisco, Ca; Bernard Persky, Craig L. Briskin, Vaishali Shetty, Goodkind Labaton Rudoff & Sucharow LLP, New York, NY.

For Roberto E. Calle Gracey, Consol Plaintiff: Ali Oromchian, Finkelstein Thompson & Loughram, San Francisco, Ca; Bernard Persky, Craig L. Briskin, Vaishali Shetty, Goodkind Labaton Rudoff & Sucharow LLP, New York, NY; Christopher J. Gray, Law Office of Christopher J. Gray, P.C., New York, NY; Christopher Lovell, Gary S. Jacobson, Lovell, Stewart, Halebian, L.L.P., New York, NY; Louis F. Burke, Louis F. Burke, P.C., New York, NY.

For Dominick Viola, Jr., Consol Plaintiff: Ali Oromchian, Finkelstein Thompson & Loughram, San Francisco, Ca; Bernard Persky, Craig L. Briskin, Vaishali Shetty, Goodkind Labaton Rudoff & Sucharow LLP, New York, NY.

For Reliant Energy Services, Inc., Defendant: Gregory Copeland, Holly Roberts, J. Michael Baldwin, James Hail, Mark Robeck, Baker Botts, L.L.P., Houston, TX; Paul Anthony Ragsua, Baker Botts LLP (NY), New York, NY; Diana L. Weiss, Orrick, Herrington & Sutcliffe [*2] LLP, New York, NY; Douglas R. Tribble, Pillsbury Winthrop LLP, San Diego, CA; Jonathan L. Abram, Hogan & Hartson, L.L.P., New York, NY.

For Centerpoint Energy Houston Electric, L.L.C., Defendant: Blossom Kan, John L. Hendricks, Orrin L. Harrison, III, Akin Gump Strauss Hauer & Feld LLP (NYC), New York, NY.

For Dynegy Marketing and Trade, Defendant: J. Michael Baldwain, Baker Botts, L.L.P., Houston, TX; Diana L. Weiss, Orrick, Herrington & Sutcliffe LLP, New York, NY; Douglas R. Tribble, Michael J. Kass, Pillsbury Winthrop LLP, San Diego, CA; Jonathan L. Abram, Hogan & Hartson, L.L.P., New York, NY; Mark Robert Hellerer, Pillsbury Winthrop Shaw Pittman, LLP (NY), New York, NY.

For Dygeny Holdings, Inc., Dygeny, Inc., Defendants: Mark Robert Hellerer, Pillsbury Winthrop Shaw Pittman, LLP (NY), New York, NY; Douglas R. Tribble, Pillsbury Winthrop LLP, San Diego, CA; Michael J. Kass, Pillsbury Winthrop LLP, San Francisco, CA.

For Aquila Energy Marketing Corp., Aquila Merchant Service, Inc., Defendants: J. Michael Baldwain, Baker Botts, L.L.P., Houston, TX; Diana L. Weiss, Orrick, Herrington & Sutcliffe LLP, New York, NY; Douglas R. Tribble, Pillsbury Winthrop LLP, San [*3] Diego, CA; Jonathan L. Abram, Hogan & Hartson, L.L.P., New York, NY.

For AEP Energy Service, American Electric Power Company, Inc., Defendants: J. Michael Baldwain, Baker Botts, L.L.P., Houston, TX; Diana L. Weiss, Orrick, Herrington & Sutcliffe LLP, New York, NY; Douglas R. Tribble, Pillsbury Winthrop LLP, San Diego, CA;

Jonathan L. Abram, Hogan & Hartson, L.L.P., New York, NY; Steven J. Routh, Hogan & Hartson, LLP, Washington, DC.

For El Paso Merchant Energy, L.P., El Paso Corporation, Defendants: J. Michael Baldwain, Baker Botts, L.L.P., Houston, TX; Diana L. Weiss, Orrick, Herrington & Sutcliffe LLP, New York, NY; Douglas R. Tribble, Pillsbury Winthrop LLP, San Diego, CA; Jonathan L. Abram, Hogan & Hartson, L.L.P., New York, NY; Stephanie J. Goldstein, Fried, Frank, Harris, Shriver & Jacobson, New York, NY.

For Williams Energy Marketing and Trading Company, Williams Companies, Inc., Defendants: J. Michael Baldwain, Baker Botts, L.L.P., Houston, TX; Diana L. Weiss, Orrick, Herrington & Sutcliffe LLP, New York, NY; Douglas R. Tribble, Pillsbury Winthrop LLP, San Diego, CA; Jonathan L. Abram, Hogan & Hartson, L.L.P., New York, NY; Jeffrey M. Shohet, Mark H. Hamer, Noah [*4] A. Katsell, DLA Piper Rudnick Gray Cary US LLP, San Diego, CA; Stanley J. Panikowski, Gray Cary Ware & Freidenrich LLP, San Diego, CA.

For Duke Energy Corporation, Defendant: Peter Joseph Kadzik, Dickenstein, Shapiro, Morin & Oshinsky, L.L.P., Washington, DC.

For CMS Energy Corporation, Defendant: J. Michael Baldwain, Baker Botts, L.L.P., Houston, TX; Diana L. Weiss, Orrick, Herrington & Sutcliffe LLP, New York, NY; Douglas R. Tribble, Pillsbury Winthrop LLP, San Diego, CA; Jonathan L. Abram, Hogan & Hartson, L.L.P., New York, NY; Banks Brown, Patrick S. Sinclair, Robert E. Rice, McDermott, Will & Emery, New York, NY.

For Sempra Energy, Defendant: Melvin Arnold Brosterman, Stroock & Stroock & Lavan LLP, New York, NY.

For Enserco Energy, Inc., Defendant: Richard P. Swanson, Thelen, Reid & Priest, L.L.P., New York, NY.

For WD Energy Services, Encana Corporation, Defendants: J. Michael Baldwain, Baker Botts, L.L.P., Houston, TX; Diana L. Weiss, Orrick, Herrington & Sutcliffe LLP, New York, NY; Douglas R. Tribble, Pillsbury Winthrop LLP, San Diego, CA; Jonathan L. Abram, Hogan & Hartson, L.L.P., New York, NY; Robert A. Sacks, Sullivan & Cromwell, Los Angeles, CA. [*5]

For Entergy-Kock Trading, L.P., Defendant: J. Michael Baldwain, Baker Botts, L.L.P., Houston, TX; Diana L. Weiss, Orrick, Herrington & Sutcliffe LLP, New York, NY; Douglas R. Tribble, Pillsbury Winthrop LLP, San Diego, CA; Jonathan L. Abram, Hogan & Hartson, L.L.P., New York, NY; Jill Diane Fairbrother, Kenneth M. Raisler, Sullivan and Cromwell, LLP(NYC), New York, NY.

For Kock Industries, Inc., Defendant: J. Michael Baldwain, Baker Botts, L.L.P., Houston, TX; Diana L. Weiss, Orrick, Herrington & Sutcliffe LLP, New York, NY; Douglas R. Tribble, Pillsbury Winthrop LLP, San Diego, CA; Jonathan L. Abram, Hogan & Hartson, L.L.P., New York, NY; Kenneth Conboy, Latham & Watkins, LLP, New York, NY.

For Cook Inlet Energy Supply, L.L.C., Defendant: J. Michael Baldwain, Baker Botts, L.L.P., Houston, TX; Diana L. Weiss, Orrick, Herrington & Sutcliffe LLP, New York, NY; Douglas R. Tribble, Pillsbury Winthrop LLP, San Diego, CA; Jonathan L. Abram, Hogan & Hartson, L.L.P., New York, NY; Mary Anne Sullivan, William H. Johnson, Hogan & Hartson, L.L.P., Washington, DC.

For Cook Inlet Region, Inc., Inupait Energy Corporation, Defendants: Mary Anne Sullivan, William H. Johnson, Hogan [*6] & Hartson, L.L.P., Washington, DC.

For Midamerican Energy Company, Defendant: J. Michael Baldwain, Baker Botts, L.L.P., Houston, TX; Diana L. Weiss, Orrick, Herrington & Sutcliffe LLP, New York, NY; Douglas R. Tribble, Pillsbury Winthrop LLP, San Diego, CA; Jonathan L. Abram, Hogan & Hartson, L.L.P., New York, NY; Robert A. Jaffe, Kutak, Rock, L.L.P., New York, NY.

For MIECO, Inc., Defendant: J. Michael Baldwain, Baker Botts, L.L.P., Houston, TX; Diana L. Weiss, Orrick, Herrington & Sutcliffe LLP, New York, NY; Douglas R. Tribble, Pillsbury Winthrop LLP, San Diego, CA; Jonathan L. Abram, Hogan & Hartson, L.L.P., New York, NY; Richard T. Marooney, Jr, King & Spalding, LLP (NYC), New York, NY.

For Idaho Power Company, Idacorp., Inc., Defendants: David H. Hetzel, Leboeuf, Lamb, Greene & Macrae, LLP, New York, NY; Dennis Kerrigan, Jr., Leboeuf, Lamb, Greene & Macrae, LLP, Hartford, CT.

For Cinergy Services, Inc., Cinergy Corp., Defendants: J. Michael Baldwain, Baker Botts, L.L.P., Houston, TX; Diana L. Weiss, Orrick, Herrington & Sutcliffe LLP, New York, NY; Douglas R. Tribble, Pillsbury Winthrop LLP, San Diego, CA; Jonathan L. Abram, Hogan & Hartson, L.L.P., New York, [*7] NY; Patrick M.

McGuirk, Steven M. Bierman, Sidley Austin Brown & Wood LLP (NY), New York, NY; Thomas K. Cauley, Chicago, IL.

For Does 1-100, Defendant, Consol Defendant: J. Michael Baldwain, Baker Botts, L.L.P., Houston, TX; Diana L. Weiss, Orrick, Herrington & Sutcliffe LLP, New York, NY; Douglas R. Tribble, Pillsbury Winthrop LLP, San Diego, CA; Jonathan L. Abram, Hogan & Hartson, L.L.P., New York, NY.

For West Coast Power, LLC, Defendant: Michael J. Kass, Pillsbury Winthrop Shaw LLP, San Diego, CA.

For Cinergy Marketing & Trading, LP, Defendant: Steven M. Bierman, Sidley, Austin, Brown & Wood, New York, NY.

For Duke Energy Trading and Marketing, L.L.C., Consol Defendant: J. Michael Baldwain, Baker Botts, L.L.P., Houston, TX; Diana L. Weiss, Orrick, Herrington & Sutcliffe LLP, New York, NY; Douglas R. Tribble, Pillsbury Winthrop LLP, San Diego, CA; Jonathan L. Abram, Hogan & Hartson, L.L.P., New York, NY; Peter J. Kadzik, Dickenstein, Shaprio, Morin & Oshinsky LLP (DC), Washington, DC.

For Coral Energy Holding, L.P., Coral Energy Resources L.P., Consol Defendants: J. Michael Baldwain, Baker Botts, L.L.P., Houston, TX; Diana L. Weiss, Orrick, Herrington & [*8] Sutcliffe LLP, New York, NY; Douglas R. Tribble, Pillsbury Winthrop LLP, San Diego, CA; Jonathan L. Abram, Hogan & Hartson, L.L.P., New York, NY; Felice Beth Galant, Robert D. Owen, Fulbright & Jaworski L.L.P., New York, NY.

For Calpine Energy Services, L.P., Consol Defendant: Richard P. Swanson, Thelen, Reid & Priest, L.L.P., New York, NY.

For E Prime, Inc., Consol Defendant: Robert C. Micheletto, Jones Day (NYC), New York, NY.

For Oneok Energy Marketing and Trading Company, L.P., Oneok, Inc., Consol Defendants: Karen Michele Crupi-Fitzgerald, Heller Ehrman, White & McAulifee, LLP (NYC), New York, NY.

For Western Gas Resouces, Inc., Consol Defendant: Jerome S. Hirsch, Peter E. Greene, Skadden, Arps, Slate Meagher & Flom, LLP (4 Times Sq, Rm 44), New York, NY; Peter S. Julian, Skadden, Arps, Slate, Meagher & Flom, New York, NY.

For Intelligence Press, Movant: Alia Lyerly Smith, Nathan Siegel, Levine, Sullivan, Kick & Schulz, L.L.P., New York, NY.

For McGraw-Hill Companies, ADR Provider: Matthew A. Leish, Victor A. Kovner, Davis Wright Tremaine LLP, New York, NY.

JUDGES: ANDREW J. PECK, United States Chief Magistrate Judge.

OPINIONBY: ANDREW J. PECK

OPINION: OPINION [*9] **AND ORDER**

ANDREW J. PECK, United States Chief Magistrate Judge :

Plaintiffs, natural gas futures traders, have moved to compel the production of documents from defendants American Electric Company, Inc. ("AEP") and Aquila Merchant Services ("Aquila" or "AMS") (for purposes of this decision, collectively "defendants"). (5/2/05 Plfs. Letter Br.) n1 Defendants claim that these documents are privileged and that their prior production of these documents to governmental agencies has not waived this privilege, since that production was pursuant to non-waiver agreements.

n1 The parties did not docket and file most of their submissions with the Clerk of Court.

For the reasons discussed below, plaintiffs' motion to compel is DENIED.

FACTS

The facts pertaining to the underlying action have been set forth in Judge Marrero's opinion denying defendants' motion to dismiss. See *In re Natural Gas Commodity Litig., 337 F. Supp. 2d 498 (S.D.N.Y. 2004).* Only those facts relevant [*10] to this motion are set forth below.

AEP's Internal Investigation

In September 2002, in response to media reports exposing the inaccurate reporting of another natural gas trading company, AEP subsidiary American Electric Power Energy Services, Inc. ("AEPES") asked all AEPES traders to certify that they had not engaged in inaccurate reporting of natural gas transactions to trade publications. (5/16/05 Routh Aff. P 2.) In October 2002, AEP dismissed five traders who had been unable to certify their trading conduct, publicly reported the dismissals, and reported them to the Federal Energy Regulatory Commission ("FERC") and the Commodity Futures Trading Commission ("CFTC"). (5/16/05 Routh Aff. P 2.) At a meeting a week later between FERC, CFTC (collectively "the governmental agencies") and AEP outside counsel Stephen Routh from Hogan & Hartson, the governmental agencies said that "AEP would have to conduct an internal investigation of the circumstances surrounding inaccurate reporting and provide the agencies with a report of that investigation before the agencies would resolve claims regarding the conduct of the AEPES traders through settlement, as opposed to through litigation. [*11] " (Id. P 3.) Hogan & Hartson retained an outside consultant, Cornerstone Research, to aid in the internal investigation. (5/16/05 AEP Letter Br. at 7.)

The internal investigation involved comparison/analysis of two different types of data, both of which have been produced to plaintiffs in this litigation. (5/16/05 Routh Aff. P 4.) The first type of data, referred to by AEP as "spreadsheet data," contained information "in a form consistent with data transmitted by natural gas traders to trade publications," reflecting daily high, low and average prices from different trading hubs or reflecting monthly trade-by-trade price and volume information for each trading hub. (Id.) While the data in these spreadsheets was in the form generally used to transmit data to the trade publications, AEP does not know whether these spreadsheets were in fact transmitted to the trade publications because the trader responsible for doing so was one of the dismissed traders. (Id.) The second type of data, referred to by AEP as "system data," was from AEP's database of "trades actually made by traders on behalf of AEP." (Id.) The system data includes data for all trades made by AEP, including [*12] "physical and financial natural gas trades as well as trades for other types of commodities." (Id. P 7.)

Aquila's Internal Investigation

Aquila's outside counsel Orrick, Herrington & Sutcliffe conducted a similar internal investigation. (5/2/05 Plfs. Letter Br. Ex. E: 7/14/03 Orrick, Herrington Letter to CFTC.) Orrick, Herrington hired the forensic accounting firm Kroll Zolfo Cooper LLC ("Kroll") to assist in the analysis. (Id.; see also Dkt. No. 279: Deacon 5/26/05 Aff. PP 1-2.) Kroll conducted an analysis comparing "trade data recorded internally by AMS to available trade data that AMS employees sent or may have sent to natural gas trade publications." (Deacon Aff. P 2.) This analysis, finalized in a Kroll Report, compared

> certain spreadsheets containing reported trading data for certain months with corresponding data recorded in AMS's internal Gas Works system. Kroll analyzed all of the trades contained on these spreadsheets and did not selectively analyze any specific individual reported trades. Kroll's analysis was limited to a review of the data contained in these documentary sources, and was not based on witness interviews or other non-documentary [*13] sources.

(Deacon Aff. P 3.) One type of data Kroll analyzed were spreadsheets that apparently were reported to trade publications, which spreadsheets were made available to plaintiffs in this case in October 2004. (Id. P 4.) A second type of data Kroll analyzed were spreadsheets containing similar trade data presumed to have been reported to the trade publications, and produced to plaintiffs in this litigation in October 2004. (Id. P 5.) The third type of data which AMS located but was not used in the Kroll Report were draft spreadsheets, which AMS produced to plaintiffs as well. (Id. P 6.) Finally, AMS produced to plaintiffs the recorded trading data from its internal Gas Works system that was analyzed in the Kroll Report. (Id. P 7.)

The Non-Waiver Agreements

AEP

In February 2003, in connection with ongoing settlement discussions between the CFTC and AEP, the CFTC requested review of a draft AEP attorney-client memorandum that "in part summarized certain data analyses undertaken by and at the direction of AEP's outside legal counsel, including" Routh. (Routh Aff. P 11.) Before producing this information to the CFTC, Routh secured [*14] the CFTC's agreement that it would keep the information confidential, that it would not consider it a waiver of privilege "with respect to any information beyond what was specifically set forth in the memorandum," and that the CFTC would not disclose information to anyone else. (Id. P 12.) Routh memorialized that agreement in a letter dated February 24, 2003 (id.), which stated:

> We are providing the enclosed Memorandum in reliance on the Division's agreement that, in deference to our concerns regarding preservation of privilege set forth below, the Division will return the Memorandum to us at our meeting scheduled for February 27, 2003 and not retain any copy.
>
> We submit this Memorandum as a selective and limited disclosure of a confidential and privileged attorney-client

> communication and of attorney work product solely for the purpose of exploring and negotiating a possible settlement and resolution of the Division's investigation as to AEPES. We intend that its privileged character be preserved. As to the Division Staff, no waiver of privilege is intended beyond the specific statements contained in the Memorandum (there is no general waiver of privilege to the subject [*15] matters discussed in the Memorandum or of any underlying information or analyses referenced in the Memorandum). As to third parties, there is no waiver of privilege at all; the information in the Memorandum is disclosed for the Division's Staff alone in furtherance of our settlement discussions and the resolution of the investigation as to AEPES.

(Routh Aff. Ex. 1: 2/24/03 Letter from Routh to CFTC.) n2

n2 At oral argument, the Court addressed whether the settlement privilege should enter into analysis of the waiver issue, and because both parties agreed it should not, it is not considered here. (See 5/19/05 Conf. Transcript ["Tr."] at 45.)

In April 2003, attorneys for FERC and the DOJ requested that AEP's counsel provide them with the same attorney-client memorandum and appendices that AEP had given the CFTC. (Routh Aff. P 13.) The governmental agencies also requested "back-up information" for and additional information on "the data analyses that had been undertaken by and at the direction [*16] of AEP's legal counsel." (Id.)

Before producing the requested documents, AEP counsel Routh secured non-waiver agreements from each agency with respect to all material produced. (Id. P 14.) The terms of the nonwaiver agreements were substantially the same as those outlined in the February 2003 letter and were memorialized in a letter dated April 15, 2003. (Id. P 14; Routh Aff. Ex. 2: 4/15/03 Routh letter to CFTC, FERC, DOJ.) The only differences were that in the April 15, 2003 letter, the privileged documents were produced in cooperation with "investigations being conducted by each [agency]," instead of as part of ongoing settlement discussions as had been the case in the February 2003 letter; there was no reference to any of the agencies returning the documents after any set point, as had been the case in the February 2003 letter; and the April 2003 letter said that in addition to being covered by attorney-client and work product privilege, the materials were within the scope of *17 C.F.R. § 145.9(d)(1)(i)-(iv)*, and that AEP requested that the government maintain the confidentiality under the *Freedom of Information Act* ("FOIA") of submitted documents, [*17] while the February 2003 only referenced that regulation at the top of the letter. (Compare Routh Aff. Ex. 1: 2/24/03 Routh Letter to CFTC (quoted above), with Routh Aff. Ex. 2: 4/15/03 Routh letter to CFTC, FERC, DOJ.)

In May 2003, in response to follow-up requests, AEP produced additional materials to the CFTC and FERC under the same non-waiver agreement. (Routh Aff. P 14.)

In September 2003, the CFTC filed a civil action against AEP in the United States District Court for the Southern District of Ohio alleging that AEP had knowingly reported inaccurate data to the trade publications and attempted manipulation. (Id. P 16.) In January 2005, the CFTC and AEP settled that litigation. (Id.) At no point during that litigation did the CFTC identify which trades had been allegedly false or knowingly inaccurate. (Id.)

Aquila

In response to a subpoena, Aquila produced "Confidential Materials" including the Kroll Report to the CFTC in July 2003 (5/2/05 Plfs. Letter Br. Ex. E: 7/14/03 Orrick, Herrington Letter to CFTC), but only after delineating the terms of a non-waiver agreement:

> Please be advised that by producing the Confidential Materials pursuant [*18] to this agreement, Aquila does not intend to waive the protection of the attorney work product doctrine, attorney-client privilege, or any other privilege applicable as to third parties. Aquila believes that the Confidential Materials are protected by, at a minimum, the attorney work product doctrine and the attorney-client privilege. Aquila believes that the Confidential Materials warrant protection from disclosure.
>
> The CFTC will maintain the confidentiality of the Confidential Materials pursuant to this agreement and will not disclose them to any third party, except to the extent that the CFTC determines that disclosure is otherwise required by law or would be in furtherance of the CFTC's discharge of its duties and responsibilities.

> The CFTC will not assert that the production of the Confidential Materials to the CFTC by Aquila constitutes a waiver of the protection of the attorney work product doctrine, the attorney-client privilege, or any other privilege applicable as to any third party. The CFTC agrees that production of the Confidential Materials by Aquila to CFTC does not effect a subject matter with regard to additional testimony, documents or other materials. Any grounds [*19] for additional production by Aquila to CFTC that may exist apart from the production provided for in this agreement shall remain unaffected by this agreement.

(Id. at 1-2.) Aquila, like AEP, also requested confidential treatment of its documents under *17 C.F.R. § 145.9* for FOIA purposes. (Id. at 2.) The CFTC counter-signed the letter as "Agreed and Accepted." (Id.) The "confidential materials" "primarily included the Kroll comparison analysis" (5/16/05 AMS Letter Br. at 2), supplemented by documents identified on Aquila's privilege log in this case (see 5/2/05 Plaintiff Letter Br. Ex. B). In September 2003, Aquila produced the same materials to the FBI after obtaining an agreement by the FBI to abide by the terms of the confidentiality agreement with the CFTC. (5/2/05 Plfs. Letter Br. Ex. B: 9/12/03 Orrick, Herrington Letter to FBI; see 5/16/05 AMS Letter Br. at 3.)

Plaintiffs' Motion to Compel

On May 2, 2005, plaintiffs moved to compel production of the documents that AEP and Aquila previously disclosed to the governmental agencies but in this litigation have withheld from plaintiffs (including the Kroll and Cornerstone [*20] Reports) because defendants claim attorney-client and/or work product privilege, and rely on the non-waiver agreements to respond to plaintiffs' waiver claim. (See 5/2/05 Plfs. Letter Br. at 2; Plfs. Letter Br. Exs. A-B: AEP & Aquila Privilege Logs.)

Plaintiffs argue that if a work product privilege applies to the documents, plaintiffs' substantial need overcomes that protection for factual material. (5/2/05 Plfs. Letter Br. at 4.) Mostly, however, plaintiffs contend that defendants' production of these documents to the governmental agencies constituted a waiver of any privilege and therefore that defendants should be compelled to produce all the withheld documents. (Id. at 8-12.) n3

n3 Plaintiffs also contended that the Court should grant their motion on the ground that defendants have put these documents "at issue." (Id. at 3.) At the May 19, 2005 discovery conference, this Court denied plaintiffs' motion on this point. (5/19/05 Conf. Tr. at 46.) Plaintiffs also contended that the "short-cut" proposal amounted to a waiver by defendants of any privilege they now claim. (5/2/05 Plfs. Letter Br. at 8 n.1.) The Court also denied plaintiffs' motion on this point at the May 19, 2005 conference. (5/19/05 Conf. Tr. at 46-47.) Finally, plaintiffs in a throw-away paragraph in their letter brief assert that "plaintiffs do not concede that defendants' submissions to the government are protected by the attorney-client or work-product privilege in the first instance. Indeed, the burden of demonstrating both that the privilege exists and has not been waived is on Defendants." (5/2/05 Plfs. Letter Br. at 8.) Defendants have clearly established that these analyses - by counsel and by consultants hired by counsel because of government investigations and potential litigation - are at least subject to the work product privilege, and plaintiffs did not renew this argument in their reply letter brief or at oral argument. The Court accordingly finds that the material is subject to the work product privilege. The issue that remains is whether defendants waived that privilege.

[*21]

ANALYSIS

I. PRIOR DISCLOSURE OF PRIVILEGED DOCUMENTS TO GOVERNMENTAL AGENCIES UNDER A NON-WAIVER AGREEMENT

Plaintiffs contend that defendants waived any privilege when they disclosed documents to the governmental agencies in connection with a previous investigation. (5/2/05 Plfs. Letter Br. at 8-12.) In contrast, defendants contend that their non-waiver agreements were sufficient to preserve the privilege.

A. State of the Law

The Second Circuit has not directly answered the question posed by plaintiffs' motion to compel: whether disclosure of privileged documents to governmental agencies in response to a subpoena constitutes a waiver of that privilege for subsequent litigations where the disclosing party (defendants, here) entered into a confidentiality, "non-waiver" agreement before producing the documents to the governmental agencies. In *In re Steinhardt Partners, L.P., 9 F.3d 230, 235 (2d*

Cir. 1993), the Second Circuit held that the defendant Steinhardt had waived its work product privilege when it voluntarily submitted a privileged memorandum to the SEC in a previous investigation. The Second Circuit in Steinhardt [*22] found the disclosure to have been voluntary despite the fact that it was made in response to an SEC subpoena, because no compulsory legal process had been necessary to compel production to the SEC. *Id. at 234*. The defendant in Steinhardt had not entered into a confidentiality agreement before disclosing its privileged documents to the government.

The Second Circuit in Steinhardt explained the background to work-product protection and waiver:

> The logic behind the work product doctrine is that opposing counsel should not enjoy free access to an attorney's thought processes. An attorney's protected thought processes include preparing legal theories, planning litigation strategies and trial tactics, and sifting through information. At its core, the work product doctrine shelters the mental processes of the attorney, providing a privileged area within which he can analyze and prepare his client's case. The doctrine grants counsel an opportunity to think or prepare a client's case without fear of intrusion by an adversary.
>
> Common sense and the practicalities of litigation define the limits of the work product doctrine. Once a party allows an adversary [*23] to share the otherwise privileged thought processes of counsel, the need for the privilege disappears. Courts therefore accept the waiver doctrine as a limitation on work product protection. The waiver doctrine provides that voluntary disclosure of work product to an adversary waives the privilege as to other parties.

In re Steinhardt Partners, L.P., 9 F.3d at 234-35 (citations & internal quotations omitted, emphasis added).

The Second Circuit in Steinhardt, after reviewing decisions from other Circuits, rejected a "selective waiver" approach, and found that Steinhardt had waived the privilege by producing the document to the SEC. *In re Steinhardt Partners, L.P., 9 F.3d at 235*. The "selective waiver" approach adopted by the Eighth Circuit preserves privilege in a civil litigation for documents previously disclosed to the government in response to litigation or investigation. See *Diversified Indus. v. Meredith, 572 F.2d 596, 611 (8th Cir. 1978)*. The Second Circuit agreed with the D.C. Circuit "that selective assertion of privilege should not be merely another brush on an attorney's palette, utilized and [*24] manipulated to gain tactical or strategic advantage." *In re Steinhardt Partners, L.P., 9 F.3d at 235* (citing *Permian Corp. v. United States, 214 U.S. App. D.C. 396, 665 F.2d 1214, 1221 (D.C. Cir. 1981)*).

Nevertheless, the Second Circuit in Steinhardt "declined to adopt a per se rule that all voluntary disclosures to the government waive work product protection." *Id. at 236*. Instead, according to the Second Circuit:

> Crafting rules relating to privilege in matters of governmental investigations must be done on a case-by-case basis. Establishing a rigid rule would fail to anticipate situations in which the disclosing party and the government may share a common interest in developing legal theories and analyzing information, or situations in which the SEC and the disclosing party have entered into an explicit agreement that the SEC will maintain the confidentiality of the disclosed materials.

Id. (emphasis added). n4

n4 Cf. *In re Grand Jury Proceedings, 219 F.3d 175, 185 (2d Cir. 2000)* (In case concerning whether corporation's chairman's grand jury testimony waived the corporation's privilege, the Second Circuit stated that "we believe that the implied waiver analysis should be guided primarily by fairness principles. . . . Since fairness depends on context, we believe it is not prudent to formulate a per se rule in this area of the law.") (citing, inter alia, Steinhardt).

[*25]

Subsequent to Steinhardt, in cases where the parties disclosed privileged material to the government in a prior litigation/investigation, the district courts within this Circuit have found significant the presence or absence of a non-waiver/confidentiality agreement. See, e.g., *Maruzen Co. v. HSBC USA, Inc., 2002 U.S. Dist. LEXIS 13288, 00 Civ. 1079, 00 Civ. 1512, 2002 WL 1628782 at *2 (S.D.N.Y. 2002)* (Since defendants, who claimed the privilege, had "explicit confidentiality agreements with the authorities satisfying Steinhardt, [and other cases], plaintiffs' motion to compel is hereby denied in all respects."); *In re Leslie Fay Cos. Sec. Litig. ("Leslie Fay II"), 161 F.R.D. 274, 282-84 (S.D.N.Y. 1995)* ("When the Company has voluntarily disclosed to the SEC the ACR [Audit Committee Report] exonerating Leslie Fay management and later sued BDO based on the report's findings," subject matter waiver of attorney-client privilege found in Report and factual underlying documents. Court found no further waiver from disclosures to U. S. Attorney's Office and bankruptcy examiner, which "were made pursuant to confidentiality agreements intended to preserve any [*26] privilege applicable to the disclosed documents. . . . We think that the May 23 [confidentiality] agreement satisfies the standard articulated in Steinhardt."); *In re Leslie Fay Cos. Sec. Litig. ("Leslie Fay I"), 152 F.R.D. 42, 44 (S.D.N.Y. 1993)* (Court need not determine whether Audit Committee Report constitutes work product "because we find that the Audit Committee waived any work product immunity it may have had when it voluntarily disclosed the Report to the SEC without first obtaining a confidentiality agreement."); see also, e.g., *Spanierman Gallery, Profit Sharing Plan v. Merritt, 2003 U.S. Dist. LEXIS 22141, 00 Civ. 5712, 2003 WL 22909160 at *3, 5 (S.D.N.Y. Dec. 9, 2003)* (defendant waived attorney-client and work product privileges for documents produced to FBI; defendant "took no precautions to preserve the privilege when the documents were produced to the FBI. They were not labeled 'confidential' or 'privileged,' and there was no agreement with the FBI that the documents were to be treated as privileged and confidential, and should not be produced to third parties."); *Bank of America v. Terra Nova Ins. Co., 212 F.R.D. 166,172-73 (S.D.N.Y. 2002)* [*27] (disclosure of work-product material to government agencies in hope they would prosecute person who stole from company is not trial preparation, so waiver found; Court notes that "when material is disclosed to a law enforcement agency without any agreement regarding confidentiality, there is a strong potential that the material may ultimately become public and thus available to an adversary." "In re Steinhardt left open the possibility that a waiver might not be found if there is an explicit agreement to maintain confidentiality, see *9 F.3d at 236* - a circumstance that does not exist in this case.")

It appears that while the Second Circuit in Steinhardt declined to adopt a per se waiver approach, the majority of Circuits have adopted such a position, leaving the Second Circuit (and the different Eighth Circuit approach) in the minority. See, e.g., *In re Columbia/HCA Healthcare Corp. Billing Practices Litig., 293 F.3d 289, 302-07 (6th Cir. 2002)* (adopting per se waiver approach for attorney-client and work product privilege), n5 cert. denied, *539 U.S. 977, 124 S. Ct. 27 (2003); United States v. MIT, 129 F.3d 681, 686, 688 (1st Cir. 1997)* [*28] (rejecting selective waiver approach, finding attorney-client and work product privileges waived by disclosure to government agency, but leaving open issue of whether waiver would apply to opinion work product documents); *Westinghouse Elec. Corp. v. Republic of the Philippines, 951 F.2d 1414, 1418, 1426-30 (3d Cir. 1991)* (Finding attorney-client and work product privileges waived because of prior disclosure of privileged documents to governmental agency; even if government and disclosing party had entered into a confidentiality agreement, result would be the same.); *In re Chrysler Motors Corp. Overnight Evaluation Program Litig., 860 F.2d 844, 846-47 (8th Cir. 1988)* (defendant waived work product privilege for documents sought by government which defendant had disclosed to adversary in civil litigation, despite confidentiality agreement); *Permian Corp. v. United States, 214 U.S. App. D.C. 396, 665 F.2d 1214, 1217-18, 1219-22 (D.C. Cir. 1981)* (attorney-client privilege was waived when party disclosed documents to the SEC, regardless of intent to preserve privilege against other government agencies; affirmed district court's [*29] finding that work product privilege had not been waived as to other documents because of written confidentiality agreement); cf. *Genentech, Inc. v. United States ITC, 122 F.3d 1409, 1417 (Fed. Cir. 1997)*(rejecting limited waiver approach in an "inadvertent disclosure" case); n6 see generally Theodore R. Lotchin, No Good Deed Goes Unpunished? Establishing a Self-Evaluative Privilege for Corporate Internal Investigations, *46 Wm. & Mary L. Rev. 1137, 1157 (2004)* ("The disclosure of confidential information to a federal agency will usually waive the privilege for all future cases regarding communication on the same subjects, especially if the disclosure took place during the course of an investigation or administrative proceeding. Although this precedent is firmly established, several federal circuits have declined to adopt a per se rule that every voluntary production by a corporate client waives the attorney-client and work product privileges.") (fns. omitted); Jay G. Martin, Strategies for Boards of Directors Conducting Internal Investigations, 1479 PLI/Corp 473, 485 (2005) ("Recent cases are divided on whether providing [*30] these materials to the government, even under a confidentiality or nonwaiver agreement, operates as a waiver of the attorney-privilege and work product privileges as to third parties. Recent decisions favoring waiver outnumber those rejecting waiver."); Andrew J. McNally, Comment, Revitalizing Selective Waiver: Encouraging Voluntary Disclosure of Corporate Wrongdoing by Restricting Third Party Access to Disclosed Materials, *35 Seton Hall L. Rev. 823, 828 (2005)* ("In most jurisdictions, a corporation's disclosure of sensitive materials to a government agency constitutes a complete waiver of the otherwise applicable privileges. A corporation's initial disclosure of otherwise privileged materials to the government, according to most courts, waives those privileges as to all other parties; thus, civil litigants seeking to sue the corporation will typically be granted unfettered access to the disclosed materials. Even confidentiality arrangements between the disclosing corporation and the government agency are seldom sufficient to permit the successful assertion of privilege against a civil plaintiff if a previous disclosure was made.") (fns. omitted); Mark Robeck et al. [*31] , Corporate Governance in the Face of Government Investigations, 17 No. *2 Health Law. 20, 26 (2005)* ("The majority rule in the circuits is that a voluntary disclosure of information operates as a waiver of the surrounding privileges in subsequent actions, therefore disallowing argument for protection when future plaintiffs demand the same information provided to the government. Therefore, anything produced to the government should be expected to end up in the hands of plaintiffs in subsequent civil actions via the discovery process and requests to the government agency through the Freedom of Information Act. Despite this rule, corporations may be able to safeguard their privileges via a written agreement with the government agency.") (fns. omitted); Kara Altenbaumer-Price, Assessing Risks of Sharing Internal Investigations: Target Firms Cooperating with Government Risk Waiving Their Privilege, N.Y.L.J., Mar. 21, 2005, at S2 ("The D.C., 1st, 3d and 6th circuits have completely rejected the idea that the attorney-client privilege or work-product doctrine protection are not waived by virtue of the 'selective waiver' or 'limited waiver' doctrine by production to the [*32] government, even if the government and the company enter into a confidentiality agreement. . . . The Federal, 2d and 4th Circuits have rejected the 'selective waiver' doctrine but have not addressed it in a context in which the government and the company have entered into a confidentiality agreement. The 8th Circuit alone has unqualifiedly adopted the 'selective waiver' doctrine . . . The majority rule clearly provides, particularly absent a strong confidentiality agreement, that disclosure to the government will destroy the protections of the attorney-client privilege and work-product doctrine.") (citations omitted); Lee G. Durst & Ariane J. Sims, Cooperation With Government Probes, Subsequent Civil Litigation, N.Y.L.J., May 13, 2005, at 4 ("The cases discussed above indicate that the typical defenses against claims of waiver as related to documents produced to the government during the course of an investigation may not hold much weight in today's jurisprudence. Indeed, with the exception of the Eighth Circuit, which still permits the application of the limited waiver doctrine [fn. citing Diversified omitted], the best possible preemptive protection against waiver seems [*33] to be the existence of a detailed, explicit and unconditional agreement with the government that the documents are to be treated confidentially and that production does not constitute any form of waiver as to third parties."); David Francescani & Michael Autuoro, Caught Between a Rock and a Hard Place, N.Y.L.J., June 20, 2005, at S10 ("The doctrine of selective waiver, first set forth by the Eighth Circuit in 1978, has been rejected in most of the jurisdictions considering the issue. Although the Second Circuit has not been openly receptive to selective waiver, it has left open the possibility of whether disclosure of work product to the government under a confidentiality agreement constitutes a waiver.") (fns. omitted); Jerold S. Solovy & Robert L. Bryan, Unwaiver, National L.J., Apr. 4, 2005, at 11 ("If you care about the privilege, don't disclose the material. Don't assume that production with a subpoena pointed at your head is enough. Don't count on an agreement with the government in case A to persuade the judge in case B. You might as well try to put Humpty Dumpty back together again as unwaive a waived privilege.").

n5 The Sixth Circuit in Columbia noted that a "review of the positions presented by the various courts reveals three general opinions on the issue - selective waiver is permissible; selective waiver is not permissible under any situations; and selective waiver is permissible in situations where the Government agrees to a confidentiality order." *Id., 293 F.3d at 295* (citations omitted). The Second Circuit does not explicitly fall into any of those three categories, but would appear to be closest to the last category; indeed, the Sixth Circuit in Columbia categorized the Second Circuit's position, based on Steinhardt and district court decisions, as falling in the third group. *293 F.3d at 300-01*. [*34]

n6 District court decisions in those Circuits which have not decided the issue mostly have rejected the selective waiver approach. Compare, e.g., *Hobley v. Burge, 2004 U.S. Dist. LEXIS 6858, No. 03 C 3678, 2004 WL 856439 at *7 (N.D. Ill. Apr. 21, 2004)* (work product privilege waived because City had previously disclosed documents to Special Prosecutor); *In re Bank One Secs. Litig., 209 F.R.D. 418, 423-25 (N.D. Ill. 2002)* (in accord with Westinghouse and Columbi/HCA Healthcare, defendant Bank One's voluntary production to governmental investigative body, Office of the Comptroller of the Currency, waived its work product privilege because the relationship was adversarial notwithstanding existing confidentiality agreement); *United States v. Bergonzi, 216 F.R.D. 487, 494, 496-98 (N.D. Cal. 2003)* (company waived its attorney-client and work product privileges when it disclosed documents to government where the confidentiality agreements were not unconditional).

appeal dismissed as moot, *403 F.3d 1048, 1050 (9th Cir. 2005)* ("Given our finding of mootness, we do not reach [company's] argument that we should recognize a form of 'selective' or 'partial' waiver . . ."); *United States v. South Chicago Bank, 1998 U.S. Dist. LEXIS 17444, No. 97 CR 849, 1998 WL 774001 at *4-5 (N.D. Ill. Oct. 30, 1998)* (report produced to governmental regulatory agency under confidentiality agreement waived privilege); with, e.g., *In re McKesson HBOC, Inc. Secs. Litig., 2005 U.S. Dist. LEXIS 7098, No. 99-CV-20743, 2005 WL 934331 at *9-10 (N.D. Cal. Mar. 31, 2005)* (Company's confidentiality agreements with the government were sufficient to preserve work product privilege as to the extent possible under the law, that disclosure of the protected materials will not reach adverse parties."); *Saito v. McKesson HBOC, Inc., 2002 Del. Ch. LEXIS 139, No. Civ. A. 18553, 2002 WL 31657622 at *11 (Del. Ch. Nov. 13, 2002)* (applies selective waiver rule: McKesson HBOC, due to its confidentiality agreement, reasonably expected its privilege would be preserved in disclosure of documents to SEC), aff'd, *870 A.2d 1192 (Del. 2005)*; cf. *LaBelle v. Philip Morris Inc., No. 2-98-3235-23, 2000 WL 33957169* at *5-7 (D.S.C. Oct. 23, 2000) (defendants waived attorney-client and work product privileges for documents produced to government in response to grand jury subpoena despite confidentiality agreement); *In re M & L Bus. Mach. Co., Jobin v. Bank of Boulder, 167 B.R. 631, 637 (D. Colo. 1994)*, ("Production of documents under a grand jury subpoena does not automatically vitiate the attorney-client privilege, mush less in an unrelated civil proceeding brought by a non-governmental entity. This is especially true in a case such as this, where the record demonstrates that the [defendant] has consistently sought to protect its privilege" through production pursuant to a confidentiality agreement); *In re M & L Bus. Mach. Co., Jobin v. Bank of Boulder, 161 B.R. 689, 695-97 (D. Colo. 1993)* (recognizing split in circuits on limited waiver and that 10th Circuit had yet to rule on the issue, and holding defendant had not waived its attorney-client privilege through previous disclosure of documents to United States Attorney in connection with grand jury investigation for purposes of subsequent bankruptcy proceedings because defendant had entered into a letter agreement with the government which specifically expressed intention to preserve confidentiality of documents with respect to third parties including subsequent proceedings).

[*35]

B. Application of the Legal Standards to This Case

While the Second Circuit has neither re-examined Steinhardt in a case dealing directly with this issue, nor instructed how much weight to give to a confidentiality agreement with the government agency, this Court is not free to adopt the so-called majority view, this Court is bound by *Steinhardt* until the Second Circuit (or Supreme Court) reverses or otherwise modifies it. See, e.g., *United States v. Collado, No. 99-1218, 201 F.3d 433 (table), 1999 WL 1212647 at *1 (2d Cir. 1999)* ("The fact that there is a split among the circuits on this issue, in no way changes our obligation to follow binding precedent of this court.") (citation omitted), cert. denied, *530 U.S. 1264, 120 S. Ct. 2724 (2000)*; *United States v. Foont, 901 F. Supp. 729, 734 n.1 (S.D.N.Y. 1995)* ("This Court is bound by Second Circuit precedent on the matter; defendant's arguments about circuit splits are of no avail in this forum."), aff'd, *93 F.3d 76 (2d Cir. 1996)*; *Bass v. Coughlin, 800 F. Supp. 1066, 1071 (N.D.N.Y. 1991)* ("When [*36] the Court of Appeals announces a principle of law for this circuit, it remains the law until the case is overruled or reversed."), aff'd, *976 F.2d 98 (2d Cir. 1992)*. As discussed above, the Second Circuit in Steinhardt rejected the Eighth Circuit's "selective waiver" approach, but declined to adopt a per se rule that disclosure to the government always waives the privilege. In adopting a case-by-case approach, the Second Circuit specifically referred to one factor relevant here - "situations in which the [government agency] and the disclosing party have entered into an explicit agreement that the [government agency] will maintain the confidentiality of the disclosed materials." *In re Steinhardt Partners, L.P., 9 F.3d 230, 236 (2d Cir. 1993)*. The district court decisions in this Circuit have relied on the presence of an explicit confidentiality agreement to find no waiver from production of work product material to the government. (See cases cited at pages 11-12 above.)

Here, both AEP and Aquila had explicit written confidentiality and non-waiver agreements with the government agencies. (See pages 4-7 above.) Under *Steinhardt*, that [*37] goes a long way to a finding of non-waiver here. In this Court's view, however, Steinhardt does not create a "per se" rule that if there is a confidentiality/non-waiver agreement with the government, the privilege is not waived. While that is an important factor, this Court also must examine other relevant factors (although Steinhardt does not provide any further guidance on the factors this Court should consider).

The second most important factor here (besides the non-waiver agreements), is that both AEP and Aquila have produced to plaintiffs in this litigation the factual documents underlying the work product analyses provided to the government agencies. For example, if the analyses had been based on oral information from defendants' traders, or if the underlying factual trade data was no longer available, plaintiffs would have made a strong showing of substantial need for the analyses defendants produced to the governmental agencies. The analyses, however, were not based on oral information but documents, and those underlying documents have been produced to plaintiffs here. (See Dkt. No. 279: Deacon 5/26/05 Aff. P 3: The Kroll Report "was limited to a review of the [*38] data contained in [the] documentary sources, and was not based on witness interviews or other nondocumentary sources."; id. PP 4-7: identifies by Bates numbers the spreadsheets containing the data upon which the Kroll Report was based, which documents were produced to Plaintiffs; 5/16/05 AEP Letter Br. at 8: The underlying data AEP and Cornerstone used in their analyses was produced to plaintiffs.) Plaintiffs and their experts therefore can perform their own analyses of the trading data and the data reported to the trade publications. To the extent that defendants and defendants' experts disagree with plaintiffs' analyses, plaintiffs will receive defendants' current analyses of the data during the expert discovery period. (See 5/19/05 Conf. Tr. at 32: AEP counsel Routh: "There are analyses that can be done. We have not said that they can't be. . . . If [plaintiffs] focus on that, or ultimately if their experts do, we will have all of this out in experts discovery but it will be discovery of the testifying experts analysis, not of [counsel's] analysis.") Plaintiffs do not have a substantial need for the analyses that defendants' counsel and experts provided to the government. [*39] Since the data used in defendants' analyses has been provided to plaintiffs, plaintiffs suffer no hardship by not having defendants' analyses. (See 5/16/05 AMS Letter Br. at 14; 5/16/05 AEP Letter Br. at 21-23.)

Accordingly, because defendants had explicit written confidentiality and non-waiver agreements with the governmental agencies, and because plaintiffs have not shown a substantial need for defendants' experts' and counsels' analyses, having been provided the underlying documents and data on which the analyses were based, under *Steinhardt*, the Court finds that defendants did not waive the work product privilege and the documents at issue need not be provided.

CONCLUSION

For the reasons discussed above, plaintiffs' motion to compel production of defendants' privileged documents given to governmental agencies pursuant to a confidentiality nonwaiver agreement is DENIED. n7

n7 Plaintiffs also claim that as to a few of the documents, the privilege was waived by defendant AEP's inadvertent but sloppy production to plaintiffs. The Court will address that issue in a separate Opinion.

[*40]

SO ORDERED.

Dated: New York, New York

June 21, 2005

Andrew J. Peck

United States Chief Magistrate Judge

NOTES

26

MEMORANDUM OF AMICUS CURIAE UNITED STATES CHAMBER OF COMMERCE CONCERNING INTERPRETATION OF "LOSS"

Submitted by:

Lawrence J. Zweifach

Heller Eherman LLP

IN THE UNITED STATES DISTRICT COURT
FOR THE SOUTHERN DISTRICT OF TEXAS
HOUSTON DIVISION

UNITED STATES OF AMERICA,	§	
Plaintiff,	§	
vs.	§	CR. NO. H-03-363 (Werlein, J.)
DANIEL BAYLY, DON BOYLE, JAMES BROWN, WILLIAM FUHS, ROBERT FURST,	§	
Defendant.	§	

INTRODUCTION

The Chamber of Commerce of the United States ("the Chamber") is the world's largest business federation, representing an underlying membership of more than three million companies and professional organizations of all sizes and in all industries. Members of the Chamber are affected by and active in all U.S. and foreign markets and in all phases of corporate and public finance. The Chamber advocates the interests of its members in matters before the courts. Congress, and the Executive Branch, and regularly files amicus briefs such as this one in cases that raise issues of vital concern to its memberships.

At least one sentencing issue raised in this proceeding—the proper definition of "loss" in cases arising out of allegations of securities fraud—is a recurring question of great importance to the business community.[1] The issue typically arises when a misrepresentation is disclosed and the value of a stock subsequently declines, raising the questions whether and to what extent the -loss" in value is attributable to the misrepresentation. In that setting, the real stock market reaction that resulted in the alleged "loss" can be analyzed to determine the extent to which the misrepresentation was its cause. And, in that routine setting. not even the Government would suggest that expert speculation about the amount of inflation when shares were purchased should he substituted for an analysis of the actual stock price decline that occurred.

This case, however, arises in an atypical context—where a company is bankrupt and the price of a stock had plummeted to zero *before* the specific misrepresentation at issue was disclosed. In this context, there has been no "loss" following disclosure of a misrepresentation and *a fortiori*, there is no objective, market-based decline to use to measure "loss." There is only an expert's speculation about what would have happened if the misrepresentation had been disclosed before the stock price went to zero. Under civil law, such speculation is legally inadequate to demonstrate "loss"; the Chamber submits that it is even more problematic to use that speculation to increase exponentially criminal punishment. *Cf. United States v. Downs*, 123 F.3d 637, 643 (7th Cir. 1997) ("[t]his estimate of loss similarly has the advantage of not `making the term of a criminal sentence turn on conjecture").

The legal foundations of our economy include reasonable limits on corporate liability, such as the limited liability of corporations, *see United States v. Bestfoods*, 524 U.S. 51 (1998), the business judgment rule for corporate officers and directors, *see Kamen v. Kemper Financial Services, Inc.*, 500 U.S. 90 (1991). proof of intent, and the requirement of "loss" at issue here. These reasonable limits enable corporations to exist and provide jobs. Corporations could not effectively perform this function if the securities laws were deemed violated merely because a company proved unprofitable, or even went bankrupt. *See Huddleston v. Herman & MacLean*, 640 F.2d 534, 549 (5th Cir. 1981), *aff'd in part. rev 'd in part on other grounds*, 459 U.S. 375 (1983).

---

1. Of course, the defendants here were charged with wire fraud but not securities fraud. In this brief, the Chamber does not address at this time whether shareholder loss can properly be used as "loss" in a case that does not charge and prove all the elements of securities fraud, including materiality. Similarly, the Chamber does not address at this time whether the factual predicate for any "loss" amount must be found by the jury.

In the criminal context, when a business fails, it is vital that corporate officers and employees do not face draconian increases in criminal punishment when there is no causal connection between a defendant's misrepresentation and the losses of that company. Criminal laws should not so disproportionately punish corporate crimes that, for example, companies choose not to go public, individuals choose not to serve as officers, directors or outside advisers, and companies avoid novel but legitimate transactions, to the detriment of the entire economy. *Cf.* H. R. Rep. No. 104-50, at 20 (1995) ("[f]ear of litigation keeps companies out of the capital markets" and "businesses suffer as auditors and directors decline engagements and board positions"); *Central Bank of Denver, NA. v. First Interstate Bank of Denver, NA.*, 511 U.S. 164, 189 (1994) ("[t]his uncertainty and excessive litigation can have ripple effects. For example, newer and smaller companies may find it difficult to obtain advice from professionals").

The legal rules crafted in high profile cases such as this one have economic effects across the board. The Chamber submits that it is vital that the rule of law that emerges from this case fit logically within the structure of securities law and reflect the focused purpose of the "loss" requirement under securities law and the Sentencing Guidelines. It is important that hard cases not make bad law, even when the hard case involves Enron. Rather, the governing rule of law used by this Court should maintain the balance between the appropriate punishment of criminal wrongdoing and the reasonable limits on liability reflected in corporate law generally and securities law specifically.

The Government's approach to defining loss under Guideline § 2F1.1 is untethered from the applicable securities law and common law context that is informed by the reasonable limits on corporate liability for "loss" reflected in our legal system. The Government's approach could well deter members of the Chamber and other businesses from engaging in economically beneficial conduct. Thus, while the Guidelines place individuals convicted of violating securities laws on notice that they face increased criminal punishment based on real losses attributable to their actions, they do not—and should not—be deemed to enhance criminal punishment based on subjective and speculative claims of inflated value.

The Chamber addresses three issues. First, we demonstrate that in order to increase defendants' sentences for "actual loss," the Government must prove that the defendants' misrepresentations caused an actual decline in the price of Enron's stock, and that the Government did not and cannot do so. Second, we show that the Government cannot use the decline in price of Enron's stock—a decline that *preceded* disclosure of the misrepresentation at issue here—as proof that the stock declined as a result of defendants' misrepresentation. (Put differently, the Government cannot show that the decline which actually occurred was attributable to defendants' later-disclosed misrepresentation.) Finally, the Chamber shows that the word "loss" has the same definition in Guideline § 2F1 .1's phrases "actual loss" and "intended loss." This Guideline provision seeks to assign responsibility for specific concrete harms and attempted harms, and here there is no proof that defendants intended to cause any decline in Enron's stock's price (as the subsequent sale of the parked barges at a substantial profit demonstrates).

ARGUMENT

I. There Is No "Actual Loss" Unless There Is Proof That The Defendants' Conduct Caused An Actual Decline in Stock Price.

Under the Sentencing Guidelines, the offense level for fraud crimes may increase based on several factors. including "loss." See Guidelines § 2F1.1. Guideline § 2F 1.1 incrementally increases punishment based on the amount of the `actual loss" attributable to a defendant's fraud. The loss increments start at "More than 52,000" and end at "More than $80.000.000." *Id.*

As set forth in detail in the briefs of the United States and Defendants, the word loss" has an established meaning in the context of federal securities law and in the common law of fraud: It is the "decline in value of the security" that was "caused by the fraud." Brief for the United States as *Amicus Curiae* Supporting Petitioners at 22, *Dura Pharms., Inc. v. Broudo*, No. 03-932 (U.S. filed Sept. 13. 2004) ("U.S. Brief in *Dura*"). The same word "loss" is also used in Guideline § 2F 1.1. and the same definition should apply.

1. In civil securities law and at common law. "loss" is established only if the price of a stock or security "actually decline[s] as a result of [the] alleged misrepresentation." *Semerenko v. Cendant Corp.*, 223 F.3d 165. 184-85 (3d Cir. 2000) (securities law).[2] *See Bastien v. Petren Res. Corp., 892 F.2d 680, 683 (7th Cir. 1990) ("what securities lawyers call 'loss* causation' is the standard common law fraud rule"); *Restatement (Second) of Torts* § 548A & cmt. b (1977) (*"Restatement"*) (stating requirement). This interpretation of "loss" has also been codified in the Private Securities Litigation Reform Act of 1995 ("PSLRA"), Pub. L. No. 104-67, § 101(b), 109 Stat. 737, 743-49. See 15 U.S.C. § 78u-4(b)(4) (the misrepresentation at issue must have "caused the *loss* for which the plaintiff seeks to recover damages") (emphasis supplied). Indeed, in a related provision. the PSLRA defines the actionable "loss" as "the *depreciation* in value of the . . . security" resulting from disclosure of the misrepresentation. See id. § 77l(b) (emphasis added). This makes clear that "loss" exists only if a misrepresentation is disclosed and this causes the stock to decline in

---

2. *See also Emergent Capital Inv. Mgmt., LLC v. Stonepath Group, Inc.*, 343 F.3d 189, 198-99 (2d Cir. 2003); *Bastian v. Petren Res. Corp.*, 892 F.2d 680, 684-85 (7th Cir. 1990); *First Interstate Bank of Nev., N.A. v. Chapman & Cutler*, 837 F.2d 775. 779-80 (7th Cir. 1988); *Robbins v. Koger Props., Inc.*, 116 F.3d 1441, 1147-49 (11th Cir. 1997).

value. *See also* S. Rep. No. 104-98. at 7 (1995) (describing loss under 15 U.S.C. § 78u-4(b)(4) as "the loss in the value of their stock . . . caused by the [securities law] violation and not by other factors").

Thus, for purposes of federal securities law and the common law of fraud, a misrepresentation that artificially inflates the price of a security does not cause a "loss" when the stock is initially purchased at the inflated price. There is no "loss" attributable to the misrepresentation unless and until the truth is subsequently revealed and the price of the security declines as a result. And where, before disclosure of the alleged misrepresentation, the value of a security declines for other reasons—for example, because of a recession—that earlier decline is not a "loss" attributable to the misrepresentation.

In an apt footnote, in *Huddleston*, 640 F.2d at 549, the Fifth Circuit used a transaction involving a ship to illustrate that an investor has suffered no "loss" caused by fraud if the security's value declines for reasons unrelated to the fraud:

> For example, an investor might purchase stock in a shipping venture involving a single vessel in reliance on a misrepresentation that the vessel had a certain capacity when in fact it has less capacity than was represented in the prospectus. However the prospectus does disclose truthfully that the vessel will not be insured. One week after the investment the vessel sinks as a result of a casualty and the stock becomes worthless. In such circumstances, a fact-finder might conclude that the misrepresentation was material and relied upon by the investor *but that it did not cause the loss*. [*Id.* at 529 n.25 (emphasis supplied).][3]

Thus, "if false statements are made in connection with the sale of corporate stock. losses due to a subsequent decline in the market, or insolvency of the corporation brought about by business conditions or other factors [that] in no way relate to the representation[.] will not afford any basis for recovery." W. Page Keeton et al., *Prosser and Keeton on the Law*

---

3. The *Restatement (Second) of Torts* provides another useful illustration:

> A, seeking to sell to B the municipal bonds of C County, fraudulently tells B that the county has received full payment for the bond issue. B purchases the bonds in reliance upon this statement. Subsequently the county is paid in full, but the bonds are held void by the supreme court of the state on the ground that a court had no jurisdiction to issue certain orders with respect to them. As a result B suffers pecuniary loss. A is not liable to B for the loss. [*Restatement* § 548A cmt. b, illus. I.]

In this example, the defendant did not cause the loss even though the plaintiff's purchase price was inflated because of the defendant's misrepresentation. Instead, the loss had a different, unrelated cause—to wit, that with or without full payment, the bonds were void

of Torts § 110. at 767 (5th ed. 1984). *See also Restatement* § 548A cmt. b (explaining that if "the value of the stock goes down after the sale, not in any way because of the misrepresented financial condition, but as a result of some subsequent event that has no connection with or relation to its financial condition"—*e.g.*, "because of the sudden death of the corporation's leading officers"—there is "no liability"). This "loss" requirement "is intended to 'fix a legal limit on a person's responsibility, even for wrongful acts.'" *Castellano v. Young & Rubicam. Inc.*, 257 F.3d 171, 187 (2d Cir. 2001) (quoting *First Nationwide Bank v. Celt Funding Corp.*, 27 F.3d 763, 769 (2d Cir. 1994)).

The Government concedes that, under civil securities law and the common law, "loss" is defined by the actual, post-disclosure decline in the value of a stock. As the Government explained in a recent brief to the United States Supreme Court:

> [E]ven if the security's price declines after the purchase for reasons unrelated to the fraud, the investor has still suffered no loss caused by the fraud and thus has no right to recovery.
>
> It might be argued that the possibility of recoupment does not alter the fact that an investor who pays too much for a security suffers a loss by virtue of the overpayment. *Such an argument would he without merit. "Loss" means a decline in value of-the security. and its fraud-on-the-market case. that necessarily occurs at some point after the security has been purchased* [U.S. Brief in *Dura* at 22 (emphasis in original).]

2. Under fundamental principles of statutory construction. "loss-should have the same meaning—a "decline in the value of the security" "caused by the fraud"—under Guideline 2F 1.1. The "same test" should apply because of the "linguistic consistency" and related subject matters of the securities fraud statutes and the Guideline. *See Holmes Group. Inc. v. Vornado Air Circulation Sys., Inc.*, 535 U.S. 826. 830 (2002).

To date, the question of "loss" under Sentencing Guideline § 2F 1.1 has arisen in the typical case described *supra* at 2. That is, following the disclosure of a misrepresentation, a stock's price has declined, and the court determines the extent to which that decline is attributable to the misrepresentation. As Defendants explain (Defs. Br. 16-18), and as the Government acknowledges (Govt. Br. 21), in *none* of these cases did the sentencing court determine "loss" by assessing the amount of artificial inflation at the time of purchase. Instead, these courts used the actual decline to measure "loss" and considered the effect of factors other than the misrepresentation that might have exacerbated the decline.

This uniformly-used methodology—measuring the actual decline in stock price *and assessing the extent to which other causes alter that measurement*—is inconsistent with the Government's view that "loss" equals the amount of the artificial inflation at the time of purchase. Indeed, in *United States v. Grabske*, 260 F. Supp. 2d 866 (N.D. Cal. 2002), the court explicitly rejected the Government's contention that "loss" is defined by "the extent to which the fraud inflated the price of the stock," and instead required "pro[of] that the fraud inflated the price of the stock and that the investors 'lost' that inflation after the fraud was revealed." *Id.* at 870. And, the court repeatedly made clear that the Government is required to prove an actual decline attributable to the defendant's conduct. as the civil and common law require. *See id.* at 869-71. In sum, the only cases directly addressing "loss" under Guideline § 2E1.1 define "loss" just as civil securities law and the common law do.

Like its civil law analogues, Guideline § 2F 1.1 is focused *not* on determining whether a misrepresentation has occurred (a jury has already made that determination), but instead on calibrating a sanction based on the "loss" attributable to a defendant. A defendant convicted of a securities law violation will be criminally punished for his or her fraud: and that sentence may be increased by a number of factors that the Chamber does not address here. The issue presented under Sentencing Guideline § 2F1.1 is solely whether the criminal sentence should be increased based specifically on the amount of the "loss" attributable to the defendant's acts.

It is, accordingly, entirely appropriate to interpret § 2F 1.1 to increase punishment only if the misrepresentation directly causes a stock's loss of value. The law routinely punishes the same act more or less severely based on the amount of harm it causes. *See Payne v. Tennessee*, 501 U.S. 808, 819 (1991) ("the assessment of harm caused by the defendant as a result of the crime charged has understandably been an important concern of the criminal law, both in determining the elements of the offense *and in determining the appropriate punishment*") (emphasis supplied). Guideline § 2F 1.l is focused precisely on the relationship between the enhancement of punishment and the "loss" attributable to the defendant. It does not enhance punishment based on the general importance of compliance with the securities laws or on the complexity or deliberate nature of the fraud; other provisions of the law and the Guidelines address these points. It is, accordingly, wrong to make Guideline § 2F 1.1 a catch-all for consideration of all aspects affecting a defendant's culpability, as the Government has done here. Rather, it is clearly appropriate to define "loss" under

Guideline 2F t .1 as it has been defined under civil securities laws and in the common law of fraud.

Finally, if there were any doubt that "loss" under Guideline § 2F1.1 should be defined as established law provides, that doubt would have to be resolved in defendants' favor under the rule of lenity. The "rule has been applied not only to resolve issues about the substantive scope of criminal statutes. but to answer questions about the severity of sentencing." *United States v. R.L.C.*, 503 U.S. 291, 305 (1992) (plurality opinion); *see also United States v. Batchelder*, 442 U.S. 114, 121 (1979) (rule of lenity "applies to sentencing as well as substantive provisions"); *Albertaz v. United States,* 450 U.S. 333, 342 (1981) (same); *Bifulco v. United States*, 447 U.S. 381, 387 (1980) (same). This circuit, like virtually all others to consider the question, has applied the rule of lenity to interpretation of sentencing provisions. *See. e.g., United States v. Kinder*, 946 F.2d 362, 367 (5th Cir. 1991); *United States v. Sherrod*, 964 F.2d 1501, 1505 (5th Cir. 1992).

The rule of lenity requires courts faced with ambiguity or more than one plausible reading of a criminal law to take the narrowest view. *See McNally v. United States*, 483 U.S. 350, 359-60 (1987) (citing cases). As the Supreme Court explained in *Bell v. United States*, 349 U.S. 81, 83 (1955), it is "a presupposition of our law to resolve doubts in the enforcement of a penal code against the imposition of a harsher punishment." Here, the meaning of "loss" in Guideline § 2F 1.1 is, at the very least, ambiguous, in light of the time-honored definition of "loss" for violations of securities law and fraud. The rule of lenity thus mandates the application of that established definition. This requires proof that the misrepresentation caused a specific decline.

3. None of the Government's attempts to justify adopting a different definition of "loss" under Guideline § 2F 1.l withstand scrutiny.

First, the Government relies on a comment in the Guidelines that gives an example of "actual loss" as "the amount by which the stock was overvalued," to argue that an "actual loss" attributable to the defendant's misrepresentation occurs when a stock is purchased at an inflated price. Guideline § 2F1.1, cmt. n.8(a). This argument ignores the next sentence of the same comment. which gives an example where "the loss is the difference between the amount paid by the victim for the product and the amount for which the victim could resell the product received." *Id.* In the latter example, there is no loss until the hidden problem is disclosed and the resale price declines. Putting the two comments together, it is certainly appropriate to *measure* loss as "the amount by which the stock was overvalued," if a decline attributable to a disclosure of defendant's misrepresentation later occurs and establishes the amount of such overvaluation. Indeed. in the typical case, this pattern will occur. But, in cases such as this one—where the stock declines for reasons other than the misrepresentation—there is no "loss" to measure.[4] Ultimately, the Guidelines nowhere suggest that the same word "loss" should be defined to mean one thing under federal securities law and common law—*viz.*, "depreciation in value of the subject security" after disclosure of the defendant's misrepresentation, 15 U.S.C. § 771(h)—and something entirely different under federal criminal law.

Second, the Government claims that the civil definition of "loss" does not apply because it reflects and serves only the limited purpose of the civil rule—to find and compensate the particular purchasers of stock who were harmed by the misrepresentation. The Government argues as follows:

- The purpose of a civil suit is compensation for individuals who incurred losses based on a misrepresentation.
- In the civil context, an artificial inflation in stock price will not injure the purchaser if he or she resells the stock at the artificially inflated price; but for purposes of the criminal law, the absence of damage to a particular individual is irrelevant because "some investor has still paid too much for the stock." Govt. Br. 8.
- Thus, in the civil setting, a plaintiff's suit may be dismissed because that particular plaintiff has resold the stock at the inflated price and has not suffered a "loss." In contrast, in the criminal setting, it is irrelevant which plaintiff is injured; a defendant's punishment

4. In demonstrating that "loss" is not measured by the artificial inflation in the stock's value at the time of purchase in the civil context in *Dura*, the Government itself rebutted an argument similar to the one it makes here. The Senate Report for the PSLRA stated only that "the plaintiff would have to prove that the price at which the plaintiff bought the stock was artificially inflated as the result of the misstatement or omission." S. Rep. No. 104-98, at 15. The Government noted that if this statement were "an exhaustive description of the plaintiffs burden," then "loss" could be proven based on such artificial inflation. U.S. Brief in *Dura* at 27. But, the Government refused to treat this statement as exhaustive, and instead noted that the Report did not "explain whether additional proof would be required" beyond inflation. *Id.* Similarly, here, "the amount by which the stock was overvalued" might equal purchase-time inflation in some circumstances, but not in those cases where the stock price declines for reasons other than the misrepresentation.

should always be enhanced based on the "loss" that someone always incurs.

The civil definition of "loss," however, is not merely a way for the courts to locate an appropriate plaintiff. As the Government acknowledged in its *Dura* brief, there are situations in which a misrepresentation does not result in a "loss" for any plaintiff—*e.g.* where, as here, a stock loses all value for reasons unrelated to the defendant's misrepresentation before the misrepresentation is revealed. *See* U.S. Brief in *Dura* at 22. Indeed, this is also illustrated by the sunken ship footnote in *Huddleston*, where no plaintiff was injured because the misrepresentation about capacity did not cause the loss when the uninsured ship sank. *See supra* at 6. Conversely. the Government itself explained in *Dura*, that no plaintiff would incur a "loss" when investors "bought [inflated] stock in a company that falsely claimed to be insured," if the company "acquired insurance a week later, before any of its assets were damaged," and then performed well. U.S. Brief in *Dura* at 24.

Moreover, in a civil class action where no loss was caused because revelation of the misrepresentation did not cause a stock price decline, the court does not merely substitute a later-selling class representative. Rather, the court dismisses the entire class action because the absence of a post-disclosure decline means no plaintiff has incurred a loss from the misrepresentation. *See e.g.. Lentell v. Merrill Lynch & Co.*, 396 F.3d 161, 164. 175-76 & n.4 (2d Cir. 2005); *Robbins v. Koger Props., Inc.*, 116 F.3d 1441, 1449 (11th Cir. 1997).

Thus, although the Chamber agrees that the transfer of loss from one purchaser to another "does not reduce the overall harm to society or the magnitude of the crime," (Govt. Br. 16), neither an original purchaser nor any subsequent purchaser has suffered a "loss" attributable to the defendant's misrepresentation in civil law unless and until the misrepresentation is revealed and the value of the stock declines. When such a decline never occurs, the harm to society and the magnitude of the crime are less, meaning that, in the criminal context, a sentence should not be enhanced based on "loss."

The cases cited by the Government are not to the contrary. In *United States v. Deavours*, 219 F.3d 400 (5th Cir. 2000), and *United States v. Lane*, 323 F.3d 568 (7th Cir.), *cert. denied*, 540 U.S. 818 (2003), the courts increased sentences based on all victims' aggregate loss directly attributable to a defendant's misrepresentation without regard to the loss suffered by any particular individual. Neither case suggests that an aggregate loss can be proven or calculated if no person ever incurs a loss attributable to the misrepresentation: and that is the situation when a stock price declines entirely for reasons independent of the defendant's misrepresentation.

The Government implicitly acknowledges that its first attempted distinction of loss in the civil and criminal contexts fails. when it says that "[c]omplications with [its] reasoning arise . . . when a stock price declines all the way to zero ... without explicit disclosure of the fraud" based on "independent factors" such as a "downturn in the economy." Govt. Br. 17. But, the Government argues that "[b]y the time of criminal sentencing. a jury has found beyond a reasonable doubt that the defendant engaged in material fraudulent conduct"; the "only issue remaining is an assessment of the severity of that conduct": and defendants should not escape enhancements "because of the fortuity that the company collapsed purportedly before their fraud was revealed," which "does nothing to reduce their culpability." *Id.* at 17-18.

This argument ignores that Guideline § 2F 1.1 does not address whether the defendant misrepresented material facts or the level of his "culpability." This provision is focused exclusively on the incremental increase in punishment warranted by the amount of "loss" attributable to a misrepresentation. As noted above, other provisions of the Guideline take into account other aspects of a defendant's blameworthiness; § 2F1.1 should not be used as a catch-all to enhance criminal punishment .based on generalized views of a defendant's culpability.

As an *amicus*, it would not be appropriate for the Chamber to address fact-specific errors related to the Government's calculation of the amount by which Enron's stock was artificially overvalued ($43.8 million). But, we respectfully submit that the Government's theory of "loss" allows proof of the amount in ways that are (a) fundamentally inconsistent with the Supreme Court's decision in *Basic Inc. v. Levinson*, 485 U.S. 224 (1988), adopting the efficient-markets hypothesis; and (b) so speculative that they are inconsistent with fundamental criminal law principle of fair notice and with the Sentencing Guidelines' goal of uniform treatment of similarly-situated defendants.

Basic makes clear that in securities fraud cases. the law presumes that publicly-traded securities such as Enron's trade in an efficient market. The "premise [is] that the market price of shares traded on well-developed markets reflects all publicly available information, and, hence, any material misrepresentations." *Id.* at 246. The guiding assumption is that an efficient market promptly and fully values all material public information (true and false). and that a market price on a given day reflects that valuation in real time. *See, e.g.*, R. Dennis, *Materiality and the Efficient Capital Market Model: A Recipe for the Total Mix*, 25 Wm. & Mary L. Rev. 373, 374-75 (1984), *cited in Basic*, 485 U.S. at 246 n.24. This means that "when a stock is traded in an efficient market, the materiality of *disclosed* information may be measured post hoc by looking to the movement, in the period immediately following disclosure, of the price of the firm's stock." *Oran v. Stafford*, 226 F.3d 275. 282 (3d Cir. 2000) (emphasis supplied).

Accordingly, in an efficient market, the price of a security at the time of a purchase cannot by itself indicate how much value (if any) the market placed on an alleged, but still undisclosed, misrepresentation about the company. Only after the misrepresentation is disclosed can the market's price indicate the effect that particular piece of information had on price. And, by definition, a price decline that precedes a disclosure cannot have been caused by that disclosure and cannot measure the value of information withheld prior to the disclosure; instead, that price decline must have been caused by other company, industry, and market factors. Similarly, once a misrepresentation is exposed, if the security's price does not promptly decline, there is no basis for concluding that the misrepresentation was inflating the stock price prior to disclosure. The efficient market—the premise that underlies the securities law—would have said otherwise.

The Government's proposed interpretation of "loss" in the Guidelines, however, does not require proof of a negative market price reaction to the disclosure of a misrepresentation, and is for that reason fundamentally inconsistent with the efficient-markets hypothesis. It focuses only on the beginning of the transaction without requiring any consideration of how the transaction played out, and thus finds "loss" where none occurs—*e.g.*, where a stock declines before a misrepresentation is disclosed or where the misrepresentation is exposed and the market does not respond negatively. In contrast, the established definition of "loss" is consistent with the premise of an efficient market. because it requires that an investment "loss" be traced directly to specific market price reactions that are deemed to promptly and accurately value all disclosed, material information.

Equally to the point, the Government's approach creates difficult problems of proof which threaten unwarranted findings of indeterminate and massive "loss[es]." Where "loss" is defined by a post-disclosure decline in a stock's value, the amount of loss can be proven through assessment of objective factors such as reported prices. One method for doing so is an "event study," a "statistical regression analysis that examines the effect of an event, such as an allegedly fraudulent statement or omission, on a dependent variable, such as a company's stock price." *In re World Access, Inc. Secs. Litig.*, 310 F. Supp. 2d 1281, 1298 n.10 (N.D. Ga. 2004). But the Government's "inflation" approach provides no objective check on expert speculation about loss. Indeed, only subjective opinion testimony about the degree of inflation can support the amount of loss in an "inflation" approach. *Cf. First Nationwide Bank v. Gelt Funding Corp.*, 27 F.3d 763, 770 (2d Cir. 1994) (describing the "unworkable difficulties in ascertaining what amount of the plaintiffs injury as caused by the defendant's wrongful action as opposed to other external factors, and in apportioning damages between causes"). This method of assessing "loss" is particularly troubling in the Guideline setting where substantially increased criminal sanctions will occur arbitrarily in some cases but not others, based on subjective and unpredictable opinion testimony.

This case effectively illustrates the point. The Government's expert (Prof Saunders) could not look to the market and assess the effect of disclosure on the value of Enron's stock, because Enron's stock lost all value as the result of intervening events that led to bankruptcy before the misrepresentations at issue were disclosed. Instead, Prof. Saunders applied several controversial analytical techniques to attempt to derive the amount by which the misrepresentation inflated the stock. There can be no objective check on such expert testimony about loss because the market never actually reacted to a disclosure of the misrepresentation. Such expert opining about inflation is so extremely speculative that it is an unlawful basis upon which to award civil damages. *See supra*, at 5-8. It is likewise a vague, arbitrary and hence unacceptable basis for adding years to a defendant's prison sentence.

II. The Government Has Not Proven An Actual Loss Under The Established Standard.

In the alternative, the Government claims that it proved "a revelation of defendants' fraud followed by a decline in Enron's stock price," establishing "loss" under the applicable standard. Govt. Br. 24. Specifically, the Government asserts that Enron's disclosures in the fall of 2002 "encompassed the disclosure of the massive conspiracy *of which the instant fraud was a part . . . to wit, that Enron engaged in earnings manipulation*" which "resulted in a precipitous decline in the price of the stock." *Id.* (emphasis supplied). Unpacking this argument, it is clear that the Government does not mean that the Nigerian barge parking transaction was disclosed in the fall of 2001—it is undisputed that it was not. *See id.* at 25 (conceding that there was no "disclosure of the details of the Nigerian barge deal at that time"). Instead, the Government is equating the 2001 disclosure of "Enron's fraudulent accounting practices"—a disclosure of massive fraud which resulted in the restatement of four and one-half years of financial statements. the termination of Enron's CFO. and an SEC investigation—with the disclosure of the barge-parking transaction. *Id.* at 24-25. And, the Government is claiming that because the undisclosed barge transaction was similar to part of the disclosed accounting fraud, the decline that followed the disclosure of Enron's massive fraudulent practices can be attributed to individuals at Merrill Lynch who participated in the barge-parking transaction. This argument is of particular concern to the Chamber as it misinterprets both civil and criminal law.

This government argument is the worst sort of bootstrapping. It holds individuals who participated in a specific transaction responsible for numerous other separate transactions, overriding any reasonable attribution of responsibility for conduct. And, its logic would attribute to defendants responsibility not simply for the loss allegedly caused by the barge transaction, but for the entirety of the billions of dollars lost in Enron's collapse and bankruptcy (a consequence of the argument that makes it so implausible that the Government simply ignores it). Indeed, the Government's logic necessarily leads to the conclusion that defendants here (and any minor or limited participant in any fraudulent transaction in connection with Enron during the relevant period) would bear the same level of responsibility for the "losses" of Enron's bankruptcy as would any principals at Enron who planned and executed Enron's massive fraud. And, the argument runs roughshod over a basic fact—the barge transaction was not disclosed until *after* Enron went bankrupt; thus, Enron would have descended into bankruptcy even without the barge transaction and its disclosure (indeed. as defendants note, the barge transaction was ultimately profitable). How then can any misrepresentation related to the barge transaction have caused the Enron bankruptcy in the relevant legal sense?

The civil case law does not remotely support the Government's argument. The Government misleadingly claims that the "loss" arising out of Enron's collapse is attributable to the barge-transaction misrepresentation because Enron's collapse somehow "relates to the type of earnings manipulation involved in the Nigerian barge deal." *See* Govt. Br. 25 (emphasis added). But, civil law does not attribute responsibility for "loss" based on a family resemblance between frauds. It requires that the stock price decline be attributable to disclosure of "the falsity of the" specific prior misrepresentation alleged. *Lentell*, 396 F.3d at 175 & n.4. *See also Rob-*

bins, 116 F.3d at 1448 (holding that "loss" was not established because the decline in stock value was attributable to the company's concern "that future financing would not be available to sustain its sales of properties—not because it discovered that past accounting errors had overstated its cash flow"); *In re WorldCom Inc. Secs. Litig.*, 2005 WL 375314, at *6 (S.D.N.Y. Feb. 17, 2005) ("[a] concealed fact cannot cause a decrease in the value of a stock before the concealment is made public").

Most directly on point is *Miller v. Schweickart*, 413 F. Supp. 1062 (S.D.N.Y. 1976). There plaintiffs asserted that the defendant broker-dealer's general partners were employing "parking" transactions as a device to falsify the broker-dealers' financial position and engage in bond trading beyond that which its capital would support, exposing that capital to unreasonable risk of dissipation if market conditions worsened. *Id.* at 1067. Specifically, plaintiffs claimed that after the defendant's parking transaction, the broker-dealer "had similar transactions with others during the subsequent period" and "[a]s a result, substantial losses were sustained in those transactions (all unrelated to any dealings with [defendant])." *Id.* In an argument virtually identical to that made by the Government here, the plaintiffs contended "that the concealment of the nature of the [defendant's] transaction in early 1972 substantially assisted the general partners to continue their "parking" *with others* without detection or restraint and thus contributed to the collapse of [the broker-dealer]. *Id.*

The court held that "[t]his far-fetched theory of causation must fail as a matter of law." *id.*, explaining:

> To accept plaintiffs' theory would extend liability for fraud beyond the immediate and foreseeable consequences of one's wrongdoing and *in effect make [the defendant] the permanent accomplice of the [broker-dealer's] general partners in all their subsequent parking transactions with others*; it would subject [defendant' to strict liability for any future depredations by those general partners long after [defendant] had ceased to have any dealings with [the broker-dealer], even for deeds done with others years later, of which [defendant] had no knowledge. *This is causation run riot*. . . . To allow a jury to find a causal relationship between [defendant's] transactions, which terminated in early 1972, and the collapse of [the broker-dealer] more than two years later in July 1974, would permit it to engage in sheer speculation of the rankest type. [*Id.* at 1068 (emphasis supplied)]

The Government's argument here fails by perfect analogy. It is attempting to attribute Enron's collapse to a single transaction completed before the collapse and never disclosed until after the collapse, based on the resemblance between the barge-parking transaction and different misrepresentations whose revelation actually led to Enron's collapse.

SAN FRANCISCO & LIVE WEBCAST PROGRAM SCHEDULE

DAY ONE: 9:00 A.M. - 5:00 P.M.

MORNING SESSION: 9:00 A.M. - 12:45 P.M.

9:00 **Introduction & Overview**
- Hot issues and cutting-edge developments
- Trends and predictions

David Siegel

9:15 **Prosecuting the Securities Fraud Action**
- Strategies and objectives
- Use of individual non-class actions
- Preparing your case for trial
- Trying your case – lessons for the plaintiff/defendant

Patrick J. Coughlin, Robert S. Gans, Sherrie R. Savett

10:15 Break

10:30 **Defending the Securities Class Action**
- Pleading motions
- Handling "confidential witnesses"
- Dealing with the problem of multiple fronts
- Preparing for trial: in Limine motions, Daubert motions, and other pre-trial battles

Seth Aronson, Bruce G. Vanyo, Peter A. Wald

11:45 **Securities Auditor Liability**
- Impact of PCAOB
- The SEC-Auditor relationship
- The Company-Auditor relationship
- Potential Auditor liability

Phillip R. Rotner, Peter A. Wald

12:45 Lunch Break

AFTERNOON SESSION: 1:45 P.M. - 5:00 P.M.

1:45 **Loss Causation and Damages**
- Aggregate v. per share damages - recent decisions *(Worldcom, Oxford Healthcare, America West, Clarent)* and tactical considerations
- Attacking the 'value line' - Daubert motions revisited
- Loss causation in the post-*Dura* world

Prof. Allan W. Kleidon, Daniel P. Lefler, Alan Schulman

2:45 **Settlement Procedures and Trends in Securities Actions**
- Mediation techniques
- Settlement trends
- Use of experts
- Valuing cases

U.S. Magistrate Judge Edward Infante (Ret.), Dr. Marsha Kramer Mayer, Alan Schulman

4:00 **Directors' & Officers' Liability Insurance**
- State of the D&O insurance industry
- New products
- Current coverage/hot issues
- Loss mitigation insurance

Meredith Nelson Landy, Anthony M. Santoro, Jr.

DAY TWO: 9:00 A.M. - 4:30 P.M.

MORNING SESSION: 9:00 A.M. - 12:30 P.M.

9:00 **SEC Enforcement Initiatives**
- Latest developments
- Financial fraud
  - Actions against auditing firms and other gatekeepers
  - Actions against third parties, including banks and customers
- Cases involving mutual funds and other regulated entities

Marc Fagel, Robert C. Freise

10:00 Break

10:15 **How to Deal Effectively with the SEC**
- Is there value to cooperation?
- Impact of the Securities Fraud Deterrence & Investor Restitution Act, H.R. 2179
- Is there a corporate attorney-client privilege?
- Trends in penalties

Robert C. Friese, Martin N. Gelfand

11:00 **The Expanding Responsibilities and Liabilities of Corporate Directors**
- Expanded risks for the "independent director" after Worldcom, Disney and Oracle
- Developments in corporate governance and derivative cases

David J. Berger, Ralph C. Ferrara, Darren J. Robbins

12:30 Lunch Break

AFTERNOON SESSION: 2:00 P.M. - 4:30 P.M.

2:00 **Developments in Internal Investigations**
- Impact of the Amendments to the Organizational Sentencing Guidelines: In what limited situations will an organization need to waive its attorney-client privilege?
- Best practices and strategies for conducting internal investigations

David H. Kistenbroker, Harry A. Olivar, Jr.

3:00 Break

3:15 **Criminal Investigation & Prosecution of Securities Violations**
- Why corporations are indicted
  - Have the rules changed since Arthur Andersen?
  - Update on the DOJ's principles of federal prosecution of business organizations
- Why corporations are not indicted
  - Negotiating deferred and non-prosecution agreements
  - Update on the implications of Merrill Lynch and other agreements avoiding corporate indictment
- Update on corporate sentencing: Impact of the new Amendments to the Organizational Guidelines - the litigation dilemma
- Parallel proceedings: The interaction among the DOJ, SEC, and private litigants

Debra Wong Yang

4:15 **Closing Remarks**

David Siegel

NEW YORK CITY PROGRAM SCHEDULE

DAY ONE: 9:00 A.M. - 5:00 P.M.

MORNING SESSION: 9:00 A.M. - 12:45 P.M.

9:00 Introduction & Overview

- Hot issues and cutting-edge developments
- Trends and predictions

Colleen P. Mahoney

9:15 Prosecuting the Securities Fraud Action

- Strategies and objectives
- Use of individual non-class actions
- Preparing your case for trial
- Trying your case – lessons for the plaintiff/defendant

Daniel L. Berger, Stuart M. Grant, Robert A. Wallner

10:15 Break

10:30 Defending the Securities Class Action

- Pleading motions
- Handling "confidential witnesses"
- Dealing with the problem of multiple fronts
- Preparing for trial: in Limine motions, Daubert motions, and other pre-trial battles
- Loss causation/damages

Jonathan M. Hoff, Brad S. Karp, Laurie B. Smilan, James B. Weidner

11:45 Securities Auditor Liability

- Impact of PCAOB
- The SEC-Auditor relationship
- The Company-Auditor relationship
- Potential Auditor liability

Alan S. Fox, Michael R. Young

12:45 Lunch Break

AFTERNOON SESSION: 1:45 P.M. - 5:00 P.M.

1:45 Corporate Governance Litigation

- Defining the Independent Director
- Executive compensation and the business judgment rule
- Changes in Delaware law

Vice Chancellor Stephen P. Lamb, Theodore N. Mirvis

2:45 Settlement Procedures and Trends in Securities Actions

- Mediation techniques
- Settlement trends
- Use of experts
- Valuing cases

Bruce D. Angiolillo, Richard Bemporad, Frederick C. Dunbar

4:00 Directors' & Officers' Liability Insurance

- State of the D&O insurance industry
- New products
- Current coverage/hot issues
- Loss mitigation insurance

Vincent G. Caracciolo, Joseph P. Monteleone

DAY TWO: 9:00 A.M. - 4:30 P.M.

MORNING SESSION: 9:00 A.M. - 12:30 P.M.

9:00 SEC & NASD Enforcement Initiatives

- Latest developments
- Financial fraud
  - Actions against auditing firms and other gatekeepers
  - Actions against third parties, including banks and customers
- Cases involving broker dealers, mutual funds and other regulated entities

Wayne M. Carlin, Barry Goldsmith

10:00 Break

10:15 How to Deal Effectively with the SEC & NASD

- Is there value to cooperation?
- Is there a corporate attorney-client privilege?

Wayne M. Carlin, Barry Goldsmith, Colleen P. Mahoney, Derek M. Meisner

11:00 Loss Causation and Damages

- Aggregate v. per share damages - recent decisions *(Worldcom, Oxford Healthcare, America West, Clarent)* and tactical considerations
- Attacking the 'value-line' - Daubert motions revisited
- Loss causation in the post-*Dura* world

Scott D. Musoff, Lyle Roberts

12:30 Lunch Break

AFTERNOON SESSION: 2:00 P.M. - 4:30 P.M.

2:00 Developments in Internal Investigations

- Impact of the Amendments to the Organizational Sentencing Guidelines: In what limited situations will an organization need to waive its attorney-client privilege?
- Best practices and strategies for conducting internal investigations

Harvey R. Kelly, Derek M. Meisner

3:00 Break

3:15 Criminal Investigation & Prosecution of Securities Violations

- Why corporations are indicted
  - Have the rules changed since Arthur Andersen?
  - Update on the DOJ's principles of federal prosecution of business organizations
- Why corporations are not indicted
  - Negotiating deferred and non-prosecution agreements
  - Update on the implications of Merrill Lynch and other agreements avoiding corporate indictment
- Update on corporate sentencing: Impact of the new Amendments to the Organizational Guidelines - the litigation dilemma
- Parallel proceedings: The interaction among the DOJ, SEC, and private litigants

Andrew J. Levander, Lawrence J. Zweifach

4:15 Closing Remarks

Colleen P. Mahoney

FACULTY

SAN FRANCISCO*

CHAIR: **David Siegel**, Irell & Manella, Los Angeles

Seth Aronson
O'Melveny & Myers
Los Angeles

David J. Berger
Wilson Sonsini Goodrich & Rosati
Palo Alto

Patrick J. Coughlin
Lerach Coughlin Stoia Geller Rudman & Robbins LLP
San Francisco

Marc Fagel
Associate District Administrator
Securities and Exchange Commission
San Francisco

Ralph C. Ferrara
LeBoeuf, Lamb, Greene & MacRae, L.L.P.
Washington, D.C.

Robert C. Friese
Shartsis Friese LLP
San Francisco

Robert S. Gans
Bernstein Litowitz Berger & Grossman LLP
San Diego

Martin N. Gelfand
Irell & Manella LLP
Los Angeles

Magistrate Judge Edward Infante (Ret.)
San Francisco

David H. Kistenbroker
Katten Muchin Rosenman LLP
Chicago

Professor Allan W. Kleidon
Cornerstone Research
Menlo Park

Dr. Marcia Kramer Mayer
Senior VP
NERA Economic Consulting
New York City

Daniel P. Lefler
Irell & Manella
Los Angeles

Meredith Nelson Landy
O'Melveny & Myers
Los Angeles

Harry A. Olivar, Jr.
Quinn Emanuel Urquhart Oliver & Hedges, LLP
Los Angeles

Darren J. Robbins
Lerach Coughlin Stoia Geller Rudman & Robbins LLP
San Diego

Phillip R. Rotner
Deloitte & Touche
New York City

Anthony M. Santoro, Jr.
AIGTS
New York City

Sherrie R. Savett
Berger & Montague, P.C.
Philadelphia

Alan Schulman
Bernstein Litowitz Berger & Grossmann LLP
San Diego

Bruce G. Vanyo
Wilson Sonsini Goodrich & Rosati
Palo Alto

Peter A. Wald
Latham & Watkins LLP
San Francisco

Debra Wong Yang
US Attorney
Central District of California
U.S. Department of Justice
Los Angeles

** Webcast will be broadcast of San Francisco faculty.*

NEW YORK CITY

CHAIR: **Colleen P. Mahoney**, Skadden, Arps, Slate, Meagher & Flom LLP
Washington, D.C.

Bruce D. Angiolillo
Simpson Thacher & Bartlett LLP
New York City

Richard Bemporad
Lowey Dannenberg Bemporad & Selinger, P.C.
White Plains, New York

Daniel L. Berger
Bernstein Litowitz Berger & Grossmann LLP
New York City

Vincent G. Caracciolo
Senior Vice President
Specialty Casualty
Liberty International Underwriters
New York City

Wayne M. Carlin
Wachtell, Lipton, Rosen & Katz
New York City

Frederick C. Dunbar
Senior Vice President
NERA Economic Consulting
New York City

Alan S. Fox
PricewaterhouseCoopers LLP
New York City

Barry Goldsmith
Executive Vice President, Enforcement
NASD
Washington, D.C.

Stuart M. Grant
Grant & Eisenhofer P.A.
Wilmington

Jonathan M. Hoff
Cadwalader, Wickersham & Taft LLP
New York City

Brad S. Karp
Paul, Weiss, Rifkind, Wharton & Garrison LLP
New York City

Harvey R. Kelly
Managing Director
AlixPartners LLC
New York City

The Honorable Stephen P. Lamb
Vice Chancellor
Delaware Court of Chancery
Wilmington

Andrew J. Levander
Dechert LLP
New York City

Derek M. Meisner
Kirkpatrick & Lockhart Nicholson Graham, LLP
Boston

Theodore N. Mirvis
Wachtell, Lipton, Rosen & Katz
New York City

Joseph P. Monteleone
Duane Morris LLP
New York City

Scott D. Musoff
Partner
Skadden, Arps, Slate, Meagher & Flom LLP
New York City

Lyle Roberts
Wilson Sonsini Goodrich & Rosati
Reston, Virginia

Laurie B. Smilan
Latham & Watkins LLP
Reston, Virginia

Robert A. Wallner
Milberg Weiss Bershad & Schulman LLP
New York City

James B. Weidner
Clifford Chance US LLP
New York City

Michael R. Young
Willkie Farr & Gallagher LLP
New York City

Lawrence J. Zweifach
Heller Ehrman LLP
New York City

Program Attorney: Ellen A. DiLapi

Nor can "loss" be established based on speculation that an earlier disclosure of a specific fact "would have" triggered a series of events that ultimately "would have" led to other more important disclosures. *See Robbins*, 116 F.3d at 1448. Like the Government's family-resemblance argument, this attenuated notion of "loss" attribution would allow massive damages to be leveraged out of the hypothetical consequences from a minor misstatement. *Cf. Holmes v. Securities Investor Prot. Corp.*, 503 U.S. 258, 287 (1992) (Scalia, J., concurring in the judgment) ("for want of a nail, a kingdom was lost is a commentary on fate, not the statement of a major cause of action against a blacksmith").

This kind of speculative, attenuated "loss" determination has no place in civil securities litigation which calculates "loss" based on the market's actual reaction to disclosure of a specific misrepresented fact. It certainly has no place in the determination of "loss" for purposes of enhancing criminal punishment.

III. To Prove "Intended Loss," the Government Must Prove That Defendants Intended Enron's Stock To Decline When The Contrary Is Clearly True.

As the authors of the Guidelines signaled by again using the word "loss" in the phrase "intended loss." The Government must prove not that defendants intended to inflate the value of Enron's stock, but instead that defendants specifically intended Enron's stock price to decline by a particular amount (here $43.7 million). Indeed, if "loss" did not bear the same meaning of "decline" in the phrases "actual loss" and "intended loss," then it would be a simple matter for the Government to circumvent Guideline § 2F 1.1's instruction that criminal punishment be calibrated to the harm attributable to the misrepresentation. The Government could simply invoke the concept of "intended loss," posit that defendants intend all the potential consequences of any misrepresentation, and offer speculation about what those consequences might have been.

The Fifth Circuit has also made clear, moreover, that "intended loss" under Guideline 2F1.1 "refer[s] to actual intent, not constructive intent." *United States v. Henderson*, 19 F.3d 917, 928 (5th Cir. 1994). Thus, for example, where a defendant fraudulently obtains a loan that he intends to repay, "the intended loss is zero." *Id.* at 928. Here, too, it is apparently undisputed that defendants intended the barge transaction to produce real profits and thus not to harm Enron or its stock price.

For the reasons set forth by defendants, the Government failed to prove that the defendants intended to inflict any "loss" by engaging in the barge transaction at issue—let alone the $43.8 million that the Government speculated was the amount by which the aggregate purchase price of Enron stock was artificially inflated. See Defs. Br. 25. Even assuming that the Government proves that defendants sought artificially to inflate Enron's 1999 stock price by allowing the company to book $12 million of revenues in 1999 instead of 2000, that does not prove that defendants intended to cause a decline in the value of Enron's stock. To the contrary, defendants intended that the barges would be sold at a significant profit so that Enron ultimately could recognize real earnings based on that transaction. and that is what occurred.

It is true, as the Government states. that defendants sometimes intend to cause the loss of the full amount of money they put at risk. But, in cases that involve only an intent to mislead temporarily. no such intent is proven. That is why the primary case relied upon by the Government. *United States v. Deavours*, 219 F.3d 400 (5th Cir. 2000), does not assist its cause. That case involved a "'Ponzi scheme'" in which "'a swindler promises a large return for investments made with him.'" *Id.* at 402. The swindler "'pays the promised return on the initial investments in order to attract additional investors. The payments are not financed through the success of the underlying venture but are taken from the corpus of the newly attracted investments.'" *Id.* In such cases, a defendant intends from the inception of a scheme that a fraud victim's money will be misused, and any apparent payback to an initial victim is "not to compensate the victims for their losses, or to extricate [the defendant] from wrongdoing, but conversely to extend [the] criminal activities and the profitability thereof—and to place yet more property of innocent victims at risk." *Id.* at 403. *See id.* at 404 (any payments made were "as amplification of the fraudulent scheme").

Here, in contrast, at most the alleged intent was temporarily to mislead investors about Enron's returns in 1999 by prematurely injecting returns from the barge transaction into its balance sheet. The defendants' specific intent, however, plainly included the actual realization of those returns so that the false temporary effect of the transaction would be replaced by a real effect. This scheme is not remotely the equivalent of a Ponzi-type scheme whose ultimate intent is permanently to defraud.[5]

Neither of the other cases identified by the Government as "securities fraud case[s] that use intended loss rather than actual loss as the appropriate measure of loss under Guideline 2F1.1" remotely support such an approach to sentencing in this case. In *United States v. Manas*, 272 F.3d 159 (2d Cir. 2001), only an "intended loss" occurred, because the defendants' fraud came to light in a government sting operation "so that the intended victims of defendants' fraud never actually suffered an economic loss." *Id.* at 160. In contrast, the fraud alleged here was not an attempt that failed because it was part of a sting operation. The fraud alleged here was fully consummated. Thus, here the real-world actual harm of zero serves as an objective check against speculation about a grossly disproportionate intended harm. This objective check confirms that, at most, defendants intended a temporary inflation in Enron's stock but no lasting effect because the barge would be genuinely sold at substantial profit. Because "loss" in a securities case means a subsequent decline in stock price, *supra*, at 5-9, such a temporary price inflation is not an intended loss. *Manas* does not support supplanting the real-world, actual loss from a fully consummated fraud with conjecture about intended loss.

United States v. Graye, 2003 WL 282195 (S.D.N.Y. Feb. 10, 2003), is similarly inapposite. The scheme at issue did not come to fruition, and there was no dispute about the amount of harm that the defendants intended.

In sum, "intended loss" should be defined to mean "intended decline," just as "actual loss" means "actual decline." Moreover, the "intended loss" measure should be reserved for situations in which an attempt to defraud occurred but was not completed—and thus there is no way to measure "actual loss"—or where there is proof that the defendants specifically intended to cause an ascertainable decline.

---

5. The Government generically claims that defendants always intend to cause the full amount of loss "placed at risk" by a fraudulent scheme, but cases that state this rule uniformly involve a specific intent to deprive investors of the full value of their investment. *See United States v. Dahlstrom*, 180 F.3d 677, 685 (5th Cir. 1999) (a scheme to sell securities in a company whose only product was commercially worthless); *United States v. Wimbish*, 980 F.2d 312, 315-16 (5th Cir. 1992) (a scheme to pass checks that was only partially successful, more akin to theft in the court's view than to fraud), *abrogated on other grounds by Stinson v. United States*, 508 U.S. 36 (1993); *Lane*, 323 F.3d at 590 (holding that the unsecured portion of a fraudulently obtained loan is the intended loss, in part because it is "'has the advantage of not "making the term of a criminal sentence turn on conjecture,'" even though the underlying project succeeded and no loss actually occurred). In each of these cases, the defendant intended to cause a loss that was mitigated by some fortuity not of the defendant's making.

CONCLUSION

For all of the foregoing reasons, the Chamber respectfully requests that the word "loss" in Guideline § 2F1.1 be given its established meaning under securities law and the common law—*viz.*, the decline in price attributable to a defendant's misrepresentation.

Dated: March 25, 2005

Respectfully submitted

Carter G. Phillips
Richard D. Bernstein
Virginia A. Seitz
(Motions for *pro hac vice* admission pending) SIDLEY AUSTIN BROWN & WOOD LLP 1501 K Street, N.W.
Washington, D.C. 20005
(202) 736-8000

Counsel for *Amicus Curiae*

Robin S. Conrad
NATIONAL CHAMBER LITIGATION CENTER, INC.
1615 H Street, N.W.
Washington, D.C. 20062

Of Counsel

CERTIFICATE OF SERVICE

The undersigned hereby certifies that a true and complete copy of the foregoing document was served via Federal Express on counsel for the United States government and for defendants at the Fallowing addresses this twenty-fifth day of March, 2005.

Andrew Weissman
Matthew W. Friedrich
Kathryn Reummter
DEPARTMENT OF JUSTICE
ENRON TASK FORCE
1400 New York Avenue. N.W.
Washington, DC 20530
(counsel for U.S. government)
Telephone: (202) 514-0666
Facsimile: (202) 353-3165

Richard Schaeffer
Peter J. Venaglia
Brian Rafferty
DORNBUSH MENSCH
MANDELSTAM
& SCHAEFFER. LLP
747 Third Avenue
New York, NY 10017
(counsel for Daniel Bayly)
Telephone: (212) 759-3300
Facsimile: (212) 753-7673

Sidney K. Powell
Deborah Pearce
POWELL & PEARCE
1854A Henderson Road
No. 228
Asheville, N.C. 28803
(counsel for James A. Brown)
Telephone: (828) 651-9543
Facsimile: (828) 684-5343

Thomas A. Hageman
Marla Thompson Poirot
GARDERE WYNNE
SEWELL LLP
1000 Louisiana
Suite 3400
Houston, TX 77002-5007
(Counsel for Daniel Bayly)
Telephone: (713) 276-5064
Facsimile: (713) 276-6064

Lawrence J. Zweifach
Holly Kulka
HELLER EHRMAN WHITE
& MCAULIFFE LLP
120 West 45th Street
21st Floor
New York, NY 10036-4041
(counsel for James A. Brown)
Telephone: (212) 832-8300
Facsimile: (212) 763-7600

David Spears
RICHARDS SPEARS KIBBE
& ORBE L.L.P.
One World Financial Center
29th Floor
New York, NY 10017
(counsel for William R. Fuhs)
Telephone: (212) 530-1800
Facsimile: (212) 530-1801

Ira Lee Sorkin
CARTER LEDYARD
& MILLBURN LLP
2 Wall Street
New York. NY 10005
(counsel for Robert S. Furst)
Telephone: (212) 732-3200
Facsimile: (212) 732-3232

____

Richard D. Bernstein

NOTES

NOTES

Program Schedule and Faculty